LIMNOLOGY *in North America*

LIMNOLOGY
in North America

Edited by DAVID G. FREY

Madison, Milwaukee, and London, 1966

THE UNIVERSITY OF WISCONSIN PRESS

Published by
THE UNIVERSITY OF WISCONSIN PRESS
Madison, Milwaukee, and London
U.S.A.: Box 1379, Madison, Wisconsin 53701
U.K.: 26–28 Hallam Street, London, W. 1

Reprinted 1966

Printed in the United States of America
Library of Congress Catalog Card Number 63–7540

Acknowledgments

It should immediately be obvious even to the casual reader that a book of this scope could not have been written by one person. Each chapter reveals and reflects the intimacy of long personal acquaintance with the region or topic presented. The editor is deeply grateful to each of the chapter contributors for so generously giving of his time and thoughtful attention in the preparation of this volume. It has truly been a cooperative venture for the general consolidation and advancement of the science of limnology.

The editor also appreciates the thoughtfulness, efficiency, and even forbearance with which Miss Joan Krager and her associates at the University of Wisconsin Press have handled this assignment. Moreover, the Cartographic Laboratory of the University of Wisconsin has done an excellent job in preparing many of the maps in the book. This has saved the chapter authors countless headaches and has greatly improved the overall quality of the illustrations.

Finally, the American Society of Limnology and Oceanography wishes to acknowledge the financial support of the National Science Foundation in producing this book, which has resulted in a market price considerably lower than would otherwise have been possible.

DAVID G. FREY

Bloomington, Indiana
1 September 1962

Contents

Contributors

Alfred M. Beeton
Environmental Research
Bureau of Commercial Fisheries
Biological Laboratory
U.S. Fish and Wildlife Service
Ann Arbor, Michigan

Clifford O. Berg
Department of Entomology and Limnology
Cornell University
Ithaca, New York

W. H. Bradley
U.S. Geological Survey
Washington 25, D.C.

John L. Brooks
Department of Biology
Yale University
New Haven, Connecticut

Robert S. Campbell
Department of Zoology
University of Missouri
Columbia, Missouri

Graciela C. Candelas
Department of Biology
University of Puerto Rico
Río Piedras, Puerto Rico

Gustavo A. Candelas
Department of Biology
University of Puerto Rico
Río Piedras, Puerto Rico

Kenneth D. Carlander
Department of Zoology and Entomology
Iowa State University
Ames, Iowa

David C. Chandler
Great Lakes Research Division
Institute of Science and Technology
University of Michigan
Ann Arbor, Michigan

Gerald A. Cole
Department of Zoology
Arizona State University
Tempe, Arizona

Edward S. Deevey, Jr.
Department of Biology
Yale University
New Haven, Connecticut

J. S. Dendy
Department of Zoology-Entomology
Auburn University
Auburn, Alabama

Samuel Eddy
Department of Zoology
University of Minnesota
Minneapolis 14, Minnesota

W. T. Edmondson
Department of Zoology
University of Washington
Seattle 5, Washington

David G. Frey
Department of Zoology
Indiana University
Bloomington, Indiana

F. E. J. Fry
Department of Zoology
University of Toronto
Toronto 5, Ontario, Canada

Shelby D. Gerking
Department of Zoology
Indiana University
Bloomington, Indiana

Gerald E. Gunning
Department of Zoology
Tulane University
New Orleans 18, Louisiana

Arthur D. Hasler
Department of Zoology
University of Wisconsin
Madison 6, Wisconsin

G. E. Hutchinson
Department of Biology
Yale University
New Haven, Connecticut

William H. Irwin
Department of Zoology
Oklahoma State University
Stillwater, Oklahoma

P. A. Larkin
Institute of Fisheries
University of British Columbia
Vancouver 8, British Columbia, Canada

George H. Lauff
Sapelo Island Research Foundation
Sapelo Island, Georgia

Vianney Legendre
Service de la Recherche
Ministère de la Chasse et des Pêcheries
Montreal, Quebec, Canada

Daniel A. Livingstone
Department of Zoology

Duke University
Durham, North Carolina

Walter G. Moore
Department of Biological Sciences
Loyola University
New Orleans 18, Louisiana

Joe Kendall Neel
Water Supply and Pollution Control
U.S. Public Health Service
Kansas City 6, Missouri

T. G. Northcote
Institute of Fisheries
University of British Columbia
Vancouver 8, British Columbia, Canada

Robert W. Pennak
Department of Biology
University of Colorado
Boulder, Colorado

M. W. Smith
Fisheries Research Board of Canada
Biological Station
St. Andrews, New Brunswick, Canada

Clarence M. Tarzwell
U.S. Department of Health, Education, and
   Welfare
Public Health Service
Robert A. Taft Sanitary Engineering Center
Cincinnati 26, Ohio

James L. Yount
Midge Research Laboratory
Entomological Research Center
Florida State Board of Health
Winter Haven, Florida

Introduction

Limnology is the study of all inland waters and of the external influences that affect the nature of the waters and the processes going on in them. Hence, it is concerned not only with the life in these waters, the fixation and utilization of energy, and the complex interrelationships among the various organisms, but also with the chemistry and physics of the waters, the geology, meteorology, hydrology, and bioecology of their drainage basins, and the progressively greater influence of man on the total complex of life and processes in these waters. Indeed, the dependence of man, his animals, his agriculture, and his industries on water has created critical problems of adequate supply and satisfactory quality of water in many parts of the world. These problems are bound to increase as the world's population increases and as industrial technology advances. Because of his striving to comprehend all the intricate relationships in waters, the limnologist will play a progressively greater role in meeting these problems and in effectively managing our water resources. Water is a renewable but not an inexhaustible natural resource.

In comparison with many other sciences, limnology is still young in years, although already reasonably mature. From its descriptive beginnings around the turn of the century it has developed rapidly. Progressive sophistication in instrumentation and experimentation here as in other sciences is resulting in a mushrooming of our accumulated knowledge and understanding of limnological processes. Such growth inevitably results in fragmentation and specialization of interests as it becomes increasingly more difficult for any one individual to remain cognizant of all advances in the field and to integrate them into his thinking. The problems of communication among scientists, the orderly development of ideas and theories, and the retrieval of pertinent information from the world's literature are of paramount importance.

Stimulated by the Fifteenth Congress of the International Association of Limnology, held in Wisconsin in August 1962, the present volume attempts to remedy some of this fragmentation by presenting a summary of the development and current status of limnology in North America. The continent has been divided into a number of geographical areas based mainly on political subdivisions (see map on next page) for each of which at least one limnologist active in the area has generously given his time to summarize its limnology. The several topical chapters not included in this map are apparent from the Table of Contents. In this presentation we are interested not only in reviewing the significant work that has already been done but also in describing the limnological resources of each region and, at least by inference, in suggesting directions that further limnological work might take. It is anticipated that this book will stimulate further study and integration, and even before its publication a few of the chapter authors have already obtained research grants for the investigation of problems disclosed by their summaries.

The authors have operated within a general framework laid out by the managing editor, but each has been given considerable latitude and freedom of decision in developing his chapter. Thus, the chapters are almost as diverse in their presentations as are the interests and backgrounds of their authors. Initial allotments of pages proved quite unrealistic in many instances,

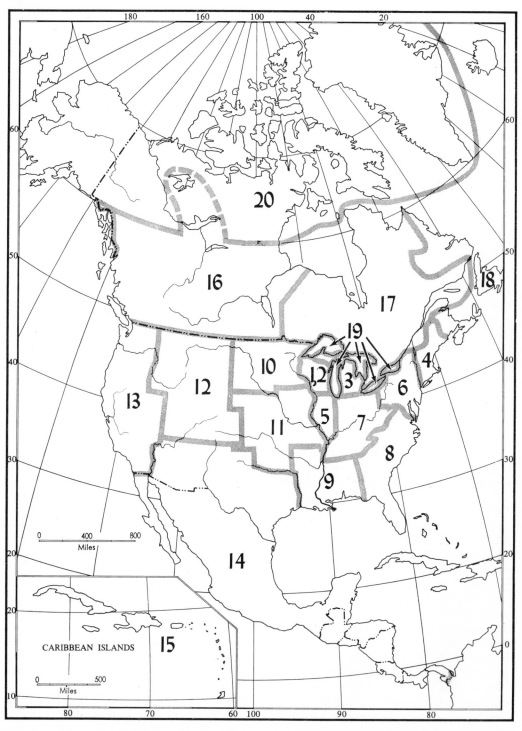

Numbers assigned to geographical areas represent chapter numbers in this book.

Prepared by the University of Wisconsin Cartographic Laboratory.

so that the volume is considerably larger than originally planned. However, our general attitude was that the book would have to be as large as necessary to accomplish the stated objectives.

Even in spite of its size the volume is not complete, and the individual chapter authors will be the first to admit this. The body of literature is so extensive that in many instances only a sampling has been presented, based on the judgment of the chapter author. The bibliographies for the chapters are sufficiently large, however, so that from the references listed a person interested in any particular subject should be able to locate other references in the desired area.

One large body of literature that has not been adequately covered in this book, more so in some chapters than in others, is the general subject of fishery biology and fish management. As a result of the very extensive effort in this area supported by the conservation departments of the various states and by the Federal Aid in Fish Restoration Program (Dingell-Johnson Program), there is a tremendous volume of mimeographed and processed reports published locally and primarily for local use. Such literature is difficult to obtain and evaluate, and much of it, although directly concerned with one component of the aquatic biota, is somewhat peripheral to limnology as treated in this book. Persons interested in this aspect of applied limnology can consult the following books for further information and lists of references: Hubbs and Eschmeyer (1938), Carlander (1950, 1953), Lagler (1952), Rounsefell and Everhart (1953), Vibert and Lagler (1961), Lagler *et al.* (1962).

A second major topic of applied limnology that has not been treated exhaustively, for to do so would probably require a volume as large as the present one, concerns man's use and reuse of water. Involved here are not only the effects of domestic, agricultural, and industrial pollution on the quality of lakes and rivers but also the conflicting use of water bodies for power development, industry, fish production, recreation, etc. The recreational and aesthetic aspects of water bodies are more difficult to evaluate in terms of dollars than are the other uses, but there are hopeful signs that the planners of multipurpose projects will take these "peripheral" functions into account and make due allowance for them in the total operation of the projects.

With the increasing use of our waters for residential sites and for recreational purposes, as well as for water supply, power development, and waste disposal, and with the resulting relentless and largely irreversible changes in the nature of these waters, it is time we take steps to identify and set aside prime examples of our various kinds of lakes, ponds, streams, springs, bogs, etc. for future study. Some states have already moved in this direction, and other progress is being made through Nature Conservancy and by the establishment of national parks, forests, primitive areas, and wilderness areas by the various governments of North America. This is encouraging, but it is only a partial solution. What is needed is a coordinated effort by the limnologists of North America and other continents as well to preserve some of the natural aquatic areas of the world before they are irreparably altered. The International Association of Limnology established a committee in 1959 to investigate this matter and initiate appropriate action.

Another topic that has been handled in varying detail by the chapter authors concerns faunistic and floristic studies. Many of these are very important for the proper identification of species, but to include all of them would greatly enlarge the book without resulting in a commensurate increase in the presentation of limnological processes. The specialist in a group will already be aware of the important papers in his field. The non-specialist will probably rely, at least initially, on the new edition of *Fresh-Water Biology, Aquatic Invertebrates of the United States, Aquatic Insects of California,* or on some of the important regional works, especially those concerning aquatic insects.

For the purposes of this book North America is considered to extend from Panama northward, including Greenland and the Caribbean islands. This is a tremendous area, with great regional variations in topography, geology, and climate, as a result of which the limnological resources, particularly lakes, are very unevenly distributed. The glaciated portion of the continent is most richly supplied with lakes, and it is this region that supported the first studies in limnology on the continent and continues to support very extensive research programs. Even the desert and steppe regions, however, have aquatic resources with an abundance of fascinating present-day limnological problems, and if one adds the dimension of time to his conceptual framework, the large pluvial lakes of the Great Basin, the changes in drainage patterns, the speciation that has occurred with isolation of spring runs, etc., all become fair game for study.

By far the greatest amount of limnological research in North America has been conducted by persons associated with universities. The earliest generation of limnologists—Birge, Juday, Welch, Ward, Whipple, Needham, Scott, Eigenmann, Coker, etc.—nearly all had their primary training in zoology, and hence the subsequent generations of limnologists have likewise been dominated by persons having their primary training in zoology. This is a matter of tradition rather than design, since limnology is interdisciplinary in nature and could be taught equally well in departments of botany, geology, meteorology, sanitary engineering, etc. In more recent time persons with primary training in these other fields are selecting limnology as their main area of research, which is resulting in a wholesome diversification and freshness of approach.

The teaching of limnology in North America and the total research output are now being greatly expanded by limnologists' moving to other universities and to positions with state governments or with various federal organizations. A survey in 1952 (Frey, 1953), for example, showed that at that time some course in limnology was being offered at 66 separate locations in the United States, involving about 750 students per year. In 1930 Needham listed only 16 institutions in the United States and Canada that offered courses in limnology. Certainly the number of institutions offering training in this subject and the number of students receiving such training is much greater now than in 1952. Moreover, with the increasing availability of research support, a progressively larger number of students is receiving graduate training to the master's or Ph.D. degree. This is a healthy sign.

Another healthy sign is the fact that limnology and oceanography in North America have a common professional organization—the American Society of Limnology and Oceanography—and a common journal—LIMNOLOGY AND OCEANOGRAPHY. Aquatic processes are much the same, whether the water is salty or fresh. Both fields are advancing rapidly, and both can profit by sharing ideas, theories, and methods. Persons with oceanographic training are now studying the Laurentian Great Lakes, and limnologists are em-

ployed by the various oceanographic institutions. The Caspian Sea, which is six times larger than Lake Superior, is considered a lake, although salty, and is being studied by Russian limnologists. The problems of primary productivity, feeding mechanisms, energy transfer in ecosystems, biogeochemical transformations, density stratification, water movements, etc. are general problems, not the prerogative of any one group of scientists. Hence, the present book, although restricted in scope by the title and available publication space, concerns the aquatic environment in general. It should be of value to the oceanographers, too, in helping understand the overall development of aquatic research.

One of the potential deficiencies of any multi-authored volume such as this is that general contributions not specifically related to one chapter or another tend to be slighted. Accordingly, I have prepared an annotated list of books and monographs that have served or seem destined to serve as important summaries or source materials in the development of limnology in North America. This list is entirely subjective and is not complete. Not included, for example, are the many monographic treatments of regional importance, particularly those from Illinois, Wisconsin, Michigan, New York, and Connecticut. These can be found in the separate chapters. Also, of the half-dozen or so textbooks in ecology, I have included only the two that are most closely related to limnology. Of the various books concerned more specifically with oceanography, only the classic by Sverdrup *et al.* has been included. In recent years symposium volumes and review articles have become progressively more important as means of scientific communication. These, likewise, have been largely neglected in this list.

Annotated list of references

AMERICAN PUBLIC HEALTH ASSOCIATION. 1960. Standard methods for the examination of water and wastewater; including bottom sediments and sludges. 11th ed. Amer. Pub. Health Assoc., New York. 626 p. This book has served as a ready reference for chemical, physical, and bacteriological methods of water analysis, and in the more recent editions plankton and benthos have also been included. First edition in 1905.

CARLANDER, K. D. 1950. Handbook of freshwater fishery biology. W. C. Brown, Dubuque, Iowa. 281 + v p.

————. 1953. First supplement to handbook of freshwater fishery biology. W. C. Brown, Dubuque, Iowa. 277–429 + vi p.

CARPENTER, KATHLEEN E. 1928. Life in inland waters, with especial reference to animals. Macmillan, New York. 267 + xviii p. A general introduction to the biology of fresh waters.

CLARKE, F. W. 1924. The data of geochemistry. 5th ed. U. S. Geol. Surv., Bull. 770, 841 p. A compilation of chemical analyses that has been widely used as a reference and for establishing the mean ionic composition of inland waters. A revision of this work by D. A. Livingstone will soon be published by the U.S. Geological Survey.

CLARKE, G. L. 1954. Elements of ecology. John Wiley & Sons, New York. 534 + xiv p. Being primarily an oceanographer and a limnologist, Clarke has included many illustrations from aquatic ecosystems in his textbook.

COKER, R. E. 1954. Streams, lakes, ponds. Univ. North Carolina Press, Chapel Hill. 327 + xviii p. This is a very readable account of freshwater hydrobiology, with a good chapter on density currents in reservoirs.

DAVIS, C. C. 1955. The marine and fresh-water plankton. Michigan State Univ. Press, East Lansing. 562 + xi p. An attempt to treat the composition and general life conditions of all plankton.

EDDY, SAMUEL, AND A. C. HODSON. 1961. Taxonomic keys to the common animals of the North Central States, exclusive of the parasitic worms, insects and birds. 3rd ed. Burgess Publ. Co., Minneapolis. 162 + v p. This well-illustrated key, although not confined to aquatic animals, is useful for the beginning student in working with all aquatic groups except insects. First edition in 1950.

EDMONDSON, W. T. (ed.). 1959. Fresh-water biology. 2nd ed. John Wiley & Sons, New York. 1248 + xx p. This revision of the 1918 classic by Ward and Whipple serves as the most comprehensive single source book for the systematics of all organisms in our inland waters except parasites and aquatic vertebrates.

FASSETT, N. C., with revision appendix by E. C. OGDEN. 1957. A manual of aquatic plants. 2nd ed. Univ. Wisconsin Press, Madison. 405 + ix p. The standard book on the aquatic plants of the northeastern quarter of the United States. First edition in 1940.

FREY, D. G. 1953. The teaching of limnology in the United States. Sci. Monthly, 76(5): 290–296.

GALTSOFF, P. S., et al. 1937. Culture methods for invertebrate animals. Comstock Publ. Co., Ithaca, New York. 590 + xxiii p. This book is a useful source of reference for culture methods developed by various investigators for freshwater, marine, and terrestrial invertebrates.

HUBBS, C. L., AND R. W. ESCHMEYER. 1938. The improvement of lakes for fishing; a method for fish management. Inst. Fish. Research, Michigan Conserv. Dept., Bull. No. 2, 233 p.

HUTCHINSON, G. E. 1957. A treatise on limnology. Vol. I. Geography, physics, and chemistry. John Wiley & Sons, New York. 1015 + xiv p. The first of several projected volumes reviewing and integrating the entire field of limnology. It is indispensable for anyone seriously working in the field.

LAGLER, K. F. 1952. Freshwater fishery biology. W. C. Brown, Dubuque, Iowa. 350 + x p.

LAGLER, K. F., J. E. BARDACH, AND R. R. MILLER. 1962. Ichthyology. John Wiley & Sons, New York. In press.

MORGAN, ANN H. 1930. Field book of ponds and streams; an introduction to the life of fresh water. Putnam, New York. 448 + xvi p. An entertaining and helpful guide for the beginner to the life in fresh water.

MOULTON, F. R. (ed.). 1939. Problems of lake biology. Amer. Assoc. Advance. Sci., Publ. 10. Science Press, Lancaster, Pennsylvania. 142 p. This is a volume of papers by G. L. Clarke, F. E. Eggleton, F. E. J. Fry, A. T. Henrici, R. W. Pennak, G. W. Prescott, D. S. Rawson, W. L. Tressler ,and L. R. Wilson concerned with the importance of various groups of organisms in the overall economy of lakes and with the chemical and physical metabolism of lakes and the utilization of solar energy.

MOULTON, F. R., AND FLORENCE HITZEL (eds.). 1949. Limnological aspects of water supply and waste disposal. Amer. Assoc. Advance. Sci., Washington, D.C. 87 p. Another symposium volume, containing papers by J. N. Wilson, S. L. Chang, A. F. Bartsch and W. S. Churchill, W. M. Van Horn, J. B. Lackey, B. H. Ketchum et al., C. E. Taft, and J. B. Moyle. The papers, although concerned chiefly with the sanitary aspects of limnology, are of general interest as well, especially the paper by Moyle on the long-term effects of $CuSO_4$ on lake metabolism.

MUENSCHER, W. C. 1944. Aquatic plants of the United States. Comstock Publ. Co., Ithaca, New York. 374 + x p. A second book on aquatic plants, which, although it covers a wider area, is less comprehensive than the one by Fassett because the definition of aquatic plants is more restricted.

NEEDHAM, J. G. 1930. The teaching of hydrobiology and aquiculture in American universities. Science, 71: 265–266.

NEEDHAM, J. G., AND J. T. LLOYD. 1937. The life of inland waters; an elementary textbook of freshwater biology for students. 3rd ed. Comstock Publ. Co., Ithaca, New York. 438 p. The first edition of this book, published in 1916, was the first general book devoted exclusively to freshwater hydrobiology in North America. The book is organism oriented and contains relatively little information on limnological processes.

NEEDHAM, J. G., AND P. R. NEEDHAM. 1935. A guide to the study of freshwater biology. Comstock Publ. Co., Ithaca, New York. 88 p. A handy, well-illustrated guide to the common aquatic organisms of the Cornell region, which has been widely used by generations of students in eastern North America.

NEEDHAM, J. G., et al. 1941. A symposium on hydrobiology. Univ. Wisconsin Press, Madison. 405 + ix p. This symposium, held at the University of Wisconsin while Birge and Juday were still active, represents a substantial summary of the status at that time of many aspects of limnology.

NEEDHAM, P. R. 1940. Trout streams; conditions that determine their productivity and suggestions for stream and lake management. Comstock Publ. Co., Ithaca, New York. 233 + x p. A book summarizing Needham's extensive experience in the study and management of trout streams and containing a general description of stream limnology.

ODUM, E. P., in collaboration with H. T. ODUM. 1959. Fundamentals of ecology. 2nd ed. Saunders, Philadelphia. 546 + xvii p. This ecology textbook is included in the list because of its excellent presentation of ecosystem ecology and of the energy relationships in communities. H. T. Odum collaborated in the latter section, in particular. First edition in 1953.

PENNAK, R. W. 1953. Fresh-water invertebrates of the United States. Ronald Press, New York. 769 + xix p. With the accumulation of additional information the 1918 edition of *Fresh-water biology* became so out of date that Pennak single-handedly attempted to remedy the situation—a monumental undertaking. The book is authoritative, in that each of the individual chapters was carefully read by a specialist in the group of organisms concerned. The book enjoys a wide popularity among students and limnologists.

RAINWATER, F. H., AND L. L. THATCHER. 1960. Methods for collection and analysis of water samples. U.S. Geol. Surv., Water-Supply Paper 1454. 301 + ix p. Another book on the analysis of water samples, which is well documented and contains many helpful procedures.

REID, G. K. 1961. Ecology of inland waters and estuaries. Reinhold, New York. 375 + xvi p. Reid has attempted the difficult task of describing the ecology of estuaries, which are transitional between pure limnology and pure oceanography.

RICKER, W. E. 1958. Handbook of computations for biological statistics of fish populations. Fish. Research Board Canada, Bull. 119, 300 p. A standard book in its field, first published in 1948 as *Methods of estimating vital statistics of fish populations,* Indiana Univ. Publ., Sci. Ser. No. 15.

ROUNSEFELL, G. A., AND W. H. EVERHART. 1953. Fishery science, its methods and applications. John Wiley & Sons, New York. 444 + xii p.

RUSSELL, I. E. 1895. Lakes of North America; a reading lesson for students of geography and geology. Ginn & Co., Boston. 125 + xi p. One of the very early descriptions of some of the major lakes of North America, well written and fascinating to read.

———. 1898. Rivers of North America. Putnam, New York. 327 p. An equally interesting description of the rivers.

RUTTNER, FRANZ. 1952. Fundamentals of limnology. 2nd ed. Univ. Toronto Press, Toronto. 242 + xi p. This book is included in the list, not because it was written by a North American, but because its English translation gives the American student an acquaintance with and appreciation of one of the foremost limnologists of Europe. The third edition

of this book has now been published in Germany, and the English translation will appear early in 1963. It represents the best single account of limnological principles and processes.

SELLERY, G. C., with a chapter by C. H. MORTIMER. 1956. E. A. Birge. Univ. Wisconsin Press, Madison. 221 + vii p. Birge's long and active life, both as a limnologist and as an administrator, is well documented in this book. The chapter by Mortimer is of special interest to limnologists, since it attempts to assess critically Birge's contributions to the development of limnology.

SMITH, G. M. 1950. The fresh-water algae of the United States. 2nd ed. McGraw-Hill, New York. 719 + vii p. A general account of the systematics and biology of the freshwater algae. First edition in 1933.

STRICKLAND, J. D. H. 1960. Measuring the production of marine phytoplankton. Fish. Research Board Canada, Bull. 122, 172 + viii p. Strickland has prepared a careful and critical review of the various methods of measuring primary production, which are applicable to freshwater as well as marine situations.

STRICKLAND, J. D. H., AND T. R. PARSONS. 1960. A manual of sea water analysis. Fish. Research Board Canada, Bull. 125: 185 + vi p. Besides listing methods for the analysis of micronutrients and the components of particulate organic matter, this bulletin has a good discussion of measuring photosynthesis by oxygen production and radiocarbon uptake.

SVERDRUP, H. U., *et al.* 1942. The oceans; their physics, chemistry, and general biology. Prentice-Hall, New York. 1087 + x p. This has been a famous standard textbook and reference in general oceanography. North American books on oceanography since that time have been more restricted in scope.

USINGER, R. L. (ed.). 1956. Aquatic insects of California. Univ. California Press, Berkeley. 508 + ix p. Although a regional work as far as species are concerned, this book presents keys to the immature stages and adults of all genera of aquatic insects in North America. It represents our best single volume at this level.

VIBERT, R., AND K. F. LAGLER. 1961. Pêches continentales, biologie et aménagement. Dunod, Paris. 720 + xxiv p.

WARD, H. B., AND G. C. WHIPPLE. 1916. Freshwater biology. John Wiley & Sons, New York. 1111 + ix p. This extensive series of keys to species of the aquatic biota served many generations of aquatic biologists and did much to stimulate interest in freshwater organisms.

WELCH, P. S. 1952. Limnology. 2nd ed. McGraw-Hill, New York. 538 + xix p. The first edition published in 1935 was the first North American book in limnology that attempted to describe the interaction between aquatic organisms and their environment. It has had a great influence through its use by students and as a source of reference. Regretfully, the second edition includes relatively few of the major advances in limnology in the intervening years.

————. 1948. Limnological methods. Blakiston, Philadelphia. 381 + xviii p. This book is a useful reference for methods of surveying lakes and studying their biota. The chemical methods described are quite elementary by modern standards, so that some other source would have to be consulted for these.

WHIPPLE, G. C., revised by G. M. FAIR AND M. C. WHIPPLE. 1927. The microscopy of drinking water. 4th ed. John Wiley & Sons, New York. 586 + xix p. The first edition of this book published in 1899 might be considered the first general book in limnology, even antedating Forel's *Handbuch der Seenkunde,* although giving more emphasis to the strictly biological side of limnology. Later editions considered thermal and chemical stratification and other limnological processes. It has been one of the important books for giving sanitary engineers some background in general limnology, in contrast to the many books that have been written specifically as manuals for water supply treatment and waste disposal.

Conversion Factors for Units of Measurement

The editor has made no attempt to solicit or require uniformity throughout the book in units of length, area, volume, mass, and temperature. Some authors have endeavored to convert all measurements to the metric system, whereas others have quoted directly the units of measurement used in the papers being cited. Each approach has points in its favor. One argument for the direct approach is that it obviates awkward decimals, which obviously do not represent sampling intervals selected in planning a series of observations or experiments. To enable anyone to convert from the American system to the metric system or vice versa, the following brief table of conversion factors has been assembled. These factors do not apply in all instances to the English system because of the slight differences in definition of units of length, area, and volume.

Multiply	By	To Obtain	LENGTH	Multiply	By	To Obtain
in	2.540	cm		cm	0.394	in
ft	0.305	m		m	3.281	ft
yd	0.914	m		m	1.094	yd
mi	1.609	km		km	0.621	mi

Multiply	By	To Obtain	AREA	Multiply	By	To Obtain
yd^2	0.836	m^2		m^2	1.196	yd^2
acres	0.405	ha		ha	2.471	acres

Multiply	By	To Obtain	VOLUME	Multiply	By	To Obtain
ft^3	2.832×10^{-2}	m^3		m^3	35.314	ft^3
yd^3	0.765	m^3		m^3	1.308	yd^3
acre-ft	1233.49	m^3		m^3	8.107×10^{-4}	acre-ft
gal	3.785	L		L	0.264	gal

Multiply	By	To Obtain	MASS	Multiply	By	To Obtain
lb	0.454	kg		kg	2.205	lb

Multiply	By	To Obtain	CONCENTRATION AND RATE	Multiply	By	To Obtain
ft^3/sec*	1.699	m^3/min		m^3/min	0.589	ft^3/sec*
lbs/acre	1.121	kg/ha		kg/ha	0.892	lbs/acre
grains/gal	1.712×10^{-2}	g/L		g/L	58.418	grains/gal

TEMPERATURE

$F = 9/5\ C + 32$

$C = 5/9\ (F - 32)$

* ft^3/sec is also abbreviated cfs and cusec.

LIMNOLOGY *in North America*

1 | *David G. Frey*

Wisconsin: The Birge-Juday Era

A remarkable chapter in the development of the science of limnology extends from 1875, when the young E. A. Birge became an instructor at the University of Wisconsin, to the early 1940's. Chancey Juday, who was Birge's close associate for more than four decades, retired in 1942 and died in 1944. Birge lived until 1950, just 15 months short of his 100th birthday, but although he was active during most of his later years, his last papers were published in 1941 (Juday and Birge, 1941; Juday, Birge, and Meloche, 1941). Juday and Hasler (1946) cite a paper by Birge as being in press in the 1945 volume of the *Transactions of the Wisconsin Academy of Sciences, Arts, and Letters,* but this was never published.

The accomplishments of these two men and their associates are outstanding. Since a mere listing of their more than 400 publications occupies 21 printed pages (Juday and Hasler, 1946), I cannot aspire in a single chapter to give a critical appraisal of this vast effort in terms of its overall impact on the development of limnology. This has already been done in part for Birge, and to a lesser extent for Juday, in a very lucid essay by Mortimer (1956), which may be read and reread with profit by limnologists young and old.

The studies of Birge and Juday, although they are largely what is known today as descriptive limnology, are of interest not merely for their limnological descriptions of Wisconsin lakes but also for their significant contribution to our

understanding of limnological processes in general. "To summarize their impact on limnology in a few words is difficult; but I believe he [Birge] will be chiefly remembered because he laid bare the mechanics of stratification, and showed (with Juday) how the living processes of photosynthesis, respiration, and decay combine to produce a concurrent stratification of the dissolved gases. The Wisconsin partners will further be remembered for their chemical analyses and crop estimates of plankton; and for the extensive survey of water chemistry and plankton in northeastern Wisconsin" (Mortimer, 1956). To this should be added the pioneering studies of Birge and Juday and their associates on transmission of solar radiation by water.

Another important consideration is that Birge and Juday developed a program in limnology in which persons of many different primary interests participated—chemists, physicists, bacteriologists, algologists, plant physiologists, geologists, etc. Most of these persons were staff members and students from the University of Wisconsin, but during the operation of the Trout Lake Laboratory more and more persons from outside the state and even from outside the United States became associated with the program. Hence, the story of limnology in Wisconsin is not merely that of Birge and Juday, although they were the motivating force, but also that of their many associates. A chronological listing of the papers and reports arising from this total effort closely parallels the general development of the science of limnology, as reflected by changing rationale, methods of attack, and problems being investigated.

Contribution 719, Department of Zoology, Indiana University.

Fig. 1.1.—E. A. Birge. Portrait by Harold Hone.

Fig. 1.2.—Chancey Juday. Portrait by Harold Hone.

The men

Birge (Fig. 1.1) was born in 1851 in Troy, New York. He received his A.B. and A.M. degrees from nearby Williams College in Massachusetts, where he had already started working on Cladocera (Brooks *et al.*, 1951). "His early interest in the planktonic crustacea and the chance which brought him to the shores of Mendota combined to start him on an exploration of the world in which lake plankton live" (Mortimer, 1956).

Promotions were more rapid in those times. Birge became a professor at Wisconsin in 1879 after only four years as an instructor, including time off to complete his Ph.D. at Harvard in 1878. During 1880–81 he studied at Leipzig with Carl Ludwig, working on the nerve fibers and ganglion cells in the spinal cord of the frog. On his return to Wisconsin he constituted a one-man department of biology, teaching courses in zoology, botany, bacteriology, human anatomy, and physiology. Later when a separate Department of Zoology was organized, he served as its first chairman until 1906.

Birge became more and more involved in administrative work at the university. These facets of his life, as well as his impact on the univer-

sity and community in general, are detailed in the book by Sellery (1956). Among other responsibilities he was appointed Dean of the College of Letters and Science in 1891, and he served as Acting President of the university from 1900–1903 and as President from 1918–25.

His early studies on the plankton Crustacea of Lake Mendota (Birge *et al.*, 1895; Birge, 1897) represent the first real beginning of limnology in Wisconsin and of Birge as a limnologist. His earlier studies (Birge, 1878, 1879, 1881, 1892, 1893) were primarily faunistic. The study on the seasonal distribution of the plankton in lakes led him directly into an investigation of thermal stratification and chemical changes in the hypolimnion.

Fortunately, through the establishment of the Wisconsin Geological and Natural History Survey in 1897, of which Birge served as Director until 1919, he was able to initiate a broad program of obtaining basic morphometric data on the lakes of southeastern Wisconsin, and he was also able to hire a full-time biologist to help direct and carry out the limnological activities of the survey. This biologist was Chancey Juday.

Juday (Fig. 1.2) was born in 1871 at Millersburg along the northern edge of the lake district in Indiana. Very likely as a boy he was stimulated by lakes and by the excitement of discovering the diversity of life they contain. At Indiana University, where he obtained the A.B. and A.M. degrees (in 1896 and 1897) and much later an honorary LL.D., he came into contact with Carl Eigenmann, who in 1895 had established a biological station on Turkey Lake (now known as Lake Wawasee) only a few miles from Juday's home (Frey, 1955). It was perhaps inevitable that Eigenmann and Juday should get together, and that Juday should participate in the summer research program at Turkey Lake. Juday's first papers (1896, 1897, 1903) are concerned with Turkey Lake and Winona Lake, to which the station was relocated in 1899, and with Lake Maxinkuckee (Juday, 1902, 1920c), where he spent some time in 1899 studying the amount of plankton in the water and the diel movements of the plankton Crustacea.

Juday was appointed Biologist of the Wisconsin Geological and Natural History Survey in 1900. His first assignment, appropriately, was to study the diel migration of· zooplankton in Mendota and other lakes of southeastern Wisconsin (Juday, 1904a), but after only a year he had to withdraw because of health, and for the next few years he served on the biology or zoology staffs of the universities of Colorado and California. During these years he studied the fishes and fisheries of Colorado and Lake Tahoe (Juday, 1904b, 1905, 1906a, 1907b, 1907d, 1907e) and the marine Cladocera (Juday, 1907a) and ostracods (Juday, 1906b, 1907c) of the San Diego region.

In 1905 he rejoined the Wisconsin Geological Survey as Biologist, a position he held until 1931. In 1908 he was appointed Lecturer in Limnology in the Department of Zoology at the University of Wisconsin, and from this time until 1941 (serving as Professor of Zoology from 1931) he taught and directed the training of graduate students in limnology and fisheries.

The early efforts of Birge and Juday as a team were concentrated on the Madison lakes, especially Lake Mendota, and on other lakes of southeastern Wisconsin. These studies were either problem oriented or lake oriented. The volume on dissolved gases (Birge and Juday, 1911) Mortimer (1956) regards as "the most outstanding single contribution of the Wisconsin School."

Fig. 1.3.—Sketch of original three buildings at the Trout Lake Limnological Laboratory. From Juday and Birge, 1930.

This study led directly into quantitative studies of plankton standing crops (Birge and Juday, 1922) and still later to an investigation of the dissolved organic content of lake waters (Birge and Juday, 1926, 1927a, 1927b, 1934) as a means of studying the differences among lakes in their ability to produce organic matter.

After 1917 their effort shifted away from the Madison region. During the period 1921–24 they carried out an intensive chemical and biological investigation of Green Lake, the deepest (72 m) lake in the state and also the deepest lake in the United States (exclusive of the Great Lakes) between the Finger Lakes of New York and the mountain lakes in the West. Unfortunately the results were never completely analyzed and published (Juday, 1924a, 1924b).

The study on dissolved gases was based mainly on lakes in southeastern Wisconsin, although many lakes in the northeastern and northwestern lake districts were examined briefly. Birge and Juday believed it might be desirable to shift their base of activities from near Madison to the northern part of the state. Birge had previously spent part of the summer of 1892 in northern Wisconsin (Birge, 1893), and a preliminary survey in August 1924 (Juday and Birge, 1930) showed the lakes in the northeastern district to be diversified both in biology and in chemistry. Accordingly, in June 1925 a summer field station was established on Trout Lake (Fig. 1.3) with the close cooperation of the State Forestry Headquarters there. Juday served as the Director of this laboratory until his retirement in 1942. The approach here was not so much problem oriented or lake oriented, but rather it was concerned with surveying large numbers of lakes for various chemical and biological properties and studying the range of variation of these properties and their presumed controls, especially as related to drainage and seepage categories.

Many students, both undergraduate and graduate, were involved in these studies. Many senior investigators from the University of Wisconsin and from other states or nations were attracted to the Trout Lake Laboratory to conduct studies of interest. Some of the persons associated with this period of research are Manning, Pennak, Hasler, Twenhofel, Whitney, Woltereck, Kozminski, Wilson, Potzger, and others. Regardless of one's opinion concerning the value of survey-type programs, he must admit that a large volume of basic information concerning limnology derived from these efforts.

If the aim of limnology is the better understanding of the environmental control of living processes, it is a debatable point whether, for a given effort, more knowledge is to be gained by concentrating on a problem selected for one lake or organism, or by the wider survey of the kind we are reviewing. Or, stated differently, did Birge [and Juday] advance more on the narrow front on Lake Mendota or in the wider campaigns in northeastern Wisconsin? This is a matter of opinion. . . . No doubt the future will show that both methods of attack, in their time and place, have value [Mortimer, 1956].

Although Birge and Juday did most of their research in Wisconsin, separately and together they carried on some short-term studies outside the state. From October 1907 to June 1908 Juday visited various limnologists and limnological laboratories in Europe (Juday, 1910), and in February 1910 he visited some lakes in Guatemala and Salvador. The resulting paper (Juday, 1915) represents one of the first studies in tropical limnology. Birge and Juday together investigated the Finger Lakes of New York (Birge and Juday, 1914, 1921) and likewise made a brief study of Lake Okoboji in Iowa (Birge and Juday, 1920). Other studies, in which the field work was carried out by their associates, concern lakes of the northwestern United States (Kemmerer et al., 1923) and Karluk Lake, Alaska (Birge and Rich, 1927; Juday et al., 1932).

Both men were active in national affairs, serving variously as president of the American Microscopical Society, American Fisheries Society, Ecological Society of America, and the Wisconsin Academy of Sciences, Arts, and Letters. Moreover, Juday was one of the persons instrumental in bringing about the birth of the Limnological Society of America, and he was elected president for its first two years. Juday was awarded the Leidy Medal by the Academy of Natural Sciences of Philadelphia in 1943, and Birge and Juday together were awarded the Einar Naumann Medal by the International Association of Limnology in 1950 in recognition of their important and numerous contributions to the field.

They were not summer vacation limnologists; their approach was the opposite of dilettante. They were by no means averse to speculation; but first of all they assiduously collected the facts. The complexity of the questions [in the dissolved gases study] have "become more and more manifest as our experience has extended to numerous lakes and to many seasons. If this report had been written at the close of the first or second year's work it would have been much more definite in its conclusions and explanations than is now the case. The extension of our acquaintance with the lakes has been fatal to many interesting and at one time promising theories." Without such "extension of acquaintance" they might never have achieved that insight into the mechanisms of stratification, interplay of sun and wind, and the quantitative bonds between plankton activities and dissolved gases, which form the unique and really valuable core of their work [Mortimer, 1956].

These are good words to remember at a time, such as the present, when there is so much emphasis on speed of publication and length of personal bibliographies.

Further information on the biographies of Birge and Juday is given in the publications by Welch (1944), Noland (1945), Brooks et al. (1951), Sellery (1956), and Mortimer (1956).

The region

In terms of its effects on limnology and limnological processes, the climate of Wisconsin is continental, with cold winters and hot summers. "In 36 of the last 50 years a minimum of $-40°$ F or lower has been recorded in some part of the State, while, on the other hand, there are very few summers during which the temperature does not reach 100° or higher in some localities" (Coleman, 1941). The temperature is considerably milder in the southern portion, with mean annual temperatures ranging from 47° F in the south to 39° F in the extreme north.

This has two consequences for limnology. In the first place, all the lakes become ice covered in winter. In the northeastern lake district the shallower lakes freeze over by mid-November, the deeper lakes not until early December. The ice generally disappears about the first of May (Juday and Birge, 1930). In southern Wisconsin, during the period 1852–1948 Lake Mendota on the average froze over on 14 December and thawed on 4 April, for an ice-cover duration of 112 days. The extremes in duration of ice cover ranged from 65 days in the winter of 1931–32 to 161 days in 1880–81. The earliest the lake has frozen over is 25 November 1857, and the latest it has thawed is 6 May 1957 (Ragotzkie, 1960).

Lake Wingra, which is nearby, is much smaller, and, as would be expected, it freezes earlier in winter than Mendota and thaws earlier in spring. The records, extending from 1877 to the present, are much less complete than for Mendota. They show, however, that on the average the lake froze over on 25 November and thawed on 29 March, for an average ice-bound period of 125 days (W. E. Noland, 1950).

Coupled with this long period of ice cover is a rather heavy snowfall. Some regions in the extreme northern part of the state average 55 to 60 in. per winter, whereas in the south the snowfall averages about 30 in. (Coleman, 1941). In those winters having a long duration of ice cover with a sufficient thickness of snow on top, at least the shallow lakes can experience great enough oxygen utilization beneath the ice to result in fish mortalities (Greenbank, 1945: this study was conducted in the neighboring state of Michigan, where conditions are roughly comparable to those of Wisconsin).

The second consequence of the continental climate for limnology is that as a result of the short springs and hot summers, thermal stratification in the lakes becomes established early, often with only an incomplete spring overturn in the smaller lakes, and within a relatively short time the temperature-depth curve exhibits the sharp sigmoid shape which is characteristic of our continental lakes throughout the summer but which is not attained by most western European lakes until late summer or even until the partial fall overturn. The three zones of a stratified holomictic lake—epilimnion, metalimnion (thermocline), and hypolimnion—are so sharply defined in the lakes of southern Wisconsin that Birge's definition of the thermocline as that stratum in which the temperature gradient equals or exceeds 1° C per meter of depth (Birge, 1904b; Birge and Juday, 1914) is quite realistic.

Also of importance to limnology is precipitation and its distribution. "The average annual precipitation in Wisconsin ranges from about 26 inches in some parts of the extreme north to about 34 inches along the extreme southern and southwestern borders. The wettest months are May to September, inclusive. . . . During this period the rainfall is fairly well distributed" (Coleman, 1941). The heaviest rainfall comes after the melting of the winter snows, which tends to reduce the vernal flood peaks in the rivers. Because of the abundant summer precipitation, all except the smallest streams flow the year around (Martin, 1932).

The bedrock geology of Wisconsin consists of pre-Cambrian and Paleozoic formations, covered by a mantle of glacial drift, except in the southwestern quarter of the state, which has long been known as the Driftless Area. There are no Mesozoic or Tertiary rocks in the state. The pre-Cambrian igneous and metamorphic rocks occur in the northern portion of the state (largely co-extensive with the Northern Highland and Lake Superior Lowland in Fig. 1.4), which is part of the Superior Upland (Fenneman, 1938) and is continuous with the vast pre-Cambrian shield of Canada. The region to the south is included in Fenneman's Central Lowland, although Martin (1932) prefers to subdivide this further into Central Plain, Western Upland, and Eastern Ridges and Lowlands provinces (Fig. 1.4).

The Central Plain is underlain mainly by a soft Upper Cambrian sandstone. The remainder of southern Wisconsin is underlain mainly by resistant Ordovician and Silurian dolomites, which, as a result of their arrangement on a broad anticlinal fold with a general north-south trend, produce a series of cuestas, with their escarpments facing westward in the Eastern Ridges and Lowlands province. Martin refers to southern Wisconsin as a belted plain, similar to those of eastern England and the Paris basin in France.

Elevations range from a low of 581 ft in the southeast along Lake Michigan to a high of 1,940 ft in the northern part of the state (Martin, 1932). In general the entire Northern Highland is a relatively high plateau with elevations ranging from 1,000 to 1,800 ft. The southwestern

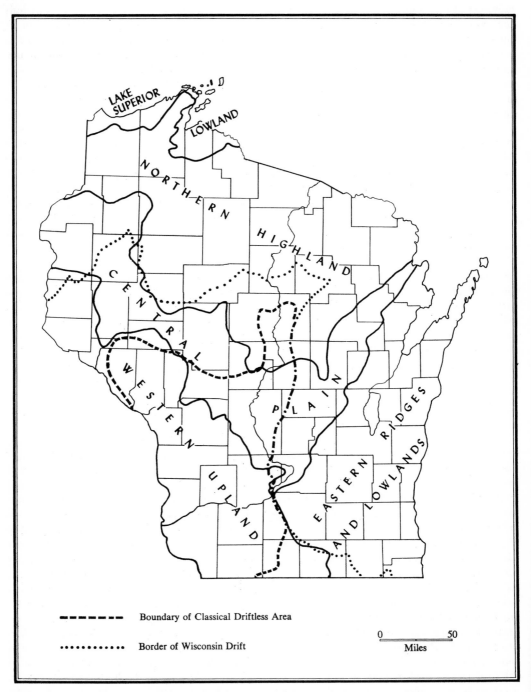

Fig. 1.4.—Physiographic provinces of Wisconsin. From Martin, 1932, and a map furnished by the Wisconsin Geological and Natural History Survey. Prepared by the University of Wisconsin Cartographic Laboratory.

quarter of the state in the Driftless Area, on the other hand, is a dissected region of steep valleys and well-developed dendritic drainages.

Three-quarters of the state definitely has been glaciated at one time or another. The most recent glacial deposits are from the Wisconsin (or Wisconsinan: see Frye and Willman, 1960) Stage, named by T. C. Chamberlin from its occurrence in Wisconsin (Chamberlin, 1894, 1895). The location of the Wisconsin Drift boundary is shown in Figure 1.4. It is well marked by an almost continuous system of end moraines. The Wisconsin Stage land surfaces are characterized by an abundance of such glacial features as drumlins, eskers, kames, and boulder trains and by several kettle moraines in the state, the one in southeastern Wisconsin, representing an interlobate moraine between the Green Bay and Michigan lobes, extending a linear distance of considerably more than 100 mi.

Between the Wisconsin Stage boundary and the boundary of the Driftless Area in the southwest are extensive regions of ground moraine, outwash, and glacial lake sediments. The Driftless Area was early noted because of the complete absence there of all igneous and metamorphic erratics, such as are common elsewhere in the state. More recently Black (1959, 1960) has claimed that "isolated deposits explainable only by glaciation are on crests of the highest ridges in all but LaCrosse County in the classical 'Driftless Area' of southwest Wisconsin. . . . Locally contorted bedrock, absence of thick residual soils and of weathering in the deposits, and absence of old loess further confirm glaciation of much, if not all, of the Driftless Area during the early Wisconsinan stage or all of it during a pre-Wisconsinan stage." The Driftless Area as originally mapped extends modestly into the neighboring states of Minnesota, Iowa, and Illinois. There are many small caves in the Driftless Area but almost none in the Eastern Ridges and Lowlands Province. Most of the karst features here either have been destroyed by glacial erosion or are buried beneath drift.

Largely because of the recency of its glaciation, Wisconsin is well provided with lakes. According to Voigt (1958) there are 8,830 lakes in the state, 4,136 of which have an area exceeding 10 acres. Included in this total are an unknown number of "flowage" lakes and reservoirs, although the vast majority of the lakes listed are natural. Every county has at least one lake, and, as would be expected, the counties in the Driftless Area generally have a smaller number and a lower density of lakes than do the counties in the glaciated region (Fig. 1.5). Vilas County leads with 968 lakes and a density of slightly more than one per mi², followed by Oneida with 830 lakes. It is little wonder that Birge and Juday established a laboratory at Trout Lake in Vilas County near the center of this northeastern lake district (Fig. 1.6).

For the state as a whole, lakes make up 2.6% of the total area, but for Vilas County they comprise 15.1% of the total land surface. Other counties have smaller percentages of their total areas in lakes. Only 1.6% of the area of Dane County is in lakes, although in this case the intensive studies on Mendota and the other lakes of the Yahara River chain (Fig. 1.7) more than compensate for any deficiency in number or acreage.

The largest natural lakes of the state are Winnebago, 558 km²; Poygan, 44.5 km²; Koshkonong, 40.0 km²; Mendota, 39.4 km². Winnebago has a maximum depth of only 6.4 m, whereas nearby Green Lake is the deepest lake in the state, with a maximum depth of 72.2 m (Juday, 1914a).

There are three well-defined lake districts in Wisconsin (Juday and Birge, 1930; Martin, 1932): (1) eastern and southeastern Wisconsin, consisting of scattered, moderate-size lakes, (2) northeastern Wisconsin (Vilas, Oneida, Iron, Forest, Lincoln, and Langlade counties), containing 34% of all the lakes in 10% of the state's area, and (3) northwestern Wisconsin (chiefly Washburn, Burnett, Polk, Barron, and Chippewa counties), containing 21% of the lakes on 8% of the area. In addition there are Lake Pepin in the Mississippi River, which is backed up behind the delta of the Chippewa River, Lake St. Croix on the lower St. Croix River, and hundreds of small flood-plain lakes ("Altwässer") in the Mississippi bottomland. These latter have not been included in the state totals.

Most of the major rivers of the state arise in the Northern Highland. The master stream of the state is the Wisconsin River, which arises at Lac Vieux Desert on the Wisconsin-Michigan border and completely traverses the state, entering the Mississippi River near the southwestern corner (Fig. 1.8). The Black, Chippewa, and St. Croix rivers are other major drainages that enter

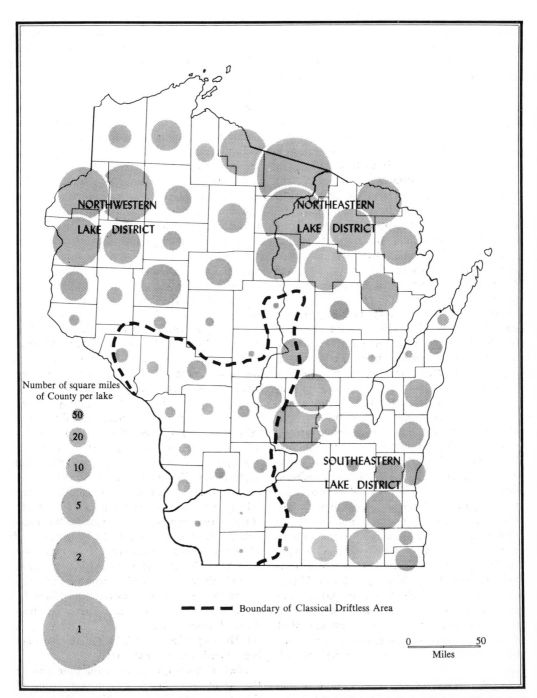

Fig. 1.5.—Density of lakes in Wisconsin by counties. The areas of the circles are proportional to the mean number of lakes per square mile. The scale at the left is the reciprocal of this, namely, the number of square miles of county for each lake. The dashed line represents the boundary of the Driftless Area, as originally described. Prepared by the University of Wisconsin Cartographic Laboratory.

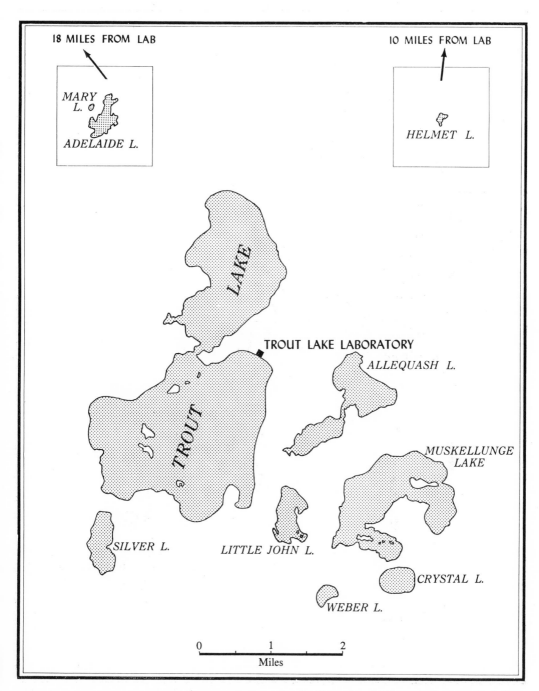

18 MILES FROM LAB

MARY L.

ADELAIDE L.

10 MILES FROM LAB

HELMET L.

LAKE

TROUT LAKE LABORATORY

ALLEQUASH L.

TROUT

MUSKELLUNGE LAKE

SILVER L.

LITTLE JOHN L.

CRYSTAL L.

WEBER L.

0   1   2
Miles

Fig. 1.6.—Location of the Trout Lake Limnological Laboratory and of some of the neighboring lakes that have been studied most intensively. Prepared by the University of Wisconsin Cartographic Laboratory.

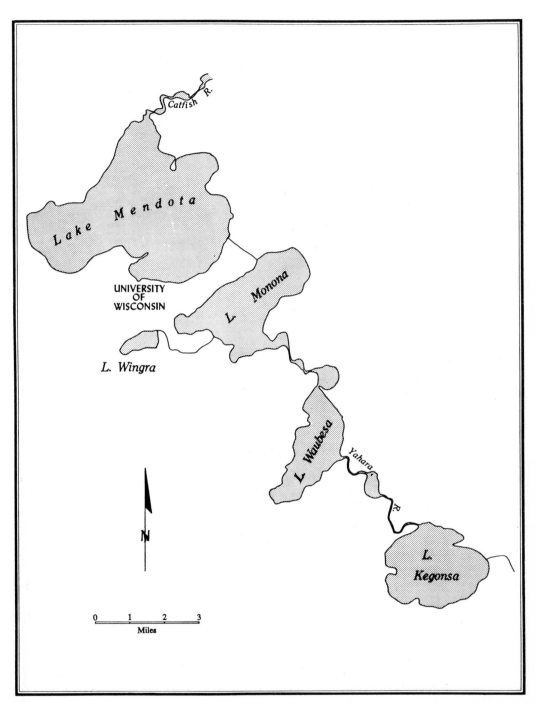

Fig. 1.7.—Lakes of the Yahara River chain at Madison, Wisconsin. The lakes are sometimes designated by numbers beginning at the south, rather than by the names shown in the figure. Thus, Kegonsa is alternately known as First Lake and Mendota as Fourth Lake. From Juday, 1914*a*, as prepared by the University of Wisconsin Cartographic Laboratory.

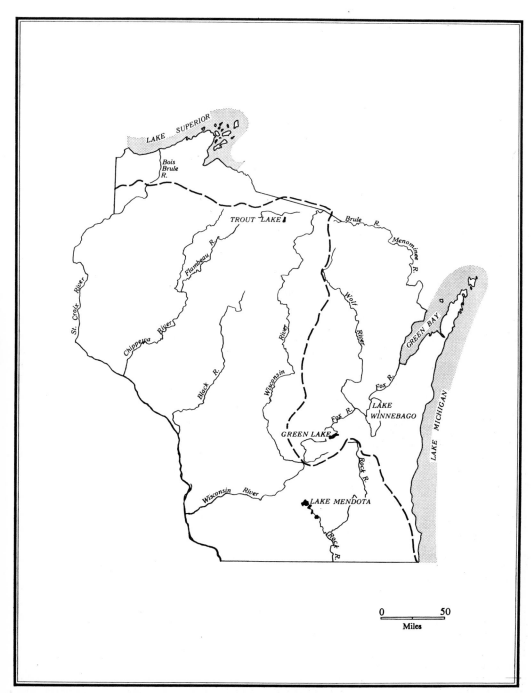

Fig. 1.8.—Major rivers of Wisconsin. The dashed line marks the approximate watershed divide between the Mississippi and Great Lakes drainages. From a map provided by the Wisconsin Geological and Natural History Survey, as prepared by the University of Wisconsin Cartographic Laboratory.

cera. Realizing that his knowledge of the Cladocera in the southern United States was very
deficient, he undertook a brief collecting trip to
New Orleans and Texas in 1903, and he profited
greatly from the subsequent collecting by and
correspondence with Mr. E. Foster of the New
Orleans *Daily Picayune.*

Birge's chapter on Cladocera for *Fresh-Water
Biology* was completed by 1910 (Birge, 1910*d*),
even though the volume was not published until
1918. His paper of 1910 detailed the taxonomic
changes that were to appear in his monograph
and presented some of his general views regarding relationships among the Cladocera. These last
two efforts on the Cladocera (1910*d*, 1918*a*) were
those of a mature, thoroughly competent investigator. But, whatever Birge's goals may have been
originally, he abandoned further work on the
systematics of Cladocera after 1910. Moreover,
no one else has subsequently undertaken so detailed a study of Cladocera in general. His monograph in *Fresh-Water Biology* remains to this
day the definitive treatment of our Cladocera,
except as it has been modified by Brooks (1959)
in the revised edition.

In the monograph (1918*a*) Birge listed 113
species for the United States, of which he described 14. He noted that:

A majority of the species found in this country are
found also in Europe. Where a species is peculiar to
this region it is often but slightly different from the
European form. The student of Cladocera should presume that any species is probably intercontinental, although it may prove to be more restricted in its range.
The study of our forms has not gone far enough to
enable us to speak of the local distribution of each
species within the general area which it covers, but it
is known that rare species are very irregularly distributed. On the whole, the fauna of the various regions
of the country is strikingly similar, but with some
forms peculiar to each region. The southern states contain numerous species which are common to them and
to South America, but are not found in the northern
states.

A word of caution should be inserted, however.
Birge himself recognized that the monograph was
incomplete. For the small species of *Alona,* for
example, he noted that "there are species and
numerous varieties besides those listed." Our
intensive work on the chydorids and their exuviae
in lake sediments has revealed quite a substantial
number of species even in the Midwest that are
not included in Birge's monograph. The gap is
greatest in the South, where quite a number of

new species and new records of species, previously described from South America and elsewhere in the Tropics, occur. A person using the
monograph should not assume that it is complete.
Specimens not agreeing with the descriptions or
figures may, in fact, be undescribed.

Both Birge and Juday at various times examined collections made by other persons and reported on the species recovered. These papers are
of limited value, since they contain very little
information besides names of species and places
and dates of collecting. These comprise reports by
Birge on Lake St. Clair and some nearby lakes in
Michigan (Birge, 1894), Turkey Lake in Indiana
(Birge, 1895*a*), some lakes of the Sierras and
Rocky Mountains in which he described *Macro-
thrix montana* (Birge, 1904*a*), and Lakes Amatitlan and Atitlan in Guatemala (Birge, 1908*b*).
Except for the recording of the marine clado-
ceran, *Evadne tergestina,* near San Diego (Juday,
1907*a*) and the listing of Cladocera in Turner's
Lake, Maine (Juday, 1923*b*), all the rest of
Juday's papers involving the identification of
Cladocera are concerned with Canada and Alaska
(Juday, 1920*a*, 1926*a*, 1927; Juday and Mutt-
kowski, 1915).

Zooplankton

Although in his early years at Wisconsin Birge
was concerned chiefly with the systematics of the
Cladocera, he was not unaware of their ecology.
The shift in Birge's dominant interest from the
systematics of the Cladocera to their ecology and
finally to limnology in its broadest sense was occasioned by a brief and incompletely documented
paper by Francé (1894) on diel migration, which
demonstrated that in Lake Balaton the zooplankters come to the surface at night and do
not descend to greater depths until about dawn,
where they remain until early afternoon. Cladocera migrated first, followed by copepods. The
pattern was modified somewhat by weather conditions.

Since Mendota is about twice as deep as Balaton, although much smaller in area, Birge was
interested in ascertaining how extensive the migration might be in a deeper lake and also at
what rate it occurred. Accordingly, he assigned
this problem to two undergraduate students—
Olson and Harder—for their undergraduate
theses. They did most of the collecting and all
the counting. Birge designed a vertical tow net

that could be opened at any desired depth by means of a messenger and then closed again by a second messenger after the net had been pulled through a desired thickness of water, generally 3 m. By this means the 18-m water column at a station marked by a buoy was sampled by 3-m strata at 3-hour intervals day and night during four periods from 5 July to 4 August 1894.

The results were surprising and unanticipated (Birge *et al.,* 1895). During July only the uppermost 12 m of the lake were tenanted by copepods and Cladocera. More than 90% occurred in the uppermost 9 m, and about 50% occurred in the top 3 m. (In a subsequent paper Birge [1898] stated that 95% or more of the zooplankton occurred above the thermocline.) Of the 6 dominant species, the only variation from this pattern of greatest abundance towards the top and decrease with depth was *Daphnia pulicaria* (*D. schödleri*), which was largely confined between 6 and 15 m depth in its distribution. These patterns of distribution were constant day and night. There was no evidence for any diel migration, unless it was confined within the uppermost 3 m.

These findings so surprised and stimulated Birge that he continued sampling into the autumn. At this time he also began studying the thermal structure of the lake. He noted that in the autumn the distribution of the Cladocera changed gradually over a two-week period from the surface concentration characteristic of summer to an approximately uniform distribution from surface to bottom, which coincided with the cooling phase of the lake and the development of homothermy. Concerning the summer distribution, Birge noted that "the crustacea apparently stopped [in their vertical distribution] rather abruptly either somewhat above or somewhat below the 10 m level." This would mark the approximate upper limit of the thermocline, but there is no evidence that Birge at this time was aware of the summer thermal structure of lakes.

What started as the assignment of a routine research problem to undergraduates became Birge's introduction to limnology. The questions raised by the vertical distribution of the planktonic Crustacea stimulated him to continue these studies for two more years (Birge, 1898). He obtained 333 series of six successive 3-m samples each over the 2-year period, and of equal importance he measured the temperature distribution in the water column on each sampling date, using the simplest of equipment—a Meyer flask and a laboratory thermometer graduated to 0.2° C. When a thermophone was finally obtained in July 1896, Birge checked the accuracy of the Meyer flask method and decided that, for the purposes of his present study at least, the temperature readings were sufficiently accurate. Whereas in the previous paper all results of zooplankton distribution had been expressed as percentages, in the present study they were expressed as numbers of organisms per m^3 or per m^2 of lake surface. Birge calculated an efficiency factor for the net by comparing the net catches with those of a metal tube 3 m long and 10 cm in diameter.

The seasonal and vertical distributions of the planktonic crustaceans were described in detail for the two-year period, and these were then related to the annual temperature cycle of the lake. Birge was surprised that the changing seasonal abundance of the limnetic Crustacea was determined primarily by fluctuations in abundance of the seven perennial species. The periodic species contributed relatively little to the total. He noted in addition that "most of the littoral forms of crustacea also appear occasionally in the plankton, especially after storms, as also do Hydrachnids and Ostracoda." These, however, comprised less than 1% of the total plankton. The course of the cycles of abundance was remarkably similar in the various years, although the magnitude of the peaks varied. Birge believed the location of the peaks was determined primarily by temperature, as affecting the cycles of growth and reproduction of the various species, and the magnitude of the peaks by food supply. He made a special point of the occurrence in the plankton of *Chydorus sphaericus,* which is generally considered to be a littoral form, noting that it occurs almost exclusively when blue-green algae are abundant.

The pattern of vertical distribution noted in the previous paper was confirmed and extended: the entomostraca occur throughout the water column during the cold months of the year and are confined mainly above the thermocline in summer. Through attempts to determine the exact lower limit of the Crustacea, Birge concluded that "the crustacean population usually passes into the thermocline and often towards its lower part, but that here it ends often with great abruptness." Furthermore, "the number of algae also declines very rapidly at the thermocline and those which are obtained below this level are dead or dying." Birge concluded that:

The crustacea are not excluded from the deeper water of the lake by the low temperature of the water, as is proved by the occurrence of the same species in the far colder water of other lakes in the same district. The exclusion is due to the accumulation of the products of decomposition in the lower water, which remains entirely stagnant after the thermocline has been formed, and is never exposed to the action of sun and air. This water in Lake Mendota acquires an offensive smell and a disagreeable taste. . . . The products of decomposition of the algae and crustacea of winter and spring remain stored in the deeper water, and undoubtedly the addition of this store of nutritive material to the surface water of the lakes as the thermocline gradually moves downward is one of the factors which occasions the enormous increase of the vegetable plankton in late summer and autumn.

This same idea had been expressed earlier by FitzGerald, (1895). Later Birge cited some studies by Drown on various ponds in Massachusetts, which demonstrated that frequently the content of dissolved oxygen declined rapidly and even totally disappeared below the thermocline. Up to this time Birge had made no chemical studies himself, and hence he could not decide whether the decomposition products or reduced oxygen was the primary factor in eliminating limnetic Crustacea from the deep water of Mendota in summer. Obviously the next step in this developing program was to study the seasonal chemistry of the water.

Birge (1898) was still disturbed by the apparent lack of diel migration in Mendota. In a more detailed investigation of the top 3 m, using a pump and a horizontal tow net, he found that there was indeed a diel migration, but that it was confined to the uppermost 1 or $1\frac{1}{2}$ m, rather than extending over the entire depth of the lake as Francé had found.

The word "thermocline" has been used in the previous discussion. This term was proposed by Birge (1898) as a synonym for the *Sprungschicht* of the German investigators.

Birge (1898) presented a detailed analysis of the annual thermal regime of Mendota for the two years. He noted many phenomena that are now part of our general understanding of the thermal dynamics of lakes—the lowering of the thermocline during summer, the increase in water temperature beneath the ice, the marked rise in temperature of the bottom water during the destruction of thermal stratification in autumn,

the variations in position and thickness of the thermocline under various wind stresses, etc. He had already reached a general understanding of the interplay of sun and wind in setting up the thermal structure, as evidenced by the statement that "the warmth of the surface water received from the sun is distributed by the wind through a certain depth of the lake, a depth which is proportional to the violence of the wind and the area of the lake." Through his observations during two full years on Mendota and single visits to neighboring lakes he had reached the conclusion that the temperature of the bottom water in different lakes and its variation from year to year in the same lake is controlled by four factors—(1) the depth of the lake, (2) the area in relation to depth, (3) the shape of the lake and the nature of its surroundings, and (4) the temperature and wind movement during the spring warm-up. Brief summaries of these two major zooplankton studies were also published elsewhere (Birge, 1895b, 1897).

Thus, Birge, who only two years earlier had been interested mainly in the systematics of the Cladocera, was now a limnologist interested in "the natural history of an inland lake as 'a unit of environment,' to employ Eigenmann's appropriate phrase." He had already been led into a study of the seasonal thermal regime of Mendota. He realized that the chemistry of the water, especially during periods of stratification, would be important to understand, and he already anticipated the interplay between organisms and environment in the development of this stratification and the control of seasonal cycles of plankton. He was aware of the importance of sun and wind in controlling the seasonal stratification. Here, in essence, is Birge, the limnologist. He and his associates subsequently investigated all these fields, and more besides, constantly keeping in mind the totality of organic and inorganic processes going on in a body of water.

All this was going on while Juday was still a youth in his mid-twenties. He, too, was interested in plankton, and, significantly, his initial approach was concerned with biomass rather than numbers. In Turkey Lake he studied the horizontal and vertical distribution of plankton collected with a vertical tow net and concentrated by centrifuge (Juday, 1897). Most of the plankton occurred in the uppermost 3 m, with very little below 6 m. A similar study, but of lesser scope, was made on Maxinkuckee (Juday, 1902, 1920c), in which the plankton was confined almost entirely to the uppermost 12 m, and in which there was positive evidence of upward migration at night. During the Maxinkuckee study Juday used a simple pump for obtaining some deep-water samples from known depths. Because of this background and research interest and because of Birge's frequent contacts with Eigenmann at this time, it seems almost inevitable in retrospect that Juday should have been hired as Biologist in the newly formed Wisconsin Geological and Natural History Survey.

Birge was still interested in the diel migration of the Crustacea, which undoubtedly explains Juday's intensive study of this phenomenon in 30 lakes of southeastern Wisconsin, including Mendota, during his first year with the survey (Juday, 1904a). Using a pump and garden hose, Juday sampled at half-hour intervals during the periods encompassing sunset and sunrise, and even throughout the night. He found that although quite a number of species exhibited diel migration, the extent of movement for the same species varied greatly from lake to lake and even from one time to another in the same lake. He believed that light was the chief factor responsible for downward movement, but that other unspecified factors were more responsible for the upward movement. He also confirmed Birge's earlier observations on the very shallow daily readjustments of species in Mendota. Returning to Indiana briefly in the summer of 1901, Juday made similar studies on Winona Lake (Juday, 1903). He found a marked diel migration in *Epischura lacustris, Chaoborus,* and *Leptodora.* Shifts in the distribution of *Diaptomus* and *Cyclops* are possibly obscured by Juday's failure to distinguish species in these genera.

Unfortunately, because of Juday's health, which necessitated his leaving for several years shortly after he had arrived, and because of Birge's increased administrative responsibilities as Acting President of the university, there was a period of relative quiescence in limnology at Wisconsin.

Copepods and other early limnology

One can argue convincingly that Birge was not the first limnologist in Wisconsin. In 1883 C. D. Marsh, who was four years Birge's junior in age, became a Professor of Natural Science at Ripon College, just seven miles from Green Lake. According to his widow (Mrs. Florence W. Marsh,

1938), he had been interested in minute forms of freshwater life since boyhood. It is little wonder then that he was attracted to Green Lake, in spite of the difficulties of horse and buggy travel. Marsh's early trips to Green Lake and to other neighboring lakes awakened an interest in copepods, which he retained throughout his life. He became an authority on this group of microcrustacea, in the same way as Birge on the Cladocera. The two men complemented each other nicely, and they maintained a constant exchange of specimens and information.

Whereas Birge originally was interested in the pure systematics of the Cladocera, Marsh from the beginning was interested in environmental relationships as well. He recorded some depth profiles of Green Lake based on soundings made through the ice some years earlier by C. A. Kenaston, also of Ripon College, and he likewise measured surface and bottom temperatures with a deep-sea thermometer loaned by the U.S. Commissioner of Fish and Fisheries (Marsh, 1892b). To his surprise he found both *Pontoporeia* and *Mysis* in the deep water, the first reported instance of this in any of the smaller inland lakes of North America (Marsh, 1892a). In August of 1893, before Birge's students began a similar study, Marsh undertook an investigation of the diel migration of plankton Crustacea in Green Lake. A brief report on the early stages of this work was presented in 1894 and a final report in 1898. He used a vertical tow net (he called such a device a "dredge," as did Birge) that could be closed at any depth. There was a marked concentration of entomostraca toward the surface at night, although not all species exhibited such an upward migration. The Miller-Casella deep-sea maximum-minimum thermometer took so long to reach equilibrium that Marsh measured only surface and bottom temperatures, but these observations are presented in graphical form for two entire years. If Marsh had had an instrument that reached thermal equilibrium more rapidly and was more amenable to being operated from a sailboat, it is conceivable he would have anticipated Birge and FitzGerald in describing the annual thermal cycle of a lake.

He was disturbed by the great variability among replicate plankton samples. He considered depth of water as one of the chief controls in the geographic distribution of copepods, and he suggested dividing lakes into shallow and deep lakes

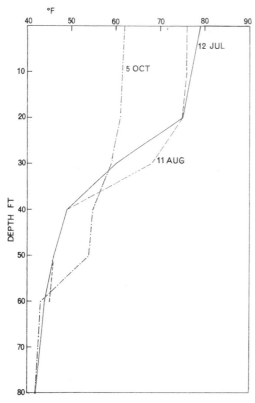

Fig. 1.9.—Thermal stratification in Pine Lake, Wisconsin, in 1879. From data given by Gifford and Peckham, 1882.

on the basis of their copepod faunas, with a dividing line at 40 m. Later (Marsh, 1901) he revised this to 30 or 35 m. This represents one of the very early attempts to recognize different kinds or types of lakes on the basis of organisms that live in them.

When the Wisconsin Geological and Natural History Survey began operations, Marsh was hired to construct a bathymetric map of Green Lake (Marsh, 1899). Subsequently he made a comparative study of the net plankton of Green and Winnebago lakes as representing deep and shallow lakes, respectively, with less intensive observations on about 30 other lakes, including some in the northern forested region (Marsh, 1903). Seasonal curves for the individual species of entomostraca and for the total volume of plankton were given. An interesting observation was that the cladoceran *Eurycercus lamellatus,* which is generally considered a littoral form, bulked large in the summer plankton of Lake Winnebago, forming a significant item in the diet

of the sheepshead (*Aplodinotus grunniens*).

Marsh left Ripon College in 1903 to obtain his Ph.D. from the University of Chicago, after which he joined the staff of the U.S. Department of Agriculture, investigating the poisoning of domestic animals by various forage plants. During this period of governmental employment, which lasted 25 years, he continued his interest in the systematics of the copepods. He examined collections from all parts of the United States and published 35 papers on his results, which are listed in a carefully prepared bibliography on pages 57–58 of his 1933 paper. Included are revisions of North American *Diaptomus* (Marsh, 1907) and *Cyclops* (Marsh, 1910), as well as the chapter on copepods in *Fresh-Water Biology* (Marsh, 1918).

Other systematic studies on copepods include those by Juday (1914*b*, 1923*a*, 1925) and Juday and Muttkowski (1915), the latter containing descriptions of two copepods—*Diaptomus pribilofensis* and *Heterocope septentrionalis*—that are widespread in the North American Arctic, as well as the papers by Wright (1927, 1928). In addition Bere (1931*a*, 1935) did some work on copepods parasitic on fish.

A few other early studies deserve mention. One of the most interesting of these is the measurement of subsurface temperatures in Pine Lake by Gifford and Peckham (1882), with a "self-registering thermometer" made by Hicks of London. Although most of the time only the surface and bottom temperatures were measured, on six occasions the temperature was measured at 10-ft intervals to depths as great as 80 ft. Gifford and Peckham themselves made no detailed analysis of the data, but the series for 12 July and 11 August, when plotted, show a very nice sigmoid curve, and the series for 5 October shows a substantial lowering of the thermocline (Fig. 1.9). The bottom water of Pine Lake remained at 41–42° F throughout the season from 11 May to 5 October. The authors found a uniform temperature on 2 December, concerning which they remarked that "probably in a larger lake this condition would not be reached before January."

Another early study was made by Hoy (1872) on the deep-water fauna of Lake Michigan. Based first on an analysis of the stomach contents of deep-water fishes, the study was supplemented by some dredgings on 24 June 1870. Hoy obtained *Mysis relicta* (named *M. diluvianus* by Stimpson) and a new species of cottid, both of which Hoy regarded as marine forms providing evidence of a former direct connection between Lake Michigan and the sea!

Another early study is that of Trelease (1889) on the blooms of blue-green algae in Mendota and Monona. The blooms were not of equal intensity in all years. That of 1882 in Mendota was so bad (chiefly *Microcystis* and *Coelosphaerium*) it prevented boating along the Madison shore. One interesting observation was on the production of horizontal rainbows by refraction or diffraction of light from floating colonies of blue-green algae partially projecting through the smooth water surface. This same phenomenon was noted later by Juday (1916*a*, 1920*b*).

Limnology: 1911–23

Dissolved gases

Ever since the study on the seasonal changes in the vertical distribution of plankton Crustacea and the suggestion that these organisms were eliminated from the bottom water in summer by chemical changes, Birge had wanted to begin a study of lake chemistry. In 1904 a gasometric method for determining O_2, CO_2, and N_2 was finally worked out with the help of two chemists at the university, and this method was subsequently used in 1905 to study the gas content principally of Mendota. Juday returned in August of that year. Whether it was at his instigation or Birge's is not certain, but in the subsequent summers the unmodified Winkler method was used for dissolved oxygen, and titrations to the methyl orange and phenolphthalein endpoints with $N/44$ Na_2CO_3 and $N/44$ HCl, as appropriate, were used in determining free CO_2, half-bound CO_2, and fixed CO_2. Gaseous nitrogen was not determined after the early part of 1906 (Birge and Juday, 1911).

I should add, parenthetically, that the concepts of "bound CO_2," and "half-bound CO_2," originally proposed by Seyler (see Juday, Birge, and Meloche, 1935), have led to some confusion. They are based first of all on the assumption that any alkalinity to the methyl orange endpoint results primarily from calcium (or magnesium) carbonate and bicarbonate, which is not true for all surface waters and certainly not true of those hypolimnions in which ammonia accumulates during summer stratification (Ohle, 1952).

Second, the interpretation of titration results is made even more difficult by Ohle's (1952) study, which showed that the carbon dioxide equilibrium is really an "inequilibrium," which follows the law of mass action very slowly under certain conditions, and that in hard-water lakes during periods of photosynthesis there can be considerable quantities of colloidal $CaCO_3$ in the water, which do not affect the pH or conductivity but do affect the methyl orange alkalinity. Third, most persons today generally report their results as parts per million of methyl orange alkalinity, but since it is not always clear whether $N/44$ acid (as recommended by Birge and Juday) or $N/50$ acid (as recommended by the American Public Health Association, 1955) was used in the titrations, the results may not be interpretable by the reader. To the writer it seems that the European practice of reporting methyl orange alkalinity as the number of milliequivalents of acid (acid combining capacity = SBV) required to titrate one liter of water to the methyl orange endpoint is least ambiguous and much to be preferred.

During the five years of study a tremendous amount of information on water chemistry, temperatures, and plankton was accumulated from 156 lakes in the three major lake districts of the state. Juday gradually was given almost complete responsibility for the study, and he took full charge of the field parties in the last two seasons. Birge, in spite of his heavy administrative duties, however, reported that he gave almost daily attention to the work and constantly reviewed the progress of the program. The final report (Birge and Juday, 1911) certainly represents one of the milestones of limnology.

In the meantime, Birge's concepts regarding ecological unity of lakes were being sharpened, and he was revealing himself more and more as a master essayist. His address in 1903 as President of the American Microscopical Society was "The thermocline and its biological significance" (Birge, 1904*b*). In this he described how the depth and extent of warming of a lake are determined by the interplay between the velocity and duration of the wind and the "thermal resistance to mixture" of the water. He distinguished between and illustrated two types of lakes—those with no zooplankton below the thermocline in summer and those with zooplankton in this region. As yet he had no terms for the zones above and below the thermocline, although he sometimes referred to them as the superthermocline and subthermocline. (He proposed the terms epilimnion and hypolimnion in a later paper [Birge, 1910b].) In two ideas he was not quite correct according to our current concepts. He considered that only slow water movements occurred in the hypolimnion, and he believed that plankton algae are kept in suspension by vital rather than mechanical means.

In his 1906 essay Birge presented a description of the seasonal change in oxygen content of Mendota, obtained the previous year by the laborious gasometric technique. He compared the conditions in Mendota briefly with those in Green Lake and with two lakes showing a metalimnetic oxygen maximum. "The amount of oxygen in the lower water depends not merely on the length of time that the bottom water is cut off from the external air, but it depends also upon the amount of decomposable material discharged into it by the upper water and on the volume of the lower water, which, in turn, depends on the depth of the lake." In this statement he combined the concepts of morphometry and productivity as controlling the O_2 content of the hypolimnion, which Thienemann (1928) later developed in greater detail. Birge also cited temperature as an important influence on oxygen content through its effect on the rate of decomposition in deep water, and he noted that small lakes have a greater relative contribution of decomposable organic matter from the littoral zone than do large lakes.

As President of the American Fisheries Society, Birge presented an address on "The respiration of an inland lake" (Birge, 1907b). Comparing a lake to an organism, or more specifically to the blood of an organism, Birge described the annual cycle of respiration in relation to the thermal cycle— a full inspiration in autumn, a less complete one in spring, none at all under the ice in winter, and only shallow respiration in summer. This essay, along with others, reflects Birge's overall view of a lake as a unit of environment—as an individual with physiological processes analogous to those of an organism.

In the second gas essay Birge (1910e) discussed the seasonal stratification of temperature, oxygen, nitrogen, carbon dioxide, and carbonates (expressed as CO_2) of Lake Mendota and then compared these conditions with those of lakes elsewhere in the state. In this essay, which is liberally documented by graphs showing stratification, Birge further developed his ideas regarding the interplay among productivity of plankton, the sun-wind factor, and the volume of deep water in determining the oxygen content of deep water in summer. Because of the large area of Mendota, the resulting low thermocline (and, therefore, small volume of deep water) and high temperature of the bottom water, and the great quantities of decomposable material that rain into the deep water, the oxygen here disappears rapidly and completely. For these reasons, Birge regretted somewhat that Mendota had been selected for such detailed study.

Other lakes showed different conditions. Green Lake had abundant oxygen in deep water throughout the summer (and also contained *Pontoporeia* and *Mysis*, as noted earlier by Marsh [1892a]). Some of the lakes exhibited oxygen maxima or minima in the thermocline. Birge noted that although the gas picture varied from lake to lake, certain patterns were emerging. This is further evidence of Birge's increasing interest in lake typology. He pointed out, too, that hard-water lakes have a greater carbon dioxide reserve than soft-water lakes and, therefore, generally have more plankton. As a result, the soft-water lakes in northeastern Wisconsin typically had better oxygen conditions in deep water during stratification than did those in the southeast. Birge related the oxygen content of the hypolimnion to its volume and the quantity of decomposable matter discharged into it.

In another paper from this period Birge (1910b) developed the concept of "thermal resistance to mixture" and asserted that the magnitude of this quantity increases the farther the water temperature departs from 4° C. And in the paper in which he proposed the terms *epilimnion* and *hypolimnion* (Birge, 1910c), he refused to accept Wedderburn's conclusion that the great vertical excursions of the thermocline in Loch Ness are the result of *temperature seiches* (internal seiches) and not the direct result of wind blowing the warm surface water from one side of the lake to another. Mortimer (1956) gives a more detailed exposition of this deficiency in Birge's otherwise excellent insight into limnological processes.

In the meantime some lesser papers were being published as an outcome of these studies. Juday

(1908*a*) briefly described the work of the Wisconsin Survey, noting among other things that whereas the calcium content of deep water increases during summer stratification, magnesium remains essentially unchanged. He further noted the occurrence of cocoons or cysts of *Cyclops bicuspidatus* in the deep-water sediments of Mendota in summer, an observation recorded in greater detail in a separate paper (Birge and Juday, 1908, which incidentally was the first paper published jointly by these men).

In this latter paper Birge and Juday reported that although the occurrence of *Cyclops* cysts at the surface of the deep-water sediments in Lake Mendota is largely coincident with the period of summer stratification and hence of oxygen depletion, the immature copepods begin to encyst while there is still adequate oxygen at the bottom and begin to excyst before oxygen is restored to the bottom by the fall overturn. The occurrence of these cysts was also noted in several other lakes, two of which had oxygen in the hypolimnion throughout the summer. At this time Birge and Juday did not have any device for sampling the lake bottom on an areal basis. They merely noted that the cysts were abundant.

Juday (1908*b*) was also interested in the effects of oxygen depletion on other animals occurring in deep water. He found eleven kinds of Protozoa and one rotifer that were active when no oxygen was present. *Chaoborus* (*Corethra*) was abundant in the oxygen-free water of the hypolimnion. An ostracod and a fingernail clam remained alive but inactive during the anaerobic period, as shown by aquarium experiments. When the clams were placed in aerated water, they quickly resumed activity. *Tubifex, Limnodrilus,* and a nematode were active under anaerobic conditions also. Wanting to make certain that oxygen was really lacking, Juday used two different titration procedures plus the gasometric procedure previously developed at Wisconsin. All gave negative results. Hence, there was quite a variety of animals that either appeared to remain active during anaerobic conditions lasting about 3 months or else survived these extreme conditions through dormancy and inactivity.

The newly discovered story of oxygen depletion in deep water was also being related to fish distribution. Lake trout were being stocked widely at this time, but with relatively infrequent success. Juday and Wagner (1908) found that Lake Kawaguesaga, in which stocking had been repeatedly unsuccessful, had no oxygen below a depth of 10.5 m, whereas in Trout Lake, in which lake trout were known to occur and were in fact caught in experimental gill nets, oxygen extended to the bottom. Moreover, Juday and Wagner found that perch and crappies placed in water pumped from the oxygenless hypolimnion of Mendota rapidly died. Such relationships as these are common knowledge now, but at the time they opened up new vistas for the fishery biologists.

All these essays and incidental reports were mere previews of the final report (Birge and Juday, 1911), which, in spite of its volume, is scarcely more than a summary of the tremendous amount of work accomplished. In the introduction Birge reviewed the annual cycle of thermal stratification, superposed on which is the utilization and production of O_2 and CO_2 by biological processes in a lake. For the first time in his writings Birge used the terms *zone of photosynthesis* and *zone of decomposition*, although he did not define them as we do today. He related the thickness of the zone of photosynthesis to the color and turbidity of the water, somewhat anticipating the later studies on light transmission. He regarded the supply of carbon dioxide, including the "half-bound" CO_2 in the bicarbonate reserves, as probably the chief controlling factor in productivity. The shape of the lake basin was likewise regarded as an important factor in productivity. The carbon dioxide removed from the epilimnion by the sinking of dead and dying plankton "is only partially replaced from the air or other sources. Since this is the case, the form of the lake basin is of importance in the economy of the lake. A lake with shoal margins, offering a chance for much decomposition above the thermocline, will produce—other things being equal—more plankton than a lake of similar area, but with steep slopes and deep water. In the latter case, almost all matter manufactured near the surface is decomposed in deep water below the region of circulation; and therefore is more or less permanently withdrawn from the possibility of being used again."

Birge returned again and again to likening lakes to organisms. He regarded as one of the chief values of their study the demonstration of the "existence of physiological processes in lakes as complex, as distinct, and as varied as those of one of the higher animals." To understand the gas story thoroughly, information was needed on the quantitative aspects of plankton and of the bacterial processes of decomposition. One of the big unanswered questions was why lakes varied so tremendously in their productivity and their ability to support plankton. The horizons of Birge and Juday had now broadened to include almost all aspects of descriptive limnology. Eventually they and their associates actively investigated many of them, using experimental procedures more and more in the later years of this period.

In the main body of the final report Juday described the annual cycles of oxygen and carbon dioxide stratification in Lake Mendota and a number of other Wisconsin lakes. The utilization of oxygen in the hypolimnion was brought about primarily by the decomposition of phytoplankton raining down from above, and "the rapidity of the decrease of oxygen in the lower water depends chiefly on three factors, the quantity of decomposable material, the temperature of the water, and the volume of water below the thermocline." Instances of supersaturation in the thermocline were associated with decreases of free CO_2, fixed (bound) CO_2, and silica and were properly related to the photosynthetic activities of algae.

Three categories of lakes were described, based on the amounts of fixed CO_2 present: *soft water lakes* with less than 5 cc/L, *medium water lakes* with 5 to 22 cc/L, and *hard water lakes* with more than 22 cc/L. (These classes were later [e.g., Wilson, 1935] redefined in terms of ppm of bound CO_2: 0–10, 10–30, and >30 ppm, respectively.) All lakes examined in northeastern and northwestern Wisconsin were either soft- or medium-water lakes, whereas all lakes of southeastern Wisconsin were hard-water lakes. In most of the medium- and hard-water lakes, the surface waters in summer were alkaline to phenolphthalein through withdrawal of half-bound (bicarbonate) CO_2. No measurements of pH were available at this time. Alkalinity and acidity were defined in relation to the phenolphthalein endpoint rather than to pH 7 as is done today.

Juday also divided lakes into those that circulate throughout the summer and those that are stratified. The latter were in turn classified into three types on the basis of the oxygen content of the hypolimnion: (1) abundant oxygen throughout summer, (2) disappearance of oxygen from a part of the hypolimnion, (3) disappearance of oxygen from all or nearly all of the hypolimnion. The

distribution of plankton, based on pump collections, was related to the various types of oxygen distribution.

Some initial studies were made on metallic ions, on the gases of anaerobic decomposition, and on the greater content of inorganic nitrogen compounds in the hypolimnion in summer.

In a final section Juday listed a variety of unsolved problems, some of which are prophetic of later studies undertaken by the Wisconsin limnologists:

The sunlight in the zone of photosynthesis offers numerous problems both quantitative and qualitative; the relation between transparency and color of water and the depth to which photosynthesis may extend; the relation of light conditions to the rate of liberation of oxygen by chlorophyl-bearing organisms, and especially the rate of liberation and accumulation of this gas in the excess oxygen stratum; the factors, whether due to light or other causes, which fix a lower limit of depth for the manufacture of excess oxygen. . . .

Hence, we see in this monograph an emerging understanding of the interaction between growth and decomposition of the plankton and the physical factors of thermal stratification and basin morphometry in controlling the chemistry of the hypolimnion. We also see some of the first attempts to classify lakes on the basis of their hardness and the summer oxygen content of the hypolimnion. One of the big advantages of these extensive monographs by Birge and Juday is that they contain great volumes of primary data, which have enabled subsequent limnologists to make new interpretations. Thus, Hutchinson (1938) used the data from Lake Mendota and Green Lake in developing the theory of areal hypolimnetic oxygen deficits. According to his analysis, Green Lake, in spite of its deep-water *Pontoporeia, Mysis,* and whitefish, is actually more productive than Mendota. The large volume of its hypolimnion makes it morphometrically oligotrophic.

Thermal capacity of lakes

Wishing to determine how widely applicable to other lake regions their conclusions on the Wisconsin lakes were, Birge and Juday, with support from the U.S. Bureau of Fisheries, studied the Finger Lakes of New York at various times from 1910 to 1912 (Birge and Juday, 1914). In this and subsequent joint papers Birge was responsible for reporting on the temperature and hydrography, Juday on the dissolved gases and plankton.

Birge was becoming more and more interested in the mechanics of thermal stratification, the means whereby water below the surface becomes warmed, and the total amount of heat a lake has stored at the time of maximum summer conditions. In this paper (Birge and Juday, 1914) and one published the next year (Birge, 1915), Birge compared the heat budgets of first-class American lakes with those of comparable European lakes for which data were available. First-class lakes were defined as those of sufficient size (at least 10 km long and 2 km wide) and depth (mean depth at least 30 m) to permit the lake "to acquire the maximum amount of heat possible under the weather conditions."

Birge noted that on the whole the heat budgets of European lakes were smaller than those of comparable North American lakes, which he explained mainly as the result of the much warmer epilimnions in the American lakes. He noted that "the August temperature conditions in the lakes of central Europe, in general, resemble those of American lakes in June. In the European lakes a relatively thick epilimnion is not formed in early and mid-summer as in ours, and a well-marked epilimnion is hardly developed in these lakes until the surface begins to cool. From this fact comes the statement, not uncommon in European writers on lakes, that the thermocline is a phenomenon which develops during the cooling period of a lake. No student of American lakes would make such a statement, since the epilimnion is fully formed in July, even in a large lake, while in smaller lakes it may be well developed in June or even in May." Because the heat content of the epilimnion can vary greatly during the summer with changes in the weather, Birge proposed later (Birge and Juday, 1920) that for purposes of comparing the heat budgets of American lakes, a mean epilimnial temperature of 23° C be used, rather than the temperature actually measured.

Forel calculated heat budgets from the heat content of a column of water at the position of maximum depth. Halbfass used the entire heat content of a lake. Birge rejected both of these as being unsuitable for comparing lakes and used instead the average amount of heat per square centimeter of lake surface. For this procedure he acknowledged the priority of Wojeikoff in 1902 and Wedderburn in 1910. He also suggested that the best measure of heat income under most conditions is the *wind distributed heat,* which is de-

fined as all the heat in a lake above 4° C. Later (1915) he suggested this be called the *summer heat income*. The total amount of heat stored in a first-class lake in the latitude of Madison at maximum summer conditions represents $\frac{1}{3}$ to $\frac{1}{2}$ of the 60,000 cal/cm^2 that is delivered to the lake during summer stratification.

Birge approached the question of stability of stratification through a consideration of the amount of work required for the wind to move the warmed surface water down to the various depths in the lake (Birge, 1916). Schmidt was also considering stability of stratification but from a different approach. Schmidt calculated the amount of work that would be required to distribute all the heat in a lake uniformly and hence bring it back to indifferent equilibrium (homothermy), whereas Birge calculated the amount of work required to produce the existing thermal stratification. Birge regarded his method as more simple and direct, although Schmidt's method is now generally considered more useful (Mortimer, 1956).

To help obtain an estimate of the magnitude of *in situ* absorption of solar radiation, Birge had an instrument (called a pyrlimnometer) constructed in 1912 for measuring solar energy directly at any depth (Birge, 1922). This instrument consisted of a series of 20 iron-constantan thermocouples, the junctions of which were covered with blackened silver discs. The instrument was sensitive to energy inputs as low as 0.006 cal/cm^2 per min. Hence, the initial studies on solar radiation at Wisconsin were based on total energy rather than spectral composition.

With this instrument in hand Birge and Juday revisited the Finger Lakes in 1918 (Birge and Juday, 1921). From measurements of the transmission of solar radiation through the water and assuming that all the subsurface radiation is absorbed and stored, Birge calculated that the maximum warming of the Finger Lakes by direct penetration of solar radiation was about 16% of the summer heat income, which was about the same as in Mendota. In Lake Okoboji (Birge and Juday, 1920) this amounted to about 20%. Because of the rapid rate of absorption of solar radiation, chiefly the infrared, about 95% of the heating by direct absorption is confined to the top 5 m. Curves for the total heat content with relation to depth were partitioned into direct solar heat and wind-distributed heat. Birge and Juday were at-

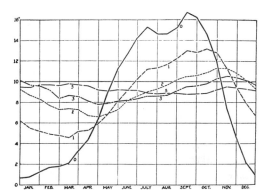

Fig. 1.10.—Mean annual fluctuations of temperature in the sediments of Lake Mendota over a three-year period at the 12-m station. The number associated with each curve is its depth in the sediments. From Birge, Juday, and March, 1928.

tracted to Lake Okoboji by the high deep-water temperatures reported by Tilton, but these were judged to be in error.

Birge and Juday studied the thermal structure of Lake Mendota over a 16-year period. During this time the mean annual heat budget (from winter minimum to summer maximum) was about 23,000–24,000 cal/cm². Two problems that were still unresolved were the amounts of energy absorbed by the sediments each year and the effect of the sediments in warming the water beneath the ice in winter. By means of electrical resistance thermometers (Birge, 1922) Birge and Juday (Birge *et al.*, 1928) measured the mud temperatures at 0.5-m intervals from the surface to 5 m, at water depths of 8, 12, 18, and 23.5 m, throughout the years 1918–20, with scattered observations beginning in 1916 and extending into 1921. They found that the annual energy budget of the sediments was about 2,000 cal/cm², hence roughly 10% of the annual energy budget of the water. Over winter about 650 cal/cm² were given up by the mud to the water, which represented only about one-fourth of the total heat gain beneath the ice. Most of the remainder was ascribed to the penetration of solar radiation through the ice.

Heat transmission varied according to the nature of the sediments. At the 8-m station this amounted to 57% per m, whereas at the deeper stations with more organic sediments it was about 50% per m. The lag in transmission from meter to meter was about one month (Fig. 1.10).

Quantitative plankton

Another monumental study by Birge and Juday was that on the plankton of the Madison lakes, chiefly Mendota (Birge and Juday, 1922). Emphasis in this study was on the amount of plankton present in the lake at a given time, its seasonal variation, and the seasonal variation in its chemical composition, expressed as nitrogen, crude protein, ether extract, carbohydrates, crude fiber, nitrogen-free extract, and ash. The chemical work was done by Schuette of the Chemistry Department, or under his direction, using methods he had reported earlier (Schuette, 1918). The voluminous report, which was written largely by Juday, represented a culmination of his early interests in the biomass aspects of plankton.

All samples were collected at a single station in Mendota, and the data from these were then extrapolated to the entire lake. This involved certain assumptions that were not critically examined. Massive water samples (2,000–38,000 L each, although most were in the 10,000–20,000 L range) were pumped from the various depths in the water column. From 1911 through 1914 only net plankton was studied, but from 1915 through 1917 nannoplankton was sampled as well. The nannoplankton was concentrated by means of a DeLaval centrifuge developed for clarifying oils and varnishes. Tests showed that this centrifuge recovered 98% of the algae and Protozoa, as well as 25–50% of the bacteria. Smaller samples were taken for determining the genera, or in some instances the species, of organisms present, although this aspect of the study is completely subsidiary to the biomass aspects. During this intensive study, more than 2 million liters of water were strained, yielding 1.3 kg dry weight of net plankton for chemical analyses. About half this amount of nannoplankton and detritus was obtained.

Juday reported that "the various forms reach their maximum numbers at different times of the year, some even in winter, so that there is no definite harvest time [as in agriculture] at which this material may be collected and the annual production of it thereby determined. The plankton, therefore, must be considered as a 'standing crop' since it is present at all seasons of the year and since it does not possess any definite period of maturity; in other words, it constitutes a continuous stream of life which presents different degrees of abundance during the course of its annual cycle."

The annual cycle of plankton standing crop or biomass in Mendota exhibited peaks in spring and autumn at the time of the overturns and lesser amounts during summer and winter (Fig. 1.11). Nannoplankton was of much greater relative importance in the spring bloom than in the fall bloom. Diatoms were the dominant organisms at both these times. During a two-year period the standing crop of plankton in Mendota averaged 240 kg/ha expressed as dry organic matter. Live (wet) weight would be approximately 10 times greater. On the average the weight of nannoplankton in the standing crop was about 5 times greater than that of the net plankton. Juday defined nannoplankton as all organisms that slip through the finest bolting silk net, not merely those smaller than 25 μ as Lohmann had originally defined the term.

Birge (1923) discussed the results of this study in more general terms, pointing out that the average standing crop of offshore phytoplankton in Mendota was about 2 tons wet weight per acre and that of the zooplankton about 200 lbs per acre.

Certain minor studies and observations were made in connection with the plankton investigation that were prophetic of future studies by

Birge and Juday and their co-workers. Thus, several analyses of the organic nitrogen content of Mendota water before and after centrifugation showed a much higher content of dissolved organic nitrogen than of nannoplankton or net plankton nitrogen, the figures being 758.0, 103.5, and 21.5 mg/m^3, respectively. Juday considered and rejected Pütter's theory concerning the uptake of dissolved organic matter in the nutrition of higher organisms, largely because Pütter had neglected the nannoplankton.

Quantitative studies on the role of bacteria in the plankton were begun in 1919. Direct counts gave about 10 times as many bacteria as culture methods, but even the highest numbers obtained (60,000/ml) are much lower than we now know occur in lake waters (Kuznezow, 1959). Hence, Juday's calculations of the biomass of bacteria in Mendota and his opinion as to their importance are low by a corresponding amount.

Juday realized that the big problem for the future was not the measurement of the instantaneous biomass but the rate of turnover, or in other words the productivity. Standing crop merely represents the momentary balance between losses and gains in the population. Without presenting

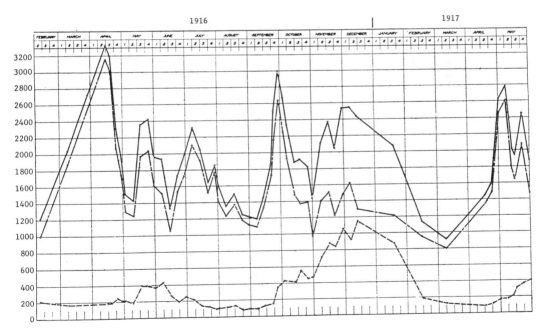

Fig. 1.11.—Fluctuations in standing crop of dry organic matter of net plankton (*bottom line*), nannoplankton (*middle line*), and total plankton (*top line*) in Lake Mendota in 1916–17, in mg per m^3 of water. From Birge and Juday, 1922.

any real basis for his opinion, he stated that the mean turnover rate probably "will be found to fall somewhere between one and two weeks during the greater part of the year."

Juday had already developed the plankton trap associated with his name (Juday, 1916b), but interestingly this device up to this time had been used only to test the efficiency of the pump used in collecting the massive samples of net and nanno-plankton.

In several other studies of this period (Birge and Juday, 1914, 1920, 1921) Juday related the vertical distribution of zooplankton to the chemical and thermal stratification of the lakes. Unfortunately, as in the dissolved gases paper (Birge and Juday, 1911), the organisms were grouped into such large categories (Crustacea, nauplii, rotifers, diatoms, and all other algae) that only the grosser aspects of vertical distribution could be perceived.

In the Lake Okoboji paper (Birge and Juday, 1920) Juday used the term mesolimnion as equivalent to thermocline, and in the plankton monograph (Birge and Juday, 1922) he used the term exclusively for this stratum. Later (e.g., Juday and Birge, 1932) he readopted the term thermocline.

Transmission of solar radiation

One of the fields of limnological research most closely associated with Birge and Juday—mainly with Birge, although most of the papers are co-authored with Juday—and in which they made some of their greatest contributions is that of the transmission of solar radiation and the factors influencing the differences in this transmission observed from lake to lake and from one depth to another in the same lake. Four papers based on field studies in southeastern Wisconsin and at the Trout Lake Laboratory were published jointly (Birge and Juday, 1929b, 1930, 1931, 1932; the paper listed as 1929a in the references is essentially a summary of the 1929b paper), and one significant paper was published on laboratory studies (James and Birge, 1938).

As mentioned previously, Birge became interested in radiant energy early in his career after he had "discovered" the seasonal cycle of thermal stratification in Mendota. In an attempt to measure the penetration of solar energy into lakes, he used a black-bulb thermometer in 1900–1901 to depths of 5 m in Mendota and in 11 other lakes.

These results were never published, although they agreed substantially with those presented in the first paper (Birge and Juday, 1929b).

In 1912 studies on transmission were initiated using a pyrlimnometer, at first with iron-constantan thermocouples and later with bismuth-silver thermocouples. This instrument converts the entire solar spectrum into energy units. In the first study the radiation was reported as $g \cdot cal/cm^2$, but in later studies the energy at any depth was always expressed as a percentage of the incident energy at the surface. Likewise, the spectral composition at any depth was based on the percentage that the energy in each color region, defined on the basis of wave length, comprised of the total energy at that level.

The results of these studies are well known. They showed that almost none of the infrared radiation and very little of the ultraviolet radiation were transmitted through more than 1 m of lake water. Hence, below a depth of 1 m the solar energy is almost entirely in the visible portion of the spectrum. Likewise, because only about half of the energy of solar radiation is in the visible portion of the spectrum, even distilled water transmits only about 47% of the total spectral energy through 1 m of water.

In the lakes reported on in the first paper, the top 10 cm of water absorbed 40–65% of the incident radiation. Birge at this time was still primarily interested in the thermal aspects of solar radiation and their effects on lakes. During the period 15 April to 15 August Mendota receives on the average about 60,000 cal/cm², of which the top meter of water absorbs 74%. Most of this heat is used in evaporation, is returned to the air during the daily warming-cooling cycle, or is distributed by the wind to greater depths.

Below a depth of 1 m, a lake maintains a characteristic transmission through the epilimnion and frequently into the metalimnion, except in highly colored waters. The pyrlimnometer used by Birge and Juday was progressively modified so that its lower limit of usefulness was extended from 1% to 0.1% and eventually to 0.01% or less of the surface radiation. In the hypolimnion they found that there was frequently a reduced transmission, especially near the bottom, resulting from increased turbidity and color. In some of the clearest lakes, however, the characteristic transmission was maintained from a depth of 1 m to the bottom.

In 1930 (Birge and Juday, 1931) the pyrlimnometer was fitted with a series of interchangeable filters so that the spectral composition of the light at different depths in the top 10 m could be studied. These studies demonstrated that "transmission is determined by three main factors: (1) the selective action of water, which is transparent to short wave radiation and opaque to long waves; (2) the selective action of stain which acts more strongly on the short wave radiation and is effective in proportion to the amount and kind present; (3) the action of suspended matter—organic and inorganic—which offers more obstruction to short wave radiation, but is not definitely selective." These studies provided a description of the spectral changes of light with increasing depth in lakes having different levels of dissolved color and turbidity.

In the last published study by Birge on this subject (James and Birge, 1938) measurements of the absorption of monochromatic light of different wave lengths in the laboratory enabled the resolution of the total transmission curve into the three components controlled respectively by the water itself, colors (both dissolved and colloidal), and suspensoids.

Other studies of solar radiation in relation to lakes were made by Pietenpol, Whitney, and Davis. Pietenpol (1918) carried out one of the earliest studies on the selective absorption of visible light by means of a spectrophotometer. Some of his data were subsequently used by Birge and Juday (1931) for comparison. Whitney (1937, 1938a) discovered a microstratification in lakes, as indicated by changes in light transmission over short vertical distances. He found that whereas the transmission in the epilimnion was generally uniform, in the metalimnion and hypolimnion the water was stratified alternately into more transparent and less transparent layers, which varied in thickness from only a few centimeters to about two meters. Replicate transmission curves from different places in the same lake showed a marked correspondence, indicating a definite layered condition within the stratified part of the lake. There was some correlation between numbers of bacteria and transparency. "The fact that the greatest changes in transparency usually occur in regions of relatively large temperature change may indicate that a lake acts as a filter or sorting machine in which particles of different sizes, shapes, and densities slowly sink

and accumulate at levels of similar densities as determined by temperature and other physical conditions" (Whitney, 1938).

In another study Whitney (1938c) extended Birge's measurements on light transmission to intensities as small as 2×10^{-6} of surface light by means of a photoelectric cell and an amplifier. Measurements of light intensity at any depth were made with the thermopile (pyrlimnometer) and with the photocell face up, then with the photocell face down to determine the amount of scattering. The ratios of scattered light to direct light intensity ranged from 1/20 to 1/180. Later papers by Whitney (1941b, 1941c) represent an expansion of these studies.

Davis (1941) was interested in the loss of light at the surface by reflection from the surface and by scattering upward out of the water by suspensoids. Surface loss did not vary with surface roughness so long as the sun was within 50° of the zenith. Surface loss was somewhat greater for diffuse skies than for clear skies, and the loss of red light was less than for total light at relatively high zenith angles.

Limnology: The last two decades (1924–44)

Much of the limnological work reviewed up to this point resulted principally from the efforts of the two pioneer limnologists, with the help of relatively few associates and assistants. But during the last two decades of the Birge-Juday era, limnology was being pushed forward on broad fronts both in the Madison area and at the newly formed Trout Lake Laboratory. At the University of Wisconsin zoologists, botanists, chemists, bacteriologists, geologists, and others were being drawn more and more into a cooperative program. Each summer at Trout Lake up to a dozen or more assistants and visiting investigators were studying all kinds of limnological problems. During this interval more than 260 papers were published by the Wisconsin group and their associates. The peak came in the late '30's and early '40's, with as many as 34 papers listed for a single year (Juday and Hasler, 1946). During this period the *Transactions of the Wisconsin Academy of Sciences, Arts, and Letters* were dominated by the enormous and varied limnological output of this group of limnologists, sometimes to the virtual exclusion of other studies. Since I cannot hope to do justice to all these papers, I shall have to summarize them briefly by major topics.

Methods and equipment

The Wisconsin limnologists were fortunate in having available Mr. J. P. Foerst, the mechanic and instrument maker in the Department of Physics. Often merely from rough sketches or from suggestions as to the kinds of data needed, Foerst was able to devise items of equipment, many of which are standard items even today for the inland limnologist—Kemmerer water bottle, Juday plankton trap, case for reversing thermometer, Ekman dredge, Foerst centrifuge, etc. These items and others are described by Juday (1916b, 1926c, 1929) and Birge (1922). After leaving the university, Foerst and his brother, H. M. Foerst, established the Foerst Mechanical Specialties in Chicago for manufacturing these items of equipment.

The Department of Chemistry at the university developed or modified many methods for the analysis of chemical substances in water and in the residues of aquatic plants and animals. Many of the chemical analyses of these materials were made by the staff members themselves (Kemmerer, Schuette, Robinson, Meloche) or by students under their direction. Thus, Schuette (1918), as already mentioned, developed methods for the microanalysis of plankton residues, the results of which formed such an integral part of the plankton monograph (Birge and Juday, 1922). Later Schuette and Hoffman (1922) and Schuette and Alder (1927, 1929a, 1929b) carried out a series of short studies on the chemical composition of various aquatic plants. Kemmerer and Hallett (1927a, 1927b, 1927c) improved the methods for the microanalysis of ammonia, carbon, and loss on ignition. Taylor (1928) developed new micro methods for the analysis of lake water residues. Black (1929) turned his attention to lake sediments. Robinson and Kemmerer (1930a, 1930b, 1930c) reported on the methods for determining Kjeldahl nitrogen, organic phosphorus, and silica in waters.

V. W. Meloche was one of the very important contributors in the cooperative lake program. Titus and Meloche (1931) described the determination of total phosphorus, and Meloche with various other persons (Meloche and Setterquist, 1933; Meloche et al., 1938; Lohuis et al., 1938; Meloche and Pingrey, 1938; Knudson, Juday, and Meloche, 1940) reported on methods for determining calcium and magnesium and also presented results of studies on the silica, sodium, and po-

tassium contents of lake waters. In addition Meloche with Juday and Birge (Juday, Birge, and Meloche, 1935, 1938, 1941) reported on detailed chemical analyses of lake waters and sediments. These will subsequently be described in somewhat greater detail. Many other chemical, physical, and biological methods were developed or modified, but these were more commonly described in papers of broader scope.

Chemistry of lake waters

Nitrogen compounds and dissolved organic matter.—As already mentioned, some preliminary analyses made during the plankton study (Birge and Juday, 1922) showed that the amount of dissolved organic matter in lake waters considerably exceeded the amount of particulate organic matter. Investigation of this problem was continued in 1922–24 (Domogalla et al., 1925), chiefly on Lake Mendota. After being run through a centrifuge to remove the particulate matter, large samples of water were evaporated at low heat under vacuum. The residues were analyzed for amino and non-amino nitrogen, protein, peptone, and diamino acid nitrogen. The content of inorganic nitrogen as ammonia, nitrite, and nitrate was also studied. Large seasonal changes were observed in all components, with a high in winter and a low in summer. There was a sudden and marked increase in ammonia and nitrate in February. It was felt that these seasonal changes were probably closely related to changing activities of the biota. An indication that protein itself was present in the water was the formation of a precipitate with phosphotungstic acid.

In another study this same year (Peterson et al., 1925) free amino acids were demonstrated in Mendota. Tryptophane, tyrosine, and histidine occurred at mean concentrations of about 13 mg/m³, cystine at 4 mg/m³. Arginine was also found. The dissolved nitrogen was separated into 12 components, which accounted for 90% of the total.

Domogalla et al. (1926) related the seasonal variations in ammonia and nitrate content of Mendota to the activity of ammonifying, nitrifying, and nitrate-reducing bacteria. Beneath the ice both ammonia and nitrate increased markedly since the dissolved oxygen did not become completely exhausted, whereas during the more severe summer stratification ammonia increased but nitrate decreased. These changes were related to bacterial populations.

Domogalla and Fred (1926) presented graphs and tables showing the annual cycles of ammonia, nitrate, organic nitrogen, soluble phosphorus, and rates of nitrification and nitrate reduction for all five lakes at Madison. Lake Monona at this time was receiving the treated sewage effluent from Madison, which considerably influenced its nitrogen chemistry and that of the two lower lakes—Waubesa and Kegonsa. Domogalla claimed to be able to demonstrate the direct utilization of ammonia by algae in Monona.

Birge and Juday (1927*a*; the paper listed as 1927*b* contains essentially the same information, and the paper published the previous year is a brief preliminary report of the same results) were concerned with the origin and significance of the large amounts of dissolved organic matter in fresh water. The average nitrogen to carbon ratio of this material was 1 to 15, whereas that of the plankton in Mendota was 1 to 7.1 and in two other Madison lakes about the same. The ratio in rooted aquatics was 1 to 17, but Birge and Juday calculated that the annual production of rooted aquatics in Mendota was scarcely one-third of the mean standing crop of dissolved organic matter and, hence, could scarcely serve as its source. They concluded that the plankton was the chief source, and that the disparity in the nitrogen to carbon ratios resulted from a more ready utilization of the nitrogen components in the material.

Birge and Juday (1927*b*) divided lakes into two classes according to the major source of the dissolved organic matter: those with the major source within the lake itself (chiefly plankton) were called *autotrophic,* whereas those with a considerable portion from outside the lake as extractives from soils and peat were called *allotrophic.* Evidence indicated that the quantity of dissolved organic matter was quite constant for a given lake, varying relatively little with depth or time. Hence, as in mineral analyses, a single sample of water should be adequate to define this characteristic.

Birge and Juday considered that the dissolved organic matter has about the same potential food value as plankton itself, since the proportions of free amino, peptide, and non-amino nitrogen are about the same, and since five free amino acids

were already demonstrated to occur. However, even though the quantity of this material is much greater than that of particulate organic matter, its great dilution would present a problem in its utilization, at least by animals. Many of the net algae are too large to be eaten by the zooplankton, but the quantity of nannoplankton and fine detritus is many times the weight of all Crustacea and rotifers and, hence, should provide adequate particulate food for them. Birge and Juday indicated that the whole problem of the nutrition of the plankton was very much unsettled.

The last paper (Birge and Juday, 1934) presented data from 529 lakes in the northeastern lake district. Whereas in the lakes of southeastern Wisconsin reported previously, there was little detectable outside influence on the amount of dissolved organic matter, the northeastern lakes exhibited the entire spectrum from clear seepage lakes to very dark-colored drainage lakes. In the clearest lakes, including Lake Michigan, the dissolved organic content was about six times that of the plankton, from which Birge concluded that "the plankton is the primary source of about 6 times its own weight of dissolved organic matter in the waters of those lakes which derive little or no organic matter from outside sources." He showed, however, that this simple ratio could not be used in partitioning the dissolved organic matter of higher carbon lakes into external and internal sources. As noted elsewhere, the summer standing crops of plankton in these soft-water lakes were only a fourth to a half as great as those in the hard-water lakes of southeastern Wisconsin.

Within a radius of 25 mi of the Trout Lake Station there are more than 500 lakes. Juday and Birge conducted a general chemical, physical, and biological survey of these lakes, many of them being visited only once but some of them being visited regularly in successive summers. A complete set of field determinations comprised 19 different chemical, physical, and biological items. Except for the few lakes that were singled out for special study, the remainder lose their identity in the subsequent reports; they are merely tallied in the appropriate range of the particular character being considered. In their early years Birge and Juday were concerned with the lake as a unit of environment. At the

Trout Lake Laboratory they were concerned with all the lakes in a particular region and the frequency distribution of these lakes over the total ranges of the particular variables being considered. The resulting papers lack the satisfying unity of the ecosystem approach, and one feels that many significant interrelationships may have been overlooked as a result.

One of the main contributions of this series of studies was to show the lake in relation to its watershed. The isolated *seepage lakes* (those without surface inlet or outlet) as a statistical group tended to be quite different in nearly all characteristics studied from the *drainage lakes* (those that are in direct surface connection with their watershed).

Transparency, color, and specific conductance (Juday and Birge, 1933).—Transparency measured in the northeastern lakes with a 10-cm Secchi disc ranged from 0.3 m to 13.6 m. In general, seepage lakes had higher transparencies than drainage lakes, which is related to the higher dissolved color of the latter. Color was more important than the amount of plankton in influencing transparency. The dissolved color, which ranged as high as 340 ppm on the Pt-Co scale, remained fairly constant for two or more months during the summer. Some lakes showed about the same color from surface to bottom, whereas others showed a marked increase toward the bottom. In a few of the latter this resulted from iron rather than vegetable stain. There was a distinct positive relationship between dissolved color and organic carbon in the water, as would be expected. The carbon to nitrogen ratio increased with increasing color.

Specific conductance varied from 6 to 132 micromhos (reciprocal megohms), which is on the whole much less than that in the lakes of southeastern Wisconsin. The specific conductance was quite characteristic of a given lake, tending to remain approximately the same from one year to the next. Specific conductance showed a strong positive relationship with fixed CO_2 and with total Ca and Mg, these being the dominant cations in the water. In some of the lakes there was no appreciable increase in specific conductance and fixed CO_2 in the hypolimnion over the summer, whereas in others there was. The role of biological activity in modifying the specific conductance was not discussed in sufficient detail.

Mineral content.—Juday, Birge, and Meloche

(1938) reported on analyses for silicon, iron, manganese, calcium, magnesium, fluoride, chloride, sulfate, and ammonia, nitrite, and nitrate nitrogen in more than 500 lakes of northeastern Wisconsin. Ranges and frequency distributions were given for each of these substances, as well as the distribution with depth and the relation to the general chemical conditions in the lakes. Stratification was related largely to biological activity of various types. An interesting result was that whereas manganese was seldom found in surface waters, iron in quantities up to 2 mg/L occurred in the surface waters of 74 lakes. The paper is valuable mainly for the description of the mineral content of a whole lake region, without giving much insight into the dynamics of particular lakes.

Lohuis *et al.* (1938) analyzed the sodium and potassium contents of lakes in northeastern Wisconsin. Drainage lakes contained more total dissolved solids and also more total Na and K than seepage lakes, but the latter had a higher proportion of Na and K. The total amount of alkali, reported as potassium, generally ranged between 2 and 4 ppm. In drainage lakes sodium and potassium were approximately equal in abundance, whereas in seepage lakes there was generally less sodium than potassium.

Meloche *et al.* (1938) studied the silica content of Mendota during the period of 1935–36 and related this to the abundance of diatoms. During summer stratification there was a distinct increase in silica in the hypolimnion. The increase in diatoms in fall was related to the upward transport of silica during fall turnover. An incidental feature of the paper is that it contains a description of the Kemmerer water sampler as currently constructed.

Phosphorus.—The results of the first paper (Juday *et al.*, 1927) were included in the second (Juday and Birge, 1931), which reported the phosphorus content of 479 lakes in northeastern Wisconsin. The mean summer content of soluble phosphorus was 0.003 mg/L and of organic phosphorus (obtained by subtracting soluble from total phosphorus) was 0.020 mg/L, although the modal value of the organic phosphorus was 0.014 mg/L. Contrary to what would be expected, there was not always a decrease in soluble phosphorus over summer, even in stratified lakes. Stratified lakes with little plankton exhibited essentially no increase in hypolimnetic phosphorus during summer stratification, whereas those richer in plankton generally showed an increased content of soluble phosphorus, and frequently of organic phosphorus as well, in the deep water. This paper, as most others of this chemical series, was concerned less with interpretation of results than with their descriptive presentation. The main value is in showing the range of phosphorus contents in lake waters of one compact lake district.

Dissolved oxygen and oxygen consumed (Juday and Birge, 1932).—The oxygen content of the surface waters of more than 500 lakes in northeastern Wisconsin averaged only 82% of saturation. This was surprising but unexplained. It checked with 88% saturation recorded in this lake district in 1907–1910, and it contrasted with the average condition of 100% saturation in the lakes of the northwestern and southeastern lake districts. Juday and Birge compared the unmodified Winkler method with the Rideal-Stewart modification, and, finding no significant difference between these methods, they continued to use the standard Winkler because of its greater convenience.

Juday and Birge considered the applicability of lake types to the lakes of northeastern Wisconsin. Defining oligotrophy and eutrophy on the basis of the late summer oxygen content of the hypolimnion, they accepted the extremes of the trophic series but not the intermediate stages proposed by Naumann. Because of great differences between the brown-colored lakes of northeastern Wisconsin and those of western Europe, they rejected dystrophy as representing a separate type of lake.

In their discussion of oxygen deficits they considered the absolute and actual deficits for the entire lake, not just for the hypolimnion. Various analyses were made of percentage saturation for entire lakes and of the hypolimnion to epilimnion ratios as proposed by Thienemann. Unfortunately, the concept of areal hypolimnetic deficit was only getting started in Norway at this time, so that the analyses made are not too significant in terms of modern limnology.

Oxygen consumed was measured not by biochemical-oxygen-demand methods but by hot acid digestion with potassium permanganate. An average of about 40% of the total organic carbon in the water was oxidized by this procedure. The total amount of oxygen consumed varied directly with the dissolved color and organic carbon in the water.

Eh, pH, and carbon dioxide.—As already mentioned, Juday and Birge in their early work considered a water sample alkaline or acid according to its color reaction to phenolphthalein. Their first paper involving the measurement of pH was that by Juday, Fred, and Wilson (1924), in which they followed changes in pH with season and depth in Lake Mendota for a two-year period from 1919 to 1922. Single series of observations were obtained in summer from six other lakes in southeastern Wisconsin. They observed that in summer particularly, and to a somewhat lesser extent under the ice in winter, the upper waters had a substantially higher pH than the lower waters. They ascribed the summer differences to the photosynthetic activity of algae towards the surface and to the decomposition of organic matter in the hypolimnion.

Prior to 1932 all their pH measurements were made by colorimetric comparison. In that year, however, Freeman *et al.* (1933) devised a calomel-quinhydrone cell for measuring pH *in situ*. A similar cell was used for measuring the pH of water samples hauled to the surface. The two methods gave essentially the same results, and both were considered superior to the calculation of pH from titration data for free and bound CO_2.

In an extensive paper on carbon dioxide and pH, Juday, Birge, and Meloche (1935) reviewed the basis for the concepts of free, half-bound, and bound CO_2. In this paper the effects of watershed on controlling the chemistry of lakes were clearly apparent. Seepage lakes tended to have lower pH, more free CO_2, and less bound CO_2 in their surface waters than did drainage lakes. Although pH generally decreased toward the bottom of a lake, associated with increases in free CO_2 and bound CO_2, Lake Mary exhibited an increase in pH—a phenomenon Yoshimura had designated by the term dichotomous stratification. Lake Mary is now known to be quite definitely meromictic.

Allgeier *et al.* (1941) measured the oxidation-reductional potential (Eh) by means of an *in situ* probe. Values ranged from $+0.512$ to $+0.077$ volt in the water to a low value of -0.140 volt in the mud. These values were higher than those obtained by previous investigators. Lakes with abundant oxygen in deep water exhibited little reduction in Eh toward the bottom, whereas lakes with reduced oxygen and brown-water lakes (they used the term dystrophic here as a general descriptive term) generally exhibited a marked reduction. The investigators showed that in addition to dissolved oxygen ferrous iron and hydrogen sulfide helped control the *Eh* levels, and they suggested that organic reducing systems were probably active as well.

Sediments

The brief study by Black (1929) represented the first investigation in Wisconsin of the chemistry of lake sediments. Black analyzed surficial sediments of several Wisconsin lakes and three Alaskan lakes for SiO_2, Fe_2O_3, Al_2O_3, CaO, MgO, P_2O_5, SO_4, CO_2, and organic carbon. The results, presented in tables, were only partially related to the depositional environments. Black noted, as Birge and Juday (1911) had earlier, that relatively little Mg occurs in the sediments even of hard-water lakes because of the high solubility of $MgCO_3$ relative to $CaCO_3$. Two brief experiments were conducted on gas production by Mendota sediments at room temperature and in a refrigerator. More than half of the gas produced anaerobically was methane.

Steiner and Meloche (1935) were concerned with the carbohydrate fraction in the organic analyses of Birge and Juday (1934), because to the extent that this material is ligneous, it would not be readily available as food to organisms. They found that lignin comprised 30 to 48% of the organic matter of lake sediments, 18% of net plankton, and 10 to 20% of nannoplankton. The lignin content was generally higher in sediments of northeastern lakes than of southeastern.

Juday, Birge, and Meloche (1941) put out a second extensive paper on the chemistry of lake sediments, involving 18 lakes in northeastern Wisconsin and 3 in southeastern Wisconsin. The same substances were measured as in the paper by Black and by the same methods, except that in the sediments of soft-water lakes, the content of organic matter was approximated by loss on ignition. Sediments of the northeastern lakes had an average organic content three times greater than that of the southeastern lakes. This was related to the higher lignin content reported by Steiner and Meloche and also to the greater abundance of mud bacteria in the southeastern lakes, the unstated assumption being that the organic matter of the sediments is more readily

decomposed in the hard-water southeastern lakes. Results of the analyses were given in tabular form.

W. H. Twenhofel, a geologist at the University of Wisconsin, was a well-known authority on sediments and sedimentation. He began investigating lake sediments as an aid to understanding the depositional environment of freshwater rocks. He was interested in transport of materials, as indicated by mechanical analysis, in the diagenesis of sediments with the potential production of petroleum, and in other geological problems. His early studies were based on surficial samples collected with an Ekman dredge and on partial cores obtained with a weight-driven pipe 6 ft long of Twenhofel's own design. Although this sampler was sometimes driven more than 6 ft into the sediments, it never collected 6 ft of material. Because the stratigraphic relationships were inexact, Twenhofel analyzed only the top, middle, and bottom of each core. In later studies Twenhofel and his associates obtained complete cores with a Jenkin corer from several northeastern lakes. On one occasion the Wilson sampler was used.

The first study was on Mendota (Twenhofel, 1933) and the second on Monona (Twenhofel, 1937). In both these lakes there was a black, soupy sediment at the top (which Twenhofel first called "ooze" and then "sludge"), with lighter-colored and firmer sediments below. Twenhofel thought this represented a diagenetic series—that the deeper, light-colored sediments were like the sludge when first deposited, but that they subsequently suffered a loss of organic content by biological activity. More recently Murray (1956) has related this almost abrupt change in sediment type in these lakes to the influence of man in the region, bringing about an increased importation of clastics and a decline in hypolimnetic oxygen, resulting in the deposition of ferrous sulfide in the sediments. Neither geologist established any chronology for the sediments of these lakes.

A similar study was made on Devils Lake in southern Wisconsin (Twenhofel and McKelvey, 1939), which is a very soft-water lake in a quartzite basin. As expected, SiO_2 was the chief inorganic constituent of the sediments, and there was little or no Ca and Mg. The organic content was estimated at 15–20% of the dry weight. The nitrogen content of the sediments varied from

0.018–0.88%. Bacterial analyses run by Janice Stadler showed smaller total counts than in Mendota. Chloroform and ether extracts yielded 1–9 lbs "oil" per ton dry weight of sediments.

Attention was also turned to Crystal Lake in the northeastern lake district (Twenhofel and Broughton, 1939). This lake was selected because of its extremely soft water and absence of dissolved color. A large part of the paper is devoted to the mechanical analysis of the sediments. A few cores that penetrated into sand indicated that the maximum thickness of the sediments was about 3 m, which gave a mean annual accumulation of 0.25 mm/yr based upon a time interval of 10,000 years. Lignin comprised about half the organic matter. The numbers of bacteria were small (Carpenter, 1939), being only about 1/1000 those of Mendota muds. Aerobic and facultative bacteria decreased markedly with depth.

Conger (1939), a diatom specialist, studied the diatoms in the cores from Crystal Lake. He found a much greater diversity than expected, 85 species in all, most of which were epiphytic and benthonic. Planktonic species were generally in the minority. The flora was more diverse at the bottom of the cores, and there was evidence that the depositional environment of the early sediments was less acid and richer in nutrients than subsequently. Several middle samples were dominated by *Fragilaria construens*, indicating rich·"blooms" of this species. In some places pine pollen and other types comprised more than 50% of the mass of the sediments. Conger's study is interesting in being one of the first to utilize diatoms in interpreting previous ecological conditions in a lake.

Little Long Lake in Vilas County was selected for study because of complete enclosure by forest, absence of any organized drainage, and the very dark brown color of its water (Twenhofel and McKelvey, 1942). About half of the dry weight of the sediments was organic matter, of which lignin comprised 40–69%. At the surface the sediments consisted of more than 90% water, whereas at greater depths they were more compact. The SiO_2 content was low, and there was no Ca or Mg. Bacterial counts were likewise low. The maximum thickness of sediments, as measured by a spud sampler, was only about 10 ft.

The next two studies (Twenhofel *et al.*, 1942, 1944) were frustrating for Twenhofel in that the

sediments of the lakes investigated consisted mainly of a greenish-yellow gel (algal gyttja) composed of floccules or sphaerules about 2 mm in diameter. Attempts at removing the organic matter by H_2O_2 or concentrated H_2SO_4 were unsuccessful, and hence the mechanical analyses were virtually meaningless. Twenhofel concluded that the sediment accumulated as floccules, which had incorporated pollen grains, diatoms, sponge spicules, and small amounts of clastics, and that they probably were not transported at all after primary deposition. In addition to the ordinary collection of surface samples with an Ekman dredge, complete cores were collected with a Jenkin sampler. As a result, information was obtained regarding progressive changes in sediment chemistry, as well as in the total thickness of the sediments. These latter were 30.3 ft in Grassy Lake, 4.7 m in Nebish, 5.9 m in Little John, and 42.5 ft in Allequash.

The sediments were approximately the same from surface to bottom, indicating to Twenhofel that there had been little diagenesis. The water content of these sediments was generally 90% or even higher, so that the 30 ft of sediment in Grassy Lake would represent a postglacial accumulation of only 1.5 ft dry sediment in the deepest part of the lake and scarcely more than 2 in. in the shoreward portions. Except at the bottom, the organic content of the sediments averaged 65–70%, with lignin comprising about a third. Using the Dumas method, Twenhofel obtained a nitrogen content of about 4% in the sediments of Grassy Lake.

Twenhofel did not observe any horizontal structuring or stratification in the sediments of any of the lakes he studied. Without any definite evidence except observation of the activity of oligochaetes in sediment samples in bottles, he attributed this to the activities of organisms, rather than to redeposition by currents. Unfortunately no chronologies were established for these cores, although pollen diagrams were later constructed for a number of localities in northeastern Wisconsin, including Crystal Lake and a nearby bog (Wilson and Cross, 1941). As a minor matter of interest, in his last paper (Twenhofel *et al.*, 1944) Twenhofel was willing to abandon the term "sludge" in favor of gyttja.

In a general paper Twenhofel and McKelvey (1941) described the conditions of sedimentation in freshwater lakes, the types of sediments occurring in them and the types of rocks that would result, the presumed diagenesis after deposition, and the general absence of stratification in freshwater sediments of their experience.

In another general paper Conger (1942) discussed the various factors that may control the production of diatomaceous deposits in lakes. The northeastern lake district is especially good for investigating this problem, since the sediments of some of them consist of 60–75% SiO_2, chiefly diatoms. Five such lakes, including Crystal Lake, were listed.

Studies on the pollen chronology of Wisconsin lake and bog sediments during this period were conducted chiefly by Wilson, and Potzger and their associates. In chronological sequence these are Hansen (1937), Wilson (1937), Wilson and Galloway (1937), Wilson (1938), Wilson and Webster (1942a, 1942b), Potzger (1942), Potzger and Keller (1942), Potzger and Richards (1942), Potzger (1943), Wilson and Webster (1944). No summary will be attempted of these papers here, since in most instances they have little to do with interpretation of earlier limnological conditions. The paper of Wilson (1932) might also be mentioned, as representing a description of the site which has since resulted in the firm correlation by radiocarbon dating between the Two Creeks interstadial of North America and the Alleröd of Europe.

Bacteria

Birge and Juday early recognized the importance of bacteria in controlling the chemical conditions in lakes, in providing sources of particulate food for the water-filtering zooplankters, and in bringing about the regeneration of plant nutrients. Their early studies on numbers of bacteria in Mendota were continued by Fred et al. (1924) and Snow and Fred (1926). Bere (1933) was one of the early persons to make direct microscopic counts of bacteria in waters. Studies of this type were extended by Stark and McCoy (1938) to the lakes of northeastern Wisconsin.

Studies on the numbers of bacteria and their function and physiology in bottom sediments were carried out by Allgeier et al. (1932, 1934), Williams and McCoy (1934, 1935), Henrici and McCoy (1938), Carpenter (1939), and Erikson (1941). Miscellaneous studies were carried out by Hardman and Henrici (1939), Stadler and

ZoBell (1939), Zobell (1940), and Zobell and Stadler (1940a, 1940b).

During this interval quite a number of persons received Masters' and Ph.D. degrees in bacteriology on problems directly related to limnology. These include Yvette Hardman, Mary A. Jansky, Dorothy E. Kinkel, and William H. Stark. No attempt was made to compile a total list of such persons and the titles of their dissertations.

Benthos of Lake Mendota

In 1913 at Juday's suggestion, Muttkowski (1918) commenced a study of the littoral benthos of Mendota. The littoral zone was defined as extending down to 7 m. The offshore limit of the rooted aquatics at a depth of 5 or possibly 6 m was generally co-extensive with a shell zone, marking the lower limit of wave action. Quantitative samples were collected from areas of 1 m² marked out on the bottom, and qualitative samples were collected from greater depths by means of a special rake and net. Quantitative results were expressed only as numbers of individuals per m². Nearly all the immature insects were raised to adults, enabling positive identification of species. Hence, distribution, habitat preferences, and phenology were described in terms of species rather than genera or families, as is commonly done in such studies.

Muttkowski presented a very nice discussion of the phenology of the population growth and emergence of the various insect species over the course of the year. Much of the population dynamics is associated, probably causally, with the seasonal growth of attached algae and higher aquatics. Early in the spring *Cladophora* dominates the plant community until a water temperature of about 16°C is reached, after which the rooted aquatics gain the ascendancy. *Sialis* makes a massive shoreward migration in early May from fairly deep water. The new brood of larvae remain in the littoral zone until fall overturn, when they migrate downward into the aphytal zone. Muttkowski related the distribution of the various species to depth and habitat and recorded the apparent optimum conditions.

In the summer of 1916 Muttkowski extended his studies to deeper water by means of the Ekman dredge, but he did not publish his results. Juday continued these studies until August 1918, concentrating mainly on the deep-water zone within the 20-m contour. His paper (Juday, 1921*b*) included Muttkowski's results as well.

Besides merely counting numbers of individuals in each dredge haul, Juday obtained mean wet weights and dry weights of individual organisms from which standing crops could be calculated. These amounted to 697 kg/ha wet weight (excluding *Pisidium*) in the deep-water zone and 360 kg/ha in the intermediate zone (7–20 m). *Chaoborus* dominated in the deep-water zone, and *Chironomus* in the intermediate zone.

Only 6 kinds of macro-invertebrates were found in the deep-water zone: *Limnodrilus, Tubifex, Pisidium idahoense, Corethra punctipennis, Chironomus tentans,* and *Protenthes choreus.* *Limnodrilus* outnumbered *Tubifex* about 4 to 1, and together they constituted about 58 kg/ha live weight. *Pisidium,* as already noted, becomes dormant during the long anaerobic period of summer stratification. *Chaoborus* (*Corethra*) exhibits a very marked population maximum in winter and almost disappears from the deep-water sediments during emergence time in summer.

Higher aquatic plants

The first study of rooted aquatic plants in Wisconsin was that of Denniston (1922) on Lake Mendota, based on samples collected in 1912. Distribution along the shore seemed to be governed by bottom type and degree of exposure, whereas depth distribution was believed governed by light. There was little or no zonation parallel to shore.

Two of the most significant early studies on the quantitative aspects of aquatic plants were those by Rickett (1921, 1924) on Mendota and Green Lake. Rickett carefully collected all the plants within a reference frame measuring ½ m on a side that was lowered to the bottom. In water no more than 2–3 m deep, simple diving sufficed, whereas at greater depths a diving hood was employed. In Green Lake Rickett was impressed by the marked decline in visual light intensity near the lower limit of the rooted plants: at 7 m the impression was that of fairly bright sunlight, whereas almost darkness prevailed at 10 m. Had SCUBA been available at that time, Rickett undoubtedly would have become a devotee.

Of the 21 species present in Mendota, *Vallisneria spiralis* made up about one-third of the total biomass and the 6 species of *Potamogeton* together about one-half. *Cladophora* was important early in the year. In the 26% of the lake bottom occupied by aquatic plants, the biomass averaged 2,019 kg dry weight per ha. Rickett arbitrarily set up three depth zones: 0–1 m, 1–3 m, and greater than 3 m. The percentages of the total biomass in each of these zones were 30%, 45%, and 25%, respectively. The lower limit of plant growth (*Ceratophyllum*) was generally about 5 m, although in a few localities it extended to 6.5 m.

In Green Lake there were 27 species of macrophytes, of which *Chara* constituted about 50% of the total dry weight. The plants extended to greater depths than in Mendota—to 8 m along the average shore and up to 10 m on shallow slopes, although only to 4 or 5 m on very steep slopes. The mean crop in the plant zone (29% of the lake bottom) was 1,780 kg dry weight per ha, distributed among the depth zones by the percentages 9%, 40%, and 50%, respectively. The greater percentage in deep water is related to greater light transmission in Green Lake than in Mendota and perhaps also to the colder temperatures at these depths. *Chara, Myriophyllum,* and *Ceratophyllum* were abundant in the deep water. Birge provided the information that 1% levels of surface light in summer occur at about 8 m in Green Lake and 4 m in Mendota.

On the basis of a brief visit to the northeastern lake district, Fassett (1930) described a number of growth forms of aquatics, which in addition to the now-recognized categories of submerged, floating leaf, and emergent plants included a fourth category of short, stiff rosettes. He further noted that in Crystal Lake (a very transparent lake) the bottom was bare from 6 to 15 m, but that at greater depths there was an almost continuous carpet of *Fontinalis flaccida* and *Drepanocladus fluitans.*

Studies comparable to those of Rickett were carried out in the northeastern lake district by Wilson (1935, 1937, 1941) and by Potzger and Van Engel (1942). The results of these studies, summarized in Table 1.1, show that the soft-water and medium-hard-water lakes of northern Wisconsin have much smaller annual crops than do the hard-water lakes of the southeast. The number of species is comparable, or even greater, as is the percentage of the total lake bottom

TABLE 1.1

Summer crops of higher aquatic plants in Wisconsin lakes[a]

Lake	Area (ha)	Max. depth (m)	Color (ppm)	Bound CO_2 (ppm)	No. spp.[b] aquatics	% Lake bottom occupied	Max. depth occupied (m)	Total dry wt. (kg)	Av. crop on occupied bottom (g dry wt./m²)
Southeastern lakes									
Mendota	3940	26	14	34	20	26	5(6.5)	2,100,000	202
Green	2972	72	5	38	27	29	8(10)	1,527,900	178
Northeastern lakes									
Little John	67.2	6	18	12	13	31	3	112	0.52
Muskellunge	372	21	8	10	31	52	7	883	0.45
Silver	87.2	19	4	17	15	23	6	17	0.08
Trout	1583	35	6	20	36+	27	6.5	321	0.07
Sweeney	63.5	6	52	18	27	30	2.3	332	1.73
Weber	15.6	13	1	2	8	34	5	894	16.8

[a] Sources of data are the following: *Mendota:* Rickett (1921); *Green:* Rickett (1924); *Little John, Muskellunge, Silver:* Wilson (1935); *Trout:* Wilson (1941); *Sweeney:* Wilson (1937); *Weber:* Potzger and Van Engel (1942). Data on color and bound CO_2 for certain lakes were obtained from Juday and Birge (1933) and Juday, Birge, and Meloche (1935). Morphometric data for Weber Lake (Juday and Birge, 1941) were used for recalculating some of the data in Potzger and Van Engel (1942).

[b] Includes only *Chara* and *Nitella* among the algae. In Mendota *Cladophora* is important in spring and early summer. In Green Lake Rickett lists 6 species of algae other than charophytes that may be abundant at times. *Nostoc* is locally abundant in Lake Muskellunge.

colonized by the plants. The differences in production are a reflection of the basic differences in the lakes. The lakes of the two districts differ not only in mineral content of the water but also in bottom type. The northeastern lakes, located in a sandy outwash plain, frequently have sandy bottoms with organic sediments occurring some distance offshore. The sandy sediments are frequently colonized by rosette-type plants (*Isoetes,* etc.), which have relatively little dry-weight biomass.

Another major difference between the two lake regions is that in the northern lakes studied, Zone I (0–1 m water depth) had from 60 to 76% of the total biomass, except in Weber Lake (studied by Potzger and Van Engel) where 29% of the total biomass occurred in Zone I.

Wilson intended to use the same methods as Rickett, but he soon decided it was too uncomfortable working at the cold temperatures near the lower limits of the colonization zones. He adopted, therefore, a lightened Petersen dredge, which sampled 625 cm² of bottom. Potzger and Van Engel, on the other hand, maintained that the dredge Wilson used was not so efficient as the standard Petersen dredge, which was considerably heavier and sampled 729 cm² of bottom. Comparison showed that the standard Petersen dredge collected four to five times as much material as

did the modified dredge. However, even increasing Wilson's crop estimates by this factor still leaves them about two orders of magnitude smaller than those of the southern lakes.

Wilson, Potzger, and Van Engel were concerned with communities or associations of plants in relation to soil type and depth zone. Wilson was also interested in the successional relationships of the communities, from primitive lakes with inorganic soils to advanced lakes with organic soils. In a review paper (Wilson, 1939a) he attempted to relate the distribution and abundance of aquatic plants to various environmental factors. Light was of particular importance in depth distribution. Some species had their lower limit at 70% of surface light, whereas others extended down to 2% (Wilson, 1941).

Fishes

While he was on the zoology faculty of the University of Wisconsin, A. S. Pearse was interested in the faunistic and general ecological relationships in lakes. His studies of this period included a number on the food of fishes (Pearse, 1915, 1918, 1921a, 1921b, 1924), the habits of the black crappie (Pearse, 1919) and the yellow perch (Pearse and Achtenberg, 1920), a study on the chemical composition of fishes (Pearse, 1925), and a study on the general ecology of lake fishes

(Pearse, 1934). In later years Couey (1935) and Nelson and Hasler (1942) also investigated the food habits of fishes.

Juday and Birge had been receiving research support from the U.S. Bureau of Fisheries for some years, but with the establishment of the Trout Lake Laboratory they also began receiving support from the Wisconsin Conservation Department for conducting studies on growth rates, food habits, general life histories, and management of fishes, including creel censuses. Studies of this kind led to the Ph.D. degree for most of the later students associated with Juday, as described in a subsequent section.

This phase of aquatic investigations in Wisconsin may be considered to have started with the study by Wright (1929) on the growth of the rockbass. From this time on there was a steady succession of papers concerned with various aspects of fishery biology and management. Included are a number of papers by Ralph Hile on the cisco (Hile, 1936a, 1936b, 1938) and the rockbass (Hile, 1941, 1942, 1943), and one by Hile and Deason (1934) on the whitefish. Hile was also interested in the bathymetric distribution of fishes in response to chemical and thermal stratification (Hile and Juday, 1941).

Many of the other papers in fishery biology of this period were written either by Juday, based on data gathered by W.P.A. workers, or by students who received their Ph.D.'s under Juday's supervision (Schneberger, Schloemer, Bennett, Spoor, and Frey). Of these papers only those based in whole or in part on Ph.D. theses are listed in the bibliography here. The remainder may be obtained from the bibliography by Juday and Hasler (1946).

One important paper of this period described the method developed by Schnabel (1938) for estimating the size of a fish population in a lake by marking and recapturing. Another interesting note by Woodbury (1942) ascribed the mortality of some fish to oxygen embolism, developed when the fish moved out of a zone of supersaturation.

Photosynthesis, productivity, community structure

In the last decade of his productive life as a limnologist, Juday began turning his attention to the measurement of the rates of energy fixation and the subsequent utilization of this energy within the trophic structure of the ecosystem. These are central problems in all phases of ecol-

ogy today. Juday and his associates carried out some pioneer studies in this area and made some fundamental contributions. The big background of information on the light climate, chemical regime, and standing crops of plankton and other habit communities in Wisconsin lakes was put to good use in these studies.

In the early studies cultured algae or concentrations of naturally occurring algae and higher aquatics were placed in light and dark bottles and suspended at various depths in lakes of contrasting color and transparency. Photosynthesis was computed then from changes in the oxygen content of the bottles.

Schomer (1934) selected three lakes with contrasting amounts of dissolved color for experiments beginning in 1932. He placed active tips of *Elodea, Ceratophyllum,* and *Chara* in light and dark bottles, and he did the same with cultures of *Coccomyxa* and *Chlorella.* In general, maximum photosynthesis was at the surface on dull days and below the surface on bright days. The compensation level was inversely related to dissolved color, being at 10–15 m in the clearest lake and at 1–2 m in the darkest lake. Schomer considered the larger plants to be of less value in such experiments than algae, and in all subsequent experiments algae were used.

The results of 1933 were described by Schomer and Juday (1935) and in a somewhat abbreviated version by Juday and Schomer (1935). Using the same two species of cultured algae as in the previous year, the authors calculated the oxygen production per million cells per 3-hour exposure period in the middle of the day and related this to the quantity of radiation received at each level as measured by the pyrlimnometer. Again they found that the depth of the maximum rate of photosynthesis and the depth of the compensation level were directly related to the transparency of the water. Maximum percentage utilization of the light occurred at depths where energies of 1.2 to 8 cal/cm^2 per 3 hours were being received, which was roughly 1% of the surface radiation in the two less transparent lakes and 4% in the most transparent. In all lakes the percentage of available energy utilized by the algae increased with depth, reaching values as high as 11% in the darkest lake. Efficiencies at the surface were unrealistically low, because they were calculated from total radiation, not merely from that in the visible portion of the spectrum.

In Crystal Lake the compensation level for the cultured algae occurred at 16.5 m, although Juday (1934a) had earlier pointed out that three species of mosses thrive in this lake at depths between 18 and 20 m. Maximum production of oxygen in all the series was 0.528 mg/million cells per 3 hours.

Curtis and Juday (1937) wished to determine if naturally occurring algae had responses similar to those observed for the cultured algae. Accordingly they ran experiments comparable to those of the previous years with cultured *Chlorella* as a control against *Chlorella* from sponges and colonies of *Ophridium*, two species of *Anabaena* that were available in relatively pure composition, *Gloeothece*, *Gloeotrichia*, a filamentous diatom growing in shallow water, and *Spirogyra*. Dissolved color in the lakes used ranged from 0 to 364 ppm on the Pt-Co scale. The filamentous diatom was the only species that always had its maximum photosynthesis at the surface. The others had their maxima below the surface during intense illumination.

Curtis and Juday conducted one of the very early bioassays of productivity in this study. They suspended cultured *Chlorella* cells in filtered Trout Lake water having a total CO_2 content (free, half-bound, and bound) of 38.2 mg/L and in water from Crystal Lake having a CO_2 content of only 5.5 mg/L. Both series of bottles, including dark bottles, were then suspended in parallel in Trout Lake. The algae in the Trout Lake water produced $2\frac{1}{2}$ times as much oxygen as those in the Crystal Lake water, which represented a utilization of 40% of the total CO_2 in the Crystal Lake water but only 15% of that in the Trout Lake water. Available CO_2 may have been a limiting factor, although the authors admitted that other unmeasured factors might have been equally important.

The following year (1936), W. M. Manning, a plant physiologist in the Department of Botany at Wisconsin, joined the summer program at Trout Lake with a much more sophisticated approach toward productivity (Manning, Juday, and Wolf, 1938b). *Chlorella* was used as in previous years, plus *Cladophora*, two species of *Anabaena*, and active tips of *Potamogeton, Vallisneria,* and *Sagittaria*. Records of surface radiation were made with a recording solarimeter, and of subsurface radiation with the pyrlimnometer. In all instances the photosynthesis accomplished was plotted as a function of light intensity (ergs/

cm²/sec) rather than as a function of depth in the water. The curves are similar in shape, naturally, with maximum photosynthesis generally at a value less than surface illumination. *Cladophora*, which was collected from surface waters, was the only plant studied that exhibited maximum photosynthesis at the surface on bright days. In the three higher aquatic plants there was no definite evidence of light adaptation over the natural depth ranges of the species. Manning also determined quantum efficiencies of the various algae used, finding considerably lower values than had been reported previously, although the values for *Chlorella* obtained in the field agreed with those he had previously determined in the laboratory (Manning *et al.,* 1938; Manning, Juday, and Wolf, 1938a). Later he also demonstrated that non-chlorophyll pigments can play a part in photosynthesis (Dutton and Manning, 1941).

The first study of the amount and distribution of chlorophyll in lakes was carried out by Kozminski (1938) in 1937. On the basis of vertical series from 17 lakes in the Trout Lake region, Kozminski attempted to establish five types of chlorophyll distribution, which subsequently were shown by Riley and by Manning and Juday (1941) to have no typological significance. The chlorophyll content of the various samples ranged as high as 386 mg/m³. Kozminski predicted that the mean chlorophyll content of the trophogenic zone would turn out to be a good index of lake productivity, since in the lakes studied this showed a general correlation with trophic level inferred from other parameters.

Most surprising was the high concentration of chlorophyll in the hypolimnion of some lakes at depths far below the 1% level. Some of this was inactive chlorophyll, probably resulting from the sinking of dead phytoplankton out of the zone of production, but some was definitely active. Kozminski suggested a relationship between depth of lake and the development of such a concentration zone, as influenced by the availability of regenerated plant nutrients at depths where there was still at least a trace of light. This explanation anticipated a similar one proposed later by Gessner (1949).

Manning and Juday (1941) attempted to obtain an estimate of primary productivity in an entire lake from the depth distribution of chlorophyll, the production of 7 mg of oxygen per hour per 1 mg of chlorophyll at optimum light, the variation in this value with light intensities above and below the optimum, and the measured light intensities in the lake at meter depth intervals and at hour time intervals throughout the day. The productivity varied from 14 to 44 kg glucose/ha per day for the seven lakes studied. The authors showed that in two lakes the deep-water concentration of chlorophyll found by Kozminski resulted from settling of phytoplankton. In Scaffold Lake, on the other hand, samples of water from 10 m, which were anaerobic and far below the 1% level of light (light intensity $< 10^{-5}$ at 6 m), actively photosynthesized at normal light intensities on being aerated. The organism involved was later reported to be *Pelogloea bacillifera* (Dutton and Juday, 1944).

Perhaps the most important study in this series was the last one (Juday, Blair, and Wilda, 1943), in which the daily productivity for an entire lake was determined from continuous records of dissolved oxygen at several depths, as measured by dropping mercury electrodes (Manning, 1940). Temperature was also recorded continuously at these depths, the dropping mercury electrodes were periodically checked by the Winkler method, light at all depths was measured with the pyrlimnometer, chlorophyll content of the water was determined, and light and dark bottle series of the lake water itself were run to determine rates of respiration and to obtain an independent check on productivity calculated from the *in situ* oxygen changes. Productivities measured by the dropping mercury electrodes ranged from 13 to 34 kg O_2/ha per day. Respiration ranged from 48 to 71% of the oxygen produced on clear and partly cloudy days to over 200% on one cloudy day.

Rates of production measured by the light and dark bottle series varied with length of exposure, in general the shorter exposure times having higher rates. Juday related this largely to increase in bacteria, based on observations by Fred *et al.* (1924) that bacteria in Mendota water samples in bottles increased 10 to 20 fold when suspended at depth for 8 days, and on similar observations by Stark *et al.* (1938). Accordingly, he recommended that the exposure time for light-dark bottle series based on oxygen changes should not exceed 48 hours. Rates of turnover were calculated from the glucose production per day in relation to the standing crop of centrifuged plankton.

Juday recommended that *in situ* oxygen values, measured continuously or at close intervals and supplemented by measurements of dark-bottle respiration, would suffice to give a general picture of the metabolic changes occurring in a lake. This paper anticipated by some years more recent attempts to determine productivity from diel *in situ* changes in oxygen, carbon dioxide, and *p*H.

In 'two other papers of this period Juday attempted to set up an energy budget for Mendota (Juday, 1940) and to investigate the relationships between various components of the standing crop of organic matter (Juday, 1942).

The mean annual solar radiation reaching Mendota over a 28-year period amounted to 118,872 cal/cm². The physical energy budget consisted of melting ice (3,500 cal), annual heat budget of water (24,200 cal), annual heat budget of bottom sediments (2,000 cal), evaporation (29,300 cal), losses at surface (28,500 cal), and conduction, convection, and radiation (31,000 cal). The basis for estimating the last term was the least satisfactory.

Assuming that the phytoplankton has a turnover rate of one week, assuming that it uses in its own metabolism one-third of the energy fixed, and making allowances for respiration rates of the various other components of the biota, Juday calculated that the biological energy utilization amounted to about 1% of the total energy actually entering the lake. Related to light energy alone, this percentage would be about twice as great.

In the later paper Juday (1942) compared the summer standing crops in two soft-water lakes in northeastern Wisconsin (Weber, Nebish) with those in two hard-water lakes in southeastern Wisconsin (Mendota, Green). The various components of the biota considered were phytoplankton, higher aquatics, zooplankton, benthos, and fish (only in the two northern lakes), plus dissolved organic matter. The community structure in each of the northern lakes was illustrated graphically by a triangle, similar to the well-known Eltonian pyramids. Although plant production was much smaller in the two northern lakes, the ratio of the standing crop of plants to that of benthos and zooplankton suggested a greater efficiency among the animals of soft-water lakes. In all four lakes the standing crop of dissolved organic matter was greater than that of the living organisms. In the hard-water lakes the dissolved organic matter was relatively more abundant than in the soft-water lakes.

Weber Lake is particularly interesting because

attempts were made during the 1930's to increase its production by the addition of fertilizers. The quantities of fertilizers added are summarized by Potzger and Van Engel (1942), and a brief progress report on the experiment is contained in Juday and Schloemer (1938a). In each of the four years 1932-35 commercial mineral fertilizers were added to the lake, without any appreciable effects on the standing crop. In 1936 the addition of 3,000 lbs of soybean meal resulted in a marked increase in everything except fish and dissolved organic matter, and this effect persisted through 1938 without the addition of any more fertilizer. In 1939 the addition of 2,000 lbs of cottonseed meal further increased the standing crops of phytoplankton, bottom flora, zooplankton, and benthos. This increase persisted through 1940, but the standing crops declined in 1941. The data on the standing crops in these various years were summarized by Juday (1942). The conclusion was reached that productivity in the northern lakes is limited not so much by mineral nitrogen and phosphorus as by the general CO_2 supply and perhaps by various essential organic factors in the water.

Biotal and general biological studies

The major studies of this general category are listed in Table 1.2.

Miscellaneous studies

Cole (1921) investigated the respiratory mechanisms of the benthic animals living under anaerobic conditions in summer. As a result of experimental oxidation of guaiacum or benzidene under conditions of darkness, he claimed that decomposing plant tissues give off small amounts of atomic oxygen, even under anaerobiosis, and that this oxygen is utilized by the animals.

Pennak (1939, 1940) studied the psammolittoral organisms in sandy beaches of 15 Wisconsin lakes. He obtained extensive data on the quantitative horizontal and vertical distribution of the various organisms and on the chemistry of the psammolittoral environment. Pennak paid special attention to the tardigrades, copepods, and rotifers, with only incidental observations on the other groups of organisms.

One other subject that should be mentioned is the cultural eutrophication of the Madison lakes. For a long time the sewage effluent from Madison was emptied into Lake Monona. This created such large blooms of algae that attempts were made to control the algae with copper sulfate beginning in 1918. Domogalla (1935) reviewed the outcome of this treatment. In 1926 a new sewage treatment plant was constructed, the effluent of which was discharged into the Yahara River just above Lake Waubesa. Subsequently, Lakes Waubesa and Kegonsa were treated with $CuSO_4$ along with Monona.

The long-term effects of accumulation of copper in lake sediments have caused concern to biologists. However, Mackenthun and Cooley (1952) showed by experiments that the present levels of copper in the sediments of Monona are not appreciably toxic even to *Pisidium* over a 60-day period.

The already productive lakes at Madison were being so seriously affected by the sewage plant

TABLE 1.2

Summary of major taxonomic, distributional, and life history studies on aquatic organisms during the Birge-Juday era

Group	References (listed in bibliography)
Algae	Smith (1916a, 1916b, 1918b, 1920, 1924); Prescott (1944)
Higher aquatic plants	Fassett (1940, 1957)
Protozoa	Juday (1919); Noland (1925a, 1925b); Noland and Finley (1931)
Sponges	Jewell (1935, 1939); Neidhoefer (1938, 1940)
Rotifers	Harring and Myers (1922, 1924, 1926, 1927); Myers (1930); Edmondson (1940)
Hirudinea	Bere (1931b)
Mollusks	Baker (1914, 1924, 1928); Morrison (1929, 1932a, 1932b)
Cladocera	Birge (1879, 1892, 1893, 1910d, 1918a); Woltereck (1932)
Copepoda	Marsh (1893, 1907, 1910, 1918, 1933); Lehmann (1903); Birge and Juday (1908); Juday (1914b, 1923a, 1925); Juday and Muttkowski (1915); Wright (1927, 1928)
Malacostraca	Marsh (1892a); Holmes (1909); Jackson (1912); Juday and Birge (1927); Creaser (1932)
Water mites	Marshall (1903, 1914, 1921, 1929, 1930, 1931–40)
Insects	Vorhies (1905, 1909); Dickinson (1936)
Fishes	Wagner (1908, 1911); Pearse (1934); Greene (1927, 1935)

effluent that the Governor of Wisconsin in 1941 appointed a committee to investigate this problem. The committee found in an intensive two-year study that the effluent from the Madison sewage disposal plant contributed 75% of the total inorganic nitrogen and 88% of the total inorganic phosphorus entering Lake Waubesa. The blooms of algae in this lake were so heavy as a result that the water from Waubesa was the major source of both nitrogen and phosphorus in Lake Kegonsa. These investigations were reviewed briefly by Sawyer (1947). Because of these findings, the sewage effluent from Madison is now diverted by conduit around the lakes, entering the Yahara River below Lake Kegonsa.

Training of graduate students

In spite of the large overall limnological output during this era, relatively few students received graduate degrees under the direct supervision of Birge or Juday. During the late 1800's Birge supervised a number of Bachelor's theses (those of Olson, Harder, and Merrill having already been mentioned) and a few Masters' theses, including those of Julius Nelson and Ruth Marshall. Birge never had any Ph.D. students.

Juday, on the other hand, supervised the Ph.D. research of 13 students between 1928 and 1940. Most of the later dissertations were concerned with growth rates of fishes in Wisconsin, which reflected the need Juday felt for studying fishes as one of the biotal components of the total ecosystem and also reflected the continuing financial support from the U.S. Bureau of Fisheries and the Wisconsin Conservation Department for "practical" investigations. All these dissertations are listed below; those which have been published may be found in the references.

1928 Edward Joseph Wimmer. A study of two limestone quarry pools. (Wimmer, 1929)
1928 Stillman Wright. Studies in aquatic biology. I. A chemical and plankton study of Lake Wingra. 35 p. II. A revision of the South American species of *Diaptomus*. (Wright, 1927) III. A contribution to the knowledge of the genus *Pseudodiaptomus*. (Wright, 1928)
1929 Abraham H. Wiebe. Productivity of fish ponds. I. The plankton. 95 + ii p. Published as Investigations of plankton production in fish ponds. (Wiebe, 1930)
1930 Willis L. Tressler. Limnological studies of Lake Wingra. 35 + v p. Published by W. L. Tressler and B. P. Domogalla as Limnological studies

of Lake Wingra. (Tressler and Domogalla, 1931)
1931 J. P. E. Morrison. A report on the Mollusca of the northeastern Wisconsin lake district. (Morrison, 1932a) Studies on the life history of *Acella haldemani* ("Desh." Binney). (Morrison, 1932b)
1932 Ruby Bere. The bacterial content of some Wisconsin lakes. 27 p. The effect of freezing on the number of bacteria in ice and water from Lake Mendota. 18 p. Copepods parasitic on fish of the Trout Lake region, with descriptions of two new species. (Bere, 1931a)
1933 Edward Schneberger. The growth of yellow perch (*Perca flavescens* Mitchill) from Nebish, Silver and Weber lakes in Vilas County, Wisconsin. 73 p. (Schneberger, 1935)
1936 William A. Spoor. The age and growth of the sucker, *Catostomus commersonii* (Lacépède), in Muskellunge Lake, Vilas County, Wisconsin. 90 p. (Spoor, 1938)
1937 Arthur D. Hasler. The physiology of digestion of plankton Crustacea. I. Some digestive enzymes of *Daphnia*. (Hasler, 1935) II. Further studies on the digestive enzymes of A. *Daphnia* and *Polyphemus*, B. *Diaptomus* and *Calanus*. 13 + ii p. (Hasler, 1937)
1938 Robert W. Pennak. The ecology of the psammolittoral organisms of some Wisconsin lakes, with special reference to the Tardigrada, Copepoda, and Rotatoria. 180 p. (Pennak, 1940)
1939 George W. Bennett. Limnological investigations in Wisconsin and Nebraska. I. The limnology of some gravel pits near Louisville, Nebraska. 63 p. II. The growth of the large mouthed black bass, *Huro salmoides* (Lacépède), in the waters of Wisconsin. (Bennett, 1937) III. Growth of the small-mouthed black bass, *Micropterus dolomieu* (Lacépède), in Wisconsin waters. (Bennett, 1938)
1939 Clarence L. Schloemer. The age and rate of growth of the bluegill, *Helioperca macrochira* (Rafinesque). 113 p.
1940 David G. Frey. Growth and ecology of the carp, *Cyprinus carpio* Linnaeus, in four lakes of the Madison Region, Wisconsin. 248 p. Partially published. (Frey, 1942)

During the period from 1920 through 1940, when the program of cooperative lake studies was being rapidly expanded, students in other departments were likewise obtaining Ph.D.'s based on limnological research. The departments most directly involved were Bacteriology, Botany, Chemistry, and Geology. No attempt was made to search out all the pertinent dissertations of this period, although the total number probably equals or even exceeds that of Juday's students.

References

This list of references includes all the limnological publications of Birge and Juday, some of which are not listed in the previous bibliography by Juday and Hasler (1946). Although the present list is extensive and covers quite completely the limnological output of this period, it does not include many papers on the growth, ecology, and management of fishes or on the parasites of fishes and other organisms. Some of the lesser taxonomic papers have also been omitted. These may be found in the listing by Juday and Hasler. Finally, a few of the papers listed in the present bibliography have not been summarized in the text because of space limitations.

ALLGEIER, R. J., B. C. HAFFORD, AND CHANCEY JUDAY. 1941. Oxidation-reduction potentials and pH of lake waters and of lake sediments. Trans. Wisconsin Acad. Sci. Arts Lett., **33**: 115–133.

ALLGEIER, R. J., W. H. PETERSON, AND CHANCEY JUDAY. 1934. Availability of carbon in certain aquatic materials under aerobic conditions of fermentation. Intern. Rev. Hydrobiol., **30**: 371–378.

ALLGEIER, R. J., W. H. PETERSON, CHANCEY JUDAY, AND E. A. BIRGE. 1932. The anaerobic fermentation of lake deposits. Intern. Rev. Hydrobiol., **26**: 444–461.

AMERICAN PUBLIC HEALTH ASSOCIATION. 1955. Standard methods for the examination of water, sewage, and industrial wastes. 10th ed. APHA, AWWA, FSIWA. Amer. Pub. Health Assoc., New York. 522 + xix p.

BAKER, F. C. 1914. The molluscan fauna of Tomahawk Lake, Wisconsin, with special reference to its ecology. Trans. Wisconsin Acad. Sci. Arts Lett., **17**: 200–246, pl. 11–17.

———. 1924. The fauna of the Lake Winnebago region; a quantitative and qualitative survey with special reference to the Mollusca. Trans. Wisconsin Acad. Sci. Arts Lett., **21**: 109–146.

———. 1928. The fresh water Mollusca of Wisconsin. I. Gastropoda. II. Pelecypoda. Wisconsin Geol. Nat. Hist. Surv., Bull. 70, 507 + xx p., pl.–28; 495 + vi p., pl. 29–105.

BENNETT, G. W. 1937. The growth of the large-mouthed black bass in the waters of Wisconsin. Copeia, 1937(2): 104–118.

———. 1938. Growth of the small-mouthed black bass in Wisconsin waters. Copeia, 1938(4): 157–170.

BERE, RUBY. 1931a. Copepods parasitic on fish of the Trout Lake region, with descriptions of two new species. Trans. Wisconsin Acad. Sci. Arts Lett., **26**: 427–436.

———. 1931b. Leeches from the lakes of northeastern Wisconsin. Trans. Wisconsin Acad. Sci. Arts Lett., **26**: 437–440.

———. 1933. Numbers of bacteria in inland lakes of Wisconsin as shown by the direct microscopic method. Intern. Rev. Hydrobiol., **29**: 248–263.

———. 1935. Further notes on the occurrence of parasitic copepods on fish of the Trout Lake region, with a description of the male of *Argulus biramosus*. Trans. Wisconsin Acad. Sci. Arts Lett., **29**: 83–88.

BIRGE, E. A. 1878. On Crustacea cladocera collected at Cambridge, Mass., 1876, and at Madison, Wis., 1877. Ph.D. Thesis, Harvard Univ.

———. 1879. Notes on Cladocera. Trans. Wisconsin Acad. Sci. Arts Lett., **4**: 77–112.

———. 1881. Notes on Crustacea in Chicago water supply, with remarks on the formation of the carapace. Chicago Med. J. and Exam., **44**(6): 584–590, 1 pl.

———. 1892. Notes and list of Crustacea Cladocera from Madison, Wisconsin. Trans. Wisconsin Acad. Sci. Arts Lett., **8**: 379–398.

———. 1893. Notes on Cladocera, III. Trans. Wisconsin Acad. Sci. Arts Lett., **9**: 275–317.

———. 1894. A report on a collection of Cladocera, mostly from Lake St. Clair, Michigan, p. 45–47, 1 table. *In* J. E. Reighard. A biological examination of Lake St. Clair. Bull. Michigan Fish Comm., **4**: 1–60.

———. 1895a. Cladocera [of Turkey Lake, Indiana]. Proc. Indiana Acad. Sci., **5**: 244–246.

———. 1895b. On the vertical distribution of the pelagic crustacea of Lake Mendota, Wis., during July, 1894. Biol. Centr., **15**: 353–355.

———. 1897. The vertical distribution of the limnetic crustacea of Lake Mendota. Biol. Centr., **17**: 371–374.

———. 1898. Plankton studies on Lake Mendota. II. The Crustacea of the plankton from July, 1894, to December, 1896. Trans. Wisconsin Acad. Sci. Arts Lett., **11**: 274–448.

———. 1901a. The cone net. J. Appl. Microscop., **4**: 1405–1407.

———. 1901b. Report of the Limnological Commission. Trans. Amer. Microscop. Soc., **22**: 193–196.

———. 1904a. Report on the Cladocera, p. 149–153, pl. 25. *In* H. B. Ward, A biological reconnaissance of some elevated lakes in the Sierras and Rockies. Studies Zool. Lab., Univ. Nebraska, No. 60, p. 127–154.

———. 1904b. The thermocline and its biological significance. Trans. Amer. Microscop. Soc., **25**: 5–33, pl. 1, 2.

———. 1906. Gases dissolved in the waters of Wisconsin lakes. Trans. Amer. Fish. Soc., 1906: 143–163.

———. 1907a. The oxygen dissolved in the waters of Wisconsin lakes. Rept. Wisconsin Comm. Fish., 1907: 119–140. (This is the same article as Birge, 1906.)

———. 1907b. The respiration of an inland lake. Trans. Amer. Fish. Soc., 1907: 223–241.

———. 1908a. The respiration of an inland lake. Popular Sci. Month., **72**: 337–351. (This is the same article as Birge, 1907b.)

———. 1908b. [Phyllopoda] p. 203–205. *In* S. E. Meek, The zoology of lakes Amatitlan and Atitlan, Guatemala, with special reference to ichthyology.

Field Columbian Museum, Zool. Ser., **7**(6) : 159–206.

——. 1910*a*. The apparent sinking of ice in lakes. Science, N.S., **32** : 81–82.

——. 1910*b*. An unregarded factor in lake temperatures. Trans. Wisconsin Acad. Sci. Arts Lett., **16**(2) : 989–1004, pl. 64, 65.

——. 1910*c*. On the evidence for temperature seiches. Trans. Wisconsin Acad Sci. Arts Lett., **16**(2) : 1005–1016, pl. 66.

——. 1910*d*. Notes on Cladocera, IV. Trans. Wisconsin Acad. Sci. Arts Lett., **16**(2) : 1017–1066.

——. 1910*e*. Gases dissolved in the waters of Wisconsin lakes. Bull. U.S. Bur. Fish., **28** : 1273–1294.

——. 1913. Absorption of the sun's energy by lakes. Science, **38** : 702–704.

——. 1915. The heat budgets of American and European lakes. Trans. Wisconsin Acad. Sci. Arts Lett., **18**(1) : 166–213. (Fig. 1 separate.)

——. 1916. The work of the wind in warming a lake. Trans. Wisconsin Acad. Sci. Arts Lett., **18**(2) : 341–391.

——. 1918*a*. The water fleas (Cladocera), p. 676–740. *In* H. B. Ward and G. C. Whipple, Fresh-water biology. John Wiley & Sons, New York.

——. 1918*b*. Coefficients of absorption in various lake waters. Notes on the foregoing paper [Pietenpol, q.v.]. Trans. Wisconsin Acad. Sci. Arts Lett., **19**(1) : 580–593.

——. 1922. A second report on limnological apparatus. Trans. Wisconsin Acad. Sci. Arts Lett., **20** : 533–552, pl. 39, 40.

——. 1923. The plankton of the lakes. Trans. Amer. Fish. Soc., **52** : 118–130.

——. 1929. Fish and their food. Trans. Amer. Fish. Soc., **59** : 188–194.

——. 1936. Biology of Lake Mendota. Tech. Club of Madison, 1936 : 11–12.

——. 1938. Note [re C. D. Marsh], p. 541–543. *In* Mrs. Florence W. Marsh, Professor C. Dwight Marsh and his investigations of lakes. Trans. Wisconsin Acad. Sci. Arts Lett., **31** : 535–543.

BIRGE, E. A., AND CHANCEY JUDAY. 1908. A summer resting stage in the development of *Cyclops bicuspidatus* Claus. Trans. Wisconsin Acad. Sci. Arts Lett., **16** : 1–9.

——. 1911. The inland lakes of Wisconsin. The dissolved gases of the water and their biological significance. Wisconsin Geol. Nat. Hist. Surv., Bull. 22, 259 + x p.

——. 1914. A limnological study of the Finger Lakes of New York. Bull. U.S. Bur. Fish., **32** : 525–609, pl. 111–116.

——. 1920. A limnological reconnaissance of West Okoboji. Univ. Iowa Studies Nat. Hist., **9**(1) : 1–56, 1 pl.

——. 1921. Further limnological observations on the Finger Lakes of New York. Bull. U.S. Bur. Fish., **37** : 210–252.

——. 1922. The inland lakes of Wisconsin. The plankton. I. Its quantity and chemical composition. Wisconsin Geol. Nat. Hist. Surv., Bull. 64, 222 + ix p.

——. 1926. The organic content of lake water. Proc. Natl. Acad. Sci., **12** : 515–519.

——. 1927*a*. Organic content of lake water. Bull. U.S. Bur. Fish., **42** : 185–205.

——. 1927*b*. The organic content of the water of small lakes. Proc. Amer. Phil. Soc., **66** : 357–372.

——. 1929*a*. Penetration of solar radiation into lakes, as measured by the thermopile. Bull. Natl. Research Council, **68** : 61–76.

——. 1929*b*. Transmission of solar radiation by the waters of inland lakes. Trans. Wisconsin Acad. Sci. Arts Lett., **24** : 509–580.

——. 1930. A second report on solar radiation and inland lakes. Trans. Wisconsin Acad. Sci. Arts Lett., **25** : 285–335.

——. 1931. A third report on solar radiation and inland lakes. Trans. Wisconsin Acad. Sci. Arts Lett., **26** : 383–425.

——. 1932. Solar radiation and inland lakes. Fourth Report. Observations of 1931. Trans. Wisconsin Acad. Sci. Arts Lett., **27** : 523–562.

——. 1934. Particulate and dissolved organic matter in inland lakes. Ecol. Monogr., **4** : 440–474.

BIRGE, E. A., CHANCEY JUDAY, AND H. W. MARCH. 1928. The temperature of the bottom deposits of Lake Mendota; a chapter in the heat exchanges of the lake. Trans. Wisconsin Acad. Sci. Arts Lett., **23** : 187–231, tables 17–20 in appendix.

BIRGE, E. A., O. A. OLSON, AND H. P. HARDER. 1895. Plankton studies on Lake Mendota. I. The vertical distribution of the pelagic crustacea during July, 1894. Trans. Wisconsin Acad. Sci. Arts Lett., **10** : 421–484, pl. 7–10.

BIRGE, E. A., AND W. H. RICH. 1927. Observations on Karluk Lake, Alaska. Ecology, **8** : 384.

BLACK, C. S. 1929. Chemical analysis of lake deposits. Trans. Wisconsin Acad. Sci. Arts Lett., **24** : 127–133.

BLACK, R. F. 1959. Friends of the Pleistocene [report of meeting]. Science, **130** : 172–173.

——. 1960. The "Driftless area" of Wisconsin was glaciated. Program 1960 Ann. Meetings, Geol. Soc. Amer. : 59.

BORDNER, J. S. 1939. Inventory of northern Wisconsin lakes. Wisconsin State Planning Board, Div. Land Econ. Inventory, Bull. 5, 64 p.

BROOKS, J. L. 1959. Cladocera, p. 587–656. *In* W. T. Edmondson (ed.), Fresh-water biology. 2nd ed. John Wiley & Sons, New York.

BROOKS, J. L., G. L. CLARKE, A. D. HASLER, AND L. E. NOLAND. 1951. Edward Asahel Birge (1851–1950). Arch. Hydrobiol., **45** : 235–243.

BROUGHTON, W. A. 1941. The geology, ground water and lake basin seal of the region south of the Muskellunge Moraine, Vilas County, Wisconsin. Trans. Wisconsin Acad. Sci. Arts Lett., **33** : 5–20.

CARPENTER, P. L. 1939. Bacterial counts in the muds of Crystal Lake—an oligotrophic lake of northern Wisconsin. J. Sediment. Petrol., **9** : 3–7.

CHAMBERLIN, T. C. 1894. Glacial phenomena of North America, p. 724–774. *In* James Geikie, The great ice age and its relation to the antiquity of man. 3rd ed. D. Appleton, New York.

————. 1895. Classification of American glacial deposits. J. Geol., **3**: 270–277.

CHASE, W. J., AND L. E. NOLAND. 1927. The history and hydrography of Lake Ripley (Jefferson County, Wisconsin). Trans. Wisconsin Acad. Sci. Arts Lett., **23**: 179–186.

COLE, A. E. 1921. Oxygen supply of certain animals living in water containing no dissolved oxygen. J. Exptl. Zool., **33**: 293–320.

COLEMAN, F. H. 1941. Supplementary climatic notes for Wisconsin, p. 1199–1200. *In* Climate and man, Yearbook of Agriculture. U.S. Dept. Agr.

CONGER, P. S. 1939. The contribution of diatoms to the sediments of Crystal Lake, Vilas County, Wisconsin. Amer. J. Sci., **237**: 324–340, pl. 1–2.

————. 1942. Accumulation of diatomaceous deposits. J. Sediment. Petrol., **12**(2): 55–66.

COUEY, F. M. 1935. Fish food studies of a number of northeastern Wisconsin lakes. Trans. Wisconsin Acad. Sci. Arts Lett., **29**: 131–172.

CREASER, E. P. 1932. The decapod crustaceans of Wisconsin. Trans. Wisconsin Acad. Sci. Arts Lett., **27**: 321–338.

CURTIS, J. T., AND CHANCEY JUDAY. 1937. Photosynthesis of algae in Wisconsin lakes. III. Observations of 1935. Intern. Rev. Hydrobiol., **35**: 122–133.

DAVIS, F. J. 1941. Surface loss of solar and sky radiation by inland lakes. Trans. Wisconsin Acad. Sci. Arts Lett., **33**: 83–93.

DENNISTON, R. H. 1922. A survey of the larger aquatic plants of Lake Mendota. Trans. Wisconsin Acad. Sci. Arts Lett., **20**: 495–500. (Table 2 folded in.)

DICKINSON, W. E. 1936. The mosquitoes of Wisconsin. Bull. Pub. Museum, Milwaukee, **8**(3).

DOMOGALLA, B. P. 1935. Eleven years of chemical treatment of the Madison lakes: Its effect on fish and fish foods. Trans. Amer. Fish. Soc., **65**: 115–121.

DOMOGALLA, B. P., AND E. B. FRED. 1926. Ammonia and nitrate studies of lakes near Madison, Wisconsin. J. Amer. Soc. Agron., **18**: 897–910.

DOMOGALLA, B. P., E. B. FRED, AND W. H. PETERSON. 1926. Seasonal variations in the ammonia and nitrate content of lake waters. J. Amer. Water Works Assoc., **15**: 369–385.

DOMOGALLA, B. P., CHANCEY JUDAY, AND W. H. PETERSON. 1925. The forms of nitrogen found in certain lake waters. J. Biol. Chem., **63**: 269–285.

DUTTON, H. J., AND CHANCEY JUDAY. 1944. Chromatic adaptation in relation to color and depth distribution of freshwater phytoplankton and large aquatic plants. Ecology, **25**: 273–282.

DUTTON, H. J., AND W. M. MANNING. 1941. Evidence for carotenoid-sensitized photosynthesis in the diatom *Nitzschia closterium*. Amer. J. Botan., **28**: 516–526.

EDMONDSON, W. T. 1940. The sessile Rotatoria of Wisconsin. Trans. Amer. Microscop. Soc., **59**: 433–459.

ENTEMAN, MINNIE M. 1900. Variations in the crest of *Daphnia hyalina*. Amer. Nat., **34**: 879–890.

ERIKSON, DAGNY. 1941. Studies on some lake-mud

strains of *Micromonospora*. J. Bacteriol., **41**: 277–300.

FASSETT, N. C. 1930. The plants of some northeastern Wisconsin lakes. Trans. Wisconsin Acad. Sci. Arts Lett., **25**: 157–168.

————. 1940. A manual of aquatic plants. McGraw-Hill, New York. 382 + vii p.

————. 1957. A manual of aquatic plants. 2nd ed. Revision appendix by Eugene C. Ogden. Univ. Wisconsin Press, Madison. 405 + ix p.

FENNEMAN, N. M. 1902. On the lakes of southeastern Wisconsin. Wisconsin Geol. Nat. Hist. Surv., Bull. 8, 178 + xv p.

————. 1938. Physiography of eastern United States. McGraw-Hill, New York. 714 + xiii p.

FIELD, J. B., C. A. ELVEHJEM, AND CHANCEY JUDAY. 1943. A study of the blood constituents of carp and trout. J. Biol. Chem., **148**: 261–269.

FIELD, J. B., LYNN L. GEE, C. A. ELVEHJEM, AND CHANCEY JUDAY. 1944. The blood picture in furunculosis induced by *Bacterium salmonicida* in fish. Arch. Biochem., **3**: 277–284.

FITZGERALD, DESMOND. 1895. The temperature of lakes. Trans. Amer. Soc. Civil Engineers, **34**(756): 67–109; Discussion, 110–114.

FLANIGON, T. H. 1942. Limnological observations on three lakes in eastern Vilas County, Wisconsin. Trans. Wisconsin Acad. Sci. Arts Lett., **34**: 167–175.

FORBES, S. A. 1890. Preliminary report upon the invertebrate animals inhabiting Lakes Geneva and Mendota, Wisconsin, with an account of the fish epidemic in Lake Mendota in 1884. Bull. U.S. Fish. Comm., **8**: 473–487, pl. 72–74.

FRANCÉ, R. H. 1894. Zur Biologie des Planktons. Biol. Centr., **14**(2): 33–38.

FRED, E. B., F. C. WILSON, AND AUDREY DAVENPORT. 1924. The distribution and significance of bacteria in Lake Mendota. Ecology, **5**: 322–339.

FREEMAN, STEPHEN, V. W. MELOCHE, AND CHANCEY JUDAY. 1933. The determination of the hydrogen ion concentration of inland lake waters. Intern. Rev. Hydrobiol., **29**: 346–359.

FREY, D. G. 1942. Studies on Wisconsin carp. I. Influence of age, size, and sex on time of annulus formation by the 1936 year class. Copeia, 1942(4): 214–223.

————. 1955. The Winona Lake Biological Station. Amer. Inst. Biol. Sci. Bull., **5**(3): 20–22.

FRIES, CARL, JR. 1938. Geology and ground water of the Trout Lake region, Vilas County, Wisconsin. Trans. Wisconsin Acad. Sci. Arts Lett., **31**: 305–322.

FRYE, J. C., AND H. B. WILLMAN. 1960. Classification of the Wisconsinan Stage in the Lake Michigan glacial lobe. Illinois State Geol. Surv., Circ. 285, 16 p.

GESSNER, FRITZ. 1949. Der Chlorophyllgehalt im See und seine photosynthetische Valenz als geophysikalisches Problem. Schweiz. Z. Hydrol., **11**: 378–410.

CIFFORD, ELIZABETH M., AND G. W. PECKHAM. 1882. Temperature of Pine, Beaver and Okauchee lakes, Waukesha County, Wisconsin, extending from May to December, 1879; also particulars of depths of

Pine Lake. Trans. Wisconsin Acad. Sci. Arts Lett., 5: 273–275.

GREENBANK, JOHN. 1945. Limnological conditions in ice-covered lakes, especially as related to winterkill of fish. Ecol. Monogr., 15: 343–392.

GREENE, C. W. 1927. An ichthyological survey of Wisconsin. Papers Michigan Acad. Sci. Arts Lett., 7: 299–310.

———. 1935. The distribution of Wisconsin fishes. Wisconsin Conserv. Comm. 235 p.

HANSEN, H. P. 1937. Pollen analyses of two Wisconsin bogs of different age. Ecology, 18: 136–148.

HARDMAN, YVETTE. 1941. The surface tension of Wisconsin lake waters. Trans. Wisconsin Acad. Sci. Arts Lett., 33: 395–404.

HARDMAN, YVETTE, AND A. T. HENRICI. 1939. Studies of freshwater bacteria. V. The distribution of *Siderocapsa treubii* in some lakes and streams. J. Bacteriol., 37: 97–104, pl. 1.

HARRING, H. K., AND F. J. MYERS. 1922. The rotifers of Wisconsin. Trans. Wisconsin Acad. Sci. Arts Lett., 20: 553–662, pl. 41–61.

HARRING, H. K., AND F. J. MYERS. 1924. The rotifer fauna of Wisconsin. II. A revision of the notommatid rotifers, exclusive of the Dicranophorinae. Trans. Wisconsin Acad. Sci. Arts Lett., 21: 415–549, pl. 16–43.

HARRING, H. K., AND F. J. MYERS. 1926. The rotifer fauna of Wisconsin. III. A revision of the genera Lecane and Monostyla. Trans. Wisconsin Acad. Sci. Arts Lett., 22: 315–423, pl. 8–47.

HARRING, H. K., AND F. J. MYERS. 1927. The rotifer fauna of Wisconsin. IV. The Dicranophorinae. Trans. Wisconsin Acad. Sci. Arts Lett., 23: 667–808, pl. 23–49.

HASLER, A. D. 1935. The physiology of digestion of plankton crustacea. I. Some digestive enzymes of Daphnia. Biol. Bull., 68: 207–214.

———. 1937. The physiology of digestion in plankton crustacea. II. Further studies on the digestive enzymes of (A) Daphnia and Polyphemus; (B) Diaptomus and Calanus. Biol. Bull., 72: 290–298.

HATHAWAY, E. S. 1927. The relation of temperature to the quantity of food consumed by fishes. Ecology, 8: 428–434.

———. 1928. Quantitative study of the changes produced by acclimatization in the tolerance of high temperatures by fishes and amphibians. Bull. U.S. Bur. Fish., 43(2): 169–192.

HENRICI, A. T., AND ELIZABETH McCOY. 1938. The distribution of heterotrophic bacteria in the bottom deposits of some lakes. Trans. Wisconsin Acad. Sci. Arts Lett., 31: 323–361. (Fig. 1 separate.)

HILE, RALPH. 1936a. Age and growth of the cisco, *Leucichthys artedi* (Le Sueur), in the lakes of northeastern Highlands, Wisconsin. Bull. U.S. Bur. Fish., 48: 211–317.

———. 1936b. Summary of investigations on the morphometry of the cisco, *Leucichthys artedi* (Le Sueur), in the lakes of the northeastern Highlands, Wisconsin. Papers Michigan Acad. Sci. Arts Lett., 21: 619–634, pl. 62.

———. 1938. Morphometry of the cisco, *Leucichthys artedi* (Le Sueur), in the lakes of the Northeastern Highlands, Wisconsin. Intern. Rev. Hydrobiol., 36: 57–130.

———. 1941. Age and growth of the rock bass. *Ambloplites rupestris* (Rafinesque), in Nebish Lake, Wisconsin. Trans. Wisconsin Acad. Sci. Arts Lett., 33: 189–337.

———. 1942. Growth of the rock bass, *Ambloplites rupestris* (Rafinesque), in five lakes of northeastern Wisconsin. Trans. Amer. Fish. Soc., 71: 131–143.

———. 1943. Mathematical relationship between the length and the age of the rock bass, *Ambloplites rupestris* (Rafinesque). Papers Michigan Acad. Sci. Arts Lett., 28: 331–341.

HILE, RALPH, AND H. J. DEASON. 1934. Growth of the whitefish, *Coregonus clupeaformis* (Mitchill), in Trout Lake, northeastern Highlands, Wisconsin. Trans. Amer. Fish. Soc., 64: 231–237.

HILE, RALPH, AND CHANCEY JUDAY. 1941. Bathymetric distribution of fish in lakes of the northeastern Highlands, Wisconsin. Trans. Wisconsin Acad. Sci. Arts Lett., 33: 147–187.

HOLMES, S. J. 1909. Description of a new subterranean amphipod from Wisconsin. Trans. Wisconsin Acad. Sci. Arts Lett., 16(1): 77–80.

HOY, P. R. 1872. Deep-water fauna of Lake Michigan. Trans. Wisconsin Acad. Sci. Arts Lett., 1: 98–101.

HUTCHINSON, G. E. 1938. On the relation between the oxygen deficit and the productivity and typology of lakes. Intern. Rev. Hydrobiol., 36: 336–355.

JACKSON, H. H. T. 1912. A contribution to the natural history of the amphipod, *Hyalella knickerbockeri* Bate. Bull. Wisconsin Nat. Hist. Soc., 10: 49–60.

JAMES, H. R., AND E. A. BIRGE. 1938. A laboratory study of the absorption of light by lake waters. Trans. Wisconsin Acad. Sci. Arts Lett., 31: 1–154.

JEWELL, MINNA E. 1935. An ecological study of the fresh-water sponges of northeastern Wisconsin. Ecol. Monogr., 5: 461–504.

———. 1939. An ecological study of the fresh-water sponges of Wisconsin. II. The influence of calcium. Ecology, 20: 11–28.

JUDAY, CHANCEY. 1896. Hydrographic map of Turkey Lake. Proc. Indiana Acad. Sci. (Frontispiece), 1895.

———. 1897. The plankton of Turkey Lake. Proc. Indiana Acad. Sci., 1896: 287–296.

———. 1902. The plankton of Lake Maxinkuckee, Indiana. Trans. Amer. Microscop. Soc., 24: 61–62.

———. 1903. The plankton of Winona Lake. Proc. Indiana Acad. Sci., 1902: 120–133.

———. 1904a. The diurnal movement of plankton crustacea. Trans. Wisconsin Acad. Sci. Arts Lett., 14: 534–568.

———. 1904b. Fishes of Boulder County, Colorado. Univ. Colorado Studies, 2(2): 113–114.

———. 1905. List of fishes collected in Boulder County, Colorado, with description of a new species of Leuciscus. Bull. U.S. Bur. Fish., 24: 223–227.

———. 1906a. The food of the trout of the Kern River Region. Bull. U.S. Bur. Fish., 25: 43–49.

———. 1906b. Ostracoda of the San Diego region. I.

Halocypridae. Univ. California Publ. Zool., **3**(2): 13–38, pl. 3–7.

———. 1907a. Cladocera of the San Diego region. Univ. California Publ. Zool., **3**(10): 157–158.

———. 1907b. Notes on Lake Tahoe, its trout and trout-fishing. Bull. U.S. Bur. Fish., **26**: 133–146.

———. 1907c. Ostracoda of the San Diego region. II. Littoral forms. Univ. California Publ. Zool., **3**(9): 135–156, pl. 18–20.

———. 1907d. Studies on some lakes in the Rocky and Sierra Nevada Mountains. Trans. Wisconsin Acad. Sci. Arts Lett., **15**(2): 781–793, pl. 48–50.

———. 1907e. A study of Twin Lakes, Colorado, with especial consideration of the food of the trouts. Bull. U.S. Bur. Fish., **26**: 147–178, pl. 3.

———. 1908a. Resumé of the recent work on lakes by the Wisconsin Geological and Natural History Survey. Intern. Rev. Hydrobiol., **1**: 240–242.

———. 1908b. Some aquatic invertebrates that live under anaerobic conditions. Trans. Wisconsin Acad. Sci. Arts Lett., **16**: 10–16.

———. 1908c. [Copepoda] p. 205. In S. E. Meek, The zoology of lakes Amatitlan and Atitlan, Guatemala, with special reference to ichthyology. Field Columbian Museum, Zool. Ser., **7**(6): 159–206.

———. 1910. Some European biological stations. Trans. Wisconsin Acad. Sci. Arts Lett., **16**(2): 1257–1277.

———. 1913. Air in the depths of the ocean. Science, N.S., **38**: 546–547.

———. 1914a. The inland lakes of Wisconsin. II. The hydrography and morphometry of the lakes. Wisconsin Geol. Nat. Hist. Surv., Bull. 27, 137 + xv p.

———. 1914b. A new species of Diaptomus. Trans. Wisconsin Acad. Sci. Arts Lett., **17**(2): 803–805.

———. 1915. Limnological studies on some lakes in Central America. Trans. Wisconsin Acad. Sci. Arts Lett., **18**: 214–250.

———. 1916a. Horizontal rainbows on Lake Mendota. Monthly Weather Rev., **44**: 65–67.

———. 1916b. Limnological apparatus. Trans. Wisconsin Acad. Sci. Arts Lett., **18**(2): 566–592, pl. 34–38.

———. 1919. A freshwater anaërobic ciliate. Biol. Bull., **36**: 92–95.

———. 1920a. The Cladocera of the Canadian Arctic Expedition, 1913–18. Rept. Canadian Arctic Exped., 1913–18, Vol. 7: Crustacea, Part H: Cladocera, p. 3E–8E.

———. 1920b. Horizontal rainbows. Science, N.S., **51**: 188.

———. 1920c. The plankton, p. 105–110. In B. W. Evermann and H. W. Clark, Lake Maxinkuckee, physical and biological survey. Vol. II. Indiana Dept. Conserv., Indianapolis.

———. 1921a. Observations on the larvae of Corethra punctipennis Say. Biol. Bull., **40**: 271–286.

———. 1921b. Quantitative studies of the bottom fauna in the deeper waters of Lake Mendota. Trans. Wisconsin Acad. Sci. Arts Lett., **20**: 461–493.

———. 1922. Limnological observations on Lake George. A biological survey of Lake George, New York. New York Conserv. Comm., 1921: 37–51.

———. 1923a. An interesting copepod from the Finger Lakes, New York. Science, **58**: 205.

———. 1923b. The water-fleas, p. 16–17. In A scientific survey of Turners Lake, Isle-au-Haut, Maine, New York State Museum. Published privately.

———. 1924a. The productivity of Green Lake, Wisconsin. Verh. intern. Verein. Limnol., **2**: 357–360.

———. 1924b. Summary of quantitative investigations on Green Lake, Wisconsin. Intern. Rev. Hydrobiol., **12**: 1–12.

———. 1925. Senecella calanoides, a recently described fresh-water copepod. Proc. U.S. Natl. Museum, **66**(Article 4): 1–6.

———. 1926a. Freshwater Cladocera from southern Canada. Canadian Field-Nat., **40**: 99–100.

———. 1926b. Sand flotation on lakes. Science, N.S., **64**: 138.

———. 1926c. A third report on limnological apparatus. Trans. Wisconsin Acad. Sci. Arts Lett., **22**: 299–314.

———. 1927. Freshwater Cladocera from the east shore of Hudson and James bays. Canadian Field-Nat., **41**: 130–131.

———. 1929. Limnological methods. Arch. Hydrobiol., **20**: 517–524.

———. 1934a. The depth distribution of some aquatic plants. Ecology, **15**: 325.

———. 1934b. Growth of game fish. Field and Stream, December, 1934: 7–72.

———. 1935. Chemical composition of large aquatic plants. Science, **81**: 273.

———. 1937. Trout Lake. The Limnological Laboratory. The Biologist, **18**: 177–182.

———. 1938a. Fish records for Lake Wingra. Trans. Wisconsin Acad. Sci. Arts Lett., **31**: 533–534.

———. 1938b. Wisconsin lakes and fish investigations. Progr. Fish-Cult., **39**: 18–21.

———. 1940. The annual energy budget of an inland lake. Ecology, **21**: 438–450.

———. 1942. The summer standing crop of plants and animals in four Wisconsin lakes. Trans. Wisconsin Acad. Sci. Arts Lett., **34**: 103–135.

———. 1943. The utilization of aquatic food resources. Science, **97**(2525): 456–458.

JUDAY, CHANCEY, AND G. W. BENNETT. 1935. The growth of game fish in Wisconsin waters. Mimeographed report, 13 p.

JUDAY, CHANCEY, AND E. A. BIRGE. 1927. Pontoporeia and Mysis in Wisconsin lakes. Ecology, **8**: 445–452.

———. 1930. The highland lake district of northeastern Wisconsin and the Trout Lake limnological laboratory. Trans. Wisconsin Acad. Sci. Arts Lett., **25**: 337–352.

———. 1931. A second report on the phosphorus content of Wisconsin lake· waters. Trans. Wisconsin Acad. Sci. Arts Lett., **26**: 353–382.

———. 1932. Dissolved oxygen and oxygen consumed in the lake waters of northeastern Wisconsin. Trans. Wisconsin Acad. Sci. Arts Lett., **27**: 415–486.

———. 1933. The transparency, the color and the specific conductance of the lake waters of northeastern Wisconsin. Trans. Wisconsin Acad. Sci. Arts Lett., **28**: 205–259.

———. 1941. Hydrography and morphometry of some

northeastern Wisconsin lakes. Trans. Wisconsin Acad. Sci. Arts Lett., **33**: 21–72.

JUDAY, CHANCEY, E. A. BIRGE, G. I. KEMMERER, AND R. J. ROBINSON. 1927. Phosphorus content of lake waters of northeastern Wisconsin. Trans. Wisconsin Acad. Sci. Arts Lett., **23**: 233–248.

JUDAY, CHANCEY, E. A. BIRGE, AND V. W. MELOCHE. 1935. The carbon dioxide and hydrogen ion content of the lake waters of northeastern Wisconsin. Trans. Wisconsin Acad. Sci. Arts Lett., **29**: 1–82.

JUDAY, CHANCEY, E. A. BIRGE, AND V. W. MELOCHE. 1938. Mineral content of the lake waters of northeastern Wisconsin. Trans. Wisconsin Acad. Sci. Arts Lett., **31**: 223–276.

JUDAY, CHANCEY, E. A. BIRGE, AND V. W. MELOCHE. 1941. Chemical analyses of the bottom deposits of Wisconsin lakes. II. Second report. Trans. Wisconsin Acad. Sci. Arts Lett., **33**: 99–114.

JUDAY, CHANCEY, J. M. BLAIR, AND E. F. WILDA. 1943. The photosynthetic activities of the aquatic plants of Little John Lake, Vilas County, Wisconsin. Amer. Midland Nat., **30**: 426–446.

JUDAY, CHANCEY, E. B. FRED, AND F. C. WILSON. 1924. The hydrogen ion concentration of certain Wisconsin lake waters. Trans. Amer. Microscop. Soc., **43**: 177–190.

JUDAY, CHANCEY, AND A. D. HASLER. 1946. List of publications dealing with Wisconsin limnology 1871–1945. Trans. Wisconsin Acad. Sci. Arts Lett., **36**: 469–490.

JUDAY, CHANCEY, CLARENCE LIVINGSTON, AND HUBERT PEDRACINE. 1938. A census of the fish caught by anglers in Lake Waubesa in 1937. Mimeographed report, 7 p.

JUDAY, CHANCEY, AND V. W. MELOCHE. 1943. Physical and chemical evidence relating to the lake basin seal in certain areas of the Trout Lake region of Wisconsin. Trans. Wisconsin Acad. Sci. Arts Lett., **35**: 157–174.

JUDAY, CHANCEY, AND R. A. MUTTKOWSKI. 1915. Entomostraca of St. Paul Island, Alaska. Bull. Wisconsin Nat. Hist. Soc., **13**: 23–31.

JUDAY, CHANCEY, W. H. RICH, G. I. KEMMERER, AND ALBERT MANN. 1932. Limnological studies of Karluk Lake, Alaska, 1926–30. Bull. U.S. Bur. Fish., **12**: 407–436.

JUDAY, CHANCEY, AND C. L. SCHLOEMER. 1936. Growth of game fish in Wisconsin waters. Fourth report. Mimeographed report, 17 p.

JUDAY, CHANCEY, AND C. L. SCHLOEMER. 1938a. Effect of fertilizers on plankton production and on fish growth in a Wisconsin lake. Progr. Fish-Cult., **40**: 24–27.

JUDAY, CHANCEY, AND C. L. SCHLOEMER. 1938b. Growth of game fish in Wisconsin waters. Fifth report. Mimeographed report, 26 p.

JUDAY, CHANCEY, AND EDWARD SCHNEBERGER. 1930. Growth studies of game fish in Wisconsin waters. Mimeographed report, 7 p.

JUDAY, CHANCEY, AND EDWARD SCHNEBERGER. 1933. Growth studies of game fish in Wisconsin waters. Second report. Mimeographed report, 10 p.

JUDAY, CHANCEY, AND H. A. SCHOMER. 1935. The utilization of solar radiation by algae at different depths in lakes. Biol. Bull., **69**: 75–81.

JUDAY, CHANCEY, AND L. E. VIKE. 1938. A census of the fish caught by anglers in Lake Kegonsa. Trans. Wisconsin Acad. Sci. Arts Lett., **31**: 527–532.

JUDAY, CHANCEY, AND GEORGE WAGNER. 1908. Dissolved oxygen as a factor in the distribution of fishes. Trans. Wisconsin Acad. Sci. Arts Lett., **16**: 17–22.

KEMMERER, GEORGE, J. F. BOVARD, AND W. R. BOORMAN. 1923. Northwestern lakes of the United States: Biological and chemical studies with reference to possibilities in production of fish. Bull. U.S. Bur. Fish., **39**: 51–140.

KEMMERER, GEORGE, AND L. T. HALLETT. 1927a. An improved method of organic microcombustion. Ind. Engr. Chem., **19**: 173–176.

KEMMERER, GEORGE, AND L. T. HALLETT. 1927b. Improved micro-Kjeldahl ammonia distillation apparatus. Ind. Engr. Chem., **19**: 1295–1296.

KEMMERER, GEORGE, AND L. T. HALLETT. 1927c. Micro determination of carbonate carbon. Ind. Engr. Chem., **19**: 1352–1354.

KNUDSON, H. W., CHANCEY JUDAY, AND V. W. MELOCHE. 1940. Silicomolybdate method for silica. Ind. Engr. Chem., Anal. Ed., **12**: 270–273.

KNUDSON, H. W., V. W. MELOCHE, AND CHANCEY JUDAY. 1940. Colorimetric analysis of a two-component color system. Ind. Engr. Chem., Anal. Ed., **12**: 715–718.

KOZMINSKI, ZYGMUNT. 1938. Amount and distribution of the chlorophyll in some lakes of northeastern Wisconsin. Trans. Wisconsin Acad. Sci. Arts Lett., **31**: 411–438.

KUZNEZOW, S. I. 1959. Die Rolle der Mikroorganismen im Stoffkreislauf der Seen. (Translated from the Russian by Alfred Pochmann.) VEB Deutscher Verlag der Wissenschaften, Berlin. 301 + x p.

LAPHAM, I. A. 1876. Oconomowoc Lake, and other small lakes of Wisconsin, considered with reference to their capacity for fish-production. Trans. Wisconsin Acad. Sci. Arts Lett., **3**: 31–36.

LATHBURY, ALISON, AND R. A. BRYSON. 1958. Studies of the physiographic features of Lake Mendota. I. Sublacustrine gullies. Unpublished.

LEHMANN, HARRIET. 1903. Variations in form and size of *Cyclops brevispinosus* Herrick and *Cyclops americanus* Marsh. Trans. Wisconsin Acad. Sci. Arts Lett., **14**(1): 279–298, pl. 30–33.

LOHUIS, DELMONT, V. W. MELOCHE, AND CHANCEY JUDAY. 1938. Sodium and potassium content of Wisconsin lake waters and their residues. Trans. Wisconsin Acad. Sci. Arts Lett., **31**: 285–304.

MACKENTHUN, K. M., AND H. L. COOLEY. 1952. The biological effect of copper sulphate treatment on lake ecology. Trans. Wisconsin Acad. Sci. Arts Lett., **41**: 177–187.

MANNING, W. M. 1938. Photosynthesis. J. Phys. Chem., **42**(6): 815–854.

———. 1940. A method for obtaining continuous records of dissolved oxygen in lake waters. Ecology, **21**: 509–512.

———. 1943. Physical factors influencing the accuracy of the dropping mercury electrode in measurements of photochemical reaction rates. Trans. Wisconsin Acad. Sci. Arts Lett., **35**: 221–233.

MANNING, W. M., AND R. E. JUDAY. 1941. The chlorophyll content and productivity of some lakes in northeastern Wisconsin. Trans. Wisconsin Acad. Sci. Arts Lett., **33**: 363–394.

MANNING, W. M., CHANCEY JUDAY, AND MICHAEL WOLF. 1938*a*. Photosynthesis in *Chlorella*. Quantum efficiency and rate measurements in sunlight. J. Amer. Chem. Soc., **60**: 274–278.

MANNING, W. M., CHANCEY JUDAY, AND MICHAEL WOLF. 1938*b*. Photosynthesis of aquatic plants at different depths in Trout Lake, Wisconsin. Trans. Wisconsin Acad. Sci. Arts Lett., **31**: 377–410.

MANNING, W. M., J. F. STAUFFER, B. M. DUGGAR, AND FARRINGTON DANIELS. 1938. Quantum efficiency of photosynthesis in *Chlorella*. J. Amer. Chem. Soc., **60**: 266–274.

MARSH, C. D. 1892*a*. On the deep-water Crustacea of Green Lake. Trans. Wisconsin Acad. Sci. Arts Lett., **8**: 211–213.

———. 1892*b*. Notes on the depth and temperature of Green Lake. Trans. Wisconsin Acad. Sci. Arts Lett., **8**: 214–218, pl. 6.

———. 1893. On the Cyclopidae and Calanidae of central Wisconsin. Trans. Wisconsin Acad. Sci. Arts Lett., **9**: 189–224, pl. 3–6.

———. 1894. On the vertical distribution of pelagic Crustacea in Green Lake, Wisconsin. Amer. Nat., **28**: 807–809.

———. 1898. On the limnetic Crustacea of Green Lake. Trans. Wisconsin Acad. Sci. Arts Lett., **11**: 179–224, pl. 5–14.

———. 1899. Hydrographic map of Green Lake. Wisconsin Geol. Nat. Hist. Surv., Map No. 7.

———. 1901. The plankton of fresh water lakes. Trans. Wisconsin Acad. Sci. Arts Lett., **13**: 163–187.

———. 1903. The plankton of Lake Winnebago and Green Lake. Wisconsin Geol. Nat. Hist. Surv., Bull. 12, 94 + vi p.

———. 1907. A revision of North American species of Diaptomus. Trans. Wisconsin Acad. Sci. Arts Lett., **15**: 381–516, pl. 15–28.

———. 1910. A revision of the North American species of Cyclops. Trans. Wisconsin Acad. Sci. Arts Lett., **16**(2): 1067–1134, pl. 72–81.

———. 1918. Copepoda, p. 741–789. *In* H. B. Ward and G. C. Whipple, Fresh-water biology. John Wiley & Sons, New York.

———. 1933. Synopsis of the calanoid crustaceans, exclusive of the Diaptomidae, found in fresh and brackish waters, chiefly of North America. Proc. U.S. Natl. Museum, **82**(18): 1–58, pl. 1–24.

MARSH, MRS. FLORENCE W. [Mrs. C. D.]. 1938. Professor C. Dwight Marsh and his investigation of lakes. Trans. Wisconsin Acad. Sci. Arts Lett., **31**: 535–543.

MARSHALL, RUTH. 1903. Ten species of Arrenuri belonging to the subgenus Megalurus Thon. Trans. Wisconsin Acad. Sci. Arts Lett., **14**: 145–172, pl. 14–18.

———. 1914. Some new American water mites. Trans.

Wisconsin Acad. Sci. Arts Lett., **17**(2): 1300–1304, pl. 92–93.

———. 1921. New American water mites of the genus Neumania. Trans. Wisconsin Acad. Sci. Arts Lett., **20**: 205–213, pl. 2–4.

———. 1929. The morphology and developmental stages of a new species of Piona. Trans. Wisconsin Acad. Sci. Arts Lett., **24**: 401–404.

———. 1930. The water mites of the Jordan Lake region. Trans. Wisconsin Acad. Sci. Arts Lett., **25**: 245–253.

———. 1931–40. Preliminary list of the Hydracarina of Wisconsin. Part I. The red mites. Trans. Wisconsin Acad. Sci. Arts Lett., **26**: 311–319 (1931); Part II, Trans. Wisconsin Acad. Sci. Arts Lett., **27**: 339–357 (1932); Part III, Trans. Wisconsin Acad. Sci. Arts Lett., **28**: 37–61 (1933); Part IV, Trans. Wisconsin Acad. Sci. Arts Lett., **29**: 273–297 (1935); Part V, Trans. Wisconsin Acad. Sci. Arts Lett., **30**: 225–251 (1937); Part VI, Trans. Wisconsin Acad. Sci. Arts Lett., **32**: 135–165 (1940).

MARSHALL, W. S., AND N. C. GILBERT. 1905. Notes on the food and parasites of some fresh-water fishes from the lakes at Madison, Wis. Rept. U.S. Bur. Fish., 1904: 513–522.

MARTIN, LAWRENCE. 1932. The physical geography of Wisconsin. 2nd ed. Wisconsin Geol. Nat. Hist. Surv., Bull. 36, 608 + xxiii p.

MELOCHE, V. W., G. LEADER, L. SAFRANSKI, AND CHANCEY JUDAY. 1938. The silica and diatom content of Lake Mendota water. Trans. Wisconsin Acad. Sci. Arts Lett., **31**: 363–376.

MELOCHE, V. W., AND KATHERINE PINGREY. 1938. The estimation of magnesium in lake water residues. Trans. Wisconsin Acad. Sci. Arts Lett., **31**: 277–283.

MELOCHE, V. W., AND T. SETTERQUIST. 1933. The determination of calcium in lake water and lake water residues. Trans. Wisconsin Acad. Sci. Arts Lett., **28**: 291–296.

MERRILL, HARRIET BELL. 1893. The structure and affinities of *Bunops scutifrons* Birge. Trans. Wisconsin Acad. Sci. Arts Lett., **9**(2): 319–342, pl. 14–15.

MORRISON, J. P. E. 1929. A preliminary list of the mollusca of Dane County, Wisconsin. Trans. Wisconsin Acad. Sci. Arts Lett., **24**: 405–425.

———. 1932*a*. A report on the mollusca of the northeastern Wisconsin lake district. Trans. Wisconsin Acad. Sci. Arts Lett., **27**: 359–396.

———. 1932*b*. Studies on the life history of *Acella haldemani* ("Desh." Binney). Trans. Wisconsin Acad. Sci. Arts Lett., **27**: 397–414.

MORTIMER, C. H. 1956. 'An explorer of lakes, p. 165–211. *In* G. C. Sellery, E. A. Birge. Univ. Wisconsin Press, Madison.

MURRAY, R. C. 1956. Recent sediments of three Wisconsin lakes. Bull. Geol. Soc. Amer., **67**: 883–910.

MUTTKOWSKI, R. A. 1918. The fauna of Lake Mendota. A qualitative and quantitative survey with special reference to the insects. Trans. Wisconsin Acad. Sci. Arts Lett., **19**(1): 374–482.

MYERS, F. J. 1930. The rotifer fauna of Wisconsin. V. The genera Euchlanis and Monommata. Trans.

Wisconsin Acad. Sci. Arts Lett., **25**: 353–413, pl. 10–26.

NEEDHAM, J. G., *et al.* 1941. A symposium on hydrobiology. Univ. Wisconsin Press, Madison. 405 + ix p.

NEESS, J. C., AND W. W. BUNGE, JR. 1956. An unpublished manuscript of E. A. Birge on the temperature of Lake Mendota. I. Trans. Wisconsin Acad. Sci. Arts Lett., **45**: 193–238.

NEESS, J. C., AND W. W. BUNGE, JR., 1957. An unpublished manuscript of E. A. Birge on the temperature of Lake Mendota. II. Trans. Wisconsin Acad. Sci. Arts Lett., **46**: 31–89.

NEIDHOEFER, J. R. 1938. *Carterius tenosperma* (Potts), a species of fresh-water sponge new to Wisconsin. Trans. Amer. Microscop. Soc., **57**: 82–84.

———. 1940. The fresh-water sponges of Wisconsin. Trans. Wisconsin Acad. Sci. Arts Lett., **32**: 177–197, pl. 1–27.

NELSON, M. M., AND A. D. HASLER. 1942. The growth, food, distribution and relative abundance of the fishes of Lake Geneva, Wisconsin, in 1941. Trans. Wisconsin Acad. Sci. Arts Lett., **34**: 137–148.

NOLAND, L. E. 1925*a*. Factors influencing the distribution of fresh water ciliates. Ecology, **6**: 437–452.

———. 1925*b*. A review of the genus Coleps with descriptions of two new species. Trans. Amer. Microscop. Soc., **44**: 3–13.

———. 1945. Chancey Juday. Limnol. Soc. Amer., Spec. Publ. 16: 1–3.

NOLAND, L. E., AND H. E. FINLEY. 1931. Studies on the taxonomy of the genus Vorticella. Trans. Amer. Microscop. Soc., **50**: 81–123.

NOLAND, W. E. 1950. The hydrography, fish, and turtle population of Lake Wingra. Trans. Wisconsin Acad. Sci. Arts Lett., **40**(2): 5–58.

O'DONNELL, D. J. 1943. The fish population in three small lakes in northern Wisconsin. Trans. Amer. Fish. Soc., **72**: 187–196.

OHLE, WALDEMAR. 1952. Die hypolimnische Kohlendioxyd-Akkumulation als produktionsbiologischer Indikator. Arch. Hydrobiol., **46**(2): 153–285.

OLIVE, E. W. 1905. Notes on the occurrence of *Oscillatoria prolifica* (Greville) Gomont in the ice of Pine Lake, Waukesha County, Wisconsin. Trans. Wisconsin Acad. Sci. Arts Lett., **15**(1): 124–134.

PEARSE, A. S. 1915. On the food of the small shore fishes in the waters near Madison, Wisconsin. Bull. Wisconsin Nat. Hist. Soc., **13**: 7–22.

———. 1918. The food of the shore fishes of certain Wisconsin lakes. Bull. U.S. Bur. Fish., **35**: 245–292.

———. 1919. Habits of the black crappie in inland lakes of Wisconsin. Rept. U.S. Comm. Fish. for 1918. Appendix 3. Bur. Fish. Documents 867: 1–16.

———. 1921*a*. Distribution and food of the fishes of Green Lake, Wis., in summer. Bull. U.S. Bur. Fish., **37**: 253–272.

———. 1921*b*. The distribution and food of the fishes of three Wisconsin lakes in summer. Univ. Wisconsin Studies in Sci., No. 3, 61 p.

———. 1924. Amount of food eaten by four species of fresh-water fishes. Ecology, **5**: 254–258.

———. 1925. The chemical composition of certain fresh-water fishes. Ecology, **6**: 7–16.

———. 1934. Ecology of lake fishes. Ecol. Monogr., **4**: 475–480.

PEARSE, A. S., AND HENRIETTA ACHTENBERG. 1920. Habits of yellow perch in Wisconsin lakes. Bull. U.S. Bur. Fish., **36**: 293–366, pl. 83.

PENNAK, R. W. 1939. The microscopic fauna of the sandy beaches, p. 94–106. *In* Problems in lake biology. Amer. Assoc. Advance. Sci., Publ. No. 10.

———. 1940. Ecology of the microscopic metazoa inhabiting the sandy beaches of some Wisconsin lakes. Ecol. Monogr., **10**: 537–615.

PETERSON, W. H., E. B. FRED, AND B. P. DOMOGALLA. 1925. The occurrence of amino acids and other organic nitrogen compounds in lake waters. J. Biol. Chem., **63**: 287–295.

PIETENPOL, W. B. 1918. Selective absorption in the visible spectrum of Wisconsin lake waters. Trans. Wisconsin Acad. Sci. Arts Lett., **19**(1): 562–579.

POTZGER, J. E. 1942. Pollen spectra from four bogs on the Gillen Nature Reserve, along the Michigan-Wisconsin state line. Amer. Midland Nat., **28**: 501–511.

———. 1943. Pollen study of five bogs in Price and Sawyer counties, Wisconsin. Butler Univ. Botan. Studies, **6**: 50–64.

POTZGER, J. E., AND C. O. KELLER. 1942. A pollen study of four bogs along the southern border of Vilas County, Wisconsin. Trans. Wisconsin Acad. Sci. Arts Lett., **34**: 149–166.

POTZGER, J. E., and RUTH R. RICHARDS. 1942. Forest succession in the Trout Lake, Vilas County, Wisconsin area: A pollen study. Butler Univ. Botan. Studies, **5**: 179–189.

POTZGER, J. E., AND W. A. VAN ENGEL. 1942. Study of the rooted aquatic vegetation of Weber Lake, Vilas County, Wisconsin. Trans. Wisconsin Acad. Sci. Arts Lett., **34**: 149–166.

PRESCOTT, G. W. 1944. New species and varieties of Wisconsin Algae. Farlowia, **1**(3): 349–385.

RAGOTZKIE, R. A. 1960. Compilation of freezing and thawing dates for lakes in North Central United States and Canada. Tech. Rept. No. 3, NR 387-022, Nonr 1202 (07).

RICKETT, H. W. 1920. A quantitative survey of the flora of Lake Mendota. Science, N.S., **52**(1357): 641–642.

———. 1921. A quantitative study of the larger aquatic plants of Lake Mendota. Trans. Wisconsin Acad. Sci. Arts Lett., **20**: 501–527. (Tables 4–6 folded in.)

———. 1924. A quantitative study of the larger aquatic plants of Green Lake, Wisconsin. Trans. Wisconsin Acad. Sci. Arts Lett., **21**: 381–414, 2 pl.

ROBINSON, R. J., AND GEORGE KEMMERER. 1930*a*. Determination of organic phosphorus in lake waters. Trans. Wisconsin Acad. Sci. Arts Lett., **25**: 117–121.

ROBINSON, R. J., AND GEORGE KEMMERER. 1930*b*. The determination of Kjeldahl nitrogen in natural waters. Trans. Wisconsin Acad. Sci. Arts Lett., **25**: 123–128.

ROBINSON, R. J., AND GEORGE KEMMERER. 1930*c*. Determination of silica in mineral waters. Trans.

Wisconsin Acad. Sci. Arts Lett., **25**: 129–134.

SAWYER, C. N. 1947. Fertilization of lakes by agricultural and urban drainage. J. New England Water Works Assoc., **61**: 109–127.

SCHLOEMER, C. L. 1936. The growth of the muskellunge, *Esox masquinongy immaculatus* (Garrard), in various lakes and drainage areas of northern Wisconsin. Copeia, 1936(4): 185–193.

——. 1938. A second report on the growth of the muskellunge, *Esox masquinongy immaculatus* (Garrard), in Wisconsin waters. Trans. Wisconsin Acad. Sci. Arts Lett., **31**: 507–512.

SCHLOEMER, C. L., AND RALPH LORCH. 1942. The rate of growth of the wall-eyed pike, *Stizostedion vitreum* (Mitchill), in Wisconsin's inland waters with special reference to the growth characteristics of the Trout Lake population. Copeia, 1942(4): 201–211.

SCHNABEL, ZOE EMILY. 1938. The estimation of the total fish population of a lake. Amer. Math. Monthly, **45**: 348–352.

SCHNEBERGER, EDWARD. 1935. Growth of the yellow perch (*Perca flavescens* Mitchill) in Nebish, Silver and Weber lakes, Vilas County, Wisconsin. Trans. Wisconsin Acad. Sci. Arts Lett., **29**: 103–130.

SCHOMER, H. A. 1934. Photosynthesis of water plants at various depths in the lakes of northeastern Wisconsin. Ecology, **15**: 217–218.

SCHOMER, H. A., AND CHANCEY JUDAY. 1935. Photosynthesis of algae at different depths in some lakes of northeastern Wisconsin. I. Observations in 1933. Trans. Wisconsin Acad. Sci. Arts Lett., **29**: 173–193.

SCHUETTE, H. A. 1918. A biochemical study of the plankton of Lake Mendota. Trans. Wisconsin Acad. Sci. Arts Lett., **19**: 594–613.

SCHUETTE, H. A., AND HUGO ALDER. 1927. Notes on the chemical composition of some of the larger aquatic plants of Lake Mendota. II. Vallisneria and Potamogeton. Trans. Wisconsin Acad. Sci. Arts Lett., **23**: 249–254.

SCHUETTE, H. A., AND HUGO ALDER. 1929a. Notes on the chemical composition of some of the larger aquatic plants of Lake Mendota. III. *Castalia odorata* and *Najas flexilis*. Trans. Wisconsin Acad. Sci. Arts Lett., **24**: 135–139.

SCHUETTE, H. A., AND HUGO ALDER. 1929b. A note on the chemical composition of Chara from Green Lake, Wisconsin. Trans. Wisconsin Acad. Sci. Arts Lett., **24**: 141–145.

SCHUETTE, H. A., AND ALICE E. HOFFMAN. 1922. Notes on the chemical composition of some of the larger aquatic plants of Lake Mendota. I. Cladophora and Myriophyllum. Trans. Wisconsin Acad. Sci. Arts Lett., **20**: 529–531.

SELLERY, G. C. 1956, E. A. Birge. Univ. Wisconsin Press, Madison. 221 + vii p.

SMITH, G. M. 1916a. A monograph of the algal genus *Scenedesmus* based upon pure culture studies. Trans. Wisconsin Acad. Sci. Arts Lett., **18**(2): 422–530, pl. 25–38.

——. 1916b. A preliminary list of algae found in Wisconsin lakes. Trans. Wisconsin Acad. Sci. Arts Lett., **18**(2): 531–565.

——. 1918a. The vertical distribution of Volvox in the plankton of Lake Monona. Amer. J. Botan., **5**: 178–185.

——. 1918b. A second list of algae found in Wisconsin lakes. Trans. Wisconsin Acad. Sci. Arts Lett., **19**(1): 614–654, pl. 10–15.

——. 1920. Phytoplankton of the inland lakes of Wisconsin. I. Myxophyceae Phaeophyceae, Heterokonteae, and Chlorophyceae exclusive of the Desmidiaceae. Wisconsin Geol. Nat. Hist. Surv., Bull. 57, 243 p., pl. 1–51.

——. 1924. Phytoplankton of the inland lakes of Wisconsin. II. Desmidiaceae. Wisconsin Geol. Nat. Hist. Surv., Bull. 57, 227 p., pl. 52–88.

SNOW, LETITIA M., AND E. B. FRED. 1926. Some characteristics of the bacteria of Lake Mendota. Trans. Wisconsin Acad. Sci. Arts Lett., **22**: 143–154, pl. 4.

SPOOR, W. A. 1938. Age and growth of the sucker, *Catostomus commersonii* (Lacépède), in Muskellunge Lake, Vilas County, Wisconsin. Trans. Wisconsin Acad. Sci. Arts Lett., **31**: 457–505, pl. 1.

STADLER, JANICE, AND C. E. ZoBELL. 1939. Evidence for the aerobic decomposition of lignin by lake bacteria. J. Bacteriol., **38**: 115.

STARK, W. H., AND ELIZABETH McCOY. 1938. Distribution of bacteria in certain lakes of northern Wisconsin. Centr. Bakteriol. Parasitenk. C., **96**: 201–209.

STARK, W. H., JANICE STADLER, AND ELIZABETH McCoy. 1938. Some factors affecting the bacterial population of fresh-water lakes. J. Bacteriol., **36**: 653–654.

STEINER, JOHN, AND V. W. MELOCHE. 1935. A study of ligneous substances in lacustrine materials. Trans. Wisconsin Acad. Sci. Arts Lett., **29**: 389–402.

TAYLOR, F. H. L. 1928. A complete systematical analysis of lake water residues by a new micro method. Unpublished thesis, Univ. Wisconsin, 57 p.

THIENEMANN, AUGUST. 1928. Der Sauerstoff im eutrophen und oligotrophen Seen. Die Binnengewässer, Bd. 4, 175 p.

THWAITES, F. T. 1929. Glacial geology of part of Vilas County, Wisconsin. Trans. Wisconsin Acad. Sci. Arts Lett., **24**: 109–125.

TITUS, LESLIE, AND V. W. MELOCHE. 1931. Note on the determination of total phosphorus in lake water residues. Trans. Wisconsin Acad. Sci. Arts Lett., **26**: 441–444.

TITUS, LESLIE, AND V. W. MELOCHE. 1933. A microextractor. Ind. Engr. Chem., Anal. Ed., **5**: 286–288.

TRELEASE, WILLIAM. 1889. The "working" of Madison lakes. Trans. Wisconsin Acad. Sci. Arts Lett., **7**: 121–129, pl. 10.

TRESSLER, W. L., AND B. P. DOMOGALLA. 1931. Limnological studies of Lake Wingra. Trans. Wisconsin Acad. Sci. Arts Lett., **26**: 331–351.

TWENHOFEL, W. H. 1933. The physical and chemical characteristics of the sediments of Lake Mendota, a fresh water lake of Wisconsin. J. Sediment. Petrol., **3**: 68–76.

——. 1937. The bottom sediments of Lake Monona, a fresh-water lake of southern Wisconsin. J. Sediment. Petrol., **7**: 67–77.

TWENHOFEL, W. H., AND W. A. BROUGHTON. 1939. The sediments of Crystal Lake, an oligotrophic lake in Vilas County, Wisconsin. Amer. J. Sci., 237: 231–252.

TWENHOFEL, W. H., S. L. CARTER, AND V. E. Mc-KELVEY. 1942. The sediments of Grassy Lake, Vilas County, a large bog lake of northern Wisconsin. Amer. J. Sci., 240: 529–546.

TWENHOFEL, W. H., AND V. E. McKELVEY. 1939. Sediments of Devils Lake, a eutrophic-oligotrophic lake of southern Wisconsin. J. Sediment. Petrol., 9: 105–121.

TWENHOFEL, W. H., AND V. E. McKELVEY. 1941. Sediments of fresh-water lakes. Bull. Amer. Assoc. Petrol. Geol., 25: 826–849.

TWENHOFEL, W. H., AND V. E. McKELVEY. 1942. The sediments of Little Long (Hiawatha) Lake, Wisconsin. J. Sediment. Petrol., 12: 36–50.

TWENHOFEL, W. H., V. E. McKELVEY, S. A. CARTER, AND HENRY NEISON. 1944. The sediments of four woodland lakes, Vilas County, Wisconsin. I and II. Amer. J. Sci., 242: 19–44, 85–104.

VOIGT, L. P. 1958. Wisconsin Lakes. Wisconsin Conserv. Dept., Publ. 218–58, 35 p.

VORHIES, C. T. 1905. Habits and anatomy of the larva of the caddis-fly, *Platyphylax designatus*, Walker. Trans. Wisconsin Acad. Sci. Arts Lett., 15(1): 108–123, pl. 7–8.

———. 1909. Studies on the Trichoptera of Wisconsin. Trans. Wisconsin Acad. Sci. Arts Lett., 16: 647–738, pl. 52–61.

WAGNER, GEORGE. 1908. Notes on the fish fauna of Lake Pepin. Trans. Wisconsin Acad. Sci. Arts Lett., 16(1): 23–37.

———. 1911. The cisco of Green Lake, Wisconsin. Bull. Wisconsin Nat. Hist. Soc., 9: 73–77.

WELCH, P. S. 1944. Chancey Juday (1871–1944). Ecology, 25(3): 271–272.

WHITNEY, L. V. 1937. Microstratification of the waters of inland lakes in summer. Science, N.S., 85: 224–225.

———. 1938a. Microstratification of inland lakes. Trans. Wisconsin Acad. Sci. Arts Lett., 31: 155–173.

———. 1938b. Continuous solar radiation measurements in Wisconsin lakes. Trans. Wisconsin Acad. Sci. Arts Lett., 31: 175–200.

———. 1938c. Transmission of solar energy and the scattering produced by suspensoids in lake waters. Trans. Wisconsin Acad. Sci. Arts Lett., 31: 201–221.

———. 1941a. A multiple electromagnetic water sampler. Trans. Wisconsin Acad. Sci. Arts Lett., 33: 95–97.

———. 1941b. A general law of diminution of light intensity in natural waters and the percent of diffuse light at different depths. J. Opt. Soc. Amer., 31: 714–722.

———. 1941c. The angular distribution of characteristic diffuse light in natural waters. J. Marine Research, 4: 122–131.

WIEBE, A. H. 1930. Investigations of plankton production in fish ponds. Bull. U.S. Bur. Fish., 46: 137–176.

WILLIAMS, F. T., AND ELIZABETH McCOY. 1934. On the role of microorganisms in the precipitation of calcium carbonate in the deposits of fresh water lakes. J. Sediment. Petrol., 4: 113–126.

WILLIAMS, F. T., AND ELIZABETH McCOY. 1935. The microflora of the mud deposits of Lake Mendota. J. Sediment. Petrol., 5: 31–36.

WILSON, L. R. 1932. The Two Creeks forest bed, Manitowoc County, Wisconsin. Trans. Wisconsin Acad. Sci. Arts Lett., 27: 31–46.

———. 1935. Lake development and plant succession in Vilas County, Wisconsin. I. The medium hard water lakes. Ecol. Monogr., 5: 207–247.

———. 1937. A quantitative and ecological study of the larger aquatic plants of Sweeney Lake, Oneida County, Wisconsin. Bull. Torrey Botan. Club, 64: 199–208.

———. 1938. The postglacial history of vegetation in northwestern Wisconsin. Rhodora, 40: 137–175.

———. 1939a. Rooted aquatic plants and their relation to the limnology of freshwater lakes, p. 107–122. *In* Problems in lake biology. Amer. Assoc. Advance. Sci., Publ. No. 10.

———. 1939b. A temperature study of a Wisconsin peat bog. Ecology, 20: 432–433.

———. 1941. The larger aquatic vegetation of Trout Lake, Vilas County, Wisconsin. Trans. Wisconsin Acad. Sci. Arts Lett., 33: 135–146, 2 pl.

WILSON, L. R., AND A. T. CROSS. 1941. A study of the plant microfossil succession in the bottom deposits of Crystal Lake, Vilas County, Wisconsin, and the peat of an adjacent bog. Amer. J. Sci., 241: 307–315.

WILSON, L. R., AND E. F. GALLOWAY. 1937. Microfossil succession in a bog in northern Wisconsin. Ecology, 18: 113–118.

WILSON, L. R. AND RUTH M. WEBSTER. 1942a. Fossil evidence of wider post-Pleistocene range for butternut and hickory in Wisconsin. Rhodora, 44: 409–414.

WILSON, L. R., AND RUTH M. WEBSTER. 1942b. Microfossil studies of three northcentral Wisconsin bogs. Trans. Wisconsin Acad. Sci. Arts Lett., 34: 177–193.

WILSON, L. R., AND RUTH M. WEBSTER. 1944. Fossil evidence of wider post-Pleistocene range for butternut and hickory in Wisconsin—a reply. Rhodora, 46: 149–155.

WIMMER, E. J. 1929. A study of two limestone quarry pools. Trans. Wisconsin Acad. Sci. Arts Lett., 24: 363–399.

WOLTERECK, RICHARD. 1932. Races, associations and stratification of pelagic daphnids in some lakes of Wisconsin and other regions of the United States and Canada. Trans. Wisconsin Acad. Sci. Arts Lett., 27: 487–521.

WOODBURY, L. A. 1942. A sudden mortality of fishes accompanying a supersaturation of oxygen in Lake Waubesa, Wisconsin. Trans. Amer. Fish. Soc., 71: 112–117.

WRIGHT, STILLMAN. 1927. A revision of the South American species of *Diaptomus*. Trans. Amer. Microscop. Soc., 46: 73–121.

———. 1928. A contribution to the knowledge of

the genus *Pseudodiaptomus*. Trans. Wisconsin Acad. Sci. Arts Lett., **23**: 587–599.

———. 1929. A preliminary report on the growth of the rock bass, *Ambloplites rupestris* (Rafinesque), in two lakes of northern Wisconsin. Trans. Wisconsin Acad. Sci. Arts Lett., **24**: 581–595.

ZoBELL, C. E. 1940. Some factors which influence oxygen consumption by bacteria in lake water. Biol. Bull., **78**: 388–402.

ZoBELL, C. E., AND JANICE STADLER. 1940a. The effect of oxygen tension on the oxygen uptake of lake bacteria. J. Bacteriol., **39**: 307–322.

ZoBELL, C. E., AND JANICE STADLER. 1940b. The oxidation of lignin by lake bacteria. Arch. Hydrobiol., **37**: 163–171.

$\underset{\Large 2}{}$ | *Arthur D. Hasler*

Wisconsin 1940–1961

Experimental limnology

The major emphasis of limnological work in Wisconsin in recent years has been away from the classical, descriptive limnological work so thoroughly done by Birge and Juday and toward the more experimental limnology which has been made possible by modern apparatus development and automation.

A phase of experimental limnology was started at Wisconsin by the suggestion that blooms of algae on Lake Mendota were not so frequent in years when there were dense growths of large aquatic plants. To test this hypothesis experimentally, Hasler and Jones (1949) studied changes in the numbers of algae in four ponds (3.64 m diameter by 1 m deep) built of silo concrete blocks in a large pond (Fig. 2.1). Because of their unique construction, all four tanks contained the same water and the same initial inoculum of plankton. Two of the experimental ponds contained dense introductions of *Anacharis canadensis* with smaller amounts of *Potamogeton foliosus*, whereas the other two tanks were free of plants. In both years of the experiment there was unequivocal evidence that the planktonic algae were suppressed in the ponds with dense growths of aquatic plants.

In the late 1940's interest developed in the possibility of using small lakes as experimental models for limnological studies. Cather Lake, in northwestern Wisconsin, was initially used for this type of study, because it contained brown-stained water which prevented the full utilization of the sun's energy. Its limnological characteristics were investigated from 1948 to 1949, and in 1950

commercial hydrated lime, $Ca(OH)_2 + Mg(OH)_2$, was added in sufficient quantity to change the pH from 5.4 to 7.1 and the carbonates from 5.0 mg/L $CaCO_3$ to 20 mg/L $CaCO_3$ (Hasler *et al.*, 1951). A marked clearing of the water resulted, which enabled sufficient light to penetrate into the thermocline for photosynthesis.

This before-and-after type of experiment was improved by concurrent observations on the two halves of an hourglass-shaped lake which was divided by an earthen barrier erected at the constriction (Fig. 2.2). To one of these lakes, Lake Peter, lime was added which raised the pH from 5.9 to 7.3. The mean standing crop of zooplankton responded by increasing to 0.81 g dry weight/ m^2 in the treated portion (Peter) as compared with 0.64 g/m² in the untreated half (Paul) (Johnson and Hasler, 1954). Later there was a 60% increase in the depth of the euphotic zone of the treated portion of Peter-Paul Lake, but

Fig. 2.1.—Experimental silo-ponds 3.6 m in diameter erected inside a large hatchery pond. After Hasler and Jones, 1949.

55

Fig. 2.2.—Aerial view of Lake Paul (left) and Lake Peter, showing the separating barrier. After Johnson and Hasler, 1954.

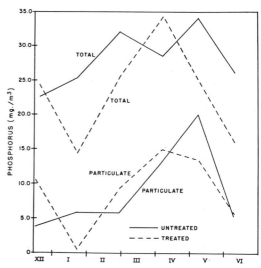

Fig. 2.4.—Total and particulate phosphorus in the two portions of Peter-Paul Lake. After Stross and Hasler, 1960.

readings taken two years later by Stross and Hasler (1960) showed a total increase of 160%, a change from 2.7 to 7.0 m.

The decline in the concentration of dissolved oxygen in the thermocline of the untreated portion was due mainly to a high rate of respiration. A faster rate of oxygen depletion in this portion was readily apparent (Fig. 2.3). Presumably, no excess oxygen was produced during the daylight period, because both production and consumption of oxygen were 28.5 μg/L per hr. In the treated portion, however, the values were 38.7 and 12.2 μg/L per hr, respectively, an oxygen demand of only 32% of that produced.

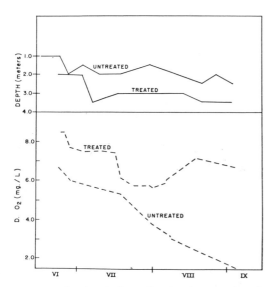

Fig. 2.3.—Depth of the epilimnion in treated and untreated portion of Peter-Paul Lake and the changes in concentration of dissolved oxygen in each portion during the summer of 1956. After Stross and Hasler, 1960.

Because the lakes circulated completely only in autumn, iron was homogeneously distributed for only a brief period prior to its loss from suspension. At the time of turnover, the iron concentration was 0.20 mg/L in the lime-treated lake (Peter) and 0.65 mg/L in the untreated portion. It was assumed from this result that lime eliminated about 70% of the iron. In the summer, iron went into solution in the hypolimnion of the untreated lake (4.3 mg/L) to a greater extent than it did in the treated twin (1.8 mg/L).

A set of six measurements taken during the winter-to-spring period suggested that partial removal of iron did not inhibit the normal precipitation of phosphorus (Fig. 2.4). Instead, loss of phosphorus in the treated portion seemed to occur more rapidly and resulted in an average concentration of 22.0 μg/L as compared to 28.0 μg/L in the untreated part of Peter-Paul Lake. A non-biological precipitation was thought to be the major cause for the loss, because the plankton was extremely sparse during the period.

Subsequently, Stross et al. (1961) found important differences in the plankton produced by the two lakes. They computed a turnover rate for Daphnia of 2.1 weeks in the lime-treated lake and 4.6 weeks in the untreated twin, which suggested that the changed conditions were associated with a rapid increase in the size of the population. Hence, this method of analyzing the effect was more dramatic, as well as more biologically realistic, than when the differences were measured by the conventional basis of standing crop only.

Plankton studies

The problem of enumeration by sampling, as applied to plankton populations, has certain peculiarities, such as the apparent non-randomness of the populations as they are encountered in nature. In saying that natural populations are non-random, Neess (1949) means that the interaction between these populations and the sampling methods used on them produces sample distributions that do not fulfill all of the postulates necessary to validate tests of significance and other forms of statistical estimation from which conclusions are drawn.

The unsatisfactory quantitative performance of net samplers stimulated the search for an improved volumetric sampler. The first of these to be used extensively was the Juday trap; large-sized Kemmerer bottles were also used for this purpose, but the most recent sampler is the Clarke-Bumpus sampler, which has a conical net with a meter mounted in the mouth so that water passing through can be measured independently of length of tow or rate of towing.

Ricker (1938) concluded that the *Daphnia* of Cultus Lake showed little tendency toward a Poisson–non-random distribution in terms of hauls with an ordinary tow net, and further that a series of hauls taken at a central station in the lake were equivalent in their content to a series of similar size spread over the entire lake. In the years 1944, 1945, and 1946, samples of zooplankton were taken by Neess and Jones in the Gardner Ponds with a Juday trap. Review of these data indicated many erratic fluctuations which were uncorrelated from pond to pond and could not be explained in terms of known variables. Neess re-examined the assumption that organisms were uniformly distributed for use in the sampling done in Gardner Ponds and Cultus Lake.

A grid of 12-foot squares was superimposed on one of the ponds, and 10-liter samples were taken with a Juday trap at 60 intersections. Later, a similar experiment involving 35 samples was performed in Lake Mendota. Following this, replicate samples of approximately 400 L each were taken in the pond and in Lake Mendota

with the Clarke-Bumpus sampler, using the same general scheme.

The results of these experiments are summarized in Table 2.1. In most instances the ratio s^2/m is greater than 1, which leads to the general conclusion that, for this kind of sampling, the populations of organisms concerned are Poisson–non-random.

The Clarke-Bumpus sampler is approximately as accurate in measuring water volume as the Juday trap but handles much larger amounts at one time. Table 2.1 compares the Clarke-Bumpus sampler with the Juday trap. In Lake Mendota hauls were taken on the same day and in Gardner Pond C on different days, which explains the difference in means in the latter case. In Lake Mendota the distributions of sampler catches were essentially random for most organisms, whereas in terms of the Juday trap they remained clumped. In Gardner Pond C the difference is much more striking. Here, where the distribution of organisms is strongly irregular, the trap is an inadequate sampler.

As a result of the sampling studies initiated by

TABLE 2.1

Distributions of common summer zooplankters in Lake Mendota and Gardner Ponds (summer, 1947), based on Clarke-Bumpus and Juday trap samples at 0–1 meter: m, mean number of organisms per liter; s^2, single haul variance

Species	Clarke-Bumpus		Juday trap	
	m	s^2 (s^2/m)	m	s^2 (s^2/m)
LAKE MENDOTA				
Daphnia longispina	36	106 (2.9)	26	67 (2.6)
Diaptomus sp.	10	29 (2.9)	11	38 (3.4)
Cyclops viridis	6	4 (0.7)	7	13 (1.9)
Copepod nauplii	20	15 (0.8)	39	180 (4.6)
Chydorus sp.	26	63 (2.4)	31	70 (2.3)
Lecane sp. (Rotatoria)	24	75 (3.1)	35	126 (3.6)
Asplanchna sp. (Rotatoria)	9	8 (0.9)	11	38 (3.4)
GARDNER C[a]				
Daphnia longispina	68	395 (5.8)	184	8,649 (47.0)
Diaptomus pallidus	27	81 (3.0)	48	3,249 (67.0)
Copepod nauplii	—	— —	108	4,624 (43.0)
Bosmina longirostris	—	— —	11	400 (36.0)

[a] In Gardner Pond C, coarser netting on the Clarke-Bumpus allowed the smaller nauplii and *Bosmina* to escape.

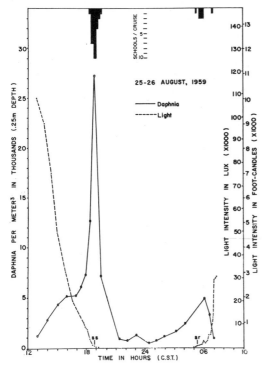

25-26 AUGUST, 1959

—— Daphnia
------ Light

SCHOOLS / CRUSE

LIGHT INTENSITY IN LUX (X1000)

LIGHT INTENSITY IN FOOT-CANDLES (X1000)

DAPHNIA PER METER³ IN THOUSANDS (.25m DEPTH)

TIME IN HOURS (C.S.T.)

Fig. 2.5.—White bass activity and related environmental factors. Schooling activity (bar graph), numbers of *Daphnia* at 0.25-m depth (——), and light intensity (------) over approximately 24 hr. *sr* = sunrise, *ss* = sunset. After McNaught and Hasler, 1961.

Neess, a joint Zoology-Meteorology program of coordinated measurement of currents, temperatures, and zooplankton density was undertaken. Ragotzkie and Bryson (1953) demonstrated that concentrations of plankton were produced in regions of near-surface convergence, since the phototropic response of the *Daphnia* kept substantial numbers of them near the surface. This explains some large-scale non-random distributions not observed by Neess.

The zooplankters of the genus *Daphnia* comprise the bulk of the food of the white bass (*Roccus chrysops*) in Lake Mendota. In 1961 McNaught and Hasler (1961) correlated the *Daphnia* aggregations with the feeding behavior of the white bass. The pattern of feeding activity of the white bass was shown to correspond with the morning and evening surface concentrations of *Daphnia* (Fig. 2.5). The compact schools of white bass, conspicuous at the surface of Lake Mendota from May through October, were

observed to be most numerous in regions of high concentrations of air-locked and free-swimming *Daphnia*.

These studies on vertical migration of plankton have recently been extended to determine the rate of ascent and descent of *Daphnia* in this same area of Lake Mendota (McNaught and Hasler, in preparation). The rates of movement during the dawn rise seem to correspond to the rate of change in light intensity at that time. The evening ascent to the surface is probably related to other factors in addition to light intensity, because the consistent timing, which is characteristic of the dawn migration, is not realized at dusk.

Diptera studies

Dugdale (1955) studied the ecology of the populations of those species of *Chironomus* inhabiting the profundal and sublittoral bottom of Lake Mendota. Larvae of two species (*Chironomus plumosus* L. and one which closely resembles *C. rempelii* Thien.) make up almost the entire bulk of the dipteran larvae in the regions of the lake studied. The combined standing crops of the two species for the entire lake varied between 270 and 455 kg/ha wet weight. Crops of emerging insects, which were estimated from corrected decreases in larval standing crops during periods of adult emergence, amounted to 835 metric tons or 294 kg/ha wet weight for the entire lake for 1954.

A simple mathematical model was developed by Dugdale, which established quantitative relations among growth, mortality, net and gross productivities, and standing crop. From this, certain rates were derived, along with the distribution of production throughout the year and the relations between maximum standing crop and net productivity.

In each of the species studied, the life cycle appeared to last two years. Each of the species showed two periods of adult emergence during the year, one in spring (May, June), the other in late fall (November). The periods of emergence were almost the same for both (deepwater) species. In *C. plumosus* the same regions of the lake did not appear to contribute equally to the two hatches. The sublittoral regions provided most of the spring adults, and the deeper regions most of those hatched in fall. Periods of emergence were correlated with high oxygen concentrations and maximum temperatures in the deeper waters, although the exact mechanism that triggers pupation was not found. Eggs were shown not to hatch in the laboratory in the absence of oxygen.

Dugdale found that pupae arrived at the surface of the lake only during a brief period shortly after sunset, a time of day when the probability of low wind velocity at the water surface is maximum. Newly hatched adults disappeared rapidly from the surface of the lake but appeared diurnally in large mating swarms along the edges of the lake. Females made oviposition flights over the lake at sunset and dawn only; the fate of females after oviposition is not known, although they are still capable of flight at this time. Length of the imaginal portion of the life cycle was estimated to be no more than two or three days, on the basis of laboratory studies of weight losses of adults at various relative humidities.

Dugdale and Neess (unpublished) estimated that 15% of the total budget of iron in Lake Mendota is removed from the lake by emerging adults which are blown ashore by the winds during emergence.

Mature larvae were found in large numbers, actively swimming between lake bottom and surface during periods of adult emergence and at the same time of day at which pupal movements occurred.

Studies on ion transport

It is a well-known axiom in limnology that a lake is generally wasteful of the phosphorus that enters it via effluents from the surrounding watershed. In fact, the bottom water and mud of these lakes contain sufficient nutrients to bring them into a eutrophic condition, but owing to the seasonal stratification of the water, nutrients accumulate near or on the bottom of the basin, where they are unavailable to the aquatic organisms in the euphotic zones above. Investigations have shown that phosphorus, added to the water, invariably collects at the water-mud interface, where it is subsequently incorporated into the mud. Zicker *et al.* (1956) added further to this knowledge by showing that radiophosphorus applied to the surface of the mud does not diffuse readily into the water in an undisturbed system. In laboratory studies with miniature, simulated lake-mud systems, radiophosphorus added to the mud at depths greater than

2 cm from the surface did not diffuse into the overlying water.

In 1947 Hasler (1947) reviewed the instances of eutrophication of lakes throughout the world and predicted a worsening of the nuisance conditions in lakes receiving domestic wastes. He also pointed to the great stores of phosphorus in Lake Mendota (1.1 million metric tons P under the 10 m contour) and re-emphasized how wasteful lakes are with the phosphorus they receive. In a later work Hasler (1957) proposed that lakes might be refertilized with their own phosphorus.

In an aquarium experiment circulation of the water above phosphorus-rich mud with the aid of air bubbles showed that bubbles of compressed air would lift P^{32} from the bottom water to the surface. In practice, bottom deposits could be harrowed to produce clouds of sediment, while bubbles of compressed air could be simultaneously introduced into the hypolimnion in order to transport the phosphorus-rich particles to the trophogenic zone in a thermally stratified lake.

In tests under summer conditions (Schmitz and Hasler, 1958; Schmitz, 1958) air was used to bring hypolimnetic water up into the euphotic zone of a small experimental lake, Sawmill Pond, with a maximum depth of 7.1 m and an area of 1250 m². Air was delivered through small perforations spaced along the length of an air conductor which was suspended just above the lake bottom. The daily rate of flow was 101 L/m³ of lake volume, under a pressure of 1 atm at 20° C. An almost homoiothermal condition

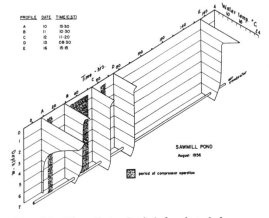

Fig. 2.6.—The effect of air-induced turbulence on the thermal stratification of Sawmill Pond. After Schmitz and Hasler, 1958.

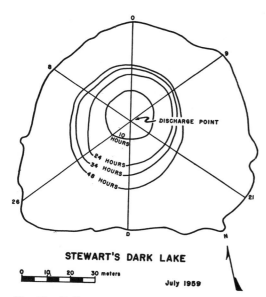

STEWART'S DARK LAKE

0   10   20   30 meters

July 1959

Fig. 2.7.—Sodium-24 was released near the center of Stewart's Dark Lake at a depth of 8 m. The outlines mark the approximate horizontal movement of the radioactive material. After Likens and Hasler, 1960.

was observed after only 4½ hours of treatment (Fig. 2.6). The concentrations of soluble phosphorus became isometric with depth. Prior to treatment, soluble phosphorus exhibited typically high concentrations in the 2- to 3-m zone. The absolute content of the total phosphorus in the upper 2 m was higher in every case than the mean of the pretreatment values.

In an experiment conducted in Tub Lake (0.7 ha) in which lower daily rates of treatment (5.6 L of air/m³ of lake volume) were used, radioactive phosphorus which had previously been placed in the hypolimnion could be brought to the surface (Sparr, 1958). In this case the thermocline was lowered, but it retained its identity.

The amount of work theoretically required to compress the air to the necessary hydrostatic pressure was compared with the change in volume of the epilimnion resulting from the treatment. This was done in order to provide a basis for comparison of treatments in lakes of different sizes. The values obtained ranged from 8.17 × 10² g · cm to 19.4 × 10² g · cm for the work applied to each cubic meter of lake volume for each cubic meter of increase in volume of the epilimnion.

Tests under conditions of ice cover were also conducted by Schmitz with essentially the same

physical installation. Daily additions of 3.4 and 1.9 L of air/m³ of lake volume were applied in two consecutive years on Katharine Lake (6.1 ha). These applications maintained areas of open water continuously and concentrations of dissolved oxygen at about 7 and 2 mg/L, respectively. Under normal conditions the oxygen concentration in this water is less than 3 mg/L and periodically less than 1 mg/L. Average water temperatures were reduced to as low as 0.7° C at the higher rate of treatment.

Extending the use of radionuclides in experimental limnology, Hasler proposed that lakes could be used as models of the sea in studies designed to study the physical-biological transport of nuclides in marine situations.

From preliminary studies (Likens and Hasler, 1962a) conducted in a small, chemically stratified lake (Stewart's Dark Lake) in northwestern Wisconsin, dipteran midges were found to transport measurable quantities of radioiodine (I^{131}) from the deep water of this lake to the shoreline. The radioiodine was first detected in samples of adult midges collected in lighted shoreline traps 20 days after its release within the lake.

The physical transport within Stewart's Dark Lake was measured by using Na^{24}. The results of replicated experiments showed that radiosodium was transported horizontally in all directions from its release point deep within the lake at a maximum rate of about 16–18 m per day (Fig. 2.7). No appreciable vertical transport of the radiosodium was measured during the experimental periods.

Sodium-24 was also used to measure the physical movement in an ice-covered lake (Tub Lake) in northwestern Wisconsin (Likens and Hasler, 1962b). The results showed that the radiotracer (Na^{24}) was transported horizontally a maximum distance of 15–20 m during the first 24 hours of replicated experiments. Subsequent horizontal displacement was somewhat slower but reached a maximum distance of almost 30 m from the release point in 3 days. Some vertical movement was indicated by the results but was of very low velocity.

Physical limnology

Geological studies

The sedimentation in Lake Mendota has changed abruptly in the recent past. Murray (1956) found this change recorded in cores by a buff marl overlain by 1–14 in. of black gyttja, the interface between the two sediments being very sharp. The marl and gyttja differ in being high-carbonate–low-clastic and low-carbonate– high-clastic sediments, respectively, but their organic content is essentially the same. The change in sedimentation is ascribed to increased deposition of clastic material in the lake as a consequence of farm and domestic practice.

Contemporaneous with this increased clastic deposition, there has been an increase in the biological productivity of the lake with an accompanying hypolimnetic oxygen deficiency. The black color of the gyttja was found to result from the presence of ferrous sulfides deposited under conditions of oxygen deficiency and not from organic content as previously supposed.

The sediments of Trout Lake, a medium-softwater, oligotrophic lake in northern Wisconsin, have high organic content and are dark green. Where complete sections of the sediments are available, the distribution of organic content shows increased organic deposition with the advance of time. The most recent sediments show a slight decrease in organic content which is ascribed to recently increased clastic deposition.

Lake Wingra is a shallow, hard-water, advanced eutrophic lake, near Lake Mendota. Its recent bottom deposits consist of a gray marl, which in shallow water becomes shell marl.

No evidence was found to support the theory that important diagenetic changes are taking place in any of the sediments studied. Changes in the sediments that have taken place after deposition, exclusive of compaction and water loss, appear to be restricted to the upper few inches of the most recent record.

Current studies

After some preliminary testing, the free drogue was adopted as the most suitable means for measuring the slow currents encountered in a lake. The modal current velocities (Lathbury *et al.*, 1960) in about 3000 integrated observations of 2 to 33 minutes duration were found to be at the lower limit of sensitivity of all but the most refined of propeller or rotor-type current meters. (See Ragotzkie and Bryson, 1953, previously mentioned, on plankton vs. currents.)

When the question arose concerning the rate at which the waters of University Bay were replaced by water from the rest of Lake Mendota, a line of observing points was established across the mouth of the bay to measure the current profiles at various times.

Bryson and Ragotzkie (1955) found replacement rates from less than one to several days per complete change. They also found that University Bay was normally occupied by a clockwise gyre, the rotation rate of which was nearly constant and independent of the current velocity. This is characteristic of inertial motion. The period of this rotational motion is nearly a half pendulum day.

This same study revealed that a jet of particularly high velocity extended out into the lake along one side of a peninsula (Picnic Point) and often displayed a countercurrent along the left side of the jet next to the shore. Associated with this jet was a density structure (Suomi and Bryson, 1952) comparable to that in the vicinity of the Gulf Stream.

With the observational techniques gained in these studies, several other projects involving large numbers of observations were undertaken. Clarke and Bryson (1959) analyzed the flow pattern at Second Point Bar. From this study a complete synoptic picture of the vertical and horizontal currents was obtained. As a by-product, a rapidly developing countercurrent below the surface was found following diminution of the stress from surface wind (Bryson and Bunge, 1956).

Several long series of current measurements carried out by Lathbury *et al.* (1960) yielded evidence that currents within the hypolimnion are not primarily due to seiches (either surface or internal) but are mainly due to redistribution of density by the wind.

Shulman and Bryson (1961) found that wind-driven currents deviate to the right of the wind in a pattern which fits the logarithmic spiral hodograph of classical theory, even though they do not extend to the predicted depths. The depth of frictional influence was found to be a few meters rather than tens of meters. At the same time, about 700 current observations at 10-cm depth intervals with simultaneous wind observations were used by Haines and Bryson (1961) to establish the ratio of water velocity to wind velocity (wind factor). They showed that a constant wind factor f for each depth could be found only if the non-wind-driven current was first subtracted and if the wind speed at a height of 5 m was below about 5.7 m/sec.

Wave studies

The first wave studies concentrated on the long-period standing waves generally known as the seiche. After Bryson and Kuhn (1955) established that the period calculated with the simplest assumptions was a good approximation of the observed period, they showed that the seiche crest rotated about a nodal point and that the seiche period was unaffected by an ice cover. Studies of the amplitude suggested that the decay rate of the seiche might be attributed to the stress of the seiche current on the bottom.

In another study by Bryson and Stearns (1959) the seiche currents through the mouth of South Bay, Manitoulin Island, Ontario, were computed from observed seiche amplitudes. The current values were then used to estimate the rate of exchange between bay water and Lake Huron water.

The persistent thermal fluctuations observed in the lake when stratified drew the attention of Bryson and Ragotzkie (1960) to the shorter, progressive internal waves, which were found to be present in all observations. Using a large triangular array of thermopiles, the speed, wavelength, amplitude, and direction of motion were studied. No particular origin for the waves was found.

Twice in ten years the study of C. H. Mortimer (Scottish Marine Laboratory) on the internal waves of Lake Michigan has been sponsored by the University of Wisconsin. A twelve-year analysis of domestic water-intake temperatures disclosed large fluctuations in thermocline depth, initiated and largely controlled by the wind, but also propagated as internal waves counterclockwise around the basin. These studies are to be continued and enlarged.

Heat budget studies

From the mean heat content of the lake and standard climatic data, monthly contributions of sun and air to the heat stored in the lake were computed by Dutton and Bryson (1962). These atmospheric contributions to the heat budget of the lake are particularly important climatic parameters, especially in their ecological impact. Using the concept of the thermal structure of lakes as a significant indicator of the climate, the study of the lake heat budgets has been extended into the Canadian Arctic. Here, and in the Subarctic, lake heat budget data have been gathered since 1958 in connection with a study of the interrelation of climate and terrain. In these northern lakes the winter ice sheet is of great importance to the heat budget (Scott and Ragotzkie, 1962; Bunge and Bryson, 1956).

Other physical limnological studies

On the bathymetric chart of Lake Mendota produced under the direction of Birge at the turn of the century, there appeared several peculiar deep holes near shore. When the lake bottom was resurveyed with an echosounder in the early 1950's, it appeared that these deep holes were actually steep-sided sublacustrine gullies leading from broad, shallow, near-shore areas down the main slopes toward broad, very flat, deep areas (Lathbury and Bryson, 1958). Their similarities, in miniature, to submarine canyons were so striking that the question of density currents in the lake immediately arose.

Density currents were observed in the lake by Bryson and Suomi (1951). They showed that the turbid runoff following periods of heavy rain flowed along the bottom and spread at the thermocline or moved deep into the hypolimnion as dictated by density relations. Field observations also showed that turbid water, of sufficient density to penetrate the thermocline, was produced by waves in the broad shallows.

Aquatic microorganisms

Among the actinomycetes to be found in soil and water are the micromonosporae, members of the genus *Micromonospora*. They are placed in the family Streptomycetaceae but are more "primitive" than the members of the genus *Streptomyces*. The diagnostic feature of *Micromonospora* is the formation of single spores, each terminating a short lateral branch of a secondary hypha (Colmer and McCoy, 1950).

Colmer and McCoy (1944) found that micromonosporae occurred in all thirteen Wisconsin lakes studied but were more numerous in the oozes of shallow bays in the southern Wisconsin lakes. These same organisms were found in the forest soils adjacent to these lakes and reached a minimum on wave-washed shores, but the study gave no proof of quantitative association between micromonosporae and water plants. The micromonosporae comprised a very high average percentage of the "total" bottom bacteria (13.4%) and of the chromogenic microorganisms (61.6%).

Studies on some lake-mud strains of *Micromonospora* were undertaken by Erikson (1941), who used some of the earliest isolates made by Henrici and McCoy from northern Wisconsin lakes and found them able to attack many strange or resistant organic substrates, such as phenols, straight-chain hydrocarbons, cellulose, pectin, chitin, rubber, etc. No attack on lignin was demonstrable, however.

Respiration studies were carried out with the blue-green alga, *Microcystis aeruginosa,* and three of its bacterial associates belonging in the genera *Flavobacterium, Bacterium,* and *Pseudomonas;* another bloom-producing alga, *Alphanizomenon flos-aquae,* two bacterial associates (*Achromobacter* sp., *Flavobacterium* sp.), *Azotobacter agile,* and *Rhodospirillum rubrum* were also used.

Of the 14 carbon substrates surveyed, glucose-1-phosphate, α-ketoglutarate, and to a lesser extent, lactate and citrate, were the ones most rapidly oxidized by *M. aeruginosa.* Glucose and fructose had no effect on respiration, whereas pyruvate was found to exert a slight toxic effect. Acetate, oxaloacetate, and succinic, fumaric, and malic acids were oxidized at comparatively slow rates, but the two amino acids (aspartic and glutamic) were poorly respired if at all.

Pseudomonas sp. was the most active of the cultures studied on almost all substrates, except on citrate where respiration was very slow. *Flavobacterium* sp. similarly displayed an appreciable oxidative ability, but the respiration was very low on oxaloacetate and acetate, and, in general, the exogenous rates on the organic acids were much lower than those displayed by *Pseudomonas* sp. The oxidative power of *Bacterium* sp., on the other hand, was somewhat intermediate.

There was a consistent increase in O_2 uptake when *M. aeruginosa* was associated with *Flavobacterium* sp. on substrates which neither organism respired to any extent when tested separately. With the other bacteria, the results were not so clear, but in every case the substrate appeared to be a significant factor in the result obtained (Zagallo, 1953).

Recently Jannasch (1960) of the University Institute for Microbiology, Göttingen, Germany, worked with W. B. Sarles on the influence of algae upon denitrification by aquatic bacteria. He attempted to detect interaction between photosynthesizing algae and denitrifying bacteria by cultivating *Chlorella* sp. with *Pseudomonas stutzeri.* Denitrification was inhibited by illumination of the mixed culture after a dark period of three hours.

Continuing these studies, Jannasch (1960) reported as follows:

The inhibition of denitrification by molecular oxygen was used as an indicator of the availability of oxygen to denitrifying bacteria. The formation of elementary nitrogen and nitrous oxide by *Pseudomonus stutzeri* was found mass-spectrometrically in water (containing 0.05% readily oxidizable organic matter and 0.008% nitrate) under aerobic conditions if suspended particulate matter was present. The formation of anaerobic micro-zones by bacterial activity is suggested. Thus, in the presence of seston or mud particles, dissolved oxygen is not available to denitrifying bacteria in the same concentration as that determined by chemical analysis. Agitation produced an increase of oxygen uptake but, at the same time, a delay of denitrification. No true "aerobic denitrification" has been found.

Vegetation studies

Andrews and Hasler (1942) worked out an acceptable method for obtaining quantitative samples of invertebrate organisms from the aquatic plants in the littoral areas of Lake Mendota. They observed a higher abundance of organisms in mixed species stands than in single species stands. They also found that those plants with the most dissected surface area harbor the largest population of animals.

An ecological investigation of the communities of large, submerged aquatic plants in Wisconsin lakes was carried out during the summers of 1952 and 1953, with emphasis on the vegetation of eutrophic lakes (Swindale and Curtis, 1957). Stands of plants were selected on the basis of homogeneity of the vegetation at single depths within uniform areas of lakes. Each stand was sampled by 20 quadrats, 0.2 m^2 in area.

Indices calculated from the joint occurrence of species within the quadrats were used to derive an order of species related to a gradient of ecological factors. The order of species thus derived was used to weight the relative frequencies of the species in each stand. The weighted relative frequencies of the species were summed for each stand, thus giving an index by which the stands might be arranged in order. When the stands were arranged according to these values and the frequencies of the species plotted against the resulting gradient, a pattern of continual change of community composition resulted which was similar to that previously designated as a vegetational continuum (Fig. 2.8).

The submerged communities often vary considerably in different parts of the same lake, those in bays and sheltered places with rich soils hav-

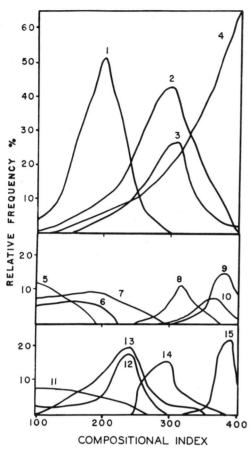

Fig. 2.8.—Relative frequency (smoothed curves) of important taxa plotted against the compositional index. Taxa: 1. *Isoetes* spp., 2. *Najas flexilis*, 3. *Vallisneria americana*, 4. *Chara* spp., 5. *Elatine minima*, 6. *Potamogeton epihydrus*, 7. *Myriophyllum tenellum*, 8. *Heteranthera dubia*, 9. *Potamogeton illinoensis*, 10. *Potamogeton zosteriformis*, 11. *Juncus pelocarpus* f. *submersus*, 12. *Eleocharis acicularis*, 13. *Potamogeton gramineus*, 14. *Anacharis* spp., 15. *Myriophyllum exalbescens*. After Swindale and Curtis, 1957.

ing communities with higher index values than the equivalent communities on the exposed shores with poorer soils. Likewise, in a single area, the communities usually vary with depth, and there are positive correlations between the position of the stands on the phytosociological gradient and the substrate at the various depths.

The majority of the plants in the stands with low indices are small, often rosette-form plants (Fig. 2.9). Those in the high-index stands tend to be plants of large stature and/or bulk, as first pointed up by Fassett (1930). There is, therefore, a continuum of plant physiognomy as well as a continuum of species in the Wisconsin lakes.

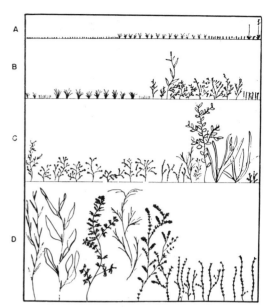

Fig. 2.9.—Diagrammatic illustration of physiognomy along the gradient in representative stands at indices of 100 (*A*), 200 (*B*), 300 (*C*), and 400 (*D*). The proportion of horizontal space occupied by each species represents its relative frequency in the community. No attempt was made to portray the actual spatial arrangement of species within each stand. After Swindale and Curtis, 1957.

With a few exceptions, the following generalizations may be made. Stands with high indices are found in lakes where water has higher conductivities (Fig. 2.10), more organic matter,

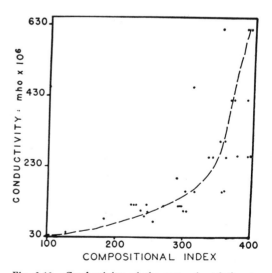

Fig. 2.10.—Conductivity of the water in relation to the compositional index. The dots represent stands for which conductivity measurements were obtained. After Swindale and Curtis, 1957.

marl, calcium, magnesium, nitrate content, and higher pH and which have less sand in their substrates than the lakes which have stands in the lower part of the gradient. There is evidence that the various factors interact with and compensate for each other in influencing the nature of the plant communities.

Ecology of fishes

Odor detection by fish

The exploration of the role of large aquatic plants in lake ecology suggested the possible problem of plant-odor detection by fish. Conditioned response tests in the laboratory on the bluntnose minnow (*Pimephales notatus*) showed that this species could distinguish the odor characteristics of 14 different species of submerged aquatic plants that grow in Lake Mendota (Walker and

Hasler, 1949). Not only could they distinguish them by the sense of smell, but also it was impossible to mask the odor of one species of plant by saturating the water with water extracts of a second species. Odors of plants were detected by this minnow in extremely high dilutions.

Homing migrations in fishes

To explain the homing of salmon, the hypothesis was proposed that young salmon are "imprinted" by an organic odor of the home stream in the early fingerling period. Each stream acquires a different odor, perhaps derived from a community of plants or their decomposition products in the stream or drainage basin. The mature salmon, returning from the sea, swims upstream in response to the water current. It rejects tributary after tributary until it detects

TABLE 2.2

Mean training scores in seconds for fishes reacting to odor stimuli. From Hasler and Wisby, 1951.

	A. Positive odor[a]: Otter Creek; negative odor[b]: Honey Creek						
Tank No.			7			8	
Month of training[c]	Odor tested	Pre-test[d]	Test[e]	Hesitation[f]	Pre-test	Test	Hesitation
First	positive	63	97	69	39	142	43
	negative	66	46	104	35	61	82
Second	positive	85	181	55	57	160	47
	negative	73	20	200	52	18	196
Third	positive	68	194	46	43	176	31
	negative	47	21	217	40	19	209
Sixth	positive	47	200	6	39	242	9
	negative	39	15	241	40	13	226
	B. Positive odor[a]: Honey Creek; negative odor[b]: Otter Creek						
Tank No.			2			3	
Month of training	Odor tested	Pre-test	Test	Hesitation	Pre-test	Test	Hesitation
First	positive	25	76	76	40	113	34
	negative	58	52	132	68	43	146
Second	positive	47	123	56	87	156	35
	negative	42	40	180	76	44	137
Third	positive	43	146	47	64	182	23
	negative	57	27	203	39	19	129
Sixth	positive	46	343	6	34	336	0
	negative	31	13	285	40	17	273

[a] Positive odor: The odor with which fish had been trained to associate reward.

[b] Negative odor: The odor with which fish had been trained to associate punishment. No punishment accompanied these tests.

[c] Records for tests made at this stage of training.

[d] Pre-test: Scores from random movement during 60 seconds preceding test.

[e] Test: Scores during 60-second period coinciding with exposure to odor.

[f] Hesitation: Scores for 5-second intervals from time they perceive the odor until enter scoring zone.

traces of the home stream. It may make faulty choices but continues the search after backtracking—a behavior pattern frequently observed. The salmon is stimulated to enter the home stream by the characteristic odor.

Hasler and Wisby (1951) showed that streams have characteristic odors by training a group of bluntnose minnows to discriminate between the waters of two chemically different Wisconsin creeks (Table 2.2). This experiment proved that olfactory organs were the sole means of discrimination in these tests: when the olfactory tissue of the trained fish was destroyed, the fish no longer responded to the training odors.

Chemical analysis of the stream waters indicated that the main difference between them was in the total organic fraction. Hasler and Wisby obtained evidence to substantiate this by separating the water into various fractions and presenting these to the fish. There was a strong indication that the odorous stimulant is a volatile organic substance.

A test of the retentive capacities of the trained minnows showed that the fish could differentiate between the odors for a comparatively long period after training ended, particularly if the learning took place in early life.

Salmon fingerlings trained in the laboratory were also able to discriminate between the odors from two Wisconsin creeks. Wisby and Hasler (1954) then captured sexually ripe coho salmon (*Oncorhynchus kisutch*) at two branches of the Issaquah River in Washington, plugged the nasal sac of half of the 302 specimens with cotton, and then placed all the fish downstream to make the run and selection of stream again. Those with plugged nasal sacs returned in random fashion, but a great majority of those from the other group again selected the stream of their first choice.

The hypothesis can be further tested by using an artificial substance to condition salmon fry in a hatchery or spawning riverlet. An artificial substance for conditioning salmon fry might then be used to decoy the returning mature fish to a different site. The artificial odor must be neither a repellant nor an attractant for the unconditioned salmon. Morpholine ($OCH_2CH_2NHCH_2CH_2$) was suggested as a compound that might fit these requirements because it is soluble in water, detectable in extremely low concentrations, and chemically stable under stream conditions.

Although home-finding in a stream system may depend upon the recognition of an odor and other yet undiscovered guideposts, it seems that the olfactory hypothesis is inadequate to explain the movements of salmon in the ocean. The initial attack on this problem was to study a less complex type of homing than that in salmon. For a number of years Hasler *et al.* (1958) studied the natural history of the white bass (*Roccus chrysops*) in Lake Mendota. They located only two major spawning grounds—Maple Bluff and Governor's Island, both on the north shore of the lake and 1.6 km apart. The white bass congregate here in late May and early June when temperatures range from 16° to 24° C.

During the spawning seasons of 1955, 1956, and 1957, the authors captured white bass in fyke nets, marked them with numbered disk tags, and transported part of the catch in open tanks to stations in the lake for daytime release and released the others on the spawning grounds. Large numbers of the displaced spawners returned to the original site from a release point 2.4 km away. About 90% of the displaced fish that were recaptured were at their "home" spawning site.

Subsequently, the "take-off" direction of displaced white bass was observed by attaching a plastic float to the fish and mapping the path of its movement (Fig. 2.11). These observations showed that the course taken upon release on sunny days was generally northerly toward the spawning grounds (Fig. 2.12). From these ob-

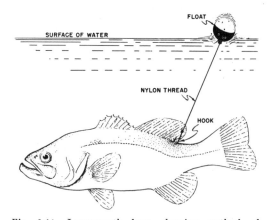

Fig. 2.11.—Largemouth bass, showing method of attaching the float which was used as an aid in tracking the course of the fish after displacement. A nylon thread connects the bobber and hook. After Hasler *et al.*, 1958.

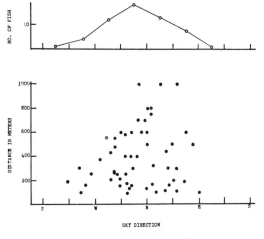

Fig. 2.12.—Direction of take-off and distance traveled by white bass after one hour from a mid-lake release point. Strength of current ignored. After Hasler *et al.*, 1958.

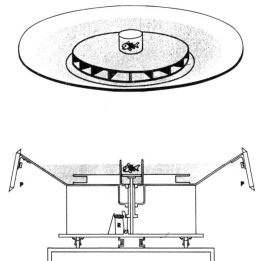

Fig. 2.13.—Training tank for determining ability of fish to use the sun in direction location: *top*, as seen from above; *bottom*, side view; *P*, periscopes. After Hasler *et al.*, 1958.

servations it appeared that the white bass in Lake Mendota were able to maintain a constant compass direction in unfamiliar territory. Once near the spawning area they appeared to locate their specific spawning ground by other cues. On cloudy days the displaced fish swam at random.

Hasler *et al.* (1958) tested the fish under the open sky in a specially designed tank where an escape or cover-seeking response could be scored (Fig. 2.13). The tank had 16 compartments arranged around a circle. None of these compartments could be seen by the fish from its starting point in the middle of the large tank, and only one of them was open. The others were covered by a metal band. In training tests, at frequent intervals, a fish was released from a cage in the center of the tank and given a small electric shock to make it seek cover in the small open compartment which was always in the same compass direction. When the fish had learned the location of the training compartment, tests were conducted in which all 16 compartments were left open. The fish usually chose the compartment in the compass direction in which it had been trained to seek shelter (Fig. 2.14). The fish learned to seek cover correctly at different times of day, allowing for the movement of the sun. Trained fish tested under completely overcast skies, however, were disoriented.

A crucial test substituted an artificial "sun" indoors for the actual sun. A sun-compass fish chose a hiding box as though it were responding to the actual sun at that specific time of day. Hence, the existence of an orientation rhythm, which is associated with the so-called "biological" clock, has been established.

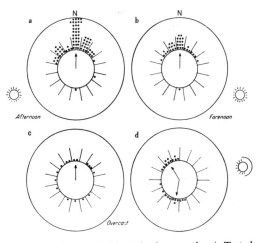

Fig. 2.14.—Scores of fish trained to north. *a*) Tested in the afternoon with 16 possible choices. *b*) Tested in the forenoon with 16 possible choices. *c*) Scores of Fish B tested under completely overcast sky on two different days. *d*) Scores of Fish B using an artificial light, where the altitude was the same as the sun. ● scores of fish trained to north and tested in the forenoon; ○ scores of same fish tested in the afternoon. After Hasler *et al.*, 1958.

Field and laboratory evidence on four different species of freshwater fish and laboratory tests on young silver salmon make it clear that many fish possess a sun-compass mechanism.

Preliminary studies suggest that the altitude of the sun plays a role in orientation. Hasler and Schwassmann (1960) trained sunfish (*Lepomis cyanellus*) to orient to the sun at Madison, Wisconsin (43° N), and then took them and the circular sun-orientation maze to Belém, Brazil (1° S). When the fish were tested where the sun appears to move counterclockwise, they continued to compensate for the azimuth curve of the sun that was "correct" for Madison. For a more extensive review of these studies, see Hasler (1960).

Perch studies

Records of Lake Mendota's perch (*Perca flavescens*) population go back to 1884. Since then two major changes have been found in the size and relative abundance of perch—a decrease in the number of fish and an increase in the average size.

In 1920 Pearse and Achtenberg (1920) estimated the perch population to be 15 million adult fish. The usual catch of anglers then, fishing through the ice with a line and two hooks, was from 200 to 400 perch per day. At this same time the average total length of the adult fish caught, as indicated by hook and line records, was 16.3 cm, and each weighed an average of 51.0 g.

By 1945 Hasler's (1945) measurements showed that the perch were 20.1 cm long on the average and weighed 127.6 g. In these ensuing years the population was alleged by anglers to have decreased substantially, but to what extent is not exactly known; however, a census of the number of fish caught during the winter of 1956 totaled nearly 1½ million perch (unpublished paper). By 1949 the weight of an average perch had risen to 178.6 g and the average length had increased to 24.4 cm (Bardach, 1949). This change in the perch population can be partially attributed to the large sporadic die-offs that were observed in 1890, 1929, 1946, and 1949.

In his study of the winter distribution of perch in Lake Mendota, Hasler (1945) found, by extensive netting under ice, that this winter population was most abundant in the deepest water of the lake, and that the fish traveled in schools of definite size-classes.

Of the environmental conditions that might influence the concentration of fish in deep water, such as oxygen content of the bottom water, temperature, and abundance of plankton Crustacea and bottom fauna, correlation with the last was the most striking. Not only were bottom-dwelling midges more abundant in the deeper stations, but the perch at these depths consumed more midges than did those at shallower depths. Even the lack of oxygen near the bottom in the deepest portions of the lake in late winter did not entirely prevent the perch from plying the bottom for food.

Work by Hasler and Whitney (1946) and Hasler and Bardach (1949) described a pre-sundown movement of schools of perch from depths of 8–12 m, where they hover in the daylight hours, onto a shelf at a depth of 6–10 m adjacent to Second Point in Lake Mendota. At sunrise the movement was reversed.

In 1953 Hasler and Villemonte (1953) saw on the oscilloscope screen of an echosounder that the schools of perch moved onto the Second Point shelf high over the bottom during their pre-sundown, inshore movement and reached their greatest concentration during the hour before sunset. The perch settled lower as twilight approached until their presence was no longer discernible on the screen.

Hasler and Villemonte also used aqualung divers to descend to the bottom at intervals during the pre- and post-sundown period. Pre-sundown observations revealed the perch, 15–28 cm in length, aggregated in tight schools with 20–25 cm between individuals. As long as there was sufficient light for the diver to see without artificial light, the fish moved in schools off the bottom. After sundown, however, the divers, aided by spotlights, found no schools of perch; instead, they observed individual fish dispersed along the lake bottom with their pectoral fins resting on the sand. When disturbed by the light or the currents from the moving diver, the fish would move briskly ahead to escape the spotlight beam and sink again to the bottom. At daybreak, they rose from the bottom, congregated in schools, and moved out to deeper water.

During summer and early fall a rapidly changing light intensity apparently initiates these movements. The light values are given in Table 2.3

for various depths in Lake Mendota for a typical clear July day during the migration hours.

Tibbles (1956) undertook a study to extend the knowledge of the movements and depth distribution of the pelagic fishes in Lake Mendota. He found by using an echosounder that there were at least three variations in sites of habitat for perch in the Second Point region of Lake Mendota during the summer: (1) the littoral population composed of juvenile and mature perch, (2) the population (chiefly mature) on the west side of the Second Point shelf, characterized by the rhythmic daily movements described above, and (3) the population of older perch found on the east side of the shelf that are recordable by echosounder even at night and therefore do not move shoreward at dusk as some do.

From a depth distribution determination for one area east of the underwater shelf at Second Point, from midsummer to early spring, Tibbles found that over 90% of the perch were caught at depths greater than 7 m in water 18 m deep. From the varying depths at which perch were caught during the summer, it is apparent that they are not restricted to a definite temperature stratum but remain in the deepest water in which there is sufficient oxygen to maintain life.

In the winter investigations (Stone, 1961) on the perch carried out from early January to mid-March, 1960 and 1961, the 24-hour activity and movement of the perch was observed by echosounder under the ice cover. By careful measurement of the tracings on the echo-chart, Stone found that the perch showed a diurnal bimodal activity cycle. At night the perch appeared to be associated in loosely knit aggregations moving very slowly on or just above the bottom, but at daybreak they became active and seemed to feed along the bottom. As the day progressed, this behavior declined, and finally most individuals were found in compact, faster-moving schools of various sizes. This change occurred at about the time of the second peak of activity. By late afternoon or sunset, activity slowed rapidly to the nocturnal pattern.

The swimming speed of the perch correlated with the daily activity cycle. Speed at night was about 30 to 60 cm/min. This increased to a morning maximum of 5 to 10 m/min at 0900 or 1000 hours, the period during which general activity is at a maximum. Swimming remained

TABLE 2.3

Relative intensities of light, in foot-candles,[a] at various times and depths for Lake Mendota on a typical July day

Depth (m)	Hours before sunset			
	2.5	2	1	0
Surface[b]	2,600	2,200	1,000	100
2	550	460	210	21
4	168	141	64	6
6	50	42	19	1.9
8	15	12	5.7	0.67
10	4	3	1.7	0.17

[a] To convert foot-candles into lux, or lumens per square meter, multiply values in table by 10.
[b] Data for surface intensities are based on Madison Weather Bureau records for a typical clear July day; underwater intensities measured with a Weston Photronic Cell.

constant at a speed of about 3 to 5 m/min for the remainder of the day, then decreased to nocturnal levels just before sunset.

There was no indication of a strong daily vertical migration during the winter studies. The majority of the perch remained within about 5 m of the bottom at all times, except for limited upward movement by a small percentage of the fish during the daylight hours. This movement appeared to be short-term excursions.

A consistent pattern of movement occurring during the day was indicated by both the continuous recordings at a fixed point and simultaneous multiple recordings in the quadrat. Records taken at stations along the shorelines adjacent to bays and in the central lake basin suggested a morning movement in a direction along the contour, but afternoon records from all stations indicated only a random movement.

By the end of April (Tibbles, 1956), water temperatures had risen, and spawning activity in the shallow water along the shore began. Then, by July, most adult perch had returned to deep water and were most abundant at the 11- to 18-m levels. By August the perch had begun to rise toward the 7-m level because of the lack of oxygen in the lower water of the lake, and usually were most abundant in the regions just above the thermocline for the remainder of the summer.

Cisco studies

Several hypotheses have been proposed to explain the decline of the cisco (*Coregonus artedii*) in Lake Mendota since 1940. The hypothesis that the decline was caused by poor survival of young fish—poor year-classes might be caused by starvation of the larval fish when the eggs hatch under the ice during unusually late springs —was disproved by incubation studies carried out by John and Hasler (1956), who estimated that the date of hatching falls no earlier than 25 April. They also found that the eggs do not hatch under the ice and doubted that they ever had in the past 70 to 75 years. They found that the date of hatching was apparently unrelated to the dates of spawning, the dates of formation and departure of the ice, or the temperatures of the water prior to the freeze-over.

John and Hasler's study of the larval cisco revealed that they require illumination in order to feed on living zooplankton, provided that the concentrations of the food organisms are not unreasonably high. If the larvae are kept in continuous darkness, they starve.

On the day of hatching, the larvae began to feed before the yolk sac had been absorbed. At temperatures between 14° and 18°C they began to swallow water and to feed on particulate matter, and by the third day they began to consume adult *Cyclops* sp. During the first week, they were more successful in feeding on dead zooplankton kept in suspension than on living zooplankton, but by the end of the week, they appeared to feed equally well on living zooplankton.

Their success in obtaining living zooplankton depended on the comparative swimming ability of the prey.

At temperatures encountered after the departure of the ice, the larvae were able to tolerate 18–20 days (108–128 degree days) of starvation. At temperatures between 3° and 4° C they withstood about 30 days of starvation.

Only rare occurrences of the cisco have been reported from Lake Mendota in recent years. This once very abundant fish has almost reached extinction. Just what changes in the catchment basin have been responsible for the decline of this species are not known, but increasing quantities of domestic sewage and severe siltation are suspected offenders.

White bass study

Horrall (1961) made a comparative study of two spawning populations of the white bass (*Roccus chrysops*) in Lake Mendota. From 1955 to 1960 the seasonal abundance, the sex ratio, and the length and age composition of the spawning populations were investigated on the Maple Bluff and Governor's Island spawning grounds.

The spawning aggregations occurred from late May through June when the temperatures ranged from 16° to 24° C. Two factors were observed to influence the seasonal timing and abundance

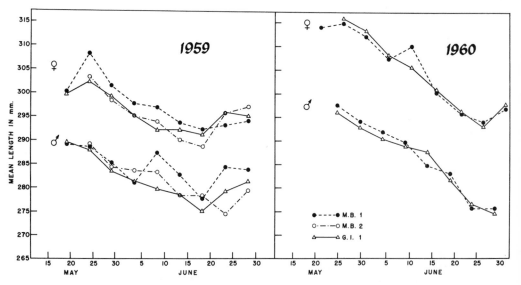

Fig. 2.15.—Mean lengths of samples of male and female white bass, by 5-day sampling periods, on the Maple Bluff and Governor's Island spawning grounds, Lake Mendota, 1959 and 1960. *M. B. 1* and *M. B. 2* represent different nets at Maple Bluff; *G. I. 1* is the netting station at Governor's Island.

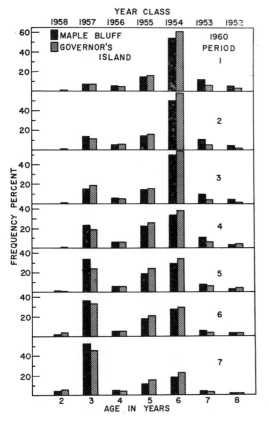

Fig. 2.16.—Age frequencies for each of the 7 periods, Maple Bluff and Governor's Island spawning grounds, Lake Mendota, 1960. Male fish only. Period 1: 23–27 May; Period 2: 28 May–1 June; Period 3: 2–6 June; Period 4: 7–11 June; Period 5: 12–16 June; Period 6: 17–21 June; Period 7: 22–26 June.

of spawners: the temperature of the water and the age composition of the population. Typically about seven year classes were represented on the spawning grounds, although one or two year classes usually were dominant. All fish three years and older were mature.

Several changes were found to occur in the composition of the spawning populations during a single spawning period. The sex ratio was found to change so that the males out-numbered the females by about 9 to 1 during the height of the spawning season. There was a progressive decrease in the mean length and age of both male and female spawners during the spawning period (Figs. 2.15 and 2.16). These changes were regular and followed similar patterns on both spawning grounds.

Spawning white bass that were tagged and released at eight different sites, including the other spawning site, returned with high accuracy to the "home" spawning site. A total of 9,071 releases and re-releases was made over a five-year period. Of the 1,384 recaptures about 89% had "homed" correctly. The evidence overwhelmingly supports the hypothesis that the white bass were homing to a specific spawning ground during the course of a single spawning season.

In addition, the preference for a specific spawning site was maintained in the succeeding spawning periods by individual fish. Out of 621 recaptures of fish one and two years after tagging, 83% were recaptured on the spawning ground where they originally had been captured.

In addition to the work on the white bass, the yellow bass (*Roccus mississippiensis*), which is a close relative of the white bass, has been studied in Lake Wingra (Helm, 1958).

Carp studies

Although carp control in its various forms has been an important part of the work of many state conservation agencies during the past 30 years, there have been relatively few opportunities to study the effectiveness of the various methods of control. Such an opportunity was made available when the need for carp control became acute in Lake Wingra in 1953.

Rates of natural mortality and recruitment were investigated by Neess *et al.* (1957) in a population of carp (*Cyprinus carpio*) in this lake. Average rates of natural mortality were found to be about 0.06 per month during the winter months of November, December, January, and February and about 0.04 per month during the others. During a two-year period in which the population was reduced by about 90% by extensive seining in addition to natural mortality, reproduction remained negligible; recruitment to the catchable portion of the population was seemingly large owing to growth of the year-classes already present at the beginning of the period.

A quantitative history of the population from 1953 to 1955 is given in Table 2.4, where an attempt was made to compare the losses caused by natural mortality with those caused by the fishery.

This extensive fishing effort (seining) demon-

TABLE 2.4

Quantitative history of the carp population in Lake Wingra from 1953 to 1955

| | | Weight, lbs | | | |
	Number of fish	Standing crop	Yield	Mortality	Pounds per acre
Population before seining of 1953	27,837	132,782			414.9
Removed by fishery in 1953	4,516		21,541		67.3
Population after seining of 1953	23,321	111,241			347.6
Natural mortality, winter of 1953–54	5,107			23,492	73.4
Population before seining of 1954	13,160	59,746			186.7
Removed by fishery in 1954	7,575		34,390		107.5
Population after seining of 1954	5,585	25,356			79.2
Natural mortality, spring 1954 to fall 1955	3,262			16,301	51.0
Catchable fish recruited, spring 1954 to fall 1955	1,773	7,978			24.9
Population before seining of 1955	3,697	21,276			66.5
Removed by fishery in 1955	1,009		5,337		16.7
Removed after seining of 1955	2,688	15,527			48.5
After seining of 1953:					
Total loss through natural mortality				39,802	
Total yield to fishery			39,727		

strated that an extremely large population of carp could be brought under control.

Muskellunge as a predator of perch

The size of the populations of bass and dwarfed perch in George and Corrine Lakes were measured by Gammon (1961) for two years prior to the introduction of 20.3–22.9 cm muskellunge fingerlings (*Esox masquinongy immaculatus*). Within a year after the introduction of the new predator, the perch in George Lake larger than 10.0 cm in length decreased from about 31,000 individuals to a density that was too low to estimate. In Corrine Lake, three years lapsed before a comparable reduction occurred (Fig. 2.17).

Gammon found that the differences in the response of the population levels of largemouth and smallmouth bass appeared to be related to a difference in the schooling tendencies and the habitat preferences of the young. Young largemouth bass school near the same type of habitat that is preferred by muskellunge, while the young smallmouth bass scatter over sandy and rocky areas. Little change in the growth rate and the length-weight relationship of either smallmouth or largemouth bass was observed to occur after the reduction of the number of perch.

About 25% of the muskellunge stocked in the spring in George Lake was unaccounted for after one and a half months, but there was no evidence of a similarly high mortality of the

muskellunge stocked in the fall in Corrine Lake. After this initial loss, a relatively constant annual mortality rate of 20 to 25% was observed in both populations.

This study of a predator-prey interaction conducted over a relatively long period has demonstrated how the introduction of a native fish but more specific predator can bring under control an explosive population of dwarfed perch.

Trout studies

After rotenone removal of resident fishes, rainbow trout (*Salmo gairdneri*) were established and maintained by stocking in some small experimental dystrophic lakes in northern Wisconsin and Upper Michigan, and the vital statistics of these populations at various levels of standing crop were followed (Johnson and Hasler, 1954). Based on a decline in growth rate at higher levels of standing crop, the carrying capacity of these lakes for pure populations of rainbow trout appeared to be approximately 45 kg/ha.

Johnson and Hasler found that most trout growth occurred from May through October, with little growth occurring during the period of ice cover from November through April. Availability of zooplankton (the principal food of these trout), size of standing crop of trout, temperature, and size of trout were considered factors determining the growth in these lakes. Analysis of these factors indicated that rate of growth at low levels of standing crop was largely regulated by length of growing season and water temperatures during that season. However, as size of standing crop increased, competition for food within the trout population apparently resulted in a slower rate of growth; this competition was found to be the most important factor in determining growth of trout at high levels of standing crop.

Natural mortality from time of stocking in May until mid-October 1952 ranged from 32 to 60% for age-group I trout and 15 to 19% for

productive behavior of the green sunfish (*Lepomis cyanellus*) and the northern redfin shiner (*Notropis umbratilis cyanocephalus*) in the University of Wisconsin Arboretum Gardner Ponds (Hunter, 1962).

Daily tabulations of the number of nests established by *L. cyanellus* during two spawning seasons revealed that nests were constructed at regular intervals of approximately eight to nine days throughout each season. However, the breed-

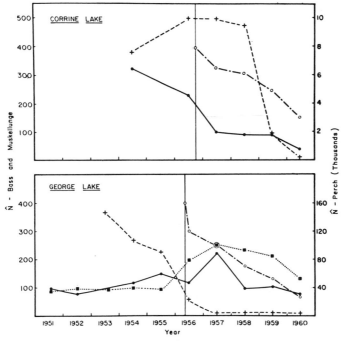

Fig. 2.17.—Estimated populations (Ñ) of perch, bass, and muskellunge in George Lake and Corrine Lake. The vertical line in each case indicates the time when muskellunge were introduced.

●————● largemouth bass   +– – – – –+ perch
■ · · · · · ■ smallmouth bass   ○– · – · –○ muskellunge

age-group II trout. The amount of natural mortality appeared to be entirely dependent on the number of trout predators present and not on the density of the trout.

This study also pointed out the suitability of dystrophic lakes or other lakes without oxygen below the epilimnion in midsummer for management as rainbow-trout lakes in areas where the mean July air temperature is less than 70° F (21° C).

Utilization of the nests of Lepomis cyanellus *by* Notropis umbratilis

Investigations were conducted on the re-

ing periods of *L. cyanellus* were found to be synchronized only when males constructed nests in colonies. When nests were isolated, the synchronization of breeding periods was not evident, and the nesting periods of individual males tended to be more irregular.

Males of *N. umbratilis* were found to establish territories over occupied sunfish nests and to form dense aggregations over the nests at times when *L. cyanellus* were spawning. Eggs collected on watch glasses which were placed inside and outside the occupied and unoccupied *L. cyanellus* nests indicated that *N. umbratilis* almost always spawned inside the occupied nests of *L. cyanel-*

lus. Although *N. umbratilis* eggs were collected throughout the period during which the sunfish nests were occupied, more *N. umbratilis* eggs were found on watch glasses during the times *L. cyanellus* were spawning than at any other time. Daily tabulations of the numbers of male *N. umbratilis* on the breeding grounds showed that more male shiners were present over the nests of *L. cyanellus* during the times when sunfish were establishing nests and spawning than at other times.

Studies on stream fishes

The Brule River in Douglas County contains populations of rainbow, brown, and brook trout. The rainbow and brown trout are migratory fishes, which spend the early part of their life in the stream, then migrate to Lake Superior, but return to the river to spawn when mature.

Hunt (1959) undertook an analysis of the role played by surface-drift insects in the diet of stream trout during the summer months. He found that this food resource was heavily exploited by all three species of trout studied and accounted for 76.5% of the total volume of food of 271 trout. Variations in the relative abundance of surface insects were regularly reflected in the percentage contribution such insects made to the total volume of food eaten by trout. On occasion, surface insects constituted 100% of the stomach contents. Surface feeding reached its peak of activity during the first two weeks in August, which coincided with the maximum abundance of insects present on the water.

The study also showed that 75% of the adult insects found on the surface of the stream had originated in the stream rather than on the land. Ephemeroptera made up an average of 49% of the available surface insects. Second in importance were the Diptera, the members of which accounted for 17% of the summer total collected with the catch-net. Coleoptera contributed 11%, Hymenoptera 8%, and Trichoptera 6%.

Studies on the rainbow trout population in the Brule River were conducted in 1960–61 by Salli (unpublished). One of the objectives of his research program was to determine the age composition of the rainbow trout population and to obtain information on the growth in the early years of life during which the trout is a resident of the stream. Analysis of the catch on two occasions when large samples were obtained by electrofishing revealed that 80–81% of the trout were one-year-old fish, 11–14% were two-year-old fish, and 5–8% were three-year-old fish. The mean total length of the rainbow trout at the time of formation of the various annuli was calculated to be 92 mm at the first annulus, 145 mm at the second annulus, and 179 mm at the third annulus.

Recent investigations on the ecology of stream fishes have also been carried out at Marquette University under the direction of R. M. Darnell. Blackburn (1959), in a study of the movement and distributional relations of the black bullhead (*Ictalurus melas*) and the tadpole madtom (*Noturus gyrinus*), found that individuals of both species concentrated in a pool area of the stream. Considerable movement within the pool by individual fish suggested that the fish were attracted by the pool conditions in general but did not remain associated with specific localized habitat features within the pool.

Meierotto (1960) investigated diurnal periodicity in activity patterns of the black bullhead in the same stream pool. He found differences between young and adults in the 24-hour patterns of activity and directions of movement. Laboratory studies in a constant environment suggested that the activity pattern of the young was endogenous. Food analyses coupled with digestion rate experiments pointed to two daily peaks of feeding by the young, which clearly did not correspond with the periods of greatest activity observed in the fish trapped in the stream.

Plantenburg (1961) studied the black bullhead to determine factors influencing the rate of digestion of its most important natural food item in the stream, the amphipod *Hyalella azteca*. On the basis of a series of laboratory feeding experiments, she described the process of morphological disintegration of the food and established seven stages which could be distinguished fairly objectively. Employing these stages as criteria, she determined that the rate of digestive disintegration of the food at 25° C was 37% faster than at 20° C. At 15° C the rate was further retarded. The presence of previously undigested food was found to retard the process.

Sound communication in fish

Schneider and Hasler (1960) reported that the sounds made by the male freshwater drum (*Aplodinotus grunniens*) are produced by a special apparatus which is located in the body cavity and is connected with the swimbladder (Fig. 2.18). This structure consists of two elongated muscles and a tendon. The muscle fibers originate from the left and right sides of the abdominal musculature and are attached to a broad central tendon, which extends between the muscles and across the swimbladder; these muscles are separated from the swimbladder by adipose tissue (Fig. 2.19). Presumably, contractions of the muscles actuate the tendon to produce sound on the swimbladder. This structure is fully developed by the time the fish are three years old.

Hydrophone records showed that the fishes in Lake Winnebago started drumming in early May and reached a maximum during the spawning season in June, after which the drumming decreased gradually in intensity until the end of August when no sounds were audible. During the spawning season, however, a daily rhythm of drumming was observed: the first sounds were heard at about 1000 hours and became more frequent in the following hours until a peak was reached in the drumming activity in the afternoon. The drumming then decreased gradually until sunset when it stopped. Schneider and Hasler found that the daily rhythm was altered by changes in weather conditions.

Analysis of the sounds from several recordings showed that mean pulse periods ranged from 36.5 to 60.2 msec, the mean duration of the pulses from 12.4 to 28.9 msec, and the intervals from 23.0 to 34.5 msec. Because only the sexually mature male produced sounds, the function appears to be mainly for communication during spawning.

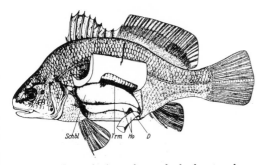

Fig. 2.18.—Lateral view of a male freshwater drum. A flap is folded back to expose to view the drumming muscle attached to the body and the swim bladder. *Schbl* swim bladder; *Trm* drumming muscle; *D* gut-digestive tract; *Ho* testes. After Schneider and Hasler, 1960.

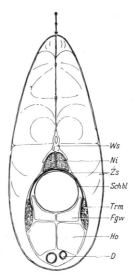

Fig. 2.19.—Schematic cross-section through the sound producing apparatus within the body cavity, showing the tendon as it passes over the swim bladder. *Ws* vertebral column; *Ni* kidney; *Zs* tendon connecting drumming muscle; *Schbl* swim bladder; *Trm* drumming muscle; *Fgw* fatty tissue; *Ho* testis; *D* gut. After Schneider and Hasler, 1960.

Endocrinology of fishes

In 1939 and 1940 Hasler *et al.* (1939, 1940) were able to advance the spawning time of rainbow trout by six weeks through intraperitoneal injections of the whole pituitary glands of carp. The muskellunge (*Esox masquinongy*) was also induced to spawn prematurely. Moreover, eggs were obtained from injected females whose spawning migration was interfered with by a newly constructed dam on the Chippewa River in Wisconsin.

As a sequel to this applied study and to learn more about the physiology and the endocrinology of fishes, hormones from the carp pituitary were shown to increase the O_2 consumption of normal goldfish but not of castrated ones (Hasler and Meyer, 1942). In addition, an assay of carp pituitary activity was devised by determining its action on producing snout-tubercles in nonspawning male minnows (Ramaswami and Hasler, 1955).

Origin and quantities of plant nutrients in Lake Mendota
by G. A. Rohlich

To obtain sufficient data to fulfill the requirements of a study on the origin and quantities

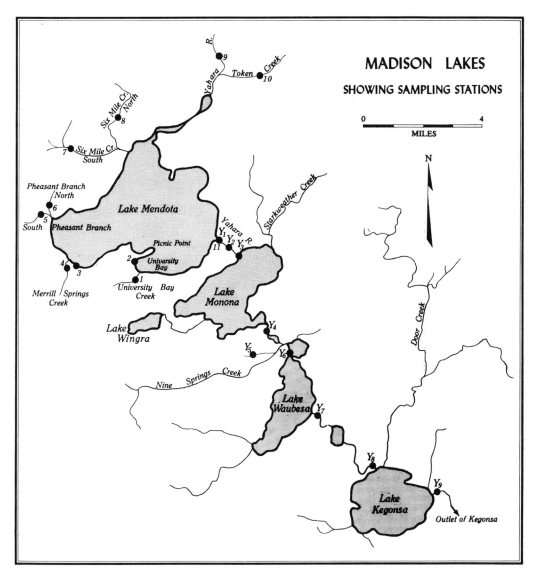

Fig. 2.20.—Location of sampling stations on the tributaries of Lake Mendota, and along the Yahara River below Lake Mendota.

1. University Bay Creek
2. University Marsh Pumping Station
3. Merrill Springs
4. Merrill Springs Creek
5. Pheasant Branch, South
6. Pheasant Branch, North
7. Six Mile Creek, South
8. Six Mile Creek, North
9. Yahara River
10. Token Creek
11. Lake Mendota Outlet: Tenney Park Locks

Stations designated Y-1, Y-2, etc., were established to obtain data on the so-called "Yahara River Survey." Prepared by the University of Wisconsin Cartographic Laboratory.

of plant nutrients, three separate sets of stations were established on Lake Mendota: the inland series, the horizontal series, and the vertical series.

Inland series.—The inland series consisted of the stations on the ten tributaries to Lake Mendota and an eleventh station on the Yahara River at the outlet of the lake (Fig. 2.20). Control devices were constructed on these streams in order to obtain accurate measurements of the flow. Since the Lake Mendota Outlet at the Tenney Park Locks is the only outflow of importance from Lake Mendota, the analyses of samples from the series of eleven stations enables the computation of the amount of nutrients retained in the lake.

Horizontal series.—The horizontal series of sampling stations were established on University Bay Creek, Pheasant Branch, and the Yahara River at the entrance to the lake. Station 1 of each of these series is located upstream on each of the streams; Station 2 is located at the mouth of each; and Station 3 is in a line with Stations 1 and 2 but in the lake proper. The samples from the stations established for this series were analyzed to determine the effect of the weedbeds and a'gae, concentrated at the mouth of the streams, on the concentration of nutrient materials originally in the stream (Emelity and Hanson, 1948, 1949; Belter and Calabresa, 1949).

Vertical series.—The vertical series of stations were located in the lake at University Bay where the water is 65 ft deep, east of Pheasant Branch Creek where the depth is 65 ft, and northeast of Picnic Point where the depth is 80 ft. At each of these stations samples were taken at the surface, at about 10 m depth, and at about 0.5 m above the lake bottom.

Measurement of flow from tributaries

At each of the eleven inland stations on Lake Mendota, suitable arrangements for stream gauging were made to obtain measurements of the flow. The control devices for flow measurement varied in design, and equations of flow for each type of device were formulated in terms of its physical characteristics and the heads of water involved. Rating curves for each control were plotted. Current meter readings were also made from time to time to check the calibration of the weirs. Continuous recording head gauges were established at eight of the stations, and rainfall

TABLE 2.5

Water balance of Lake Mendota, 1 October 1948 to 1 October 1949

INFLOW	
a) Measured tributaries—Stations 1–10 (192.27 mi² of drainage basin)	78.4 cfs
b) Unmeasured tributary area (31.87 mi² of drainage basin, by computation)	13.0 cfs
c) Precipitation onto lake surface (31.65 in.)	38.7 cfs
Total inflow (4,100,000,000 ft³)	130.1 cfs
OUTFLOW	
a) Storage	3.5 cfs
b) Evaporation (51.17 in., by computation)	58.2 cfs
c) Outflow, Station 11	70.0 cfs
d) University pumpage	1.5 cfs
Total outflow (4,200,000,000 ft³)	133.2 cfs

Unaccounted for: $133.2 - 130.1 = 3.1$ cfs $= 2.33\%$ of outflow.

gauges were installed on the drainage basins of the several streams tributary to the lake. These instruments permitted refinement of measurements and made it possible to obtain incidental information concerning the rainfall-runoff relationship for the various types and sizes of drainage areas included in this basin.

A water balance for the year 1 October 1948 to 1 October 1949 is given in Table 2.5.

In subsequent water balance studies conducted by several students and compiled by McCaskey (1955), the basin was controlled by weirs at the principal stations, namely 7, 8, 9, and 10, with the Yahara River outlet (Station 11) as the final check point in the system of flow control. Summaries of the water balance by months for the years 1951, 1952, 1953, and 1954 are available. Data for 1954 are given as an example in Table 2.6.

Analysis of water samples

Chemical analyses of water samples from the various stations consisted of determinations of pH, alkalinity, dissolved oxygen, biochemical oxygen demand, soluble phosphorus, total phosphorus, free ammonia nitrogen, total organic nitrogen, nitrite nitrogen, nitrate nitrogen, sulfates, silicates, manganese, and iron.

A summary of the phosphorus and nitrogen entering the lake from the period 1 October 1948 to 1 October 1949 is shown in Table 2.7.

TABLE 2.6

Water balance by months in water year 1954 (flow in cubic feet per second [cfs])

Inflow

Month and calendar year	Meas-ured	Unmeas-ured	Precip-itation	Stor-age	Total cfs/mo.
Oct. 1953	31.8	15.2	9.3	39.6	95.9
Nov.	33.0	15.8	6.3	17.1	72.2
Dec.	32.5	15.6	30.4		78.5
Jan. 1954	32.5	15.6	9.8		57.9
Feb.	38.5	18.5	8.4		65.4
Mar.	35.8	17.1	15.9	26.3	95.1
Apr.	44.0	21.1	69.0		134.1
May	33.8	15.7	46.5		96.0
June	47.6	22.8	107.2	13.7	191.3
July	87.0	41.6	66.5	42.7	237.8
Aug.	40.8	19.6	31.0	23.0	114.4
Sept.	39.2	18.8	52.6	20.5	131.1
					1369.7

Outflow

Month and calendar year	Out-let	Pump-age	Evapo-ration	Stor-age	Total cfs/mo.
Oct. 1953	29.3	1.5	55.2		86.0
Nov.	19.5	1.5	31.4		52.4
Dec.	16.9	1.5	9.0	39.5	66.9
Jan. 1954	19.3	1.5	12.2		33.0
Feb.	43.4	1.5	15.7	25.5	86.1
Mar.	93.6	1.5	22.5		117.6
Apr.	61.5	1.5	46.2	106.0	215.2
May	52.6	1.5	56.0	59.1	169.2
June	260.3	1.5	71.5		333.3
July	370.0	1.5	63.4		434.9
Aug.	77.6	1.5	51.6		130.7
Sept.	68.1	1.5	53.0		122.6
					1847.9

Net difference is 478 cfs/mo. excess outflow volume, or a mean flow of 39.7 cfs.

Tables 2.8 and 2.9 show the balances for the various constituents for which analyses were made for a winter period, 1 October 1948 to 1 May 1949, and for a summer period, 1 May 1949 to 1 October 1949, as well as for the full-year period. During the year, 17,362 lbs of soluble phosphorus entered the lake (Table 2.10). This corresponds to a fertilization of about 1.8 lbs per acre of lake surface. Table 2.10 also shows that the supply of soluble phosphorus and inorganic nitrogen in total number of pounds to Lakes Waubesa and Kegonsa is considerably greater than to either Lakes Mendota or Monona, and that the pounds per acre of lake surface in the three lower lakes is much higher than in Mendota.

The increase in the amount of soluble phosphorus and inorganic nitrogen to Lake Waubesa was principally from the discharge of the effluent from the Madison Nine Springs Sewage Treatment Plant during the years shown. In December 1958 this effluent was diverted to the Yahara River below Lake Kegonsa. Currently data on the Yahara River stations are being obtained to determine the composition of the water at these stations since the diversion.

Bottom muds

Studies on the composition of the bottom muds in Lake Mendota were made by Levihn (1951) and Kaneshige (1952). Sixty-seven stations were established in the central portion of Lake Mendota, and an additional 39 stations were concentrated in the University Bay area. Samples of bottom muds were collected and analyzed for soluble and total phosphorus, free ammonia, total

TABLE 2.7

Summary of phosphorus and nitrogen entering Lake Mendota, 1 October 1948 to 1 October 1949. All figures are percentages of the totals.

Sampling station	Soluble phosphorus	Total phosphorus	Inorganic[a] nitrogen	Organic nitrogen	Flow
1. Univ. Farm Creek	2.7	2.0	0.2	1.3	0.9
2. Univ. Marsh Pump	0.7	0.7	2.2	1.3	0.7
3. Merrill Springs	0.2	0.3	1.1	0.1	0.9
4. Merrill Springs Creek	0.3	0.4	1.2	0.3	0.9
5. Pheasant Branch—South	2.8	4.1	3.7	5.1	3.2
6. Pheasant Branch—North	3.5	4.5	3.4	4.1	6.4
7. Six Mile Creek—South	1.0	1.1	2.0	1.0	1.5
8. Six Mile Creek—North	39.8	27.9	12.1	37.5	20.1
9. Yahara River	34.5	34.3	30.7	28.2	31.4
10. Token Creek	14.5	24.7	43.4	21.1	34.0

[a] Inorganic nitrogen represents the summation of ammonia, nitrite, and nitrate nitrogen.

TABLE 2.8

Phosphorus and nitrogen balance in Lake Mendota. Stations 1–10 represent addition to the lake; Station 11 is the outflow.

	Winter period 1 Oct. 1948–1 May 1949		Summer period 1 May 1949–1 Oct. 1949		Water year 1 Oct. 1948–1 Oct. 1949	
	Pounds	% retained	Pounds	% retained	Pounds	% retained
Soluble phosphorus						
Stations 1–10	11,710		5,652		17,362	
Station 11	7,275		1,790		9,065	
Retained in lake	4,435	37.9	3,862	68.7	8,297	47.7
Total phosphorus						
Stations 1–10	22,984		13,043		36,027	
Station 11	18,350		7,200		25,550	
Retained in lake	4,634	20.2	5,843	44.7	10,477	28.9
Total organic nitrogen						
Stations 1–10	60,031		23,706		83,737	
Station 11	30,710		21,890		52,600	
Retained in lake	29,321	48.7	1,816	7.7	31,137	37.1
Total inorganic nitrogen						
Stations 1–10	192,310		67,397		259,707	
Station 11	25,445		13,220		38,665	
Retained in lake	166,865	86.7	54,177	80.6	221,042	81.1

The inorganic nitrogen entering the lake during the year amounted to 259,720 lbs, corresponding to a fertilization of 26.7 lbs per acre of lake surface. Most of this is in the form of nitrates. Relatively heavy contributors on a percentage basis are the University Marsh pumping station and Token Creek. The pumpage from the University Marsh contributed 2.2% of the total, while supplying only 0.7% of the flow. A concentration as high as 27 ppm of nitrate-nitrogen was recorded at this station on 29 June 1949.

It is of interest to compare these data with the fertilization of the lower lakes as shown in Table 2.10.

organic nitrogen, nitrite and nitrate nitrogen, and total iron.

Representative data from these studies are shown in Figures 2.21, 2.22, 2.23, and 2.24. Figure 2.21 shows lines of equal concentration of total phosphorus in the open lake area, and Figure 2.22 shows total phosphorus values in University Bay in the summer of 1951 and winter of 1950. Similar plots for total organic nitrogen are shown in Figures 2.23 and 2.24.

The values shown on these figures are on the basis of the dry weight of the mud. In general the data indicate that the concentrations became greater with increasing depth of water, with the exception of the area near the mouth of the Yahara River. The concentrations in University Bay indicate that a shifting of the muds occurs between summer and winter conditions. In this report only summary data have been presented. The complete data, giving the concentrations of the various constituents at each of the stations on each of the sampling dates, are available at the University of Wisconsin Library. Only the theses cited in this summary are listed in the bibliography. There are in addition 17 other unpublished theses related to these general problems.

Applied limnology

Blue-green algae and waterblooms

A project was initiated in the Botany Department of the University of Wisconsin in 1947 with the purpose of studying the nutrition of blue-green algae and of understanding the most important nutritional factors contributing to bloom development under natural conditions.

The initial work of this project was concerned with the development of a nutrient solution in which blue-green algae, and particularly the bloom-producing species, would make satisfactory growth. Modifications of one of the solutions described by S. P. Chu provided a suitable culture medium for a large number of blue-green algae, including previously uncultured bloom-

TABLE 2.9

SO_4, SiO_2, Mn, Fe, and free CO_2 balance in Lake Mendota. Stations 1–10 represent addition to the lake; Station 11 is the outflow.

	Winter period 1 Oct. 1948–1 May 1949		Summer period 1 May 1949–1 Oct. 1949		Year period 1 Oct. 1948–1 Oct. 1949	
	Pounds	% retained	Pounds	% retained	Pounds	% retained
Sulfates						
Stations 1–10	1,281,870		471,390		1,753,260	
Station 11	949,650		481,950		1,431,600	
Retained in lake	332,220	25.9	−10,560	−2.2	321,660	18.3
Silicates						
Stations 1–10	935,880		144,430		1,080,310	
Station 11	76,530		28,590		105,120	
Retained in lake	859,350	91.8	115,840	80.2	975,190	90.2
Manganese						
Stations 1–10	17,750		5,927		23,677	
Station 11	16,150		7,576		23,726	
Retained in lake	1,600	9.0	−1,649	−27.8	−49	−0.2
Iron						
Stations 1–10	14,480		6,160		20,640	
Station 11	2,350		1,605		3,955	
Retained in lake	12,130	83.8	4,555	74.0	16,685	80.7
Free CO_2						
Stations 1–10	961,975		310,945		1,272,920	
Station 11	430,460		6,030		436,490	
Retained in lake	531,515	55.2	304,915	98.2	836,430	65.7

producing organisms such as *Microcystis, Aphanizomenon,* and *Gloeotrichia* (Gerloff *et al.*, 1950a, 1950b).

The suitability of these solutions for blue-green algae culture seemed to depend primarily on the alkaline buffering provided by sodium carbonate and sodium silicate. If these constituents were omitted, the algae would grow only if the *p*H of the media was frequently adjusted to the alkaline range.

Unialgal cultures were considered essential for all nutrition studies, and bacteria-free cultures were used in most studies. Ultraviolet radiation was found the most satisfactory procedure for selectively destroying the bacteria that penetrate the gelatinous sheaths of the blue-green species.

The mineral nutrition of a number of species was quantitatively studied by Gerloff *et al.* (1950c, 1952) to determine the effects on algal growth of systematic variations in the amounts of the essential elements in the medium. The bloom-producing species were found incapable of nitrogen-fixation. In fact, the organisms studied

required much greater amounts of nitrogen than of any other essential mineral element. The requirement of the algae for phosphorus was par-

TABLE 2.10

Fertilization of the four lakes

	Soluble phosphorus		Inorganic nitrogen	
	Lbs per lake	Lbs/acre of lake surface	Lbs per lake	Lbs/acre of lake surface
Mendota (Year 1949)	17,362	1.8	259,720	27
Monona[a] (1942–43; 1943–44)	23,072 29,601	6.6 8.5	254,028 313,573	73 90
Waubesa[a] (1942–43; 1943–44)	125,384 129,366	62.0 63.6	859,113 911,085	422 448
Kegonsa[a] (1942–43; 1943–44)	107,864 118,874	34.2 37.7	527,014 490,524	168 156

[a] From Sawyer *et al.* (1945), "Investigation of the Odor Nuisance Occurring in the Madison Lakes."

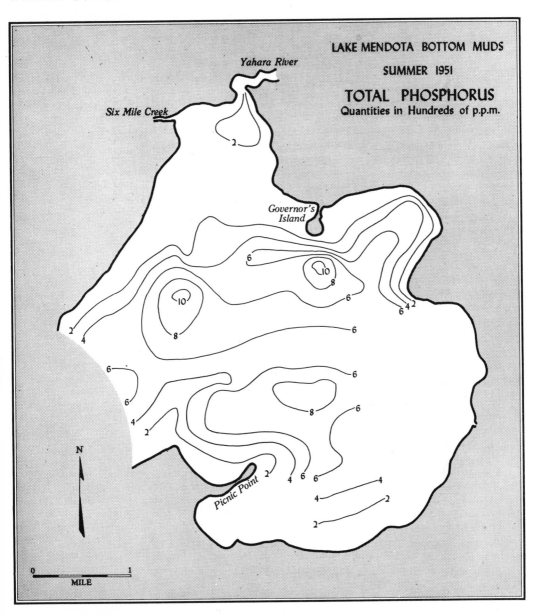

Fig. 2.21.—Distribution of total phosphorus in the surficial sediments of Lake Mendota in the summer of 1951. Values shown are in hundreds of parts per million, based on dry weight. Prepared by the University of Wisconsin Cartographic Laboratory.

ticularly interesting in view of the frequent suggestion that phosphorus supply is a limiting factor in the growth of algae in lakes and streams. The blue-green algae studied did not have an unusually high phosphorus requirement. In fact, relative to other organisms, their phosphorus requirement seemed low. Another interesting nutritional feature of the blue-green algae, in sharp contrast to higher plants, was their extremely low requirement for calcium.

Studies on the trace element requirements of the blue-green algae led to the discovery that

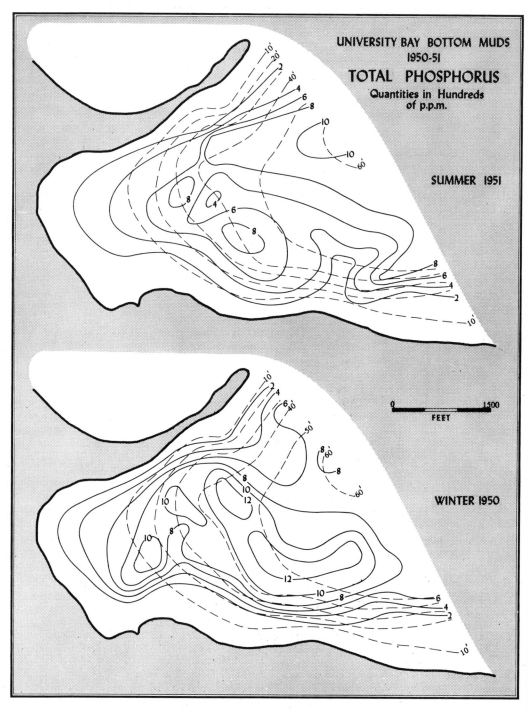

Fig. 2.22.—Distribution of total phosphorus in the surficial sediments of University Bay of Lake Mendota during the winter of 1950 and the summer of 1951. Values shown are in hundreds of parts per million, based on dry weight. The dashed lines are bottom contours in feet. Prepared by the University of Wisconsin Cartographic Laboratory.

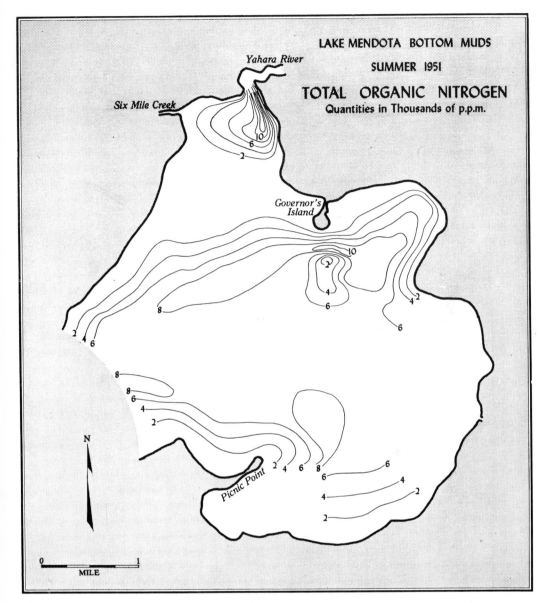

Fig. 2.23.—Distribution of total organic nitrogen in the surficial sediments of Lake Mendota in the summer of 1951. Values shown are in parts per thousand, based on dry weight. Prepared by the University of Wisconsin Cartographic Laboratory.

cobalt is an essential element for these organisms (Holm-Hansen *et al.*, 1954). This was the first demonstration that cobalt is required for green plants.

One possible means of reducing the excessive growths of algae in lakes and streams is to remove critical essential elements from effluents that flow into the water and are the primary source of the elements.

Reliable measurements of the degree to which a specific element actually limits growth of algae in nature are difficult to obtain. In the past they have been based on changes in the concentrations of various elements in lakes or streams as blooms

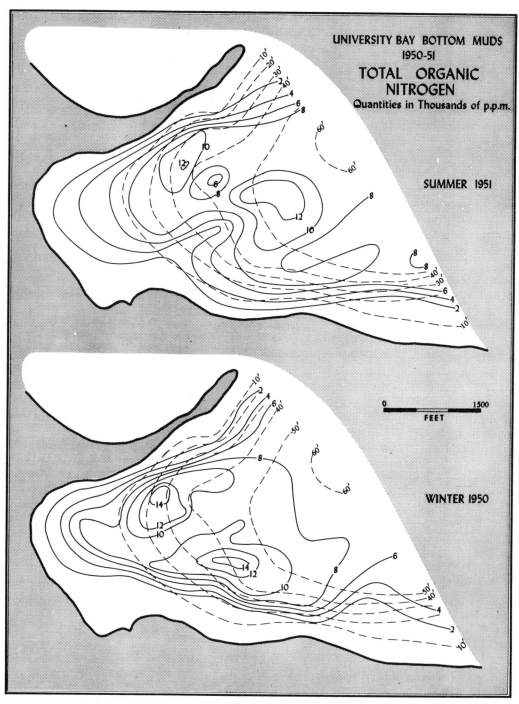

Fig. 2.24.—Distribution of total organic nitrogen in the surficial sediments of University Bay of Lake Mendota during the winter of 1950 and the summer of 1951. Values shown are in parts per thousand, based on dry weight. The dashed lines are bottom contours in feet. Prepared by the University of Wisconsin Cartographic Laboratory.

developed. Results obtained by this procedure are unreliable for several reasons. An attempt, therefore, was made to utilize the cell content of an essential element as a guide to the supply of the element in the algal environment (Gerloff and Skoog, 1954).

The effects of additions of various essential elements to lake water showed that only nitrogen, phosphorus, and iron were likely limiting factors for the growth of *Microcystis aeruginosa* in the southern Wisconsin lakes under study. Comparisons of the iron contents of cells grown in the laboratory and collected from lakes (Gerloff and Skoog, 1957a) indicated iron was much less likely to limit growth than was nitrogen or phosphorus.

The critical level—the minimum cellular concentration of an element that is necessary for maximum growth—of nitrogen in *Microcystis* was established in laboratory experiments to be approximately 4.0% and of phosphorus 0.12%. Samples of the same organism then were collected from blooms in a number of southern Wisconsin lakes. Both the nitrogen and phosphorus contents of these algae were above the critical levels, so that neither element could be considered a limiting factor in the development of blooms.

A procedure was developed (Gerloff and Skoog, 1957b) that permitted adjustment of the critical levels in accordance with the carbohydrate contents of the cells. After these adjustments were made, cellular nitrogen contents of algae in several lake samples were below the critical nitrogen level of 4.0%. The nitrogen content of the other samples was very close to the critical level. Chemical analyses indicated nitrogen to be present in the lakes in far less abundant supply relative to need than was phosphorus. Reduction of the nitrogen supply, therefore, is suggested as a possible measure for controlling algal blooms in these lakes.

Approximately 300 organic compounds were screened for selective toxicity to bloom-producing blue-green algae. In field tests (Fitzgerald and Skoog, 1954), repeated applications of 2,3-dichloronaphthoquinone reduced blooms of blue-green algae with no immediately observable, harmful effects to other organisms.

Fishery biology

A study was undertaken by Hunter (1962) on the net-avoidance behavior of carp (*Cyprinis carpio*) and other species of fish. He evaluated the size of the tank, temperature, light, and social behavior for their effect on the responses of carp to a moving net under laboratory conditions. He also studied the responses of carp to air bubbles and to nets of various colors. The responses of carp to a moving net were compared to those of nine other species of freshwater fishes.

Survival of muskellunge fry depends upon the presence of young *Daphnia* which are small enough for the fry to ingest. On the other hand, the adult *Daphnia*, which are too large to be ingested by the fry, insure an adequate brood stock for continued production of young (Johnson, 1958). To make certain that *Daphnia* is the dominant crustacean in the ponds when fry are introduced, biologists "seed" the ponds from artificial *Daphnia* cultures at strategic periods.

Because this close relationship between food size and fish size exists, legal-sized (17.8 to 25.4 cm) trout are stocked in lakes during periods when the late instar stages of *Daphnia* are abundant. Fingerling trout have been stocked during periods (summer) when the bulk of the planktonic Crustacea consisted of species that were too small for legal-sized trout to ingest but not too small for fingerlings 7.6 to 12.7 cm (Brynildson, 1961a).

Brynildson (1961b) demonstrated that rainbow trout stocked when 20.3 to 25.4 cm long in infertile Fish Lake, Dane County, could not compete with the cisco and panfish, because the latter species grazed the individuals in the zooplankton population before they reached a size large enough for the trout to ingest. Six months after release, none of these trout was found in electrofishing and gill net collections.

Young largemouth bass and carp, less than 3.8 cm in length, placed in the same ponds at Delafield Research Station, fed on small (less than 0.5 mm) cladocerans. Largemouth bass, after they became larger than 3.8 cm, generally switched to an insect diet and did not ingest many cladocerans. The carp, however, continued into adulthood to feed on the same food (cladocerans) as when they were young (Mraz and Ensign, 1960).

Priegel (1961) released 400,000 dyed walleye fry at Shiocton to follow their downstream migration in the Wolf River. The fry were released at 1500 hours on 16 May, and by 0930 hours on 18 May the fry had reached Fremont, a distance of 76 km. The fry had traveled the 76 km in only 44 hours.

Channel catfish that had been taken in nets in the Wisconsin River and tagged by Brynildson and Truog (1959) were caught on hook and line up to 155 km from the point of original capture and release within 3 months after release.

A study to determine territory and homing of wild adult and fingerling brook trout showed that displacing adult brook trout 305 m downstream did not prevent their return to their home grounds (93% return in one month). However, only 53% found their original homes when released 305 m above the area where they were originally captured. In contrast to older fish, the young-of-the-year (9 months old and 5.1 to 12.7 cm in length) wild brook trout showed less ability to return to their home grounds when moved 305 m up (12% return) or down (4% return) from their original home grounds (Hunt, 1961).

Lake sturgeon (*Acipenser fulvescens*) are normally found to remain in a particular home basin except at spawning time when they travel to sites over 161 km away to spawn before returning to their home basin. During 1960 two tagged sturgeon were taken in the northern sector of Lake Michigan's Green Bay. One of them, tagged three years previously on a spawning ground 201 km upstream from Lake Winnebago, traveled back through the lake, then over 12 power dams downstream to Green Bay, thence another 161 km northward. The other fish was tagged in Lake Winnebago in 1957, recaptured twice (spring and fall) in 1958 in the lake, and finally captured and removed in the summer of 1960 in northern Green Bay. Very high water levels in 1960, at least a 25-year maximum, are suspected by Wirth and Priegel (1961) to have initiated the downstream movement from Lake Winnebago.

Carp, which destroy rooted aquatic vegetation (mechanically and as a result of water turbidity), are controlled by seining or eradicating with fish toxicants. With an increase in the rooted aquatic vegetation, algae becomes less of a problem in fertile lakes. The loss of aquatic vegetation in ponds at Delafield Station, caused by introduction of carp, made the environment unsuitable for some of the large cladocerans, such as *Eurycercus* and *Simocephalus,* but favored the

production of small cladocerans, such as *Chydorus* and *Bosmina,* species which were generally too small to be ingested by largemouth bass over 3.8 cm in length (Mraz and Ensign, 1960).

Because planktonic Crustacea are mainly killed after application of fish toxicants, reintroduction of these organisms is often made, or a crustacean more suitable in the fish-food chain may be introduced.

The best method of maintaining adequate dissolved oxygen for fish in Cox Hollow Lake, Iowa County, during winter was accomplished by releasing oxygen-free water from the bottom of the dam at the same rate as water from a stream entered the lake (Brynildson and Truog, 1960).

It was apparent from several studies that stream trout do not grow large in a restricted environment. Trout habitat development now aims at increasing the depth of the stream water without sacrificing water velocity, which results in increased trout poundage because of an increase in growth rates (White, 1961).

During the last ten years, electrofishing has developed to a point where 60 to 90% of the trout in most Wisconsin trout streams (1.3 to 12.0 m in width) can be collected during one run with the shocking unit, and large boom shockers have, in many instances, replaced seines for collecting fish in lakes. Common salt has been added experimentally to stream and lake water low in mineral content to increase conductance. With an increase in conductance, Churchill (1961) found that there was a corresponding increase in efficiency of the electrofishing gear in catching fish.

Until very large cone nets were employed, pelagic fry of the walleye were difficult to collect. Now, however, such nets are towed in lakes to catch the fry and are set as drift nets in streams to catch the fry drifting downstream (Priegel, 1960). Yellow perch fry are also collected with these cone nets in large numbers where these fish are abundant.

Classification of waters

Regional classification of lakes and streams is a comparatively recent project. The classification of Wisconsin waters is now being undertaken by Poff (1961) on the basis of the concentration of major ions and on morphometry and its relationship to production and recreational potential.

Pollution investigations

In 1950 a systematic program of pollution investigation and control was instituted by the Wisconsin Committee on Water Pollution to check specific drainage basins in order to determine all sources of industrial and domestic pollution. Waste samples were obtained by Bartsch (1948) and Bartsch and Churchill (1949), and chemical, sanitary, and biological stream surveys were conducted to define the impact of pollution on the stream ecology. Toxic wastes are sometimes a problem, and a tabulation of materials toxic to aquatic life has been developed to serve as a guide to indicate additional bioassay determination (Mackenthun, 1952).

By 1955 essentially the entire state had been surveyed, and a continuing phase of the committee's effort has consisted of a periodic re-inventory of the impact of pollution on the many streams within the 28 drainage basins.

In 1926 joint waste utilization and stream improvement activities were begun with the pulp and paper industry. For four months, from June to September, weekly stream samples are collected by various mill personnel for dissolved oxygen, temperature, and biochemical oxygen demand. Comprehensive cross-section surveys have also been conducted by state and industry representatives to determine stream purification capacities (Wiley *et al.*, 1957); Lueck *et al.*, 1957; and Wisniewski, 1958).

In 1943 investigations were instituted by the Pulp and Paper Industry and the Committee on Water Pollution to increase the dissolved oxygen in a stream by the use of compressed air (Wiley *et al.*, 1947). About 0.5 mg/L of dissolved oxygen could be introduced by this method, but efficiencies were comparatively low. Recent experiments were instituted to study the introduction of air at hydroelectric power plants by hydro-turbine venting (Scott *et al.*, 1958; Wiley *et al.*, 1960). The dissolved oxygen increase at six power plants located on three rivers ranged from 0.35 to 1.51 mg/L, and oxygen absorption efficiencies ranged from 15 to 35% during the summer testing period.

Chemical precipitation and trickling filter treatment of cannery wastes were reported by Warrick *et al.* (1939, 1945) in connection with co-operative work undertaken by the Canners' Association and the State Board of Health.

The production of excessive and obnoxious growths of algae in the Madison lakes has plagued local residents for many years. An extensive investigation of this problem was instigated by the Governor's Committee in 1942, resulting in a two-year study of the fertilization of the waters (Sawyer *et al.*, 1945; see Table 2.10). Biological productivity was found to be a function of the loading of inorganic nitrogen on each lake, and the soluble phosphorus content was thought to become a limiting factor in the rate of biological activity and also in determining the nature of growth when its concentration fell below 0.01 mg/L (Lackey and Sawyer, 1945).

The Wisconsin Committee on Water Pollution (1949) also conducted studies on Lake Mendota concerning conditions contributing to the occurrence of aquatic nuisances. They found that fertilization of Lake Mendota takes place at a much lower rate than in the other Madison lakes, but that the bloom production is in proportion to the degree of fertilization. These studies resulted in the diversion of sewage effluent from the lake to Badfish Creek. Pre-diversion studies were made on the creek by Ernest (1957), and bi-weekly chemical and biological samples have been analyzed from the receiving stream (Mackenthun *et al.*, 1960). The diversion structure is unique in that it provides efficient hydraulic head to permit development of two cascade aeration stations for undiluted plant effluent. These step cascades, handling 18 to 20 million gallons dry weather effluent volume, add about 0.5 mg/L dissolved oxygen per foot of fall.

The subject of aquatic nuisances and their control has interested Wisconsin's citizens for many years (Wisconsin Comm. on Water Pollution, 1939). Chemical control methods have been outlined for the use of algicides and herbicides in the abatement program (Mackenthun, 1950, 1958, 1961). The impact of chemical usage upon the aquatic environment has also been of interest, and studies have been conducted on the biological effect of copper sulfate treatment (Nichols *et al.*, 1947; Mackenthun and Cooley, 1952).

Since 1956, four sewage stabilization ponds have been used in Wisconsin. A comprehensive 15-month physical, chemical, and biological investigation was made of these facilities to serve as a guide in recommending and approving future installations (Mackenthun and McNabb, 1959; McNabb, 1960a). The ice and snow cover on these ponds during the winter results in low algal and protozoan populations, a near absence of dissolved oxygen, and high concentrations of nitrogen and phosphorus.

Arising out of the stabilization pond studies, a method was developed by McNabb (1960b) for handling numerous phytoplankton samples, which involves a determination of the presence or absence of the various species in 30 eyepiece fields. This technique has been adapted to other studies, such as the determination of the relative efficiency of a commercial microstraining unit, installed at the Kenosha, Wisconsin, Water Department, in straining plankton from the Lake Michigan raw water supply (Mackenthun and Lueschow, 1961).

The development of irrigation disposal of wastes was found to be an economical method of waste treatment at suitable locations. A complete removal of effluent can be achieved by this method, which is an important factor when nutrients create aquatic nuisances (Schraufnagel, 1957, 1959).

Incidental reports have been made on Wisconsin's water use (H. E. Wirth, 1959), on a malarial survey along the upper Mississippi River (Poston and Brooke, 1942), on the flavor and aroma of fish taken from four freshwater sources (Baldwin et al., 1961), and on court decisions and water pollution control laws (Resh, 1956).

Chemical removal of nitrogen and phosphorus from sewage plant effluents

Laboratory studies showed that it was possible to remove approximately 95 to 99% of the soluble phosphates from the effluent of a sewage treatment plant (Katz, 1949). These data showed that an aluminum sulfate (alum) dosage of about 200 mg/L was required to remove the soluble phosphates effectively. In order to reduce the costs of soluble phosphate removal, however, a study was made by Lea et al. (1954) of coagulant recovery. Following the addition of alum, the aluminum hydroxide floc with its complexed phosphate was pumped from the bottom of a sedimentation basin to a recovery tank. Sodium hydroxide was added to the floc suspension until the pH of the solution was raised to approxima-

tely 11.9, which converted the insoluble aluminum hydroxide to soluble sodium aluminate and the phosphate to a soluble sodium phosphate. Addition of calcium chloride to the solution at this point resulted in the formation of insoluble tricalcium phosphate. The calcium phosphate is readily separated from the sodium aluminate solution by sedimentation and is a by-product of the process. The comparatively phosphate-free sodium aluminate is then re-used as a coagulant for removing more phosphate from the sewage effluent. Pilot plant studies confirmed the original laboratory studies.

Nesselson (1954) found that strong base anion exchangers, regenerated with common salt, performed satisfactorily for the removal of nitrate. Amberlite IR-120 has respective values of 29.7 filter-plant effluent has an exchange capacity of 19.9 to 26.8 kg/m³ as $CaCO_3$ and operates under an efficiency of 28 to 47.6 g of NaCl/g of anions removed. Nalcite SAR had respective values of 14.9 to 17.6 kg/m³ as $CaCO_3$ and 42 to 69.3 g NaCl/g of anions removed.

The removal of ammonia nitrogen by nuclear sulfonic cation exchangers was also investigated. Nalcite HCR has an exchange capacity of 36.6 to 50.3 kg/m³ as $CaCO_3$ in the treatment of activated sludge effluent and operates with an efficiency of 9.8 to 17.5 g NaCl/g cations removed. Amberlite IR-120 has respective values of 29.7 to 38.9 kg/mm³ as $CaCO_3$ and 9.1 to 18.2 g NaCl/g cations removed.

Kuhn (1956) carried out studies on air stripping in packed towers to remove ammonia nitrogen. In his studies the optimum pH for stripping was found to be 11.0. (Range of pH was 8.0 to 12.0.) The effect of air/liquid loading, expressed as m³ per min of air per liter of liquid per min was also studied at ratios of 0.29, 0.44, 0.64, 1.72, 3.34 m³/min per L/min. The respective ammonia nitrogen removals obtained at these ratios were 15.1, 28.5, 37.8, 67.0, and 78.7%.

Scientific areas

The long view for limnological research in Wisconsin took a favorable turn when the State Scientific Areas Committee was created by the Legislature of Wisconsin. There is now a provision through which important faunistic and floristic communities can be set aside, in perpetuity, for scientific research. Already, bogs, shorelines, and a cluster of five lakes have been assigned to this status. More aquatic areas, for instance different lake types, will be added as justification for them can be made.

A cooperative study of the Brule River was made by the University of Wisconsin and the Wisconsin Conservation Department. Recommendations were made for the preservation of the drainage basin and its return to the natural state. Considerable progress has been made by the Wisconsin Conservation Department in the acquisition of the Brule Bog and forest lands adjacent to the river. Several papers appeared in the Wisconsin Academy of Science between 1944 and 1945 which gave the basis for the recommendation. The following authors were contributors: E. A. Bean, W. S. Churchill, R. I. Evans, N. C. Fassett, A. D. Hasler, J. O'Donnell, E. Schneberger, J. T. Thomson.

Acknowledgments

The preparation of this section was made possible through the able editorial services of Clo Ann Loree and Ross M. Horrall. The materials used for the sections on bacteriology, meteorology, physiology of blue-green algae, paper-mill pollution, water pollution committee, applied fisheries, and chemical budget of Lake Mendota were supplied by Drs. W. B. Sarles, R. A. Bryson, G. C. Gerloff, W. Van Horn, K. M. Mackenthun, O. M. Brynildson, and G. A. Rohlich, respectively.

I would like to acknowledge the efforts of my graduate students whose works are cited here and who have enriched our knowledge of Wisconsin limnology by their devotion to research: J. D. Andrews, J. E. Bardach, C. Brynildson, R. C. Dugdale, J. R. Gammon, S. E. Jones, W. T. Helm, R. M. Horrall, R. L. Hunt, J. R. Hunter, K. R. John, W. E. Johnson, G. E. Likens, C. D. McNabb, D. C. McNaught, J. C. Neess, R. A. Ragotzkie, W. R. Schmitz, M. C. Sparr, R. G. Stross, H. O. Schwassmann, D. N. Swindale, R. D. Stone, J. J. Tibbles, T. J. Walker, E. L. Zicker.

References

ANDREWS, J. D., AND A. D. HASLER. 1942. Fluctuations in the animal populations of the littoral zone in Lake Mendota. Trans. Wisconsin Acad. Sci. Arts Lett., **34**: 137–148.

BALDWIN, R. E., D. H. STRONG, AND J. H. TORRIE. 1961. Flavor and aroma of fish taken from four fresh-water sources. Trans. Amer. Fish Soc., **90**: 175–180.

BARDACH, J. E. 1949. Contribution to the ecology of the yellow perch (*Perca flavescens* Mitchill) in Lake Mendota, Wisconsin. Ph.D. Thesis, Univ. Wisconsin.

BARTSCH, A. F. 1948. Biological aspects of stream pollution. Sewage Works J., **20**: 292–302.

BARTSCH, A. F., AND W. S. CHURCHILL. 1949. Biotic responses to stream pollution during artificial stream reaeration, p. 33–48. *In* Limnological aspects of water supply and waste disposal. Amer. Assoc. Advance. Sci.

BELTER, W. G., AND T. A. CALABRESA. 1949. The origins and quantities of algal fertilizers tributary to Lake Mendota (1949). M.S. Thesis, Univ. Wisconsin.

BLACKBURN, JOAN. 1959. A comparative study of two species of ictalurid fishes in a Wisconsin stream. M.S. Thesis, Marquette Univ.

BRYNILDSON, C., AND J. TRUOG. 1959. A progress report on the Wisconsin River catfish survey. Southern Area Invest. Memo. 252, Fish Mgmt. Div., Wisconsin Conserv. Dept., 11 p. (Mimeo.)

BRYNILDSON, C., AND J. TRUOG. 1960. The methods adopted to prevent winter-kill of fish in Cox Hollow Lake, Iowa County, during the winter of 1960. Southern Area Invest. Memo. 254, Fish Mgmt. Div., Wisconsin Conserv. Dept., 8 p. (Mimeo.)

BRYNILDSON, O. M. 1961*a*. Monthly (July) research report. Cold Water Group, Research and Plan. Div., Wisconsin Conserv. Dept., 2 p. (Ditto.)

———. 1961*b*. Trout lakes study. Annual progress report. Cold Water Group, Research and Plan. Div., Wisconsin Conserv. Dept., 21 p. (Ditto.)

BRYSON, R. A., AND W. W. BUNGE, JR. 1956. The "stress-drop" jet in Lake Mendota. Limnol. Oceanogr., **1**: 42–46.

BRYSON, R. A., AND P. M. KUHN. 1955. On the measurement of bottom stress in lakes. Trans. Amer. Geophys. Union, **36**: 612–614.

BRYSON, R. A., AND R. A. RAGOTZKIE. 1955. Rate of water replacement in a bay of Lake Mendota, Wisconsin. Amer. J. Sci., **253**: 533–539.

BRYSON, R. A., AND R. A. RAGOTZKIE. 1960. On internal waves in lakes. Limnol. Oceanogr., **5**: 397–408.

BRYSON, R. A., AND C. R. STEARNS. 1959. A mechanism for the mixing of the waters of Lake Huron and South Bay, Manitoulin Island. Limnol. Oceanogr., **4**: 246–251.

BRYSON, R. A., AND V. E. SUOMI. 1951. Midsummer renewal of oxygen within the hypolimnion. J. Marine Research, **10**: 263–269.

BUNGE, W. W., JR., AND R. A. BRYSON. 1956. Ice on Wisconsin lakes. Parts 1, 2, 3. Rept. Lakes and Streams Invest. Comm., Univ. Wisconsin, Nos. 13, 14, 15.

CHURCHILL, W. S. 1961. Five lakes studies. Monthly (Oct.) research report. Warm Water Group, Research and Plan. Div., Wisconsin Conserv. Dept., 2 p. (Mimeo.)

CLARKE, D. B., AND R. A. BRYSON. 1959. An investigation of the circulation over Second Point Bar, Lake Mendota. Limnol. Oceanogr., **4**: 140–144.

COLMER, A. R., AND ELIZABETH McCOY. 1944. Micromonospora in relation to some Wisconsin lakes and lake populations. Trans. Wisconsin Acad. Sci. Arts Lett., **35**: 187–220.

COLMER, A. R., AND ELIZABETH McCOY. 1950. Some

morphological and cultural studies on lake strains of micromonosporae. Trans. Wisconsin Acad. Sci. Arts Lett., **40**: 49–70.

DUGDALE, R. C. 1955. Studies in the ecology of the benthic Diptera of Lake Mendota. Ph.D. Thesis, Univ. Wisconsin.

DUTTON, J. A., AND R. A. BRYSON. 1962. Heat flux in Lake Mendota. Limnol. Oceanog., **7**: 80–97.

EMELITY, L. A., AND R. J. HANSON. 1948. A sanitary survey of the Yahara River. B.S. Thesis, Univ. Wisconsin.

EMELITY, L. A., AND R. J. HANSON. 1949. The origins and quantities of algal fertilizers tributary to Lake Mendota. M.S. Thesis, Univ. Wisconsin.

ERIKSON, DAGNEY. 1941. Studies on some lake-mud strains of *Micromonospora*. J. Bacteriol., **41**: 227–300.

ERNEST, L. A. 1957. A sanitary survey of the Badfish drainage ditch and creek. M.S. Thesis, Univ. Wisconsin.

FASSETT, N. C. 1930. The plants of some northeastern Wisconsin lakes. Trans. Wisconsin Acad. Sci. Arts Lett., **25**: 155–168.

FITZGERALD, G. P., AND F. K. SKOOG. 1954. Control of blue-green algae blooms with 2, 3-dichloronaphthoquinone. Sewage and Ind. Wastes, **26**: 1136–1140.

GAMMON, J. R. 1961. Contributions to the biology of the muskellunge. Ph.D. Thesis, Univ. Wisconsin.

GERLOFF, G. C., G. P. FITZGERALD, AND F. K. SKOOG. 1950a. The isolation, purification, and nutrient solution requirements of blue-green algae, p. 27–44. *In* The culturing of algae: A symposium. Charles F. Kettering Foundation. Yellow Springs, Ohio.

GERLOFF, C. C., G. P. FITZGERALD, AND F. K. SKOOG. 1950b. The isolation, purification, and culture of blue-green algae. Amer. J. Botan., **37**: 216–218.

GERLOFF, G. C., G. P. FITZGERALD, AND F. K. SKOOG. 1950c. The mineral nutrition of *Coccochloris peniocystis*. Amer. J. Botan., **37**: 835–840.

GERLOFF, G. C., G. P. FITZGERALD, AND F. K. SKOOG. 1952. The mineral nutrition of *Microcystis aeruginosa*. Amer. J. Botan., **39**: 26–32.

GERLOFF, G. C., AND F. K. SKOOG. 1954. Cell contents of nitrogen and phosphorus as a measure of their availability for growth of *Microcystis aeruginosa*. Ecology, **35**: 348–353.

GERLOFF, G. C., AND F. K. SKOOG. 1957a. Availability of iron and manganese in southern Wisconsin lakes for the growth of *Microcystis aeruginosa*. Ecology, **38**: 551–556.

GERLOFF, G. C., AND F. K. SKOOG. 1957b. Nitrogen as a limiting factor for the growth of *Microcystis aeruginosa* in southern Wisconsin lakes. Ecology, **38**: 556–561.

HAINES, DON, AND R. A. BRYSON. 1961. An empirical study of wind factor in Lake Mendota. Limnol. Oceanogr., **6**: 356–364.

HASLER, A. D. 1945. Observations on the winter perch population of Lake Mendota. Ecology, **26**: 90–94.

———. 1947. Eutrophication of lakes by domestic drainage. Ecology, **28**: 383–395.

———. 1957. Natural and artificially (air-ploughing)

induced movement of radioactive phosphorus from the muds of lakes. UNESCO Intern. Conf. Radio-isotopes, **4**: 658–675.

———. 1960. Homing orientation in migrating fishes. Ergeb. der Biol., **23**: 94–115.

HASLER, A. D., AND J. E. BARDACH. 1949. Daily migrations of perch in Lake Mendota, Wisconsin. J. Wildl. Mgmt., **13**: 40–51.

HASLER, A. D., O. M. BRYNILDSON, AND W. T. HELM. 1951. Improving conditions for fish in brown-water bog lakes by alkalization. J. Wildl. Mgmt., **15**: 347–352.

HASLER, A. D., R. M. HORRALL, W. J. WISBY, AND WOLFGANG BRAEMER. 1958. Sun orientation and homing in fishes. Limnol. Oceanogr., **3**: 353–361.

HASLER, A. D., AND S. E. JONES. 1949. Demonstration of the antagonistic action of large aquatic plants on algae and rotifers. Ecology, **30**: 359–364.

HASLER, A. D., AND R. K. MEYER. 1942. Respiratory responses of normal and castrated goldfish to teleost and mammalian hormones. J. Exptl. Zool., **91**: 391–404.

HASLER, A. D., R. K. MEYER, AND H. M. FIELD. 1939. Spawning induced prematurely in trout with the aid of pituitary glands of the carp. Endocrinology, **25**: 978–983.

HASLER, A. D., R. K. MEYER, AND H. M. FIELD. 1940. The use of hormones for the conservation of muskellunge, *Esox masquinongy immaculatus* Garrard. Copeia, 1940(1): 43–46.

HASLER, A. D., AND H. O. SCHWASSMANN. 1960. Sun orientation in fish at different latitudes. Cold Spring Harbor Symposium, **25**: 429–441.

HASLER, A. D., AND J. R. VILLEMONTE. 1953. Observations on the daily movements of fishes. Science, **118**: 321–322.

HASLER, A. D., AND L. V. WHITNEY. 1946. A combination photoelectric light meter and fish-detector. J. Wildl. Mgmt., **19**: 175–177.

HASLER, A. D., AND W. J. WISBY. 1951. Discrimination of stream odors by fishes and its relation to parent stream behavior. Amer. Nat., **85**: 223–238.

HELM, W. T. 1958. Some notes on the ecology of panfish in Lake Wingra with special reference to the yellow bass. Ph.D. Thesis, Univ. Wisconsin.

HOLM-HANSEN, O., G. C. GERLOFF, AND F. K. SKOOG. 1954. Cobalt as an essential element for blue-green algae. Physiol. Plant., **7**: 665–675.

HORRALL, R. M. 1961. A comparative study of two spawning populations of the white bass, *Roccus chrysops* (Rafinesque), in Lake Mendota, Wisconsin, with special reference to homing behavior. Ph.D. Thesis, Univ. Wisconsin.

HUNT, R. L. 1959. The role of insects of the surface-drift in the diet of Brule River trout. M.S. Thesis, Univ. Wisconsin.

———. 1961. Lawrence Creek studies. Monthly (Sept.) research report. Cold Water Group, Research and Plan Div., Wisconsin Conserv. Dept., 2 p. (Ditto.)

HUNTER, J. R. 1962. The utilization of the nests of *Lepomis cyanellus* by *Notropis umbratilis*. Ph.D. Thesis, Univ. Wisconsin.

JANNASCH, H. W. 1960. Denitrification as influenced by photosynthetic oxygen production. J. Gen. Microbiol., **23**: 55–63.

JOHN, K. R., AND A. D. HASLER. 1956. Observations on some factors affecting the hatching of eggs and the survival of young shallow-water cisco, *Leucichthys artedi* Le Sueur. Limnol. Oceanogr., **1**: 176–194.

JOHNSON, L. D. 1958. Pond culture of muskellunge in Wisconsin. Wisconsin Conserv. Dept., Tech. Bull. 17, 58 p.

JOHNSON, W. E., AND A. D. HASLER. 1954. Rainbow trout production in dystrophic lakes. J. Wildl. Mgmt., **18**: 113–134.

KANESHIGE, H. M. 1952. Chemical analysis of the bottom muds of Lake Mendota. M.S. Thesis, Univ. Wisconsin.

KATZ, W. J. 1949. The chemical removal of phosphates from sewage effluent. M.S. Thesis, Univ. Wisconsin.

KUHN, P. A. 1956. Removal of ammonia nitrogen from sewage effluent. M.S. Thesis, Univ. Wisconsin.

LACKEY, J. B., AND C. N. SAWYER. 1945. Plankton productivity of certain southeastern Wisconsin lakes as related to fertilization. Sewage Works J., **17**: 573–585.

LATHBURY, ALISON, AND R. A. BRYSON. 1958. Studies of the physiographic features of Lake Mendota. I. Sublacustrine gullies. (Unpublished.)

LATHBURY, ALISON, R. A. BRYSON, AND BERNHARD LETTAU. 1960. Some observations of currents in the hypolimnion of Lake Mendota. Limnol. Oceanogr., **5**: 409–413.

LEA, W. L., G. A. ROHLICH, AND W. J. KATZ. 1954. Removal of phosphates from treated sewage. Sewage and Ind. Wastes, **26**: 261–275.

LEVIHN, P. 1951. A sanitary survey of the Yahara River and bottom muds of Lake Mendota. M.S. Thesis, Univ. Wisconsin.

LIKENS, G. E., AND A. D. HASLER. 1960. Movement of radiosodium in a chemically stratified lake. Science, **131**: 1676–1677.

LIKENS, G. E., AND A. D. HASLER. 1962a. Biological and physical transport of radionuclides in stratified lakes. (In press.)

LIKENS, G. E., AND A. D. HASLER. 1926b. Movements of radiosodium (Na^{24}) within an ice-covered lake. Limnol. Oceanogr., **7**: 48–56.

LUECK, B. F., A. J. WILEY, R. H. SCOTT, AND T. F. WISNIEWSKI. 1957. Determination of stream purification capacity. Sewage and Ind. Wastes, **29**: 1054–1065. Also presented at the 12th Industrial Waste Conf., Purdue Univ., Lafayette, Indiana, May 13–15, 1957.

MCCASKEY, A. E., JR. 1955. Hydrological characteristics of Lake Mendota drainage basin. Ph.D. Thesis, Univ. Wisconsin.

MCNABB, C. D. 1960a. Enumeration of freshwater phytoplankton concentrated on the membrane filter. Limnol. Oceanogr., **5**: 57–61.

———. 1960b. II. A study of the phytoplankton and photosynthesis in sewage oxidation ponds in Wisconsin. Ph.D. Thesis, Univ. Wisconsin.

MCNAUGHT, D. C., AND A. D. HASLER. 1961. Surface schooling and feeding in the whitebass, *Roccus chrysops* Rafinesque, in Lake Mendota. Limnol. Oceanogr., **6**: 53–60.

MCNAUGHT, D. C., AND A. D. HASLER. The rate of movement of *Daphnia* in relation to changes in light intensity. (MS.)

MACKENTHUN, K. M. 1950. Aquatic weed control with sodium arsenite. Sewage and Ind. Wastes, **22**: 1062–1067.

———. 1952. Selected review of the literature on toxic materials affecting biological life in streams and sewage treatment processes. Wisconsin Comm. on Water Pollution, Madison, Wis., 35 p. (Mimeo.)

———. 1958. Chemical control of aquatic nuisances. Wisconsin Comm. on Water Pollution, Madison, Wis., 64 p.

———. 1961. The practical use of present algicides and modern trends toward new ones. Trans. 1960 Seminar on Algae & Metropol. Wastes, R. A. Taft Sanit. Engr. Center, Cincinnati, Ohio, Sec, TR W61-3: 148–154.

MACKENTHUN, K. M., AND H. COOLEY. 1952. The biological effect of copper sulfate treatment on lake ecology. Trans. Wisconsin Acad. Sci. Arts Lett., **41**: 177–187.

MACKENTHUN, K. M., AND L. A. LUESCHOW. 1961. Biological investigations of the city of Kenosha's municipal water micro-straining operation. Wisconsin Sect. Amer. Water Works Assoc. (Mimeo.)

MACKENTHUN, K. M., L. A. LUESCHOW, AND C. D. McNABB. 1960. A study of the effects of diverting the effluent from sewage treatment upon the receiving stream. Trans. Wisconsin Acad. Sci. Arts Lett., **49**: 51–72.

MACKENTHUN, K. M., AND C. D. McNABB. 1959. Sewage stabilization ponds in Wisconsin. Wisconsin Comm. on Water Pollution, Madison, Wis., Bull. No. WP105, 52 p.

MEIEROTTO, R. R. 1960. Analysis of diurnal periodicity in the black bullhead, *Ictalurus melas* (Rafinesque). M.S. Thesis, Marquette Univ.

MRAZ, D. F., AND A. R. ENSIGN. 1960. Largemouth bass studies in Southern Wisconsin. Evaluation of liberalized regulations and bass-carp inter-relationships. Tech. Bull., Fish Mgmt. Div., Wisconsin Conserv. Dept.

MURRAY, R. C. 1956. Recent sediments of three Wisconsin lakes. Bull. Geol. Soc. Amer., **67**: 883–910.

NEESS, J. C. 1949. A contribution to aquatic population dynamics. Ph.D. Thesis, Univ. Wisconsin.

NEESS, J. C., W. T. HELM, AND C. W. THREINEN. 1957. Some vital statistics in a heavily exploited population of carp. J. Wildl. Mgmt., **21**: 279–292.

NESSELSON, E. J. 1954. Removal of inorganic nitrogen from sewage effluent. Ph.D. Thesis, Univ. Wisconsin.

NICHOLS, M. S., T. HENKEL, AND D. McNALL. 1947. Copper in lake muds from lakes of the Madison area. Trans. Wisconsin Acad. Sci. Arts Lett., **38**: 333–350.

PEARSE, A. S., AND HENRIETTA ACHTENBERG. 1920. Habits of yellow perch in Wisconsin lakes. Bull. U.S. Bur. Fish., **36**: 297–362.

PLANTENBURG, SR. M. D. 1961. Factors influencing digestion in the black bullhead, *Ictalurus melas* (Rafinesque). M.S. Thesis, Marquette Univ.

POFF, R. J. 1961. Ionic composition of Wisconsin lake waters. Fish Mgmt. Div., Wisconsin Conserv. Dept. Misc. Rept. 4, 20 p. (Mimeo.)

POSTON, H. W., AND M. M. BROOKE. 1942. Report on malaria survey along the upper Mississippi River. Board of State Health Commissioners, Upper Mississippi River Basin (obtainable at State Board of Health, Madison, Wis.), 80 p.

PRIEGEL, G. R. 1960. Winnebago studies. Annual progress report. Research and Plan. Div., Wisconsin Conserv. Dept., 56 p. (Mimeo.)

———. 1961. Winnebago studies. Monthly (May) research report. Warm Water Group, Research and Plan. Div., Wisconsin Conserv. Dept., 6 p. (Mimeo.)

RAGOTZKIE, R. A., AND R. A. BRYSON. 1953. Correlation of currents with the distribution of adult *Daphnia* in Lake Mendota. J. Marine Research, 12: 157–172.

RAMASWANI, L. S., AND A. D. HASLER. 1955. Hormones and secondary sex characters in the minnow, *Hyborhynchus*. Physiol. Zool., 28: 62–68.

RESH, W. H. 1956. Court decisions and statutory provisions in water pollution control law. Sewage and Ind. Wastes, 28: 211–218.

RICKER, W. E. 1938. On adequate quantitative sampling of the pelagic net plankton of a lake. J. Fish. Research Board Canada, 4: 19–32.

SAWYER, C. N., J. B. LACKEY, AND R. T. LENZ. 1945. An investigation of the odor nuisance occurring in the Madison lakes, particularly Monona, Waubesa, and Kegonsa, from July 1942 to July 1944. Report on Governor's Committee, Madison, Wis., 2 v. (Mimeo.)

SCHMITZ, W. R. 1958. Artificially induced circulation in thermally stratified lakes. Ph.D. Thesis, Univ. Wisconsin.

SCHMITZ, W. R., AND A. D. HASLER. 1958. Artificially induced circulation of lakes by means of compressed air. Science, 128: 1088–1089.

SCHNEIDER, HANS, AND A. D. HASLER. 1960. Laute und Lauterzeugung beim Süsswassertrommler *Aplodinotus grunniens* Rafinesque (Sciaenidae, Pisces). Z. vergleich. Physiol., 43: 499–517.

SCHRAUFNAGEL, F. H. 1957. Dairy waste disposal by ridge and furrow irrigation. Proc. 12th Ind. Waste Conf., Purdue Univ., Lafayette, Indiana: 28–49.

———. 1959. Disposal of industrial wastes by irrigation. Pub. Health Repts., 74: 133–140.

SCOTT, JOHN, AND R. A. RAGOTZKIE. 1962. The heat budget of an ice covered inland lake. Tech. Report No. 6, Dept. Meterology, Univ. Wisconsin.

SCOTT, R. H., T. F. WISNIEWSKI, B. F. LUECK, AND A. J. WILEY. 1958. Aeration of stream flow at power turbines. Sewage and Ind. Wastes, 30: 1496–1505. Also presented at the 13th Ind. Waste Conf., Purdue Univ., Lafayette, Indiana, May 5–7, 1958.

SHULMAN, MARK, AND R. A. BRYSON. 1961. The vertical variation of wind driven currents in Lake Mendota. Limnol. Oceanogr., 6: 347–355.

SPARR, M. C. 1958. The effect of chemical and physical treatments upon light penetration and phosphorus content of bog waters. M.S. Thesis, Univ. Wisconsin.

STONE, R. D. 1961. Preliminary investigations of winter activity and movements of the yellow perch, *Perca flavescens* (Mitchill), in Lake Mendota, Wisconsin. M.S. Thesis, Univ. Wisconsin.

STROSS, R. G., AND A. D. HASLER. 1960. Some lime-induced changes in lake metabolism. Limnol. Oceanogr., 4: 265–272.

STROSS, R. G., J. C. NEESS, AND A. D. HASLER. 1961. Turnover time and production of the planktonic crustacea in limed and reference portion of a bog lake. Ecology, 42: 237–245.

SUOMI, V. E., AND R. A. BRYSON. 1952. The circulation of Lake Mendota. Trans. Amer. Geophys. Union, 33: 707–712.

SWINDALE, D. N., AND J. T. CURTIS. 1957. Phytosociology of the large submerged plants in Wisconsin lakes. Ecology, 38: 397–407.

TIBBLES, J. J. G. 1956. A study of the movements and depth distribution of the pelagic fishes in Lake Mendota. Ph.D. Thesis, Univ. Wisconsin.

WALKER, T. J., AND A. D. HASLER. 1949. Olfactory discrimination of aquatic plants by the bluntnose minnow *Hyborhynchus notatus* (Rafinesque). Physiol. Zool., 22: 45–63.

WARRICK, L. F., F. J. MCKEE, H. E. WIRTH, AND N. H. SANBORN. 1939. Methods of treating cannery wastes. Wisconsin State Board of Health and Comm. on Water Pollution, Madison, Wis., 91 p.

WARRICK, L. F., T. F. WISNIEWSKI, AND N. H. SANBORN. 1945. Cannery waste disposal lagoons. Wisconsin State Board of Health and Comm. on Water Pollution, Madison, Wis., 48 p.

WHITE, R. J. 1961. Habitat evaluation studies. Annual progress report. Research and Plan. Div., Wisconsin Conserv. Dept., 76 p. (Mimeo.)

WILEY, A. J., B. F. LUECK, R. H. SCOTT, AND T. F. WISNIEWSKI. 1957. Cooperative state-industry stream studies—lower Fox River, Wisconsin. Sewage and Ind. Wastes, 29: 76–87.

WILEY, A. J., B. F. LUECK, R. H. SCOTT, AND T. F. WISNIEWSKI. 1960. Commercial scale operation of turbine aeration on Wisconsin rivers. J. Water Pollution Control Federation, 32: 186–194. Also presented at the 14th Ind. Waste Conf., Purdue Univ., Lafayette, Indiana, May 5–7, 1959.

WILEY, A. J., L. PARKINSON, H. W. GEHM, T. F. WISNIEWSKI, AND A. F. BARTSCH. 1947. River reaeration. Paper Trade J., 124(12): 123–128.

WIRTH, H. E. 1959. Water use in Wisconsin. M.S. Thesis, Univ. Wisconsin.

WIRTH, T. L., AND G. R. PRIEGEL. 1961. Movement of tagged sturgeon from Lake Winnebago. Warm Water Group files. Research and Plan. Div., Wisconsin Conserv. Dept.

WISBY, W. J., AND A. D. HASLER. 1954. Effect of olfactory occlusion on migrating Silver Salmon *O. kisutch*). J. Fish. Research Board Canada, 11: 472–478.

WISCONSIN COMMITTEE ON WATER POLLUTION. 1939. Chemical treatment of lakes and streams with special reference to the origin and control of swimmers' itch. 19 p. (Mimeo.)

———. 1949. Report on Lake Mendota studies, 1945–47, p. 1–18. (Mimeo.)

WISNIEWSKI, T. F. 1958. Algae and their effects on dissolved oxygen and biochemical oxygen demand. R. A. Taft Sanit. Engr. Center, Cincinnati, Ohio. Tech Rept. W58–2: 157–176.

ZAGALLO, A. C. 1953. Oxidative metabolism of some bacteria and blue-green algae, alone and in association. Agronomia lusitana, 15: 315–345.

ZICKER, E. L., K. C. BERGER, AND A. D. HASLER. 1956. Phosphorus release from bog lake muds. Limnol. Oceanogr., 1: 296–303.

3 | *David C. Chandler*

Michigan

Aquatic resources

The state of Michigan possesses an abundance and great diversity of fresh waters. Within its boundaries of 58,216 mi² are more than 11,000 lakes and 43 river systems. In addition the state is almost surrounded by four of the Great Lakes—Superior, Michigan, Huron, and Erie—giving it 3,121 mi of shoreline.

These inland waters are distributed widely throughout the state in relation to geological features resulting from glaciation. Retreat of the last glacier, the Wisconsin, distributed drift in various forms and depths throughout the state and also exposed bedrock in certain areas. The relative density of lakes by counties is shown in Figure 3.1, and the general features of the surface geology are shown in Figure 3.2. Comparison of these two figures shows that few lakes occur

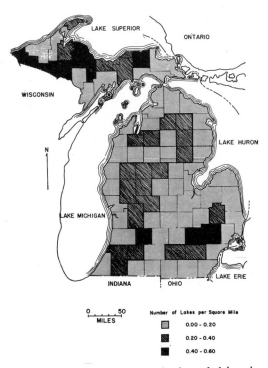

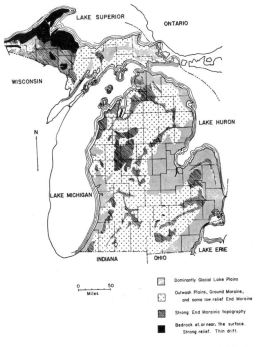

Fig. 3.1.—Michigan relative density of lakes by county.

Fig. 3.2.—Michigan generalized slope and relief. Modified from Veatch, 1953.

Fig. 3.3.—Michigan principal river systems.

in the glacial lake plains, but they are numerous in the outwash plains, morainic formation, and bedrock outcrops. Except for a few small streams in the extreme southern part of the state and in the western part of the Upper Peninsula, all waters drain directly into the Great Lakes system (Fig. 3.3).

The total area of standing water in the state of Michigan is 728,311 acres (1,138 mi^2), representing about 2% of the state's surface. Irregular distribution of the 11,037 lakes (Fig. 3.1) results in lake districts or concentrations where land and water surfaces are nearly equal. These lakes vary in area from a fraction of an acre to 20,000 acres. The maximum depth is 285 ft, with fewer than 12 lakes exceeding 100 ft. Brown (1944) states: "Approximately one-half of the lakes in Michigan are less than 10 acres in surface area, and only 19 lakes have more than 5,000 acres, while the average size for all lakes is about 66 acres. Of the 11,037 lakes in the entire state, which are less than 200 acres in area, 10,403 are natural and 182 artificial. There are 411 natural and 41 artificial lakes which have over 200 acres." The number of artificial lakes has increased since Brown's report, but it probably does not exceed 400.

Limnologically the 11,037 lakes of the state vary widely, ranging in characteristics from late

oligotrophy to dystrophy. Lakes in the western, and particularly in the southwestern, part of the Upper Peninsula are very similar to the small, soft-water seepage lakes of northeastern Wisconsin (Birge and Juday, 1911). The central part of the Upper Peninsula has many small seepage lakes, but like the eastern part it also has numerous drainage lakes of medium size with hard waters. In the Lower Peninsula most of the lakes are less than 200 acres in area, possessing distinct drainage and hard waters. Scattered throughout the Lower Peninsula are small areas of seepage lakes showing various stages of bog succession. These are small and shallow, with colored, acid waters, surrounded by sphagnum and other characteristic bog vegetation. Marl formation is common in other lakes, ranging in character from slight encrustations on exposed surfaces and fine particles mixed in the organic sediments to heavy encrustation in addition to depositions in the form of flocculates and concretions. This latter condition is particularly characteristic of the lakes in the Huron River system near Ann Arbor. Hooper's (1956) study of the chemical and morphometric characteristics of lakes in southern Michigan indicates that marl deposits begin to influence the basin shape when the total alkalinity exceeds a value of about 105 ppm. He suggests that this alkalinity value is a natural point for separating categories of Michigan lakes classified on the basis of hardness. In addition to these more common types of lakes, two unusual groups are found in the Lower Peninsula, one close to the Lake Michigan shore in the northwestern part of the state and the other forming a chain in the Cheboygan River system in the extreme north-central part of the Lower Peninsula (Fig. 3.3).

Typical of the first group is Torch Lake, with a maximum depth of 285 ft, an area of 18,770 acres, and a long, narrow, steep-sided basin. Torch and several similar lakes—Elk, Crystal, Leelanau, etc.—were once a part of Lake Michigan, having been isolated by great bars which developed in either the Algonquin or Nipissing times (Scott, 1921). Their appearance and general characteristics resemble the famous "Finger Lakes" of central New York. Their waters are cold, transparent, and hard, and their faunas resemble that of the Great Lakes, with *Mysis relicta, Pontoporeia affinis,* and *Limnocalanus macrurus* being common.

The second group of unusual lakes forms an

"inland waterway" of approximately 50 mi extending from Cheboygan on Lake Huron to within 3 mi of Little Traverse Bay of Lake Michigan. Within this group of six or seven lakes are three, Black, Mullet, and Burt, which have areas exceeding 10,000 acres. The irregular basins of this group lie in a glaciated depression, the slopes of which are conspicuously marked by shorelines of former lake levels higher than the present. Limnologically these lakes are similar, being eutrophic, marl forming, and less than 60 ft in depth, except for a small depression in Mullet with a depth of 148 ft.

The 43 principal river systems (Fig. 3.3), comprising about 36,000 mi including the main streams and tributaries, are distributed in the state in accordance with the surface geology. Draining into Saginaw Bay is the Saginaw River, the largest river in the state, with a drainage area of approximately 6,500 mi². The next three in order of size are Grand (5,514 mi²), St. Joseph (3,132 mi²), and Muskegon (2,611 mi²), all draining into Lake Michigan (Brown, 1944). These larger rivers drain the agricultural lands of the state and are of low gradient.

The northern part of the Lower Peninsula and the entire Upper Peninsula are heavily forested, and the soils are sandy. Here the rivers are of higher gradient and clearer unless colored by drainage from bog areas. Qualitative characteristics of individual river systems, including their hydrology, have been described by McNamee (1930).

During the past 25 years the Institute for Fisheries Research of the Fish Division of the Michigan Department of Conservation has mapped approximately 2,400 inland lakes as part of their fisheries program. Some of these maps are blue-line prints showing lake outline, bottom contours, weedbeds, etc.; others are simple outline maps showing depth contours. The index and price list of these maps and a catalog of more than 300 publications are available at the institute. Also, the institute has made limnological surveys or inventories of many of the lakes and streams in the state and has on file the pertinent physical, chemical, and biological data.

Topography of the state ranges from level or gently rolling in the eastern section of the Upper Peninsula and the southern part of the Lower Peninsula to hilly and rough terrain in the western part of the Upper Peninsula and the north-central part of the Lower Peninsula. Elevation varies from 600 to 2,000 ft above sea level, with the highest point in the western Upper Peninsula. The southern part of the Lower Peninsula has a comparatively flat terrain, with an average elevation of about 800 ft. In some parts of the Lower Peninsula, a portion of the land area is tributary to undrained depressions.

The Great Lakes have a stabilizing effect on temperatures in the state, and because of the prevailing westerly winds, winters are milder and summers cooler than at the same latitudes in Wisconsin and Minnesota (Eichmeier, 1959). A comparison of January mean temperatures at points of like latitude shows Lansing's temperature, 23.8° F, Madison's (Wisconsin) 19.3° F. In July the reverse is true, with Lansing's mean temperature 71.1° F, Madison's 73.1° F. Much cloudiness prevails during late fall and winter in the entire state, and for the year the numbers of cloudy and sunny days are about equal.

Precipitation is well distributed throughout the year, with the average annual rate ranging from 30 to 36 in. depending on location within the state. Snowfall variation over the state is great, ranging from an annual total of 160 in. in the northwestern portion of the Upper Peninsula to less than 30 in. in the extreme southeast. Droughts occur occasionally but usually are not of long duration. Flood frequency is relatively low, with a greater number occurring in late winter or early spring as a result of sudden warming and rain combined with snowmelt.

Prevailing winds are from the southwest over the southern part of the state and westerly over northern sections. Damaging or dangerous storms are few, but tornadoes, windstorms, and blizzards do occur occasionally.

According to Darlington (1945), two forest belts or climax formations occur in Michigan— the Deciduous Forest and the Northeastern Conifer Forest. The former occupies the southern half of the Lower Peninsula, while the Upper Peninsula lies entirely within the latter. Mixtures of the two formations occur in both the northern and southern parts of the state. The northern half of the Lower Peninsula is usually considered to be a tension zone in which the northernmost parts of the deciduous climax forest formation and the southern edge of the northeastern evergreen forest formation overlap. The major deciduous area in the Lower Peninsula lies south of latitude 43°, a line extending west of the southern tip of Lake Huron. This is often referred to as the "hardwood country," in contrast to the "softwood lands" in the northern part of the state.

Teaching and research, period 1895–1930

State agencies

Limnology in Michigan did not become a recognized discipline or a term in common usage until about 1920. Paul S. Welch offered the first course in limnology in the state in 1923 at the University of Michigan Biological Station, and in 1928 he introduced a similar course on the campus at Ann Arbor. Prior to 1920, the pursuit of natural history and ecology, as expressed in teaching, research, and surveys, laid the ground work from which limnology of the state took form.

Among the early contributors to the development of limnology, Jacob E. Reighard (Fig. 3.4) deserves special consideration. He joined the faculty of the University of Michigan in 1886, served as chairman of the Department of Zoology from 1892 to 1925, and worked closely with the Michigan Fish Commission (State Board of Fish Commissioners). His broad interests were expressed by specific researches in meteorology, anatomy, histology, embryology, fish behavior,

Fig. 3.4.—Jacob E. Reighard. 1861–1942.

underwater photography, and plankton. He is known best, probably, for his work in fish behavior, especially breeding behavior, coloration and color vision, and habitat selection. This serious interest in fish and fisheries was maintained over a decade after his retirement in 1927. His last publication (Reighard, 1942) appeared a few months after his death.

Reighard's major study of fisheries problems was undertaken in 1893, when he headed an extensive survey of Lake St. Clair for the Fish Commission, prompted by a decrease in the commercial catch of whitefish. This became a model study of a lake, stimulating state and federal agencies to establish lake and stream surveys emphasizing the measurement of environmental factors affecting fish and other aquatic organisms. Although this study was directed at a practical fishery problem, the manner in which Reighard conducted it clearly demonstrated his recognition of a lake as an ecosystem. In the introductory pages to his report on Lake St. Clair, Reighard (1894) gives the following statement of purpose:

To study carefully and in the broadest possible way the life of the lake. After examining the physical characteristics of the lake, such as the color, transparency and chemistry of the water, a study of this sort should include a determination of the kinds of animals and plants in the lake. Every species should be sought out, carefully described and figured, and a specimen of it preserved. Then the habits of each species should be known, its habitat, its food, its enemies and its parasites. The numbers of animals and plants of each species in a given volume of water should be determined and the variations in these numbers in different parts of the lake and at different seasons of the year. Such a collection of data would form a complete picture of the biology of the lake.

If this study had been done thirty years later, it probably would have borne the title "A limnological study of Lake St. Clair." The study was extended the following year, 1894, to Lake Michigan, with the base of operation at Charlevoix. The roster of personnel for these studies reads like a "Who's Who" in aquatic biology at the turn of the century: J. E. Reighard, H. B. Ward, Frank Smith, Charles Kofoid, E. A. Birge, C. Dwight Marsh, H. S. Jennings, etc.

From these studies on Lakes St. Clair and Michigan came two classical scientific reports (Reighard, 1894; Ward, 1896) dealing with the basic problems of fisheries and specific treatment of the identification and biology of the predominant plants and animals. These studies represented the first serious investigation of the Great Lakes and established a philosophy and design of lake survey that was to be followed in the state for the next several decades. Reighard continued his ecological investigation of lakes in the state (Reighard, 1913, 1929), always emphasizing behavior of organisms and their relation to environmental factors. His thinking about ecological matters is indicated in the following quotation from a paper he presented at a symposium on the trends of ecology (Reighard, 1918): "That behavior, rather than structure determines habitat; that animals select their habitats by one method or another; that an understanding of habitat selection requires a knowledge of physiological life histories; that animal communities result from habitat selection; that animals of a given community show similar or equivalent behavior to some dominant factor of the habitat; that communities succeed one another; these are some of the principles of the newer ecology."

Another lake survey, basically limnological in character, was carried out on Walnut Lake by Thomas L. Hankinson (1908). This study was supported by the Michigan Board of Geological Survey to learn as much as possible about the environmental conditions in a lake supporting a large population of whitefish, with the hope that the information would furnish a basis for establishing a policy for stocking Michigan lakes with whitefish. It is of interest to note that Jacob Reighard was an advisor on the board and that he helped outline the plan of study and supervised portions of it. Hankinson viewed the lake and its drainage basin as a unit. The physiography and geology of the area were treated in considerable detail, and the lake was divided into habitat types, each being studied carefully in respect to its physical, chemical, and biological characteristics. This study stands as a classic among lake surveys and must be considered an early form of limnological study in the state. Associated with this survey as investigators were specialists from various parts of the country, such as Reighard, University of Michigan; C. C. Adams, University of Chicago; G. N. Caulkins, Columbia University; E. A. Birge, University of Wisconsin; J. G. Needham and O. A. Johannsen, Cornell University; and R. E. Richardson, University of Illinois.

Fisheries and limnological activities conducted by the state of Michigan prior to 1924 were under the supervision of the Michigan Fish Commission, established in 1870. Its programs were either of a general survey nature or specifically directed toward practical problems of fish culture and management. The personnel carrying out these activities were often men who were not scientifically trained but who possessed direct knowledge of practical problems. Supplementing this year-round personnel were men with scientific training employed for the summer months. In 1924, when a Department of Conservation was established, the work of the state became scientifically oriented, with more specific goals and a greater emphasis on conservation. This change was effected by the energetic championing of the new approach by such men as A. G. Ruthven, P. S. Lovejoy, and others; by deforestation and the destruction of wildlife; and by results accomplished through scientific investigations.

The Conservation Department, in developing its new fish program, relied heavily upon the summer employment of university men to conduct special studies throughout the state. At first the studies were directed at isolated problems contributing very little to an overall program. By 1926 the work assumed more or less the character of a lake and stream survey, conducted cooperatively with the Michigan Land Economic Survey and employing two trained biologists, Jan Metzelaar and T. H. Langlois, the year around. For the next few years these biologists and Carl L. Hubbs, a consultant from the university, working with the trout hatchery crews, carried out the fish program for the state (Hubbs and Metzelaar, 1926).

University of Michigan

Concurrent with the state's interest in and financial support of biological surveys in the early 1900's, directed toward solution of fishery problems, was the development of a research and teaching program in natural history and ecology at the University of Michigan. The close cooperation between the activities of the state agencies and those of the University of Michigan probably should be regarded as a single effort in the development of a program in natural history and ecology. Many of the same individuals worked in both the state and university programs; the most conspicuous example was Jacob Reighard.

Reighard, as chairman of the Department of Zoology at the University of Michigan, must be credited with the development of a strong curriculum in natural history and ecology that dominated the department long after his retirement in 1927. Limnology as it exists in the department today stemmed from a series of courses and researches initiated at the turn of the century by Reighard and his staff. According to Shull (1944), the first formal course given in the department in ecology and natural history was that offered by Charles C. Adams in 1903. It was taken over in 1909 by Alexander G. Ruthven, and its subject matter was partly included in his course in zoogeography. Freshwater biology was first given by Arthur S. Pearse in 1908; in 1911 it was given by A. Franklin Shull, and it was finally incorporated in Reighard's "Natural History of Invertebrates" in 1916. Reighard's course became a part of Frank Blanchard's course, "Natural History of Animals," in 1925, but a year later "Freshwater Biology" was again made a separate course. It disappeared from the curriculum in 1928 when Paul S. Welch introduced his course in limnology, which he taught until his retirement in 1952.

Parallel with the development of a curriculum in natural history and ecology on the Ann Arbor campus was the summer program at the University of Michigan Biological Station at Douglas Lake in northern Michigan. Again, Jacob Reighard spearheaded this effort, recommending to the Board of Regents in 1900 that a biological station be established to promote the study of plants and animals in their natural habitats. The station was established in 1909 (LaRue, 1944) on Douglas Lake, and Reighard served as Director from 1909 to 1914. He served only three years in residence, but he was assisted by the following Acting Directors: A. S. Pearse in 1910 and H. A. Gleason in 1913 and 1914. In 1915 Gleason was made Director, followed by Otto C. Glasser in 1916, and George R. LaRue in 1917. LaRue served until 1940, followed by A. H. Stockard, who has been Director since that time.

The Biological Station, throughout its entire existence, has had a tremendous impact on the development of natural history and ecology, as well as limnology, in the state. *Proceedings of the Semicentennial Celebration,* June 1959, of the founding of the station gives an excellent account of its early years, growth of physical facilities, teaching and research program, and a bibliography of approximately 900 papers resulting from research at the station.

Paul S. Welch joined the Biological Station staff in the summer of 1918, and it was at this time that he seriously entered the field of limnology. His previous research interest in aquatic insects, although continued for several years, was eventually replaced by limnological studies. Until 1928, publications based on research at the Biological Station by Welch and his graduate students dealt with aquatic insects. Welch's first truly limnological paper, which appeared in 1927, dealt with the description of the physicochemical characteristics of Douglas Lake. The course in limnology introduced by Welch in 1923 dealt with the broad aspects of aquatic ecology, insects being only a small part. Presenting this course, in the absence of a textbook or organized reference sources, made him realize the urgent need of a textbook, and he proceeded to write one. The book (Welch, 1935) drew heavily upon data collected by him and his students on Douglas Lake and adjacent waters.

The great number and diversity of lakes and streams on the station's 8,900 acres and in the immediate vicinity make this an ideal situation for limnological work (Fig. 3.5). Douglas Lake has an area of 5.83 mi^2 and a maximum depth of 89 ft, possesses seven distinct depressions, is eutrophic, and has hard but slightly colored water. It is a productive lake with dense populations of benthic organisms on its diversified shoals and profundal zones; its irregular shoreline forms bays with an abundance of higher aquatic plants; and the large expanse of open waters supports a heavy plankton population with marked seasonal changes in species and numbers (Welch, 1927; Welch and Eggleton, 1932). This lake is typical of many in the northern part of the state; therefore, Welch, in writing his textbook, used data from Douglas Lake to illustrate many principles. The wealth of information collected from this body of water by Welch and his students is exceeded probably only by that obtained by Birge and Juday from Lake Mendota, Wisconsin.

The biological characteristics of the region immediately surrounding the station are given in the following description prepared by Alfred H. Stockard, Director, for the Summer Announcement of 1960:

Situated in the transition zone between coniferous forests to the north and deciduous forests to the south, the Station is surrounded by vegetation characteristic of both regions. Near it are swamps, bogs, lowlands, rich uplands, sandy uplands, and dunes, supporting both virgin and second-growth stands of characteristic vegetation. A remarkable system of lakes, streams, and bogs surrounds the Station, and

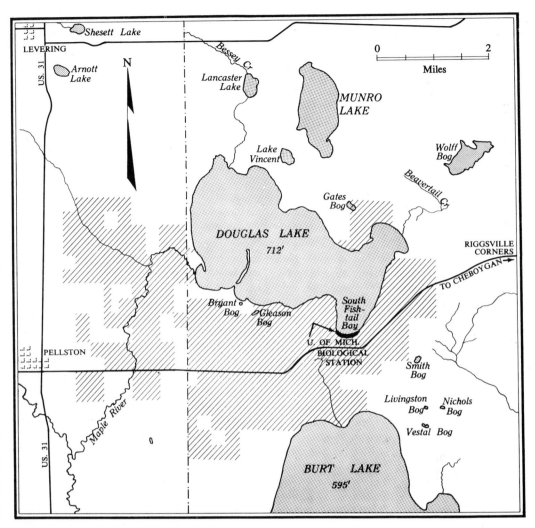

Fig. 3.5.—The University of Michigan Biological Station area. Prepared by the University of Wisconsin Cartographic Laboratory.

the upper three Great Lakes are within easy reach. The diversified topography, soil, water, and vegetation offer unusual variety of habitat and afford excellent opportunity for teaching and research in biology.

The region supports a wealth of plant species in all the major groups. More than 100 families, 400 genera, and 1,000 species of flowering plants, and a wide diversity of lower vascular plants, including more than 85 species, varieties, and hybrids of horsetails, club mosses, ferns, and conifers, have been recorded. Bryophytes are especially rich, with about 75 species of liverworts and more than 250 species of mosses. Fully 170 genera and 600 species of algae and 150 species of lichens are known. The study of the higher fungi, slime molds, and water molds now is especially productive, and the study of bacteria is only beginning.

The wide range of both terrestrial and aquatic habitats in the extensive uninhabited areas offers excellent opportunity for zoological studies. The region supports approximately 52 species of mammals, 16 of reptiles, 16 of amphibians, and 75 of fishes, and it is exceptionally favorable for the study of birds. About 150 species, including the summer residents and early autumn migrants, are present. Many of the migrants are shore birds from the far north. All resident species are nesting early in the session. They include numerous species well known in southern Michigan and also many that are known only as migrants in southern Michigan.

The invertebrate fauna is rich. Sponges, hydras, turbellarians, nematodes, gastrotrichs, bryozoans, and aquatic annelids are abundant. Mollusks known for the region include 76 species of snails, 14 of unionid clams, and a large number of sphaeriids. The small crustaceans are numerous, and the larger crustaceans, centipedes, and millipedes are represented by several species each. Insects are plentiful and include representatives of 23 orders. Spiders, pseudoscorpionids, acarinids, phalangids, and rotifers are common. Protozoans are abundant and diversified. All major groups except the strictly marine forms are plentifully represented and readily available, and both the free-living forms and the parasites of vertebrates and invertebrates can be collected easily throughout the session.

Helminth parasites, especially the larval stages of trematodes, cestodes, and nematodes, are abundant. Since the collecting of vertebrate and invertebrate hosts is easy, and a supply of pens, cages, and aquaria provides good conditions for experimentation, opportunities for research on both the parasitic protozoans and the parasitic worms are especially good.

Because of the great variety of situations and the wealth of both plant and animal species in its vicinity, the Station is especially well situated for both teaching and research in the phases of botany and zoology which require ready access to organisms in their natural habitats. Accordingly, both courses and research are centered on the major habitats and the major groups of organisms.

Teaching and research, period 1930–60

It was during this period that limnology in the state became firmly established and underwent strong development. (1) The Fish Division of the Michigan Department of Conservation, with its increasing interest in the scientific pursuit of fisheries problems, established the Institute for Fisheries Research, located on the campus at Ann Arbor. (2) A strong program in theoretical limnology was developed at the University of Michigan. (3) A program in theoretical and applied limnology was initiated at Michigan State University.

Fish Division,
Michigan Department of Conservation

In 1929 the Michigan Department of Conservation requested the University of Michigan to assist in establishing an organization to carry out investigations of the sport fishery of the state. Consequently, the Institute for Fisheries Research was established on the campus at Ann Arbor, where many specialists in fisheries and limnology resided.

Carl L. Hubbs, who had worked closely with the state's program in fisheries, became the first director and served from 1930 to 1935. Succeeding Hubbs were A. S. Hazzard (1935–55) and Gerald P. Cooper (1955 to present). According to Cooper (1957):

The Institute for Fisheries Research is the research agency of the Fish Division of the State Conservation Department, operating in cooperation with the University of Michigan. The Department furnishes the funds and the University provides the central office and laboratory facilities. The Institute Director and most of the staff are permanent employees of the Conservation Department but part of the work is done by special investigators and by candidates for advanced degrees either at the University of Michigan or at Michigan State University.

The specific problems undertaken by the Institute are as requested by the Department and at present include: lake improvement, inventory of the streams and inland lakes to determine suitable management methods, studies of migration, growth rate, food habits, spawning habits and other relationships of the principal game and forage fishes, predator studies, evaluation of fishing regulations, population studies, and determination of fish yield by creel census. Research in fish nutrition and fish diseases is also being conducted to improve the efficiency of the hatcheries.

In its *Catalog of Publications* (Cooper, 1957), the institute lists approximately 300 publications in the form of bulletins, miscellaneous publications, reprints, reports, pamphlets, maps, and lake inventories. The availability, price, and method of obtaining these publications are given in the catalog.

The institute, in addition to furnishing the Department of Conservation with information on practical problems, serves the unique function of bringing together the cooperative efforts of limnologists and fisheries biologists in a state-wide program. Many graduate students working at the University of Michigan and Michigan State University have held fellowships with the institute. These students and their major professors have directed much effort and thought toward the solution of fisheries problems of the state, although the subjects of limnology and fisheries are represented in separate curricula on the campuses.

The widely recognized success of the institute's activities since 1930 reflects the basic philosophy and objectives associated with its formation and the choice of staff to direct its program. Its three directors—Hubbs, Hazzard, and Cooper—are well known for their broad experience in teaching, research, and the practical aspects of fish management at state and federal levels. They have maintained a basic research program conducted by a competent staff and a service for dealing with practical and immediate problems in the state. The inventory surveys of Michigan waters initiated in 1886 by the state were put on a continuing basis by the institute from 1930 to 1940. With assistance from various agencies, more than 2,400 lakes have been mapped and 500 biological surveys completed. Each year special problems related to streams and lakes are solved by survey teams on the research staff, but these activities are supplementary to the research program.

The institute, as a research arm of the Fish Division, conducts studies that offer promise of solutions to practical fish management problems and supply information helpful in matters of legislation and regulation. A large part of the research is concerned directly with fish; however, a basic limnological program is strongly supported and is noteworthy for its scientific accomplishments and success in uniting the limnological interests of the state universities in a state-wide program. The effort to establish close cooperation among the scientific personnel of the Fish Division and the state universities has been an objective of the institute from its beginning (Hubbs, 1930). Limnological studies, however, have received their greatest emphasis since Frank F. Hooper joined the institute as Biologist in 1952 and Gerald P. Cooper as Director in 1955.

Hooper, with a background in fisheries biology and five years' teaching experience in the Department of Zoology of the University of Michigan, was unusually well qualified to head the limnological program of the institute. He had worked with Welch and Frank E. Eggleton in the limnological programs of both the department and the Biological Station. Also, he had carried on cooperative limnological studies with Robert C. Ball of Michigan State University and had worked closely with ichthyologists and fisheries biologists on both campuses. Complementing the interagency cooperation that Hooper personally established was the institute's program of supporting candidates for advanced degrees at the University of Michigan or Michigan State University.

The limnological studies carried on by Hooper or by graduate students fall essentially into the two categories of chemical and benthic (Hooper, 1953, 1956; Beatty and Hooper, 1958). Chemical studies have dealt with general characteristics of lakes, lake fertilization, translocation of radioactive phosphorus in streams, and iron as a factor limiting primary productivity in marl lakes. Benthic studies have been concerned with life

Fig. 3.6.—Paul S. Welch, 1882–1959.

history and distribution of aquatic midges, isopods, and amphipods. Related to these benthic studies but carried out independently of Hooper is the work on stream insects by Justin Leonard (1947; Leonard and Leonard, 1949), who for a number of years was Biologist with the institute and since 1955 Assistant Deputy Director, Michigan Department of Conservation.

University of Michigan: Limnology, 1930–52

The limnological program at the University of Michigan from 1930 to 1952 consisted of closely coordinated activities in the Department of Zoology on campus and at the Biological Station. Paul S. Welch (Fig. 3.6) and his close associate Frank E. Eggleton directed this program and followed the philosophy that instruction and research in this area would be confined to principles, without emphasis on applied aspects or other special features. Consequently, the formal courses in limnology did not treat the subjects of fisheries, water quality, or problems concerned with municipal water supply. Each of these subjects was represented in the curriculum of other departments available to interested students. The essential nature of limnology as conceived by Welch is best expressed in the following quotation from the first edition of his limnology book (1935):

Limnology may therefore be defined as that branch of science which deals with biological productivity of inland waters and with all of the causal influences which determine it. This definition does not preclude any of the necessary stress on the different animal and plant communities, since they are the direct result of the biological productivity of waters which they occupy. Inland waters differ to a striking degree in the quality and quantity of life which they contain. To understand the natural circumstances responsible for this tremendous difference in natural waters and to identify and evaluate the influences which govern a particular form of productivity are the aim and province of modern limnology.

Welch thought of productivity in terms of standing crop and not in terms of energy measurements.

To place in proper perspective the contributions of Welch to the field of limnology and the development of the program at the University of Michigan, it must be recognized that limnology as an organized subject did not exist in 1928. Limnology prior to that time was represented mainly by research activities on lakes and streams, such as those conducted by Birge and Juday in Wisconsin, Forbes and Richardson in Illinois, Scott in Indiana, and Needham in New York. A well-established university curriculum in limnology did not exist. To accomplish this and to develop a strong graduate program were major aims of Welch.

Before his book was published in 1935, the principal sources of information for his classes were his well-organized and presented lectures and assignments in such books as *The Life of Inland Waters* (Needham and Lloyd, 1930), *Life in Inland Waters* (Carpenter, 1928), *The Microscopy of Drinking Water* (Whipple *et al.*, 1927). His text on limnology and the companion volume on limnological methods (Welch, 1948) still are widely used in this country and in Europe. Through these books he exerted a tremendous influence on the teaching and the development of the subject of limnology throughout the world. The ability to organize and present clearly the elements of a previously unorganized subject, such as limnology was in 1928, characterized his scholarly and exacting approach to everything he did.

Formal courses in limnology consisted of a four-credit-hour course given each spring semester on the Ann Arbor campus and each summer at the Biological Station. Also, a course in limnological methods was given without credit on the campus when there was a demand for it, but at the station it was given each summer from 1930 to 1952, except from 1937 to 1947 when it was given in alternate years. The general course on campus consisted of formal lectures by Welch and laboratory and field studies conducted by both Welch and Eggleton. In the lectures emphasis was placed on principles explaining the physical, chemical, and biological phenomena and processes occurring in lakes. Laboratory and field exercises combined observations in the natural habits with the use of methods and analysis of data. Both Welch and Eggleton believed that students should have direct experience in the field, and, therefore, numerous field trips were taken each year. A great diversity of lakes and streams within a 20-mi radius of Ann Arbor made this plan of teaching feasible and unique. The common freshwater habitats near campus are eutrophic lakes ranging in area from 5 to 75 acres, with depths varying from 10 to 100 ft; marl lakes with deposition taking the form of encrustations, flocculent precipitates, pebbles, or large concretions; bogs and bog lakes in various stages of succession; woodland ponds; large and small streams of low gradient. About 18 mi from Ann Arbor is the university's Newcomb Tract of 206 acres bordering Base Lake, through which the Huron River flows. A small laboratory on this site has been used to implement substantially the limnological field studies on campus. Trips to these habitats were made from late February, when an ice cover was present, through spring into early June when summer stratification began. To study this great diversity of habitats many pieces of equipment were acquired by the university, resulting in a collection probably excelled by no other laboratory.

In addition to teaching limnology, Welch and Eggleton were in charge of courses in invertebrate zoology and entomology. Welch's early interest in entomology was reflected in his teaching and his research activities in the field of aquatic insects, as well as in the research interests of several of his graduate students. On the other hand, Eggleton's primary interest was limnology, with emphasis on the invertebrates. The combined interests of these two men were blended in their congenial, cooperative efforts in teaching and graduate training and in their personal research.

It was at the Biological Station that Welch gave his first formal course in limnology, and the station continued to be a place of great importance in his graduate program and in his personal research. Of his 34 doctoral students, nearly all spent at least one summer at the station, and some returned three or four summers to conduct most of their doctoral research. The station was an ideal location for the development of a course emphasizing field work, since the laboratory was located on the shore of Douglas Lake, an example of the typical eutrophic lakes of Michigan. Also, readily accessible were numerous glacial lakes differing from Douglas Lake morphometrically and chemically, an unusual series of bogs and bog lakes exhibiting a variety of chemical characteristics and stages of succession, river systems showing marked differences in gradient from source to mouth, and several springs. The Great Lakes, representing small oceans, were only 15 to 20 mi away but were used rarely. It was at the station, with unlimited opportunities for field studies, that Welch made his limnology course famous. It was a popular course because of his warm sincerity as a teacher and his direct and orderly presentation of the subject matter. Also, his national and international reputation as a limnologist attracted students year after year.

The scope and specific nature of the graduate program under the direction of Welch probably can be presented best by listing chronologically his doctoral students and the titles of their theses. Sixteen of the theses dealt with the life history, physiology, or taxonomy of insects. Welch's research interest prior to 1928 was aquatic insects, and this interest is reflected in the research of his early doctoral students. Seven theses dealt with plankton, six with life histories and physiology of aquatic invertebrates, five with some aspect of benthos, and one with fish. Many of the theses contained experimental work, but it was usually secondary to a descriptive approach. Most of these theses have been published, and many of them are listed in the bibliography of the University of Michigan Biological Station (1959).

1. A morphological and geographical study of the *Gyrinidae*. Melville H. Hatch. 1924.

2. A study of the general biology, life histories and respiration of the Haliplidae (Coleoptera). Jennings R. Hickman. 1928.

3. A contribution to the biology of *Simulium* (Diptera). Yi Fang Wu. 1928.

4. A contribution to the knowledge of taxonomy and ecology of Florida Odonata. Charles F. Byers. 1929.

5. A limnological study of the profundal bottom fauna of certain freshwater lakes. Frank E. Eggleton. 1930.

6. Contribution to the biology of the fresh-water sponges (Spongillidae). Marcus C. Old. 1930.

7. A limnological study of certain bog lakes with special reference to the macroplankton. Wilbur C. Gorham. 1931.

8. Habitat distribution and life-histories of crane-flies of northern Florida. J. Speed Rogers. 1931.

9. A study of the general biology, morphology of the respiratory system, and respiration of certain aquatic *Stratiomyia* and *Odontomyia* larvae (Diptera). Kimber C. Kuster. 1932.

10. An ecological investigation of the burrowing inner beach insects of some fresh-water lakes. J. K. Gwynn Silvey. 1932.

11. A limnological study of certain freshwater polyzoa with special reference to their statoblasts. C. J. D. Brown. 1932.

12. Limnological investigations on respiration, annual migratory cycle, and other related phenomena of freshwater pulmonate snails. Elmer P. Cheatum. 1933.

13. The fate of typical lake plankton in rivers and streams. David C. Chandler. 1934.

14. A morphological and physiological study of the respiratory system in various larval instars of *Stenelmis sulcatus* (Dryopidae; Coleoptera). M. Cimini Susskind. 1934.

15. A limnological study of *Pelmatohydra* with special reference to their quantitative seasonal distribution. Donald E. Miller. 1935.

16. A limnological study of the plankton of concretion-forming marl lakes. Marion R. Raymond. 1936.

17. Limnological relations of insects to certain emergent aquatic plants. William C. Frohne. 1937.

18. A limnological investigation of some northern Michigan Donaciini (Chrysomelidae; Coleoptera). Carl E. Hoffman. 1938.

19. A limnological investigation of the microscopic benthic fauna of Douglas Lake, Michigan. George M. Moore. 1938.

20. Vertical distribution of the Rotifera in Douglas Lake, Michigan, with special reference to submerged depression individuality. Robert S. Campbell. 1939.

21. An investigation of the gaseous plastron as a respiratory mechanism in certain adult aquatic Coleoptera. Hilda T. Harpster. 1939.

22. A limnological investigation of the dynamics of a barren, sandy, wave-swept shoal in Douglas Lake, Michigan. James W. Moffett. 1939.

23. Culicinae of certain northern Michigan bog mats,

and the limnological features influencing their production. William H. Irwin. 1940.

24. Limnological investigations of the Ephemeroptera in Douglas Lake, Michigan, with special reference to distribution of immature stages. F. Earle Lyman. 1940.

25. Mechanical effects of water turbulence on certain freshwater plankters. Joseph P. Harris. 1941.

26. A limnological investigation of Periphyton in Douglas Lake, Michigan. O. Whitney Young. 1941.

27. The fate of animals in stream drift when carried into lakes. Jack S. Dendy. 1942.

28. Relationship of the invertebrate fauna to the fish population in Third Sister Lake, Michigan. Robert C. Ball. 1943.

29. A limnological investigation of the Psammon in Douglas Lake, Michigan, with special reference to shoal and shoreline dynamics. Joe K. Neel. 1947.

30. Quantitative estimation of plankton from small samples of Sedgewick-Rafter cell mounts of concentrate samples. Robert E. Serfling. 1947.

31. Limnological relations of insects to plants of the genus *Potamogeton*. Clifford O. Berg. 1949.

32. A study of the life history, ecology and economic importance of a burrowing mayfly, *Hexagenia limbata* (Serville), in certain Michigan waters. Burton Hunt. 1950.

33. Direct effect of turbidity on fishes. I. Eugene Wallen. 1950.

34. The limnological relations of insects to certain aquatic flowering plants. Y. J. McGaha. 1951.

Professor Welch (1882–1959) published 64 research papers; the last 30 were based on work done at the Biological Station (Univ. Michigan Biol. Sta., 1959). Bound copies of these papers, along with his complete professional library, are housed in the Department of Zoology as the Paul S. Welch Library. Mimeographed copies of his complete bibliography are available in the Department of Zoology. His research interests fall into three major areas: oligochaetes, 20 papers; aquatic insects, 21 papers; and limnology, 15 papers. His publications from 1911 to 1927 were almost evenly divided between oligochaetes and insects, and after 1930 he published only on limnological subjects. Depression individuality and bog lakes were the two limnological areas of special interest to him. A third area, the limnological significance of aquatic flowering plants, received emphasis primarily through his graduate students. This was an area bringing together his early professional interests in aquatic insects and his more recent pursuit of limnology.

The importance of the Biological Station to Welch and his program in limnology is evidenced by his 33 consecutive summers as a staff member of the station. His first serious limnological study was on the depression individuality of Douglas Lake, characterized by physical and chemical conditions. He made observations and collected data on this phenomenon for many years, publishing only significant facts and leaving a wealth of unpublished data which are now a part of the Welch Library. His research on bog lakes represented a more sustained interest, resulting in five significant papers, the first appearing in 1936. They dealt with bog lakes ranging in characteristics from acid waters surrounded by sphagnum mats to highly alkaline waters with or without sphagnum mats (Welch, 1936a, 1936b, 1938a, 1939). Also in the region were bog lakes showing alternately acid and alkaline waters depending upon lake levels (Welch, 1938b). This spectrum of lakes became his research interest, resulting in publications which established him as a world authority on the subject.

Professor Eggleton's (Fig. 3.7) research interests overlapped with Welch's, resulting in several joint publications dealing with physicochemical studies and depression individuality. However, Eggleton's major research interest was benthos. His doctoral thesis, directed by Welch, was the first of eight major studies of this subject on which he published (Eggleton, 1931). He studied lakes in southern and northern Michigan and in central New York and the Great Lakes (Eggleton, 1935, 1952, 1956). However, most of his research was done in the Douglas Lake region, where he spent more than 35 summers, first as a student and then as a staff member. His publication on the deep-water fauna of Lake Michigan, based on collections by the U.S. Fish and Wildlife Service (Eggleton, 1937), represents one of the early quantitative benthic studies on the Great Lakes. His present research interest is the ecology and taxonomy of sphaeriids.

Sixteen doctoral students completed their work under the direction of Eggleton from 1943 to 1960. Most of these were concerned with the life history, ecology, and taxonomy of specific groups of aquatic invertebrates. Only two might be considered limnological, and these were plankton studies. The groups of invertebrates studied by his doctoral students, listed in order of study, are pelecypods, gastropods, amphipods, water mites, myriapods, rhabdocoels, oligochaetes, chaetognaths, nematodes, phalangids, rotifers, and isopods.

The team of Welch and Eggleton, working

*Fig. 3.7.—*Frank E. Eggleton, 1893———.

closely and amicably together from 1926 to 1952, deserves comment. It was their combined effort that resulted in the rapid development and continued growth of limnology at the University of Michigan. All teaching and research programs were jointly determined, and each man made his individual contribution. Welch was the senior member of the team but was dependent upon Eggleton for the conduct of field studies in both the teaching and research programs. Welch understood the broad implications of limnology and kept well informed on current issues and developments through a scholarly review of limnological literature and direct contact with laboratories and biological stations. An expression of his leadership was the major role he played in organizing the Limnological Society of America in 1935 and his almost complete management of it for its first ten years. The wide recognition of limnology at Michigan is accredited to Welch, but he humbly gave much credit to Eggleton, upon whose great energy, enthusiasm, and thoroughness Welch relied in this team effort.

University of Michigan: Limnology, 1953–60

At the time of Welch's retirement in 1952, Eggleton chose to assume responsibility for the development of courses and the graduate program in invertebrate zoology, leaving limnology for Welch's successor. However, between the time of Welch's retirement and the appointment of his successor, Eggleton and Hooper taught limnology at Ann Arbor, and David C. Chandler of Cornell University taught it at the Biological Station.

In September 1953 Chandler accepted the position of Professor of Zoology at the University of Michigan, assuming responsibility for the limnological program. At the same time George H. Lauff, who had just completed his doctoral work at Cornell, came to Michigan as an Instructor in Zoology to assist Chandler. The plan which Chandler and Lauff decided to pursue placed emphasis upon experimental work and the extension of the theoretical work in the department to areas outside the department. This program consisted of five parts: (1) theoretical limnology centered in the department, (2) a summer program at the Biological Station, (3) applied limnology involving an interdepartmental curriculum, (4) investigations on the Great Lakes, and (5) a combined teaching and research effort in oceanography involving the Department of Zoology and the Great Lakes Research Division of the Institute of Science and Technology.

(1) Theoretical limnology has received major emphasis, centered around an active departmental program of teaching and graduate research. The curriculum consists of three courses: "Limnology," a lecture course on general principles; "Field Studies," a laboratory course applying the principles of the lecture course to lakes and streams; and "Experimental Limnology," an advanced course applying current methods and equipment to the solution of specific problems. In addition to these courses are seminars and informal discussions limited to graduate students. Enrollment in these courses varies from 12 to 15 in the laboratory to 40 in lectures and consists of students from the departments of Botany, Conservation, Environmental Health, Fisheries, Geology, Sanitary Engineering, Wildlife Management, and Zoology.

Students working toward advanced degrees in limnology are required to pass the comprehensive examination in zoology, to spend at least one summer at a freshwater or marine station, and to take basic courses in limnology and oceanography in addition to completing doctoral research involving both field and laboratory studies. The following doctoral dissertations, completed under the direction of Chandler and Lauff since the initiation of this program in 1953, are listed chronologically to portray the specific nature of the graduate program. Only the first two have been published; several others are in press.

1. The vertical migration of *Mysis relicta* in Lakes Huron and Michigan. Alfred M. Beeton. 1957. (See Beeton, 1959.)
2. The transformation of energy by *Daphnia pulex*. Sumner Richman. 1957. (See Richman, 1958.)
3. The transformation of energy by an aquatic herbivore, *Stenonema pulchellum* (Ephemeroptera). Francesco B. Trama. 1957.
4. The application of radioisotopes to the study of lake metabolism. George W. Saunders. 1958.
5. The micro-distribution of caddis flies *Pycnopsyche lepida* and *Pycnopsyche guttifer*. Kenneth W. Cummins. 1960.
6. The effect of continuous, sub-lethal gamma radiation on the intrinsic rate of natural increase in *Daphnia pulex*. Jack Marshall. 1960.
7. Factors limiting primary productivity in a marl lake. Claire L. Schelske. 1960.
8. Uptake of radioactive heavy metals by aquatic plants. Roger W. Bachmann. 1961.
9. The interrelationship of substrate and associated parameters and their effect on the local distribution of the burrowing mayfly *Ephemera simulans*. Clyde H. Eriksen. 1961.

(2) Each summer a course in general limnology is offered at the Biological Station, usually given by either Chandler, Lauff, or George W. Saunders, a limnologist who did his graduate work under Chandler at Michigan and is now associated with the Department of Zoology and the Great Lakes Research Division. This course differs from the one on campus in that greater emphasis is placed on field work. Douglas Lake is used extensively in giving students practical experience with limnological methods and equipment which are eventually applied in a comparative study of a great diversity of waters in the region. Also, Douglas Lake is used by the staff and students in conducting experimental studies on specific organisms or lake processes. Facilities for field studies at the station are excellent both in respect to equipment and in respect to ready access to natural waters; therefore, this summer program greatly complements the more experimental and laboratory approach given on the campus. Also, the facilities of the Great Lakes Research Division are used for one or two all-day field trips each summer on Lake Michigan. Inclusion of the Great Lakes in the limnology course introduces the use of equipment and techniques essential for the study of large bodies of water.

(3) Applied limnology is represented by an interdepartmental curriculum supported by the departments of Sanitary Engineering, Environmental Health, and Zoology. The aim of this program is to combine the efforts and thinking of limnologists, sanitary engineers, and people in public health in establishing a broad training for scientific personnel working in the areas of water quality, pollution control, and water management.

(4) Limnology at the University of Michigan prior to the arrival of Chandler and Lauff in 1953 did not include the Great Lakes, except for the limited research interests of Eggleton. The university's Great Lakes Research Institute, organized in 1945,* had laid the ground work for an active program by drawing up long-term plans and by attracting the enthusiastic support of staff members from the departments of Botany, Geology, Zoology, and various groups in the College of Engineering. However, up to 1953 only isolated research projects had been carried out on the Great Lakes. Chandler and Lauff became active immediately in the Great Lakes Research Institute, assisting in the expansion of the broad interdisciplinary program as well as developing Great Lakes limnology so that it could be coordinated and integrated with the effort in the Department of Zoology. This was accomplished essentially by requiring all graduate students in limnology to devote some time to active participation, usually as a research assistant, in the field program on the Great Lakes. Only a few graduate students up to 1960 have used the Great Lakes for doctoral research, but these lakes have served to familiarize the student with the similarities between the fundamental problems and processes in large and small bodies of water. Also, since oceanographic methods and equipment are used in Great Lakes studies, students in limnology observe directly the similarities between the principles of limnology and oceanography. Research data from the Great Lakes are used extensively in the teaching program, both in the general and in the advanced courses.

(5) A course in oceanography and marine

---

* Reorganized in 1960 as the Great Lakes Research Division of the Institute of Science and Technology.

biology was first offered in the Department of Zoology in 1951 by Frederick E. Smith, an invertebrate zoologist with considerable marine experience. This offering was expanded in 1956, when John C. Ayers, formerly with Woods Hole Oceanographic Institution and Cornell University, joined the zoology staff. He, along with Charles F. Powers, an oceanographer who did his doctoral work under the direction of Ayers, heads a teaching and research program in oceanography closely integrated with the programs in limnology on the Great Lakes. The curriculum in oceanography developed from the course by Smith in 1951 to a general course in oceanography with a laboratory and an advanced lecture course in physical oceanography. In 1961 the first step in revising the curricula in oceanography and limnology was to combine the introductory courses of both subjects into a single offering, "Limnology and Oceanography." In this course the principles of the two subjects are presented, emphasizing the great similarities and treating important differences in varying detail. Advanced courses in the two subjects are given separately, but seminars integrate the two subjects at the graduate level.

An interdepartmental program in oceanography under the direction of the Graduate School was initiated in 1960, and several departments in the physical sciences and the Department of Zoology participate. The program is at both the undergraduate and graduate levels, leading to B.S., M.S., and Ph.D. degrees in oceanography. In this program students study the Great Lakes extensively as "laboratory-sized oceans," in addition to obtaining experience at a marine laboratory. Facilities of the Great Lakes Research Division of the university, including three research vessels, 34 ft, 50 ft, and 114 ft, well equipped for deep and shallow water studies, are used in this training program. Ayers, Chandler, Lauff, and Powers work together closely in carrying out the teaching and research in limnology and oceanography, especially on the Great Lakes.

Research conducted by the staff in limnology and oceanography includes studies on streams and small lakes of the state and on all the Great Lakes except Ontario. The cooperative efforts of Ayers, Chandler, Lauff, and Powers, and several scientists from other institutions have been used in attacking the problems on the Great Lakes, while individual efforts have characterized the research on streams and small lakes. Three rather distinct areas of research have been pursued by this group since 1954: (1) currents, water transport, and water masses in the Great Lakes (Ayers *et al.*, 1956, 1958; Powers and Ayers, 1960), (2) relation of substrate to distribution of benthos in streams and lakes (Lauff *et al.*, 1961b), and (3) primary productivity measurements in small and large lakes (Bachmann *et al.*, 1961).

During 1954 and 1955 the major research effort was on the problems of currents and water circulation in the basins of Lakes Huron and Michigan. The "synoptic survey method" was employed to obtain a broad picture of current patterns, temperature conditions, and chemical characteristics of the waters. Through this method standardized observations and collections were made at about 100 predetermined positions in each lake. Ten to twelve research vessels crossed the lakes simultaneously on predetermined transects on several occasions. Ayers, the senior member of this research team, used his oceanographic experience to apply for the first time the "dynamic heights method" in calculating direction and velocity of currents from temperature measurements. Publications from these studies (Ayers *et al.*, 1956, 1958; Ayers and Bachmann, 1957) represent the most complete information available on currents of the Great Lakes. More detailed studies of currents and water movements were made in Grand Traverse Bay by Lauff (1957) and by Powers and Ayers (1960) in the Straits of Mackinac.

A cooperative study by the staff, 1956–59, provided information on the distribution and nature of bottom sediments in Grand Traverse Bay and in the Straits of Mackinac (Lauff *et al.*, 1961b). This study was based on the premise that the superficial sediments give clues to the biological conditions of the overlying water and also that they are substrata for benthic organisms and spawning grounds of fish. Mechanical analyses of several hundred samples were used to give indirect hydrographic information on the nature of bottom currents, important to an understanding of circulation and movement of lake waters. These data were correlated with the distribution and biology of benthic organisms in the area.

Lauff and his graduate students have been studying the microdistribution of stream fauna in relation to the mechanical and chemical characteristics of the substrate and currents. Studies on streams in the Ann Arbor area are supplemented by well-designed experiments in the laboratory (Lauff *et al.*, 1961*a*).

Studies in primary productivity were started at Michigan in 1957 by Lauff and have been continuous through his efforts and those of his colleagues and graduate students. The studies have dealt with a comparison among lake types, using carbon-14, dissolved oxygen, and chlorophyll as methods for measuring productivity. Since 1959 most of this work has been done on Grand Traverse Bay of Lake Michigan, with the aim of developing a reliable method for estimating integral photosynthesis in the Great Lakes on a synoptic basis (Bachmann *et al.*, 1961; Trama *et al.*, 1961).

Research activities by staff members in limnology and oceanography have been carried on essentially within the Department of Zoology, but two other units within the university have greatly implemented this work. The Phoenix Memorial Laboratory, with its unexcelled research facilities, has been used extensively by the limnologists in radiation and radioisotope studies. Also, the Great Lakes Research Division of the Institute of Science and Technology, with its research vessels and well-equipped laboratories, has been freely used by both the limnologists and oceanographers. The Great Lakes research program has never been officially a part of the Department of Zoology; nevertheless, Chandler, Lauff, Ayers, and Powers, all members of the department, have devoted much of their research effort in this area. All have held joint appointments in the Department of Zoology and the Great Lakes Research Division, resulting in an integration of all efforts in the fields of limnology and oceanography at Michigan. Chandler, as Director of the Great Lakes Research Division and head of the limnological unit in the Department of Zoology, has strongly advocated this cooperative effort in the aquatic sciences.

University of Michigan:
Fisheries and ichthyology

Limnology at Michigan, since its introduction as a formal course, has essentially excluded the subject matter of ichthyology and fisheries biology. This was due in part to the personal philosophy of Welch and in part to the fact that a teaching and research program in ichthyology was started in the Museum of Zoology about 1920. Carl L. Hubbs, who had a good knowledge of both limnology and ichthyology, devoted most of his research and teaching effort to the latter field. As Curator of Fishes, he built up an unrivaled collection of North American freshwater fishes, which today remains a monument to his ability, enthusiasm, and untiring energy. From this strong beginning, ichthyology and fisheries biology have remained separate courses in the curriculum.

Hubbs served as chairman of 27 doctoral committees from 1924 to 1944, in addition to vigorously conducting personal research and taking an active part in the state's fisheries program. Among his students are five who at present occupy important positions in aquatic biology on the university campus.

Reeve M. Bailey and Robert R. Miller were appointed Curators of Fishes in the Museum of Zoology in 1944 and 1948, respectively. They expanded the fish collection, participated in the teaching program, and continued research in systematics. Also, they have kept up the ichthyological library started by Hubbs, making it one of the most complete in the country. Their graduate students work primarily in systematics; however, a broad background in aquatic ecology and limnology is required. Henry van der Schalie became Curator of Mollusks in the museum in 1934, building up a large research and teaching collection used by aquatic biologists on campus and throughout the country. Malacological research by van der Schalie and his students extends into the area of limnology, ichthyology, parasitology, and public health; therefore, there is close cooperation among staff and students in these areas. Karl F. Lagler, Chairman of the Department of Fisheries, and Gerald P. Cooper, Director of the Institute for Fisheries Research, both former students of Hubbs, head fisheries units on campus.

Formal courses in ichthyology and fisheries biology were introduced into the Department of Zoology in 1939, with Karl Lagler in charge. These courses attracted students from several departments and were taught in cooperation with ichthyologists from the Museum of Zoology, Institute for Fisheries Research, and the Great Lakes Fishery Investigations of the U.S. Fish and Wildlife Service. James W. Moffett, director of the last organization since 1950, did his graduate work with Welch and has worked closely with the aquatic biologists on campus.

The program under the direction of Lagler has been vigorous both in research and in teaching. A complete list of Lagler's publications and the masters' and doctoral theses received in fisheries biology from 1937 to 1959 is available from the Department of Fisheries. Since 1939 about 36 masters' degrees and 18 doctoral degrees have been received by students under his direction. Prior to 1953 emphasis was placed on life histories, food habits, growth, and population studies, but since then experimental studies have been undertaken. This change in emphasis occurred when Lagler, in 1950, became Chairman of the Department of Fisheries in the newly established School of Natural Resources. At this time the curriculum in fisheries was expanded, and John E. Bardach, who did his doctoral work under the direction of A. D. Hasler at the University of Wisconsin, was added to the fisheries staff. With a background in physiology and limnology, Bardach introduced experimental work into the teaching and research program of the department.

Bardach's personal research has been done primarily in the following areas: temperature sensitivity of freshwater fishes (Bardach and Bjorklund, 1957); and growth (Bardach and Menzel, 1957), movements (Bardach, 1958a), culture (Bardach, 1958b), and food selection (Bardach et al., 1959) of marine fishes in the vicinity of Bermuda. His graduate students have worked with both freshwater and marine fishes on the problems of growth, visual discrimination, utilization of food, and behavior.

Michigan State University

Limnology at Michigan State University, East Lansing, developed as a recognized program about fifteen years later than did fisheries. It was an outgrowth of the fisheries program and has remained closely associated with it. Fisheries became a part of the curriculum of the Department of Zoology in 1940 and remained there until 1950, when it was incorporated into a new Department of Fisheries and Wildlife under the direction of Peter I. Tack. The first formal course in limnology was offered by Tack in 1941 in the Department of Zoology, where he also directed work in fisheries. Limnology as taught by Tack

from 1941 to 1946 was strongly oriented toward fisheries biology, especially the practical problems of management. In 1946 Robert C. Ball, who did his doctoral work under the direction of Welch, was placed in charge of the limnological teaching and research program. Under his direction the course in limnology has become more classical, including fish only as a component of the aquatic ecosystem. This course consists of lectures and laboratory work, with very little field work. An advanced course in limnological methods affords an opportunity for students with a serious interest in the subject to have direct contact with technical equipment and methods applied to field and laboratory problems. Ball and his limnological program were transferred from zoology to the Department of Fisheries and Wildlife in 1950. Here he works closely with Tack, who teaches ichthyology, and Eugene W. Roelofs, who since 1954 has taught and directed graduate work in aquiculture and fisheries management.

The W. K. Kellogg Gull Lake Biological Station of Michigan State University, located about 55 mi southwest of Lansing, consists of 1,500 acres, containing many lakes, ponds, streams, and various types of bogs and swamps. It operates each summer for a period of eight weeks, offering a variety of biological courses, including aquatic plants, freshwater algae, aquatic insects, limnology, and ichthyology. This station does not play an important role in the graduate program of students in limnology and fisheries but provides unique training for science teachers and prospective science teachers.

In the immediate vicinity of East Lansing are numerous small natural and artificial lakes offering a great diversity of aquatic habitats for teaching and research purposes. The Red Cedar River flows through the campus, affording ready access to natural waters the year around. In addition to these waters near campus, Ball makes frequent use of experimental facilities such as hatchery ponds, lakes, and streams, owned by the State Department of Conservation.

An active undergraduate and graduate program in the Department of Fisheries and Wildlife is evidenced by 180 undergraduates, 11 masters', and 6 doctoral candidates in 1960. Since 1950, 50 masters' degrees have been conferred, 14 under the direction of Tack and 36 under Ball. Also, in this period 5 doctoral students completed their work under the direction of Tack and 8 under Ball. Limnology at Michigan State is now represented primarily by the work of Ball and his students.

Ball has maintained a good balance between fisheries and limnology in the pursuit of his personal research and in his graduate program. Among the 36 students receiving masters' degrees under his direction since 1950, 16 studied fisheries problems, such as harvesting and production of bait and pond fishes and life histories and food habits of various sport species. Ten theses were concerned with the artificial fertilization of streams, marl lakes, bog waters, and eutrophic ponds and the effects of fertilization on the production of fish and benthos. Five dealt with the movement and translocation of radiophosphorus through stream ecosystems and general characteristics of streams. One study was made on benthos and three on primary productivity in flowing water.

The doctoral program under Ball's direction has been more strictly limnological, as shown by the following list of doctoral dissertation titles since 1952. The first four have been published, and several others are in press.

1. Relationships between alkalinity and adsorption and regeneration of added phosphorus in fertilized trout lakes. Paul Howard Barrett. 1952. (See Barrett, 1952.)
2. Experimental fertilization of Michigan trout lakes. Howard Allen Tanner. 1952. (See Tanner, 1960.)
3. An ecological study of the family Tendipedidae of two fresh-water lakes in Isabella County, Michigan. LaVerne L. Curry. 1952. (See Curry, 1954.)
4. Chemical and biological effects of lime application to bog lakes in northern Michigan. Thomas Frank Waters. 1956. (See Waters, 1956.)
5. A study of nutrient accrual, uptake, and regeneration as related to primary production in a warm-water stream. Morris Leroy Brehmer. 1958.
6. Primary production, energetics, and nutrient utilization in a warm-water stream. Alfred Richard Grzenda. 1960.
7. A study of the ribonucleic acid-polyphosphate complexes isolated from *Anabaena variabilis* and synchronized *Chlorella pyrenoidosa*. David L. Correll. 1961.
8. Factors influencing the ecological distribution of *Tendipes decorus* (Joh.) in Coldwater Lake, Isabella County, Michigan. Gale R. Gleason. 1961.

Ball's personal research interests were centered around fisheries problems from 1940 to 1952, concerned with population studies (Brown and Ball, 1942), tagging experiments (Ball, 1944), relationship between available fish food and feeding habits of fish (Ball, 1946), effects of fertilizers on the production of fish food organisms and fish (Ball, 1949; Ball and Tanner, 1951), and farm pond management (Ball, 1952). Much of his research during this period was directly related to the Department of Conservation's program aimed at providing trout fishing in small lakes. Preliminary work clearly demonstrated that many lakes were suitable for trout with respect to temperature and oxygen conditions, but the feasibility of the venture had to be checked by removing warm-water fishes by chemical treatment and replacing them with trout. Ball (1949; Ball and Tanner, 1951) showed that artificial fertilization of these small lakes greatly increased the abundance of fish food organisms, but that heavy fish-kills occurred in winter. Most of Ball's research at this time was of direct interest to the State Department of Conservation, since it contributed to the solution of immediate and practical fisheries problems. In return, Ball received research funds, access to state facilities and equipment, and fellowships for graduate students.

In 1952, when Frank Hooper became Biologist with the Institute of Fisheries Research, he and Ball initiated cooperative studies in the state aimed more at fundamental problems of limnology. Since 1950 they have worked closely together, combining their practical knowledge of fisheries and interest in fundamental limnology to assist the Department of Conservation in solving state fisheries problems. They have undertaken joint studies on artificial circulation of a small lake (Hooper et al., 1953), primary productivity studies in ponds (Knight et al., 1962), and translocation of phosphorus in a trout stream (Ball and Hooper, 1962).

Many students working with Ball are supported in part by the Institute for Fisheries Research, in the same manner as students working with Lagler and Chandler at the University of Michigan. This points again to the central role of this institute in bringing together limnological and fisheries biologists of the state in a cooperative effort. Ball and Hooper deserve much credit for the success of this state-wide effort since 1952.

Another significant aspect of limnology at Michigan State University is the work in freshwater algae headed by Gerald W. Prescott since

1946. He is internationally known for his numerous publications on taxonomy and ecology of algae in the United States and in Central and South America, on water sanitation, and on the importance of phytoplankton in lake metabolism. The publication that best represents his contribution to algology and limnology is his treatise on algae of the western Great Lakes area (Prescott, 1951). In this excellent presentation of the ecology and systematics of algae, he discusses the limnological role of phytoplankton in lake metabolism and includes an extensive bibliography on Michigan and Wisconsin algae. Many of his pertinent publications are included.

Michigan's major contributions to the national development of limnology

Limnology in North America stemmed from a program in aquatic biology initiated around the turn of the century by the states of Illinois, Indiana, Ohio, Michigan, Minnesota, New York, and Wisconsin. Michigan's early contribution was primarily the concept and design of lake surveys, exemplified by the studies of Reighard (1894) and Hankinson (1908), and the curriculum in aquatic biology in the University of Michigan as early as 1904. Paul S. Welch organized and offered one of the earliest formal courses in limnology in 1923, and he probably was the first to incorporate the concept of biological productivity as the central theme. In 1935 he published the first textbook in limnology, one that was used widely and remained unrivaled for nearly fifteen years.

The University of Michigan since 1928 and Michigan State University since 1946 have supported strong active graduate teaching and research programs, accompanied by vigorous, productive staff research. Approximately 60 limnologists have received Ph.D.'s from Michigan universities since 1928, and many times this number in the areas of ichthyology-fisheries, invertebrate zoology, and ecology. More than two-thirds of these limnologists now hold important positions in aquatic biology in universities, research institutions, and state and federal agencies. These graduate programs in limnology are increasing in strength, and a greater emphasis is being placed on the experimental approach, especially in the use of radioisotopes as tracers.

Few states have been as successful as Michigan in applying the results of theoretical limnological studies to fisheries problems on a state-wide basis. This has been accomplished primarily through the activities of the Institute for Fisheries Research, the research arm of the Fish Division of the Department of Conservation, working in close cooperation with aquatic biologists in state colleges and universities. Numerous surveys of state waters as well as specific basic studies have resulted from this program, broadening the training of graduate students and solving fisheries problems in the state.

Michigan limnologists have made an outstanding contribution to the organization and development of the American Society of Limnology and Oceanography through leadership in scientific sessions and in the administration of the society's affairs. Welch served as a member of the organizational committee and as secretary-treasurer of the society from its formation in 1935 to 1945. During these first ten years, Welch carried the major responsibility of promotion and guidance of the society; again, from 1959 to the present, George H. Lauff has served as secretary-treasurer. Two Michigan men have served as president of the society: Paul S. Welch, 1946, and David C. Chandler, 1956–57; six as vice-president: Chandler, 1948–49, Justin W. Leonard, 1950–51, James W. Moffett, 1952–53, Robert C. Ball, 1955–56, Gerald W. Prescott, 1959–60, and John C. Ayers, 1961–62. Also, Frank F. Hooper served on the Executive Committee from 1957 to 1958, and many Michigan men have served on numerous secondary committees of the society.

The University of Michigan, through its Great Lakes Research Division, has offered leadership in the conduct of an interdisciplinary research program on the Great Lakes. Limnologists, oceanographers, geologists, meteorologists, etc.. have united their research efforts in the study of these laboratory-sized oceans. This research program has served to demonstrate the similarity between the principles of limnology and oceanography and the applicability of oceanographic equipment and methods in the study of large lakes. In addition to bringing the limnologists and oceanographers closer together in their thinking, the program has contributed substantially to the solution of regional water resource problems.

References

AYERS, J. C., D. V. ANDERSON, D. C. CHANDLER, AND G. H. LAUFF. 1956. Currents and water masses of Lake Huron. Great Lakes Research Div., Univ. Michigan, Ann Arbor, Publ. No. 1, 101 p.

AYERS, J. C., AND R. W. BACHMANN. 1957. Simplified computations for the dynamic height method of current determination in lakes. Limnol. Oceanogr., **2**: 155–157.

AYERS, J. C., D. C. CHANDLER, G. H. LAUFF, C. F. POWERS, AND E. B. HENSON. 1958. Currents and water masses of Lake Michigan. Great Lakes Research Div., Univ. Michigan, Ann Arbor, Publ. No. 3, 169 p.

BACHMANN, R. W., G. W. SAUNDERS, AND F. B. TRAMA. 1961. Investigations in lake metabolism—photosynthesis: A modified C^{14} technique for estimations of photosynthesis in large lakes. Great Lakes Research Div., Univ. Michigan, Ann Arbor, Publ. No. 7: 163.

BALL, R. C. 1944. A tagging experiment on the fish population of Third Sister Lake. Trans. Amer. Fish. Soc., **74**: 360–369.

———. 1946. Relationship between available fish food, feeding habits of fish and total fish production in a Michigan lake. Michigan State Univ. Agr. Expt. Sta., Tech. Bull. 206: 1–60.

———. 1949. Experimental use of fertilizers in the production of fish-food organisms and fish. Michigan State Univ. Agr. Expt. Sta., Tech. Bull. 210: 1–28.

———. 1952. Farm pond management in Michigan. Trans. 17th North Amer. Wildl. Conf.: 221–225.

BALL, R. C., AND F. F. HOOPER, 1962. Translocation of phosphorus in a trout stream ecosystem. Proc. AIBS-AEC Symposium on Radioecology. In press.

BALL, R. C., AND H. TANNER. 1951. The biological effects of fertilizer on a warm-water lake. Michigan State Univ. Agr. Expt. Sta., Tech. Bull. 223: 1–32.

BARDACH, J. E. 1958a. On the movements of certain Bermuda reef fishes. Ecology, **39**: 139–146.

———. 1958b. Marine fishes and fish culture in the Caribbean. Proc. 10th Gulf Caribbean Fish. Inst.: 132–137.

BARDACH, J. E., AND R. G. BJORKLUND. 1957. The temperature sensitivity of some American freshwater fishes. Amer. Nat., **91**: 233–251.

BARDACH, J. E., AND D. W. MENZEL. 1957. Field and laboratory observations on the growth of some Bermuda reef fishes. Proc. 9th Gulf Caribbean Fish. Inst.: 106–112.

BARDACH, J. E., H. E. WINN, AND D. W. MENZEL. 1959. The role of the senses in the feeding of nocturnal reef predators Gymnothorax moringa and G. vicinus. Copeia, 1959(2): 133–139.

BARRETT, P. H. 1952. Relationships between alkalinity and adsorption and regeneration of added phosphorus in fertilized trout lakes. Trans. Amer. Fish. Soc., **82**: 78–90.

BEATTY, L. D., AND F. F. HOOPER. 1958. Benthic associations of Sugarloaf Lake. Papers Michigan Acad. Sci., **43**: 89–106.

BEETON, A. M. 1959. Photoreception in the opossum shrimp, Mysis relicta Loven. Biol. Bull., **116**: 204–216.

BIRGE, E. A., AND C. JUDAY. 1911. The inland lakes of Wisconsin. The dissolved gases of the water and their biological significance. Wisconsin Geol. Nat. Hist. Surv., Bull. No. 22, 259 + xx p.

BROWN, C. J. D. 1944. Michigan lakes and streams. Michigan Dept. Conserv., Fish Div., Pamphlet No. 24.

BROWN, C. J. D., AND R. C. BALL. 1942. A fish population study of Third Sister Lake. Trans. Amer. Fish. Soc., **72**: 177–186.

CARPENTER, K. E. 1928. Life in inland waters. Macmillan Co., New York. 267 p.

COOPER, G. P. 1957. Catalog of publications of the Institute for Fisheries Research 1934–57. Michigan Dept. Conserv., Lansing, 24 p.

CURRY, L. L. 1954. Notes on the ecology of the midge fauna (Diptera: Tendipedidae) of Hunt Creek, Montmorency County, Michigan. Ecology, **35**: 541–550.

DARLINGTON, H. T. 1945. Taxonomic and ecological work on higher plants of Michigan. Michigan State Univ. Agr. Expt. Sta., Tech. Bull. 201, 59 p.

EGGLETON, F. E. 1931. A limnological study of the profundal bottom fauna of certain freshwater lakes. Ecol. Monogr., **1**: 233–331.

———. 1935. A comparative study of the benthic fauna of four northern Michigan lakes. Papers Michigan Acad. Sci., **20**: 609–644.

———. 1937. Productivity of the profundal benthic zone in Lake Michigan. Papers Michigan Acad. Sci., **22**: 593–612.

———. 1952. Dynamics of interdepression benthic communities. Trans. Amer. Microscop. Soc., **71**: 189–228.

———. 1956. Limnology of a meromictic, interglacial, plunge-basin lake. Trans. Amer. Microscop. Soc., **75**: 334–378.

EICHMEIER, A. H. 1959. Climate of Michigan. U.S. Dept. Com., Weather Bur., Climatography of the U.S., No. 60–20.

HANKINSON, T. L. 1908. A biological survey of Walnut Lake, Michigan. Rept. Biol. Surv., State of Michigan, State Board of Geol. Surv. (part of rept. for 1907), Lansing: 157–288.

HOOPER, F. F. 1953. Limnological features of Weber Lake, Cheboygan County, Michigan. Papers Michigan Acad. Sci., **39**: 229–240.

———. 1956. Some chemical and morphometric characteristics of southern Michigan lakes. Papers Michigan Acad. Sci., **41**: 109–130.

HOOPER, F. F., R. C. BALL, AND H. A. TANNER. 1953. An experiment in the artificial circulation of a small Michigan lake. Trans. Amer. Fish. Soc., **82**: 222–241.

HUBBS, C. L. 1930. Fishery research in Michigan. Trans. Amer. Fish. Soc., **58**: 178–182.

HUBBS, C. L., AND JAN METZELAAR. 1926. The zoological resources of Michigan. Michigan Acad. Sci., Ann. Rept.: 67–74.

KNIGHT, A., R. C. BALL, AND F. F. HOOPER. 1962. Some estimates of primary production rates in Michigan ponds. Papers Michigan Acad. Sci., **47**: 219–233.

LARUE, G. R. 1944. The University of Michigan—An encyclopedic survey. IV. The Biological Station.

Univ. Michigan, Ann Arbor: 761–769.

LAUFF, G. H. 1957. Some aspects of the physical limnology of Grand Traverse Bay. Great Lakes Research Div., Univ. Michigan, Ann Arbor, Publ. No. 2, 56 p.

LAUFF, G. H., K. W. CUMMINS, C. H. ERIKSEN, AND M. PARKER. 1961a. A method for sorting bottom fauna samples by elutriation. Limnol. Oceanogr., 6: 462–466.

LAUFF, G. H., E. B. HENSON, J. C. AYERS, D. C. CHANDLER, AND C. F. POWERS. 1961b. The bottom sediments of the Straits of Mackinac Region. Great Lakes Research Div., Univ. Michigan, Ann Arbor, Publ. No. 6, 69 p.

LEONARD, J. W. 1947. Differences in the occurrence of nymphs of two species of burrowing mayflies in fish stomachs. Ann. Entomol. Soc. Amer., 40: 688–691.

LEONARD, J. W., AND F. A. LEONARD. 1949. An annotated list of Michigan Trichoptera. Occasional Papers, Museum Zool., Univ. Michigan, No. 522, 35 p.

McNAMEE, R. L. 1930. The surface waters of Michigan hydrology and qualitative characteristics and purification for public use. Dept. Engr. Research, Univ. Michigan, Ann Arbor, Bull. 16, 321 p.

NEEDHAM, J. G., AND J. T. LLOYD. 1930. The life of inland waters. Charles C Thomas, Baltimore. 438 p.

POWERS C. F., AND J. C. AYERS. 1960. Water transport studies in the Straits of Mackinac region of Lake Huron. Limnol. Oceanogr., 5: 81–85.

PRESCOTT, G. W. 1951. Algae of the western Great Lakes area. Cranbrook Inst. Sci., Bloomfield Hills, Michigan, Bull. No. 31, 946 + xiii p.

REIGHARD, J. E. 1894. A biological examination of Lake St. Clair. Bull. Michigan Fish Comm., No. 4, 60 p.

——. 1913. An ecological reconnaissance of the fishes of Douglas Lake, Cheboygan County, Michigan, in midsummer. Bull. U.S. Bur. Fish., 33: 219–249.

——. 1918. Symposium on the trends in zoology. 3. The trends of ecology. Michigan Acad. Sci. 20th Rept.: 109–114.

——. 1929. A biological examination of Loon Lake, Gogebic County, Michigan, with suggestions for increasing its yield of small-mouth bass (*Micropterus dolomieu*). Papers Michigan Acad. Sci., 10: 589–612.

——. 1942. The breeding habits of the river chub, *Nocomis micropogon* (Cope). Papers Michigan Acad. Sci., 28: 397–423.

RICHMAN, SUMNER. 1958. The transformation of energy by *Daphnia pulex*. Ecol. Monogr., 28: 273–291.

SCOTT, I. D. 1921. Inland lakes of Michigan. Michigan Geol. Biol. Surv., Publ. 30, Geol. Ser. 25, 383 p.

SHULL, A. F. 1944. The University of Michigan—An encyclopedic survey. IV. The Department of Zoology. Univ. Michigan, Ann Arbor: 738–750.

TANNER, H. A. 1960. Some consequences of adding fertilizer to five Michigan trout lakes. Trans. Amer. Fish. Soc., 89: 198–205.

TRAMA, F. B., G. W. SAUNDERS, AND R. W. BACHMANN. 1961. Investigations in lake metabolism—photosynthesis: Chlorophyll *a* in Grand Traverse Bay with reference to its use as an index of primary productivity. Great Lakes Research Div., Univ. Michigan, Ann Arbor, Publ. No. 7: 163–164.

UNIVERSITY OF MICHIGAN BIOLOGICAL STATION. 1959. Proceedings, Semicentennial Celebration, June 16–19, 1959, Pellston, Michigan. 130 p.

VEATCH, J. O. 1953. Soils and land of Michigan. Michigan Agr. Expt. Sta., Mem. Ser. No. 7. Michigan State Coll. Press, East Lansing. 241 p.

WARD, H. B. 1896. Biological examination of Lake Michigan in the Traverse Bay region. Michigan Fish Comm., Bull. No. 6, 99 p.

WATERS, T. F. 1956. The effects of lime application to acid bog lakes in northern Michigan. Trans. Amer. Fish. Soc., 86: 329–344.

WELCH, P. S. 1927. Limnological investigation on northern Michigan lakes. Papers Michigan Acad. Sci., 8: 421–449.

——. 1935. Limnology. McGraw-Hill Book Co., New York. 471 + xiv p. (2nd ed., 1952, 538 + xi p.)

——. 1936a. A limnological study of a small sphagnum–leather-leaf–black spruce bog lake with special reference to its plankton. Trans. Amer. Microscop. Soc., 55: 300–312.

——. 1936b. Limnological investigations of a strongly basic bog lake surrounded by an extensive acid-forming mat. Papers Michigan Acad. Sci., 21: 727–751.

——. 1938a. A limnological study of a bog lake which has never developed a marginal mat. Trans. Amer. Microscop. Soc., 57: 344–357.

——. 1938b. A limnological study of a retrograding bog lake. Ecology, 19: 435–453.

——. 1939. Vertical distribution of summer temperature in the false bottoms of certain Michigan bogs. Ecology, 20: 38–46.

——. 1948. Limnological methods. Blakiston Co., Philadelphia. 381 + xviii p.

WELCH, P. S., AND F. E. EGGLETON. 1932. Limnological investigations on northern Michigan lakes. II. A further study of depression individuality in Douglas Lake. Papers Michigan Acad. Sci., 15: 491–508.

WHIPPLE, G. C., G. M. FAIR, AND M. C. WHIPPLE. 1927. The microscopy of drinking water. John Wiley & Sons, New York. 586 + xix p.

4 | *John L. Brooks*
Edward S. Deevey, Jr.

New England

The six New England states (Maine, New Hampshire, Vermont, Massachusetts, Rhode Island, and Connecticut) make a rather unhomogeneous region that is more or less united by cultural and political considerations and is usually treated as a unit in geography books. From the limnological standpoint it has been convenient to maintain this unity in treatment, since New England is the only completely glaciated political division of the United States in which lakes are common but sedimentary rocks are rare. Much less is known of the lakes of northern New England than those of Connecticut, and after a preliminary attempt at a geographic subdivision of the work, the authors of this chapter chose to divide their task by topic rather than by region; Brooks has taken main responsibility for the limnology of the larger lakes of northern New England, where biological and especially fisheries limnology has been paramount, while Deevey has concentrated on chemical and geological problems that have been studied mainly in the smaller lakes.

In this chapter Deevey has written the four sections, "History," "Physiography, climate, and vegetation," "Geology and regional limnology," and "Small lakes: Special limnological problems"; Brooks, the sections, "Limnological resources" and "The biological limnology of northern New England." Figure 4.1 is a map of New England for orientation purposes, on which are shown the drainage basins and some of the larger lakes. The newly drawn figures are the work of William Vars, delineator, Biology Department, Yale University.

New England has an honorable history of pioneering work on sanitary limnology, on the biology and hydraulics of flowing waters, and on groundwater geology, but the authors have felt incompetent to review these engineering aspects of the subject; and although fisheries limnology is too important to be similarly neglected, the fact that nearly all inland fisheries in New England are recreational rather than food-producing has biased the character and, to some extent, depressed the scientific quality of the data available for review. It is obvious that in a work of this scope marine biology and oceanography can have no place, and the authors have also excluded estuarine biology as being marine, not limnological, in practice if not in principle.

History

New England's lakes have probably never been far from the consciousness of the region's artists and poets, of which there have been many of distinction, perhaps especially in the period (*ca.* 1815–65) described by the critic Van Wyck Brooks (1936) as *The Flowering of New England.* Distinguished amateurs of natural science have been fewer in number, however, and the only figure on New England's literary scene who is also remembered today for his contribution to natural history is the strange and lonely Henry Thoreau (1817–62), who seems to have spent his days observing natural phenomena with great care and insight and his evenings writing essays extolling nature and simplicity but disparaging natural science as a proper pursuit of the "whole" man. This curious dichotomy, which owed a good deal to the contemporary German *Naturphilosophie*, persists today in the form of the "two cultures" discerned by C. P. Snow. Perhaps because limnology was not then recognized as science,

117

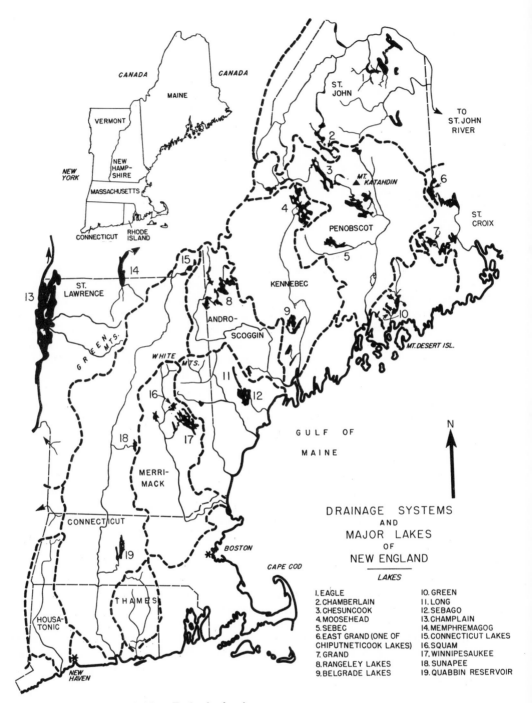

DRAINAGE SYSTEMS
AND
MAJOR LAKES
OF
NEW ENGLAND

LAKES

1. EAGLE	10. GREEN
2. CHAMBERLAIN	11. LONG
3. CHESUNCOOK	12. SEBAGO
4. MOOSEHEAD	13. CHAMPLAIN
5. SEBEC	14. MEMPHREMAGOG
6. EAST GRAND (ONE OF	15. CONNECTICUT LAKES
CHIPUTNETICOOK LAKES)	16. SQUAM
7. GRAND	17. WINNIPESAUKEE
8. RANGELEY LAKES	18. SUNAPEE
9. BELGRADE LAKES	19. QUABBIN RESERVOIR

Fig. 4.1.—General map of New England, showing
political subdivisions, drainage basins, and the largest
lakes.

Thoreau's limnology was relatively free from this philosophical strain, and two chapters of his enduring classic *Walden* are devoted to original scientific observation of high quality, easily surpassing Gilbert White's *Natural History of Selbourne*, to which the work has often been compared. Some of Thoreau's most important discoveries, including that of thermal stratification, remained unpublished in the journals until long after his death and literary enshrinement; his limnological contributions have been discussed by Deevey (1942*a*).

Although much scientific observation on New England's freshwater biology, notably the Ph.D. thesis of E. A. Birge on Cladocera, was stimulated by the appointment of Louis Agassiz as professor in Harvard College, little that can be called limnology (as more general than hydrobiology) appears to have been done until the early work of Whipple on the microscopy of Boston's public water supplies. Agassiz's own contribution to limnology was not made in New England, but on Lake Superior. The scattered data for a proper history of New England limnology have not been brought together, but it is fair to say that the modern phase of the subject began with the appointment in 1928 of G. E. Hutchinson as instructor in zoology at Yale.

Limnological resources

Most of our knowledge of New England lakes has been gained through the biological surveys conducted by the fish and game agencies of the various states. Although these surveys were admittedly aimed at the establishment of effective fisheries management programs, the surveys were sufficiently broadly based so that they have, to varying degrees, provided physical, chemical, geological, taxonomic, and ecological data, permitting a sound, if preliminary, evaluation of each lake as an ecosystem.

These state agencies have had a more sustained interest in limnology in its emphasis upon fisheries than have the many universities and colleges of New England. While members of the faculties of these academic institutions have participated in the state surveys, there has never been a limnological institute associated with any university. At institutions such as Yale University and the University of Maine, where there has been a more or less sustained interest in problems of

lake biology, the research effort has reflected the interests of individuals, rather than the concerted activity of institutes. The nearest approach to an institute is the Geochronometric Laboratory, Yale University, of which E. S. Deevey is director. This is concerned with isotopic geochemistry, including limnological and paleolimnological problems accessible to isotopic methods, as well as with radiocarbon dating.

Many academic biologists who have served on these surveys, especially the New Hampshire surveys, have achieved eminence in biology. Although many were associated with the enterprises for only a season, G. P. Cooper directed the Maine surveys from 1936 to 1944, during which period he was a staff member of the University of Maine, and E. E. Hoover initiated and directed the New Hampshire survey until his untimely death, at age 28, denied him the satisfaction of seeing it completed.

Although most of the attention of the state surveys has been devoted to ponds and lakes, the upland streams of New Hampshire's White Mountains (Hoover, 1936, 1937, 1938; Warfel, 1939) and those of the Berkshire Hills in Massachusetts (Swartz, 1942) have been examined. The results of a fisheries survey of Vermont streams will be published soon. The most complete analyses of the streams and their biota have been undertaken by the New Hampshire surveys, and various aspects of the results are treated by Behney (1937), Trippensee (1937), Rainwater (1937), and Embody *et al.* (1938). Industrial and sewage pollution, which has affected streams and rivers much more than it has the ponds and lakes, is commented upon in both the Massachusetts and New Hampshire streams surveys and is carefully detailed in the latter. The lower courses of the major rivers have been devastated by pollution, but the situation is steadily improving (see Moss, 1961). The interesting accounts of fish and fishing in colonial times as given for the Merrimack River by Marston and Gordon (1938) and for the Connecticut River (Marston, 1939; Moss, 1961) make one deplore the impoverishment of these complex and productive ecosystems that has usually accompanied the growth of human populations. The report by Warfel and Foote (1939) on the relatively unpolluted middle reaches of the Connecticut River is the only such physical, chemical, and biological survey dealing with the contemporary status of a major river in this region (but see also Moss, 1961). Data on the larger rivers of the Merrimack drainage are summarized on pages 84 and 85 of Hoover (1938) but not discussed.

About 1350 of New England's lakes have been the subject of at least primary biological surveys. For New Hampshire and Massachusetts there are published reports on approximately 460 lakes each. While the lakes reported for Massachusetts were at least 20 acres (8 ha), the minimum area considered in New Hampshire was one-half this size. In Maine, Connecticut, and Rhode Island (with 235, 154, and 41 lakes surveyed, respectively) the smallest lakes surveyed were about 25 acres (10 ha). Vermont is the only state for which biological survey reports of the lakes are not published, although bathymetric maps of 16 of the lakes of northeastern Vermont are available (Mills, 1951). In Maine, practically all the lakes that have been surveyed are within a belt extending about 50 mi (80 km) inland from the coast and running from the New Hampshire boundary northeastward to about opposite Mt. Desert Island. The innumerable lakes north of this coastal belt have not been surveyed because of their inaccessibility, except for the Rangeley lakes in the Androscoggin drainage, Moosehead Lake, which is the chief source of the Kennebec River, and Haymock Lake (reached by airplane), a small lake 25 mi (40 km) northeast of Moosehead, draining via the Allagash into the St. John River. However, 439 of the lakes in this region were visited by airplane and sampled for trace metals (Kleinkopf, 1960) but nothing else.

Although all of these state surveys have had roughly the same goal, the methods and results have not always been the same. In the following paragraphs the major items of a survey are listed with notations of special reports or omissions. While the surveys in Connecticut (Thorpe *et al.*, 1942; Wilde *et al.*, 1959) and Massachusetts (Swartz, 1942; McCabe, 1946, 1952, 1953; McCabe and Swartz, 1951; Stroud, 1955; Mullan and Tompkins, 1959) gave the most complete morphometric data, most surveys provided adequate data even though all parameters were not calculated. The conspicuous exception was the New Hampshire surveys (Hoover, 1937, 1938; Warfel, 1939), where "maximum depth" was the only depth datum provided, although soundings

were given for some lakes in Hoover (1936). The only available study of Vermont lakes (Mills, 1951) provided bathymetric maps, as well as geological information necessary for an understanding of the origin of the basins. Such detailed geological data are available for few other New England lakes, although each of the New Hampshire surveys has a chapter on the geology of the pertinent portion of the state. Other geological information may be gleaned from Figures 4.6 and 4.23.

Of the physical parameters, midsummer temperature series were standard for all surveys, but light penetration has been variously treated. Transparency (Secchi disc) values were determined in the New Hampshire, Connecticut, and Massachusetts surveys, while light extinction curves were determined by Saila and Horton (1957) in some of the Rhode Island lakes. Maine surveys gave no data on light penetration.

Vertical series of dissolved oxygen were as standard a part of the chemistry as temperature series were of the physics, and vertical series of pH determination were made on all but the Connecticut survey. Otherwise, the Connecticut survey was the only one to examine the chemistry with thoroughness (Deevey and Bishop, 1942; Deevey, 1940). Determinations of methyl orange alkalinity (summarized in section "Geology and regional limnology") and total phosphorus were made routinely in Massachusetts and sporadically in the Maine surveys. New Hampshire surveys noted alkalinities routinely, while Rhode Island surveys noted resistivity values (Saila and Horton, 1957).

The fishes represent the only group of organisms to be specifically identified on all surveys, and the ecological studies, referred to species, are that much more significant. Mention should be made of the excellent chapters on fishes in the New Hampshire series (Gordon, 1937; R. M. Bailey, 1938; J. R. Bailey and Oliver, 1939), the Connecticut report (Webster, 1942), and the extensive considerations of the ecology of the fishes of Maine lakes (Cooper, 1939a, 1939b, 1940, 1941, 1942; Cooper and Fuller, 1945, 1946). The plankton and benthos were sampled quantitatively in all surveys except that in Rhode Island. Usually the organisms were sorted into major groups and counted or weighed. Notes on phytoplankton and zooplankton with identification to genus or family were given by Edmondson and Fuller (1937), Edmondson (1938), and Cole

(1939) for some New Hampshire lakes. Gustafson (1952) classified the algae, planktonic and non-planktonic, of some lakes of northeastern Massachusetts to genus and gave the distribution of the genera in these lakes. The *Daphnia* of the extensive Maine surveys have been identified and their distribution examined in Brooks (unpublished 1).

Although the benthic organisms have been examined in a general way in all the surveys (except Rhode Island's), they have been extensively and intensively studied in Connecticut lakes only (Deevey and Bishop, 1942; Deevey, 1941*a*, 1941*b*).

Parasitological surveys of the fish have been conducted in Connecticut (Hunter, 1942), north-central Massachusetts (Sindermann, 1953), and in Maine (Meyer, 1954).

The authors wish to express thanks here to the directors and aquatic biologists of the fish and game departments of several states who were helpful in making the publications of their agencies available: James P. Galligan, Connecticut; Charles L. McLaughlin, Massachusetts; James M. MacMartin, Vermont; William A. Tompkins, Massachusetts.

Physiography, climate, and vegetation

As described in a later section, New England's geology is that of the exposed and deeply dissected roots of a Paleozoic mountain system. The present surface is "a plateau-like upland declining toward the sea, surmounted by residual mountains standing singly or in groups and ranges" (Fennenman, 1938, pp. 344–345). The maximum present altitude, Mt. Washington in the White Mountains of New Hampshire, is 1,950 m; Mt. Katahdin, the highest peak of an isolated range in central Maine, is 1,580 m above sea level, and the Green Mountains in Vermont rise to altitudes above 1,200 m. Local relief is typically of the order of 200 m near the coast and 400 m in the north. Lowlands developed on sedimentary rocks are narrow, although the wider Carboniferous districts of the southeastern portion lie a little lower than the surrounding crystalline highlands; the broadest area of Silurian sediments, in northern Maine, underlies an extensive upland with summit altitudes between 320 and 380 m. Though hardly mountainous as compared to the folded Appalachians, New England is distinctly a rugged country, in which steep slopes are common. Much of northern New England is still largely wilderness with dense forests and poor roads, and the recent presence of a stagnant ice sheet, in combination with the rough terrain, has produced a landscape exceptionally rich in lakes, many of them of spectacular beauty.

The climate of New England is maritime, in the sense that extremes of temperature are rare, and precipitation is abundant and rather evenly distributed seasonally and geographically. The coastal belt is much more maritime than the interior, however, as the isotherms of Figure 4.2 show, and whereas one winter in four is likely to be too mild to permit work on Linsley Pond in southern Connecticut, northern Connecticut has no such difficulty, and northern New England winters are of legendary severity. Climatic data are summarized in the 1941 Yearbook (U.S. Dept. Agr., 1941) and in the "Annual Summary by Sections," part of the U.S. Weather Bureau's journal *Climatological Data*. A *Hydrologic Investigations Atlas* (Knox and Nordenson, 1955), available from the U.S. Geological Survey, contains detailed maps of precipitation and runoff for New England and adjacent New York; Figures 4.3 and 4.4 are simplified versions of these maps, and Figure 4.5, taken from the same work, shows evaporation from lakes. The relatively dry interior belts are features that do not show so clearly on older maps; they express a small but significant degree of rain shadow in the lee of the Taconic-Green Mountain and White Mountain ranges, which stand athwart the eastward-moving cyclonic storm tracks.

Although three centuries of European habitation have left little primeval forest and none that is completely undisturbed, much forested country remains, and the proportion is actually increasing as the poorer agricultural land is abandoned and becomes suburban (Wright *et al.*, 1933). New England forests are diverse in type and rich in arboreal species as compared with Europe, though much less so than those of the southern Appalachians. The "climax forest," an abstract concept that appeals more to academic ecologists than to practical foresters, is of at least two types in New England; according to the outstanding work on the subject (Braun, 1950), the hemlock-white pine-northern hardwood region occupies all of northern New England, while most of Connecticut, Rhode Island, Cape Cod, and the shore south of Cape Ann belong to the oak-chestnut

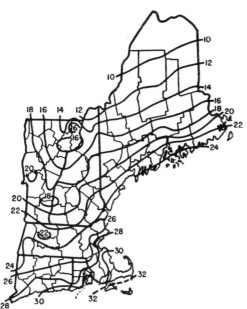

Fig. 4.2.—January and July isotherms for New England. From *Climate and Man* (U.S.D.A., 1941).

region that is more fully developed south of the glacial boundary. The dominant species in the northern forest are hemlock (*Tsuga canadensis*), sugar maple (*Acer saccharum*), and beech (*Fagus grandifolia*), with white pine (*Pinus strobus*) highly characteristic but rarely dominant. In the south the oaks *Quercus velutina*, *Q. coccinea*, *Q. alba*, and *Q. montana* are dominant, the chestnut (*Castanea dentata*) having been extinct since about 1920 as a forest tree. *Carya*, *Juglans*, *Nyssa*, *Liquidambar*, *Liriodendron*, and *Platanus* are all native to this region, but of these only *Carya* (shagbark hickory, *C. ovata*) is common so far north.

The forest types are probably distinct, but they are difficult to demonstrate in the disturbed areas near cities or on the extensive outwash plains dominated by pitch pine (*P. rigida*); what the car-window botanist is more likely to see, as he crosses the boundary from south to north, is a change in the pioneer vegetation of abandoned fields. In the south, red cedar (*Juniperus virginiana*) and gray birch (*Betula populifolia*) dom-

inate the landscape; toward the north, white pine becomes the old-field tree.

A third New England forest type, widespread but confined to higher altitudes and not easy to map, is an outlier of the boreal coniferous forest or taiga. White spruce (*Picea glauca*) and balsam fir (*Abies balsamea*) are the dominants of this forest in Canada, but in New England white spruce tends to give way to red spruce (*P. rubens*), which continues down the Appalachians. Paper birch (*Betula papyrifera*) is a characteristic pioneer species. Black spruce (*P. mariana*) is the species of bogs in northern New England, as it is throughout the Canadian taiga, and is usually accompanied by tamarack (*Larix laricina*).

Geology and regional limnology

Geologic history

All of New England belongs to the Appalachian system, an "ideal" mountain system that has served geologists as model and as laboratory for more than a century. In this account, which leans

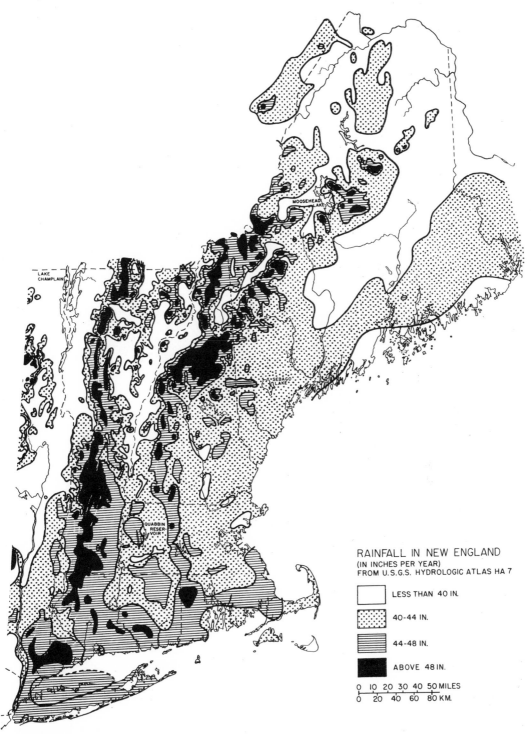

RAINFALL IN NEW ENGLAND
(IN INCHES PER YEAR)
FROM U.S.G.S. HYDROLOGIC ATLAS HA 7

LESS THAN 40 IN.

40-44 IN.

44-48 IN.

ABOVE 48 IN.

0 10 20 30 40 50 MILES
0   20   40   60   80 KM.

Fig. 4.3.—Precipitation (inches per year) in New England. Simplified from *Hydrologic Investigations Atlas HA 7* (Knox and Nordenson, 1955) by omission of some contours. The basic data are averages for the 20-year period 1930–49.

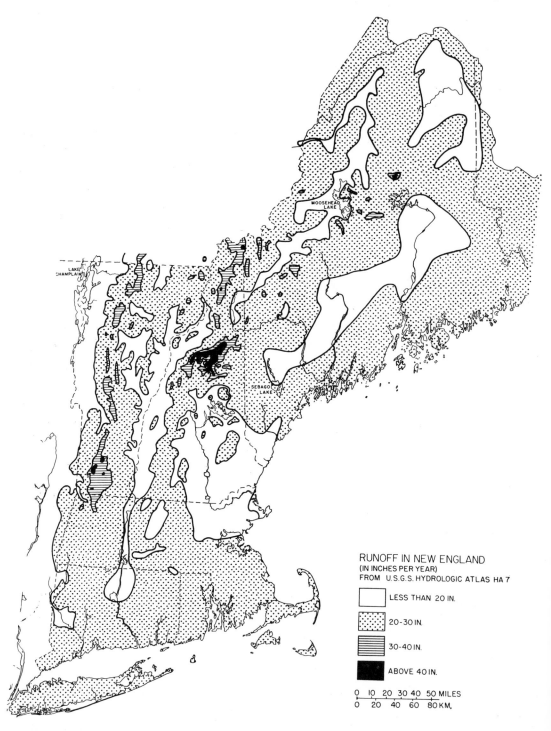

RUNOFF IN NEW ENGLAND
(IN INCHES PER YEAR)
FROM U.S.G.S. HYDROLOGIC ATLAS HA 7

☐ LESS THAN 20 IN.

▦ 20-30 IN.

▤ 30-40 IN.

■ ABOVE 40 IN.

0 10 20 30 40 50 MILES
0   20   40   60 80 KM.

Fig. 4.4.—Runoff (inches per year) in New England. Simplified from *Hydrologic Investigations Atlas HA 7* (Knox and Nordenson, 1955) by omission of some contours. The basic data are the runoff figures at a network of U.S. Geological Survey stream-gaging stations, published annually in *U.S.G.S. Water-Supply Papers*. Averages are for the 20-year period 1930–49.

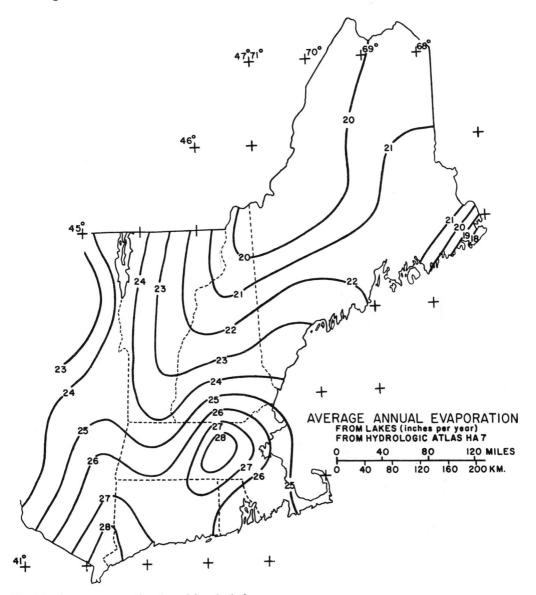

Fig. 4.5.—Average evaporation from lakes, in inches per year, computed from pan-evaporation data in New England and New York. From *Hydrologic Investigations Atlas HA 7* (Knox and Nordenson, 1955).

heavily on the recent synthesis of King (1959), modern ideas about geosynclines (e.g., Kay, 1951) play a dominant role. General geologic maps, such as the U.S. Geological Survey Geologic Map of the United States (1932, 4 sheets, 1:2,500,000) can be used for most purposes, with the realization that most "Archean" rocks mapped in New England are probably Paleozoic. Figure 4.6 is a simplified version of this map. There are new

state maps of Vermont (Doll, 1961), New Hampshire (Billings, 1955), and Connecticut (Rodgers *et al.*, 1956, 1959); other state maps are older (Massachusetts and Rhode Island: Emerson, 1917; Maine: Keith, 1933).

The Appalachian geosyncline, which bordered the eastern and southern margins of the pre-Cambrian continental shield throughout Paleozoic time, is divisible longitudinally into two parts, the

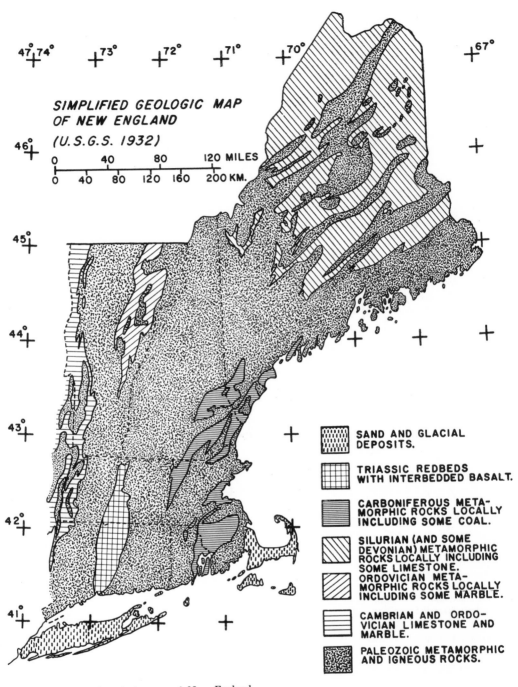

Fig. 4.6.—Simplified geologic map of New England, from the U.S. Geological Survey map of the United States, 1:2,500,000, 1932, reprinted 1960.

shelf and the *foredeep*. The proximal shelf belt received shallow-water marine and continental sediments on a continental platform that subsided very gradually and in proportion to its load; the early Paleozoic strata thicken remarkably toward the foredeep, but none was formed very far above or below sea level. This *miogeosynclinal* belt now forms the *folded* or *sedimentary Appalachians*, displayed from central New York through Pennsylvania into Tennessee and Alabama but poorly represented in New England, most of which lay farther seaward, i.e., was part of the foredeep. In this more peripheral region, which continues southward as the Piedmont of the Carolinas and Georgia, relatively intense metamorphism is the rule. The sediments (dominantly graywackes and notably lacking in carbonates) appear to have accumulated very rapidly, together with extrusive and intrusive volcanic rocks that are partly submarine, in a complex of deep-ocean troughs, the floors of which subsided even more rapidly than the troughs were filled with sediments. This foredeep is the *eugeosynclinal* belt, which now forms the *crystalline Appalachians*. "Appalachia," the hypothetical land mass that provided materials for both parts of the geosyncline, was probably a series of island arcs, perched precariously on the seaward edges of the troughs, close to the axis of the mobile belt that produced the volcanism. Though doubtless mainly volcanic, the islands must have grown in part by a kind of cannibalism, as eugeosynclinal volcanic and clastic rocks were partially remelted in the roots of the island blocks before the blocks were uplifted. At various times, episodes of mountain-making, centered in the mobile eugeosynclinal belt, uplifted major parts of the whole "Appalachia" mass and plastered it against the continent. The same crustal paroxysms that brought deep-sea deposits high above sea level as the crystalline Appalachians provided the horizontal forces that crumpled the miogeosynclinal sediments.

In consequence of this Paleozoic history, New England is a metamorphic terrain profoundly modified by volcanism. Unaltered sedimentary rocks are rare, and carbonate sediments, so common in the folded belt, are even rarer. The exceptional sediments and their histories are described in chronologic order.

Early Paleozoic.—Underlying the Great Valley of Vermont, which continues southward past Stockbridge, Massachusetts, and into northwest-

ern Connecticut, there is a narrow belt of Cambrian and Ordovician limestones, mostly metamorphosed to marble, that evidently belongs to the miogeosynclinal series. This is a transitional zone just west of the Green Mountain front (a mountain mass corresponding to the Blue Ridge that divides the crystalline Piedmont from the central sedimentary Appalachians). Some overthrusting occurred here relatively early in Paleozoic time, and the north-south–trending Taconic range, which bounds the valley on the west, is the remnant of an overthrust block of Cambrian and Ordovician rocks of more nearly eugeosynclinal facies, bodily moved several miles westward from above or perhaps even from beyond the Green Mountains. The limestones, where not protected against removal by the overthrust block, have been eroded to form a narrow lowland, merging northward with the Champlain lowland and drained southward by the upper Housatonic River. New England's hard-water lakes are largely confined to this belt.

Middle Paleozoic.—The Taconic overthrusting implies that part of New England was welded to the continental shelf as early as late-Ordovician time; some Silurian and Devonian sediments, therefore, accumulated on the newly-made platform, thereby extending the miogeosynclinal relationships eastward into eastern Vermont and even into New Hampshire and northern Maine. The widest belt of Silurian rocks, in northern Maine, is dominantly shale, but some beds of Silurian limestone occur in the valley of the Aroostook River near the New Brunswick border, and streaks of low-grade marble occur at several places within the metamorphic belt, notably in eastern Vermont near the Connecticut River.

Carboniferous.—Carboniferous sediments, probably deposited in separate basins on the growing continental platform, outcrop in the Boston basin, in a broader basin of which Narragansett Bay is now a part, and in southeastern New Hampshire and adjacent states, the last being mapped as Ordovician, Silurian, and Devonian on the newer map (Billings, 1955). These sediments are dominantly shales and sandstones, in part non-marine, and contain some highly graphitic coal but essentially no carbonate.

Triassic.—By late Triassic (probably at the end of Permian) time the Appalachian orogeny was complete, and the high mountains of New England were being deeply eroded. A broad continental basin west of what was then the mountain front received much of the debris in the form of fluviatile sand and gravel, while basaltic lavas were injected as flat-lying sheets between and in part upon the layers of clastic sediment. Subsequent arching uplifted the crust under the Triassic basin and led to the removal of most of its central portion. What is left in New England is a thick pile of *redbeds*—interbedded arkose (feldspathic sandstone) and dolerite (traprock), dipping gently eastward along the eastern flank of the arch. Though much weaker than the surrounding and underlying crystallines, these rocks have been protected by deep downdropping along faults at their eastern margin. The Triassic belt now forms a north-south–trending lowland, excavated largely by the Connecticut River in Massachusetts and Connecticut, where the edges of the traprock sills form characteristic long ridges separated by valleys developed in the weaker sandstones. A small piece of the otherwise missing central section of the arch has been separately dropped down, apparently as a graben, and now exposes Triassic sediments in the Pomperaug Valley in western Connecticut; the western flank of the arch, with westward-dipping but otherwise identical Triassic strata, is preserved beyond the Hudson River in New York and New Jersey, where one of its dolerite sills now forms the Hudson Palisades. The Triassic rocks are more soluble than other New England rocks, except the limestones, and include some thin beds of freshwater marlstone; as a result, medium-hard waters are characteristic of the central Triassic lowland, and iron is abundant enough to have been mined (as bog-iron) in a few places in colonial days.

Post-Triassic.—If any younger sediments were laid down in New England, they have been almost entirely removed. Cretaceous and younger coastal-plain sediments are exposed on Martha's Vineyard, but the rest of New England's coastal plain is now drowned. A deposit of Tertiary lignite was formerly exposed at Brandon, Vermont. The post-Triassic history is otherwise one of erosion, possibly including one or more episodes of peneplanation followed by uplift and renewed dissection. The idea of repeated peneplanation, which strongly colors the otherwise excellent account of Fenneman (1938), is considered an illusion by many modern geomorphologists.

Pleistocene.—Although all of New England was glaciated, its tough rocks and rugged topography

presented massive obstacles to erosion by moving ice, and glacial erosion is confined to obvious softening of some contours and excavation of a few deep troughs, like that now occupied by Lake Willoughby in northern Vermont. Moreover, although Pleistocene glaciation was presumably multiple in New England as elsewhere, all traces of older Pleistocene deposits appear to have been removed by the last (Wisconsin) ice. The Glacial Map of eastern United States (Flint *et al.,* 1959) is, therefore, rather uninformative in its New England sector and has not been reproduced in this chapter. It shows wide areas of undifferentiated Wisconsin till (generally thin and exceedingly stony, accounting for the "hard-scrabble" quality of much New England agriculture). Numerous bodies of mappable outwash occur mostly along valleys, and there are even more numerous bodies of ice-contact stratified drift. Terminal moraines exist as short segments near Charlestown, Rhode Island, and on Cape Cod and the offshore islands, and have been variously correlated with the moraines on Long Island and farther west. Presumably (Flint, 1953) the recorded glaciation was of late (or "classic") Wisconsin age, culminating in the construction of the Long Island end-moraines about 20 or 18 thousand years ago.

The outwash and ice-contact stratified drift are deposits of a retreating glacier, the distal zone of which stagnated and wasted away *in situ;* Flint's *Glacial Geology of Connecticut* (1930) was one of the earliest works to recognize the significance and enormous extent of dead-ice features. Two bodies of (Wisconsin) till in superposition are reported at several places in Massachusetts and Connecticut, but their absolute ages are unknown, and the New England correlatives of the late-Wisconsin substages (Iowan, Farmdale, Tazewell, Cary, Mankato, Valders) are problematic.

At Totoket, near New Haven, Connecticut, Leopold (1956) reported pollen-stratigraphic evidence of a late-glacial climatic oscillation of Alleröd type (tundra–park-tundra–tundra) but of Bölling age (13 to 12 thousand years ago), implying that the retreating glacier-margin may have paused or readvanced at Middletown, a few miles north, in Port Huron (Mankato) time, but this evidence is shaken by radiocarbon-dated pollen sections on Martha's Vineyard (Ogden, 1959, and unpublished) that seem to contradict the general interpretation of Deevey (1958). Spruce forests certainly grew in central Massachusetts in Alleröd (Two Creeks or Port Huron-Valders) time (Davis, 1958), and were disturbed but not destroyed by the Valders climatic deterioration; the implication is that the Valders ice-margin (which destroyed the Two Creeks forest in Wisconsin 11,400 years ago) lay far to the north of central Massachusetts. It is also believed that the Valders ice-margin lay to the north or northwest of Aroostook County, Maine (Deevey, 1951), and may not have crossed the St. Lawrence lowland (Terasmae, 1960; MacClintock and Terasmae, 1960).

Extensive bodies of laminated ("varved") silt and clay record the existence of glacial lakes in the Connecticut and Merrimack valleys, in the city of Providence, Rhode Island, and in the Champlain lowland of Vermont. The largest of these belongs to Lake Hitchcock, in the Connecticut valley, which was nearly 200 mi long though very narrow. If the laminations are annual, Lake Hitchcock endured for more than 4,000 years, but despite impressive similarity of "varve" sequences between the Connecticut deposits and similar clays in the Hudson valley (Antevs, 1922), other evidence is increasingly unfavorable to the view that the lamination is annual. (For limnologists the most interesting of Antevs' numerous papers on American glacial "varves" is the relatively recent one on Steep Rock Lake, Ontario [Antevs, 1951].)

Relative levels of land and sea during and after New England's glaciation have not been satisfactorily worked out, in part because much of the relevant evidence has been drowned by the eustatic rise of sea level, amounting to some 36 m in the last 11,000 years (Godwin *et al.*, 1958; Fairbridge, 1961). Late-glacial submergence, presumably the result of delayed isostatic recovery from glacial loading during the early part of the eustatic rise, brought marine clay into the Champlain lowland, into the Boston basin, and over the coastal belt of Maine to altitudes now at least 60 m above sea level (Bloom, 1960); the limnological consequences of the marine overlap are discussed later. Later, while the sea rose to about its present level, crustal upwarping raised northern New England farther and faster, but this isostatic rebound appears to have come to an end, at least in New England, several thousand years ago. The latest movement along the whole New England shore is a relative rise of the sea. Recent

tectonic subsidence is strongly suggested by this evidence, which shows that coastal marshes that began to form from 2 to 4 thousand years ago are still forming, not only south of Cape Cod but as far north as the Bay of Fundy.

Holocene.—Ignoring local chronological and vegetational details that are still far from clear, one can describe New England's postglacial climatic history as nearly identical to western Europe's: von Post's tripartite scheme (increasing, maximal, decreasing warmth) fits well with most pollen-stratigraphic data from eastern United States. The middle period of maximum warmth (Danish pollen zones V through VIII; New England zones B through C-2) is the Hypsithermal sub-age of Deevey and Flint (1957). Figure 4.7, taken from this publication, is a stratigraphic chart of the pollen zones with some external correlations supported by radiocarbon dating. The New England pollen zones were first established as a by-product of paleolimnological studies (Deevey, 1939, 1942*b*) on Linsley Pond, a locality that requires re-investigation by more modern methods. Radiocarbon dates have not been conspicuously helpful in this intensively studied region, evidently because the medium-hard waters of the Triassic lowland incorporate some ancient (C^{14}-free) carbonate (Deevey *et al.*, 1954; Oana and Deevey, 1960; Stuiver and Deevey, 1961, and unpublished); and for this reason paleolimnological studies by Deevey and collaborators have been shifted to the softer lakes of the crystalline eastern Connecticut highland.

Pollen sequences recovered from lakes and lowmoor bogs are relatively insensitive to variations of rainfall, and the raised bogs that are so much more informative in this respect have not been studied in New England. Recurrence horizons, demonstrated by fossil testaceous rhizopods as well as by more orthodox peat stratigraphy, are known in a bog in Nova Scotia (Ogden, 1960) and should be sought in the magnificent raised bogs of eastern Maine. The rest of New England has a small summer excess of evapotranspiration (Thornthwaite, 1948), and all its bogs are believed to be of the lowmoor type.

Origin of lake basins

Probably all New England lakes, except the artificial ones, owe their origin in part to Pleistocene glaciation, but the majority appear to be in rock basins and only the dams are made of glacial

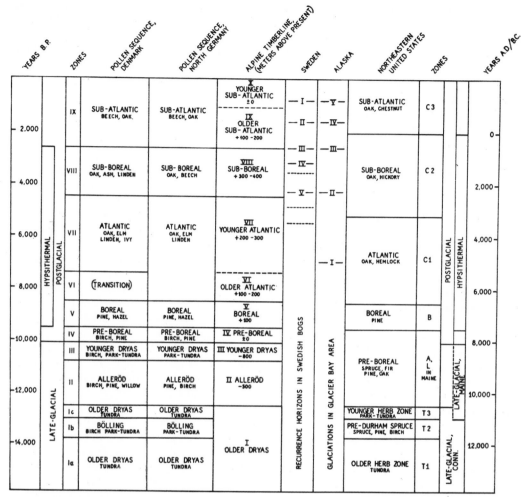

Fig. 4.7.—Stratigraphic chart of late-Pleistocene chronologies in eastern North America, with some external correlations. From Deevey and Flint, 1957, Fig. 1.

drift. Without subsurface studies, which have rarely been made, it is difficult to be sure that the height of a drift dam, where composed of till, exceeds the depth of the lake behind, but the prevailing depths are so shallow as to allow the theory that many lakes are dammed entirely by till. In one drainage basin in New Hampshire (the Merrimack: Hoover, 1938), for example, about half of 181 natural lakes surveyed are between 3 and 9 m deep (probably including the heights of the small artifical dams that are nearly universal), and these figures seem to be fair estimates of the average thickness of till, at least in the valleys where most lakes are located. (In

northern Vermont, where Mills [1951] studied the morphology and sediments of several lakes, the till is reported to be generally 12 to 15 m thick, but this is probably an overestimate; Goldthwait [1925] gives 3 to 8 m for New Hampshire, and Flint [1930] gives 3 m for Connecticut). Dams composed of ice-contact stratified drift, especially kames, are probably commoner than those of till alone, but it seems certain that unconsolidated deposits of either sort would not hold so many lakes 10 to 15 thousand years after their formation if the underlying bedrock were not full of irregularities. Kettles are of course exceedingly numerous, Linsley Pond and Walden

Pond being examples of this familiar type. Many kettles are compound or are formed in a jumbled mass of ice-contact stratified drift and till, some of which may be flowtill. Figure 4.8, a somewhat extreme example, is nonetheless an elegant illustration of complex lake-basin forms in a region of stagnant ice. (Webster Lake, also known as Lake Chargogagogmanchogagogcharbunagungamog, is distinguished for its name too; according to prob-

ably false Algonkian etymology, it means "I fish on my side, you fish on your side, nobody fish in between.")

Lake basins formed by glacial erosion are either scarce or difficult to identify, but Lake Willoughby in northern Vermont occupies a spectac-

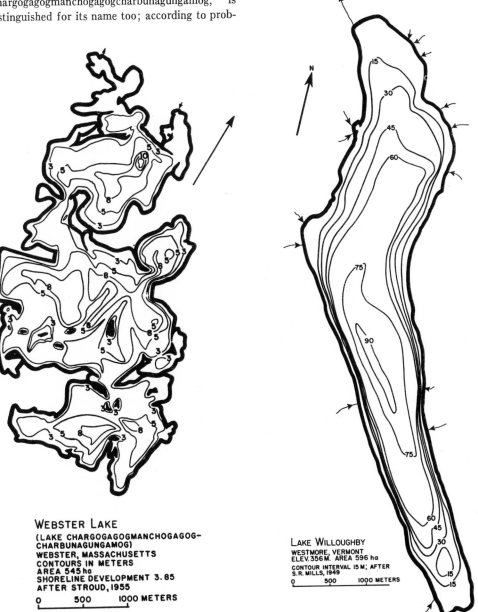

WEBSTER LAKE
(LAKE CHARGOGAGOGMANCHOGAGOG-
CHARBUNAGUNGAMOG)
WEBSTER, MASSACHUSETTS
CONTOURS IN METERS
AREA 545 ha
SHORELINE DEVELOPMENT 3.85
AFTER STROUD, 1955

0   500   1000 METERS

LAKE WILLOUGHBY
WESTMORE, VERMONT
ELEV. 356 M. AREA 596 ha
CONTOUR INTERVAL 15 M; AFTER
S.R. MILLS, 1949

0   500   1000 METERS

Fig. 4.8.—Bathymetric map of Webster Lake (Lake Chargogagogmanchogagogcharbunagungamog), Webster, Massachusetts. Redrawn, with contours converted from feet to meters, from Stroud, 1955.

Fig. 4.9.—Bathymetric map of Lake Willoughby, Westmore, Vermont. Redrawn, with contours converted from feet to meters, from Mills, 1951.

TABLE 4.1

Ionic composition of some New England waters, with comparisons

	Milliequivalents per L							Total mg/L
	HCO₃	SO₄	Cl	Ca	Mg	Na	K	
Moosehead Lake (Clarke, 1924)	0.180	0.043	0.056	0.110	0.025	0.078	0.015	16.0
Lake Winnipesaukee (Clarke, 1924)	0.164	0.083	0.045	0.135	0.058	0.104	0.015	18.2
Lake Winnipesaukee (U.S.G.S., 1958)	0.134	0.108	0.065	0.195	0.041	0.087	0.005	21
Conn. R., Pittsburg, N.H. (Clarke, 1924)	0.125	0.121	0.003	0.165	0.082	0.035	0.010	17.9
Conn. R., Middletown, Conn. (U.S.G.S.)	0.690	0.457	0.211	0.847	0.165	0.304	0.056	102
Mean, non-sedimentary basins (79 anal.)	0.233	0.113	0.051	0.230	0.083	0.078	0.014	37.5
Mean, sedimentary basins (16 anal.)	1.137	0.358	0.145	0.876	0.349	0.205	0.037	108.9
9 Nova Scotia lakes on quartzite (Gorham, 1961)	0.029	0.104	0.138	0.104	0.033	0.130	0.015	ca. 27
Uppland 1–21 (Lohammar, 1938)	0.861	0.188	0.110	0.789	0.196	0.158	0.026	87.8
Rain water, Caribou, Me. (Junge and Werby, 1958)	n.d.	0.0580	0.0085	0.0315	n.d.	0.0117	0.0038	n.d.

ular U-shaped valley (Fig. 4.9) and was the subject of a special study by E. C. Jacobs (1921), who considered the preglacial trough to have been a graben in the Ordovician rocks. Crystal Lake, nearby, provides another example (Mills, 1951). A topographic map of Maine shows a marked northwest-southeast linearity both of drainage lines and of lake basins over much of the country, and because this is parallel to the direction of ice movement, it is possible that the grain has been accentuated by glaciation. On the other hand, there are wide areas in Kennebec County where the grain strikes north-south or even northeast-southwest, athwart the lines of glacial flow as indicated by striae, and all the conspicuous topographic linearity in Maine may, therefore, reflect not glacial modeling but foliation of the rocks.

Regional limnology

Information on the chemistry of New England lake waters is extensive in some districts but very unevenly distributed. Northern Maine provides the only large body of data on limnological abundance of the trace metals Mn, Pb, Ag, Zn, Cu, Ni, Zr, Va, Mo, Cr, Sn, and Ti (Kleinkopf, 1960), while the lake waters of the whole state of Vermont (in contrast to the streams) have apparently never been analyzed chemically. Total phos-

phorus has been measured in about 50 Connecticut lakes, in about 40 Massachusetts lakes, and in more than 100 lakes of coastal Maine, but the reports of the Maine Department of Inland Fisheries and Game, so helpful in other respects, are otherwise almost devoid of chemical data.

A few representative analyses, complete for major cations and anions, are collected in Table 4.1. New England's waters are obviously very dilute and of the bicarbonate type. On the other hand, though Gorham (1961) remarks on the close similarity in concentration and in ionic proportions of his Nova Scotia lake waters to the average rain water in Newfoundland (Junge and Werby, 1958), New England lakes are, in general, not simply filled with the rain water that falls at Caribou, Maine (Figs. 4.10 and 4.11). The table shows that Nova Scotia waters are chloride, not bicarbonate, waters, owing to proximity to the ocean, and New England is much more continental. The steep fall of the isochlors over the eastern states, shown from old data in Figure 4.12 (Jackson, 1905), also brings out this point. Caribou rain water has a large excess of sulfate, presumably the result of industrial pollution of the atmosphere, and in fact has more sulfate (2.78 mg/L) than 14 of the 95 U.S.G.S. New England analyses included in the means of Table 4.1 (from which the more sulfate-rich examples were ex-

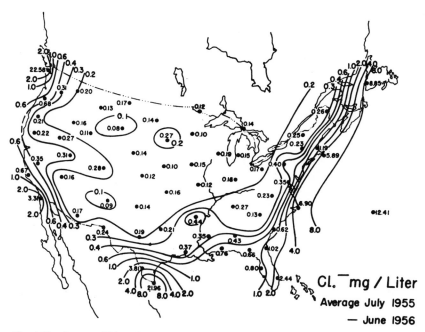

Fig. 4.10.—Average Cl in rain water, 1955, in the United States. From Junge and Werby, 1958, Fig. 1.

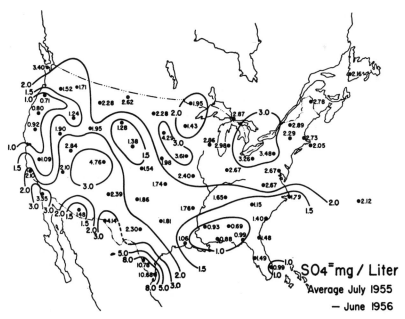

Fig. 4.11.—Average SO₄ in rain water, 1955, in the United States. From Junge and Werby, 1958, Fig. 8.

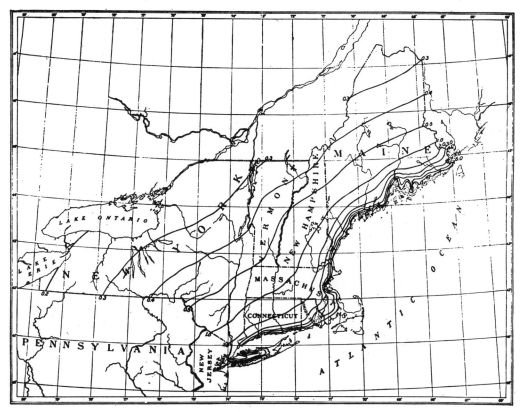

Fig. 4.12.—Isochlors for surface waters, in mg Cl per liter, in New England and New York. From Jackson, 1905.

cluded on suspicion of sulfite contamination). Atmospheric sulfate may well be increasing along with industrial CO_2; the two analyses of Lake Winnipesaukee, which are at least 30 years apart since Clarke's (1924) analysis is undated, support this suggestion. For other ions, however, it is clear that the relatively small amounts in the runoff waters are derived mainly from the rocks, not from the rain.

Figure 4.13 is a first attempt to find patterns in the distribution of bicarbonate alkalinity such as those found earlier in Connecticut (Deevey, 1940). Since many analyses give total residue only, a statistical study was first made (Fig. 4.14) on a selection of U.S.G.S. analyses (mainly streams, but excluding obviously polluted waters and the lower reaches of large rivers). As compared with Rodhe's (1949) standard bicarbonate water, some extra solutes are evident, and Table 4.1 suggests that these are both sulfates and chlorides. Nevertheless, the slope of the bicar-

bonate-salinity relationship is the same, and the regression equation has been used to convert all values to bicarbonate.

A high proportion of New England lakes are "extremely soft"—a useful addition ($HCO_3 <$ 10 mg/L) to the standard Wisconsin categories: soft, < 28; medium-hard, 28–84; hard, > 84 (L. R. Wilson, 1935). The Maine waters are so soft that the mean of 439 salinities, 13.5 mg/L (Turekian and Kleinkopf, 1956), actually implies negative bicarbonate values by the regression equation used. Hard waters, as expected, are almost strictly confined to the Cambrian-Ordovician limestone belt; however, the belt of Carboniferous metamorphic rocks in Massachusetts and New Hampshire also contains two hard localities and several that approach or exceed medium hardness. Medium-hard waters are consistently found in the Triassic lowland of southern Connecticut. (Data are lacking for the Silurian limestone belt in Aroostook County, Maine.) The streaks of

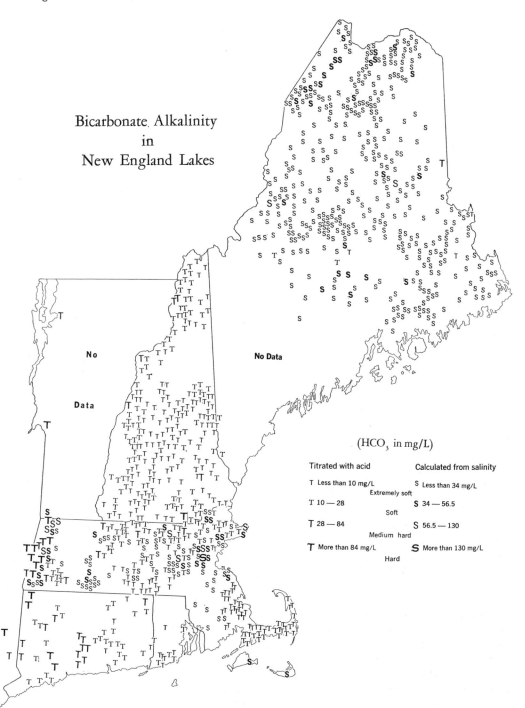

Bicarbonate Alkalinity
in
New England Lakes

(HCO₃ in mg/L)

Titrated with acid	Calculated from salinity
T Less than 10 mg/L	S Less than 34 mg/L
Extremely soft	
T 10 — 28	S 34 — 56.5
Soft	
T 28 — 84	S 56.5 — 130
Medium hard	
T More than 84 mg/L	S More than 130 mg/L
Hard	

Fig. 4.13.—Distribution of HCO₃ in surface waters of New England lakes. Sources of data: Maine, Kleinkopf, 1955; New Hampshire, survey reports of New Hampshire Fish and Game Department; Massachusetts, annual reports of Massachusetts Department of Public Health and fisheries survey reports of Massachusetts Division of Fisheries and Game; Rhode Island, Saila and Horton, 1957 (with correction of arithmetic errors in original); Connecticut, Deevey, 1940. A few analyses of small streams near lakes were taken from U.S. Geological Survey publications (Clarke, 1924; U.S.G.S., 1958, 1959; Pauszek, 1961).

impure marble that occur in Vermont and New Hampshire produce several medium-hard localities and raise several others from the "extremely soft" to the "soft" class. Some smearing of carbonate materials beyond the outcrops is to be expected in the glacial drift, accounting for medium-hard lakes in northwestern Connecticut, but the two hard waters farther southeast of this district are dammed reaches of the Housatonic River.

The trace-metal analyses of Kleinkopf (1960; Turekian and Kleinkopf, 1956) are not very informative without comparative data from other regions. All elements measured showed a variance of at least two, usually three, orders of magnitude, which makes averaging an uncertain procedure. High values for several of the metals are concentrated around known rock masses of unusual mineral composition, and they point to other rock masses that may be geochemically (or economically) interesting. Typical averages, obtained by grouping methods and assuming total salinity to be normally distributed, are as follows, in mg/m³: Cu, 11.6; Mn, 4.0; Pb, 2.6; Ti, 2.0; Ni, 0.2; Cr, 0.2 (Turekian and Kleinkopf, 1956, with correction of an arithmetic error in the original). Copper, at least, is a relatively mobile element in lakes, and in the course of a year its variation in Connecticut lakes spans the whole range of Maine data (Riley, 1939).

Total phosphorus values for Connecticut, summarized by Deevey (1940), show that this region is typical of humid regions in its phosphorus deficiency; the mean quantity in 47 lakes was 14.9 mg/m³. The lakes of the Triassic lowland, possibly because of agricultural enrichment, averaged a little higher, but Linsley Pond, much the best-studied of the lowland lakes, averaged 21 mg/m³ in 1938 and 1939. Maine data (Cooper, 1942; Cooper and Fuller, 1946) are similar; the mean for 50 lakes in the central coastal district was 14.9 mg/m³, and for 57 lakes in the Penobscot basin and on Mt. Desert Island the mean was 11.5 mg/m³. Massachusetts figures are higher. Swartz (1942) gives the mean of 9 lowland lakes as 44 ± 23 mg/m³, though the mean of 12 highland lakes was 3 ± 1 mg/m³. Snow (in McCabe, 1946) gives phosphorus data that may not be comparable with the others for methodologic reasons; if they are, and if "phosphates" means PO_4, the mean of 22 lakes in Worcester County, 1944–45, was 65.4 mg/m³. Excluding 6 lakes for which the ratio of total N to P is incredibly high,

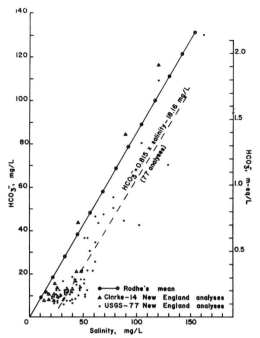

Fig. 4.14.—Regression of alkalinity (mg HCO_3 per liter) on total salinity in New England waters, from selected U.S.G.S. analyses (U.S.G.S., 1958, 1959) and from Clarke, 1924. Clarke's salinities are computed by addition of ions, and the later U.S.G.S. salinities are residues on evaporation; only the latter were used for the regression line. Rodhe's (1949) line of relationship is for more purely bicarbonate waters than those of New England.

the mean PO_4 is 86.5 mg P/m³ and the N to P ratio is 5.8. A close relationship was shown in Connecticut between total phosphorus and the standing crop of plankton as measured by chlorophyll analyses, and the relationship between plankton and nutrients was improved statistically by considering, in addition to total P, the nitrate content as observed in winter under ice (Deevey, 1940); alkalinity was found to be unimportant when the other variables were held constant statistically. When better data on productivity are available than those provided by chlorophyll analyses, it will be worthwhile to re-examine these relationships, preferably with attention to mobility of iron and within a more homogeneous series of soft and medium-hard lakes. The Connecticut and New York lakes within New England's limestone belt, Queechy Lake in particular, are very hard but rather unproductive and seem very deficient in nutrients, possibly because of iron deficiency combined with phosphorus removal by marl deposition; such lakes may not provide fair tests of the limnological importance of carbonates.

Regional differences in biological productivity are not very evident in the available data; no studies have been made with C^{14}-labeled bicarbonate. Massive weedbeds and waterblooms occur sporadically throughout the region but are typical of lakes serving as recreation centers for the numerous small cities. Most New England lakes, with their clean sandy or rocky shores and paucity of rooted vegetation, give a strong first impression of sterility. Because salmonid fishes are most prized by sportsmen, a lake's reputation as a good fishing lake depends more on its depth than on its real productivity. Its reputation is also affected by use: legends of trout-fishing in the wilderness of northern New England will probably not survive urbanization.

Attempts have been made (Hutchinson, 1941; Deevey, 1940) to use the rate of generation of the hypolimnetic oxygen deficit as a measure of productivity and thereby to obtain a regional view, but Connecticut lakes are in general too shallow for successful application of this method. Data exist for similar studies in the deeper lakes of Maine, several of which were visited more than once in the same summer by the survey parties, but the data have not been re-examined for this chapter.

No lakes in New England are known to be meromictic, although some might be expected in the fiord land of the central Maine coast, and there is an unconfirmed report, not mentioned by Saila and Horton (1957), that one of the coastal lagoons of Rhode Island had a saline monimolimnion about 1946.

The biological limnology of northern New England

Although all of New England is well provided with lakes, the larger natural lakes are all in the northern two-thirds. The natural lakes of Connecticut, Rhode Island, and Massachusetts are small. The largest bodies of inland water in these states have been recently impounded, and the largest of these impoundments is Quabbin Reservoir in central Massachusetts, with an area of 100 km² and a maximum depth of 46 m. Their presence, however, does not vitiate the generalization that the limnology of southern New England is one concerned with natural lakes seldom over 500 ha

in area. While small lakes occur abundantly in northern New England, there are in addition numerous lakes larger than 1,000 ha, the three largest being over 100 km² in area. The present section of this report then will treat these large lakes and their dominant cold-loving species of fish, while the following section on southern New England will discuss the small lakes of that subregion and their biology.

A catalogue of large lakes is out of place here, but mention must be made of the three largest (Table 4.2). Moosehead Lake, located near the center of Maine, is New England's largest lake with an area of 331 km² and the third deepest of the known lakes with a maximum depth of 75 m. A discussion of this lake and its biology will be given subsequently. Lake Winnipesaukee, New Hampshire's largest lake, with an area of 180 km² is the second largest in New England. Its maximum depth is only 51 m. Sebago Lake in southern Maine is not only the third largest (116 km²) but also the deepest, its maximum depth being 96 m. A bathymetric map of Sebago is given as Figure 4.15. Lake Willoughby in northeastern Vermont has only about one-tenth the area of Sebago yet is nearly as deep (94 m). The bathymetric map of this classic example of a lake in an ice-scoured valley is given as Figure 4.9.

As noted in a previous section, the topography of northern New England, especially New Hampshire and Vermont, exhibits considerable relief. While effects of altitude on the progression of the seasonal changes in these lakes have not been extensively studied, data relating altitude to the date on which the ice completely melted during the spring of 1940 were compiled by A. L. Grover

TABLE 4.2

The largest and deepest lakes of New England

Lake	Location	Area (km²)	Maximum depth (m)
Moosehead	Piscataquis Co., Maine	331	75
Winnipesaukee	Belknap Co., New Hampshire	180	52
Sebago	Cumberland Co., Maine	116	96
Quabbin Reservoir[a]	Hampshire Co., Massachusetts	100	46
Willoughby	Orleans Co., Vermont	6	94

[a] A recent impoundment.

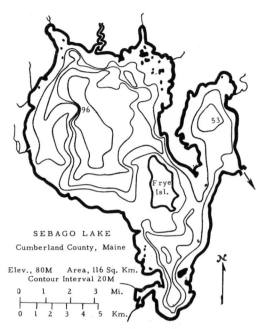

SEBAGO LAKE
Cumberland County, Maine

Elev., 80M   Area, 116 Sq. Km.
Contour Interval 20M

0   1   2   3   Mi.

0   1   2   3   4   5   Km.

Fig. 4.15.—Bathymetric map of Sebago Lake, Cumberland County, Maine. The bottom contours of Sebago, the deepest lake in New England, were drawn from depth data given in Cooper, 1939*b*. The soundings were made by W. C. Kendall in 1906, 1907. Note the deep trough trending northwest-southeast. Compare with Lake Willoughby, Figure 4.9.

(presented in Cooper, 1940). The diagram representing this relationship has been reproduced here as Figure 4.16. While the nature of this relationship is probably relatively constant from year to year, the actual date of disappearance of ice in a given lake varies considerably. Data for Rangeley Lake have been compiled by Kendall (1918). For the period between 1875 and 1915 the date varied from April 19 to May 28, while the mean date for this period was May 10. The mean date as calculated by Kendall for the period 1875–88 was May 15; for 1889–1902 it was May 8; for 1903–1915 it was May 6. In 1940 the date was May 19 (Fig. 4.16), while in 1961, the ice disappeared on May 15. A similar diagram relating the date of complete freezing in the fall to altitude has not been published. The Rangeley lakes usually freeze over in December. Thus, the period of open water in Maine lakes at altitudes above 300 m (1,000 ft) lasts approximately seven months.

Moosehead Lake

It seems desirable to introduce a discussion of the problems of the biological limnology of northern New England with a brief account of the limnology of Moosehead Lake. Moosehead Lake is the largest lake in New England (if one excludes Lake Champlain) with an area of 331 km³, although it is not the deepest (see Table 4.2) since 75 m was the greatest depth found by the Maine Fisheries and Game Survey, the chief source of information (Cooper and Fuller, 1945). Its mean depth is 16.6 m. This large lake, centered at 69° 45′ E. and 45° 45′ N., lies at the head of the Kennebec drainage system at an altitude of 319 m and constitutes the chief source of the Kennebec River (see Fig. 4.1). The irregular, 270 km-long shoreline of this elongated and lobate lake has a development of 4.2 and encloses 303 km² of water surface as well as three large and many small islands, the total area of which approximates 28 km². Figure 4.17 is a bathymetric map of Moosehead Lake.

The geology of the Moosehead area has not been studied in detail, but it seems clear that the lake basin was shaped by processes associated with the Pleistocene glaciations and had a much greater area in late-glacial time (Leavitt and

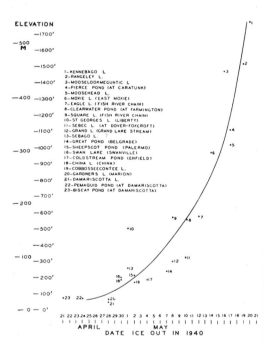

Fig. 4.16.—Diagram showing relation between elevation and the date of final disappearance of ice from various Maine lakes in spring of 1940. From Cooper, 1940, the data for which were compiled by A. L. Grover.

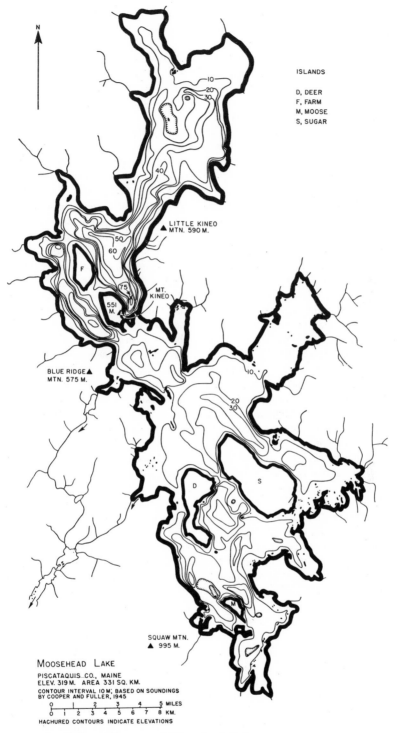

Fig. 4.17.—Bathymetric map of Moosehead Lake, Piscataquis County, Maine. Approximate bottom contours drawn from soundings given on map in Cooper and Fuller, 1945.

Perkins, 1935). The bedrock in this general region of Maine is Paleozoic metamorphic rock, complicated by a ridge of intrusive igneous rock (Paleozoic) with a northeast-southwest trend that cuts the lake in the middle (Keith, 1933). Blue Ridge Mountain (575 m), Mount Kineo (551 m), and Little Kineo Mountain (590 m) are atop this ridge in the immediate vicinity of the lake (see Fig. 4.17). Except for North Bay, which lies parallel to and just north of this ridge, the long axis of the lake and of its depressions trend more nearly northwest-southeast. This is close to the prevalent direction in which the Wisconsin ice moved over this region. It might be conjectured that these features of the present lake basin were formed by ice-scouring of a pre-existing valley or valleys oriented in the direction of the ice movement. The two deepest depressions, lying on either side of the Mount Kineo peninsula, have the steep sides and relatively flat bottoms characteristic of ice-scoured valleys.

The vertical distributions of temperature, oxygen, and pH were determined in the various parts of the lake in the summer of 1944 (Cooper and Fuller, 1945). The highest surface temperature was 22.5°, and the lowest bottom temperature was 5.5° C. However, the various depressions of the lake showed noteworthy differences in the properties of the water each contained. This "submerged depression individuality," to use Welch's term (1952), is evident in the diagrammatic north-south vertical section which Cooper and Fuller (1945) present. This section, slightly modified, is reproduced here as the lower panel of Figure 4.18. The depressions are designated by symbols which refer to the nine subdivisions of the lake as given in the upper panel of the same figure. On this outline are also indicated the course of the diagrammatic vertical section (in two parts) and the sampling stations. It is evident that the three northern basins (A, B, C) with 40% of the lake's area have most of the lake's deep water. Furthermore, all the water here below 18 m is 10° C or colder, whereas in the other basins the relatively smaller amount of water below 18 m is somewhat above 10° C, except in the Sugar Island-Deer Island trough (F) where the temperature drops to 8.5° at 46 m. Throughout the summer the epilimnion showed 95 to 105% saturation with oxygen, and the hypolimnetic waters held less than 80% of the saturation value only in Lily Bay (I), where in

August at a temperature of 11.5° the oxygen was 75 to 79% of saturation.

Essentially no information is available on the thermal and chemical properties of the water at other seasons. Comparison with the Rangeley lakes suggests that the lake freezes over during December and becomes ice-free again early in May.

Both the variety and quantity of organisms in this oligotrophic lake are scant. Phytoplankters are the sole primary producers, since rooted vegetation is virtually absent from the rocky shores (see next paragraph). Diatoms dominated the phytoplankton throughout July and August when the lake was sampled, and of the six genera represented, *Tabellaria* and *Asterionella* were the most common. *Staurastrum, Dinobryon, Volvox,* and *Ceratium* were the other algae common during the summer. The copepods (one species each of *Cyclops* and *Diaptomus* as reported by Cooper and Fuller, 1945) were the most abundant summer zooplankters. The Cladocera, while less abundant in total number, are represented by more species. There are five species of *Daphnia* alone (*D. dubia, D. galeata, D. retrocurva, D. catawba,* and *D. longiremis:* Brooks, 1957, and unpublished 1) as well as *Bosmina longirostris, Holopedium gibberum, Diaphanosoma brachyurum,* and *Leptodora kindtii.* Of the six common genera of rotifers, *Polyarthra* was commonest. Some quantitative estimates were made of the volume of the plankton collected in a Birge closing net of No. 20 bolting silk. The average settled volume of plankton in the upper 5 m was 95 cc/ m^3, while for the 5- to 10-m stratum there averaged about one-fifth as much plankton as at the surface. The value for the upper 5 m was slightly less than the average value for net-plankton volume found in the nearby Rangeley lakes (Cooper, 1940) and about half of the average midsummer volume for the same stratum of 61 much smaller coastal lakes (Cooper, 1942).

The shoreline of Moosehead Lake is composed almost entirely of rocks and boulders from several centimeters to nearly a meter in diameter. Even the shallow-water areas of fine gravel are very limited, and there are essentially no sandy beaches. The only areas of fine sediment (mud, sand) occur in small protected bays and protected stream-mouths. Attempts to use the Ekman bottom sampler indicated that over half of the bottom down to a depth of 10 m consists of rocks

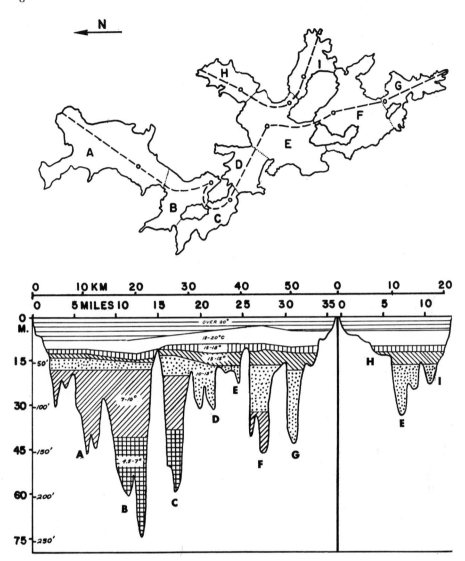

Fig. 4.18.—Lower Panel. Diagrammatic vertical section of Moosehead Lake showing mid-summer temperature distribution in individual lake basins. *Upper Panel.* The position of the hypothetical section is indicated by the interrupted lines of the outline map. The letters designating individual basins correspond to the deeps as seen in the lower panel. Modified from Figures 1 and 2 of Cooper and Fuller, 1945.

and gravel too coarse to be sampled. Between 10 and 18 m about a third of the bottom samplings were unsuccessful, and it was only below 18 m that the bottom was composed of fine-grained sediments (sand, silt, clay) and organic material. In the 228 successful Ekman samples the organisms the populations of which had the greatest biomass were, in descending order, Ephemeroptera nymphs, chironomid larvae, Odonata nymphs, amnicolid snails, oligochaetes, and sphaeriid clams. Of these the Ephemeroptera and Odonata nymphs and snails were restricted to shallow water, while the oligochaetes, chironomids, and clams occurred more or less uniformly at all depths. It may be noted that *Chaoborus* larvae, never very numerous, were found principally between 10 and 20 m. The bottom fauna is scanty; Cooper and Fuller (1945) calculated an average of 44 organisms per m² (with a volume of 0.635 cc).

Twenty-two species of fish are reported from Moosehead Lake (Cooper and Fuller, 1945). In the following list the representatives are the typical subspecies unless otherwise indicated. The two species, *Osmerus mordax* and *Salmo salar*, marked by asterisks in the list have been introduced. The absence of any of the common predatory species of the families Esocidae, Serranidae, Centrarchidae, and Percidae is noteworthy.

Osmeridae
   Osmerus mordax
Coregonidae
   Coregonus clupeaformis neo-hantoniensis
   Prosopium cylindraceum quadrilaterale
Salmonidae
   Salmo salar
   Salvelinus (Cristivomer) namaycush
   Salvelinus(Baione) fontinalis
Catostomidae
   Catostomus catostomus
   Catostomus commersonnii
Cyprinidae
   Leucosomus corporalis
   Semotilus atromaculatus
   Margariscus margarita nachtriebi
   Couesius plumbeus
   Rhinichthys atratulus
   Pfrille neogaea
   Chrosomus eos
   Notemigonus crysoleucas
   Notropis cornutus
Ictaluridae
   Ictalurus nebulosus
Anguillidae
   Anguilla bostoniensis
Cottidae
   Cottus cognatus
Gasterosteidae
   Gasterosteus aculeatus cuvieri
Gadidae
   Lota maculosa

The trophic relationships of the above-mentioned organisms of the plankton, benthos, and nekton are summarized in a diagram (Fig. 4.19) that is somewhat modified from one given in Cooper and Fuller to indicate the trophic levels of both pelagic and benthic aspects of the ecosystem. For the sake of brevity the species of fish are referred to by their generic names only in both text and diagram, except that *Salvelinus (Baione) fontinalis* is referred to as *"Salvelinus"*

and *Salvelinus (Cristivomer) namaycush* as *"Cristivomer."* The food habits of the fish are based on the stomach-content analyses done by the Maine Fisheries and Game Survey. Although *Cristivomer* is probably best placed on the fifth trophic level in this diagram because it is such a voracious piscivore, its principal food is *Osmerus* and *Catostomus*, and it therefore competes with *Salmo*, *Salvelinus*, and *Lota*. The extent of the competition between these species is considered below.

While Figure 4.19 partially indicates by its pelagic-to-benthic gradient the spatial distribution of the organisms within this ecosystem, more exact information on the distribution of the fishes within the lake during summer is presented by Cooper and Fuller (1945). Because this information bears on the matter of competition between the four large predators, it will be summarized here. To consider the species of the third trophic level first, *Osmerus* is abundant in open water away from the bottom, down to a depth of about 30 m. The two species of *Catostomus*, on the other hand, live in close relation to the bottom. Although their depth ranges overlap, *C. commersonnii* (*Catostomus 1* of Fig. 4.20) is the more abundant near the surface and extends down to about 35 m. *C. catostomus* (*Catostomus 2* of Fig. 4.20), on the other hand, was not found above 5 m and ranged down to 60 m. Although these suckers in Moosehead feed extensively on plankton, plankton only supplements the diet of benthic invertebrates more typical of both species. The incorporation of plankton, probably those plankters living not far from the substratum, into the diet of these *Catostomus* has been noted in other lakes where, as in Moosehead, the benthic invertebrates are scanty. It might be noted that, except for the introduced *Osmerus*, the adults of no species of fish besides those of *Catostomus* feed extensively on plankton. The not very abundant coregonids appear to feed exclusively in the substratum. Their depth ranges are shown in Figure 4.20. *Cottus* is even more closely associated with the substratum, and it occurs from the shallow waters down to a depth of 60 m. The cyprinids and *Gasterosteus*, which also forage on benthic invertebrates, are principally restricted to depths of less than 10 m, although they occasionally reach down to 20 m.

When the distribution of the four largest predatory fish within Moosehead is considered in re-

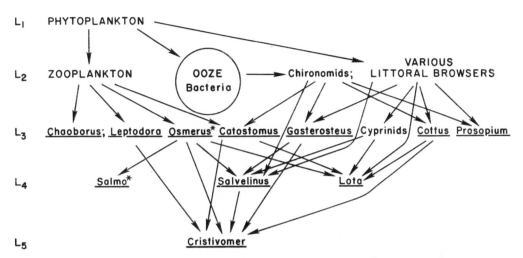

Fig. 4.19.—Food web for Moosehead Lake, based upon data, including analyses of fish stomach contents, given in Cooper and Fuller, 1945. Note that organisms are identified by group or generic names. The only instance in which a species is designated by a Latin name other than its generic name is that of the lake trout, *Salvelinus (Cristivomer) namaycush*, which is here called by its subgeneric name. "*Salvelinus*" in this diagram refers to the brook trout, *Salvelinus (Baione) fontinalis. Osmerus* and *Salmo*, indicated by an asterisk, are introduced species.

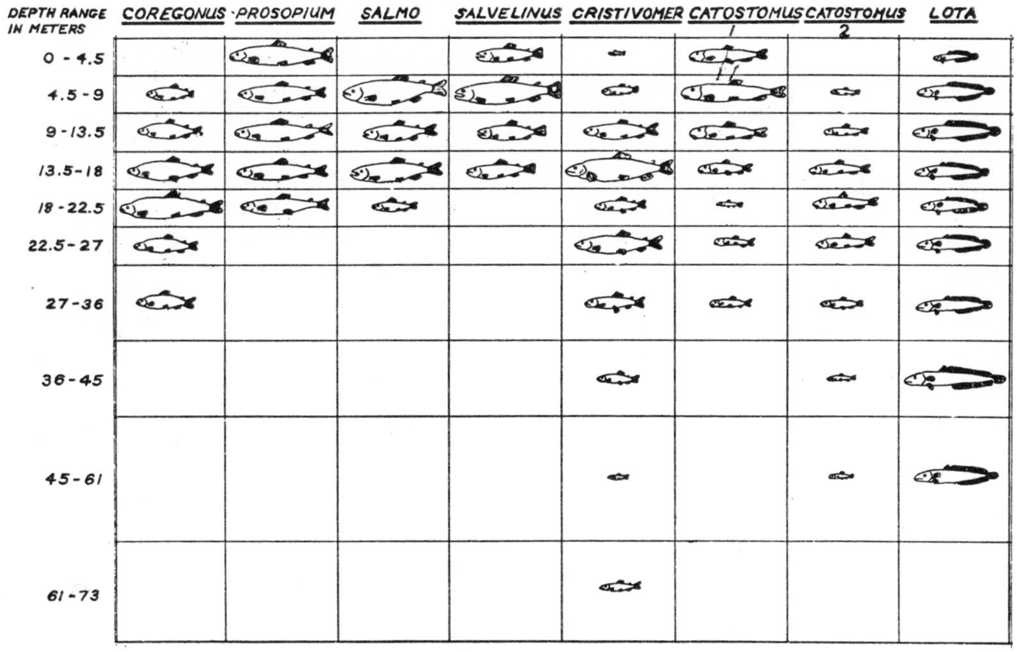

DEPTH RANGE IN METERS	COREGONUS	PROSOPIUM	SALMO	SALVELINUS	CRISTIVOMER	CATOSTOMUS 1	CATOSTOMUS 2	LOTA
0 - 4.5		fish		fish	fish	fish		fish
4.5 - 9	fish	fish	fish	fish	fish	fish	fish	fish
9 - 13.5	fish	fish	fish	fish	fish	fish	fish	fish
13.5 - 18	fish	fish	fish	fish	fish	fish	fish	fish
18 - 22.5	fish	fish	fish			fish	fish	fish
22.5 - 27	fish				fish	fish	fish	fish
27 - 36	fish				fish	fish	fish	fish
36 - 45					fish		fish	fish
45 - 61					fish		fish	fish
61 - 73					fish			

Fig. 4.20.—Diagram showing abundance in each depth zone of the larger fish in Moosehead Lake. The size of the fish at each depth interval denotes the abundance of the fish at that depth, not the size of the individuals found there. The vertical distributions given here are based on midsummer collections. *Catostomus 1 = Catostomus commersonnii; Catostomus 2 = Catostomus catostomus.* Slightly modified from Figure 7 of Cooper and Fuller, 1945.

lation to the distribution of the forage species detailed above, the food habits of the predators are easily understood. Although the abundance of these four species—*Salmo, Salvelinus, Cristivomer,* and *Lota*—at different depths is indicated in Figure 4.20, one important relationship, viz., proximity to the substratum, is not indicated. The three species of salmonids exhibit varying orientations in relation to the substratum. *Salmo* is primarily pelagic, appearing to shun the bottom. That its food is almost exclusively *Osmerus* is to be expected. *Salvelinus* has a depth range similar to *Salmo* (Fig. 4.20) except that it is common at the very surface, while *Salmo* avoids the most superficial layers during summer at least. Thus, *Salvelinus* feeds to a considerable extent on the pelagic *Osmerus* and also on insects caught at the surface and on benthic invertebrates. *Cristivomer* has the broadest distribution of the three salmonids. It ranges from the surface to the greatest depths of the lake, being most abundant at middle depths, and feeds freely in the open waters (on *Osmerus* and the cladoceran *Leptodora*) and on benthic organisms of such disparate sizes as chironomids and *Catostomus* (25 cm). *Lota* appears to be tied to the substratum more closely than any of the other three species and was found to be almost uniformly abundant over the entire bottom of the lake except for the deepest portion. In shallow waters it feeds primarily upon *Gasterosteus* and the cyprinids, while at greater depths it takes *Cottus* and *Catostomus*. The fact that *Lota* fed proportionately much less on *Osmerus* than did any of the salmonids was interpreted by Cooper and Fuller to indicate that *Lota* is less efficient at catching the very abundant but fast swimming *Osmerus*.

Three points emerge from this study of the ecology of Moosehead fishes that bear upon our subsequent discussion of the biology of the salmonid species in New England.

1. The pelagic *Salmo salar* feeds almost exclusively on *Osmerus mordax*. This dependence of freshwater salmon on *Osmerus* is true whether the two species occur naturally or have been introduced, as is the case in Moosehead.

2. *Salvelinus (Cristivomer) namaycush* in Moosehead takes a greater variety of food, but in its dependence on smelt it competes with *Salmo salar*. Both *Salvelinus (Cristivomer) namaycush* and *Salmo salar* mature (at ages V–VI and VII–VIII, respectively) at a standard length of 40–

45 cm, and both species, when of this size, feed largely on *Osmerus* (10 cm). *S. (C.) namaycush* lives longer and commonly reaches 60 or sometimes 75 cm. These large fish feed primarily upon *Catostomus* (20–25 cm). The continued coexistence of large populations of both *Salmo salar* and *S. (C.) namaycush* is maintained in Moosehead Lake by annual stocking of each. Under natural conditions in smaller lakes there is evidence (to be discussed later) that they may exclude each other.

3. The depth range of *Salvelinus (B.) fontinalis* may be restricted to relatively shallow depths by competition with *Salvelinus (C.) namaycush* (and probably *Lota*), especially in view of the sparse benthic invertebrate fauna.

Ecological-biogeographical problems

Two ecological-biogeographical problems peculiar to New England deserve consideration. These are (1) the effects of marine submergence by oceanic waters and (2) the interrelationships of the several salmonids native to northern New England. Both involve fishes the ecology of which has been noted in the preceding discussion of Moosehead Lake.

The first problem concerns the extent of the postglacial marine submergence and its biological consequences. The coastal portion of Maine and the upper half of the St. Lawrence valley in Canada are the only two extensive glaciated areas of the North American continent south of Hudson Bay that have undergone marine submergence. The northern New England coast was the only one to have been submerged by waters of the Atlantic Ocean proper, rather than by estuarine waters as was the case in the St. Lawrence Valley. As will be discussed later, the fishes *Osmerus mordax* and *Salmo salar* are the only elements of the freshwater fauna largely restricted to the area of marine submergence. This could be a consequence of the fact that the marine littoral fauna of the transgressing waters was that characteristic of open coasts, not adapted to the lowered and fluctuating salinity of the estuaries (see Bloom, 1960, for fauna of marine clays in areas of submergence). There is no evidence of any marine relict Crustacea (except for *Mysis relicta* in Lake Champlain, involved in the St. Lawrence submergence). The only New England record of a relict crustacean is that of Norton (1909) who reported *Pontoporeia affinis* from Lake Chamberlain, Maine. This lake, north of Moosehead Lake, is well outside any marine submergence. For a discussion of the significance of such occurrences, the paper of K. E. Ricker (1959) should be consulted.

The second problem is that presented by the presence of five (or four) closely related salmonids in the lakes of northern New England (further discussion follows later). All but one of these belong to the genus *Salvelinus,* and the group includes relict populations of the principally circumpolar arctic chars.

No attempt will be made to present a general biogeography of the freshwater fauna of this region. Such a summary would have to be based primarily on our knowledge of fish species, much of which has been carefully compiled by the fisheries surveys of the various states. One great difficulty with the interpretation of this body of data is the frequent transplantation of both game and forage species. Planktonic Cladocera of the genus *Daphnia,* with 11 species in New England, constitute the only other group for which accurate specific identifications from the entire region are known (Brooks, 1957, and unpublished 1). Several excellent studies of other animal groups have been confined to single states and need to be supplemented by future work in the other areas.

Marine submergence: smelt and whitefish.— The approximate position of the coastline at the time of maximum marine submergence is indicated by the dotted line in Figures 4.21 and 4.22. The geological evidence for the position of this strandline is excellent for southwestern Maine (Bloom, 1960) but is less satisfactory for other parts of Maine (Stone, 1899; Perkins, 1930; Leavitt and Perkins, 1935; Flint *et al.,* 1949, 1959). The strandline has been indicated with the greatest possible accuracy in the vicinity of lakes of interest to us here and with less accuracy in the intervening sections. References should be made to the sources noted previously for information on the refinement of the position of this highest strandline. Some areas between this highest strandline and the present coastline were not submerged. These sometime islands (see Flint *et al.,* 1949) have been omitted, since they are of no apparent concern in the present context. A detailed consideration of the geological evidence will be presented elsewhere (Brooks, in preparation 1).

Freshwater populations of two originally ma-

rine fishes, *Osmerus mordax* and *Salmo salar* (Figs. 4.21 and 4.22), are established within this once submerged area. Although the marine populations of both are anadromous, lake populations have developed only in circumscribed localities. Freshwater populations of several species of *Salmo* are known (see W. E. Ricker, 1940), often entirely unrelated to marine submergence or former glacial lakes, whereas such prior conditions are correlated with the distribution of smelt, *Osmerus eperlanus,* in the Baltic area (see Thienemann, 1950). For this reason, and especially because there is considerable evidence that in New England and the St. Lawrence area of Canada *Salmo* has established freshwater populations only where freshwater smelt provides the required food, greater interest is attached to the establishment of *Osmerus mordax* in lakes. All the lakes of New England and some of those of Canada that are inhabited by freshwater populations of *Osmerus mordax* are given in Table 4.3. Kendall (1927) is the source of most of the data used in this discussion of the smelt.

In the ocean, from which the ancestors of the lake smelt came, young smelt feed upon planktonic Crustacea, shifting to benthic organisms, chiefly Crustacea and small fish, as they mature and approach the length of 15–20 cm, which they commonly attain. In the early spring these mature fish ascend estuaries and thence enter coastal streams to spawn. Small streams are usually chosen (with the result that these spawning migrations are frequently observed and great quantities of the fish caught), although large rivers are often entered in a search for small tributaries. After some days spent in spawning, the fish return to the sea.

It can be seen in Table 4.3 that 16 of the 21 New England smelt lakes lie at altitudes less than 85 m above present sea level. There can be little question that such localities were submerged by the sea in late Wisconsin time. Isobases of postglacial crustal upwarping have not been established throughout the region, and the older geological literature is full of misconceptions and misleading inferences from the altitudes of glacial deltas, many or most of which probably record lake and not ocean levels. Erosional features of marine origin are rare, probably because the high stand of the sea at its maximum was short-lived. However, as Bloom (1960) emphasized, fossiliferous marine deposits (often in the form of

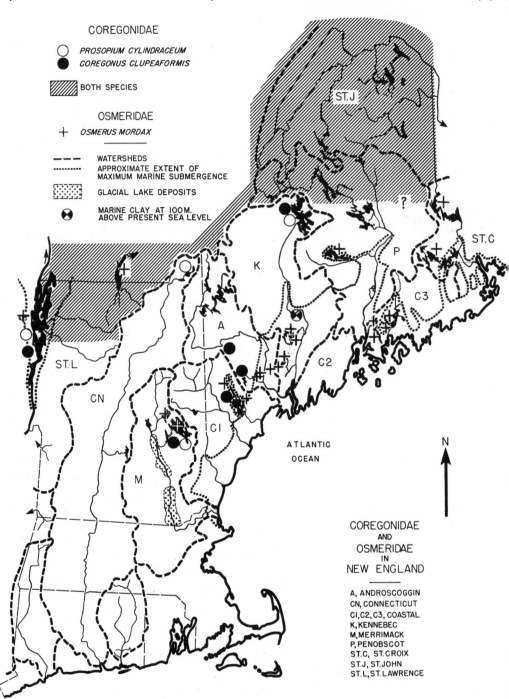

Fig. 4.21.—Natural distribution of *Osmerus mordax* and the coregonids, *Prosopium cylindraceum* and *Coregonus clupeaformis,* in New England. Dotted line approximates the position of the coastline at the time of maximum marine submergence. Stippled areas in Merrimack valley (*M*) indicate position of large glacial lakes. The major drainages of New England are indicated by the following symbols: *St. L*, St. Lawrence; *CN*, Connecticut; *M*, Merrimack; *A*, Androscoggin; *K*, Kennebec; *P*, Penobscot; *St. J*, St. John; *St. C*, St. Croix; *C₁*, *C₂*, *C₃*, separate areas drained by coastal rivers. Geological and distribution data are from various sources. See text.

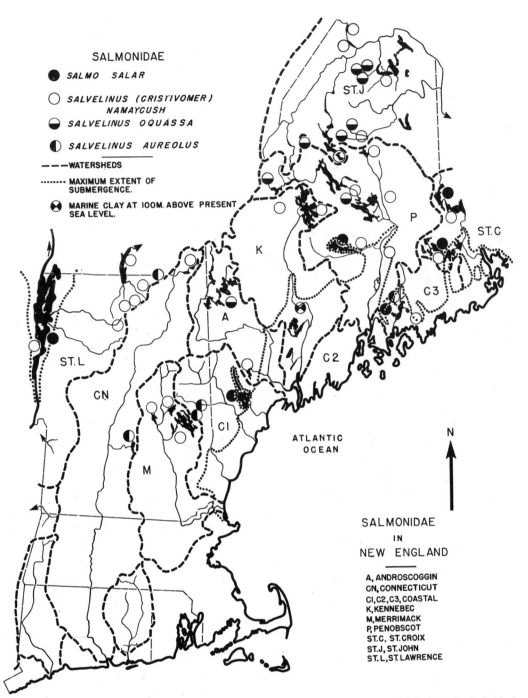

Fig. 4.22.—Natural distribution of salmonids in New England. Dotted line approximates position of coast-line at time of maximum marine submergence. *Salvelinus (Baione) fontinalis* is distributed so widely throughout the region mapped that the individual localities have been omitted for the sake of clarity. For meaning of drainage designations, see legend to Figure 4.21. Data are from various sources. See text.

TABLE 4.3

Osmerus mordax in lakes of New England and Canada

Drainage	Lake	Elev. (m)	Area (ha)	Max. depth (m)	*Osmerus* (Length in cm) "Large"	"Small"	*Salmo salar*
Merrimack	⎰Winnisquam	147	1,745	47		*?	
	⎱Winnipesaukee	154	18,000	52	(15–18; in ponds)	8–13	
	Squam	174	2,735	27		10	
Presumpscot	⎰Sebago	80	11,630	96	18–30	10–13	*
	⎰Long	81	1,970	18	20–30		
	⎱Panther	84	580	20		8–10	
Androscoggin	Taylor	73	255	13		6.5	
	Auburn	79	925	34		7	
	Sabattus	74	730	6		9	
Kennebec	⎰Cobbosseecontee	51	2,270	30		10–13	
	⎪Cochnewagan	82	155	9	15–20[a]	8–10	
	⎰Snow (Messalonskee)	71	1,435	35	30		
	⎱Great	75	3,370	21	25		
	China	60	1,585	26	*		
Coastal (Goose R.)	Swan	61	555	27	20+		
Penobscot	Toddy	48	800	37		10	
	Heart	53	30	21		10	
	Sebec	99	ca. 3,000	—	20–35	10–13	*
Coastal (Union)	Green	48	1,210	52	13–15	8–10	
St. Croix	⎰Grand (West)	98	—	—	[10]	6	*
	⎪East Grand						
	⎰ (Chiputneticook)	117	3,000	47	?	*	*
	⎱Grand Falls Lake	61	—	—	*	*	*
Coastal	Utopia (New Brunswick)	—	—	—		*	
St. Lawrence	Champlain	—	120,000	122	18	8–10	*
	Memphremagog	—	—	—	18		
	Lac des Isles	—	—	—		*	
(Saguenay R.)	Lake St. John	—	—	—		*	*

Note: Lakes in braces are closely connected.

[a] Intermediates present.

* Indicates presence of fish.

clays) unequivocally establish a minimum figure for the marine submergence. Because the clays were laid down in some depth of water, the water level must have been higher than the altitude of the clays at present. The position of the highest strandline was traced with care by Bloom (1960) in southwestern Maine, where it lies between 60 and 90 m above present sea level, rising toward the interior and to the northwest along the shore. Sebago Lake and the intimately connected Long Lake and Panther Pond were clearly estuaries of the Atlantic Ocean. Outside this well-investigated district, relationships are less clear; however, marine clays are found near Waterville, Maine, lying 100 m above present sea level. The Maine smelt lake that lies farthest inland (Sebec) is at 99 m altitude and, therefore, presents no special problem, nor do the smelt lakes of the St. Croix drainage if 60 m is taken as the minimal estimate of the probable marine submergence in that region.

The three smelt lakes in the upper Merrimack basin of New Hampshire—Winnipesaukee, Winnisquam, and Squam—are at considerably higher altitudes (147 to 174 m), but even here a close connection with the sea is not ruled out. Estuarine waters appear to have flooded the Merrimack valley as far as Manchester (Goldthwait, 1925), above which a long, narrow lake or lakes occupied the valley as far as Plymouth, which is north of the smelt localities. The available geological evidence does not prove that this was a continuous body of water at or near sea level in late-glacial time (White, 1938), but if it is safe to use the isobases of postglacial upwarping derived from Champlain Sea deposits, as Goldthwait suggested, then the Lake Winnipesaukee region, being nearer the center of glacial loading than coastal Maine, must have been uplifted to 120 or 150 m above present sea level. Presumably, therefore, the smelt reached the three lakes in the way postulated for some North German lakes (Högbom, 1917; Thienemann, 1950) that are also outside the marine limit—by short but nonmarine connections from large glacial lakes that in turn were connected to an estuary.

The lake populations of *Osmerus* are of further interest to freshwater ecologists because these smelt of both New England and Canada fall into two distinct size categories. Kendall (1927) assembled considerable data on the sizes of individuals in various lakes and recognized a "large" and a "small" form. The characteristic size of each form is given in Table 4.3. The "large" population generally attains a length of 15–30 cm and is, in this respect, more like the common marine populations. The "small" forms, usually 8–13 cm at maturity, are much more of the size and appearance of immature stages of the common marine smelt.

Two lines of evidence indicate that the size differences are determined genetically, not environmentally, as might at first be thought. One kind of evidence is provided by the results of the numerous transplantations of these freshwater smelt, undertaken by fisheries experts. When a "small" population is transplanted into a new environment, it remains "small," and "large" forms remain "large." The other evidence is the coexistence of "large" and "small" populations in 7 of the 21 lakes, populations which in the same environment have different behavioral as well as morphological characteristics.

It is axiomatic that coexisting populations do not interbreed to any serious extent. Some difference in reproductive behavior must be present if the genetic integrity of the populations is to be maintained. In the case of these populations of smelt, the difference is in the time of spawning. The "large" forms, apparently without exception in North America, ascend the tributary streams before the "small" forms, the peaks of the two migrations often being separated by several weeks. These spawning runs are noteworthy phenomena, and many observations are available (see Kendall, 1927). Never have any conspicuous differences in the spawning sites selected by the two forms been noted. The actual spawning behavior in the two forms appears quite similar. It is noteworthy that in Finnish lakes where "large" and "small" forms of *Osmerus eperlanus* occur, the "small" spawns before the "large," and, furthermore, they have different breeding sites (Reuter, 1883, quoted in Kendall, 1927). Although the reproductive isolation of the two forms in the American localities is achieved solely by the difference in spawning season, it appears to have permitted the coexistence of populations for a long period of time (thousands of years, at least). In only one lake, Cochnewegan in Maine, have intermediates between typically "large" and typically "small" forms been reported. This was observed by Atkins (quoted in Kendall, 1927), who had also studied *Osmerus* in many localities in Maine. The presence of these intermediates suggests that reproductive isolation may have broken down in this lake, with the production of a hybrid swarm. It is just possible that it was brought about by the relatively recent migration of the "small" form living in Lake Cobbosseecontee up the connecting stream to Lake Cochnewegan.

Coexisting populations of smelt would almost certainly be in strong competition for the food available in these lakes. It is noteworthy that, with the exception of Lake Cochnewegan, the lakes with both forms of smelt are all large and deep (Table 4.3; Long and Sebago Lakes should probably be considered a unit). Whereas mature "large" forms in these lakes use the same types of food as marine smelt—benthic organisms, especially Crustacea, and small fish, especially smelt—the mature "small" forms feed upon small planktonic Crustacea. In most respects these "small" lake forms seem paedogenetic derivatives of the "large" marine form. Although the mature "large" form and the mature "small" form thus do not compete greatly for food, the competition between immature "large" forms and all stages of "small" forms must be great, and this may explain why the small lakes (with the exception noted) support only one form of

Osmerus. In Lake Winnipesaukee, although both forms occur, the "large" is relatively rare in the main lake, and it alone thrives in several small tributary lakes.

The matter of the origin and relationship of the two forms is problematic. The differences between them can hardly have arisen from intra-lacustrine divergence, because isolated lakes have either one form or the other. The conclusion seems inescapable that the "small'" form and the "large" form in lakes represent two separate invasions of *Osmerus mordax* from the sea by populations which already had these divergent characteristics. Only the "large" form has been reported from the American shores of the Atlantic, although a "small" form has been reported from the European marine waters.

While it is possible that these two forms invaded—or better became acclimatized to—fresh waters at different times, it seems much more probable that these two forms coexisted in the sea, so that stocks of both size ranges were introduced at the same time into most of the lakes under consideration. Subsequent competition might have eliminated one or the other in the small lakes, while the two could continue their coexistence in the large lakes. If this supposition is correct, certain taxonomic problems arise. The "large" and "small" forms would then belong to separate species whether in lakes or in the sea.

The distribution of some species of *Coregonus* in the Baltic area is in large part coincident with that of *Osmerus* (see Thienemann, 1950). However, the two coregonids found in New England, *Prosopium cylindraceum* and *Coregonus clupeaformis*, show patterns of distribution basically different from that of *Osmerus* (Fig. 4.21). It is reasonably certain that neither whitefish occurs in any of the 15 smelt lakes of coastal Maine, with the exception of Lake Sebago and associated waters (Cooper, 1939b, 1942; Cooper and Fuller, 1946). No records are available to the author for Lake Sebec or for the lakes of the St. Croix drainage. However, two of the three smelt lakes of the Merrimack drainage have whitefish. *Prosopium* and *Coregonus* occur in both Lake Winnisquam and Lake Winnipesaukee, which can be considered a single locality.

Both species of coregonids are relatively common only in two small areas of New England, both contiguous to the St. Lawrence drainage.

The distribution of these two species, as well as of other elements of the St. Lawrence fish fauna, in the rest of New England suggests dispersal from these two areas. Lake Champlain and the waters of western Vermont draining into the St. Lawrence comprise one source area. It would seem that the whitefish have reached the Connecticut, Merrimack, and adjacent drainages from this region to the west, although the divide between the St. Lawrence and Connecticut drainages has been impassable for most species of fish. The other source area is the northern tip of Maine, which is drained by the St. John River southward through New Brunswick into the Atlantic. Since the headwaters of the St. John are broadly contiguous with the St. Lawrence drainage along a divide of relatively low relief, they have acquired a large proportion of the St. Lawrence fish fauna. From this source the coregonids have spread southwestward into the upper reaches of the Penobscot River and into Moosehead Lake at the very eastern edge of the headwaters of the Kennebec drainage. That these coregonids are otherwise lacking in the headwaters of the Kennebec and Androscoggin can doubtless be attributed to the relative impassability of the rather short divide between these drainages and that of the St. Lawrence.

Ecological interrelationships of New England salmonids.—There are either four or five species of salmonids in New England depending on one's taxonomic views. For the sake of completeness all five are considered below.

1. *Salmo salar.* Populations of Atlantic salmon spend their entire lives in fresh water in several widely separated lakes and lake systems in northern New England and eastern Canada. Each of these populations has been derived independently from the marine stock of this species. The morphological similarity of these separate populations of freshwater salmon, when compared with the marine form, is almost certainly due to the similar characteristics of the lake environments in which these forms developed. Although in the past these freshwater salmon have received taxonomic distinction from the marine form of the Atlantic salmon (see Kendall, 1935), present consensus does not recognize any distinction (Amer. Fish. Soc., 1960).

2,3. *Salvelinus* (*Salvelinus*) *oquassa* and *S.* (*S.*) *aureolus.* Representatives of the typical subgenus of *Salvelinus* are primarily circumpolar in their present distribution and are accordingly called arctic chars. The greater part of this subgenus is composed of a group of very similar, and taxonomically unresolved, species that can be referred to as the *Salvelinus (S.) alpinus* complex (see Vladykoff, 1954). The representatives of this arctic-char complex occurring in northern New England have been accorded various taxonomic treatment. Some feel that *S. (S.) oquassa* and *S. (S.) aureolus* are species distinct from each other and from other species of the subgenus, although *S. (S.) oquassa* may be identical with *S. (S.) marstoni*, the "red trout" found in several lakes in Quebec (Vladykoff, 1954). At the other extreme stands the American Fisheries Society that refers (1960) to the arctic chars as *Salvelinus alpinus* and submerges both *S. aureolus* and *S. oquassa* into it. The latter course is defensible solely for pragmatic reasons. There is abundant evidence that there are many species of arctic chars (see Berg, 1948, for example), and it is possible that *S. oquassa* and *S. aureolus,* if not distinct species, should be assimilated to two different members of the arctic-char complex.

4. *Salvelinus (Baione) fontinalis.* The brook trout shows sufficient morphological divergence from typical *Salvelinus* to be placed in a separate subgenus (see Vladykoff, 1954). It is the most widespread salmonid in the cool fresh waters, both lenitic and lotic, of New England and was much more widespread, especially in the southern portion of this area, before man's extensive modification of its environment. This species resembles the arctic chars in its relationships to its environment but is adapted to slightly warmer conditions. The present distribution of *S. fontinalis* is essentially North America east of the Mississippi, south of the southern end of Hudson Bay, and extending southward along the coast to southern New England and in the Appalachian Mountains to Georgia. Speaking in other terms, this means as far south as *S. fontinalis* can find a sufficient body of water cooler than 18°–20° C the year around.

5. *Salvelinus (Cristivomer) namaycush* differs considerably in both morphological and environmental relationships from typical *Salvelinus.* Although this morphological divergence has often been recognized by placing this species in a separate monotypic genus, *Cristivomer* (see Vladykoff, 1954), the present consensus seems to be that voiced by Morton and Miller (1954) who retain it in the genus *Salvelinus* and suggest that separate subgeneric rank, as here indicated, suffices to denote its divergent nature.

Ecologically speaking, *Salvelinus fontinalis* is the salmonid most widely distributed over New England, inhabiting both cool streams and the lakes with a sufficient body of cool, oxygenated water in midsummer. The brook trout is so nearly ubiquitous in northern New England that no attempt has been made to indicate its distribution in Figure 4.22. The next most abundant species is *Salvelinus namaycush*, although it is limited to relatively deep lakes in the northern two-thirds of New England. The two species of arctic chars, *S. (S.) oquassa* and *S. (S.) aureolus,* occur in lakes widely scattered over the northern two-thirds of New England, and the freshwater salmon is indigenous to only four lakes (lake systems) in New England, all in Maine.

The distribution pattern of *S. namaycush* is remarkably similar to that of the coregonids considered above (compare Figs. 4.21 and 4.22). Relatively common in the St. John drainage area of the northern tip of Maine and in the St. Lawrence drainage in Vermont, the lake trout also occurs in adjacent watersheds. From the St. John drainage it appears to have moved southward into the Penobscot, St. Croix, and even into the coastal drainages (C_3) and westward into Moosehead Lake and some adjacent lakes in the eastern headwaters of the Kennebec. The *Salvelinus namaycush* populations of the Connecticut and Merrimack drainages are most reasonably interpreted as having come over the relatively impassable divide from western Vermont. The population in Thompson Lake on the edge of the southern Androscoggin drainage is of problematic origin, but comparison with the coregonid pattern (*Coregonus clupeaformis* also occurs in Thompson Lake) suggests that it may have come from the drainages immediately to the west, which, however, do not support lake trout at present. Although *S. namaycush* is most frequently found in large, deep lakes, its presence in Haymock Lake, a relatively small (284 ha), only moderately deep (mean depth, 8.5 m; maximum depth, 20 m) lake (Cooper and Fuller, 1945), indicates that it tolerates a wider variety of conditions, which helps explain its distribution in often widely separated deep lakes. *Salvelinus (B.) fontinalis* and *S. (C.) namaycush* usually coexist in these lakes, and they partition the environmental resources in midsummer much as they do in Moosehead Lake (see previous section), with *S. fontinalis* being associated with the shallow bottom but also feeding at the surface and in the shallower pelagic zone. *S. (C.) namaycush* feeds not only in the deeper portions of the lake bottom but throughout the deep pelagic zone as well.

The distribution of the scattered populations of the arctic chars in New England can be interpreted in relation to competition with the two above-mentioned species. *Salvelinus (S.) oquassa* is known to occur (or to have occurred) in eight localities in northern Maine, namely, in the Rangeley Lakes (type locality) of the Androscoggin drainage, in three headwater lakes in the Penobscot drainage, and four headwater lakes in the St. John drainage (Kendall, 1914; Everhart, 1950; Migdalski, 1962). It is noteworthy that *S. (C.) namaycush* is absent from the Rangeley Lakes area, and in the upper Penobscot and St. John drainages where the lake trout occurs along with *S. (S.) oquassa*, the latter is confined to headwater lakes. *S. (S.) aureolus* has been recorded from headwater lakes in the St. Lawrence, Connecticut (Sunapee Lake, the type locality), and Coastal (C_1) drainages (see Fig. 4.22) and from a lake in the Union River in drainage area C_3.

These arctic chars are confined to the deep waters of the lakes they inhabit, going into shallow water (*S. aureolus*) or ascending tributaries (*S. oquassa*) to spawn in the autumn. They are relict populations, since the arctic chars were almost certainly as widespread in New England at the end of deglaciation as *S. fontinalis* is now. Amelioration of the climate permitted the northward movement of *S. fontinalis* which probably displaced the arctic chars from the streams and shallower portions of lakes. Being confined, however, to deeper water strata, these arctic chars are vulnerable to competition for food from, and indeed predation by, the larger *S. (C.) namaycush* and *Salmo salar* wherever the latter might invade. Transplantations of these larger salmonids have led to the extinction of several populations of arctic chars (see Kendall, 1914; Cooper, 1940; Migdalski, 1962). However, in Floods Pond in the Union River drainage (C_3), *S. (S.) aureolus* is abundant, the brook trout is common, and the introduced *Salmo salar* is also common (Cooper and Fuller, 1946). But it must be remembered

that introduced smelt would provide an extra food source for the salmon, relieving the pressure on *S. aureolus* that would otherwise occur.

The last salmonid to be considered is *Salmo salar* which is indigenous to only four groups of lakes in New England (Lake Champlain is not included in this discussion), although it has been widely transplanted. These localities (refer to Fig. 4.22)—Sebago and associated lakes of the Presumpscot River in C_1, Lake Sebec in the Penobscot drainage, Green Lake of the Union River (in C_3), and both the eastern and western series of large lakes in the St. Croix drainage— are all lakes in which *Osmerus mordax* is indigenous. *Salmo salar* has seldom been known to establish itself successfully in fresh waters, whether as a natural introduction or as a transplantation, unless a smelt population was also present. This dependence of freshwater salmon on smelt was noted in the discussion of trophic relationships in Moosehead Lake (see above). The only possible exception to this rule is Lake Ontario where there probably was a salmon population, although the smelt is unknown (Kendall, 1935). The evident association of freshwater salmon with areas of marine submergence (Fig. 4.22) may merely indicate its dependence on the prior presence of *Osmerus mordax,* because the marine salmon on its spawning migrations penetrated deeply into the New England river systems.

Examination of the ecological interrelationships in Moosehead Lake revealed considerable overlap in the feeding habits of *Salmo salar* and *Salvelinus namaycush*. Although these two coexist in several very large lakes (Fig. 4.22), these lakes all have smelt populations. There is some evidence that they may tend to exclude each other from smaller lakes to which they both have access where food may be scant and competition severe (Kendall, 1914).

Small lakes: Special limnological problems

This account inevitably emphasizes the limnology of Connecticut, and especially of Linsley Pond, the *Haussee* of the Yale group. Because the Yale program is that of a university department of zoology, not a limnological research institute, many important problems remain untouched, while work on many others, intensively prosecuted between 1937 and 1939, has become obsolete by modern standards. Figure 4.23 locates the Connec-

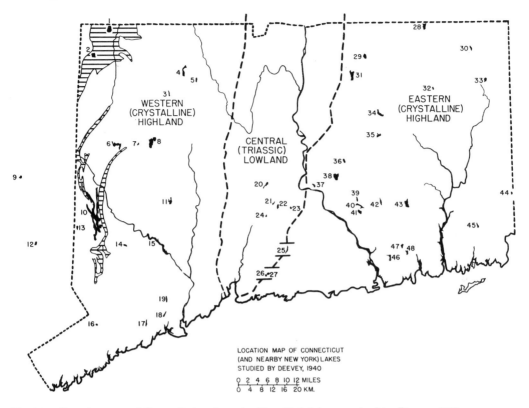

LOCATION MAP OF CONNECTICUT
(AND NEARBY NEW YORK) LAKES
STUDIED BY DEEVEY, 1940

0 2 4 6 8 10 12 MILES
0   4   8   12 16   20 KM.

Fig. 4.23.—Location map of Connecticut and nearby New York lakes examined by Deevey, 1940.

1. East Twin	9. Sylvan	17. Samp Mor-	24. North Farms	33. Alexander	40. Moodus
2. Wononsco-	10. Candlewood	tar	25. Quonnipaug	34. Waumgum-	41. Bashan
pomuc	11. Quassapaug	18. Beardsley	26. Linsley	baug	42. Hayward
3. Stillwater	12. Glenida	Park	27. Cedar	35. Columbia	43. Gardner
4. Highland	13. Ball	19. Trumbull	28. Mashapaug	36. Terramug-	44. Green Falls
5. West Hill	14. Taunton	20. Silver	29. Crystal	gus	45. Long
6. Waramaug	15. Zoar	21. Black	30. Roseland	37. Job's	46. Rogers
7. Mt. Tom	16. Moriarity's	22. Beseck	31. Shenipsit	38. Pocotopaug	47. Powers
8. Bantam		23. Dooley	32. Hall	39. Pickerel	48. Pataganset

ticut lakes that were examined in the pre-war years as part of the survey program of the Connecticut State Board of Fisheries and Game (Thorpe *et al.*, 1942). Bathymetric maps were published in 1942 as a supplement to the 1941 bulletin, now out of print and scarce, and republished with many additions (but no new chemical data) in 1959 (Wilde *et al.*, 1959). Work has continued on a few of these lakes since 1939; Table 4.4 summarizes the older data on those under more or less active investigation (Queechy Lake, in the limestone belt at Canaan, New York, is not shown on the map, Fig. 4.23). Figure 4.24 is a map of Linsley Pond.

Productivity and lake metabolism

The only data on primary productivity are for Linsley Pond, obtained by the dark-and-clear bottle method (Riley, 1940). As reworked by Hutchinson (for the unpublished second volume of the *Treatise*), the figures indicate a maximum daily gross production of 0.387 mg O_2 per cm^2 and a mean value (adjusted for the lack of mid-summer data) of 0.127 mg/cm^2 per day, representing the annual fixation of 175 g of carbon per m^2. These amounts place Linsley somewhere in the middle range of lakes studied by the method of C^{14}-uptake, as summarized by Rodhe (1958); no more can safely be said until

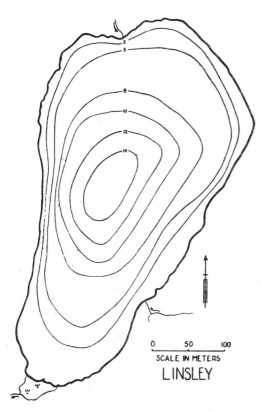

SCALE IN METERS

LINSLEY

Fig. 4.24.—Bathymetric map of Linsley Pond, North Branford, Connecticut. From Riley, 1939, Fig. 1.

the numerous sources of error in both methods are evaluated in a wide range of conditions. Consumption of oxygen, known to be exaggerated in dark bottles, was nearly uniform with respect to depth and averaged 1.2 times the production. Because no account is taken in such experiments of the quantity and productivity of rooted vegetation, consumption and production must be roughly in balance, but there is a large loss of

fixed carbon to the sediments, estimated by Riley at 2.2 metric tons per year, corresponding to an unrealized oxygen consumption one-fifth as large as that observed in the bottles. In consequence, Linsley has lost half its maximum depth since its life began, and four-fifths of its hypolimnion volume has been obliterated (Deevey, 1955).

Linsley is one of the smallest of *Hausseen,* and the high ratio of mud area to water volume (0.248 m²/m³ for the hypolimnion) forced early attention to the role of the sediments in lacustrine metabolism. In a fundamental work dealing with mechanisms of heating and mixing, with chemical events during stagnation, and with the phosphorus economy, Hutchinson (1941) showed that solutes escape from the mud when the redox state shifts toward conditions of stability for ferrous iron. During such stagnation the rate of increase of bicarbonate (balanced by NH_4^+ as well as by Fe^{++}) is a function of the area of mud in contact with the water at any depth in the hypolimnion. Similar conclusions were being reached at the same time by Einsele and by Mortimer. This means, as was also pointed out by Ohle (1959), that the metabolic CO_2 in the hypolimnion of small lakes is produced in large part anaerobically, i.e., by bacterial fermentation in the mud. Hutchinson concluded that about 50% of the total hypolimnetic CO_2 was *pelometabolic.*

This estimate (but more nearly 40%) has been confirmed by a totally different method, the use of naturally-occurring C^{13} and C^{14} as geochemical tracers (Oana and Deevey, 1960). The apparent discrepancy is accounted for by the discovery, possible only by isotopic methods, that about 10% of the total CO_2 in Linsley is ancient (C^{14}-free) and must come from solution of carbonates in the ground water. Studies of the isotopic

TABLE 4.4

Summary of data for several small New England lakes

	Linsley	Quassapaug	Quonnipaug	Rogers	Mt. Tom	Wononscopomuc	Queechy	Bantam
Area, ha	9.4	117.2	46.6	107.2	24.2	142.8	60.8	405.4
Mean depth, m	6.7	8.7	5.1	5.9	6.5	11.1	6.9	4.4
Maximum depth, m	14.8	20	14.8	20	13.9	31	13.6	7.3
Shoreline development	1.18	2.68	—	2.60	1.49	1.37	1.81	—
Vol. ratio, H/E	0.67	0.35	0.72	0.59	0.23	0.63	0.37	—
Secchi disc, mean, m	2.6	7.4	3.8	5.2	5.5	8.8	5.7	2.3
HCO_3 mg/L, surface, summer	62.5	11.4	33.1	15.3	24.1	134.0	123.1	34.9
Total P, mg/m³, mean	21	7	10	8	12	8	12	18
Organic seston, mg/L	2.9	1.2	1.1	1.5	3.6	0.7	1.8	—
Benthos, mg/cm² fresh weight	3.48	0.75	—	0.76	2.18	1.20	0.37	0.95

composition (but not the rate of production) of mud gases prove that methane is coupled to CO_2 in the fermentation processes, the CO_2 being enriched in C^{13} while the methane is depleted. All five lakes examined by Oana and Deevey were inferred, on the indirect evidence of their CO_2 pelometabolism, to be potent producers of methane. Bubbling from profundal bottoms is prominent only in Linsley, however, and methane bubbles may serve for "internal fertilization" (Ohle, 1959) only in lakes with strongly clinograde oxygen curves. The C^{14} work, begun initially on Queechy (Deevey *et al.*, 1954) as an exploration of potential errors in radiocarbon dating, is continuing (Stuiver and Deevey, 1961, and unpublished) but has been made more difficult by the artificial C^{14} produced in nuclear tests.

A similar approach to the metabolism of sulfur, using the stable S^{34} as tracer, has given preliminary indications of isotopic fractionation in the four lakes examined (Deevey *et al.*, 1962). Bacterial reduction of sulfate is expected to withdraw S^{32} preferentially, depositing it as insoluble sulfides in the mud and enriching the remaining sulfate in S^{34}. The phosphorus metabolism of Linsley was investigated by Hutchinson (1941), who followed the basic studies with an experimental injection of radiophosphorus (Hutchinson and Bowen, 1950), but the nitrogen cycle in Connecticut lakes has not been studied with comparable intensity or by the isotopic methods now available.

Some of the more exotic metabolites demonstrated in Connecticut lake waters include the vitamins thiamin (Hutchinson, 1943), niacin and biotin (Hutchinson and Setlow, 1946), and cyanocobalamin (Benoit, 1957). Free sugars (Vallentyne and Whittaker, 1956), though probably present, have not been studied in Connecticut since Vallentyne found them in Ontario lakes. Free amino acids have not been demonstrated unequivocally. A much larger fraction of the dissolved organic matter, ranging from 4.5 to 9 mg/L in Linsley, is made up of "humolimnic acids," the (partly yellow) organic acids or their salts (Shapiro, 1957) which seem to be the penultimate decomposition products of organic seston and which probably account for most of the peculiar optical properties of filtered lake water. Shapiro found these compounds to be of low molecular weight (*ca.* 450), remarkably stable toward oxidation,

and probably ectocrine in function. Their growth-promoting action in algal culture may be related to their ability to bind iron and other constituents of algal enzymes.

Plankton

Pioneering work on the components of phytoplankton was done in reservoirs of the Boston public water supply by Whipple and is summarized in his classic *Microscopy of Drinking Water* (1899); detailed data are in the annual Reports of the Massachusetts State Board (now Department) of Public Health. After these early surveys, little, other than casual collection and routine sanitary examination, was done in New England lakes until Hutchinson's (1944) attempt to elucidate the chemical conditions underlying the very variable phenology of certain common species of Linsley Pond. Several previously suggested generalizations were upset by this work, but few new ones emerged, and the matter is still full of obscurities.

Floristic and faunistic work on freshwater plankton organisms has lagged behind in New England, the impetus provided by Louis Agassiz having rather quickly been channeled into marine biology. A quantitative survey of the plankton of Linsley, Quassapaug, and Quonnipaug, using chlorophyll analysis, was made by Riley (1939), and various methods of measurement were compared in his study of Linsley (Riley, 1940); one reason for the relative neglect of Linsley's zooplankton is that it is poorly developed as compared to the phytoplankton, pelagic *Daphnia* being absent. The literature of special groups abounds in records from New England lakes, many of them in the near vicinity of Woods Hole (e.g., C. B. Wilson's *Copepods of the Woods Hole Region*, 1932), but the coverage is grossly inadequate for biogeographic or other ecological purposes. Brooks' monograph on *Daphnia* (1957) is an exception, and the seasonal life-history of *Daphnia* (in Bantam Lake) is well covered by papers on cyclomorphosis (Brooks, 1946, 1947; J. Jacobs, 1961). An examination by Brooks of the vertical distribution of limnetic *Daphnia* as it bears on problems of species associations and on the cyclomorphosis of each species is nearly ready for the press (Brooks, in preparation 2). An extension of these studies to the Rangeley Lakes of Maine is in progress (Brooks, unpublished 2; Tappa, unpublished). Edmondson's numerous records of pelagic rotifers (in contrast to his fundamental studies of sessile rotifers) are unpublished. Year-around collections of zooplankton in Queechy, Rogers, and Linsley are under study by G. B. Deevey, and life-history studies of *Cyclops bicuspidatus thomasi* and *C. scutifer* are being undertaken by Kaare Elgmork. The latter species, somewhat unexpectedly, is present in Mt. Tom Pond and Queechy Lake.

Periphyton

Edmondson's remarkable investigations of sessile rotifers (1944, 1945, 1946) must be mentioned here, but no comprehensive study of other attached organisms appears to have been made in New England lakes.

Benthos

A survey of the profundal bottom fauna of 36 Connecticut and New York lakes was made by Deevey (1941b), with emphasis on the relation of the profundal tendipedid fauna to lake typology; such data were needed if fossil tendipedids were to be correctly interpreted. The dominant type of tendipedid was shown to be related to the hypolimnetic oxygen supply, as expected, and equivalents of the European *Chironomus*, *Tanytarsus*, and *Orthocladius* lakes were found. (The *Orthocladius* lake, Lake George, is in New York.) The soft and relatively shallow (but stratified) lakes of Connecticut's eastern highland seemed to form a special and rather homogeneous type, characterized in 1937 and 1938 by a species of *Trissocladius*. Only a few species of larvae from any one lake were reared

and identified, however, and the reconnaissance has not been completed or brought up to modern taxonomic standards. Moreover, the tendipedid fauna is likely to have changed since 1938, with the increasing eutrophication of New England lakes. At any rate, no *Tanytarsus* types have been found in Quassapaug in later sampling, and *Chironomus* types have become extremely rare in Linsley.

The standing crop of profundal bottom animals (mostly measured in summer only) varied from 15.4 kg fresh weight/ha in Green Falls Reservoir to 348 kg/ha in Linsley; the latter figure is an annual mean and corresponds to an estimated 52.2 kg dry weight/ha. The total quantities seem unrelated to other properties of lakes, a conclusion recently confirmed on a larger series of lakes by Hayes (1957). Even the largest crops utilize a relatively small fraction of the available food; the annual productivity of the ooze-browsers (*Tendipes* plus oligochaetes) in Linsley was estimated at between 1 and 3% of the plankton productivity (Deevey, unpublished; these productivity calculations [Table 4.5] were reported at the East Lansing meeting of the A.S.L.O., 1955). *Chaoborus*, which makes up a major fraction of the macroscopic bottom fauna and is believed to turn its crop over twice a year, may be in part a predator on zooplankton, thus tapping a source of energy not available to the ooze-browsers.

The benthic copepods are ordinarily neglected in such studies and were very inadequately sampled in Linsley. Data are available on one species, however, the harpacticoid *Canthocamptus staphylinoides*, which spends part of its life en-

TABLE 4.5

Estimated benthic productivity for several lakes, kg/ha dry weight/year

	Beloje		Linsley	Mendota	Cedar Bog	Nipigon
	Direct est.	From max. crop				
Browsers:						
Tendipes	74.1	26.8	44.8	20.2	16	0.40
Oligochaeta	43.0	29.0	7.2	6.1	—	0.50
Amphipoda	—	—	—	—	—	1.52
Mollusca	—	—	—	3.8	—	2.74
Predators:						
Chaoborus	28.2	17.6	19.8	23.2	15	—
"Tanypus"	3.4	2.8	—	1.2	4	—
Total	148.0	76.2	71.8	54.8	35	5.93
Canthocamptus			4.5?			

cysted in the mud (Deevey, 1941a). If this species weighs about as much as *Cyclops,* and if, as Moore's (1939) data on the Douglas Lake population suggest, the animals are underestimated in the Linsley (Ekman dredge) samples by a factor of five, the productivity of this copepod alone may amount to 4.5 kg/ha dry weight, or about a tenth the productivity of *Tendipes* (Table 4.5). Because other copepods, notably *Mesocyclops edax,* were neglected, and because *Cyclops bicuspidatus* cysts are commoner than *Canthocamptus* in lakes that are somewhat larger and deeper than Linsley, the benthic copepods are probably not negligible in the energetics of lakes, and zooplankton need not be invoked to account for the massive production of *Chaoborus* in some of them.

Paleolimnology

Studies on the ontogeny of lacustrine ecosystems have taken a prominent place in the program of the Yale group. The basic methodology was suggested to Hutchinson by Gams' (1927) report of fossil tendipedids in the sediments of the Lunz lakes; if tendipedids are diagnostic of lake type, their stratigraphic sequence must yield a record of typologic succession, which is ontogeny. The problem was also taken up by Deevey (1939, 1942b, 1955), and its ramifications—into general paleoecology, into late-Pleistocene chronology, and into isotopic methods of studying both simultaneously—have been actively prosecuted. The development of the subject has made the early work obsolescent, but the conclusion of Hutchinson and Wollack (1940) that the growth of Linsley's biocoenosis was sigmoid remains the most provocative generalization and guide.

According to this view, the early postglacial lake was sterile and unproductive, but it rapidly became more and more eutrophic. Indications of an early exponential increase are found in the changing quantities of several kinds of fossils (Deevey, 1942b)—*Bosmina,* tendipedids, *Plumatella,* and epiphytic diatoms (Patrick, 1943)—as well as of total organic matter in the sediments and its component nitrogenous compounds (Hutchinson and Wollack, 1940) and pigments (Vallentyne, 1956). Later, about the beginning of Boreal time (the Hypsithermal sub-age: see Fig. 4.7), various kinds of self-limitation supposedly set in, and the lake remained in "typo-logic equilibrium" for thousands of years.

A fundamental difficulty with this concept was and is uncertainty as to time-rates of deposition in Linsley, especially in the early stages. As Livingstone (1957) pointed out, if the lower meter or two of siliceous sediment accumulated in a few years, as would be possible in a periglacial frost-thaw basin, the early exponential increase of organic components and the "silica time-scale" of Hutchinson and Wollack on which it was based would be illusory; the time scale was also known to be unreliable in its failure to distinguish diatomaceous from detrital silica. Livingstone restudied the matter, using a time-scale based on brown laminae found in the lower portion of his cores, and found indications that the exponential increase was real, but since the brown laminae are evidently not annual and are of uncertain significance, the problem remains unsettled. Radiocarbon dating is not an easy solution in this medium-hard lake and in these carbon-poor sediments, but it is being applied more indirectly in combination with a renewed attack on the pollen stratigraphy of the region.

In the course of this work the original idea has proved difficult to apply, in that the tendipedid fauna responded to the changing hypolimnetic concentration of oxygen (from a *"Tanytarsus"* to a *"Chironomus"* fauna, followed much later by a rise of *Chaoborus*), but these changes need imply no more than "morphometric eutrophication," the obliteration of part of the hypolimnion by sediments. Morphometric calculations show, however (Deevey, 1955), that Linsley must have acquired a chemically reducing hypolimnion and a *"Chironomus"* fauna long before its hypolimnion was significantly reduced in volume. But while the evidence as a whole still favors the idea that Linsley's biocoenosis underwent an exponential increase in productivity, the role that progressively warming climate may have had in directing this increase remains an unsolved problem.

Scattered data are available on the histories of several other lakes in southern New England, especially the senescent (bog) lakes that yield pollen-stratigraphic data more easily than do stratified lakes; Cedar Lake (Upper Linsley Pond), Bethany Bog, Totoket Bog, and Lidy Hite (Lyd Hyt) Pond have yielded data on loss of ignition at least, and some have been analyzed for fossil pigments (Vallentyne, 1954, 1955,

1956). These lakes are all too shallow to have been thermally stratified throughout their histories and are, therefore, less interesting than Linsley Pond, but their paleolimnology may throw light on the origin of dystrophy.

References

AMERICAN FISHERIES SOCIETY. 1960. List of common and scientific names of fishes from United States and Canada. Spec. Publ. 2.

ANTEVS, ERNST. 1922. The recession of the last ice sheet in New England. Amer. Geograph. Soc. Research Ser., No. 11, 120 + xiii p.

——. 1951. Glacial clays in Steep Rock Lake, Ontario, Canada. Bull. Geol. Soc. Amer., 62: 1223–1262.

BAILEY, J. R., and J. A. OLIVER. 1939. The fishes of the Connecticut watershed, p. 150–189. In H. E. Warfel, Biological survey of the Connecticut watershed. New Hampshire Fish, Game Dept., Surv. Rept. 4.

BAILEY, R. M. 1938. The fishes of the Merrimack watershed, p. 149–185. In E. E. Hoover, Biological survey of the Merrimack watershed. New Hampshire Fish, Game Dept., Surv. Rept. 3.

BEHNEY, W. H. 1937. Food organisms of some New Hampshire trout streams, p. 77–80. In E. E. Hoover, Biological survey of the Androscoggin Saco and coastal watersheds. New Hampshire Fish, Game Dept., Surv. Rept. 2.

BENOÎT, R. J. 1957. Preliminary observations on cobalt and vitamin B₁₂ in fresh water. Limnol. Oceanogr., 2: 233–240.

BERG, L. S. 1948. Les poissons des eaux douces de l'U.R.S.S. et des pays limitrophes. Vol. I. 4th ed. State Press, Moscow. 466 p.

BILLINGS, M. P. 1955. Geologic map of New Hampshire. U.S. Geol. Surv., Washington.

BLOOM, A. L. 1960. Late Pleistocene changes of sea level in southwestern Maine. Maine Dept. Econ. Develop., Maine Geol. Surv., Augusta, 143 p.

BRAUN, E. L. 1950. Deciduous forests of eastern North America. Blakiston, Philadelphia. 596 + xiv p.

BROOKS, J. L. 1946. Cyclomorphosis in Daphnia. I. An analysis of D. rectrocurva and D. galeata. Ecol. Monogr., 16: 409–447.

——. 1947. Turbulence as an environmental determinant of relative growth in Daphnia. Proc. Natl. Acad. Sci., 33: 141–148.

——. 1957. The systematics of North American Daphnia. Mem. Connecticut Acad. Arts Sci., 13: 1–180.

——. (In preparation, 1). Postglacial marine submergence in Maine and the distribution of freshwater smelt and salmon.

——. (In preparation, 2). The vertical distribution of limnetic species of Daphnia in Connecticut; its effect on species associations and cyclomorphosis.

——. (Unpublished, 1). The distribution of limnetic species of Daphnia in New England.

——. (Unpublished, 2). The vertical distribution of limnetic Daphnia in lakes of the Rangeley district of Maine.

BROOKS, VAN WYCK, 1936. The flowering of New England, 1815–1865. E. P. Dutton, New York. 550 p.

CLARKE, F. W. 1924. The composition of the river and lake waters of the United States. U.S. Geol. Surv., Profess. Paper No. 135, 199 + iv p.

COLE, R. M. 1939. Studies on the plankton of the Connecticut River watershed, p. 190–194. In H. E. Warfel, Biological survey of the Connecticut watershed. New Hampshire Fish, Game Dept., Surv. Rept. 4.

COOPER, G. P. 1939a. A biological survey of the waters of York County and the southern part of Cumberland County, Maine. Maine Dept. Inland Fish. Game, Fish Surv. Rept. 1: 1–58.

——. 1939b. A biological survey of thirty-one lakes and ponds of the Upper Saco River and Sebago Lake drainage systems in Maine. Maine Dept. Inland Fish. Game, Fish Surv. Rept. 2: 1–147.

——. 1940. A biological survey of the Rangeley Lakes, with special reference to the trout and salmon. Maine Dept. Inland Fish. Game, Fish Surv. Rept. 3: 1–182.

——. 1941. A biological survey of lakes and ponds of the Androscoggin and Kennebec River drainage systems in Maine. Maine Dept. Inland Fish. Game, Fish Surv. Rept. 4: 1–238.

——. 1942. A biological survey of lakes and ponds of the central coastal area of Maine. Maine Dept. Inland Fish. Game, Fish Surv. Rept. 5: 1–185.

COOPER, G. P., AND J. L. FULLER. 1945. A biological survey of Moosehead Lake and Haymock Lake, Maine. Maine Dept. Inland Fish. Game, Fish Surv. Rept. 6: 1–160.

COOPER, G. P., AND J. L. FULLER. 1946. A biological survey of the lakes and ponds of Mount Desert Island, and the Union and Lower Penobscot River drainage systems. Maine Dept. Inland Fish. Game, Fish Surv. Rept. 7: 1–221.

DAVIS, M. B. 1958. Three pollen diagrams from central Massachusetts. Amer. J. Sci., 256: 540–570.

DEEVEY, E. S. 1939. Studies on Connecticut lake sediments. I. A postglacial climatic chronology for southern New England. Amer. J. Sci., 237: 691–724.

——. 1940. Limnological studies in Connecticut. V. A contribution to regional limnology. Amer. J. Sci., 238: 717–741.

——. 1941a. Notes on the encystment of the harpacticoid copepod Canthocamptus staphylinoides Pearse. Ecology, 22: 197–200.

——. 1941b. Limnological studies in Connecticut. VI. The quantity and composition of the bottom fauna of thirty-six Connecticut and New York lakes. Ecol. Monogr., 11: 413–455.

——. 1942a. A re-examination of Thoreau's "Walden." Quart. Rev. Biol., 17: 1–11.

——. 1942b. Studies on Connecticut lake sediments. III. The biostratonomy of Linsley Pond. Amer. J. Sci., 240: 233–264, 313–338.

———. 1951. Late-glacial and postglacial pollen diagrams from Maine. Amer. J. Sci., **249**: 177–207.

———. 1955. The obliteration of the hypolimnion. Mem. Ist. Ital. Idrobiol., suppl., **8**: 9–38.

———. 1958. Radiocarbon-dated pollen sequences in eastern North America. Veröffentl. Geobotan. Inst. Rübel, Zürich, **34**: 30–37.

DEEVEY, E. S., AND J. S. BISHOP. 1942. Limnology, p. 69–121, 296–298. *In* L. M. Thorpe *et al.*, A fishery survey of important Connecticut lakes. State Geol. Nat. Hist. Surv. Connecticut, Bull. 63.

DEEVEY, E. S., AND R. F. FLINT. 1957. Postglacial hypsithermal interval. Science, **125**: 182–184.

DEEVEY, E. S., M. S. GROSS, G. E. HUTCHINSON, AND H. L. KRAYBILL. 1954. The natural C^{14} contents of materials from hard-water lakes. Proc. Natl. Acad. Sci., **40**: 285–288.

DEEVEY, E. S., MINZE STUIVER, AND NOBOYUKI NAKAI. 1962. Use of light nuclides in limnology. *In* Vincent Schultz and A. W. Klement (eds.), Radioecology. Reinhold, New York. (In press.)

DOLL, C. G., *et al.* 1961. Centennial geologic map of Vermont. Vermont Geol. Surv., Montpelier.

EDMONDSON, W. T. 1938. Notes on the plankton of some lakes in the Merrimack watershed, p. 207–210. *In* E. E. Hoover, Biological survey of the Merrimack watershed. New Hampshire Fish, Game Dept., Surv. Rept. 3.

———. 1944. Ecological studies of sessile Rotatoria. I. Factors affecting distribution. Ecol. Monogr., **14**: 31–66.

———. 1945. Ecological studies of sessile Rotatoria. II. Dynamics of populations and social structures. Ecol. Monogr., **15**: 141–172.

———. 1946. Factors in the dynamics of rotifer populations. Ecol. Monogr., **16**: 357–372.

EDMONDSON, W. T., AND J. L. FULLER. 1937. Food conditions in some New Hampshire lakes, p. 95–100. *In* E. E. Hoover, Biological survey of the Androscoggin Saco and coastal watersheds. New Hampshire Fish, Game Dept., Surv. Rept. 2.

EMBODY, D. R., C. A. GOODRUM, AND S. D. EDMOND. 1938. A statistical analysis of width measurements of a New Hampshire stream, p. 198–200. *In* E. E. Hoover, Biological survey of the Merrimack watershed. New Hampshire Fish, Game Dept., Surv. Rept. 3.

EMERSON, B. K. 1917. Geology of Massachusetts and Rhode Island. U.S. Geol. Surv., Bull. 597, 289 p.

EVERHART, W. H. 1950. The blueback trout, *Salvelinus oquassa* (Girard), in Maine. Copeia, 1950: 242.

FAIRBRIDGE, R. W. 1961. Eustatic changes in sea level, p. 99–185. *In* Physics and chemistry of the earth. Vol. 4. Pergamon Press, New York.

FENNEMAN, N. M. 1938. Physiography of eastern United States. McGraw-Hill, New York. 714 + xiii p.

FLINT, R. F. 1930. The glacial geology of Connecticut. Connecticut Geol. Nat. Hist. Surv., Bull. 47, 294 p.

———. 1953. Probable Wisconsin substages and late-Wisconsin events in northeastern United States and southeastern Canada. Bull. Geol. Soc. Amer., **64**: 897–919.

FLINT, R. F., *et al.* 1949. Glacial map of North America. Geol. Soc. Amer., Spec. Paper No. 60, revised.

FLINT, R. F., *et al.* 1959. Glacial map of the United States east of the Rocky Mountains. Geol. Soc. Amer., New York.

GAMS, HELMUT. 1927. Die Geschichte der Lunzer Seen, Moore, und Wälder. Intern. Rev. Hydrobiol. Hydrogr., **18**: 304–387.

GODWIN, HARRY, R. P. SUGGATE, AND E. H. WILLIS. 1958. Radiocarbon dating of the eustatic rise in ocean-level. Nature, **181**: 1518–1519.

GOLDTHWAIT, J. W. 1925. The geology of New Hampshire. Rumford Press, Concord, New Hampshire. 86 p.

GORDON, MYRON. 1937. Fishes of eastern New Hampshire, p. 101–118. *In* E. E. Hoover, Biological survey of the Androscoggin Saco and coastal watersheds. New Hampshire Fish, Game Dept., Surv. Rept. 2.

GORHAM, EVILLE. 1961. Factors influencing supply of major ions to inland waters, with special reference to the atmosphere. Bull. Geol. Soc. Amer., **72**: 795–840.

GUSTAFSON, A. H. 1952. The role of the algae in some Massachusetts lakes, p. 3–13, 100–104. *In* B. C. McCabe, Fisheries report for lakes of northeastern Massachusetts—1949 (to Massachusetts Div. Fish. Game). Commonwealth of Massachusetts, Boston.

HAYES, F. R. 1957. On the variation in bottom fauna and fish yield in relation to trophic level and lake dimensions. J. Fish. Research Board Canada, **14**: 1–32.

HÖGBOM, A. G. 1917. Über die arktischen Elemente in der aralokaspian Fauna, ein tiergeographisches Problem. Bull. Geol. Inst. Upsala, **14**: 241–260.

HOOVER, E. E. 1936. Preliminary biological survey of some New Hampshire lakes. New Hampshire Fish, Game Dept., Surv. Rept. 1, 77 p.

———. 1937. Biological survey of the Androscoggin Saco and coastal watersheds. New Hampshire Fish, Game Dept., Surv. Rept. 2, 160 p.

———. 1938. Biological survey of the Merrimack watershed. New Hampshire Fish, Game Dept., Surv. Rept. 3, 238 p.

HUNTER, G. W., III. 1942. Studies of the parasites of fresh-water fishes of Connecticut, p. 228–288. *In* L. M. Thorpe *et al.*, A survey of important Connecticut lakes. State Geol. Nat. Hist. Surv. Connecticut, Bull. 63.

HUTCHINSON, G. E. 1941. Limnological studies in Connecticut. IV. Mechanism of intermediary metabolism in stratified lakes. Ecol. Monogr., **11**: 21–60.

———. 1943. Thiamin in lake waters and aquatic organisms. Arch. Biochem., **2**: 143–150.

———. 1944. Limnological studies in Connecticut. VII. A critical examination of the supposed relationship between phytoplankton periodicity and chemical changes in lake waters. Ecology, **25**: 3–26.

HUTCHINSON, G. E., AND V. T. BOWEN. 1950. Limnological studies in Connecticut. IX. A quantitative radiochemical study of the phosphorus cycle in Linsley Pond. Ecology, 31: 194–203.

HUTCHINSON, G. E., AND J. K. SETLOW. 1946. Limnological studies in Connecticut. VIII. The niacin cycle in a small inland lake. Ecology, 27: 13–22.

HUTCHINSON, G. E., AND ANNE WOLLACK. 1940. Studies on Connecticut lake sediments. II. Chemical analyses of a core from Linsley Pond. Amer. J. Sci., 238: 493–517.

JACKSON, D. D. 1905. The normal distribution of chlorine in the natural waters of New York and New England. U.S. Geol. Surv., Water-Supply Paper No. 144, 31 p.

JACOBS, E. C. 1921. The geology of Lake Willoughby. Rept., Vermont State Geol., 1919–20, No. 12: 280–298 + pl. 38–43.

JACOBS, JÜRGEN. 1961. Cyclomorphosis in Daphnia galeata mendotae Birge, a case of environmentally controlled allometry. Arch. Hydrobiol., 58: 7–71.

JUNGE, C. E., AND R. T. WERBY. 1958. The concentration of chloride, sodium, potassium, calcium, and sulfate in rain water over the United States. J. Meteorol., 15: 417–425.

KAY, MARSHALL, 1951. North American geosynclines. Mem. Geol. Soc. Amer. No. 48, 143 p.

KEITH, ARTHUR. 1933. Preliminary geologic map of Maine. Maine Geol. Surv., Augusta.

KENDALL, W. C. 1914. The fishes of New England. The salmon family. I. The trout or charrs. Mem. Boston Soc. Nat. Hist., 8(1): 1–103.

———. 1918. The Rangeley Lakes, Maine, with special reference to the habits of the fishes, fish culture, and angling. Bull. U.S. Bur. Fish., 35: 489–594.

———. 1927. The smelts. Bull. U.S. Bur. Fish., 42: 217–375.

———. 1935. The fishes of New England. The salmon family. II. The salmons. Mem. Boston Soc. Nat. Hist., 9(1): 1–166.

KING, P. B. 1959. The evolution of North America. Princeton Univ. Press, Princeton, New Jersey. 189 + xviii p.

KLEINKOPF, M. D. 1955. Trace element exploration of Maine lake water. Ph.D. Dissertation, Columbia Univ., New York.

———. 1960. Spectrographic determination of trace elements in lake waters of northern Maine. Bull. Geol. Soc. Amer., 71: 1231–1242.

KNOX, C. E., AND T. J. NORDENSON. 1955. Average annual runoff and precipitation in the New England–New York area. U.S. Geol. Surv., Hydrol. Invest. Atlas HA 7, Washington.

LEAVITT, H. W., AND E. H. PERKINS. 1935. Glacial geology of Maine. Maine Tech. Expt. Sta., Bull. 30, Vol. II, 232 + viii p.

LEOPOLD, E. B. 1956. Two late-glacial deposits in southern Connecticut. Proc. Natl. Acad. Sci., 52: 863–867.

LIVINGSTONE, D. A. 1957. On the sigmoid growth phase in the history of Linsley Pond. Amer. J. Sci., 255: 364–373.

LOHAMMAR, GUNNAR. 1938. Wasserchemie und höhere Vegetation schwedischer Seen. Symbolae Botan. Upsalienses, 3(1): 1–253.

McCABE, B. C. 1946. Fisheries report for lakes of central Massachusetts—1944–45 (to Massachusetts Div. Fish. Game). Commonwealth of Massachusetts, Boston, 254 p.

———. 1952. Fisheries report for lakes of northeastern Massachusetts—1949 (to Massachusetts Div. Fish. Game). Commonwealth of Massachusetts, Boston, 115 + vi p.

———. 1953. Fisheries report for lakes and ponds of north central Massachusetts—1950 (to Massachusetts Div. Fish. Game). Commonwealth of Massachusetts, Boston, 122 + viii p.

McCABE, B. C., AND A. H. SWARTZ. 1951. Fisheries report: Plymouth County—1946; Berkshire County —1947; Barnstable County—1948 (to Massachusetts Div. Fish. Game). Commonwealth of Massachusetts, Boston, 269 + x p.

MacCLINTOCK, PAUL, AND JAAN TERASMAE. 1960. Glacial history of Covey Hill. J. Geol., 68: 232–241.

MARSTON, P. M. 1939. Notes on the Connecticut River system, p. 229–242. In H. E. Warfel, Biological survey of the Connecticut watershed. New Hampshire Fish, Game Dept., Surv. Rept. 4.

MARSTON, P. M., AND MYRON GORDON. 1938. Notes on fish and early fishing in the Merrimack River system, p. 186–197. In E. E. Hoover, Biological survey of the Merrimack watershed. New Hampshire Fish, Game Dept., Surv. Rept. 3.

MEYER, M. C. 1954. The larger animal parasites of the fresh-water fishes of Maine. Fish. Research and Mgmt. Div., Maine Dept. Inland Fish. Game, Bull. No. 1, 92 p.

MIGDALSKI, E. C. 1962. Freshwater sport fishes of North America. Ronald Press, New York. 431 p.

MILLS, J. R. 1951. A study of lakes in northeastern Vermont. Vermont Geol. Surv., Bull. 4, 54 p.

MOORE, G. M. 1939. A limnological investigation of the microscopic benthic fauna of Douglas Lake, Michigan. Ecol. Monogr., 9: 537–582.

MORTON, W. M., AND R. R. MILLER. 1954. The systematic position of the lake trout Salvelinus namaycush. Copiea, 1954(2): 117–123.

MOSS, D. D. 1961. A history of the Connecticut River and its fisheries. Connecticut State Board Fish., Game, Hartford, Connecticut, 15 p.

MULLAN, J. W. 1960. Excerpts from a special report of the Commissioners of Fisheries, filed with the State Legislature in 1866, relative to salmon and shad in the Merrimack and Connecticut rivers. Massachusetts Div. Fish. Game, Bur. Wildl. Research Mgmt., 8 p.

MULLAN, J. W., AND W. A. TOMPKINS. 1959. Trout pond management in Massachusetts. Massachusetts Div. Fish. Game, 132 p.

NORTON, A. H. 1909. Proc. Portland Soc. Nat. Hist., 2: 1–47.

OANA, SHINYA, AND E. S. DEEVEY. 1960. Carbon 13 in lake waters, and its possible bearing on paleolimnology. Amer. J. Sci. (Bradley Vol.), 258A: 253–272.

OGDEN, J. G. 1959. A late-glacial pollen sequence from Martha's Vineyard, Massachusetts. Amer. J. Sci., 257: 366–381.

————. 1960. Recurrence surfaces and pollen stratigraphy of a postglacial raised bog, Kings County, Nova Scotia. Amer. J. Sci., **258**: 341–353.

OHLE, WALDEMAR. 1959. Die Stoffwechseldynamik der Seen in Abhängigkeit von der Gasausscheidung ihres Schlammes. Vom Wasser, **25**: 127–149.

PATRICK, RUTH. VTDC. The diatoms of Linsley Pond, Connecticut. Proc. Acad. Nat. Sci., Philadelphia, **5**: 53–110 + pl. 11–12.

PAUSZEK, F. H. 1961. Chemical and physical quality of water resources in Connecticut 1955–58 (Progress report). Connecticut Water Resources Comm., Bull. 1, 79 + vii p.

PERKINS, E. H. 1930. The post-Pleistocene clays of Maine, p. 75–81. *In* L. H. Merrill and E. H. Perkins, First annual report on the geology of the State of Maine.

RAINWATER, J. H. 1937. The relationship between air and water temperatures of an Androscoggin watershed trout stream, p. 125–127. *In* E. E. Hoover, Biological survey of the Androscoggin Saco and coastal watersheds. New Hampshire Fish, Game Dept., Surv. Rept. 2.

REUTER, O. M. 1883. The smelt, p. 289. *In* O. M. Reuter and A. J. Mela, Fishes of Finland. Helsingfors. Quoted in W. C. Kendall, The smelts. Bull. U.S. Bur. Fish., **42** (1927).

RICKER, K. E. 1959. The origin of the glacial relict crustaceans in North America, as related to Pleistocene glaciation. Canadian J. Zool., **37**: 871–893.

RICKER, W. E. 1940. On the origin of kokanee, a freshwater type of sock-eye salmon. Trans. Royal Soc. Canada, Section V: 121–135.

RILEY, G. A. 1939. Limnological studies in Connecticut. I and II. Ecol. Monogr., **9**: 53–94.

————. 1940. Limnological studies in Connecticut. III. The plankton of Linsley Pond. Ecol. Monogr., **10**: 279–306.

RODGERS, JOHN, R. N. GATES, E. N. CAMERON, AND R. J. ROSS. 1956. Preliminary geological map of Connecticut. Connecticut Geol. Nat. Hist. Surv., Hartford.

RODGERS, JOHN, R. M. GATES, AND J. L. ROSENFELD. 1959. Explanatory text for preliminary geological map of Connecticut, 1956. Connecticut Geol. Nat. Hist. Surv., Bull. 84, 65 p.

RODHE, WILHELM. 1949. The ionic composition of lake waters. Verh. intern. Verein. Limnol., **10**: 377–386.

————. 1958. The primary production in lakes: Some results and restrictions of the ^{14}C method. Rapp. Procès-verbaux, Conseil Intern. Exploration Mer, **144**: 122–128.

SAILA, S. B., AND DONALD HORTON. 1957. Fisheries investigations and management in Rhode Island lakes and ponds. Div. Fish Game, Rhode Island Dept. Agr., Conserv., Fish. Publ. 3: 1–134.

SHAPIRO, JOSEPH. 1957. Chemical and biological studies on the yellow organic acids of lake water. Limnol. Oceanogr., **2**: 161–179.

SINDERMAN, C. J. 1953. Parasites of fishes of north central Massachusetts, p. 4–28. *In* B. C. McCabe, Fisheries report for lakes and ponds of north central Massachusetts—1950 (to Massachusetts Div.

Fish. Game). Commonwealth of Massachusetts, Boston.

STONE, G. H. 1899. The glacial gravels of Maine and their associated deposits. U.S. Geol. Surv. Monogr. 34, 499 p.

STROUD, R. H. 1955. Fisheries report for some central, eastern, and western Massachusetts lakes, ponds, and reservoirs—1951–52 (to Massachusetts Div. Fish. Game). Commonwealth of Massachusetts, Boston, 447 + ix p.

STUIVER, MINZE, AND E. S. DEEVEY, 1961. Yale natural radiocarbon measurements. VI. Radiocarbon, **3**: 126–140.

SWARTZ, A. H. 1942. Fisheries survey report—1942 (to Massachusetts Div. Fish. Game). Commonwealth of Massachusetts, Boston, 180 p.

TAPPA, D. W. (Unpublished.) The dynamics of the association of six limnetic species of *Daphnia* in Aziscoos Lake, Maine.

TERASMAE, JAAN. 1960. Contribution to Canadian palynology No. 2. I. A palynological study of postglacial deposits in the St. Lawrence lowlands. Geol. Surv. Canada, Dept. Mines Tech. Surv., Bull. 56: vii–xii, 1–22.

THIENEMANN, A. 1950. Verbreitungsgeschichte der Süsswassertierwelt Europas. Schweizerbart'sche Verlag., Stuttgart. 809 p.

THORNTHWAITE, C. W. 1948. An approach toward a rational classification of climate. Geograph. Rev., **38**: 55–94 + pl. 1.

THORPE, L. M., *et al.* 1942. A fishery survey of important Connecticut lakes. State Geol. Nat. Hist. Surv. Connecticut, Bull. 63, 339 p.

TRIPPENSEE, R. E. 1937. Fish population studies on some New Hampshire streams, p. 119–124. *In* E. E. Hoover, Biological survey of the Androscoggin Saco and coastal watersheds. New Hampshire Fish, Game Dept., Surv. Rept. 2.

TUREKIAN, K. K., AND M. D. KLEINKOPF. 1956. Estimates of the average abundance of Cu, Mn, Pb, Ti, Ni, and Cr in surface waters of Maine. Bull. Geol. Soc. Amer., **67**: 1129–1132.

U.S. DEPARTMENT OF AGRICULTURE. 1941. Climate and man. Yearbook of agriculture, 1941. U.S. Govt. Printing Office, Washington. 1248 + xii p.

U.S. GEOLOGICAL SURVEY. 1958. Quality of surface waters of the United States, 1954. Parts 1–4. North Atlantic slope basins to St. Lawrence River basin. U.S. Geol. Surv., Water-Supply Paper No. 1350, 415 + xi p.

————. 1959. Quality of surface waters of the United States, 1955. Parts 1–4. North Atlantic slope basins to St. Lawrence River basin. U.S. Geol. Surv., Water-Supply Paper No. 1400, 529 + xiii.

VALLENTYNE, J. R. 1954. Biochemical limnology. Science, **119**: 605–606.

————. 1955. Sedimentary chlorophyll determination as a paleobotanical method. Canadian J. Botan., **33**: 304–313.

————. 1956. Epiphasic carotenoids in post-glacial lake sediments. Limnol. Oceanogr., **1**: 252–262.

VALLENTYNE, J. R., AND J. R. WHITTAKER. 1956. On the presence of free sugars in filtered lake water. Science, **124**: 1026–1027.

VLADYKOV, V. D. 1954. Taxonomic characteristics of the eastern North American chars (*Salvelinus* and *Cristivomer*). J. Fish Research Board Canada, 11: 904–932.

WARFEL, H. E. 1939. Biological survey of the Connecticut watershed. New Hampshire Fish, Game Dept., Surv. Rept. 4, 256 p.

WARFEL, H. E., AND L. E. FOOTE. 1939. The Connecticut River, p. 122–130. *In* H. E. Warfel, Biological survey of the Connecticut watershed. New Hampshire Fish, Game Dept., Surv. Rept. 4.

WEBSTER, D. A. 1942. The life histories of some Connecticut fishes, p. 122–227. *In* L. M. Thorpe *et al.*, A fishery survey of important Connecticut lakes. State Geol. Nat. Hist. Surv. Connecticut, Bull. 63.

WELCH, P. S. 1952. Limnology. 2nd ed. McGraw-Hill, New York. 538 p.

WHIPPLE, G. C. 1899. The microscopy of drinking water. 4th ed. (1927), revised by G. M. Fair and M. C. Whipple. John Wiley & Sons, New York. 586 + xix p.

WHITE, G. W. 1938. Geology of the Merrimack watershed, p. 136–148. *In* E. E. Hoover, Biological survey of the Merrimack watershed. New Hampshire Fish, Game Dept., Surv. Rept. 3.

WILDE, C. W., *et al.* 1959. A fishery survey of the lakes and ponds of Connecticut. Connecticut State Board Fish. Game, Pond Surv. Unit, Rept. No. 1, 395 p.

WILSON, C. B. 1932. The copepods of the Woods Hole region, Massachusetts. Bull. U.S. Natl. Museum, No. 158, 635 + xix p.

WILSON, L. R. 1935. Lake development and plant succession in Vilas County, Wisconsin. I. The medium hard water lakes. Ecol. Monogr., 5:207–247.

WRIGHT, J. K., *et al.* 1933. New England's prospect: 1933. Amer. Geograph. Soc., Spec. Publ. 16, 502 + ix p.

5 | *Gerald E. Gunning*

Illinois

General description, physiography, and climate

Illinois is the lowest of the North-Central States. The average elevation approximates 632 ft (Kofoid, 1903). The range in altitude is from 1,257 ft at Charles Mound on the Illinois-Wisconsin line to 269 ft, low-water mark of the Ohio River at Cairo. The extreme length of the state is 385 mi; the extreme breadth is 218 mi. The area of Illinois is 56,625 mi² (McDannald, 1952).

Although Illinois has been classified as a prairie state, originally about two-fifths of its area was forested (Mills, 1960). The original forest area of Illinois probably exceeded 14 million acres of which only 4 million acres remain. The present forest areas of the state are principally in west-central, south-central, and southern Illinois.

Illinois is essentially a prairie plain. Relief is generally moderate to slight; it is not sufficient to exert a marked effect on climate. In spite of the absence of marked relief, the physiographic divisions of the state are readily apparent.

More than nine-tenths of the state lies within the Central Lowland (Fig. 5.1), all of which was glaciated except the Wisconsin Driftless Section in northwestern Illinois (Leighton *et al.*, 1948). The other provinces—Ozark Plateaus, Interior Low Plateaus, and Coastal Plain—lie almost entirely outside the glacial boundary in southern and southwestern Illinois.

Aided by Grant No. 367 from the Johnson Fund, American Philosophical Society, and a grant from the National Institutes of Health, U.S. Public Health Service (RG-7125).

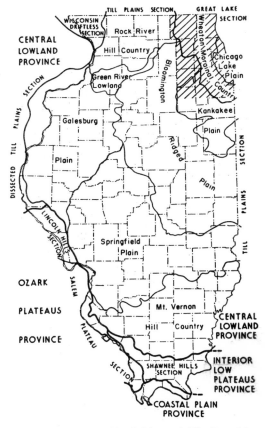

Fig. 5.1.—Physiographic divisions of Illinois and location of the Chicago region. From Suter *et al.*, 1959.

The physiographic contrasts among various parts of Illinois are due to several factors and conditions: (1) topography of the bedrock surface, (2) extent of the several glaciations, (3) differences in glacial morphology, (4) differences in age of the uppermost drift, (5) height of the glacial plain above main lines of drainage, (6) glaciofluvial aggradation of basin areas, and (7) glaciolacustrine action. For an analysis of these factors and a detailed description of the physiographic divisions, see Leighton *et al.* (1948).

When all climatic controls such as latitude, continental location, wind, and storms and their associated air masses are considered collectively, Illinois has, on the average, hot summers, cool to cold winters, and rather abundant precipitation throughout the year with a rather high degree of reliability from year to year (Page, 1949). The average is, of course, made up of pronounced day-to-day differences in temperature, wind direction and velocity, moisture condition of the atmosphere, and precipitation.

The significant climatic differences to be observed can be explained on the basis of the great north-south dimension of the state. The annual mean temperature in northern Illinois is 48° F compared with 60° F in southern Illinois. The warmest month of the year is July; the mean

monthly temperature in northern Illinois during July is 74° F compared with 80° F for southern Illinois. January is the coldest month of the year; the January mean for the extreme north is 20° F contrasted with 37° F for southern Illinois.

Precipitation varies from approximately 46 in. per year in the Shawnee Hills of southern Illinois (Fig. 5.1) to 32 in. near Lake Michigan. The difference in total precipitation between the two regions is largely due to greater winter precipitation in southern Illinois, 5% of which falls as snow (Ackermann, 1958). In northern Illinois, about 20% of the winter precipitation is snow.

A latitudinal distribution from south to north is evident with regard to average maximum monthly rainfall. March and April are peak months in southern Illinois, May has the highest average in central Illinois, and June has the highest average in northern Illinois.

The average length of the growing season varies from 140–150 days at the state line in northernmost Illinois to 200–210 days at the southern tip of the state near Cairo (Leighton, 1944).

Limnological resources

A large portion of the Illinois boundary is composed of water. The Mississippi River flows along the western boundary, to the south and east flow the Ohio and Wabash rivers, and 65 miles of Lake Michigan shoreline lie to the northeast. In addition, a number of rivers, such as the Illinois, Kaskaskia, Rock, Big Muddy, and Embarrass, add to the total surface water resources (Fig. 5.2). McDannald (1952) reported that Illinois has 4,000 mi of navigable rivers. Forbes (1928) estimated that Illinois contains 480 permanent streams with a combined length of 11,912 mi. Streams at least 20 mi long were said to compose 8,213 mi of the total. Forbes' figures do not include the Mississippi, Ohio, and Wabash.

Over 900 lakes and artificial reservoirs occur in Illinois, in addition to at least several thousand farm ponds. Bennett (1960) reported that there are 352 natural lakes in Illinois, including glacial lakes in the northern part of the state and floodplain and oxbow lakes (Fig. 5.3) along the larger rivers. He stated that most counties in Illinois have fewer than 2,000 farm ponds.

In the northern part of the state, sufficient ground water is available locally to meet the needs of municipal water systems; hence, the

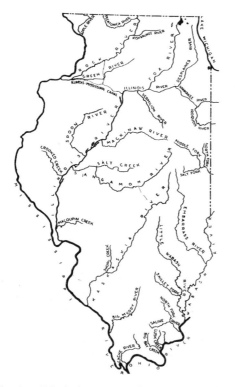

Fig. 5.2.—Principal streams of Illinois. From O'Donnell, 1935.

Fig. 5.3.—Stand of bald cypress (*Taxodium distichum*) in Horseshoe Lake, an oxbow lake 12 miles northwest of Cairo.

cities and towns do not rely on surface waters with the exception of water drawn from Lake Michigan. This is not the case in other parts of the state where sufficient ground water is not available. Rivers such as the Mississippi, Wabash, and Ohio are heavily utilized as sources of surface water. Rivers in the interior of the state, for example the Illinois, Big Muddy, and Kaskaskia, also contribute considerable water to municipal systems. Lakes Springfield and Bloomington are only two examples of many reservoirs designed for surface water storage.

Many of the larger towns and cities in southern Illinois utilize impounding reservoirs for municipal water supplies. Crab Orchard Lake, between Carbondale and Marion, Illinois, is the largest impounding reservoir (Fig. 5.4) in the state. It covers 11 mi² and has a storage capacity of 67,320 acre-feet (Ackermann, 1958).

It is a paradox that the 17 southernmost counties of Illinois should be considered a water deficiency area (Illinois State Water Survey, 1957). This region is bordered on three sides by the Mississippi, Ohio, and Wabash rivers. Several excellent developments of surface water resources lie within the region. Over 100 potential reservoir sites are available for development. The

highest mean annual rainfall within the state occurs here.

The paradox is partially explained by the fact that stream flow is highly variable in southern Illinois. This is due to a limited ground-water contribution to stream flow and a high percentage of thunderstorm-type rainfall. The average annual flow of water into the 17-county region from streams which drain an area of 7,323 mi² to the north has been estimated at 4.1 billion gallons a day (bgd) (Illinois State Water Survey, 1957). Normal runoff from the southern Illinois region, which includes 6,733 mi², was estimated at 4.3 bgd from an average rainfall of 13.8 bgd. Since a large potential water resource is present in the southern Illinois region, the water problem can be solved by proper development of the resource through construction of additional reservoirs for impounding surface water.

The tremendous industrial and municipal growth in the Chicago region (cross-hatched in Fig. 5.1) has created local problems of ground-water supply. An attempt to evaluate the continuing decline of water levels in some of the aquifers has appeared (Suter *et al.*, 1959).

Ground-water resources in the Chicago region are developed from four water-yielding units (Suter *et al.*, 1959): (1) glacial drift aquifers, (2)

Fig. 5.4.—A general view of the Crab Orchard Lake dam. The dam is 3,000 ft long and has a maximum height of 50 ft above the elevation of the stream bed formerly occupied by Crab Orchard Creek.

shallow dolomite aquifers, (3) Cambrian-Ordovician Aquifer, and (4) the Mt. Simon Aquifer.

The Cambrian-Ordovician Aquifer has been heavily utilized for ground-water supplies. Its estimated yield in 1958 exceeded 43 million gallons a day (mgd). Pumpage at Chicago has been quite extensive, resulting in a decline of artesian pressure in the Cambrian-Ordovician Aquifer amounting to as much as 660 ft since 1864 (Suter et al., 1959).

In 1957, 127.9 mgd of ground water were pumped in the Chicago region. The glacial drift and shallow dolomite aquifers yielded over half of this amount. This withdrawal resulted in no general decline in non-pumping water levels, indicating that the potential yield is considerably larger than present withdrawal (Suter et al., 1959). The results of the preliminary report indicate that future ground-water supplies should be taken from the shallow aquifers when feasible.

Southern Illinois possesses limited ground-water resources compared with northern Illinois. The ground-water potential of the 17 southernmost counties of Illinois (6,733 mi^2) has been summarized as follows (Illinois State Water Survey, 1957): 1) there are 577 mi^2 of area which are favorable for high-capacity wells of 75 gal/min or more; 2) there are 376 mi^2 in which limited development of wells appears to be possible; and 3) there are 5,780 mi^2 in which ground-water possibilities are extremely limited. Hence, utilization of surface-water resources in this area is again indicated as a desirable alternative.

Viewing the state as a whole, and not considering local or regional water supply problems, Illinois is a water-excess state. The following data from Ackermann (1958) support this view. The estimated inflow of atmospheric moisture in the air over Illinois averages about 2,000 billion gallons a day. About 5% of this amount (99 bgd) falls as some form of precipitation. Evaporation from land and water surfaces and transpiration from growing plants are estimated to return to the atmosphere about 76 bgd of the 99 bgd total precipitation. A total of 23 bgd is thus available from within the state in the form of stream flow and ground water. The latter amount, when added to the minimum flow on record of the Mississippi and Ohio rivers as well as the current pumpage and diversion from Lake Michigan, brings the grand total of mean daily surface- and ground-water supplies available in Illinois to

43 bgd. This amount is estimated to be five times the present state usage and one-sixth of the water usage for all purposes in the United States.

With regard to water quality, streams in northern Illinois generally have an average dissolved mineral content approximating 450 ppm and a hardness of about 400 ppm as $CaCO_3$. These values decrease to about 300 ppm mineral content and 250 ppm hardness in western and southern Illinois. The water of Crab Orchard Lake in southern Illinois is exceptionally low in mineral content (200 ppm) and hardness (110 ppm). All of the figures given here are approximations; refer to Larson and Larson (1957) for specific values. Many municipalities drawing water from streams and wells find it desirable to install water-softening plants as a part of the public water supply system.

History of limnological research centers

State Laboratory of Natural History

On 30 June 1858, the Natural History Society of Illinois was organized at Bloomington in the office of the Illinois State Normal University. The society was chartered by an act of the state legislature on February 22, 1861. Immediately the new society began organizing a museum and collecting literature. Stephen A. Forbes was appointed curator of the State Museum of Natural History (succeeding J. W. Powell and others) in 1872, a position he held until 1877. The Illinois Museum of Natural History at Normal was converted into a State Laboratory of Natural History by a legislative act in 1877 (Mills, 1958). Forbes became the first director.

Forbes taught zoology at the Illinois State Normal University. In addition he initiated a series of research bulletins. The first appeared in 1876 as the Bulletin of the Illinois Museum of Natural History. Number 2 of the first volume appeared in 1878 under the title Bulletin of the State Laboratory of Natural History, which runs to the beginning of Volume 13, 1918 (Mills, 1958). Henceforth, the title is Bulletin of the Illinois State Natural History Survey or Illinois Natural History Survey Bulletin. These details are given here since the bulletins contain many papers on aquatic biology in Illinois.

Forbes was appointed State Entomologist in

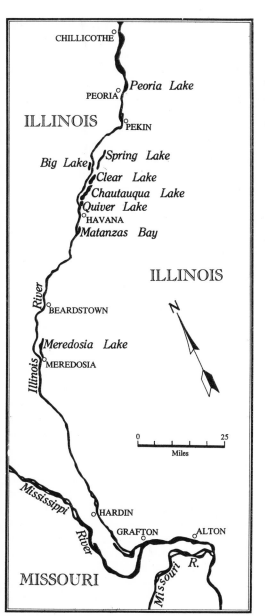

Fig. 5.5.—A portion of the Illinois River including some representative lakes along its length. Tributaries are not shown. Map prepared by the University of Wisconsin Cartographic Laboratory.

1882. On 1 July 1885, he was appointed Professor of Zoology and Entomology at the University of Illinois. The State Laboratory of Natural History was moved to Urbana by state legislative action, and Forbes remained as director of the laboratory until 1917.

Illinois Biological Station at Havana

In 1894 Professor Stephen A. Forbes established a biological station for the continuous investigation of the aquatic life of the Illinois River and adjacent waters (Forbes, 1895). Forbes intended that future studies would be done on the Mississippi River as well. He was interested in the effect on aquatic organisms of periodical overflow and gradual recession of the waters of such rivers as the Mississippi and Illinois. The main objective of the station was to be investigation, as opposed to instruction.

Some insight into why Forbes selected the Illinois River as a site for the station can be derived from a later paper (Forbes and Richardson, 1913, p. 481):

The Illinois River is peculiarly characteristic of the State of Illinois, and, next to the prairies, was its leading natural feature. The level richness of the central plateau of the state is reflected in the turbid waters and the broad sluggish current of the stream; and its wide bottomlands, originally covered with huge trees, completely flooded when the river is highest, and holding many marshes and shallow lakes at its lowest stages, are a relic of the time, not so very far remote, when the limpid waters of the Great Lakes rolled down its valley in a mighty flood on their course to the southern gulf.

The wisdom of establishing the biological station is further attested to by the following statement (Forbes, 1928, p. 277):

. . . the rivers of the country have received so little comprehensive attention from our biologists that I do not know of a single attempt anywhere in America to develop and disclose the complete biology of a river system except that which has been made by us in Illinois. . . .

Havana (Fig. 5.5) was selected as the site of the station. The bluffs along the eastern shore of the Illinois River provided a clean, hard, sand beach at their bases which was suitable for field work and ideal for camping (Bennett, 1958). An abundance of spring water occurred along the bluffs.

The laboratory was in the town itself, with a cabin boat on the Illinois River supplementing the laboratory facilities. The cabin boat contained living facilities for four men, collecting equipment, microscopes, and a small library.

The original staff of the station in 1894 included several investigators (Bennett, 1958). Frank Smith was directly in charge; his principal research interest was aquatic worms. C. A. Hart, an entomologist, was curator of collections for the State Laboratory. Adolph Hempel worked on protozoans and rotifers. Mrs. Dora Smith served as micro-technician and supervised the laboratory at Havana. A number of visiting investigators and assistants served in various capacities. Professor Forbes exercised general supervision over the station.

Forbes' interests were quite broad. In addition to his extensive fish distribution studies, he worked on food of fishes, taxonomy of crustaceans, aquatic and terrestrial insects, food of birds, plankton, benthos, and botanical problems.

C. A. Kofoid served as superintendent of the station from 1895 to 1900. His principal interest was the plankton of the Illinois River.

R. E. Richardson, who was employed in Illinois as an aquatic biologist from 1903 to 1904 and from 1909 to 1933 (East, 1958), did considerable research at Havana. Although primarily interested in bottom fauna, he collaborated with Forbes in a study of the fishes of the state and other investigations.

Illinois Natural History Survey

The State Laboratory of Natural History and the State Entomologist's Office were united in 1917 to form the Natural History Survey (Mills, 1958). Professor Forbes became the first Chief of the Survey and served in this capacity until his death in 1930.

The survey continued to maintain a boat-laboratory and other facilities on the Illinois River. Numerous investigators among the survey personnel were concerned with the physicochemical characteristics of aquatic habitats, particularly as related to their effects upon fish. A number of such studies were conducted by V. E. Shelford and his students, D. H. Thompson, and others.

Extensive surveys of the Illinois, Rock, Sangamon, Kaskaskia (Fig. 5.2), and other river systems were made. Samuel Eddy published extensively during the period 1925–34 on the plankton of various habitats in the state.

D. H. Thompson conducted aquatic research for the survey from 1923 to 1944. He was particularly interested in the dynamics of fish populations and the management of fish populations in lakes and ponds.

G. W. Bennett joined the survey staff in 1938 to work with Thompson on ponds. With D. F. Hansen assisting, these workers censused 22 artificial lakes and ponds in central and southern Illinois (Bennett, 1958). A number of reports on lake management resulted from this work.

In 1948 W. C. Starrett was employed to work on the Mississippi River. Starrett collaborated with P. G. Barnickol, and two reports on Mississippi River fishes resulted. Starrett has also been interested in bottom fauna. He was instrumental in the founding of the Midwest Benthological Society at Havana in the spring of 1953.

R. W. Larimore joined the survey staff in 1948. His study on the ecological life history of the warmouth, *Chaenobryttus gulosus*, could, in my opinion, serve as a model for future investigations of this nature.

The above account is beyond doubt a cursory one; space does not permit a listing of all members of the survey staff who have done work in the area of aquatic biology. A detailed account of the research contributions of the various Illinois biologists will be given, with appropriate literature citations, in a succeeding section.

Southern Illinois University

W. M. Gersbacher's tenure at Carbondale extended from 1929 to 1930 and from 1936 to the present. Professor Gersbacher's research has been primarily on the benthos of lakes and streams.

The aquatic biology program was bolstered in 1949 by the addition of W. M. Lewis to the zoology department. Professor Lewis established and still directs the Cooperative Fisheries Research Laboratory at Southern Illinois University. Since 1949, some 20–30 students, including this writer, have received the master's degree in zoology, specializing in fishery biology. A doctoral program is presently operative.

The training given to students here is quite broad, as evidenced by the content of some 50 publications which have appeared. These may be classified generally as follows: (1) fishery surveys of lakes and streams, (2) physicochemical studies of fishery waters, (3) general limnological studies of lakes and ponds, (4) investigations of the dynamics of fish populations, (5) fish disease and pathological problems, (6) food and feeding behavior of fishes, (7) creel censuses, (8) inquiries into the age and growth characteristics of fishes, (9) analyses of pollution and its effects on fishes, and (10) management inquiries to provide greater fish production.

Illinois Department of Conservation

The Division of Fisheries, Illinois State Department of Conservation, has contributed to aquatic research within the state. Several district fishery biologists, some of whom were trained under Professor Lewis, conduct aquatic investigations. The Division of Fisheries works closely with the Illinois Natural History Survey on fishery problems, as well as with the Cooperative Fisheries Research Laboratory at Southern Illinois University. Mr. Sam Parr served as Superintendent of the Division of Fisheries for many years; he was instrumental in the establishment of cooperative programs.

Other centers within the state

Professor V. E. Shelford, long associated with the University of Illinois and the Illinois Natural History Survey, has added to our knowledge of the aquatic biology of Illinois directly through his own research, as well as indirectly as a teacher.

Professor T. C. Dorris, who was associated with Quincy College from 1947 to 1956, studied the limnology of the Mississippi River. John Weise, also at Quincy, investigated the spring cavefish, *Chologaster agassizi,* with reference to the food chain in small spring communities.

Loren Woods of the Chicago Natural History Museum is interested primarily in the taxonomy of fishes.

Leonard Durham, formerly with the Illinois Natural History Survey, is at Eastern Illinois University, Charleston. His primary interest is fishery biology.

The Illinois State Water Survey, Illinois State Sanitary Water Board, and the Illinois State Geological Survey staffs contribute to our knowledge of the extent and quality of ground- and surface-water resources. The Illinois Academy of Science has also stimulated aquatic research.

National agencies such as the U.S. Bureau of Fisheries, U.S. Public Health Service, and U.S. Fish and Wildlife Service have conducted surveys periodically in Illinois.

Plankton

Illinois River

When Kofoid published his first paper on the plankton of the Illinois River (Figs. 5.2 and 5.5), the quantitative study of plankton had just been established as a science. The first quantitative plankton work had been done less than 10 years earlier by Hensen in Germany (Kofoid, 1897). Kofoid entered upon his now classic plankton studies with a clear conception of what he hoped to accomplish, as shown by the following passage (Kofoid, 1897, p. 1):

The scope of our plankton work upon the Illinois River and its adjacent waters includes a continuous, systematic, and exhaustive examination of the plant and animal life suspended in the waters of a river system, with a view to determining its amount and seasonal changes, its local and vertical distribution, its movement and relation to the current, the effect upon it of floods and of drouth, of light and of temperature, the organisms which compose it, their seasonal and cyclic changes, and their mutual interrelations. Added interest arises from the fact that this is the first application of this method of biological investigation to a river system and its related waters.

Kofoid reported (1897) that previous plankton researchers (Hensen, Apstein, Zacharias, Reighard, and Ward) used, without exception, the vertical-haul method of plankton collection, whereby the net is lowered to the bottom of a body of water and then raised to the surface, thus filtering a vertical column of water. Kofoid found the vertical-haul method to be generally unsatisfactory for his work at Havana. Subsequently, an oblique-haul method was used. Finally, a series of field experiments abundantly justified Kofoid's abandonment of the system of collection in which the net is drawn through the water for one in which a known quantity of water is pumped through the net.

Several advantages of the pumping method are listed in the same paper. For example, this method is widely applicable since water samples may be drawn from any desired depth; the method thus gives an accurate sampling of vertical distribution of plankton. In the same paper Kofoid described a new method of concentrating plankton collections by centrifugation as being superior to the older method of settling by gravity. The processed material was then counted by the Sedgwick-Rafter method.

Some of the major conclusions drawn from a study of 645 plankton collections made in seven localities on the Illinois River and adjacent waters between 1894 and 1899 (Kofoid, 1903) are given here.

Kofoid found that Illinois River plankton was

uniformly distributed. The average departure from the mean in short distances, for example 3 mi, approximated ± 10%. In 205 mi of the river course, the average departure in flood conditions was ± 51%.

The plankton of the river channel was subject to great seasonal and annual variations. The monthly averages of all collections indicated a period of minimum production of plankton in January-February, of rising production in March, of maximum production for the year in April-June, usually culminating in a spring maximum about the end of April and often declining to a low level in June. The average monthly production* declined gradually for the remainder of the year to the winter minimum in December.

The waters of Spoon River (Fig. 5.2), a tributary of the Illinois River, generally contained a very small amount of plankton. Chemical conditions were judged to be favorable. The recent origin of the water was believed to be the cause of the low production. When such barren waters were impounded for 10–30 days in backwater reservoirs, the waters developed an abundant plankton.

A few lakes along the Illinois River produced less plankton than did the channel waters because of excess submergent vegetation, inflow of tributary waters containing little plankton, and other causes. Most of the lakes, however, produced more plankton than did the channel waters. Phelps Lake, for example, produced the most abundant plankton of all the localities studied. The maximum production in Kofoid's records, 224.5 cc/m³, was observed in this lake on August 23, 1898.

Fluctuations in hydrographic conditions constituted the most immediately effective factor in the environment of the potamoplankton. Rising water levels usually signaled a sharp decline in plankton content per cubic meter; falling levels resulted in recovery or increase in plankton content.

Light significantly affected plankton production. The half year with more illumination and fewer cloudy days produced 1.6 to 7 times as much plankton as that with less illumination and more cloudy days.

Kofoid believed the plankton of the Illinois River to be largely autonomous. Seepage and

---

* The term "production" as used in this chapter does not embody the rate concept.

creek waters were diluents of the river plankton and added little to its diversity. The reservoir backwaters, in contrast, generally contained a more abundant plankton than the channel. The backwaters were thus a source of the channel plankton as well as a factor involved in its maintenance.

The total annual production of plankton in the Illinois River, on the basis of normal discharge and a plankton content at the mouth of the river equal to that of the average record at Havana was estimated at 67,750 m³.

Filter-paper catches indicated the presence of a plankton community (nannoplankton) approximately three times the volume of that taken by the silk plankton net. It was thus discovered that a highly significant number of organisms passed through the meshes of the plankton nets. This was, of course, a most important observation.

With the above conclusions and observations in mind, let us consider the importance of the location of the plankton-collecting stations near Havana (Fig. 5.5). This site enabled Kofoid to take collections in water that was representative of the stream as a whole. No large tributary was located near enough to disturb the water, and most of the water in the stream passing by Havana had been moving in the channel for a considerable period of time. Kofoid thus believed that conditions were favorable for a uniform distribution and development, including reproduction, of the plankton at the point where collections were made for detailed study.

In a later paper Kofoid (1908) characterized two types of plankton assemblages in the Illinois River, the summer and winter assemblages. The spring and fall aggregations were described as transitions between the other two when organisms from both summer and winter assemblages were present. "The winter plankton is characterized by a small number of species peculiar to that season, and a number of perennial forms; the summer, by a large number of summer organisms with the perennial types" (Kofoid, 1908, p. 312).

In the 1908 paper, Kofoid posed the following important question: "Is the plankton of streams (potamoplankton) different from that of lakes (limnoplankton) and ponds (heleoplankton)?" On the basis of his Illinois River work, Kofoid distinguished potamoplankton from limnoplankton and heleoplankton by the following characteristics (Kofoid, 1908): (1) It is a polymixic plankton. This is due to a mingling of planktons from all sources in the drainage basin, especially from tributary backwaters, and the consequent seeding the channel waters. (2) It is subject to extreme fluctuations in quantity and constitution. This naturally follows, considering the manifold factors which operate in the fluviatile environment and the directness with which they may affect the plankton. (3) The potamoplankton is not characterized by any species peculiar to it nor by any precise assemblages of eulimnetic organisms. It may be distinguished, in a general way only, by the greater proportion of littoral or benthal forms which are mingled with the more typical plankters.

Kofoid approached the various aspects of his endeavors with thoroughness. He identified 528 species and varieties in the plankton of the Illinois River and adjacent waters but stated that he made no effort to build up merely a long list of species. He identified, whenever possible, "the common and recurring forms" (Kofoid, 1908, p. 10).

Lake Michigan near Chicago

A fragmentary knowledge of the plankton of Lake Michigan was first gained by identifying the stomach contents of fishes that feed on plankton. Commercia' fishes, such as the lake whitefish, *Coregonus clupeaformis,** were of special interest. Professor Forbes' work in this connection will be considered later.

Eddy (1927) undertook an investigation of the plankton of Lake Michigan with the following objectives in mind: (1) to present a general picture of the plankton of Lake Michigan, (2) to determine the relative abundance of its constituent organisms, and (3) to incorporate and summarize the facts already known about the plankton of the Great Lakes. Quantitative silk-net and filter-paper collections made only at the surface and near the shore were analyzed. At the time, no work had been done on the deep-water plankton of Lake Michigan.

Eddy (1927) concluded that the stability of the lake as a biotic factor was strikingly demonstrated by comparison of data covering a time span of 40 years, which presumably showed that little or no change had occurred in the composition of the plankton during this time.

* Scientific names of fishes are those recommended by the American Fisheries Society (1960).

Many of the species were rather constantly abundant throughout the year, although some slight seasonal variations were noted, particularly for zooplankton. The plankton consisted primarily of diatoms of the genera *Asterionella, Tabellaria,* and *Fragilaria.* Limnetic algae were not conspicuous. Zooplankters were generally scarce. It was Eddy's belief that practically all the plankton originated within the limnetic area of the lake.

The first information on the deep-water plankton was published by Ahlstrom (1936), who took samples from water of 32–244 m in depth. Ahlstrom found that most species he observed in the deep-water samples of Lake Michigan were also present in the inshore surface collections that he made, although the inshore material was much richer in adventitious species. Ahlstrom characterized Lake Michigan as a *"Dinobryon* lake," with the flagellate *Dinobryon,* together with diatoms, dominating the plankton. Copepods dominated the zooplankton in bulk; protozoans dominated it in numbers. Rotifers were common. Cladocerans were usually rare. Ahlstrom could not produce supporting quantitative data, but it was his opinion that seasonal variation occurred in the plankton of Lake Michigan.

Dailey (1938) discussed seasonal periodicity of the phytoplankton of Lake Michigan. The seasonal curve for diatom periodicity conformed almost exactly with the total phytoplankton curve. Total phytoplankton showed considerable weekly variations. Spring and autumn maxima occurred in June and October, respectively. These maxima were especially attributable to *Synedra.* Hydrogen-ion concentration and temperature did not seem to be of primary importance as factors controlling diatom periodicity, but turbidity, caused by lake turnovers in the spring and fall (and by the wind action of storms), seemed to exert a very important influence on seasonal growth and pulses.

Damann (1941) noted a distinct seasonal variation in the phytoplankton of Lake Michigan. In a second paper, Damann (1945) analyzed quantitative plankton records and concluded that the plankton of Lake Michigan was dominated by diatoms from 1926 through 1942, a 17-year period. Diatoms accounted for 90% of the average total plankton. Annual generic yields of diatoms tended to reflect competition among the individual genera; the factors controlling this competition are not yet known. Concerning a second aspect, the annual average standing crop of plankton increased from 815 organisms per ml in 1938 to 1,277 organisms per ml in 1942, which was the highest annual average standing crop of plankton recorded for the entire 17-year period. Griffith (1955) reported much higher productivity than Dailey (1938) or Damann (1941); this discrepancy, she suggested, might be due to differences in counting techniques. Damann (1960) suggested that pollution, as indicated by coliform bacteria counts, does not have a direct linear relationship with the increasing trend of plankton productivity in Lake Michigan.

In summary, with regard to seasonal periodicity of the phytoplankton of Lake Michigan, most studies indicate that a distinct seasonal variation occurs.

Sinkhole ponds in southern Illinois

Sinkholes are found in various parts of the state, but they are most common in extreme southern Illinois. The funnels of sinkholes are common in areas underlain with limestone. They probably originated when water moved through the limestone and dissolved away a part of it, resulting in the formation of underground chambers. The roofs of these chambers settle and cause surface depressions that can fill with water.

Sinkholes usually have no drainage other than a vertical pit in the center which extends to the subterranean outlet. Younger sinks are usually small and deep, with steep sides extending to the pit; in the older sinks, drainage from the pit is obstructed by falling rocks and eroded soil, so that water accumulates to form a pond (Eddy, 1931). Drainage is frequently maintained to some extent through the pit of older sinks. As a result of further erosion of the sides and deposition of silt washed in following rains, the pond gradually fills and transforms to a low place containing water in wet seasons.

Eddy (1931) found an abundant plankton in several sinkhole ponds near Wetaug in southern Illinois. The plankton of these ponds, which was similar in some respects to that of rivers and other ponds, was distinguished by the abundance of several characteristic species, such as *Trichocerca multicrinis,* and by an absence or scarcity of certain other species, notably rotifers of the genus *Brachionus.* Rotifers normally occur in pond plankton. Diatoms, which are usually abun-

dant in pond and stream plankton, were noticeably rare.

The ponds ranged in age from a deep perennial pond in an apparently recent sinkhole to temporary ponds in old sinkholes that had become nearly filled. These ponds showed, to some extent, developmental stages of the plankton community as the ponds grew older and filled with silt. Ponds remaining in the perennial stage, thus containing water throughout the year, had a plankton that showed little change. As a pond reaches the temporary stage, with a gradual decrease in depth, it contains water only in the rainy seasons; the plankton organisms mingle with benthal organisms to form an aggregation characteristic of shallow water. Assemblages of both kinds of ponds were characterized in detail.

Other studies

Transeau (1916) made collections of algae in central Illinois for a period of seven years. Approximately 3,000 collections were analyzed. He concluded from his study of algal periodicity that "although algae germinate, develop vegetatively, and produce spores throughout the year, they may be conveniently grouped, on the basis of their *complete* life histories, into winter annuals, spring annuals, summer annuals, autumn annuals, ephemerals, and perennials."

Galtsoff (1924) investigated the plankton of the Upper Mississippi River. The mean content of the plankton in the river, excluding Lakes Pepin and Keokuk, averaged 14.5 cc/m³ of water. The river below Rock Island rapids carried less than 40% of the amount of plankton found above the rapids. Galtsoff described the plankton of the Mississippi River as monotonic. He found no organisms in the river plankton that could not be found in the adjacent lakes. At low-water stages the production of plankton in both Lakes Pepin and Keokuk was greater than in the adjacent parts of the river proper.

Eddy (1925) considered freshwater algal succession. He emphasized that "aquatic succession is a fundamental primary succession establishing not only a basis for terrestrial succession but completing a sere of its own. . . . Primary succession of algae may continue in two major seres, a stream or a prairie pond sere. In both seres the initial stage is very similar, starting under barren conditions and containing unicellular algae as pioneers."

The Sangamon River was subsequently studied (Eddy, 1932). This river (Fig. 5.2) flows through glacial till and occupies a well-worn valley. The current of the river is never very great at normal levels. Eddy considered the question of whether the plankton in a given part of a stream is developed there under local conditions or carried down from upstream. The latter alternative was indicated for the Sangamon River plankton, at least in part.

A monographic study of freshwater plankton communities by Eddy appeared in 1934. One purpose of this monograph was, "by studying plankton as an index to the pelagic portion of the freshwater communities, to determine the existence, rank, behavior and status of the plankton element," and each of these aspects was discussed in detail. Consider, for example, Eddy's views relevant to the factors influencing the development of plankton (Eddy, 1934, p. 62):

The important factors influencing the development of plankton are age of water (i.e., distance from source ÷ velocity), temperature, and turbidity. In the streams studied, other factors such as light, dissolved oxygen, and hydrogen-ion concentration seemed to be always sufficient to meet the requirements of the plankton. Observations on the plankton of water of different ages showed that, all other factors being favorable, a few plankton organisms usually appeared in water 6–10 days from its source, while an abundant plankton appeared in water 20 days or more from its source.

Eddy (1934) recognized four types of plankton societies or socies, characterized by their predominants as follows: (1) rivers and related waters exhibiting some degree of stability: four species of *Brachionus,* two of *Synchaeta, Filinia longiseta,* and *Moina micrura;* (2) deep lakes: *Notholca longispina, Striatella fenestrata, Daphnia retrocurva, Bosmina longispina,* and *Diaptomus minutus;* (3) temporary ponds: *Cyclops serrulatus, Camptocercus rectirostris,* and two species of *Simocephalus;* (4) moderately deep and shallow glacial lakes: *Diaptomus oregonensis,* pelagic diatoms, and blue-green algae.

The plankton studies within Illinois have thus been quite broad in terms of the number of types of habitat considered. Eddy's (1934) monograph treats the freshwater plankton of the United States in general and considers the plankton of Illinois waters in its proper perspective to plankton science as a whole.

Benthos

Illinois River and adjacent waters

The works of Richardson (1921*a*, 1921*b*, 1925*a*, 1925*b*, 1928) are milestones in the study of the benthos. Some of the conclusions Richardson reached as a result of his work on the Illinois River and adjacent waters are given below (Richardson, 1921*a*, p. 366):

In a stretch of the river above Havana, which with its adjacent lakes, is the richest part of the Illinois River system, the inshore and bottom fauna of the lakes averages in weight to the acre about twice as much as that of the river, and it is in the lakes that the fisheries give their highest yield.

Generally speaking, the richest sections of the river bottom were those with the least average slope and the slowest current and, therefore, with the most abundant sediments (Richardson, 1921*a*). The quantity of the bottom fauna diminished rapidly downstream from Chillicothe (Fig. 5.5), averaging 555 lb/acre for the upper 60 mi, 88 lb/acre for the next 42 mi, and 10.4 lb/acre for the lowermost 77 mi (all weights do not include the shells of mollusks). From Chillicothe to the mouth (Fig. 5.5), the average for the river channel was 261 lb/acre. The highest local yield was 5,196 lb/acre.

In shallow, weedy areas of lakes and backwaters the small invertebrates living on and among the weeds greatly exceeded the benthos; in one instance these invertebrates averaged 2,118 lb/acre compared with 255 lb/acre of benthos from the lakes of the same district.

Combining weed fauna and benthos, then applying joint averages to the entire area of lakes and backwater between Copperas Creek and Havana, Richardson calculated a yield of 1,447 lb/acre compared with 705 lb/acre for the unusually rich sections of river opposite the lakes (Richardson, 1921*a*).

Between 1915 and 1920, tremendous reductions occurred in numbers and poundage of small bottom animals in certain segments of the Illinois River. Numerous families and species were totally obliterated, whereas the pollutional or tolerant forms increased in frequency. These changes could be attributed to pollution from the Chicago region which increased in amount and extent (Richardson, 1921*b*). The stretch of river affected at that time was 90 mi long.

Pollution of the Illinois River often resulted in

tremendous mortality of benthal forms. Richardson (1925a) reported that in August, 1917, masses of dead snails, acres in extent, were seen floating down the Illinois River. In some places along the water front at Peoria (Fig. 5.5) the dead snails were piled up one or two feet deep.

The number of species of the 1913–15 bottom fauna exterminated by sewage in the next 10-year period in the Illinois River amounted to 12 species in Peoria Lake (Fig. 5.5), 13 species from Wesley to Copperas Creek Dam, 68–69 species from Spring Lake Canal to Havana, 24–25 species from Matanzas to Beardstown (Fig. 5.5), and almost complete extermination of adult commercial mussels as far south as Havana (Richardson, 1925b).

The effect of increasing pollution upon the major groups of the bottom fauna was reflected in a significant decrease in average numbers per square yard in all groups except the pollutional sludge worms (Tubificidae) and midge larvae (*Chironomus*), which increased tremendously in the same period (Richardson, 1928).

Benthal species were classified into seven categories with reference to the degree of tolerance of the organisms to pollution (Richardson, 1928), ranging from clean-water species to a pollutional group.

The above studies were important in that the biologist could judge, in a somewhat quantitative fashion, what constituted polluted water. Enough preliminary work had been done so that normal conditions of the bottom fauna could be generally defined. As pollution encroached upon each segment of the Illinois River farther and farther downstream, the effects of this gradual downstream progression of pollution could be studied in detail. We often find in present-day investigations that assessing the effects of pollution is difficult because of a lack of basic knowledge concerning what constitutes the normal condition.

Richardson's data provide current investigators with a sound basis for comparison in analyzing long-range changes in the benthos of the Illinois River and adjacent waters. A recent study (Paloumpis and Starrett, 1960) revealed some drastic changes in the bottom fauna of Quiver Lake (Fig. 5.5) and Lake Matanzas since the time they had been studied by Richardson in 1914–15. At Lake Matanzas the oligochaete population increased from 4.4 per square yard in 1915 to 11,007 per square yard in 1953, and

a comparable change occurred at Quiver Lake. The molluscan population of Lake Matanzas has declined greatly since 1915; the population of dipterous larvae has increased. Paloumpis and Starrett (1960) believed that siltation and other forms of pollution have been important factors in the drastic changes that have occurred in the benthos.

Other studies

Baker (1922) surveyed the molluscan fauna of the Big Vermilion River, which consisted of some 60 species and varieties. A progressive increase in number of species occurred in a downstream direction. The headwaters contained few species, the representatives of which were usually smaller than the same species from farther downstream.

Gersbacher (1937) studied small streams of the Sangamon River drainage system (Fig. 5.2) and a number of large artificial pools in central Illinois streams. He sought to establish the development or rank, from an ecological point of view, of the benthos of streams. Impounded bodies of water above dams, the age of which was known, were designated quasi-experimental pools. The conditions created by these artificial pools are characteristic of undisturbed stream bottoms. The bottoms of these newly-formed pools are devoid of animal life; communities subsequently develop on these bare areas. The bottom is mainly populated from the pools of the stream that has been dammed. Hence, one can follow the progressive development of bottom aggregations.

Gersbacher's study "strongly suggested the existence of but a single major community and its developmental stages and variations or faciations." The development of communities (Fig. 5.6) in the pools created by dams amply demonstrated this point. The latter pool development formed a basis for interpretation of the various fragments of a community found in pools of the Sangamon River and other streams. Gersbacher was convinced that "any attempt to bring the stream physiographic history into play along the lines indicated by Shelford [1911a; 1913, Chapter VI], confuses rather than clarifies an understanding of community relations in the streams under consideration at least."

Three definite successional stages in the development of bottom communities of the artifi-

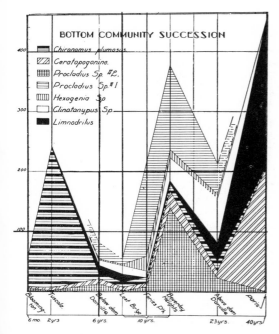

BOTTOM COMMUNITY SUCCESSION

- ▬ *Chironomus plumosus*
- ▨ *Ceratopogonina.*
- ▦ *Procladius Sp. #2.*
- ▭ *Procladius Sp. #1*
- ▥ *Hexagenia Sp*
- ☐ *Clinotanypus Sp*
- ■ *Limnodrilus*

Fig. 5.6.—A graphic representation of succession of bottom communities in the quasi-experimental areas. The three definite peaks in the graph represent the maximal abundance of different species of animals upon different ages of lake bed. Each peak represents a facies in the development of the community. From Gersbacher, 1937.

cial pools were characterized as follows: 1) *Chironomus plumosus* (on the youngest stage), 2) an unknown species of *Procladius*, and 3) *Hexagenia* sp. and *Musculium* sp. (on the oldest stage). *Limnodrilus* and members of the Ceratopogonidae (Heleidae) became extremely abundant where considerable organic material was deposited; they were not considered to be typical of succession in these reservoirs. In all of the developmental stages, fishes were considered to be the most important dominants of the community.

The communities existing in the streams of central Illinois were characterized by the same invertebrate dominants that developed in the reservoirs. The *Hexagenia-Musculium* mud bottom community was considered climax for the Sangamon River and similar streams. In mature streams, for example the Illinois River, the *Hexagenia-Musculium-Viviparus* community was climax (Gersbacher, 1937). In conclusion, biotic succession was said to constitute a guide to the interpretation of freshwater communities.

Dorris (1958) investigated four lakes occupying parts of an old stream channel on the leveed flood plain of the Mississippi River near Quincy, Illinois. He found that "bottom organisms, except tubificid worms, were virtually eliminated by severe reduction of dissolved oxygen during the summer, but were little affected by similar reduction during the winter." Fish predation seemed to be an important factor in holding bottom populations at a relatively low level. This factor, plus wave action on the bottoms, maintained a partial climax condition. The lakes were judged to be "in a condition of successional semi-stasis."

Physicochemical and pollutional aspects

Thermal stratification

Thermal stratification of the water of two artificial impoundments in southern Illinois was treated by Gersbacher (1956). Only Little Grassy Lake, an artificial reservoir near Carbondale, is considered here. The surface area of this lake is about 1,000 acres; maximum depth at spillway level is 60 ft with an average depth of 25 ft. On 28 June 1952, the range in temperature was 32° C at the surface to 13° C at a depth of 50 ft. The epilimnion extended from the surface to a depth of 8 ft, the thermocline extended from 8 to 18 ft, and the hypolimnion extended from 18 to 50 ft.

The annual temperature cycle of Lake Michigan has been discussed by a number of investigators (Church, 1942, 1945; Hough, 1958; Van Oosten, 1960; and others). Since our coverage deals mainly with that part of Lake Michigan near Chicago, I shall consider data selected from Van Oosten (1960, p. 14) for stations off Waukegan, Illinois (Table 5.1). One column of the data shows a shallow thermocline; another shows a deeper thermocline. The five temperature series shown in the table are for a localized area and are given here mainly as examples of thermal stratification. For a consideration of seiche effects, see Hough (1958, pp. 44–45). For further details consult the papers listed above.

Surface currents of Lake Michigan

Johnson (1960) studied surface currents in Lake Michigan. Our discussion will be limited to his South Haven (Michigan)–Waukegan (Illinois) transect. Recovery of drift bottles indicated a "general west-to-east drift in which the north-

TABLE 5.1

Temperature of Lake Michigan near Waukegan, Illinois, 1930 and 1931. Braces indicate thermoclines. From Van Oosten, 1960.

Cruise 12 Station 23 11 Nov. 1930 Max. depth 34 m Air 13.8° C		Cruise 2 Station 112 11 May 1931 Max. depth 56 m Air 13.5° C		Cruise 6 Station 112 30 June 1931 Max. depth 55 m Air 26.8° C		Cruise 16 Station 149 22 Oct. 1931 Max. depth 68 m Air 16.3° C		Cruise 17 Station 149 2 Nov. 1931 Max. depth 75 m Air 10.3° C	
Depth (m)	Temp. (° C)	Depth (m)	Temp. (° C)	Depth (m)	Temp. (° C)	Depth (m)	Temp. (° C)	Depth (m)	Temp. (° C)
S[a]	5.8	S[a]	4.8	S[a]	20.9	S[a]	11.8	S[a]	11.0
2	5.8	5	4.4	4	20.3	5	11.6	5	11.0
5	5.8	10	4.4	8	15.2	10	11.6	10	11.0
10	5.8	15	4.4	10	9.8	15	11.6	15	11.0
15	5.8	20	4.3	12	7.5	20	11.6	20	10.9
20	5.8	30	4.2	14	6.6	25	11.6	25	10.8
25	5.8	40	4.1	16	6.3	28	11.6	35	10.8
30	5.8	45	4.1	18	6.2	30	11.6	40	10.6
34	5.8	56	4.1	20	6.0	33	11.3	44	5.8
				25	5.5	35	10.0	47	5.0
				30	5.0	40	7.9	50	4.8
				35	4.7	53	4.9	75	4.7
				40	4.7	68	4.8		
				45	4.4				
				55	4.4				

S[a] = surface.

erly movements predominated slightly above those toward the south. Time-areal distribution of recoveries from this transect suggested no gyral motion of surface water in southern Lake Michigan during the time the units were adrift."

With respect to tides in Lake Michigan, Mills (1953) observed that they are of minor consequence. A difference in levels of about 5 cm was reported.

Erosion silt and turbidity

Ellis (1936) considered erosion silt as a factor operating in aquatic environments. He pointed out that the erosion silt loads in inland streams had reduced the millionth-intensity depth for light penetration (the depth at which light is reduced to one millionth of its surface intensity) from 15,000–34,000 mm or more to 1,000 mm or less. The 1934 summer average for the Mississippi River above Alton, Illinois, was given as 500 mm or less.

Platner (1946) considered siltation in the Upper Mississippi River to be a serious pollution problem from the standpoint of its effects on the river fisheries.

Since 1820, the Corps of Engineers of the U.S. Army has been in charge of improvement work on the Mississippi River. The main objective of the Corps has been the maintenance of

a channel of sufficient depth for boats and barges. In the early years, the Corps attempted to keep the channel open by dredging, accompanied by the construction of wing dams. Prior to 1930, no permanent cross-stream dams had been built (Carlander, 1954). Dredging and wing dams proved inadequate as measures to keep the channel open. In 1930 Congress authorized improvement by means of locks and dams, supplemented by dredging operations. At present there are 26 dams (Fig. 5.7) between Minneapolis and the mouth of the Missouri River (Carlander, 1954). The general effect of these dams has been the conversion of the Mississippi River into a number of river lakes to keep the channel open for shipping. Sedimentation in the river still constitutes a serious problem.

An excellent study including sedimentation data for Crab Orchard Lake in southern Illinois has appeared (Stall *et al.,* 1954). The 1951 sedimentation survey of the lake showed a capacity loss of 0.43% per year. In 11.2 years the lake had lost 4.84% of its original capacity. The measured rate of sedimentation was 2.8 tons/ acre per year. Physical and chemical characteristics of the lake sediment indicated that sheet erosion in the watershed was the main source of sediment. Gully erosion was a secondary source.

Jackson and Starrett (1959) discussed turbidity and sedimentation at Lake Chautauqua, Illinois (Fig. 5.5). Turbidity ranged from less than 25 ppm to 800 ppm. Resuspension of sediment particles, which were originally carried in and deposited in the lake by flood waters of the Illinois River, caused the high turbidities. The removal by commercial fishermen of over two million pounds of fish from the lake in an eight-year period had no apparent effect upon turbidity.

An acid stream: the Big Muddy River

Most of the streams of Illinois are alkaline: Jewell's (1922) values for midstream waters of the Mississippi, Illinois, Kaskaskia, Embarrass,

Fig. 5.7.—Map of a portion of the Upper Mississippi River showing 26 U.S. Corps of Engineers dam and navigation locks. From Carlander, 1954.

Vermilion, and Sangamon (Fig. 5.2) ranged from pH 7.4 to 8.5, or higher. The water of the Big Muddy, however, varied from pH 5.8 to 7.1.

A large part of the Big Muddy River and its tributaries lies in the coal fields of southern Illinois. Waters pumped from the coal mines are usually strongly acid. Ground water in parts of the area is also frequently acid. Jewell (1922) referred to the Big Muddy River as a "Natural Acid Stream"; she based this designation on the presence of acid springs in the watershed, admitting, however, that the acidity of the stream was often greatly increased by human agencies.

A later study (Walker, 1952) reported mean monthly pH values for the Big Muddy River ranging from 6.3 to 7.2. The waters of the river system were described as predominantly acid. Average monthly total acidity generally ranged from 13.2 to 161 ppm (as equivalent $CaCO_3$, based on titration with NaOH to the phenolphthalein endpoint). However, Oak Branch Creek, a tributary of the Little Muddy River, exhibited total acidity values as high as 750 ppm. Oak Branch Creek is typical of streams heavily polluted by coal-mine wastes.

As one might expect, extensive fish-kills have been associated with the drainage of mine wastes into the Big Muddy River and its tributaries (Lewis, 1955). Walker (1952) emphasized that the sublethal effect of such pollutants is probably even more important than the lethal effect; examples are reduction of food organisms, destruction of fish spawn, and the like. Even though the activity of coal mines in the region has decreased greatly, such pollution is still a serious problem in some localities.

Sewage pollution

The enormous pollution problem created in the Illinois River by sewage from the Chicago region has already been considered. Pollution is widespread, but we will mention briefly only that in the Ohio River.

Streeter and Phelps (1958) have considered pollution and natural purification of the Ohio River, which forms the southeastern boundary of Illinois. This river is important to the state since it is a navigable stream and also is an important source of surface water. The authors state that permissible limits of pollution for this river are generally given in bacteriological rather than chemical terms. "Nevertheless, the possibilities existing for at least a partial depletion of the reserve oxygen supply of the river, under conditions of pollution already approaching a critical stage from a bacterial standpoint in certain zones, could hardly be neglected in any consideration of the general problem."

This paper is very important since the findings have general application to most polluted streams. The authors concluded that "the oxygen self-purification of the Ohio River is a measurable phenomenon, governed by definite laws and proceeding according to certain fundamental physical and biochemical reactions." This was a sound approach to an understanding of pollution problems. The 1958 paper is a reprint of an older paper published in 1925.

Industrial wastes

Industrial pollution of our inland waters is certain to increase as we become more and more industrialized. Each year many fish-kills occur in Illinois, although few are brought to the attention of the public.

A published report (U.S. Public Health Service, 1961) for 1960 lists eight fish-kills in Illinois. Only two are discussed here: (1) A fish-kill occurred on the Kankakee River (Fig. 5.2) near Kankakee, Illinois, on 15 September 1960. Industrial wastes were believed to be a partial cause of the kill. Five miles of the river were affected, in which more than 3,000 fishes were reported killed. The duration of the critical effect was two days. (2) A fish-kill occurred on the Sangamon River (Fig. 5.2) near Kincaid, Illinois, on 28 July 1960. In this instance, mining operations were believed to be responsible. More than 65,000 fishes were estimated to have been killed, of which 51% were game fishes. Twenty-six miles of river were affected by the pollutant.

The evaluation of the cause and extent of such fish-kills presents a difficult problem to the limnologist or fishery biologist who must cope with the situation.

Physicochemical characteristics of strip-mine ponds

Over 20,000 acres of strip-mined land (Fig. 5.8) are present in southern Illinois. The stripping method of mining coal involves removal of the soil above coal strata immediately under the surface of the earth, usually 20 to 40 ft deep.

Very deep strata require shaft mines for the practical removal of coal.

Lewis and Peters (1955) studied the physicochemical characteristics of strip-mine ponds in three strip-mined areas of southern Illinois. They found that high concentrations of dissolved oxygen occur in the lower thermoclines of these ponds during the summer. Some ponds have extensive hypolimnions. The pH values ranged from roughly 3 to 8; the majority of the ponds were slightly basic, although some were extremely acid. Chemical conditions of the ponds, which ranged from 4 to 30 years of age at the time of the survey, were not associated with age. The nature of the exposed soils surrounding the ponds (Fig. 5.9) was believed to be more important than age in determining the chemical characteristics of the water. One of the most striking characteristics of strip-mine water in southern Illinois proved to be a high salt content. Specific conductance ranged from 900 to 4,000 micromhos in the strip-mine ponds. Four farm ponds in the vicinity of the strip mines had specific conductance values ranging from 100 to 250 micromhos. Some of the strip-mine ponds

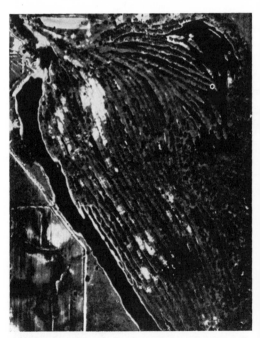

Fig. 5.8.—Aerial view of a portion of the Pyatt stripped area in southern Illinois. The largest pond in the figure (far left) covers a surface area of about 16 acres; a small part of the pond is not shown. Courtesy of W. M. Lewis.

Fig. 5.9.—Strip-mine pond near Pyatts (Perry County), Illinois. The water of this pond is characterized by low turbidity and a bright green color.

supported fish populations, whereas others appeared to be devoid of fishes.

Fishes

Ichthyological surveys

When the Illinois Natural History Society was formed, approximately three-fourths of the Illinois fishes had been described and named by such distinguished early ichthyologists as Rafinesque, LeSueur, Girard, Agassiz, Kirtland, and Mitchill (Ross, 1958). During the next 40 years, when Forbes and his associates were studying the fishes of Illinois intensively, the majority of the remaining Illinois fishes were described by Forbes, Cope, Gilbert, Nelson, and Jordan.

Among the more comprehensive early ichthyological studies are the following: (1) Kennicott (1855) considered the fishes of Cook County, listing 30 species for that area. (2) Nelson (1876) produced a partial catalogue of the fishes of Illinois which included 156 species with notes on their distribution. (3) Jordan (1878) catalogued the fishes of the state using Nelson's collections, a large collection made by Forbes in southern Illinois, Jordan's own collections from Illinois, and specimens borrowed from the U.S. National Museum. Jordan's list comprised 177 species. (4) Forbes (1884) catalogued the fishes of the state. (5) Large (1903) published a fourth list of the fishes of Illinois.

Forbes and his associates studied the fish fauna of Illinois for some 30 or more years before the work culminated in their classic publication, *The Fishes of Illinois* and *Atlas*, by Forbes and Richardson (1908). A second edition appeared in 1920. As a publication covering the freshwater fishes of a single state, this work stood as the best in its field for some 40 years. The book listed the species of fishes, their habits, life history, distribution, and so forth. Forbes used a method of showing relationships between individual species of fishes and preferences of certain kinds of fishes with respect to features of the physical environment. Although the method was useful in Forbes' time and was revolutionary for that period, it has recently been criticized for valid reasons (Bennett, 1958, p. 167).

O'Donnell (1935) published an annotated list of Illinois fishes. One of the main values of his work was in the application of scientific names currently in use to the fishes covered by Forbes and Richardson (1908, 1920). Most of these name changes were made to conform with the manual of Jordan (1929). O'Donnell's work is the latest state-wide coverage of the fishes of Illinois. Other studies have been regional or local in scope. The following investigations and the drainage or region treated are mentioned as examples: (1) Champaign County: Thompson and Hunt (1930); (2) Mississippi River at Keokuk, Iowa: Coker (1930); (3) Kaskaskia River: Luce (1933); (4) Mississippi River (Caruthersville, Missouri, to Dubuque, Iowa): Barnickol and Starrett (1951); (5) Jordan Creek, Vermilion County: Larimore *et al.*, 1952; (6) Clear Creek, Union County: Lewis and Elder (1953); (7) Pine Hills Swamp, Union County: Gunning and Lewis (1955); (8) Big Muddy River: Lewis (1955); and (9) Southern Illinois, 16 southernmost counties: Gunning and Lewis (1956). Those studies published after 1935 will be of value when a state-wide coverage is again attempted.

Food habits

The first comprehensive inquiries into the kinds of food eaten by fishes were made by Forbes (1878, 1880*a*, 1880*b*, 1883*a*, 1883*b*, 1888*a*, 1888*b*). This was a new area of investigation. The following statement from Forbes (1880*a*, p. 20) points out the importance of a knowledge of the food of fishes:

It is through the food relation that animals touch

each other and the surrounding world at the greatest number of points, here they crowd upon each other the most closely, at this point the struggle for existence becomes sharpest and most deadly; and, finally, it is through the food relation almost entirely that animals are brought in contact with the material interests of man.

Forbes (1880b) found that the food of many species of fishes differs greatly according to age; he could divide the life of most fishes into two periods, and some into three, with respect to the various kinds of food they consumed during each period of life. Forbes noted a remarkable similarity in the food of the young fishes of various species whose later foods were widely different. A classic example is the following (Forbes, 1880b, p. 72):

The full-grown black bass feeds principally, for example, on fishes and crawfishes, the sheepshead on mollusks, and the gizzard-shad on mud and algae, while the catfishes are nearly omnivorous; yet these are all found to agree so closely in food when very small that one could not possibly tell from the contents of the stomachs which group he was dealing with.

In the concluding paper of the series (1888b), Forbes summarized in a general way the food habits of the fishes he studied. For example, the burbot (*Lota lota*) was characterized as piscivorous, the pirateperch (*Aphredoderus sayanus*) was described as insectivorous, the freshwater drum (*Aplodinotus grunniens*) was characterized as a mollusk eater, the paddlefish (*Polyodon spathula*) was described as a plankton feeder (Crustacea), and so forth. Forbes considered it a remarkable fact that plant food is generally an unimportant part of the diet of fishes. Fishes, mollusks, insects, and crustaceans appeared to be the principal classes of animal food.

Forbes believed that his observations were evidence "that fishes are not mere animated machines . . . but that psychological preferences as well as physical capabilities have something to do with their choice of food" (1888b, p. 503).

Recently, Lewis and his associates have conducted a number of investigations on various aspects of the food and feeding behavior of largemouth bass (*Micropterus salmoides*). Dubets (1954) developed a gastroscope which permitted him to examine the stomach contents of live bass without sacrificing the fish. He found that over 50% of the bass taken in nature with an electrical device had empty stomachs. The gizzard

shad (*Dorosoma cepedianum*) was utilized heavily as food by the bass, a fact corroborated by Schneidermeyer and Lewis (1956).

Tarrant (1960) studied the choice made by largemouth bass, under aquarium conditions, between two sizes of green sunfish (*Lepomis cyanellus*). Tarrant proved experimentally the supposition that larger bass prefer larger fish as food items, and smaller bass prefer smaller fish in comparison. He suggested that the relative sizes of forage and predator fishes should be considered when the problem of population balance is analyzed.

Lewis *et al.* (1961) tested food preference of largemouth bass, under aquarium conditions, for a number of food items present in the natural environment. The golden shiner (*Notemigonus crysoleucas*) stood pre-eminent among the food items presented to and utilized by the bass. Gizzard shad were not included in this series of experiments.

Physiology

About 1915 a number of workers became interested in the physiological effects upon fishes of various pollutants, gases, and so forth. Shelford (1917) concluded from an experimental study of the effects of several pollutants on fishes that essentially all of the products of coal distillation are very toxic to fishes. A subsequent paper (Shelford, 1918) described the apparatus used in some of his physiological studies. Wells (1918), under Professor Shelford's direction, studied the resistance of fish to carbon dioxide and carbon monoxide. He reported that fishes are very sensitive to small changes in carbon dioxide content of the water. Carbon monoxide was, of course, found to be lethal. In the same year (1918), Powers published a monograph on the goldfish (*Carassius auratus*) as a test animal for the study of toxicity. Shelford (1923) observed the reactions of fishes to varying hydrogen-ion concentrations. Thompson (1925) discussed movements of fishes in the Illinois River from areas of oxygen deficiency to regions where the oxygen content of the water was more suitable. Thompson pointed out that the most important effect of an excess of sewage is the reduction of dissolved oxygen to a point where fish life is excluded from immense areas of water. Clausen (1936), also under Professor Shelford's direction, studied oxygen consumption in freshwater fishes under laboratory conditions. His hourly determinations of oxygen utilization by fishes presumably showed a rhythm for species inhabiting relatively quiet water, whereas no definite rhythm was found in those species inhabiting rapidly flowing water.

Thompson (1928) described the "knothead malformation" of carp (*Cyprinus carpio*), based on his work in the Illinois River system. The malady was compared with rickets in the higher vertebrates. Rachitic carp may be recognized by the bulging of the opercles, which is often so extreme that respiration is hampered. The knothead condition in carp was believed to be due to a deficiency of vitamin D.

Bennett (1948) described winter-kill of fishes in a 10-acre lake caused by oxygen deficiency below an ice cover in the winter of 1944–45. As a result of the winter-kill, 4,000 pounds of dead fish were collected when the ice went out in March. Such winter-kills were said to occur with considerable frequency in the north and central sections of Illinois when winters are severe and the ice on lakes and ponds is covered with snow for periods longer than 15 days.

Behavioral considerations

Richardson (1913*a*) observed breeding of the carp (an introduced species) in the vicinity of Havana. On 6 May 1911, for example, more than 1,000 carp were observed spawning. Spawning females were taken with dipnets. The situations suitable for carp spawning sites were discussed in detail. A second paper (Richardson, 1913*b*) described the breeding habits of several other fishes of the area including the bowfin (*Amia calva*).

Thompson and Hunt (1930) discussed downstream winter migration of larger stream fishes. Movement to deeper pools was presumably brought on by colder water temperatures. The fishes were said to cease feeding in the winter. In the spring, the fishes ascended the upper reaches of the streams again and resumed feeding.

Luce (1933) tagged 587 fishes to see if they migrated. He summarized his results as follows (p. 71):

While no extremely large migrations have come to our notice from fishes tagged in the Kaskaskia or any other Illinois waters, we were surprised to learn that the catfishes, and in particular the black bullhead, make rather extensive migrations covering distances 10, 20, or even 40 miles upstream within a few days or weeks.

Brown (1937) studied reactions of largemouth bass to colors by means of training experiments. Bass were most attracted by red. Both color and intensity were found to play roles in the responses of the bass to objects.

Shoemaker (1952), of the University of Illinois, investigated homing of fishes in Lake Myosotis, New York. Pumpkinseeds (*Lepomis gibbosus*) and yellow bullheads (*Ictalurus natalis*) returned to home areas with a high degree of accuracy, 86% and 95%, respectively, following experimental displacement.

Larimore (1952) treated home pools and homing behavior of smallmouth bass (*Micropterus dolomieui*) in Jordan Creek, Illinois. The bass showed a significant tendency to remain in the pool in which they were tagged. Bass displaced experimentally showed a marked tendency to return to the home pool.

Larimore (1957) described in detail several behavioral characteristics of the warmouth. Topics included, for example, were general activity and disposition, defense of the nest area, orientation, the spawning act, and parental care.

Louder (1958) investigated escapement of fishes over lake spillways. He indicated that the loss of larger fish, largemouth bass for example, in the spring was considerable. Heavy losses of fish appeared to be correlated with season rather than magnitude of water flowing over the spillways. He observed that heavy losses often occurred in a very short time. The behavioral factors involved in these losses are not known.

Ecology

Forbes (1907, 1909) considered the distribution of Illinois fishes. He stated (Forbes, 1909, p. 432):

The 150 native species of Illinois fishes here recognized are so distributed within and without the state as to indicate an unequal commingling of the faunae of the surrounding territories, southeastern species preponderating over southwestern, northeastern over northwestern, eastern over western, and southern over northern.

The fish population of the Illinois Basin was considered to be typical of the fishes of the entire state, since it contained four-fifths of the fish species known from Illinois. Forbes' tabular data (Table 5.2) showed the relationships of the

TABLE 5.2

Species composition of the fishes in ten districts of the state of Illinois, using the Illinois Basin as a basis for comparison. Modified from Forbes, 1909.

District	Species in district	Species not found in Illinois Basin
Illinois Basin	128	—
Lake Michigan	57	9
Cairo	101	8
Wabash	95	6
Galena	44	2
Saline	55	2
Mississippi	97	3
Rock River	92	3
Kaskaskia	69	1
Big Muddy	42	0

fish populations, in terms of species composition, of ten districts in the state. For example, the Illinois, Mississippi, and Rock rivers (Fig. 5.2) were found to have quite similar populations. The effect of various climatic, geological, and ecological factors upon the distribution of the fishes was discussed.

Shelford (1911a, 1911b, 1911c) described succession of fishes in streams and ponds. He concluded (1911a) that fishes have definite habitat preferences which cause them to be definitely arranged, linearly, in streams which have a graded series of conditions from source to mouth. In a second paper, the fish populations of a series of ponds at the south end of Lake Michigan were studied (1911b). The species of fishes were said to occur in an orderly fashion from pond to pond depending upon the age of the ponds. The fish population of a younger pond was believed to represent a stage in the developmental history of older ponds. A third paper (1911c) included a consideration of some of the causes of succession. Shelford later published a book, *Animal Communities in Temperate America* (1913), which developed additional aspects of succession.

A number of ecological studies of fishes have appeared since Shelford's, but the scope of this chapter will not allow treatment of all of them. Five have been chosen in order to show the broad range of topics covered by the Illinois investigations: (1) Hansen (1951) studied the biology of the white crappie (*Pomoxis annularis*) in Illinois. Various aspects of the life history of this fish were investigated. (2) Lewis (1953) analyzed the gizzard shad population of Crab Orchard Lake. Die-offs occur periodically in this shad population. In October, 1952, by counting sample strips, he estimated that over 10 million dead shad were strewn along the shoreline. Such die-offs may control the age and size distribution of the shad population. Most shad in the lake were found to be four years old or less. (3) Gunning and Lewis (1955) investigated a natural, undisturbed, spring-fed swamp (Pine Hills Swamp; Fig. 5.10) in the Mississippi bottoms of southern Illinois. Steep limestone bluffs shade the swamp and afford a microclimate which controls the development of plant communities and also indirectly affects the distribution of the fish population. Seventy-five per cent of the fishes taken were collected from the spring-fed portion of the swamp, which appeared to provide the most suitable fish habitat. (4) Weise (1957) studied the spring cavefish populations of several springs

Fig. 5.10.—A portion of the Pine Hills Swamp characterized by mosquito fern (*Azolla mexicana*), four species of duckweed (e.g., *Lemna minor*), hornwort (*Ceratophyllum demersum*), and other aquatic plants. Of 23 species of fishes inhabiting the swamp, only the banded pygmy sunfish (*Elassoma zonatum*) was taken here (Gunning and Lewis, 1955).

Fig. 5.11.—A spring, choked with watercress (*Nasturtium officinale*) and other aquatic plants, which flows into the Pine Hills Swamp. The spring cavefish (*Chologaster agassizi*) inhabits subterranean waters under the bluffs during the day but may be observed in the spring at night.

along the bases of the bluffs overlooking the Pine Hills Swamp. The spring cavefish occupies subterranean waters during the day but ventures into the connecting springs (Fig. 5.11) at night where it feeds, mainly on amphipods (*Gammarus*). (5) Larimore *et al.* (1959) studied the re-establishment of stream fish in Smiths Branch, a small warm-water stream in Vermilion County, Illinois, after a severe drought had virtually destroyed the fish population in 1953 and 1954. Re-establishment of the stream fish population began as soon as the stream resumed its flow. Twenty-five of the species of fishes formerly present had entered Smiths Branch by the end of the first summer after the population was destroyed in 1953. Three species of fishes were significantly absent; among these was the longear sunfish (*Lepomis megalotis*), which did not appear again until the fall of 1955. The remaining two species had not appeared when final collections were made in September, 1957. The various aspects of the recovery of the fish population, as well as of the invertebrates present, were considered.

Fishery management

This topic is judged to be beyond the scope of this book on the basis of editorial policy. Hence, it will be given only cursory attention.

The Illinois Natural History Survey has long been active in the study of commercial fisheries and fishery management procedures. Bennett (1958) has covered the activities of the survey thoroughly in this regard. An example of the type of work done by the survey personnel has recently appeared (Hansen *et al.*, 1960), in which hook-and-line catches in fertilized and unfertilized ponds were compared. The fertilization program used at Dixon Springs, Illinois, was of apparent benefit to bluegill fishing but of doubtful benefit to largemouth bass fishing. Whether the improvement in the quality of bluegill fishing attributed to fertilization was sufficient to be detected by sport fishermen was questionable for at least two of the three fertilized ponds studied.

Lewis and his associates have conducted several fishery management studies dealing with age and growth of fishes, pollution, water quality, creel censuses, and the like, as previously mentioned. Only two of these will be given as examples: (1) Lewis and Peters (1956) studied the toxicity of coal-mine slag drainage to fishes. They concluded that the lethal effect of slag drainage is due to the free acid which it contains. Such information is, of course, useful in the formulation of management policies. (2) Cole (1960) recommended impounding the acid waste-water from coal-mining operations and treating such impoundments with lime to produce an alkaline *p*H. The net effect of such action would be the reduction of pollution and, consequently, the prevention of fish-kills that often result from coal-mining operations.

Other studies

Baker (1910) studied the ecology of the Skokie Marsh area, paying particular attention to the study of mollusks. In his opinion, this work represented one of the first attempts to apply the ecological method, already being used by botanists of the day (e.g., Cowles), to the study of mollusks. Some taxonomists believed that ecological studies would not aid in ascertaining specific differences. However, Baker's ecological study definitely aided in specific and varietal determinations for several species of snails.

Adams (1915, p. 3) put the study of ecology

TABLE 5.3

Representative taxonomic, floristic, and faunistic works for the state of Illinois

Author & date	Annotation
Baker, F. C., 1911	Lymnaeidae of North and Middle America; recent and fossil
Britton, M. E., 1944	Catalog of Illinois algae
Burks, B. D., 1953	Mayflies (Ephemeroptera) of Illinois
Forbes, S. A., 1876	List of Illinois Crustacea
Frison, T. H., 1929	Fall and winter stoneflies (Plecoptera) of Illinois
Frison, T. H., 1935	Stoneflies of Illinois
Frison, T. H., 1942	Stoneflies of North America; particular reference to Illinois
Garman, Philip, 1917	Damselflies (Zygoptera) of Illinois
Hart, C. A., 1895	Insects of the Illinois River
Hempel, Adolph, 1896	New species of rotifers and Protozoa
Hempel, Adolph, 1899	Protozoa and Rotifera of the Illinois River
Hoff, C. C., 1942	Ostracods of Illinois
Jones, G. N., 1945	Flora of Illinois
Kofoid, C. A., 1898	Description of *Pleodorina illinoisensis*
Kofoid, C. A., 1899	Keys to genera and species of Volvocinae
Malloch, J. R., 1915	Midges (Chironomidae) of Illinois
Moore, J. P., 1901	Leeches (Hirudinea) of Illinois
Ross, H. H., 1944	Caddis flies (Trichoptera) of Illinois
Schacht, F. W., 1897	North American species of *Diaptomus* (Copepoda)
Schacht, F. W., 1898	Three genera of copepods, family Centropagidae
Underwood, L. M., 1886	American Crustacea north of Mexico; 313 species
Ward, H. B., 1899	Contains complete bibliography of plankton to the year 1899

into clear focus with the following words:

While some naturalists view the animal from a more or less dynamic standpoint, they do not include a similar conception of the relation of an animal to its environment. Still others view the environment more or less dynamically but do not extend this conception to the animal, and thus both of these conceptions lack completeness and are not thoroughgoing and consistent.

Adams emphasized that one of the most interesting and fundamental aspects of ecology considers the dependence of an animal upon its environment and at the same time orients it in the gamut of energies and substances.

Stickney (1922) conducted an interesting investigation on a small stream called the "Boneyard" at Champaign-Urbana, Illinois. An outstanding result of this study was the observation that dragonfly nymphs (*Libellula pulchella*) lived unharmed for over six months in alternating foul and fresh water which was as strongly acid as pH 1.0.

Waterman (1926) investigated nine sphagnum bogs in Lake and McHenry counties, Illinois. All were located in undrained depressions of Late Wisconsin Drift of the Valparaiso Moraine. In each case, bog vegetation was found over the deepest part of the depression with a very shallow zone, containing no bog plants, surrounding the former. In his opinion, the sphagnum bogs of Illinois were slowly dying out in an unfavorable environment.

Kurz (1928) studied the influence of sphagnum and other mosses on bog reactions. He concluded that bogs, in the general sense, are not necessarily acid in reaction, and that acidity is not prerequisite for peat preservation. The conditions under which a bog may remain circumneutral were described.

Hoff (1943) observed seasonal changes in the ostracod fauna of temporary ponds in Champaign County. He could not explain the seasonal changes observed but believed that a factor other than temperature may control the seasonal appearance of some species.

Dexter (1956) compared the gastropod faunas of five separate drainage systems in Champaign County. Even though these drainages have no direct connections with one another, Dexter found no significant differences among the gastropod faunas of the five streams. All contained essentially the same common species of gastropods. He suggested that aquatic birds and mammals may be responsible for the general distribution of these forms.

Taxonomic, floristic, and faunistic studies are valuable to the aquatic biologist, but the scope of this chapter prevents an extensive consideration of them. Table 5.3 is presented in lieu of a detailed treatment. A brief annotation is given for each paper, thus enabling the reader to determine whether or not the contents are of interest.

The Section of Faunistic Surveys and Insect Identification of the Illinois Natural History Survey has produced many valuable studies. These were discussed by Ross (1958), who listed an extensive bibliography.

A number of parasitologists at the University of Illinois, including Professor H. B. Ward, Professor H. J. Van Cleave, Professor R. R. Kudo, and the students of each of these men, deserve mention for the work they have done on the parasites of fishes.

Summary of major limnological contributions

Few papers on Illinois limnology have had the impact on biological thought produced by Forbes' "The lake as a microcosm" (1925). Forbes emphasized the necessity for "taking a comprehensive survey of the whole as a condition to a satisfactory understanding of any part" (Forbes, 1925, p. 537). For example, he supposed that an individual wished to become acquainted with the largemouth bass. In Forbes' opinion, one would learn little if he limited himself to that species alone. He must study also the species upon which it depends for its existence and the various conditions upon which these species depend. He must likewise consider the competitors of the bass and the conditions affecting their prosperity. In Forbes' words: "By the time he has studied all of these sufficiently he will find that he has run through the whole complicated mechanism of the aquatic life of the locality, both animal and vegetable, of which his species forms but a single element."

The ultimate goal of Forbes and his associates at the Illinois Biological Station at Havana was to disclose the complete biology of a river system. The extent to which this goal was realized should be evident from the material already presented. These investigators set a fine example for subsequent biologists to follow.

Kofoid conducted the first extensive quantitative study on the plankton of a river system. He found that the lakes adjacent to the Illinois River generally had a richer plankton than the Illinois River proper. Richardson observed the same relationship for bottom fauna. Kofoid discovered a significant plankton community, the nannoplankton, which went undetected when the traditional plankton nets were used; his filter-paper catches of nannoplankton were three times the volume of net plankton. Kofoid characterized potamoplankton, on the basis of his Illinois River studies, so that this community was distinctly recognizable when compared with lake or pond plankton.

Richardson amply demonstrated the deleterious effects of sewage pollution on the bottom fauna of the Illinois River as the pollution gradually extended farther and farther down the river from its source at Chicago. His lists of the number of species exterminated by the pollution, coupled with his general observations, leave little doubt as to the extent of the devastation.

Two standard reference works resulted, in whole or in part, from Illinois aquatic biology efforts. *The Fishes of Illinois,* by Forbes and Richardson (1908, 1920), stood as the best coverage of the fishes of an entire state for some 40 years, as stated previously. *Fresh-Water Biology,* by Ward, Whipple, and collaborators (1918), was a joint effort by several persons. It has, of course, been revised recently.

Shelford and his students have contributed a great deal to our knowledge of the concept of succession in aquatic communities. Professor Shelford treated succession of fishes, Professor Eddy described succession in plankton communities, and Professor Gersbacher considered the development of the benthos.

Within the past twenty years, much of the aquatic biology effort of the Illinois Natural History Survey has dealt with management problems. Bennett, for example, has done significant work on the largemouth bass-bluegill stocking combination for artificial lakes and the effect of periodic lake drawdowns in maintaining a balanced fish population.

At Southern Illinois University the majority of studies have dealt with some aspect of fishery management. Lewis and his associates are presently conducting a series of studies on pathogens of warm-water fishes, particularly those fish species produced commercially in hatcheries.

With the passage of time, many of the problems that confronted early limnologists have still remained with us. Problems involving sewage pollution, industrial wastes, ample municipal water supplies, sedimentation of rivers and reservoirs, and similar problems are faced at the present time. We must hope that biological knowledge will continue to advance at the same or a faster pace to enable us to cope with the re-

maining old problems and new problems as they
arise.

Acknowledgments

Dr. William M. Lewis, Southern Illinois University, read the manuscript critically and arranged
for my use of the university library facilities.

Appreciation is expressed for numerous courtesies extended to me by the personnel of the Illinois Natural History Survey including Dr. G.
W. Bennett, Dr. R. W. Larimore, Dr. D. F. Hansen, and Mrs. R. R. Warrick.

Several of my colleagues, including Dr. Franklin Sogandares-Bernal, Dr. Royal D. Suttkus, and
Dr. D. Eugene Copeland, have reviewed the manuscript during the various stages of its development.

Mr. Leon Trice aided in the preparation of the
illustrations.

References

ACKERMANN, W. C. 1958. Water resources of Illinois. *In* Atlas of Illinois resources. I. Water resources and climate. Dept. of Registration and Educ., Springfield, 58 p.

ADAMS, C. C. 1915. An outline of the relations of animals to their inland environments. Illinois Lab. Nat. Hist. Bull., 11(1): 3–32.

AHLSTROM, E. H. 1936. The deep-water plankton of Lake Michigan, exclusive of the Crustacea. Trans. Amer. Microscop. Soc., 55: 286–299.

AMERICAN FISHERIES SOCIETY, Committee on Names of Fishes. 1960. A list of common and scientific names of fishes from the United States and Canada. Spec. Publ. No. 2, 102 p.

BAKER, F. C. 1910. The ecology of the Skokie Marsh Area, with special reference to the Mollusca. Illinois Lab. Nat. Hist. Bull., 8(4): 441–499.

———. 1911. The Lymnaeidae of North and Middle America, recent and fossil. Chicago Acad. Sci., Spec. Publ. 3, 539 p.

———. 1922. The molluscan fauna of the Big Vermilion River, Illinois. Illinois Biol. Monogr., 7(2): 7–126.

BARNICKOL, P. G., AND W. C. STARRETT. 1951. Commercial and sport fishes of the Mississippi River between Caruthersville, Missouri, and Dubuque, Iowa. Illinois Nat. Hist. Surv. Bull., 25(5): 267–350.

BENNETT, G. W. 1948. Lake management reports. 5. Winter-kill of fishes in an Illinois lake. Illinois Nat. Hist. Surv., Biol. Notes 19, 9 p.

———. 1958. Aquatic biology, p. 163–178. *In* A century of biological research. Illinois Nat. Hist. Surv. Bull., 27(2).

———. 1960. Sport fishing on lakes. *In* Atlas of Illinois resources. III. Forest, wildlife, and recreational resources. Dept. of Registration and Educ., Springfield, 47 p.

BRITTON, M. E. 1944. A catalog of Illinois algae. Northwestern Univ. Studies Biol. Sci. Med., No. 2, 177 p.

BROWN, F. A., JR. 1937. Responses of the largemouth black bass to colors. Illinois Nat. Hist. Surv. Bull., 21(2): 33–56.

BURKS, B. D. 1953. The mayflies, or Ephemeroptera, of Illinois. Illinois Nat. Hist. Surv. Bull., 26(1): 1–216.

CARLANDER, H. B. 1954. A history of fish and fishing in the Upper Mississippi River. Upper Mississippi River Conserv. Comm., Wisconsin Dept. Conserv., 96 p.

CHURCH, P. E. 1942. The annual temperature cycle of Lake Michigan. I. Cooling from late autumn to the terminal point, 1941–42. Univ. Chicago, Inst. of Meteorol., Misc. Rept. No. 4, 48 p.

———. 1945. The annual temperature cycle of Lake Michigan. II. Spring warming and summer stationary periods, 1942. Univ. Chicago, Inst. of Meteorol., Misc. Rept. No. 18, 100 p.

CLAUSEN, R. G. 1936. Oxygen consumption in fresh water fishes. Ecology, 17: 216–226.

COKER, R. E. 1930. Studies of common fishes of the Mississippi River at Keokuk. U.S. Bur. Fish., Document 1072: 141–225.

COLE, V. W. 1960. Impounding and liming acid mine drainage. Ind. Wastes, 5(1): 10–11.

DAILEY, W. A. 1938. A quantitative study of the phytoplankton of Lake Michigan collected in the vicinity of Evanston, Illinois. Butler Univ. Botan. Studies, 4(6): 65–83.

DAMANN, K. E. 1941. Quantitative study of the phytoplankton of Lake Michigan at Evanston, Illinois. Butler Univ. Botan. Studies, 5: 27–44.

———. 1945. Plankton studies of Lake Michigan. I. Seventeen years of plankton data collected at Chicago, Illinois. Amer. Midland Nat., 34: 769–796.

———. 1960. Plankton studies of Lake Michigan. II. Thirty-three years of continuous plankton and coliform bacteria data collected from Lake Michigan at Chicago, Illinois. Trans. Amer. Microscop. Soc., 79: 397–404.

DEXTER, R. W. 1956. Comparison of the gastropod fauna in the drainage systems of Champaign County, Illinois. Amer. Midland Nat., 55: 363–368.

DORRIS, T. C. 1958. Limnology of the Middle Mississippi River and adjacent waters. Lakes on the leveed floodplain. Amer. Midland Nat., 59: 82–110.

DUBETS, HARRY. 1954. Feeding habits of the largemouth bass as revealed by a gastroscope. Progr. Fish-Cult., 16(3): 134–136.

EAST, B. B. 1958. Former technical employees, p. 215–218. *In* A century of biological research. Illinois Nat. Hist. Surv. Bull., 27(2).

EDDY, SAMUEL. 1925. Fresh water algal succession. Trans. Amer. Microscop. Soc., 44: 138–147.

———. 1927. The plankton of Lake Michigan. Illinois Nat. Hist. Surv. Bull., 17(4): 203–232.

———. 1931. The plankton of some sink hole ponds in southern Illinois. Illinois Nat. Hist. Surv. Bull., 19(4): 449–467.

———. 1932. The plankton of the Sangamon River in the summer of 1929. Illinois Nat. Hist. Surv. Bull., 19(5) : 469–486.

———. 1934. A study of fresh-water plankton communities. Illinois Biol. Monogr., 12(4) : 1–93.

ELLIS, M. M. 1936. Erosion silt as a factor in aquatic environments. Ecology, 17: 29–42.

FORBES, S. A. 1876. List of Illinois Crustacea, with descriptions of new species. Illinois Museum Nat. Hist. Bull., 1(1) : 3–25.

———. 1878. The food of Illinois fishes. Illinois Lab. Nat. Hist. Bull., 1(2) : 71–89.

———. 1880a. The food of fishes. Illinois Lab. Nat. Hist. Bull., 1(3) : 19–70.

———. 1880b. On the food of young fishes. Illinois Lab. Nat. Hist. Bull., 1(3) : 71–85.

———. 1883a. The food of the smaller fresh-water fishes. Illinois Lab. Nat. Hist. Bull., 1(6) : 65–94.

———. 1883b. The first food of the common whitefish (*Coregonus clupeaformis* Mitchill). Illinois Lab. Nat. Hist. Bull., 1(6) : 95–109.

———. 1884. A catalogue of the native fishes of Illinois. Illinois Fish Comm. Rept. for 1884: 60–89.

———. 1888a. Studies of the food of fresh-water fishes. Illinois Lab. Nat. Hist. Bull., 2(7) : 433–473.

———. 1888b. On the food relations of fresh-water fishes: a summary and discussion. Illinois Lab. Nat. Hist. Bull., 2(8) : 475–538.

———. 1895. Illinois State Laboratory of Natural History, Champaign, Illinois. Biennial Rept. of the Director, 1893–94. Illinois Fish Comm. Rept. for 1892–94: 39–52.

———. 1907. On the local distribution of certain Illinois fishes: An essay in statistical ecology. Illinois Lab. Nat. Hist. Bull. 7(8) : 273–303.

———. 1909. On the general and interior distribution of Illinois fishes. Illinois Lab. Nat. Hist. Bull., 8(3) : 381–437.

———. 1925. The lake as a microcosm. Illinois Nat. Hist. Surv. Bull., 15(9) : 537–550.

———. 1928. The biological survey of a river system —its objects, methods, and results. Illinois Nat. Hist. Surv. Bull., 17(7) : 277–284.

FORBES, S. A., AND R. E. RICHARDSON. 1908. The fishes of Illinois. Illinois State Lab. Nat. Hist., Urbana. 357 p.; Atlas with 102 maps.

FORBES, S. A., AND R. E. RICHARDSON. 1913. Studies on the biology of the upper Illinois River. Illinois Lab. Nat. Hist. Bull., 9(10) : 481–574.

FORBES, S. A., AND R. E. RICHARDSON. 1920. The fishes of Illinois. 2nd ed. Illinois State Journal Co., Springfield. 357 p.

FRISON, T. H. 1929. Fall and winter stoneflies, or Plecoptera, of Illinois. Illinois Nat. Hist. Surv. Bull., 18(2) : 341–409.

———. 1935. The stoneflies, or Plecoptera, of Illinois. Illinois Nat. Hist. Surv. Bull., 20(4) : 281–471.

———. 1942. Studies of North American Plecoptera with special reference to the fauna of Illinois. Illinois Nat. Hist. Surv. Bull., 22 : 235–355.

GALTSOFF, P. S. 1924. Limnological observations in the Upper Mississippi, 1921. U.S. Bur. Fish., Document 958: 347–438.

GARMAN, PHILIP. 1917. The Zygoptera, or damselflies, of Illinois. Illinois Lab. Nat. Hist. Bull., 12: 411-- 587.

GERSBACHER, W. M. 1937. Development of stream bottom communities in Illinois. Ecology, 18: 359–390.

———. 1956. Thermal stratification of the water of two artificial impoundments of southern Illinois. Trans. Illinois Acad. Sci., 48: 34–36.

GRIFFITH, R. E. 1955. Analysis of phytoplankton yields in relation to certain physical and chemical factors in Lake Michigan. Ecology, 36: 543–552.

GUNNING, G. E., AND W. M. LEWIS. 1955. The fish population of a spring-fed swamp in the Mississippi bottoms of southern Illinois. Ecology, 36: 552–558.

GUNNING, G. E., AND W. M. LEWIS. 1956. Recent collections of some less common fishes in southern Illinois. Trans. Illinois Acad. Sci., 48: 23–26.

HANSEN, D. F. 1951. Biology of the white crappie in Illinois. Illinois Nat. Hist. Surv. Bull., 25(4) : 211–266.

HANSEN, D. F., G. W. BENNETT, R. J. WEBB, AND J. M. LEWIS. 1960. Hook-and-line catch in fertilized and unfertilized ponds. Illinois Nat. Hist. Surv. Bull., 27(5) : 345–390.

HART, C. A. 1895. On the entomology of the Illinois River and adjacent waters. Illinois Lab. Nat. Hist. Bull., 4(6) : 149–273.

HEMPEL, ADOLPH. 1896. Descriptions of new species of Rotifera and Protozoa from the Illinois River and adjacent waters. Illinois Lab. Nat. Hist. Bull., 4(10) : 310–317.

———. 1899. A list of the Protozoa and Rotifera found in the Illinois River and adjacent lakes at Havana, Illinois. Illinois Lab. Nat. Hist. Bull., 5(6) : 301–388.

HOFF, C. C. 1942. The ostracods of Illinois. Illinois Biol. Monogr., 19: 1–196.

———. 1943. Seasonal changes in the ostracod fauna of temporary ponds. Ecology, 24: 116–118.

HOUGH, J. L. 1958. Geology of the Great Lakes. Univ. Illinois Press, Urbana. 313 p.

ILLINOIS STATE WATER SURVEY. 1957. Potential water resources of southern Illinois. Rept. of Invest., 31, 97 p.

JACKSON, H. O., AND W. C. STARRETT. 1959. Turbidity and sedimentation at Lake Chautauqua, Illinois. J. Wildl. Mgmt., 23 : 157–168.

JEWELL, M. E. 1922. The fauna of an acid stream. Ecology, 3 : 22–28.

JOHNSON, J. H. 1960. Surface currents in Lake Michigan, 1954 and 1955. U.S. Fish and Wildl. Serv., Spec. Sci. Rept., Fish. No. 338, 120 p.

JONES, G. N. 1945. Flora of Illinois. The Univ. Press, Notre Dame. 317 p.

JORDAN, D. S. 1878. A catalogue of the fishes of Illinois. Illinois Lab. Nat. Hist. Bull., 1(2) : 37–70.

———. 1929. Manual of the verebrate animals of the northeastern United States inclusive of marine species. World Book Co., Yonkers on Hudson. 446 p.

KENNICOTT, ROBERT. 1855. Catalogue of animals observed in Cook County, Illinois. Illinois Agr. Soc.

Trans. for 1853–54, **1**: 577–595.

KOFOID, C. A. 1897. Plankton studies. I. Methods and apparatus in use in plankton investigations at the biological experiment station of the University of Illinois. Illinois Lab. Nat. Hist. Bull., 5(1): 1–26.

———. 1898. Plankton studies. II. On *Pleodorina illinoisensis,* a new species from the plankton of the Illinois River. Illinois Lab. Nat. Hist. Bull., 5(5): 273–300.

———. 1899. Plankton studies. III. On *Platydorina,* a new genus of the family Volvocidae, from the plankton of the Illinois River. Illinois Lab. Nat. Hist. Bull., 5(9): 419–440.

———. 1903. Plankton studies. IV. The plankton of the Illinois River 1894–99, with introductory notes upon the hydrography of the Illinois River and its basin. I. Quantitative investigations and general results. Illinois Lab. Nat. Hist. Bull., 6(2): 95–635.

———. 1908. Plankton studies. V. The plankton of the Illinois River, 1894–99. II. Constituent organisms and their seasonal distribution. Illinois Lab. Nat. Hist. Bull., 8(1): 2–361.

KURZ, HERMAN. 1928. Influence of sphagnum and other mosses on bog reactions. Ecology, **9**: 56–69.

LARGE, THOMAS. 1903. A list of the native fishes of Illinois with keys. Appendix to Illinois Fish Comm. Rept. for 1900–1902: 1–30.

LARIMORE, R. W. 1952. Home pools and homing behavior of smallmouth black bass in Jordan Creek. Illinois Nat. Hist. Surv., Biol. Notes 28: 1–12.

———. 1957. Ecological life history of the warmouth (Centrarchidae). Illinois Nat. Hist. Surv. Bull., 27(1): 1–83.

LARIMORE, R. W., W. F. CHILDERS, AND CARLTON HECKROTTE. 1959. Destruction and re-establishment of stream fish and invertebrates affected by drought. Trans. Amer. Fish. Soc., **88**: 261–285.

LARIMORE, R. W., Q. H. PICKERING, AND LEONARD DURHAM. 1952. An inventory of the fishes of Jordan Creek, Vermilion County, Illinois. Illinois Nat. Hist. Surv., Biol. Notes 29: 1–26.

LARSON, T. E., AND B. O. LARSON. 1957. Quality of surface waters in Illinois. Illinois State Water Surv. Bull., **45**: 1–135.

LEIGHTON, M. M. 1944. Illinois resources, an atlas. Illinois Post-War Planning Commission, Chicago. 185 p.

LEIGHTON, M. M., G. E. EKBLAW, AND LELAND HORBERG. 1948. Physiographic divisions of Illinois. Illinois State Geol. Surv., Rept. of Invest., **129**: 16–33.

LEWIS, W. M. 1953. Analysis of the gizzard shad population of Crab Orchard Lake, Illinois. Trans. Illinois Acad. Sci., **46**: 231–234.

———. 1955. The fish population of the main stream of the Big Muddy River. Trans. Illinois Acad. Sci., **47**: 20–24.

LEWIS, W. M., AND DAVID ELDER. 1953. The fish population of the headwaters of a spotted bass stream in southern Illinois. Trans. Amer. Fish. Soc., **82**: 193–202.

LEWIS, W. M., G. E. GUNNING, EDWARD LYLES, AND

W. L. BRIDGES. 1961. Food choice of largemouth bass as a function of availability and vulnerability of food items. Trans. Amer. Fish. Soc., **90**: 277–280.

LEWIS, W. M., AND CHARLES PETERS. 1955. Physico-chemical characteristics of ponds in the Pyatt, Desoto, and Elkville strip-mined areas of southern Illinois. Trans. Amer. Fish. Soc., **84**: 117–124.

LEWIS, W. M., AND CHARLES PETERS. 1956. Coal mine slag drainage: toxicity to representative fishes. Ind. Wastes, **1**: 145–147.

LOUDER, DARRELL. 1958. Escape of fish over spillways. Progr. Fish-Cult., 20(1): 38–41.

LUCE, W. M. 1933. A survey of the fishery of the Kaskaskia River. Illinois Nat. Hist. Surv. Bull., 20(2): 71–123.

McDANNALD, A. H. (ed.). 1952. The new modern encyclopedia: A library of world knowledge. Wm. H. Wise and Co., Inc., New York. 1494 p.

MALLOCH, J. R. 1915. The Chironomidae, or midges, of Illinois, with particular reference to the species occurring in the Illinois River. Illinois Lab. Nat. Hist. Bull., 10(6): 275–543.

MILLS, H. B. 1953. Some conservation problems of the Great Lakes. Illinois Nat. Hist. Surv., Biol. Notes 31: 1–14.

———. 1958. From 1858 to 1958, p. 85–103. *In* A century of biological research. Illinois Nat. Hist. Surv. Bull., 27(2).

———. 1960. Forest resources. *In* Atlas of Illinois resources. III. Forest, wildlife, and recreational resources. Dept. of Registration and Educ., Springfield, 47 p.

MOORE, J. P. 1901. The Hirudinea of Illinois. Illinois Lab. Nat. Hist. Bull., **5**: 479–547.

NELSON, E. W. 1876. A partial catalogue of the fishes of Illinois. Illinois Museum Nat. Hist. Bull., 1(1): 33–52.

O'DONNELL, D. J. 1935. Annotated list of the fishes of Illinois. Illinois Nat. Hist. Surv. Bull., 20(5): 473–500.

PAGE, J. L. 1949. Climate of Illinois. Univ. Illinois Press, Urbana. 275 p.

PALOUMPIS, A. A., AND W. C. STARRETT. 1960. An ecological study of benthic organisms in three Illinois River flood plain lakes. Amer. Midland Nat., **64**: 406–435.

PLATNER, W. S. 1946. Water quality studies of the Mississippi River. U.S. Fish and Wildl. Serv., Spec. Sci. Rept. No. 30, 75 p.

POWERS, E. B. 1918. The goldfish (*Carassius carassius*) as a test animal in the study of toxicity. Illinois Biol. Monogr., 4(2): 7–73.

RICHARDSON, R. E. 1913a. Observations on the breeding of the European carp in the vicinity of Havana, Illinois. Illinois Lab. Nat. Hist. Bull., 9(7): 387–404.

———. 1913b. Observations on the breeding habits of fishes at Havana, Illinois, 1910 and 1911. Illinois Lab. Nat. Hist. Bull., 9(8): 405–416.

———. 1921a. The small bottom and shore fauna of the middle and lower Illinois River and its connecting lakes, Chillicothe to Grafton: Its valuation;

its sources of food supply; and its relation to the fishery. Illinois Nat. Hist. Surv. Bull., **13**(15) : 363–522.

———. 1921*b*. Changes in the bottom and shore fauna of the Middle Illinois River and its connecting lakes since 1913–15 as a result of the increase, southward, of sewage pollution. Illinois Nat. Hist Surv. Bull., **14**(4) : 33–75.

———. 1925*a*. Changes in the small bottom fauna of Peoria Lake, 1920 to 1922. Illinois Nat. Hist. Surv. Bull., **15**(5) : 327–388.

———. 1925*b*. Illinois River bottom fauna in 1923. Illinois Nat. Hist. Surv. Bull., **15**(6) : 391–422.

———. 1928. The bottom fauna of the middle Illinois River, 1913–25; its distribution, abundance, valuation, and index value in the study of stream pollution. Illinois Nat. Hist. Surv. Bull., **17**(12) : 387–475.

Ross, H. H. 1944. The caddis flies, or Trichoptera, of Illinois. Illinois Nat. Hist. Surv. Bull., **23** : 1–326.

———. 1958. Faunistic surveys, p. 127–144. *In* A century of biological research. Illinois Nat. Hist. Surv. Bull., **27**(2).

Schacht, F. W. 1897. The North American species of *Diaptomus*. Illinois Lab. Nat. Hist. Bull., **5**(3) : 97–223.

———. 1898. The North American Centropagidae belonging to the genera *Osphrantium, Limnocalanus,* and *Epischura*. Illinois Lab. Nat. Hist. Bull., **5**(4) : 225–270.

Schneidermeyer, Frank, and W. M. Lewis. 1956. Utilization of gizzard shad by largemouth bass. Progr. Fish-Cult., **18**(3) : 137–138.

Shelford, V. E. 1911*a*. Ecological succession. I. Stream fishes and the method of physiographic analysis. Biol. Bull., **21** : 9–35.

———. 1911*b*. Seasonal succession. II. Pond fishes. Biol. Bull., **21** : 127–151.

———. 1911*c*. Seasonal succession. III. A reconnaissance of its causes in ponds with particular reference to fish. Biol. Bull., **22** : 1–38.

———. 1913. Animal communities in temperate America. Univ. Chicago Press, Chicago. 362 p.

———. 1917. An experimental study of the effects of gas waste upon fishes, with especial reference to stream pollution. Illinois Lab. Nat. Hist. Bull., **11**(6) : 381–412.

———. 1918. Equipment for maintaining a flow of oxygen-free water, and for controlling gas content. Illinois Lab. Nat. Hist. Bull., **11**(9) : 573–575.

———. 1923. The determination of hydrogen ion concentration in connection with fresh-water biological studies. Illinois Lab. Nat. Hist. Bull., **14**(9) : 379–395.

Shoemaker, H. H. 1952. Fish home areas of Lake Myosotis, New York. Copeia, 1952(2) : 83–87.

Stall, J. B., J. B. Fehrenbacher, L. J. Bartelli, G. O. Walker, E. L. Sauer, and S. W. Melsted. 1954. Water and land resources of the Crab Orchard Lake basin. Illinois State Water Surv. Bull., **42** : 1–53.

Stickney, Fenner. 1922. The relation of the nymphs of a dragon fly (*Libellula pulchella* Drury) to acid and temperature. Ecology, **3** : 250–254.

Streeter, H. W., and E. B. Phelps. 1958. A study of the pollution and natural purification of the Ohio River. III. Factors concerned in the phenomenon of oxidation and reaeration. Pub. Health Bull.. 146 (first published 1925) : 1–75.

Suter, Max, R. E. Bergstrom, H. F. Smith, G. H. Emrich, W. C. Walton, and T. E. Larson. 1959. Preliminary report on ground-water resources of the Chicago region, Illinois. Illinois State Water Surv. and Illinois State Geol. Surv., Cooperative Ground-Water Rept., **1** : 1–89.

Tarrant, R. M., Jr. 1960. Choice between two sizes of forage fish by largemouth bass under aquarium conditions. Progr. Fish-Cult., **22**(2) : 83–84.

Thompson, D. H. 1925. Some observations on the oxygen requirements of fishes in the Illinois River. Illinois Nat. Hist. Surv. Bull., **15**(7) : 423–437.

———. 1928. The "knothead" carp of the Illinois River. Illinois Nat. Hist. Surv. Bull., **17**(8) : 285–320.

Thompson, D. H., and F. D. Hunt. 1930. The fishes of Champaign County : A study of the distribution and abundance of fishes in small streams. Illinois Nat. Hist. Surv. Bull., **19**(1) : 5–101.

Transeau, E. N. 1916. The periodicity of freshwater algae. Amer. J. Botan., **3** : 121–133.

Underwood, L. M. 1886. List of the described species of fresh water Crustacea from America, north of Mexico. Illinois Lab. Nat. Hist. Bull., **2**(5) : 323–386.

U.S. Public Health Service. 1961. Pollution-caused fish kills in 1960. U.S. Pub. Health Serv., Publ. No. 847 : 1–20.

Van Oosten, John. 1960. Temperatures of Lake Michigan, 1930–32. U.S. Fish and Wildl. Serv., Spec. Sci. Rept., Fish. No. 322, 34 p.

Walker, C. R. 1952. Physico-chemical characteristics of the Big Muddy River and tributaries with special emphasis on pollution. Presented at 14th Midwest Wildl. Conf., Des Moines, Iowa, 16 p. (Mimeo.)

Ward, H. B. 1899. Freshwater investigations during the last five years. Trans. Amer. Microscop. Soc., **20** : 261–336.

Ward, H. B., and G. C. Whipple. 1918. Fresh-water biology. John Wiley & Sons, New York. 1111 p.

Waterman, W. G. 1926. Ecological problems from the sphagnum bogs of Illinois. Ecology, **7** : 255–272.

Weise, J. G. 1957. The spring cave-fish, *Chologaster papilliferus*, in Illinois. Ecology, **38** : 195–204.

Wells, M. M. 1918. The reactions and resistance of fishes to carbon dioxide and carbon monoxide. Illinois Lab. Nat. Hist. Bull., **11**(8) : 557–571.

6 Clifford O. Berg

Middle Atlantic States

Introduction

Physiography

The Middle Atlantic States—New York, Pennsylvania, New Jersey, Maryland, and Delaware—comprise an area of 115,379 mi², bounded approximately by the 38th and 45th parallels north latitude and the 73rd and 81st meridians west longitude. Relief and physiography are quite varied. The highest elevations in the area are in the Adirondack and Catskill Mountains in New York and the Allegheny Plateau in west-central Pennsylvania and western Maryland. More than half of this five-state area was covered by the continental ice sheet during Wisconsin glaciation (Fig. 6.1), and this northern section is richly supplied with glacially produced lakes.

Physiographic features of the Middle Atlantic States can be grouped into 12 regions or provinces (Fig. 6.2), most of which are characterized by moderate to bold relief and generally good drainage (U.S. Dept. Agr., N.E. Post-war Planning Comm., 1943). Much of the area is seriously lacking in calcium and other essential nutrients, and the natural waters of these regions are edaphically oligotrophic.

The Adirondack Mountain region, with peaks rising 4,000 ft to more than 5,000 ft above sea level, has the greatest elevations and some of the oldest rock formations in the five-state area. These chiefly pre-Cambrian granites, schists, and gneisses are decidedly lime poor, and the later intrusives fail to supply the needed calcium and other important minerals. Most of the glacially produced lakes of this region remain pure, beautiful, and relatively unspoiled by man, but they

are exceptionally unproductive limnologically. Inasmuch as the Adirondack Mountain region has relatively low solar radiation and the lowest temperatures and shortest frost-free period of the entire five-state area, the causes of oligotrophy are as much meteorological as edaphic.

The plateau-like Adirondack Foothills, chiefly upper Cambrian and Ordovician, have elevations of 700 to 2,000 ft. The glacial lakes of this section have higher potential productivity because of both the occurrence of limestone and the higher temperatures associated with lower elevations.

The Ontario-Oneida-Champlain Lake Plain, along the shores of the lakes mentioned and also in the St. Lawrence and Hudson River valleys, is characterized by low relief, elevations of only 100 to 500 ft, and the occurrence of lacustrine deposits laid down in a glacial lake. These deposits consist mainly of calcareous silts and clays, derived from limestones and shales of Ordovician and Devonian age. Although there is an overwash of sandy material in some places, this province has much better supplies of calcium than most of the five-state area. Like the Coastal Plain, the Lake Plain has some flat and level land that is subject to imperfect drainage.

The Limestone Belt of central New York extends from Albany westward to Buffalo—across the northern ends of the Finger Lakes—in the lowlands lying north of the Northern Appalachian Plateau. A smaller arm diverges off northwestward from Albany and extends approximately to the outlet of Lake Ontario. In some places, the surface consists of deep glacial till derived from limestone and alkaline shales and lacustrine deposits from these materials. In others, there are

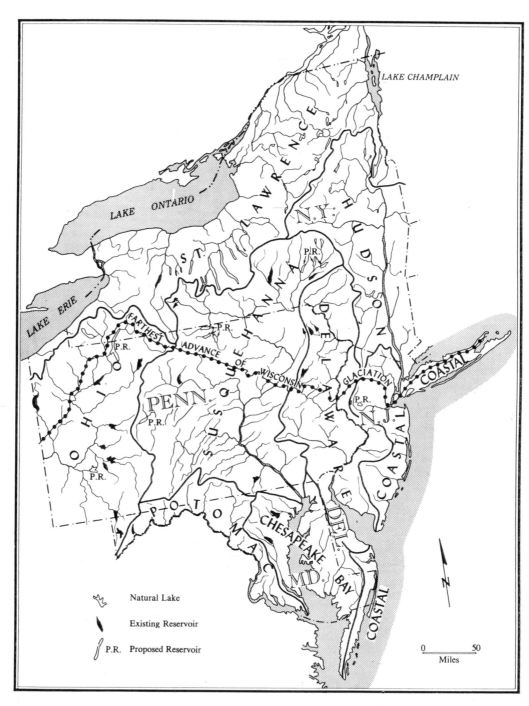

Fig. 6.1.—Water resources, drainage, and glaciation of the Middle Atlantic States. Modified from U.S. Geological Survey map: U.S. Water Resource Development. Edition of September 1958. Prepared by the University of Wisconsin Cartographic Laboratory.

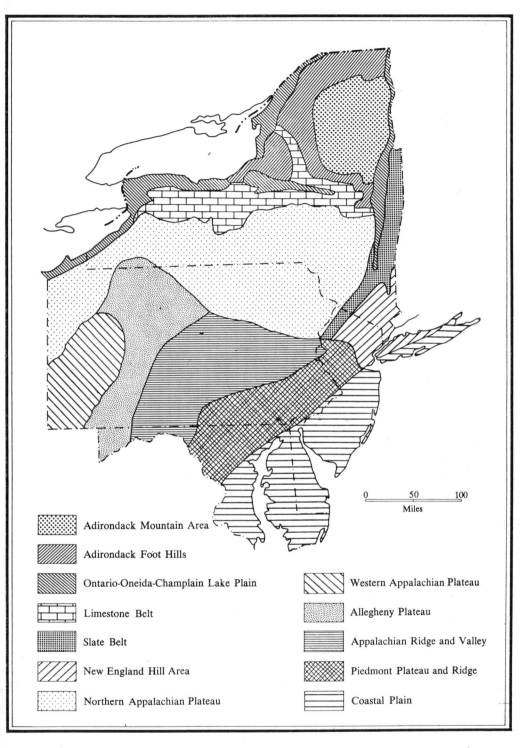

Adirondack Mountain Area

Adirondack Foot Hills

Ontario-Oneida-Champlain Lake Plain

Limestone Belt

Slate Belt

New England Hill Area

Northern Appalachian Plateau

Western Appalachian Plateau

Allegheny Plateau

Appalachian Ridge and Valley

Piedmont Plateau and Ridge

Coastal Plain

Fig. 6.2.—Physiographic regions of the Middle Atlantic States. Modified from figure in Northeast Agricultural Atlas, U.S. Dept. Agr., Northeast Post-war Planning Comm., 1943 (B.A.E. Neg. 43114). Prepared by the University of Wisconsin Cartographic Laboratory.

outcrops of intact parent strata, especially Onondaga limestone. In an area that suffers rather general impoverishment in calcium, the different limnological conditions observed in the Limestone Belt are quite remarkable.

The narrow Slate Belt, 20 to 50 mi wide, extends northerly from northwestern New Jersey and eastern New York, principally in the Hudson Valley. It is a northern extension of the Appalachian Ridge and Valley region into the glaciated area, and the southern part shows the characteristic ridge and valley conformation. Small limestone belts characterized by hard-water lakes occur within this region.

The New England Hill region occurs in a belt of hills, low ridges, and valleys, extending into southeastern New York and northeastern New Jersey. The entire region consists of till and outwash from Wisconsin glaciation. The dominant rock types are granite, gneiss, and schist, with smaller areas of sandstone, shale, and conglomerate.

The plateau top of the Northern Appalachian Plateau in southern New York and northern Pennsylvania ranges from 1,500 to 2,000 ft in elevation. The geologic material consists of Devonian, gray, acid sandstones and shales over much of the province, with some limestone material and mixed alkaline and acid gray shales and sandstones along the northern border. The southern border of this province coincides quite closely with the farthest advance of Wisconsin glaciation.

The remaining provinces may be of less interest limnologically. Lying primarily in the unglaciated area, they contain very few natural lakes. The Western Appalachian Plateau is severely dissected into narrow ridges and V-shaped valleys, along which the terrace and bottom lands have limited development. The rock formations are Carboniferous, gray, acid and calcareous shales and sandstones in horizontal positions.

Rising from 1,800 to 3,000 ft above sea level, the Allegheny Plateau has the second highest elevations in the five-state area. Although there are many deep, steep-sided valleys and gorges, much of the original undulating plateau top remains. The major geological formations are gray, acid sandstones and shales, chiefly of Carboniferous age.

In the Appalachian Ridge and Valley region, parallel high mountain ridges alternate with fairly broad areas of low ridges and some smooth valleys. The present characteristic topography was produced by differential geologic weathering of the parent materials. These differ greatly in hardness, ranging from acid gray sandstone and conglomerate to gray shale and cherty and fairly pure limestone. This topography has resulted in a remarkable trellis drainage pattern, with the great majority of streams flowing in directions parallel to the longitudinal axis of this arcuate region. Those in Maryland and south-central Pennsylvania flow predominantly south-southwest into the Potomac River. Above the Potomac-Susquehanna divide, they flow northeast to the Susquehanna River or (beyond this river) southwest to it. Because the region arcs more to the east, tributaries of the Schuylkill and Lehigh have more nearly east-west orientations. Water gaps eroded through the long ridges enable the major rivers to flow through and also permit the uniting of a few tributary streams.

The Piedmont Plateau is undulating to hilly and even somewhat mountainous along the western edge. Elevation of the plateau proper is 300 to 600 ft, but the ridges often rise above 1,000 ft. For the most part, drainage is good.

The Coastal Plain of southeastern Maryland, all but the northern end of Delaware, the southern three-fifths of New Jersey, and Long Island has the lowest elevations (0 to 300 ft), lowest relief, and some of the lowest soil nutrients and lime found in the entire area. Reflecting especially the paucity of calcium, natural waters of the ecologically famous Pine Barrens of New Jersey have some of the lowest pH and alkalinity values and deepest brown colors found anywhere in the United States.

As evidenced by the large number of natural lakes north of the line that marks the farthest advance of the Wisconsin ice sheet and their paucity south of that line, the great majority of the lakes in the Middle Atlantic States occupy basins that were produced, directly or indirectly, by Pleistocene glaciation. Flint (1947) and Hutchinson (1957) have discussed thoroughly the glacial processes involved, making specific references to several of the lakes in this area. Among the basin-forming processes considered to be indirect effects of glaciation are uplift and tilting as the North American Continent rebounded after deglaciation (Lake Champlain), excavation of plunge pools by tremendous waterfalls carrying the melt water during deglaciation (Fayetteville Green Lake), and thaw or thermokarst lakes formed in regions of permafrost near but not under the continental ice sheet (the explanation advanced by Wolfe [1953] for numerous small basins south of the farthest advance of glaciers in New Jersey).

Drainage

Drainage is predominantly eastward to the Atlantic Ocean, the only exception being a section composed of approximately the western third of Pennsylvania, a much smaller area of New York at and near its southwest corner, and a still smaller area at the western tip of Maryland (Fig. 6.1). This section drains to the west and south, through the Ohio and Mississippi rivers, to the Gulf of Mexico. The Atlantic drainage is carried by five major river systems, several smaller rivers that flow into Chesapeake Bay, and the still smaller coastal streams of New Jersey, Delaware, and Maryland. (1) The largest and best-known of the five large river systems, the St. Lawrence, drains the Laurentian Great Lakes northeastward, through Canada, to the Gulf of St. Lawrence. A band of north- and west-sloping country that extends across the northwest edge of this five-state area in New York and Pennsylvania, including the Erie and Ontario lake plains, the entire Finger Lakes region, and the western and northern foothills and slopes of the Adirondack Mountains, drains into this system. (2) Another broad band, comprising virtually the entire eastern edge of New York State south of the divide in the Adirondacks, drains primarily southward, via the Hudson River, into the harbor of New York City. (3) South and west of the Hudson, the Delaware River arises in the Catskill Mountains of southeastern New York and flows essentially southward between Pennsylvania and New Jersey, draining eastern Pennsylvania and Delaware and western New Jersey into Delaware Bay. (4) The largest river of Atlantic drainage in the United States, the Susquehanna, arises west and north of the Delaware River and drains south-central New York, a large area in central Pennsylvania, and a bit of northeastern Maryland into Chesapeake Bay. (5) Most of western and southern Maryland (as well as the eastern panhandle of West Virginia and much of northern Virginia) drains into Chesapeake Bay via the Potomac River.

Climate

A humid, continental climate, with rainfall that usually is adequate throughout the year, prevails throughout the five-state area. From a limnological point of view, the favorable effects of this are partly counterbalanced by a high incidence of cloudiness, which screens out much solar radiation and reduces the caloric energy available for photosynthesis.

The maps of normal daily solar radiation given by Visher (1954) show that New York and New England especially, but also the adjacent states to the south, receive appreciably less sunshine than most of the country at most seasons of the year. Minimal readings for the year are recorded on 21 December, when the region south and east of Lakes Erie and Ontario averages less than 100 langleys ($\equiv$ g·cal/cm² of horizontal surface), most of the five-state area gets 100–150 langleys per day, and the only section that averages more than 150 is Delaware and the southeastern tips of Maryland and New Jersey. Maximal readings on 21 June show a reversal of the usual trend for the year, with northern and western New York averaging more than 550 langleys per day, while southeastern New York and the four states to the south receive less.

Temperature extremes for the area are found in the Adirondack Mountains and the Lower Chesapeake Bay region, where there are average annual frost-free periods of only 90 days and more than 200 days, respectively. These two regions are further contrasted by average annual temperatures of $<40°$ and $>55°$ F, by average January temperatures of $<16°$ and $>38°$ F, and by average annual minima of $<-30°$ and $>5°$ F. The average annual snowfall on sections of the western slopes of the Adirondacks is more than 140 in., and there is at least one inch of snow on the ground on an average of 140 days of the year. In the Lower Chesapeake Bay the comparable figures are less than 20 in. and less than 20 days (U.S. Dept. Agr., 1941).

Average annual precipitation varies from more than 50 in. in sections of the Adirondacks and just north of New York City to slightly less than 30 in. in sections of western New York State. The precipitation is well distributed throughout the year but is somewhat heavier during the summer months in most regions. Constancy of a relatively good supply of rainfall is indicated by figures for the average annual precipitation for the 10 driest years in 40 years—more than 35 in. in the Adirondacks and more than 25 in. throughout the area.

Surprisingly small wet-bulb depressions attest to the high relative humidities characteristic of the area. Even in the season and at the time of day when relative humidities are lowest—at noon in midsummer—averages as low as 50% are not found anywhere in the five-state area, and by 8 P.M. on an average July day most of the area has 65% humidity or higher.

The high humidities and cool temperatures result in relatively low evaporative losses from lakes. On isoline maps of evaporation from reservoirs and shallow lakes in the United States, Visher (1954) indicated that these water losses vary from less than 20 in. per year in the Adirondacks to 30–40 in. in southern and eastern sections of the five-state area.

A higher than average incidence of cloudiness is more or less typical of the entire area and especially characteristic of certain sections. The largest section in the continental United States that averages less than 80 clear days per year comprises most of western New York (Binghamton to Buffalo, including all of the Finger Lakes region) and a narrowing belt that extends southwesterly through the Allegheny Plateau of Pennsylvania and western Maryland into West Virginia. This high annual incidence of cloudiness is caused by summer and winter cloud belts, which differ in their causes and in the positions of their foci but have their marginal areas superimposed.

The summer (June through August) concentration of clouds is centered over the Appalachian and Allegheny regions. These clouds are formed because warm, moisture-laden air is forced upward and cooled below the dew point. Radiation fog, which is very common in the mountain valleys on summer mornings, adds to the screening effect of the clouds. Because of the combination of clouds and fog, this region gets the smallest percentage of possible sunshine (less than 60%) and the lowest average number of hours of sunshine per day (fewer than 8) in the five-state area in summer.

Winter cloudiness, however, has twin foci southeast of Lakes Erie and Ontario, areas where the prevailing westerly winds move off the lakes. This cloudiness illustrates one of the pronounced

effects exerted by the Great Lakes on local weather. The warmer winter temperatures of these lakes cause the moisture content of cold air moving over them to increase. This results in clouds and snow squalls over the lakes and on the down-wind shores. Local topographic features on the southeast shores of these lakes cause upslope flow, resulting in additional condensation, which produces the well-known snow belts of Buffalo and Watertown. From December through February, it is these regions that get the smallest percentage of possible sunshine (less than 30%) and fewer than three hours of sunshine per day. The recent meteorological study of the Great Lakes by Petterssen (1960) included a special effort "to isolate the effects which are due to the transfer of heat from the water to the air during typical winter conditions." Petterssen mentioned effects of the lakes on cloud development and concluded that "heat transfer from the Lakes to the air exerts . . . a dominating influence on the weather systems."

The marked concentration of fruit growing in a sharply delimited belt just south and east of Lakes Erie and Ontario illustrates another important control exerted by these lakes on the climate of adjacent regions. Although this fruit belt is determined in part also by edaphic factors, the single most important control seems to be the moderating effect of these lakes on temperatures, greatly reducing the risk of frosts in late spring and early fall.

Visher (1954) summarized the influence of the Great Lakes on climatic conditions as follows:

The Great Lakes on the average depress exceptionally high temperatures about 3° to 5° and elevate exceptionally low ones 10° to 15°; they prolong the frost-free period conspicuously, by 40 to 50 percent; they slightly decrease precipitation except snowfall, which they increase fully 50 percent; they decrease summer rainfall partly by reducing thunderstorm frequency and intensity, torrential rains being notably less frequent and less heavy than at some distance inland. The Lakes increase the number of days receiving some precipitation and the number of cloudy and foggy days. In summer, however, they have more sunshine than most of the South, or the North Pacific or Atlantic coasts.

To attain some order for the many facts that should be presented in a summary of the limnological resources and contributions of the Middle Atlantic States, a geographic division into states is used here. The progression from New York, through Pennsylvania, New Jersey, and Delaware, to Maryland moves from a glaciated region richly endowed with lakes to unglaciated country, the last two states having no natural lakes. As must be expected from this fact alone, the volume of limnological work to be reported from New York exceeds that from any of the neighboring states to the south. Yet workers in the other states have made many significant and valuable contributions to limnological knowledge. Limnologists of these densely populated and heavily industrialized states have taken an effective interest in pollution and its effects, with particular reference to industrial pollution of streams. The brackish bays and estuaries of Maryland, Delaware, and New Jersey are among the most studied and best known habitats of this type in the world, and a high percentage of the information gained there can be applied directly toward the solution of freshwater problems.

New York

Limnological resources and surveys

The rich limnological resources of New York State range from shared interests in Lakes Erie, Ontario, and Champlain down through thousands of smaller natural lakes, ponds, marshes, and streams to farm ponds and man-made impoundments for power, flood control, and water supplies. The most carefully figured quantitative estimates ever made of these are the following figures supplied by the State Conservation Department. There are nearly three and a half million acres of lakes in the state. This includes the New York State territorial waters of the three large lakes mentioned above, which make up almost four-fifths of the total. Including only the streams that are sufficiently large and permanent to have been seriously considered for stocking with trout, New York has 70,000 mi of streams. There are also 20,000 farm ponds in the state.

It is clearly impossible to describe the many limnological resources of New York here. The most helpful alternative, indicating where much of this information is available, seems to be a summary of the surveys that have been made of them.

The first and most comprehensive series of biological surveys of lakes and streams done by any state agency in this country was conducted by the New York State Conservation Department in the 14 summers of 1926–39, inclusive (New York State Conserv. Dept., 1927–40). These surveys were made "to determine the most practical methods of increasing fish production," and the ultimate goals were to make sound recommendations concerning stocking policies. Whether interested specifically in stocking policies or not, limnologists working in this state find much useful information in the data on which these recommendations are based. Limnological factors that bear on the suitability of waters for various fishes were extensively investigated by the most competent aquatic biologists available, and the published reports include basic limnological information on a great number of lakes and streams.

These surveys were initiated with studies of the Genesee River System, carried out by a staff of 14 scientists working under the direction of Dr. Emmeline Moore, Investigator in Fish Culture. Each summer thereafter was devoted to the study of another river system, major portion of a large river system, or group of smaller systems constituting a watershed. This endeavor grew rapidly, and the staff for the survey of the Erie-Niagara System in 1928 included 41 scientists who worked in the field from mid-June to mid-September. Coverage of the entire state was completed when the survey of streams, lakes, and bays of the Lake Ontario Watershed was published in 1940.

In addition to studies of fish species, their food, rates of growth, parasites and predators, the carp and lamprey problems, and other matters of concern primarily to fisheries biologists, each survey has some papers of greater general interest to limnologists. Hydrographic maps of lakes and ponds are presented in some of these, and each of the later surveys includes a limnological study of selected lakes in the area (see Tressler and Bere, 1938). These usually emphasize the plankton, giving identifications of common genera and vertical distribution diagrams of the dominant groups. A paper on aquatic vegetation appears in each survey (most of them written by W. C. Muenscher), and the papers on supplies of natural fish food (primarily by P. R. Needham) give qualitative and roughly quantitative appraisals of the macroscopic benthos. The chemical investigations (chiefly by H. M. Faigenbaum) include measurements of temperature, dissolved oxygen, alkalinity, pH, CO_2, and in some instances also the sources and types of pollution and the biochemical oxygen demand (B.O.D.). A comprehensive hydrographic and biological survey of the eastern end of Lake Erie was made cooperatively with other agencies within and outside of the state during the third summer of field work and was published in 1930. Vessels especially equipped for hydrographic studies were first used on the Great Lakes in this survey. A map given in the last report shows which survey covers each section of the state. Although each year's survey is reported in a group of papers written by the various specialists on the staff, all papers of a given survey are bound together in one volume.

A currently active series of studies, focusing attention on the prevention and abatement of pollution of public waters, was initiated when the New York State Water Pollution Control Law was enacted in 1949. These include analyses of dissolved oxygen, B.O.D., coliform bacteria counts, and volume of stream flow, especially during drought conditions when low dilution factors create problems in disposing of wastes. The studies are made by the Bureau of Environmental Sanitation, State Department of Health, to advise the Water Pollution Control Board concerning the classification of public waters with respect to standards of purity and to make recommendations concerning the best usage of waters in the public interest. In the first eight years following 1949, waters of 35 drainage basins, comprising 51% of the area of New York, were surveyed (New York State Water Pollution Control Board, 1957). Efforts have been concentrated on fresh, surface waters, but tidal waters and ground waters also are to be classified. Reports are published on each drainage basin when the study of it is completed (New York State Water Pollution Control Board, 1950———).

In addition to routine studies of drainage basins, the Water Pollution Control Board conducts some research with available personnel and contracts for additional research as funds permit. These have been published as *Research Reports*, Nos. 1–7, chiefly on relative efficiency of various methods of treating different wastes, effects of different wastes on surface and ground waters, and a statistical analysis of drought flows of New York rivers (New York State Water Pollution Control Board, 1959–60).

Another currently active series of surveys and analyses of interest to limnologists is conducted cooperatively by the U.S. Geological Survey and the New York State Department of Commerce. These are made to determine the chemical and physical quality of water resources, particularly to appraise their industrial utility. Reports resulting from this survey give the concentrations of 12 ions that occur commonly in natural waters, in addition to total dissolved solids, total and non-carbonate hardness, pH, color, and specific conductance. This is supplemented by information on precipitation, runoff, and yield (gallons per minute) of various wells. Published reports (Beetem, 1954; Pauszek, 1959; Mattingly, 1961) are concerned with waters of the Allegheny, Genesee, Susquehanna, and St. Lawrence River basins. A study of the chemical and physical quality of waters of the Delaware River Basin has been made, and a report is being prepared. The surveys have concentrated primarily on streams, but unpublished data have been obtained on about 20 lakes in the state and are of particular interest limnologically.

The U.S. Geological Survey Surface Water Branch has established gauging stations on practically every major stream in the state and publishes extensive runoff data in the annual *Water Supply Papers*. In cooperation with the Water Resources Commission, State Department of Conservation, the U.S. Geological Survey Ground Water Branch is investigating the ground-water resources and publishing the results in bulletins, each of which covers the waters of one county (see Cushman, 1953).

Some regional limnology

Lakes illustrating some of the variety found in New York State are shown in Figure 6.3 and are characterized in Tables 6.1 and 6.2. Locations of the Adirondack League Club, the Brandon Ponds, and all other lakes listed in the tables are shown on the map (Fig. 6.3). Other lakes discussed in this section but not included in Tables 6.1 and 6.2 are located and named. The Finger Lakes are listed in the tables under the Northern Appalachian Plateau, although their basins are largely in the New York Limestone Belt. While their water chemistry undoubtedly is affected by the edaphic conditions of both regions, these lakes probably reflect, in the main, the influences of the Northern Appalachian Plateau, because all their major inlets flow primarily through soils of that region

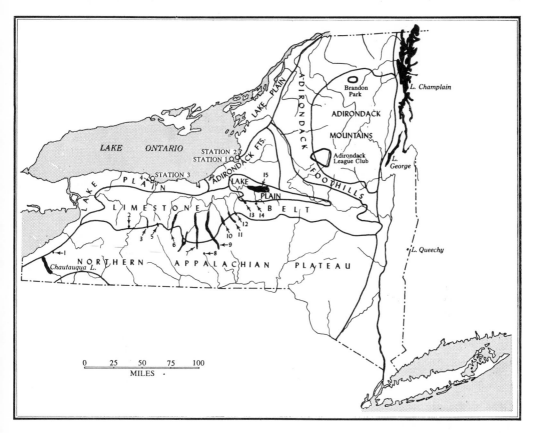

Fig. 6.3.—Some lakes and physiographic regions of New York State. Lakes listed in Tables 6.1 and 6.2 are numbered (west to east) as follows: 1, Cassadaga; 2, Silver; 3, Conesus; 4, Long Pond; 5, Canadice; 6, Canandaigua; 7, Seneca; 8, Cayuta; 9, Cayuga; 10, Owasco; 11, Skaneateles; 12, Otisco; 13, Onondaga; 14, Fayetteville Green; 15, Oneida. Compiled from various sources and prepared by the University of Wisconsin Cartographic Laboratory.

and enter the lakes near their south ends. Only two lakes included in Table 6.2, both located near the northern edge of the Limestone Belt, are considered representative of that region in the sense of getting their water primarily from its drainage.

The lakes listed in Tables 6.1 and 6.2 are grouped according to physiographic regions, and these are arranged in descending order of mean elevation. All hydrographic and chemical data for the small Adirondack lakes at Brandon and the Adirondack League Club are taken from a current thesis at Cornell University (Schofield, 1962). Chemical data for the other lakes are from the previously mentioned surveys made by the U.S. Geological Survey and the New York

State Department of Commerce. Hydrographic data for the lower-lying lakes southwest of the Adirondacks are from a variety of published and unpublished sources including Birge and Juday (1914), articles in *The Conservationist* (New York State Conservation Dept.), and records from limnology class trips at Cornell University. All lakes included in these tables are natural, and all were formed, directly or indirectly, by glaciation.

The great range in surface elevations of the lakes shown in Table 6.1 is exceeded by the range in elevations of their deepest points—from 174 ft below sea level to almost 2,300 ft above. Both the largest and deepest lakes that lie entirely within the Middle Atlantic States (Oneida and Seneca) are listed here. As indicated in Table 6.1,

TABLE 6.1

Hydrographic data on selected New York lakes.[a] Unless indicated by a footnote, lakes are normally stratified in summer and oxygen in the hypolimnion is depleted.

Lakes	Elevation (ft)	Surface area	Drainage area	Max. depth (ft)	Mean depth (ft)	Secchi disc (ft)
Adirondack League Club						
2nd Bisby Lake[b]	2100	114 acres	1739 acres	62	22	16
Canachagala Lake	2130	329 acres	1191 acres	37	14	15
East Lake	1900	33 acres	595 acres	38	16	14
Green Lake	1700	26 acres	31 acres	41	18	19
Honnedaga Lake[b]	2167	762 acres	3453 acres	190	53	85
Jones Lake[b]	2300	57 acres	305 acres	29	6	29
Panther Lake[b,c]	1900	43 acres	260 acres	23	13	18
Pico Lake	2200	31 acres	702 acres	40	12	—
Rock Pond	2000	18 acres	156 acres	65	24	13
Brandon Park ponds						
Bear Pond	1560	5 acres	65 acres	19	15	13
Black Pond	1584	25 acres	115 acres	58	25	16
Follensby Jr. Pond	1566	148 acres	4390 acres	29	13	8
Long Pond[b,c]	1568	44 acres	1345 acres	10	5	4
Wolf Pond[b,c]	1539	27 acres	950 acres	7	4	3
No. Appalachian Plateau						
Canadice Lake	1092	1.0 mi²	12 mi²	83	54	13
Canandaigua Lake[b]	686	16.6 mi²	175 mi²	274	128	12
Cayuga Lake[b]	381	66.4 mi²	813 mi²	435	179	17
Cayuta Lake	1317	0.6 mi²	—	26	—	5
Conesus Lake	818	5.2 mi²	89 mi²	59	—	21
Otisco Lake	734	2.9 mi²	34 mi²	66	33	10
Owasco Lake[b]	710	10.3 mi²	208 mi²	177	96	—
Seneca Lake[b]	444	67.7 mi²	707 mi²	618	290	27
Silver Lake	1356	1.2 mi²	—	37	—	16
Skaneateles Lake[b]	867	13.9 mi²	73 mi²	297	143	34
New York Limestone Belt						
Fayetteville Green Lake	419	67 acres	—	192	104	31
Lake Plain						
Oneida Lake[b,c]	370	80.0 mi²	1265 mi²	55	<20	8

[a] The writer is grateful to C. L. Schofield and F. H. Pauszek for permission to use the unpublished data in Tables 6.1 and 6.2 and to the former for help in preparing the tables.
[b] Oxygen not depleted.
[c] Not stratified in summer.

there are important physical, chemical, and biological differences associated with morphometry. Wherever possible, the figure given for Secchi disc transparency is an average of several readings taken at different seasons. In most of the New York lakes that develop thermal stratification in the summer, depletion of dissolved oxygen in the hypolimnion seriously limits the benthic fauna.

The contrasts in annual cycles of thermal stratification and circulation are among the most fundamental physical differences in New York lakes. Most of them are stratified in summer and winter and circulating completely every spring and fall. A few relatively shallow ones are stratified under the ice in winter but potentially in complete circulation whenever ice-free. Cayuga and Seneca are stratified in summer but are usually open, virtually homothermous, and in full circulation throughout the winter. Fayetteville Green Lake is chemically stratified and has never been known to circulate completely.

As indicated by Secchi disc readings that vary from 3 to 85 ft and by the data in Table 6.2, the chemical and biological conditions in New York lakes also are remarkably divergent. In part, these differences are the direct results of the morphometric and circulatory contrasts already noted. To an even greater degree, they are caused by marked differences in edaphic and meteorological conditions and by cultural influences. Adequacy of dissolved oxygen in hypolimnion waters of the deep Finger Lakes is due rimarily to their morphometry, but the same condition in much shallower lakes in the Adirondacks is caused by edaphic and meteorological actors. Dissolved nutrients are in such short supply that they severely limit fish production in Adirondack lakes. In other New York lakes, nutrients are so concentrated that problems of overproduction of weeds, midges, and coarse fish are created. This problem of overproduction of the "wrong" organisms and the problem of pollution often associated with overproduction are growing as the population density increases throughout the Middle Atlantic States.

Some facts of regional limnology are evident from the data in Table 6.2. The analyses on which these data are based are not replicated for each lake, but the relatively small variations found among lakes of each physiographic region compared with the great differences among the means of different regions indicate that there are real and considerable regional distinctions. The soft-water lakes of both Adirondack groups have pH, conductivity, alkalinity, calcium, magnesium, bicarbonate, and sulfate values so far below those of the lower-lying lakes that there is no overlap in the ranges of any of these columns. Although slight overlaps occur with respect to sodium and potassium, chloride, and nitrate, the means for these ions also are much lower in the Adirondack Lakes. These nutrient-poor Adi-

TABLE 6.2

Chemical characteristics of representative New York lakes

Lakes	pH	Conductivity (micromhos)	Alkalinity	Ca	Mg	Na+K	Fe	HCO₃	SO₄	Cl	NO₃
Adirondack League Club											
2nd Bisby Lake	6.3	24	3.0	2.0	0.5	1.9	0.28	4	5.1	0.4	0.29
Canachagala Lake	5:5	21	1.5	1.6	0.5	1.2	0.04	2	5.9	trace	0.08
East Lake	5.9	39	10.0	4.3	0.8	1.4	0.17	12	4.6	1.2	0.38
Green Lake	5.4	17	2.0	1.1	0.5	0.9	0.16	2	6.4	trace	0.11
Honnedaga Lake	4.9	30	0.5	1.6	0.6	1.6	<0.04	1	6.4	1.7	0.57
Jones Lake	5.8	25	3.0	2.1	0.6	1.5	0.08	4	5.5	0.5	0.22
Panther Lake	6.0	39	11.0	4.2	0.8	1.5	0.04	13	6.1	trace	0.34
Pico Lake	4.3	38	0.0	1.5	0.8	3.0	0.40	0	5.8	1.8	0.55
Rock Pond	6.4	31	6.0	3.1	0.6	1.9	0.06	7	5.1	0.7	0.39
Brandon Park Ponds											
Bear Pond	5.9	39	10.0	3.3	1.3	1.8	0.09	12	6.0	0.04	1.21
Black Pond	5.9	22	3.0	1.9	0.6	1.3	0.11	4	6.2	trace	0.32
Follensby Jr. Pond	5.8	47	14.5	4.6	1.6	1.2	0.30	18	6.3	trace	0.53
Long Pond	6.0	40	7.5	4.0	1.3	0.9	0.72	9	4.8	2.2	0.32
Wolf Pond	5.3	35	2.0	3.1	1.3	0.1	1.22	2	3.9	4.1	0.81
No. Appalachian Plateau											
Canadice Lake	7.0	104	27.9	12	2.8	3.2	0.04	34	17	2.3	0.4
Canandaigua Lake	8.1	271	103.3	35	9.7	7.5	0.04	126	28	5.1	1.7
Cassadaga Lake	7.7	184	75.4	29	3.8	2.2	0.09	92	12	3.1	0.6
Cayuga Lake	7.4	596	105.7	47	9.6	61.0	0.02	129	55	88	2.8
Conesus Lake	7.7	309	108.2	40	11.0	9.4	0.05	132	31	13.0	0.9
Otisco Lake	7.3	265	110.6	40	8.5	2.3	0.00	135	19	5.7	1.1
Owasco Lake	7.5	253	99.2	36	7.4	4.3	0.04	121	20	4.8	3.4
Seneca Lake	7.1	646	104.9	40	10.0	85.6	0.02	128	39	125	1.6
Silver Lake	7.5	237	80.3	35	6.7	3.8	0.01	98	35	5.2	1.8
Skaneateles Lake	7.5	231	93.4	36	6.2	2.9	0.18	114	16	3.6	2.0
New York Limestone Belt											
Fayetteville Green Lake	7.5	1960	157.4	400	62	14.6	0.02	192	1050	24	4.7
Onondaga Lake	7.7	5010	106.6	472	13	538	0.28	130	167	1460	11.0
Lake Plain											
Lake Erie	7.1	318	104.1	41	8.1	11.5	0.47	127	26	20.0	2.3
Long Pond	7.1	431	95.9	47	9.7	23.0	0.22	117	52	38.0	2.8
Oneida Lake	7.8	238	65.6	31	7.2	4.9	0.10	80	42	4.5	2.1
Lake Ontario—1	7.9	306	92.6	38	8.0	10.4	0.05	113	25	23.0	0.7
Lake Ontario—2	7.2	108	40.2	14	3.4	4.1	0.10	49	9	4.8	0.6
Lake Ontario—3	6.9	459	98.4	54	10.0	24.1	0.43	120	61	41.0	4.2

rondack waters are able to dissolve very little mineral matter from the ancient, granitic rocks of that region. Practically all water-soluble materials originally contained in the rocks have leached away long ago.

Another regional distinction suggested in Table 6.2 is the much greater concentration of nutrient salts in lakes of the Limestone Belt than in those of either the Northern Appalachian Plateau to the south or the Lake Plain to the north. Although figures for the Limestone Belt are based on only two lakes, the higher values for magnesium, bicarbonate, and alkalinity and the strikingly higher concentration of calcium almost certainly reflect true regional trends. In fact, the real differences between average soil influences of the Limestone Belt and those of adjacent regions probably are even greater than the tabular data on these ions indicate. As noted previously, waters of the lakes grouped to represent the Northern Appalachian Plateau in Table 6.2 undoubtedly are enriched somewhat by minor drainage from the Limestone Belt.

With respect to certain other ions, the values shown are unusually high in the two lakes that were analyzed in the Limestone Belt and are not truly representative of that region. The very high values for chloride, nitrate, and sodium in Onondaga Lake are due in part to domestic and industrial pollution. Salt springs, which emerged in that area in such volumes that they were once used commercially, may also contribute. Although the sulfate content of Limestone Belt lakes probably averages higher than that of lakes in adjacent regions, the figure given for Fayetteville Green Lake is clearly exceptional. This lake is not polluted, but it seems to be influenced appreciably by the gypsum deposits that occur in its immediate vicinity. Since the conductivity figures for these two lakes reflect the exceptional concentrations of sulfate in one and of chloride in the other, these conductivity readings probably are too high to represent the mean of Limestone Belt lakes. However, the true mean must be appreciably above that of adjacent regions because of the high values of calcium, magnesium, and bicarbonate that characterize the region.

The much higher concentration of sodium and chloride in Cayuga and Seneca than in all the other Finger Lakes presents an interesting problem. Salt strata underlie the whole Finger Lakes region. These evidently were formed during the

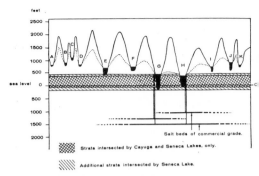

Fig. 6.4.—Diagram of the Finger Lakes (west to east) showing elevations, depths, and locations of major salt beds. Vertical scale 100 times horizontal. Sections of the lakes pass through deepest parts. Salt bed depths represented as found near south ends of lakes. Solid line between lakes represents heights of ridges near south ends, in Northern Appalachian Plateau. Broken line shows decreased relief at north ends, in Limestone Belt. See text for implications of salt beds and shaded strata. The lakes are as follows: A, Conesus; B, Hemlock; C, Canadice; D, Honeoye; E, Canandaigua; F, Keuka; G, Seneca; H, Cayuga; I, Owasco; J, Skaneateles; K, Otisco. Modified from Birge and Juday, 1914.

Paleozoic Era, when the region was a part of the Appalachian geosynclinal sea. Arid periods resulted in much evaporation and salt deposition in extensive horizontal strata. Periods of wetter climate produced beds of other materials, and this alternation of climatic conditions resulted in the accumulation of "bed after bed of sand, mud, lime and salt, one above the other" (Von Engeln, 1961). At the close of this era, the entire region was uplifted with scarcely any deformation of these horizontal deposits, although a southward regional dip reaches 50 ft per mi in some localities.

Salt is being extracted by four commercial plants in the region, two being located on the shores of each of these lakes, at or near their south ends. These locations were dictated by the thickness, purity, and depth of the salt beds, the economy of shipping out the product by barges, and the desirability of locating in the lowest position possible in the region, thus requiring the least drilling down to the salt-bearing strata. The two beds being extracted are 1,500 and 1,928 ft below ground level at the Cayuga Lake installations, or 1,087 and 1,515 ft below sea level (Fig. 6.4). No general leaching from these depths up to the level of the lake basins is at all likely. The mines remain dry, and if ground water is not seeping down into them, it almost certainly is not percolating upward from them, either.

The first explanation of this situation that comes to mind is the possibility of salt enrichment of Cayuga and Seneca lakes by washings from the commercial plants. However, the water analyzed could not reflect localized influences from these operations, and it does not seem likely that salt losses from these plants could maintain such high concentrations throughout these large lakes. The samples analyzed were taken near the north end of Cayuga Lake and at the north end of Seneca—approximately 30 and 34 mi, respectively, from the nearest commercial installations. The salt enrichment required to build up and maintain the concentrations observed in these lakes can be approximated from the volumes of Cayuga and Seneca, 333 and 546 billion ft³, respectively (Birge and Juday, 1914), and the computation by Henson *et al.* (1961) that the water volume of Cayuga is being replaced by through-flow every nine years. The salt losses at the commercial plants seem completely inadequate to account for the maintenance of these high concentrations in the lakes.

Among the alternative · hypotheses available, one seems especially intriguing. The present maximum depths of Cayuga and Seneca lakes are 54 and 174 ft below sea level. None of the other Finger Lakes basins approaches such depths, the closest being Canandaigua with a maximum depth at 412 ft above sea level. It follows that salt strata or seepages of connate water at any depth between the surface and the bottom of Cayuga Lake would be intersected by both Cayuga and Seneca but not by any other lake in the region (Fig. 6.4). The greater concentrations of sodium and chloride in Seneca (about 1.4 times that of Cayuga for both ions) may reflect the fact that it intersects more horizontal strata.

Salt beds that did not satisfy standards of purity were found at lesser depths than the ones now being extracted. The possibility that the very deep basins of these two lakes may be intersecting the most superficial of these is plausible when the regional dip is considered. If it averages as much as 50 ft/mi, as some geologists believe, then the commercial salt bed that is only 1,087 ft below sea level at Myers (6 mi from the south end of Cayuga) should outcrop approximately at the north end of the lake. Indeed, there are salt springs at Howlands Island, just north of Cayuga, which may mark the outcropping of this stratum.

Any bed of lower grade salt superficial to this might well be intersected by the lake basin.

Some of the wells drilled near the south end of Cayuga Lake prove useless because of their high salt content. This evidence of salt slightly above, as well as below, the level of Cayuga Lake, even at its south end, seems significant in this context. The fact that it may be due to connate water rather than beds of crystallized salt does not negate the essential hypothesis that the great depths of Cayuga and Seneca lakes may expose them to influences from which the shallower lakes of the region are effectively isolated. This suggests a dimension in regional limnology that has not received much attention in the literature— the possibility that the chemistry of a lake can be affected significantly by the deep-lying strata intercepted by its basin as well as by the surficial lithology of its watershed.

The analyses from three shore-zone stations of Lake Ontario are given as the last three entries in Table 6.2. These three might have been averaged together as was done for the two Lake Erie stations, but it seems desirable to show how widely such figures can range in a lake of this size. The water of station Ontario-1 probably is more nearly representative of open lake conditions than either of the others. It was collected 100 ft offshore at Nine Mile Point, northeast of Oswego. The Ontario-2 sample was collected 300 ft out from the mouth of the Salmon River at Selkirk. The very low values obtained there for nearly all ions indicate that the lake water at that point is greatly diluted by the water of this Adirondack Foothills stream. Station Ontario-3 is west of Rochester in Braddock Bay, which is culturally enriched.

Four contrasting patterns of stratification

To provide a closer look at the contrasting limnological conditions in New York, four lakes regularly visited by limnology classes at Cornell University during recent years will be considered in somewhat greater detail.

Small, shallow Cayuta Lake was formed by the morainic damming of a preglacial valley (Von Engeln, 1961). It is stratified directly in summer and inversely, under the ice, in winter, and it circulates completely in spring and fall. Respiration and decomposition of organic matter use up all of the dissolved oxygen in the deepest waters during summer stratification. Thus, Cayuta

Fig. 6.5.—Cladophora balls at the shoreline of Cayuta Lake. Photo by J. F. Clovis.

serves as an example of the many dimictic, eutrophic lakes about which students read and provides a basis for comparison with the more unusual lakes visited.

One oddity of Cayuta Lake may deserve mention here. The green alga *Cladophora,* which is well known as either a felty covering layer or an unattached and much branched colony, forms very compact balls two inches and more in diameter in this lake (Fig. 6.5). This growth habit, not reported from many American lakes, is ascribed by some to a genetic variation, and it was once even regarded as sufficient basis for establishing a distinct genus. Others (Clovis, 1955) believe that the balls result from mechanical action as growing filaments are rolled back and forth over a gently sloping bottom by wave action. The fact that plant fibers, pine needles, and other non-living material have been found rolled into similar compact balls could be cited in support of this purely mechanical explanation.

Considerably more has been written about Cayuga Lake. The papers concerned with its physical limnology will be reviewed briefly here. With the other Finger Lakes, it was introduced into limnological literature in a classic study of Birge and Juday (1914). This paper is an outstanding contribution on the hydrography, temperature structures, annual heat budgets, dissolved oxygen, carbon dioxide, and net plankton of the ten lakes visited, changing them at once from limnological unknowns to some of the best known lakes in North America. It seems all the more remarkable when one considers how little time was spent in the field to gather data, how efficiently that time must have been spent, and how carefully and thoroughly the data were worked up to derive the maximum meaning from them.

A second and equally well-known paper on the Finger Lakes by these pioneer American limnologists (Birge and Juday, 1921) concentrates on Cayuga, Seneca, and Canandaigua lakes, with particular reference to heat budgets, heat distribution, and qualitative and quantitative plankton analyses, including nannoplankton.

The next major limnological contribution on Cayuga Lake (Burkholder, 1931) extends appreciably the knowledge of its phytoplankton and that of 12 minor lakes and ponds in its drainage basin. The information presented is both qualitative and quantitative, including data on seasonal and vertical distribution. In the introductory section useful data are given on the physical limnology of Cayuga and the smaller lakes and ponds, especially on temperature, transparency, and chemical factors. The first year-around study of the thermal structure of Cayuga is included in this section.

A second year-around study of temperatures in Cayuga Lake (Hess, 1940) corroborates Burkholder's conclusion that it normally experiences only two limnological "seasons" per year, summer stratification and winter circulation.

Henson (1959) published on evidence of internal waves, and Henson *et al.* (1961) presented the most complete account extant of the physical limnology of Cayuga Lake. As stated in Henson's introduction, "This publication is a compendium of the physical features of Cayuga Lake and its environment. It treats of the geological, meteorological, hydrological, and historical aspects of the Finger Lakes region, and summarizes three years of observations on the temperature, oxygen concentration, hydrogen-ion concentration, and alkalinity of Cayuga Lake. Temperature is considered to be the pivotal point for events in the lake, and the thermal aspects have been emphasized." The long bibliography helpfully brings together much widely scattered literature on Cayuga Lake, including many references in addition to those cited in the text.

A doctoral research project now being concluded on Cayuga Lake, the work of H. H. Howard on primary production, has included further observations on transparency and thermal structure.

Since the literature is confused with respect to the annual cycle of thermal stratification and circulation in Cayuga Lake, the essential facts should be presented briefly here. Even when the facts are known, it is impossible to place Cayuga anywhere in the best system of thermal classification of lakes, which makes no provision for such a cycle. Hence, a modification of the system is suggested.

Except in unusually cold years, Cayuga Lake remains open, in full circulation, and virtually homothermous throughout the winter (Fig. 6.6). The data of Burkholder (1931), Hess (1940), Henson *et al.* (1961), and Howard (personal communication) all agree on this conclusion. Although the water temperature dropped below 4° C every winter, the lake circulated completely throughout all six of the winters that it was under observation by these workers, developing ineffective and ephemeral stratification only during periods of unusually calm, cold weather. The lowest temperature series ever recorded for Cayuga Lake is Hess' record (1940 of homoiothermy at 1.3° C in April 1940. Summer stratification begins in May or June and continues until early November.

The confusion and misleading statements in the literature are difficult to explain. Birge and Juday (1914) stated correctly that Seneca and Cayuga lakes are rarely frozen except at the ends, and they listed only nine years since 1796 that Cayuga was known to have been frozen more nearly completely. Yet Needham and Lloyd (1916) indicated that the expected winter temperatures in Cayuga Lake are 0° C at the surface and 4° C at the bottom, and they discussed a dimictic annual cycle (one with inverse stratification in winter) as though it applied to Cayuga. Hutchinson's classification of Cayuga as a dimictic lake (1957, Fig. 132) may have been based on this misleading discussion.

The paper by Henson *et al.* (1961) contains a good description of the usual annual cycle of thermal stratification and circulation in Cayuga Lake, unfortunately followed by an untenable suggestion for its classification. The authors pointed out (p. 28) that although Hutchinson placed Cayuga as a first class, temperate, dimictic lake, it does not fit his definition because it does not normally have two periods of mixing per year. Then, evidently to create a category into which Cayuga's annual cycle would fit, they suggested 'that the term *dimictic* be defined on the basis of the water passing through the 4° threshold twice in a year without including the necessity

that the lake undergo an intermediate period of inverse stratification" (Henson *et al.*, 1961, p. 29).

However, *dimictic* clearly means having *two* periods of circulation per year. It would be inappropriate and very confusing to broaden this definition to include Cayuga and other lakes that have only one circulation period annually and normally experience no stable inverse stratification. This is exactly what the term *warm monomictic* is intended to convey.

The confusion of Henson and his associates stems from the fact that Cayuga does not fit into Hutchinson's definition of warm monomictic lakes, either. Hutchinson stated (1957, p. 438) *"warm monomictic* will be employed as a substitute for tropical, implying winter circulation above 4° C." That last restrictive phrase, an unfortunate holdover from the Forel system of thermal classification, eliminates from this category some of the best-known warm-stratifying lakes in the world that circulate only once each year. Cayuga, Seneca, all five of the St. Lawrence Great Lakes (except the shallow western end of Lake Erie, which freezes and establishes stable inverse stratification), and many other large, deep lakes in Europe, Japan, and Canada all cool below 4° C, yet they normally fail to develop effective inverse stratification and continue to circulate completely throughout the winter.

To set the lower limit of warm monomictic lakes precisely at 4° C is to assume that lakes which cool below that temperature can be expected to be inversely stratified *ipso facto*. They cannot be. Even dimictic lakes destined to freeze and develop a stable stratification of 4° water lying beneath colder, less dense water do not normally have bottom waters remaining constant at 4° while the upper waters cool to zero and freeze. Langmuir (1938) reported complete circulation in Lake George, New York, continuing into the autumn while the entire lake cooled, virtually homothermously, to about 1.2° before a covering of ice formed. This pattern, with subsequent warming of the lower waters to establish the typical temperature curve of inverse stratification, is known for several lakes. In fact, it is considered usual to have "a relatively long period of autumnal circulation until the lake is well below 4° C before freezing and winter stratification are established" (Hutchinson, 1957, p. 452). If this is usually true even of lakes known to be

A

frozen and stratified later in the winter, there seems to be no logical reason to expect non-freezing lakes to stratify as they cool through the thermal point of maximum density.

The recent data on Cayuga Lake indicate that the "4° threshold" has no practical effect on the autumnal circulation, and suggest that this concept has been generally overemphasized in limnology. All workers who obtained vertical temperature series in Cayuga throughout the year found that it becomes homothermous in the autumn at a point appreciably above 4°. Then it cools to well below this point with no noticeable change in its free and complete circulation pattern as it passes the "threshold." Thus, in Cayuga, the point of maximum density proves to be no threshold at all in the sense of controlling stratification or circulation, and this evidently is true also of other large, exposed lakes.

It is suggested that the phrase "above 4° C." in the quoted definition of warm monomictic lakes should be deleted and perhaps replaced by the simple stipulation that these lakes do not freeze over completely in most winters. Freezing must be prerequisite or corequisite to the establishment of stable inverse stratification in all large

lakes that are well exposed to fresh winds. Presence or absence of a complete ice cover is an easily observed criterion, and it would certainly have a higher correlation with winter-stratified versus winter-circulating lakes than the boundary now set at 4° C. The definition should be thus enlarged to include all lakes with annual cycles that include only warm (direct) stratification and one circulation period, regardless of whether or not they remain above 4° C throughout the year.

Oneida Lake, the largest lake entirely within New York State and "the most productive lake in the Northeastern States" according to fisheries biologists, has also been characterized by Mozley (1954) as "one of the most productive lakes I have seen on any continent." Studies have been made of the mollusks and other benthic animals (Baker, 1916, 1918) and the fish (Adams and Hankinson, 1928), and some data have been obtained on the physical limnology. Dence and Jackson (1959) pointed out that the total alkalinity expressed as $CaCO_3$ increased from an average value of 13.5 ppm in 1927 to 82 ppm in 1954. Together with this increase, there was an increase in organic seston from 2.25 mg/L in

Fig. 6.6.—Cayuga Lake on 3 February 1961, the sixteenth day of a severe cold wave (views northward). Official temperature records for the 16-day period show a high of 24° F, a low of —25° F, and three successive days (Feb. 1–3) on which the 24-hour means were below zero. The lake appeared from Ithaca to be completely frozen.

A (facing page): View from above the Cornell campus at south end of lake. Bend of lake to left, with delta of Salmon Creek jutting out from east shore just beyond, is 6 mi from south end.

B: From over the east shore at "big bend." Delta of Salmon Creek is in foreground, and patches of open water appear between it and Taughannock delta on west shore, middle distance.

C: From edge of ice, 5 mi beyond the bend, open water extends northward throughout the visible portion of the lake. Photos by the author.

1927 to 12.7 mg/L in 1954, as well as a change in phytoplankton dominance from diatoms in 1927 to blue-green algae in recent years, occasionally in densities that cause odor nuisances. Marked changes in the fish fauna also were reported.

Although separated from Cayuga by less than 40 mi and subjected to essentially the same climatic conditions, Oneida Lake has an annual cycle of thermal stratification and circulation essentially the opposite of that of Cayuga. The morphometric causes and the chemical and biological results of this contrasting circulation pattern are of considerable limnological interest.

Being shallow in relation to its great area (Table 6.1) and completely exposed to winds that sweep across the flat Lake Plain, Oneida Lake is so vigorously wind-swept that it continues to circulate completely throughout the summer whenever fresh winds blow. Muenscher (1928, p. 142) wrote, "Temperature records show that the water of Oneida lake becomes relatively warm rather early in the summer. The lake is too shallow to show any vertical stratification. At no time was the bottom temperature more than 4° C. colder than at the surface; in four out of six series of readings the bottom temperature was only about 0.5° lower than at the surface." Ten vertical series of temperature taken at different stations by J. L. Forney on 18 and 28 July and 9 and 18 August 1956 gave no gradient quite so high as 4°, and both series taken on 9 August showed homothermy at 24° C. Records from most other summers show similar situations, making it quite evident that Oneida Lake goes through most summers alternating between weak, ephemeral stratification and homothermy. In winter it freezes quite early and develops such a thick layer of ice that many of the fishermen elect to drive their cars right out onto it.

Lacking any stable stratification in summer, Oneida cannot be regarded as a dimictic lake. It is like cold monomictic lakes in having inverse stratification but no effective direct stratification and in having only one period of complete circulation annually, in summer. But Oneida is completely different biologically from the arctic-alpine lakes usually considered cold monomictic, its failure to stratify in summer being due to the warming of bottom waters as well as surface waters rather than the failure of any of the water to become very warm.

The obvious alternative to classifying it as cold monomictic is to regard Oneida as a "third order" lake, defined (Whipple, 1898, as quoted by Hutchinson, 1957, p. 439) as a lake "in which thermal stratification never develops, the whole lake remaining in circulation even in summer." Lakes of the third order are further characterized as "so shallow that they never stratify thermally." Students point out, however, that Oneida Lake is not too shallow to stratify inversely in winter, that it is more than twice as deep as the approximate maximum depth (25 ft) suggested by Whipple (1898) for third order lakes, and that there are many shallower lakes in New York that remain effectively stratified throughout the summer (Table 6.1). This dilemma can best be resolved by more emphasis on the relation between maximum depth and exposure to wind stirring (rather than on depth alone) as the essential determinant of summer stratification and by explicitly labeling the defined stratification as summer stratification only.

Instructive studies of Fayetteville Green Lake have been made by limnologists at the College of Forestry at Syracuse University. Eggleton's rather exhaustive study (1956) presents considerable information on its geological history, physiography and morphometry, biohermic deposits (Fig. 6.7), temperature structure, conductivity, color, transparency, dissolved oxygen, pH, alkalinity and free CO_2, and H_2S. Somewhat less is given on plankton, phytobenthos, and zoobenthos. Jackson and Dence (1958) published a brief analysis of primary productivity in this meromictic body of water.

Forested hills almost completely enclose this small, deep lake and shelter it so well from wind-stirring that waves as much as a foot high are rare. With this morphometry and degree of shelter, it was almost inevitable that this lake would sooner or later pass through periods of spring and fall homothermy without circulating completely. When this happened, a rich mineral content characteristic of lakes in the Limestone Belt concentrated especially in the stagnant lower waters, and a monimolimnion heavily loaded with dissolved salts developed.

In a class trip to Fayetteville Green Lake on 17 December 1956, water samples were collected at depths selected to show whether the abrupt changes in concentrations of dissolved salts expected at the chemocline really occur. Water was collected at 0, 18, 25, and 50 m, the first two being above the chemocline indicated by the oxygen and alkalinity data of Eggleton (1956) and the last two below it. Greater changes were expected between the 18 m and the 25 m strata than between any other strata in the vertical series, despite the fact that they were much closer together in vertical distance. The Soils Testing Laboratory at Cornell University ran quantitative analyses for certain selected ions, the results of which are recorded in Table 6.3. These were in the nature of preliminary tests and no fine de-

Fig. 6.7.—Marl shelf extending far out over the transparent water at Dead Man's Point, Fayetteville Green Lake. Photo by D. E. Koob.

gree of precision is claimed. Yet all 0 and 18 m values are in approximate agreement with those recorded for surface waters of this lake by chemists of the U.S. Geological Survey and the New York State Department of Commerce (Table 6.2), and the trends shown in the deeper waters seem interesting enough to warrant publication. All ions analyzed except NO_3 are more concentrated below the chemocline than above it. The sharp decrease in NO_3 in the monimolimnion is to be expected because of the low redox potential there.

Occurrence of the four contrasting circulation patterns illustrated by Cayuta, Cayuga, Oneida, and Fayetteville Green lakes all within a 40-mi radius provides an unusual opportunity to observe the limnological importance of morphometric characteristics and relative exposure to wind-stirring.

Cornell University

A course entitled "General Limnology" was initiated at Cornell University by the late Professor James G. Needham in 1908. He wrote (Needham, 1946), "In 1907 I returned to join the staff of the Department as Assistant Professor of Limnology. It was given to me to initiate a new course of university instruction, and to break ground in a little developed field. . . . My own special field of limnological research was to be the biology of fresh water insects, and that justified my placement in a department of entomology."

Being an exceptionally enthusiastic student of the aquatic insects, Needham also was very successful in stimulating similar interests in others. Some of North America's outstanding students of aquatic insects were trained at Cornell during the period of his active service there, and the list of Cornell contributions on these insects includes at least one major work on every important group. When Professor Comstock retired as the first head of the Department of Entomology in 1914, he recommended that Needham be appointed to succeed him. Professor Needham filled this important position effectively from then until his own retirement in 1936. Needham was one of the founders of the Limnological Society of America and its second president in 1937. Included among his other honors were presidency of the Entomological Society of America in 1919 and vice-presidency of the Ecological Society of America in 1936.

With the addition to the staff of such men as O. A. Johannsen (aquatic Diptera), J. T. Lloyd (Trichoptera), Robert Matheson (medical entomology), and P. W. Claassen (Plecoptera), the Department of Entomology at Cornell became one of the world's greatest assemblages of aquatic entomologists. G. C. Embody joined the department in 1911 and broadened the work in freshwater biology with his course and research work in aquiculture.

Outstanding publications on aquatic insects from Cornell faculty and graduate students concern the Plecoptera (Needham and Claassen,

TABLE 6.3

Distribution of certain ions (in ppm) above and below the chemocline in Fayetteville Green Lake, 17 December 1956

Depths (m)	Ca	Mg	Na	K	Mn	Alkalinity (total)	Cl	NO_3	pH
0	481	79	13	3	.01	143	24	4.4	7.8
18	474	86	13	3	.02	163	31	4.8	7.8
25	615	118	25	5	.30	266	59	0.6	7.0
50	627	106	29	5	.22	343	58	0.2	7.2

1925; Claassen, 1931, 1940), Ephemeroptera (Needham *et al.*, 1935), Odonata (Needham and Heywood, 1929; Needham and Westfall, 1955), aquatic Hemiptera (Hungerford, 1919), aquatic Diptera (Johannsen, 1934, 1935, 1937*a*, 1937*b*; Alexander, 1920; Townes, 1945), and Trichoptera (Lloyd, 1921; Betten, 1934).

Notable contributions on other freshwater organisms are devoted to the aquatic plants (Moore, 1915; Muenscher, 1944) and freshwater biota in general (Morgan, 1930; Needham and Needham, 1962).

Although Cornell pioneered in aquatic biology and produced students who have distinguished themselves by noteworthy contributions, relatively little of this work has been in the field that is now the central focus of limnology. It was left for Birge and Juday to initiate research on the physical limnology of the Finger Lakes. Even after this subject had been opened by their two excellent studies (Birge and Juday, 1914, 1921), it was not immediately taken up at Cornell. The freshwater biologists on this campus evidently were more interested in, and preoccupied by, their own excellent research. Those concerned exclusively with the aquatic insects were not very much interested in work on the Finger Lakes, the insect faunas of which are not nearly so rich as those of the many ponds, marshes, and streams of this region. As interest developed in fish and fisheries, more and more work was done on these lakes, especially on Cayuga, but only a small part of this would be called limnology today. The comparatively minor emphasis originally placed on limnology in the strict sense is attested to by the professional careers followed by students with advanced degrees in freshwater sciences from Cornell. Famous ichthyologists and entomologists began to emerge nearly a century ago—David Starr Jordan in 1872 and John Henry Comstock in 1874. By contrast, no graduate student from Cornell undertook a professional career in limnology until less than a decade ago.

Dr. Needham was succeeded in the limnology course by C. McC. Mottley, A. D. Hess, D. A. Webster, D. C. Chandler, and the writer. There was a major shift in emphasis from the natural history of aquatic insects and fish to physical limnology when D. C. Chandler began to teach the course in 1949. Since then, much of the general limnology course, most of the advanced course, and the doctoral investigations of one

student (Maciolek, 1961) have dealt exclusively with physical limnology. Other doctoral problems have been biological, at least in part, but clearly in the realm of limnology as distinguished from natural history studies (Lauff, 1953; Henson, 1954; and the plankton studies of Bradshaw, Cowell, and Howard, still in progress).

At the same time, efforts are again being made to emphasize the area in which the Department of Entomology and Limnology has traditionally done its outstanding freshwater work—research in the natural history of aquatic insects. Student demand for such studies continues at a high level, and Cornell is peculiarly well qualified to help satisfy that demand. The writer's own research has been chiefly on the natural history of aquatic insects, with particular emphasis currently on a group of semi-aquatic flies having larvae that kill and consume snails (Berg, 1961). His graduate students have studied natural history of aquatic insects (Flint, 1960; Neff, 1960; Foote, 1961) and mollusks (Clarke and Berg, 1959), as well as the topics currently regarded as more strictly limnological.

Studies of the natural history of aquatic insects have resulted in many conclusions of considerable interest to limnologists, but most of the papers concerned are published in entomological journals where limnologists do not find them. Although space does not permit any extensive review of this literature here, a single example which recalls the Pütter hypothesis may point up the limnological significance that some entomological studies have and the great need for better liaison between these two fields.

Microorganisms and particulate organic matter had been considered essential in the nutrition of mosquito larvae until Cornell entomologist Hinman (1930) demonstrated the development of *Aedes aegypti* in pond water filtered through a Berkefeld filter. Hinman may not have eliminated the possibility of subsequent invasion of the filtrate by bacteria on which the larvae could have fed, but later experiments by Trager (1936) and others removed all doubt that these larvae can develop in media containing no particulate matter. Work of these researchers has stimulated interest outside of the Middle Atlantic States, and a considerable literature has accumulated. It is now generally believed that most mosquito larvae depend, in part at least, on dissolved food materials. Lea *et al.* (1956) reared *A. aegypti* larvae through to emergence of normal adults in a chemically defined medium consisting of amino acids, vitamins, glucose, cholesterol, and salts. A more recent study (Singh and Micks, 1958) is concerned with the effects of larval development and metabolism on the chemical composition of the medium.

Some of the studies most closely related to limnology are carried out in the Department of Conservation at Cornell, which was formed in the College of Agriculture in 1949. The staff men particularly concerned are J. P. Barlow (oceanography), E. C. Raney (ichthyology), A. M. Phillips (fish culture and nutrition), and D. A. Webster, A. W. Eipper, J. L. Forney, and W. A. Flick (fisheries biology). Barlow's studies of eutrophication in highly enriched brackish waters of the Long Island estuaries that receive drainage from duck ponds parallel much freshwater research on polluted situations (Barlow and Myren, 1961). Barlow also is sponsoring student research on limnetic zooplankton of Cayuga Lake, with particular reference to the relation of respiratory rates to age distribution of the population. Phillips' studies on the influence of the composition of water (especially its calcium content) on metabolism of trout and their direct absorption of dissolved substances are well known (Phillips *et al.*, 1961, and earlier papers in this series). Because of his fisheries work in the Finger Lakes and in lakes of the Adirondacks, Webster has become interested in the limnology of these waters (Webster, 1954, 1961) and has sponsored some student research in this field (Hatch and Webster, 1961). Forney (1957) has investigated the chemical characteristics of New York farm ponds, and Eipper's study (1959) of the effects of herbicides on plants and fish in farm ponds includes additional notes on physical and chemical conditions.

J. M. Kingsbury, Department of Botany, sponsors some limnologically oriented student research as an outgrowth of his fine work in phycology (Koob, 1959; Mason, 1961).

Two men now in the Department of Zoology have directed student research in limnological problems, and one also carries on important limnological research of his own. L. C. Cole (animal ecology and biometrics) has directed several limnologically oriented doctoral problems (Potash, 1956; Maguire, 1959; McManus, 1960). J. R. Vallentyne (limnology and biogeochemistry) is

studying the decomposition of organic compounds (especially proteins, amino acids, chlorophylls, and carotenoids) in lake waters and sediments and is directing student research on sedimentation and the banding of sediments in Cayuga Lake. Vallentyne is well known among limnologists for his studies of organic matter in fossils and lake sediments (Jones and Vallentyne, 1960) and his use of sedimented pigments in interpreting lacustrine history (Vallentyne, 1957; Vallentyne and Swabey, 1955). Since his field of interest and competence is not represented by anyone else at Cornell, his appointment here has filled a lacuna, modernized the outlook, and helped to establish a balance between natural history studies and physical limnology.

The preceding list of staff men who are interested and competent in at least some phase of limnology is long but by no means exhaustive. Limnology at Cornell is no longer restricted to a single department and dominated by one towering personality. Here, as elsewhere, the subject has outgrown departmental bounds. Various phases of it are studied in many departments, each of which alone possesses the background and technical skills now required for competent pursuit of the limnological problems in its subject area. As all aspects of this broad field have become more technical and abstruse, limnologists have increasingly sought expert guidance in other disciplines.

The newly approved Field of Water Resources at Cornell is sponsored cooperatively by the Departments of Agricultural Economics, Agricultural Engineering, Conservation, Economics, Entomology and Limnology, Geology, Hydraulics, Regional Planning, and Sanitary Engineering. This program supplies an interdisciplinary approach to a problem that increases in urgency every year in the Middle Atlantic States. Although the region has a good supply of rainfall, well distributed throughout the year, there are local and temporal shortages, especially in centers of population and industrial development. Pollution problems are far more widespread than are shortages, and the maintenance of water quality is becoming more and more difficult and expensive. The current awareness of this problem in the region is indicated by the books published on it recently (Blake, 1956; Bordne, 1960; Martin *et al.*, 1960), by the 1959 action of the New York State Legislature, which created the Temporary

State Commission on Water Resources Planning, and by the Water Resources Planning Law that was enacted recently, following the recommendations of that commission (New York Temporary State Comm. on Water Resources Planning, 1960).

New York State Museum

The New York State Museum is outstanding among state institutions in North America in the production of authoritative papers on natural history. Among the biological, geological, and ethnological papers published, some are devoted exclusively to fresh waters and their biotas, and many more include incidental discussions of these matters.

The State Museum was organized, in 1836, as the State Geology and Natural History Survey, a name that is still retained for the comparable institution in some states. The original staff of seven men included James E. DeKay, zoologist, who wrote the text for the *Zoology of New York* (1842–44). This five-volume work on the mammals, birds, reptiles, amphibians, fishes, mollusks, and crustaceans established a foundation on which the many subsequent works could build.

In 1845 the Regents of the University of the State of New York were placed in charge of the State Cabinet of Natural History, the antecedent of the State Museum. Annual Reports of the Regents on the State Cabinet of Natural History (later the Science Division and still later the State Museum) were published from 1848 through 1944. The State Cabinet of Natural History officially became the New York State Museum of Natural History in 1870.

The museum acquired the collection of fishes made in the New York State Conservation Department's extensive biological survey of lakes and streams in the 1920's and 1930's. The number of specimens may total near 70,000, and this collection has been termed "the finest and most valuable state fish collection extant" (Palmer, 1953).

The many fine publications of the State Museum are of even more interest to limnologists than are its extensive holdings of aquatic animals and plants. Major early papers in this category concern the mollusks (Marshall, 1895; Letson, 1905), fishes (Bean, 1903), aquatic insects (Needham and Betten, 1901; Needham *et al.,* 1903, 1905; Felt, 1904), higher Crustacea (Paul

mier, 1905), hydrology (Rafter, 1905), and glacial waters and evolution of drainage systems (Fairchild, 1909, 1925). The recent works probably of greatest interest to limnologists are devoted to Trichoptera (Betten, 1934), blackflies (Stone and Jamnback, 1955), crayfishes (Crocker, 1957), and pondweeds (Ogden, 1953). Limitations of space do not permit the listing of lesser papers devoted to fresh waters and their biotas. Many of these, as well as major publications concerned only incidentally with limnological matters, are cited in bibliographies of the papers listed above.

Other limnologists, institutions,
and lakes of New York

It has proved impossible to integrate this section, summarizing unrelated bits of information from widely scattered points around the state. The order of presentation is a geographic one, progressing from west to east across New York.

While employed from 1930 to 1939 as an instructor in biology at the University of Buffalo, W. L. Tressler probably contributed as much as any other individual has contributed to limnological information on the lakes of New York State. He participated in the biological surveys of the State Conservation Department in 1931, 1933, 1934, 1935, 1936, and 1937, serving as director of either the limnology division or the plankton division during the last five of those years. In these surveys, he made significant contributions to knowledge of several lakes, including Chautauqua, a warm, eutrophic lake near the southwest corner of New York that has been famous for muskellunge fishing (Tressler and Bere, 1938). Later, he chose Chautauqua Lake for one of the early year-round surveys of limnological conditions (Tressler *et al.,* 1940). Tressler launched a course in limnology at the University of Buffalo, and he wrote his well-known chapter in *Problems in Lake Biology* while teaching there (Tressler, 1939). He joined the staff of the University of Maryland in 1940, where he helped to organize a course in hydrobiology. Since 1950, he has been connected with the Navy Hydrographic Office.

Chautauqua Lake is typical of the many lakes in North America that are developing acute problems because of too much cultural enrichment. The dense and extensive growths of aquatic plants detract greatly from the enjoyment of fishing and swimming, and the great swarms of midges (Fig. 6.8) make life around the lake almost intolerable on some summer evenings. Bay (1960) considers that midge control by extensive larviciding may be feasible but possibly not advisable, particularly since the seasons when midge populations will reach problem proportions cannot be predicted in advance on the basis of present knowledge.

No one at the University of Buffalo is now interested primarily in limnology, and the course is not being taught there currently (C. M. Osborn, personal communication). The present course in aquatic biology includes some of the subject matter once covered in limnology.

Another institution in Buffalo, Canisius College, has become known among limnologists because of the phycological studies of J. L. Blum (1956, 1960). Blum's work on the ecology of algae in rivers and streams is quite noteworthy.

The State Conservation Department's program of flooding unproductive wetlands to create waterfowl marshes has led to interesting new information on the biochemical changes induced in the soils and waters soon after flooding (Cook and Powers, 1958). Pronounced thermal and chemical stratification was recorded in water averaging only three feet in depth. Excessive concentrations of iron and manganese, evidently toxic to *Potamogeton* and other duck food plants, were noted. Occasional drainage was recommended, with aeration of the marsh soils to reduce their capacity to produce conditions favoring the solution of these substances.

W. A. Dence has taught a course in limnology every fall for many years at the College of Forestry at Syracuse. Dence's limnological work has been primarily on lakes near Syracuse (Jackson and Dence, 1958; Dence and Jackson, 1959).

Staff men in the Department of Civil Engineering at Syracuse University are interested in pollution problems in Oneida Lake and are making a study of chemical and microbiological conditions there.

Of the papers of G. J. Schumacher, phycologist at Harpur College, Endicott, his recent study of the effect of current on mineral uptake and respiration (Whitford and Schumacher, 1961) is of greatest interest limnologically. "Inherent current demand" is ascribed to the need for rapid exchange of materials with the water, a conclusion that may have general applicability to stream-

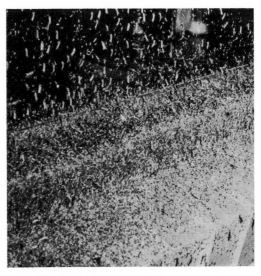

Fig. 6.8.—Two-hour accumulation of midges on window and window sill, Chautauqua Lake, 1959. Photo by E. C. Bay.

inhabiting organisms said to exhibit this phenomenon.

R. M. Crowell, St. Lawrence University, Canton, has recently compiled a catalogue of the distribution and ecological relationships of North American water mites, which many limnologists would find useful (Crowell, 1961).

Frey (1953) included Vassar College, Poughkeepsie, as one of the institutions in the United States offering a course in limnology. M. E. Pierce indicates that this course is now called ecology but that the emphasis is still decidedly limnological (personal communication). Her research concerns the effects of aquatic herbicides on benthic and planktonic organisms (Pierce, 1961).

Limnologists at Yale University have visited Queechy, Glenida, Sylvan, George, and Canada Lakes in eastern and southeastern New York and have learned a great deal about them (see Oana and Deevey, 1960, and earlier papers by Deevey and others). Queechy Lake, in the Slate Belt near the New York-Massachusetts boundary, has been studied intensively over many years as a convenient hard-water lake of a type that is rare in Connecticut. The very significant contributions made by the Yale group on bottom fauna, redox potential, regional limnology, copepod encystment, carbon-13, carbon-14, and sulfur-34 studies, pollen stratigraphy, and lacustrine history are too well known among limnologists to require any summary here. Reference to this work is given in the chapter on New England.

Pennsylvania

The occurrence of lakes in Pennsylvania is limited by the fact that a relatively small proportion of the state was glaciated. The Gazetteer of Lakes and Ponds of the *Water Resources Inventory Report* (Pennsylvania Water Supply Comm., 1917*b*) lists 424 bodies of water, but their combined area totals only 23,531 acres or less than 0.001 of the area of Pennsylvania. Of the 254 lakes larger than 20 acres listed in this gazetteer, 241 are in the northeastern portion of the state, and 9 of the remaining 13 are in the northwestern part. The concentration of lakes in these glaciated sections and their almost complete absence in the large unglaciated area indicate that glacial processes have been the dominant means of producing lake basins in recent geological time.

Table 6.4 is based on data in the Gazetteer of Lakes and Ponds. It shows that Conneaut Lake, near the northwestern corner of Pennsylvania, has the greatest surface area of any natural lake in the state. However, Harvey Lake is much deeper and has a greater volume. All lakes listed in this table except Conneaut are in the northeastern quarter of Pennsylvania. Some of the data given, especially those for mean depth and volume, are only approximate. Artificial lakes were included in this part of the *Water Resources Inventory Report* unless they served primarily as storage reservoirs. The latter are discussed in Parts 6 and 7 of the inventory report, devoted to water supply and water power, respectively. Since many storage reservoirs were thus excluded

from the Gazetteer of Lakes and Ponds, and since many more reservoirs have been impounded since 1917, the total surface area of lakes, ponds, and impoundments in Pennsylvania now is much greater than the 23,531 acres indicated in this gazetteer. Indeed, a single reservoir impounded since that time, Pymatuning, has a surface area equal to about two-thirds of that total.

Limnologists may be interested also in the Gazetteer of Streams (Pennsylvania Water Supply Comm., 1917*a*), which lists 4,419 named streams and gives for each the location of source and of mouth, the length, course, and rate of fall, the stream to which it is tributary, the basin or sub-basin, the drainage area, and the topography and geology of the region.

There is no comprehensive biological survey of the streams and lakes of Pennsylvania. The Pennsylvania Fish Commission has undertaken surveys of some lakes and streams to diagnose conditions before making recommendations for improvement of fishing, but these have not been published. Reports on individual lakes, most of them written in a popular style to interest sports fishermen, are scattered through the literature. But overall watershed appraisals, such as those given in the biological surveys of the New York State Conservation Department, have not been made.

Extensive chemical analyses of stream waters were undertaken by cooperative efforts of state agencies and the U.S. Geological Survey, and several reports on the industrial utility of surface waters have been published (see Beamer, 1953). For each stream surveyed, these reports give rate of flow, temperature, color, pH, conductivity, total dissolved solids, total and car-

TABLE 6.4

Largest Pennsylvania lakes listed in 1917 Gazetteer

Lake or pond	Area (acres)	Maximum depth (ft)	Mean depth (ft)	Volume (acre-ft)	Drainage (mi²)	Elevation (ft)	County
Conneaut Lake (Natural)	928	65	34	17160	27.9	1072	Crawford
Harvey Lake (Natural)	658	102	50	23732	7.2	1226	Luzerne
Shohola Falls Dam (Artificial)	570	11	6	2164	60.0	1151	Pike
Pocono Lake (Artificial)	510	27	9	4248	79.0	1636	Monroe
Promise Lake Pond (Artificial)	422	15	10	2349	3.5	1727	Pike
Crystal Lake (Natural)	420	—	—	5085	2.3	1937	Luzerne
Pecks Pond (Artificial)	300	8	4	810	8.0	1149	Pike
Lake Jean (Natural)	296	20	10	—	3.5	2220	Luzerne & Sullivan
Stillwater Lake (Artificial)	272	10	6	1334	14.2	1814	Monroe
Lake Carey (Natural)	263	34	22	3782	4.5	915	Wyoming

bonate hardness, and the concentrations of each of 13 common ions.

The seriousness of pollution in thickly populated and heavily industrialized Pennsylvania is indicated by the large proportion of research in the state devoted to pollution problems and by the existence there of the only commercial agency in the United States offering consulting services in aquatic biology as a business. The work of "Consulting Biologists" in Philadelphia has been predominantly on pollution, with particular reference to heated effluents (Wurtz and Dolan, 1960). C. B. Wurtz believes (personal communication) that businesses of this sort will expand markedly during the coming decade.

Four institutions should be mentioned in connection with teaching and research in general limnology in Pennsylvania. These are the University of Pittsburgh, the Academy of Natural Sciences of Philadelphia, Lehigh University, and the Pennsylvania State University.

Pennsylvania State University

A course in general limnology that was started in 1939 is being taught by E. L. Cooper at the Pennsylvania State University. Cooper's research interests are largely in the field of fish ecology and behavior (Cooper, 1959). B. G. Anderson, also of the Department of Zoology and Entomology at Pennsylvania State University, has made several important studies on the biology of *Daphnia,* including work on toxicity thresholds (Anderson 1948). A recent doctoral thesis from this department (Boyd, 1957) on the use of *Daphnia* in the bioassay of insecticides is a logical extension of Anderson's earlier studies.

University of Pittsburgh

Limnological work at the University of Pittsburgh includes basic research in general limnology conducted at the Pymatuning Laboratory and studies of more applied aspects made in Pittsburgh at the main campus and at the Mellon Institute.

The Pymatuning Laboratory (Fig. 6.9) was established in 1949 at Pymatuning Reservoir near Linesville, Pennsylvania, by the University of Pittsburgh. The program of the laboratory consists entirely of instruction and research in ecology, with special emphasis on limnology.

Pymatuning Reservoir is located on the state line, partly in Crawford County, Pennsylvania, and partly in Ashtabula County, Ohio. It is a shallow, eutrophic, and highly productive body of water that was created in 1934 by two dams on the Shenango River. A reservoir of approximately 13,000 acres is impounded by the main (lower) dam, and one of about 2,500 acres is held by the upper dam. This upper lake lies entirely within a waterfowl sanctuary not open to the public. It is on this Sanctuary Lake that Pymatuning Laboratory is located. The two basins of the main lake are almost completely separated by a causeway, and the entire reservoir is commonly regarded as comprising three distinct lakes. The land now under impoundment was an extensive swamp thought to represent the last evolutionary stage of a glacial lake (Shepps *et al.,* 1959). The first limnological study of this reservoir (Tryon and Jackson, 1952) describes it in greater detail.

Near the reservoir are extensive swamps and marshes, smaller lakes, and several bog ponds and pothole ponds. Conneaut Lake, the largest natural lake in Pennsylvania, is only 12 mi to the east, and Lake Erie is only 40 mi to the north. Jutting out from the south shore of Lake Erie, the sandspit of Presque Isle provides ponds of known ages from two years to 300 years. The Allegheny River, the upper Ohio River, the Shenango River, and several smaller streams are within working distance of the laboratory. Stripmine ponds are found in some of the area to the east and south.

Independent investigators are encouraged to work at the laboratory, where table space and living accomodations can be obtained. Boats and motors and considerable limnological field and laboratory equipment are available.

Two of the most notable contributions from this productive laboratory are the symposia, *Man and the Waters of the Upper Ohio Basin* (Tryon and Shapiro, 1956) and *The Ecology of Algae* (Tryon and Hartman, 1960). The former points up the great changes wrought by man's activities on quality and quantity of water resources in this area. *The Ecology of Algae* is of value particularly because of the thorough reviews of the recent literature made by each contributor and the fine lists of references that have resulted.

A brief discussion of the research of the men on the permanent laboratory staff will indicate some of the major emphases at Pymatuning. The

Fig. 6.9.—View (southwestward) of Pymatuning Reservoir. Sanctuary Lake makes up foreground and left side of picture; Middle Lake is right of causeway. State Fish Hatchery is in foreground, Pymatuning Laboratory on second point extending from causeway into Sanctuary Lake (with laboratory buildings hidden by trees). Photo by courtesy of C. A. Tryon, Jr.

director, C. A. Tryon, Jr., is studying fish productivity in impoundments of the upper Ohio River in connection with primary productivity studies of these impoundments. Standardized unit trawl catches of several common species of fish are being made, and instantaneous growth rates of individuals are being determined.

R. T. Hartman has studied seasonal changes in the phytoplankton of Pymatuning Reservoir (Hartman and Graffius, 1960) and the persistence of reservoir phytoplankton in downstream areas of the Shenango River (Hartman and Himes, 1961). His chapter on algae and their metabolites in natural waters in Tryon and Hartman (1960) is documented with many examples of effects of metabolites on freshwater organisms from the literature and from his own research. Field studies have been coupled with laboratory studies in an investigation of the production of extracellular metabolites by algae and their role in influencing the development and composition of natural phytoplankton communities.

E. J. Kormondy has contributed significantly to knowledge of the ecology, life history, and systematics of the Odonata (Kormondy, 1959). Studies of this group are continuing, with particular emphasis on phenology and emergence rates. Kormondy is also pursuing an investigation of the physical, chemical, and biological characteristics of the evolutionary series of ponds on Presque Isle sandspit. Working primarily with vascular plants, mollusks, and arthropods in these ponds, he hopes to correlate stages in succession, productivity levels, physical and chemical properties, and species compositions.

R. C. Dugdale is interested in cycles of nitrogen and other important nutrients in lakes. He has studied sources of phosphorus and nitrogen in lakes of Alaska (Dugdale and Dugdale, 1961), and he is currently working on cycles of nitrogen and associated elements at Pymatuning. The uptake of molybdenum by phytoplankton in Pymatuning Reservoir, where a seasonal depletion of this element occurs, is being compared with the nitrogen-fixing activity. Dugdale is leaving on 1 September 1962 to join the staff of the Institute of Marine Science of the University of Alaska.

Instructive studies also have been made in Pymatuning Reservoir on the limnetic Cladocera (Borecky, 1956), the heterotrophic bacteria (Morgan and Gainor, 1960), and the protozoan populations (Orr, 1954).

Some of the limnological studies based at the main campus of the University of Pittsburgh concern radioactive wastes and their effects on aquatic organisms. W. J. Woods studied composition and productivity of aquatic ecosystems of the upper Ohio River there recently with a grant from the Atomic Energy Commission. Woods left Pittsburgh 1 June 1962 to go into marine research at the University of North Carolina.

The important problems created by industrial pollution of natural waters, with particular reference to acid drainage from coal mines, seem to be more or less centered in Pennsylvania. It is, therefore, appropriate that an institution in this state, the Mellon Institute of Industrial Research of the University of Pittsburgh, evidently is doing the most research on this subject.

In a broad survey of the fundamental research projects at the Mellon Institute on water pollution abatement, Hoak (1954) discussed pollution problems created by the pickle liquor and other wastes of the steel industry and by cyanides in plating-waste water, and the steps taken to solve these problems. Hoak has contributed several other published papers on water supply and pollution control, including special reference to the origin of tastes and odors in drinking water (Hoak, 1957) and the physical and chemical behavior of suspended solids (Hoak, 1959). In papers presented orally but apparently not yet published, he has discussed the thermal pollution problem and diel variation of dissolved oxygen in seven natural streams of western Pennsylvania. In the latter, he found surprisingly high concentrations of dissolved oxygen, even at night, in streams considered moderately to heavily polluted.

S. A. Braley has probably given more study than anyone else to the problem of acid mine drainage (Braley, 1954). He has concluded (Pennsylvania Sanit. Water Board, 1951) that neutralization of these wastes is uneconomical and impractical, and he has turned his attention instead to abatement of acid by "mine sealing."

His laboratory studies of the oxidation of pyritic conglomerates (Braley, 1960) demonstrated that forms of FeS_2 naturally associated with veins of coal will oxidize to produce $FeSO_4$ and H_2SO_4 when exposed to the air. Thus, the source of acid drainage seems to be the exposure of iron pyrites in open (especially abandoned) mines and the dissolution of the resultant acid in water flowing through the mines.

The problem of acid mine wastes is elucidated further by studies of W. W. Leathen concerned with the bacterial inhabitants of mine effluents and their role in acid formation. Leathen found that two autotrophic bacteria were invariably present in effluents from bituminous coal mines (Leathen, 1953). The sulfur-oxidizing *Thiobacillus thiooxidans* does not enhance acid formation of the most common sulfurous constituent present, but a hitherto unknown bacterium that oxidizes iron compounds contributes appreciably to the total acidity of mine waters. Measures to inhibit bacterial activity within the mine were suggested.

The Academy of Natural Sciences of Philadelphia

Research contributions of the Limnology Department at the Academy of Natural Sciences of Philadelphia were kindly summarized by Dr. Ruth Patrick, Chairman. The following is quoted with her permission.

The first scientific group to become actively interested in limnology in Pennsylvania was the Academy of Natural Sciences of Philadelphia which established a Limnology Department in 1948. The main research contributions of this department have been as follows:

Population structure of species

1. In natural rivers the various major groups of aquatic organisms are represented by numerous species most of which have relatively small populations. The numbers of species do not change a great deal in a given area under seasonal changes although the kinds of species vary greatly. The effect of pollution is to reduce the numbers of species in certain groups (fish, insects, lower invertebrates and diatoms) and often some of the more tolerant species develop large populations. These findings were set forth by Patrick in 1949.

2. Subsequent work has shown that in the rivers of eastern United States and adjacent areas, the numbers of collectable species of the major systematic groups of organisms (algae, protozoa, lower invertebrates, insects and fish) in similar ecological areas are quite similar although the kinds of species vary greatly. It is believed that this similarity in

numbers of species is due to the fact that the numbers of niches for species occupancy are similar. The great variation in kinds of species collected at any given time even in the same area is due in part to the fact that the number of species available to occupy these niches is greater than the number of niches. Thus any change in the environment will favor one as opposed to another. As a result the one not so well suited to the immediate environmental conditions will not be able to compete and its populations will be greatly reduced or eliminated.

3. The structure of each diatom population has been shown to closely simulate a normal curve and the sample collected is a truncated normal curve. These findings are in line with the findings stated above for other forms of aquatic life. That is the population is composed of many species most of them composed of fairly small populations. A few are more common than the rest and a few are very rare (Patrick, Hohn and Wallace, 1954).

*The establishment of the fauna and
flora in a new stream area*

The establishment of the fauna and flora in a new stream area as well as the development of the area physically and chemically have been studied. The results of these studies show that the establishment of a fauna in a new area is dependent on the laying of eggs in the area or the invasion of hundreds of very small organisms from upstream areas. The establishment of a fauna is very precarious and necessitates the attempt to live in an area of a great many more individuals of a species than those that are successful. Although larvae of various ages drift downstream they do not establish a fauna in the new area. The organisms with the shortest reproductive cycles were those which most quickly established a normal complement of species.

The bed of the river is the slowest part of a river to develop. The changes toward the development of a substrate similar to that in a natural river bed occur faster in the slack water areas than in the areas of fast moving water. The bacteria in the soil under fast moving water is a few orders of magnitude less than that in soil under slow moving water.

A brief summary of the limnological interests of the professional staff will indicate some additional work of this department. Along with her investigations of biological indicators of stream conditions mentioned above (Patrick, 1949, 1961), Dr. Patrick is well known for her studies of the systematics, ecology, and distribution of diatoms. She wrote the chapter on Bacillariophyceae in the revised edition of *Fresh-water Biology* (Patrick, 1959) and has cooperated in a recent study of the diatoms of northern Alaska (Patrick and Freese, 1960). Earlier papers, including other important regional studies of diatoms, are cited in these recent works.

Francis Drouet has made significant contributions on the blue-green algae (Drouet and Daily, 1956). With support from the National Science Foundation, he is now studying the Oscillatoriaceae.

John Cairns, Jr., and Arthur Scheier have worked primarily on toxicity of various chemicals to aquatic organisms and the ways in which toxicity is affected by temperature, hardness of water, and other variables (Cairns and Scheier, 1957, 1958). W. S. Hart is working on taxonomic and other aspects of freshwater Crustacea. C. W. Reimer is studying the taxonomy and distribution of diatoms (Reimer, 1959a, 1959b). S. S. Roback is best known in limnological circles for his work on chironomid larvae (Roback, 1953, 1957).

In addition to the hydrobiologists listed above, there are a few whose studies concern brackish and marine species exclusively and a few who are employed elsewhere during the academic year but work routinely at the academy during the summer. One of the latter, Dr. Mary Gojdics, is well known because of her book on the genus *Euglena* (Gojdics, 1953). The Limnology Department trains an average of three or four college students every summer, and a Ph.D. student of the diatoms is usually studying there.

Because of the research on effects of temperature and various chemicals common in industrial wastes on aquatic organisms, the Limnology Department of the Academy of Natural Sciences is well qualified to evaluate the conditions in rivers used for waste disposal. This special knowledge was put to practical use in 1957, when the Limnology Department was requested to make biological studies of the Delaware River for the Interstate Commission on the Delaware River (Incodel). "Diatometer" studies, biological surveys of all groups of aquatic organisms, and studies of fish populations were used to judge the suitability of the river to support aquatic life (Acad. Nat. Sci. Philadelphia, Limnol. Dept., 1959). The former method involves an assessment of the numbers and kinds of diatoms that attach to clean glass slides suspended in the water (Fig. 6.10) and the computation of a ratio of the number of species to the number of individuals in the dominant species. It offers an approach to the difficult problem of bioassay of conditions in a river, which requires a minimum of time and effort for the collecting of samples.

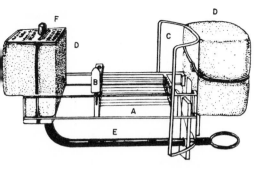

Fig. 6.10.—The "Catherwood Diatometer," a device for suspending clean glass slides in the river for attachment of diatoms and other periphytic organisms. *A*, slide holder; *B*, retaining bar; *C*, deflector; *D*, styrofoam float; *E*, brass rod for attachment; *F*, identification tag. From Acad. Nat. Sci., Philadelphia, Limnology Dept., 1959.

Lehigh University

B. B. Owen, who has been engaged with F. J. Trembley and B. W. Parker in the limnological research at Lehigh University, has kindly written a report of that work. In the summary that follows, the writer has drawn freely on that very helpful report.

Although research in limnology is carried out chiefly by the Department of Biology, many individuals in other divisions of the university are keenly interested in water problems. The Institute of Research of Lehigh University coordinates the efforts of all interested parties through its Water Resources Research Council.

The Biology Department includes six biologists in the rank of assistant professor or higher and twenty-one graduate students. Approximately two-thirds of this staff is now actively engaged in limnological or related research. Since this represents a trend of comparatively recent origin, most of the problems discussed here are still under investigation. Unfortunately, much of the interesting limnological material even from completed projects has been released only in reports of limited circulation written for sponsoring agencies.

A continuing series of limnological surveys on lakes and streams within the northeastern part of the country was begun about 25 years ago by F. J. Trembley. Between 55 and 60 reports of such projects have been issued to the parties especially concerned but usually have not been published. In most cases these were intended to serve as a basis for improved fisheries manage-ment, but the limnological data accumulated in them has also been of inestimable help in other studies made within the area.

Under the sponsorship of the Pennsylvania Power and Light Company, a four-year survey has been made to determine the effects of heated condenser discharge water upon aquatic life (Lehigh Univ., Inst. of Research, 1960–61). The site of this work is a steam-electric generating plant on the Delaware River about 10 mi above Easton, Pennsylvania, where river water totaling 120,000 gpm is circulated and returned to the river at a temperature about 15° C higher than the intake temperature. Because the Delaware River at this point is more nearly in its natural condition than are most streams in the Northeast, heat effects are observable there with a minimum of interference from other man-made alterations.

Observations were made on the distribution of heated water at various points after it enters the river and on the water chemistry above and below the effluent. A drop in dissolved oxygen from 1 to 4 ppm below normal river value was observed at collecting stations in the path of the effluent stream, but other chemical changes were insignificant.

A comprehensive survey of the river biota was undertaken at a number of points, some directly in the path of the heated water discharge, some upstream, and some downstream. Most groups of plants and invertebrate animals showed a decline in numbers of species, and usually of individuals also, in water heated above its seasonal temperature. However, the blue-green algae and certain diatoms of the family Fragilariaceae became much more abundant in the raised temperatures. A periphyton population index representing a ratio of the number of species to the number of individuals in the dominant species decreased wherever temperature was elevated above normal and proved to be a remarkably sensitive index of water temperature.

Although almost all fish left the heated zone during summer months, they seemed to be attracted there in large numbers in winter. The winter congregation has made the place famous among fishermen. None of the 43 species found in the survey disappeared completely from the area, but the overall effect of heated effluents on fish production has not been determined.

Under the sponsorship of the Interstate Com-

mission on the Delaware River (Incodel), automatic sensing and recording devices have been
developed and assembled in such a way as to
provide continuous half-hourly sampling of dissolved oxygen, specific conductivity, pH, temperature, turbidity, and certain weather conditions
pertinent to these water quality measurements.
The first station containing these instruments is
located at Riegelsville about 10 mi downstream
from Easton, Pennsylvania, and has been in operation since August 1958 (Parker *et al.*, 1960).
Other stations have begun operation more recently, one above Martin's Creek, Pennsylvania,
and another at Montague, New Jersey. Although
the immediate goal of this work is to facilitate
the detection of pollution in the river, a number
of long-term projects have been initiated to
investigate correlations between biological phenomena and the physicochemical characteristics
that are permanently recorded by these stations.
A. R. Morris, who has worked with Prof. Parker on
this project since its inception, is undertaking a
doctoral research program along related lines.

Since 1957 work has been under way to determine the effects of adding cement mill stack dust
to mineral-deficient and acid waters such as are
found in lakes and streams in the Pocono Plateau
and many other areas of the Northeast. Sponsored by Incodel, work on this project has already provided a demonstration under laboratory
conditions, as well as in several lakes, which indicates that biological productivity can be greatly
increased in such waters by use of this abundant
industrial waste product. Work is in progress to
determine the stability of chemical changes induced by addition of stack dust, to develop
methods for continuous feeding of stack dust to
streams, and to investigate the long-term biological consequences of such treatment.

During the past six years a study has been
made of a site where fuel oil is stored by flotation on top of water in an abandoned quarry.
The work was undertaken to develop means of
insuring biological digestion of phenolic compounds which diffuse from the oil into the water
below and which thus might contaminate streams
and ground water nearby. Through fertilization
and aeration, the digestion was speeded to the point
where no detectable water-soluble extractives of
fuel oil are released downstream from the quarry.

Under the sponsorship of local industry, an
extensive survey of the Lehigh River and tribu-

taries was started in 1958. The populations of
fish, macroinvertebrates, and microorganisms in
the periphyton are being studied along with water
chemistry at various sites to provide a factual
basis for description of conditions in this highly
polluted river both above and below the sites of
industrial activity.

During the past three years a detailed limnological survey has been made for the purpose of
fisheries management at the recently completed
Green Lane Reservoir. This body of water is
currently the site of an additional project which
seeks to determine the effect of such an impoundment upon the plankton and periphyton in
streams by comparing the populations of these
microorganisms at various sites above and below
the reservoir.

A taxonomic, ecological, distributional, and
historical survey of the fishes in the middle Delaware Basin has recently been undertaken as a
doctoral program by J. Mihursky, who has also
been importantly involved in several other of the
preceding projects. The information obtained
should be of particular interest to limnologists
because of the scarcity of published information
on this subject and the need of base-line data
by which to assess later developments arising
from the rapid rate of ecological change now
being witnessed in this river.

New Jersey

The many productive bays and estuaries along
New Jersey's Atlantic Coast command much
more economic interest than do the lakes centered in the northern counties. To a lesser degree, the same may be true of academic interest
in the state. It is natural that much of the aquatic research effort would be channelled into these
commercially valuable brackish and marine
waters, and it seems quite understandable that
the first textbook of limnology to include estuaries (Reid, 1961) was written in New Jersey.
Valuable research has come from the entire
coastal strip. Much has been done at Raritan
Bay because of its nearness and accessibility to
hydrobiologists at Rutgers University. Even more
has been done on the very large and economically important Delaware Bay and Estuary,
where the New Jersey Oyster Research Laboratory is operating, and neighboring states also are
conducting hydrographic and hydrobiological research. Much of this marine and brackish-water

research can be applied directly to the solution of strictly limnological problems, but limitations of space preclude a complete discussion of it here.

Toth and Smith (1960) presented data that illustrate three edaphically distinct regions of New Jersey (Table 6.5). In showing a good correlation between soil constituents and the characteristics of the water in each region, they illustrated incidentally the principle that a lake is no richer than the soils of its drainage basin. The regions are the Northern Uplands or Appalachian Province (glaciated and residual areas northwest of the fall line), the Inner Coastal Plain, and the Outer Coastal Plain (western and eastern portions of Coastal Plain, respectively, as shown in Fig. 6.11). The Northern Uplands are naturally richer in soil nutrients than is the Coastal Plain, and contributions from such agricultural practices as liming and fertilizing have added to the natural fertility. The Inner Coastal Plain contains a greater proportion of fine matter in the soils than the Outer Coastal Plain, contributing greater fertility and better moisture retention. This region of the well-known greensand soils is the most intensively cultivated area of the state. With its greater extent of very sandy soils, the Outer Coastal Plain is low in fertility and susceptible to droughts. Both regions have wide flats of wet land, but the extent of marsh and swamp is greater in this outer region. Because of these disadvantages, there is little agriculture on the Outer Coastal Plain. The marked contrast in average character of waters of the two Coastal Plain regions reflects differences in natural soil fertility, which have been exaggerated by agricultural practices.

Most of the lakes of New Jersey are concentrated in the region that was covered by Wisconsin glaciation. This section of the Northern Uplands contains the deepest and most productive lakes and the greatest variety with respect to limnological characteristics. South of the glaciated region, especially below the fall line on the Coastal Plain, large lakes are rare. Most lakes of the Inner Coastal Plain are slightly acid and poorly buffered, but some appear to be just as productive as lakes of the Northern Uplands. Lakes of the Outer Coastal Plain are usually shallow and impoverished in calcium and other nutrients. These are characterized by low *p*H values, and some have extremely dark, brown waters and

TABLE 6.5

Soil minerals and associated conductivity, alkalinity, and productivity of waters in New Jersey

	Northern Uplands	Inner Coastal Plain	Outer Coastal Plain
Soil constituents[a]			
Nitrogen	0.15	0.07	0.02
Phosphoric acid	0.20	0.10	0.005
Calcium	0.50	0.13	0.01
Magnesium	0.65	0.30	0.04
Potassium	2.25	1.15	0.20
Sodium	1.50	0.43	0.10
Water characteristics			
Conductivity (micromhos)	343[b]	258[c]	93[c]
Methyl orange alkalinity (ppm)	35[d]	16[d]	6[d]
Productivity (lbs of fish/ acre)	220[e]	110[f]	30[b]

[a] Average percentages in each region.
[b] Mean of 8 streams.
[c] Mean of 6 streams.
[d] Mean of all lakes and ponds inventoried in Lake and Pond Survey.
[e] Mean of 12 lakes and ponds.
[f] Mean of 4 lakes and ponds.
Temperatures for conductivity measurements were not specified. Modified from Toth and Smith, 1960.

sharply limited biotas. There are very few trout lakes in New Jersey, because almost all lakes sufficiently deep and sheltered to stratify in summer suffer depletion of dissolved oxygen in the hypolimnion.

In addition to information obtained in the fisheries survey and in studies of theoretical limnology at Rutgers University discussed later, state and federal agencies working on applied problems have collected miscellaneous limnological data throughout the state. For example, the New Jersey Division of Water Policy and Supply has records of weekly water analyses and plankton samplings from Wanaqua River dating back to about 1929. The State Department of Health and the U.S. Geological Survey have routine water analyses in lakes and streams and sediment data on many of the principal streams. New Jersey is also importantly involved in the cooperative interstate study of the Delaware River discussed under Pennsylvania.

Fisheries survey

An extensive survey of the limnological resources was started just over a decade ago by the New Jersey Division of Fish and Game. Results of this survey are published (New Jersey

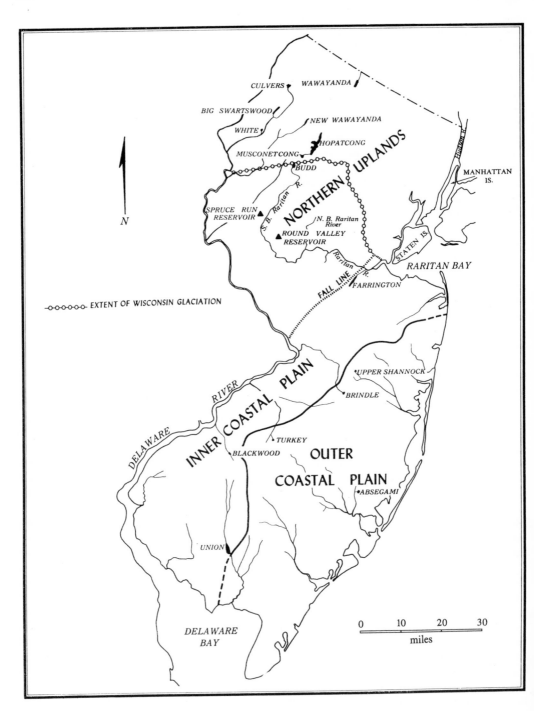

Fig. 6.11.—Three edaphically distinct regions of New Jersey and lakes characteristic of them. Compiled from various sources and prepared by the University of Wisconsin Cartographic Laboratory.

TABLE 6.6

Representative lakes and ponds of New Jersey

Lake or pond	Area (acres)	Maximum depth (ft)	Mean depth (ft)	Thermally stratified	Secchi disc (ft)	Alkalinity (ppm)		pH	
						Surface	Bottom	Surface	Bottom
Hopatcong	2,685	58	18	Yes	7–8	26	32	7.3	6.7
Musconetcong	329	10	5	No	10	23	23	7.1	7.1
New Wawayanda	103	109	39	Yes	9.5	128	188	8.1	7.1
Wawayanda	225	82	30	Yes	9	15	28	7.2	6.8
White	65	44	22	Yes	7	135	235	9.1	7.3
Culvers	585	49	28	Yes	12	76	65	7.0	6.3
Big Swartswood	494	42	22	Yes	4	52	73	7.2	7.0
Budd	376	14	6	No	6.5	21	23	7.9	6.9
Union	898	27	9	Yes	4.7	14	15	6.0	6.0
Blackwood	25	7	3.5	No	4	22	25	6.9	6.6
Farrington	290	23	6	Yes	10.5	15	30	6.7	6.5
Brindle	—	8	—	Yes	2.3	6	68	4.3	5.8
Upper Shannock	7.5	6.5	4	No	5.5	6	9	4.5	4.7
Absegami	68	9	5	No	3.5	3	7	4.4	5.0

Dept. Conserv. and Econ. Develop., 1950, 1951, 1957) as *Fisheries Survey Report*, Nos. 1–3, each written by several contributors. Although intended primarily for sports fishermen, these reports contain a commendable amount of fundamental limnological data. Report No. 1 (1950) concerns 19 lakes, including the largest and best-known ones in the state, and 18 smaller ponds, comprising a total area of about 8,900 acres. Report No. 2 (1951) includes 28 impoundments or small lakes, and No. 3 (1957) embraces 40 more, making a total of about 100 surveyed and reported upon.

The discussion of each lake or pond gives such information as location, drainage, area, maximum depth, approximate mean depth, elevation, bottom type, whether natural or impounded, and whether oxygen in the hypolimnion becomes depleted in the summer. A table of limnological characteristics given in the appendix of each report indicates for each body of water the presence or absence of thermal stratification when surveyed, the Secchi disc reading, color, methyl orange and phenolphthalein alkalinity, and pH. An appendix on aquatic vegetation includes a table of the common macrophytes and an estimate of the relative abundance of each in each lake. Hydrographic maps of these lakes and ponds are published separately as supplements to the reports. In addition to the reports already published, one on coastal streams and estuaries, one on aquatic plants, and an additional survey of lakes and ponds are now in preparation.

Table 6.6 and the discussion to follow are based upon data of R. F. Smith, "A general dis-

cussion of lakes surveyed. . ." (in New Jersey Dept. Conserv. and Econ. Develop., 1950, 1951). Lakes included in Table 6.6 have been selected primarily to present a general cross section of limnological conditions in New Jersey and secondarily to introduce some of the largest and best-known New Jersey lakes into limnological literature. The mean depths given are approximate. In most instances the total alkalinity given is entirely methyl orange alkalinity; phenolphthalein alkalinity contributed only a small proportion of the total given for surface waters in a few lakes. The first eight lakes listed are in the glaciated northern region. The next three are impoundments of the Inner Coastal Plain, and the last three are impoundments of the Outer Coastal Plain.

The largest and best-known lake in the state, Hopatcong, is 7 mi long and lies at an elevation of 924 ft in the piedmont region of north-central New Jersey. It is partly artificial and once consisted of two lakes joined by a branch of the Musconetcong River. A dam constructed about 1831 raised the lower lake about 12 ft, thus connecting it with the upper lake. Lake Hopatcong is dimictic and eutrophic, with neutral, only slightly brownish water and a total alkalinity of about 30 ppm. It is a popular fishing lake, especially for eastern chain pickerel, *Esox niger*. This species grows rapidly there, large pickerel being taken especially in winter by ice-fishermen.

Lake Musconetcong, typical of the shallow lakes of New Jersey and many other states, has developed serious weed problems (chiefly *Myriophyllum spicatum*) as a result of cultural eutrophication. Until a weed control program was initiated a few years ago, fishing and swimming were deteriorating every year. In addition the dense and extensive weed growths created an odor problem in late summer when these masses of plants began to decompose.

New Wawayanda Lake, the deepest in New Jersey, is the only lake of those surveyed in 1950 in which the volume of the hypolimnion exceeds that of the epilimnion. The hypolimnion maintains adequate supplies of dissolved oxygen throughout the summer and supports a population of brown trout, *Salmo trutta*.

Wawayanda (or "Old Wawayanda") also retains some oligotrophic tendencies and seems well suited for salmonid fishes. The survey crew found heterograde oxygen curves on both surveys in 1951. A metalimnetic oxygen minimum found near the 20-ft depth on 4 July evidently persisted, intensified, and rose slightly toward the surface between then and 10 September. Below that level, much of the water down to 70 ft in the 80-ft basin had 4 or even 5 ppm of dissolved oxygen throughout most of the summer.

White Lake, near the western edge of northern New Jersey in Warren County, is one of the uncommon marl lakes of the state. The survey crew found a metalimnetic oxygen maximum there on 14 July and reported quantities of H_2S in the bottom deposits. Typical of marl lakes, a heavy shelf of $CaCO_3$ encroaches from the shore and drops off sharply into deep water. It would be interesting to see whether heterograde oxygen curves, with opposite tendencies in the metalimnion, recur in Wawayanda and White lakes each summer and, if so, to determine why this happens.

Culvers, Big Swartswood, and Budd are popular north Jersey fishing lakes. They are primarily natural, but water levels have been raised by dams.

Union, Blackwood, and Farrington lakes represent the southern, central, and northern sections, respectively, of the Inner Coastal Plain. The former is easily the largest lake on the New Jersey Coastal Plain. It is located in an intensively cultivated area just north of Millville, at an elevation of 26 ft. The rich farm land in its drainage basin no doubt contributes importantly toward a productivity that is well above the average for soft-water lakes.

Blackwood is a warm, shallow impoundment in southern Camden County and is popular for panfish and carp fishing. Because of warm waters and rich agricultural drainage, growth rates of fish are excellent.

Farrington Lake functions primarily as a reservoir, supplying water to New Brunswick, but is also much used for boating and fishing. Like most New Jersey lakes more than 15 ft deep, it stratifies thermally in the summer. By 28 August 1950 the upper 10-ft stratum was the only water that held enough dissolved oxygen to support a fish population permanently.

Brindle Lake at Fort Dix, Upper Shannock Pond at Collier's Mills Shooting Ground, and Lake Absegami about 15 mi north of Atlantic City illustrate some of the pecularities of small lakes in the Pine Barrens which most ecologists consider roughly co-extensive with the Outer Coastal Plain. Since the most intensely pigmented waters of this region originate in cedar swamps, they are known as "cedar waters." Brindle Lake has the darkest brown water of all lakes surveyed in 1950, and a Secchi disc reading of only 2.3 ft. Sunlight is extinguished at a shallow depth, and an oxygen deficit, making the water unsuitable for development of fish, extended from the bottom up to a depth of only 3 ft. This evidence of stable stratification even in very shallow impoundments is characteristic of "cedar waters." Since all radiant energy is absorbed in a relatively thin surface stratum, the temperature differential resulting from direct absorption is much sharper than that of more transparent waters. Pakim Pond, a few miles south of Fort Dix, has even darker water and a Secchi disc reading of 1 ft. Upper Shannock is less deeply pigmented than many Pine Barrens ponds but is fully as acid as the average. The only game fish present in Lakes Absegami and Brindle is *Esox niger*, and a substandard growth rate characterizes even this acid-tolerant species in both lakes. Good fishing is provided in Lake Absegami by the northern yellow bullhead, *Ictalurus natalis prothistius*, and by a particularly dense population of the American eel, *Anguilla bostoniensis*.

Two large reservoirs are now under construction. Round Valley Reservoir, near Lebanon, will have an area of 2,350 acres and a maximum depth of 200 ft. Spruce Run Reservoir, near Clinton, will have an area of 1,290 acres.

Rutgers University

The only institution of New Jersey that offers course work in limnology is Rutgers, the State University, at New Brunswick. This course was founded by the late Dr. Thurlow Nelson, best known for his researches on shellfish, who also did much work in limnology with the New Jersey Division of Water Policy and Supply. Since its foundation, the course has been taught by H. H. Haskin, G. K. Reid, E. T. Moul, and F. B. Trama. The course is currently being taught co-operatively by Trama, a zoologist, and Moul, a botanist.

Students of the origins of lake and pond basins would be interested in studies of numerous pond basins of the New Jersey Coastal Plain by Peter E. Wolfe, Geology Department, Rutgers University. Wolfe (1953) attributed these to frost-thaw action and subsidence in the periglacial zone during Pleistocene time, when the Continental Ice Sheet stood just north of the Coastal Plain. He likened them to subsidence thaw basins being formed in the Arctic now. Such alternative hypotheses as wind deflation, solution depression, and meteorite scarring were considered but rejected on what appears to be good geological evidence.

The most thorough limnological study made of any lake in New Jersey (Smith, 1960) presents considerable data on Turkey Lake, a small, shallow, unstratified seepage lake in the Pine Barrens. It differs from most south Jersey "cedar waters" in its clarity and lack of color, evidently resulting from low dissolved and suspended organic matter. Chemical analyses that included monitoring throughout daily and annual cycles indicate a stable pH of 4.1–4.5, oxygen values that remain below saturation levels (attributed by Smith to high B.O.D.), extremely low nitrates and phosphates, considerable quantities of iron (with an important role in trophic dynamics being ascribed to iron), and some of the lowest values of hardness known for natural waters (total dissolved solids 15.8 mg/L, alkalinity 1.5–7.5 mg/L).

The restricted biota suggests limiting factors of a chemical nature. Quite possibly the low calcium content is insufficient to counteract toxic effects of heavy metals. The production of the floc communities evidently raises the total primary production considerably, and Smith concludes, "The trophic structure suggests a system surprisingly high in primary producers and consumers but disproportionately low at the secondary and tertiary levels."

Another recent limnological contribution from the Zoology Department at Rutgers (Woods, 1960) is a synecological study of a small stream located at the eastern edge of the piedmont region of New Jersey and considered typical of upland and piedmont regions.

A project included in the research of graduate students of E. T. Moul and H. H. Haskin on Raritan Bay illustrates the frequent applicability of principles learned in brackish-water studies to the solution of strictly freshwater problems. This study of the phytoplankton of Raritan Bay (Patten, 1961a, 1961b) has developed to the point that it elucidates abstract principles of negentropy flow in communities of plankton, which presumably are equally applicable in freshwater situations.

Other studies at Rutgers include some unpublished theses on freshwater plants (Renlund, 1953; Keller, 1954; Patten, 1954). In addition Moul and M. F. Buell are currently engaged in a study of algal vegetation of bogs at Helmetta, New Jersey. Miss Joan Hellerman is initiating a qualitative and quantitative study of the diatom flora of Mohonk Lake, New York, a small, deep lake near Poughkeepsie.

F. B. Trama (personal communication) has indicated that future research there probably will center on stream ecology, effects of impoundment on water quality, and diurnal changes in phytoplankton. He expects the new reservoirs mentioned previously to be important assets to course work and research efforts of the limnologists at Rutgers. Trama's early research work was principally on fish toxicity studies and stream pollution, but he has since become interested in bioenergetics and primary productivity (Trama et al., 1961).

Delaware

Delaware has no natural lakes, and aquatic biologists of the state have necessarily channelled their interests into brackish bays and estuaries, marine environments, freshwater streams, and small artificial impoundments. The majority of research of limnological significance has come from Delaware Bay and Estuary. This is not surprising when the paramount commercial importance of this great bay and estuary system is considered.

Some information about freshwater habitats of Delaware can be gleaned from a series of four papers, *Fisheries Publications*, Nos. 1–4, of the Delaware Board of Game and Fish Commissioners (Harmic, 1952, 1954a, 1954b, 1955). These are written for sports fishermen, and the limnological data included are of the elementary survey type.

Publication Nos. 1, 3, and 4 are surveys of 40 impoundments. In addition to creel censuses, stomach analyses, and other data of interest to the fisherman, they present hydrographic maps, notes on location, surface area, water level control, drainage basin, and dominant vegetation. For many of these impoundments, there are two or three vertical series of temperature, dissolved oxygen, CO_2, and pH. In most instances, the series from a given pond are all taken the same day, in summer, at different stations in the pond. A summary of the macroscopic benthos found at each of three stations and an indication of the volume of net plankton per m^3, based on one vertical haul, complete the limnological data.

Publication No. 2 (Harmic, 1954a) is a survey of the Christina Watershed, an area of about 100,000 acres in the northern end of the state. A table of physical, chemical, and biological characteristics is given for each of seven streams tributary to this system. For three stations in each stream, data are presented on width, average depth, velocity, volume of flow, water color, suspended solids, bottom type, water temperatures on three or more summer days, dissolved oxygen, CO_2, pH, and the number and volume (by displacement) of macroscopic bottom animals per ft^2 of bottom.

These surveys indicate that almost all of the fresh waters of Delaware are slightly acid, the pH ranging typically between 6 and 7 but with extremes of 5.2 and 7.2. A single impoundment, Noxontown Pond, had pH values of 8.2–8.6. No alkalinity measurements are given, but the pH readings and the alkalinity data from nearby waters in Maryland and New Jersey suggest that Delaware waters also are very soft.

Practically all Delaware impoundments are small, shallow, and warm, with no stable summer stratification and no problem of oxygen depletion. The largest body of standing, fresh water in the state, Lum's Pond, is an impoundment of somewhat more than 200 acres just north of the Chesapeake and Delaware Canal in the northern quarter of the state. Although it is only 10 ft deep, it also seems to be one of the deepest impoundments in Delaware. Except for the Hockessin quarry pits which have depths of 22 and 25 ft, the deepest contour line seen on any map was one at 12 ft.

Limnologists whose interests extend into cognate disciplines would welcome the Delaware Intrastate Water Resources Survey (Delaware Basin Surv. Coordinating Comm., 1959), which brings together under one cover reports from all the state commissions, boards, and departments concerned with water resources. The Water Pollution Commission at Dover, which has done important research on pollution of estuarine waters, contributed one of the most substantial reports in this survey. The Civil Engineering Department, University of Delaware, has written an informative report of work it has done on measurement of rainfall, runoff, and stream discharge. The Delaware Geological Survey, which has published several bulletins and reports on water resources, ground-water problems, and artesian pressures, contributed another section. Other reports by the State Board of Health, the State Soil Conservation Commission, the Board of Game and Fish Commissioners, and other interested agencies complete this survey. As the first state-wide survey covering the important and rapidly growing problem of maintaining an adequate supply of pure water, this report on Delaware's water resources and projected needs may well serve as a model for others to follow.

Individuals and state agencies of Delaware have contributed toward cooperative studies of the Delaware River, sponsored by the Interstate Commission on the Delaware River (Incodel) and reported under the state of Pennsylvania.

As mentioned above, the Delaware River, Estuary, and Bay constitute a remarkably valuable interstate resource, the lower reaches of which have been the object of much scholarly, cooperative research. The chief contributors in Delaware have been workers at the University of Delaware Marine Laboratories at Lewes and Newark. The Marine Laboratories have accumulated a considerable portion of the existing hydrographic data on the estuary, concentrating particularly on salinity, temperature, dissolved oxygen, pH, and surface transparency. Some of this information, stressing variations in salinity, temperature, and dissolved oxygen with seasons and with distance between Philadelphia and the bay mouth, is presented graphically in the *Biennial Report* (Marine Lab., Univ. Delaware, 1954). Reports on plankton studies, benthos, and fisheries also are included. Shuster (1959) added data on morphometry, plankton, and fisheries, and additional information is contained in papers in *Estuarine Bulletin,* a quarterly publication of the Marine Laboratories.

Maryland

Far more research of limnological value has come from the brackish waters than from the fresh waters of Maryland. In fact, if limnology is defined strictly as the study of natural lakes, there has been no study of limnology in Maryland, for there is no natural lake in the state. If it is recognized, however, that much of limnological knowledge—instrumentation, techniques, and concepts—is common to limnology and oceanography, and if the limnological value of much of the basic research in brackish-water bays and estuaries is duly appreciated, the significant contributions of Maryland to limnological knowledge will be evident. Indeed, the artificiality of the boundary that has been set up between these two sciences probably is nowhere quite so evident as in great, brackish bays such as the Chesapeake. Fresh waters being fed in throughout the 200-mi length of this great bay blend with ocean waters that flow in at its mouth with every incoming tide. This produces a very gradual shift in salinity that defies anyone to say where the province of limnology ends and that of oceanography begins. Like the taxonomist who has discovered a continuum of intermediate forms completely bridging the gap between two "species" everyone had considered distinct, the brackish-water scientist who works in a continuum of habitats ranging from freshwater to marine may be seeing this matter in the clearest perspective.

But the common methodology and principles of the two sciences are even more important to the point being stressed here than is the physical blending of fresh and salt waters. The brackish-water scientist discovers this common ground because he constantly uses both limnological and oceanographic literature. Limnologists and oceanographers who could profit by doing the same sometimes fail to see the advantages to be gained by it. For this reason also, the research worker in brackish waters is more likely to appreciate the essential unity of these two sciences.

The fragments of information published on fresh waters of Maryland include a sportsmen's classification of the streams (Van Deusen, 1954). Unpublished reports by H. J. Elser, of the Maryland Department of Research and Education, give hints about limnological conditions in impoundments. From these, it seems that *p*H values near neutrality and very low alkalinities characterize the fresh waters throughout the state. Total alkalinities (as $CaCO_3$) of only 7 to 22 ppm and *p*H values from 6.0 to 7.2, with a single pond reported at 7.8, were noted by Elser.

Deep Creek Lake, an impoundment of 3,900 acres practically at the western tip of the state, is the largest body of fresh water in Maryland. It is reported as having a maximum depth of 72 ft, average depth of 26.5 ft, Secchi disc reading of 8 to 12 ft, and a low alkalinity of 7 ppm. One summer survey report indicated temperatures of 73° F at the surface and 49° F at the bottom, characterized the *p*H as "about neutral," and stated that there was a depletion of oxygen below 32 ft.

Loch Raven Reservoir, about 10 mi north of Baltimore, has an area of 2,500 acres, a maximum depth of 69 ft, and an average depth of about 40 ft. A total alkalinity of 12 ppm, a *p*H of 7.0, and a poorly developed thermocline at about 30 ft have been reported. Oxygen below the thermocline ranged from 4 to 0 ppm.

Similar data are available on some lesser impoundments, and serious limnological studies of a few freshwater habitats have been made, primarily by personnel of two institutions, the Chesapeake Biological Laboratory at Solomons Island and the Chesapeake Bay Institute at Baltimore.

Considerable information on surface and underground water resources has been obtained by the Maryland Department of Geology, Mines and Water Resources and by the U.S. Geological Survey, Ground Water Branch. Singewald (1945) summarized these extensive data in an easily usable form. Bulletins published by the department present more detailed data on surface and ground-water resources for each county.

Even without any natural lakes Maryland reportedly has a greater percentage of its area under water than does any other state. This indicates the geographic dominance of the Chesapeake Bay and suggests a reason why almost all of the limnologically significant research from Maryland has come from this bay and estuaries connected with it. Another reason is found in the paramount economic importance of the Chesapeake, especially its role in navigation, waste disposal, and the fish, shellfish, and crab industries.

The Chesapeake has commanded great academic as well as economic interest, and the aquatic research of Maryland has been concentrated primarily on it. This research has come chiefly from the two productive Chesapeake institutes to be discussed.

Chesapeake Biological Laboratory

Although its first two publications were issued earlier, the Chesapeake Biological Laboratory is usually considered to date from 1931 when the original laboratory building was completed. From 1941 to 1961 it was administered by the Commission on Research and Education, Maryland Department of Research and Education. In 1961 the commission and the department, with all staff and physical assets, were transferred to the University of Maryland as the newly created Natural Resources Institute.

In its *Final Report* (Hawkins *et al.*, 1961) the Maryland Department of Research and Education listed 172 research contributions, 52 papers in an educational series, and 27 additional titles of publications that it has issued. Most of these came from the Chesapeake Biological Laboratory. Although marine and brackish-water studies have dominated the work of this institute, many of these papers are of interest and value to limnologists. Brief descriptions of a few of these will indicate the types of research that have been done.

In the first comprehensive work on the hydrography of estuarine waters in the Solomons region, Newcombe *et al.* (1939) presented considerable data on temperature, salinity, dissolved oxygen, transparency, phosphates, nitrite and ammonia nitrogen, and silicon. These were monitored to obtain seasonal trends throughout the year, surface-to-bottom variations, magnitudes of hourly changes, and annual maxima and minima of the various elements. Additional studies on distribution of the phosphates were presented by Newcombe and Lang (1939) and Newcombe and Brust (1940) for the bay proper and the estuary of the Patuxent River, respectively. Lesser contributions were made by these authors on alkalinity and dissolved oxygen.

Studies in small, shallow, eutrophic ponds on the coastal plain were made by Conger (1943) and Thompson (1947). Conger studied the generation of marsh gas, which he estimated somewhat crudely at 90 ft³/acre per day in a sen-

escent, 10-acre lake in summer. Thompson's study of freshwater dinoflagellates is a well-illustrated, but probably not complete, guide to identification of these phytoplankters for the state.

Morse (1947) and Nash (1947) made instructive contributions on plankton of the Patuxent estuary. The former paper is a study of seasonal variation in surface plankton populations carried out during two full years. Nash presented data on seasonal variations in surface and deep-water plankton densities. He also examined the physical and chemical factors usually considered in limnological studies and attempted to correlate plankton densities with these factors. Nash reported a single period of thermal stratification from March to August and a single period of overturn from September to February throughout the length of the Patuxent estuary and in the region of the Chesapeake Bay opposite the mouth of the estuary.

Beaven (1960) summarized temperature and salinity records in the mouth of the Patuxent River for a 20-year period, reporting remarkably little deviation in temperatures from the average annual pattern. His cited literature includes papers on the physical hydrography of the Chesapeake Bay and its other estuaries.

A series of papers on pollution of the Patapsco River estuary (Olson *et al.*, 1941; Davis, 1948; Garland, 1952) contributes importantly toward making Baltimore Harbor one of the most carefully studied harbors in the world with respect to pollution and its control.

Tressler and Smith (1948) presented an ecological study of seasonal distribution of Ostracoda of the Solomons Island region. Although only marine and brackish-water species are included, students of this subclass who work exclusively in fresh waters still find this thorough study very useful.

An illustrated guide to the genera of phytoplankton organisms of the Chesapeake Bay (Griffith, 1961) includes many genera that occur in fresh waters. Although intended specifically for workers in the Chesapeake Bay, it should prove quite helpful throughout that general region.

Three bibliographies from the Chesapeake Biological Laboratory would be of interest to limnologists. Mansueti (1955) contributed a guide to key works on the natural resources of Maryland with special reference to zoology, botany, and geology. Schwartz (1960) presented a bibliography of more than 1,200 titles (published and unpublished papers) on Maryland tidewater fisheries. A bibliography on effects of external forces (electricity, electronics, explosives, light, magnetism, mechanical agitation, radiation, and sound) on aquatic organisms (Schwartz, 1961) may be most useful of all to limnologists. It also contains more than 1,200 titles, many of which concern freshwater organisms.

Maryland Tidewater News was published periodically from 1944 to 1959 by the Chesapeake Biological Laboratory, when it was superseded by *Chesapeake Science*. Both journals contain some papers of limnological interest.

Chesapeake Bay Institute

In some senses, the Chesapeake Bay Institute is the same organization as the Department of Oceanography, Johns Hopkins University, which is staffed entirely by men holding research appointments at C.B.I. It is, in fact, affiliated with the Johns Hopkins University, and the two organizations share office and research facilities. Although its focus of research interest is more on marine than on freshwater studies, the Chesapeake Bay Institute has contributed significantly to limnological knowledge.

In a recent paper describing the Chesapeake Bay Institute study of the Baltimore Harbor, Carpenter (1960*b*) wrote:

The Institute is a research contract division whose main field of interest is the physical and chemical behavior of estuaries and other shallow water systems. One of the principal efforts of this group is a continuing study of the Chesapeake Bay system, which has been underway for the last ten years, with joint support from the State of Maryland, the Commonwealth of Virginia, and the Federal Government, primarily the U.S. Navy. The Baltimore Harbor study is an intensive survey of a limited area of special interest, which has been subjected to extensive use and misuse by man.

Research vessels of C.B.I. (Fig. 6.12) conduct cruises throughout the Chesapeake Bay directed toward a better understanding of its physical and chemical hydrography. The properties studied include temperature structure, dissolved oxygen, salinity, *p*H, alkalinity, inorganic phosphate, turbidity, and current direction and speed, all surveyed at the surface and at various depth intervals. Records obtained on these surveys go back to 1949. Studies have also been made of various tributary estuaries, such as those of the Patapsco (Baltimore Harbor), Magothy, Rappahannock,

Fig. 6.12.—Chesapeake Bay Institute Research Vessel *Maury*, occupying station. Hose aft carries water from known depths for analyses in shipboard laboratory. Photo by courtesy of Susan S. Raup.

York, Choptank, Patuxent, James, and St. Marys rivers. In most instances the techniques and principles followed on these survey cruises are the same as those used in limnological investigations.

A brief account of the recent work of some of the research staff at C.B.I. will illustrate the applicability of much of their research to the solution of freshwater problems.

D. W. Pritchard, Director of C.B.I. and Chairman of the Department of Oceanography, is interested in dynamics of circulation, turbulence, and diffusion, and in disposal of radioactive wastes, in estuarine and near-shore waters (Pritchard, 1959). Quite apart from this major research work on salt and brackish waters, he is well known in limnological circles for his studies of reservoirs, with particular reference to circulation patterns and water quality. Pritchard (1958) directed attention to the problem of reduced oxygen content in turbine discharges from hydroelectric power plants. Since the reduced oxygen content often causes mass mortality of aquatic organisms below the dam, it acts as a very potent pollutant. Understanding of seasonal fluctuations in dissolved oxygen in reservoirs, of stratification and circulation patterns, effects of intake levels of turbines, retention times in reservoirs, and low-flow periods will guide the hydro power companies in combating this problem. Anderson and Pritchard (1960) made a comprehensive study of water circulation and evaporation in Lake Mead, which is well known to limnologists. The work of Pritchard and Carpenter (1960) on turbulent diffusion in estuarine and inshore waters should be studied by all limnologists interested in this subject because of the techniques that are discussed.

Although he was working exclusively with marine microorganisms, W. R. Taylor (1960) made important contributions to culture techniques that can advantageously be adopted and widely used in limnology. He pointed out that the data obtained from classical (static) culture experiments to determine uptake rates of radioactive trace elements may not be representative of the processes occurring in the natural marine environment. As the phytoplankton population in laboratory containers goes through all phases of the growth curve during an experiment, the cells change physiologically. It follows that the biochemical mechanisms controlling the uptake of trace metals do not remain constant throughout the experiment. As nutrients are consumed and excreted products accumulate, the environment changes in response to metabolic activity. As an example of the complications that can result, Taylor mentioned the increase in *p*H during photosynthesis with resultant alteration in the solubilities of certain trace elements frequently employed as the isotopic material under study.

The point made applies as well to freshwater as to marine investigations, and it seems that it should be extended to include all research directed toward precise data on metabolic rates of phytoplankton, whether radioactive trace elements are utilized or not. Metabolic rates are strongly affected by the accumulation of waste products. It follows from this fact alone that the validity of conclusions about metabolic rates based on long-term experiments in closed vessels is open to grave doubts.

Fig. 6.14.—An underway sampler, gimbals-mounted on *Tracer*, illustrating portability of entire rig. Turner fluorometer used in dye diffusion studies is visible at left under canopy. Photo by courtesy of Susan S. Raup.

To solve this problem, Taylor suggested the use of the chemostat, a continuous-flow growth apparatus introduced by bacteriologists to maintain both the population and the medium at a constant level. This consists of a growth chamber, a stirring device to assure homogeneity, and a discharge system to remove medium and cells at the same rate as new medium is being supplied (Fig. 6.13). Taylor modified this device for studies of photosynthetic organisms and experimented with the use of light, B-complex vitamins, inorganic and organic phosphorus compounds, and other nutrients to limit and control phytoplankton population growth. He concluded that in radioactive uptake studies, nutrient-limiting chemostat experiments are appreciably more precise than is any experiment using light as the limiting factor.

J. H. Carpenter is interested in the chemistry of fresh and salt natural waters, including the solubility of gases in distilled, fresh, and sea waters, the trace metals, and the development of ultrasensitive tracer techniques for tagging water

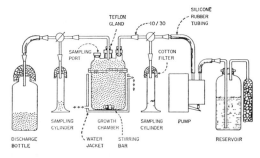

Fig. 6.13.—Chemostat system for continuous culture of phytoplankton organisms. Modified from Fig. 20, Chesapeake Bay Institute Technical Rept. 21, by W. R. Taylor.

masses. He has worked with Pritchard in investigations of circulation patterns of reservoirs and developed a highly sensitive tracer material, the fluorescent dye Rhodamine B (Carpenter, 1960a), which has attracted considerable attention here and abroad. This organic pigment can be detected by appropriate measurements with a filter fluorometer in concentrations as low as 1 part in 10^{11} (Fig. 6.14). It is quite soluble, non-toxic, safe and easy to store and handle, and it is available commercially at relatively modest cost. This dye gives results comparable to radioactive tracers without their real and psychological hazards. It is superior to fluorescent materials previously used in being more sunfast and in having greater sensitivity to detection.

Carpenter (1957) studied major cations in waters ranging from fresh to marine, with special reference to techniques presently used in such analyses and the possibility of improving them. He pointed out the advantages of flame photometry for the estimation of sodium and potassium and of complexometric titration of calcium and magnesium following ion-exchange separation. The new knowledge gained by this research, as well as that resulting from Carpenter's work on tracers to analyze circulation patterns, is completely applicable to freshwater studies.

B. Kinsman is interested in stochastic processes applied to turbulence and wind waves and in the application of statistics and stochastic processes to design of field surveys. Kinsman (1960) shed considerable light on wind-generated waves in Round Bay, near the mouth of the Severn River. Since this study is concerned with short fetches, it is particularly pertinent to inland lakes.

The work of R. C. Whaley (1960, 1961) on Conowingo Reservoir points up several types of brackish-water research that can be used in limnology. Conowingo is a main-stream reservoir on the Susquehanna River, four miles above the tidewaters of the Chesapeake Bay. In this project Whaley used current drags, thermistor bead thermometers, dye tracers, and hydrophotometers perfected and tested by colleagues at C.B.I. in the Chesapeake Bay. He made significant contributions on the water movements in relation to inflow, outflow, wind, and thermal stratification, the seasonal and spatial temperature structure, the seasonal and spatial distribution of oxygen and pH, and sedimentation and transparency. His data on primary production are less conclusive,

but they give an interesting indication of high rates in comparison with those known for lakes at comparable latitudes. This may be due not only to a very high influx of allochthonous materials but also to the beneficial effects of turbulent flow in constantly exposing the phytoplankton to new supplies of nutrients and in dispersing metabolic wastes, as stressed by Odum (1957).

Johns Hopkins Department of Sanitary Engineering and Water Resources

The Department of Sanitary Engineering and Water Resources at Johns Hopkins University has made limnological contributions of considerable interest, particularly in the area of pollution abatement.

A bibliography on biochemical oxygen demand (Hull, 1959a), containing about 290 titles, is valuable to anyone whose work touches on this subject. A bibliography by the same author (Hull, 1959b) on the effects of impoundment on water quality is less comprehensive but also very useful. Hull has accumulated a card file of several hundred references covering all aspects of water resources in the Potomac River Basin. He hopes to make this also generally available as a bibliography.

Shapiro (1957) presented chemical analyses of the coloring matter of natural waters and reported the effects of these substances on pure cultures of phytoplankton. He concluded that these materials originate as a result of decomposition in soil and possibly in sediments. Shapiro suggested the name "humolimnic acids" to indicate the probable relation but improbable equivalence of these substances with so-called "humic" acids.

In an interesting study of a metalimnetic minimum in dissolved oxygen that became more pronounced as the summer progressed, Shapiro (1960) found a non-migrating population of copepods in that stratum. He attributed the oxygen minimum primarily to their respiration and pointed out that its intensification during the summer was correlated with an increase in density of the copepod population.

Other papers by personnel of this department concern Baltimore Harbor, the Potomac River, the Delaware River, and others, with particular reference to pollution and its effects, oxygen balance, allowable loading, and related subjects. Current research projects include an investigation of low-flow augmentation for stream pollution abatement and an extension of various phases of the project on coloring matter of natural waters mentioned previously.

University of Maryland

The only limnology course, strictly defined, taught in Maryland is given at the University of Maryland at College Park. The teaching of aquatic biology there started as a course in hydrobiology (fresh and salt water) taught by W. L. Tressler and R. A. Littleford. The limnology course was first given when the class work was divided into fresh- and salt-water studies in 1955. It has been taught by D. A. Livingstone, E. B. Henson, and (currently) R. G. Stross. Stross has worked on lime-induced changes in lake metabolism (Stross and Hasler, 1960). He is now studying the influences of major nutrients and of grazing by animals on growth rates of phytoplankton. Henson studied with D. C. Chandler at Cornell University and has contributed significantly to our knowledge of the limnology of Cayuga Lake (Henson, 1959; Henson *et al.,* 1961). Livingstone, who is now at Duke University, is best known for his studies of pollen profiles and lacustrine history in arctic America (Livingstone, 1955; Livingstone *et al.,* 1958).

References

ACADEMY OF NATURAL SCIENCES OF PHILADELPHIA, Limnology Department. 1959. Biological studies of the Delaware River for the Interstate Commission on the Delaware River (Incodel), 1957–59. 123 p.

ADAMS, C. C., AND T. L. HANKINSON. 1928. Ecology and economics of Oneida Lake fish. Roosevelt Wildl. Ann., 1(2 & 3): 239–548.

ALEXANDER, C. P. 1920. The crane-flies of New York. II. Biology and phylogeny. Cornell Univ. Agr. Expt. Sta., Mem. No. 38: 691–1133.

ANDERSON, B. G. 1948. The apparent thresholds of toxicity to *Daphnia magna* for chlorides of various metals when added to Lake Erie water. Trans. Amer. Fish. Soc., 78: 96–113.

ANDERSON, E. R., AND D. W. PRITCHARD. 1960. Circulation and evaporation, p. 125–147. *In* W. O. Smith, C. P. Vetter, G. B. Cummings, and others, Comprehensive survey of sedimentation in Lake Mead, 1948–49. U.S. Geol. Surv., Profess. Paper No. 295.

BAKER, F. C. 1916. The relation of mollusks to fish in Oneida Lake, New York. New York State Coll. Forest., Tech. Publ. 4, 366 p.

———. 1918. The productivity of invertebrate fish

food, on the bottom of Oneida Lake, with special reference to mollusks. New York State Coll. Forest., Tech. Publ. 9, 264 p.

BARLOW, J. P., AND R. T. MYREN. 1961. Oxygen resources of tidal waters. Water & Sewage Works J., 108: 68–71.

BAY, E. C. 1960. The feasibility and advisability of chironomid control with special reference to Chautauqua Lake, N.Y. Ph.D. Thesis, Cornell Univ. (L.C. Card No. Mic 60-6505), 184 p. Univ. Microfilms. Ann Arbor, Mich. (Dissertation Abstr. 21: 1715).

BEAMER, N. H. 1953. Chemical character of surface water in Pennsylvania 1949–51. Pennsylvania Dept. Com., Publ. 26, 96 p.

BEAN, T. H. 1903. Catalogue of the fishes of New York. New York State Museum, Bull. 60, 784 p.

BEAVEN, G. F. 1960. Temperatures and salinity of surface water at Solomons, Maryland. Chesapeake Sci., 1: 2–11.

BEETEM, W. A. 1954. Chemical quality of water resources of the Conewango Creek basin, New York. New York State Dept. Com., and U.S. Geol. Surv., Albany, 58 p.

BERG, C. O. 1961. Biology of snail-killing Sciomyzidae (Diptera) of North America and Europe. XI Intern. Kong. Entomol. Wien 1960, Verhandlungen, 1: 197–202.

BETTEN, CORNELIUS. 1934. The caddis flies or Trichoptera of New York State. New York State Museum, Bull. 292: 1–576.

BIRGE, E. A., AND CHANCEY JUDAY. 1914. A limnological study of the Finger Lakes of New York. Bull. U.S. Bur. Fish., 32: 525–614.

BIRGE, E. A., AND CHANCEY JUDAY. 1921. Further limnological observations on the Finger Lakes of New York. Bull. U.S. Bur. Fish., 37: 210–252.

BLAKE, N. M. 1956. Water for the cities. Syracuse Univ. Press, Syracuse. 341 p.

BLUM, J. L. 1956. The ecology of river algae. Botan. Rev., 22: 291–341.

———. 1960. Algal populations in flowing waters, p. 11–21. *In* C. A. Tryon, Jr., and R. T. Hartman, The ecology of algae. Edwards Bros., Ann Arbor.

BORDNE, E. F. 1960. Water resources of a western New York region, etc. Syracuse Univ. Press, Syracuse. 149 p.

BORECKY, G. W. 1956. Population density of the limnetic Cladocera of Pymatuning Reservoir. Ecology, 37: 719–727.

BOYD, J. E. 1957. The use of *Daphnia magna* in the microbioassay of insecticides. Ph.D. Thesis, Pennsylvania State Univ. (L.C. Card No. Mic 58-69), 205 p. Univ. Microfilms. Ann Arbor, Mich. (Dissertation Abstr. 18: 51).

BRALEY, S. A. 1954. Acid mine drainage. Mechanization, 18(1): 87–89, (2): 113–115, (3): 96–98, (4): 137–138, (5): 97–98, (6): 105–107, (8): 101–103.

———. 1960. Special report on the oxidation of pyritic conglomerates. Coal Ind. Advisory Comm. to the Ohio River Valley Water Sanit. Comm., Research Project No. 37–06, Mellon Inst., 32 p.

BURKHOLDER, P. R. 1931. Studies in the phytoplankton of the Cayuga Lake basin, New York. Bull.

Buffalo Soc. Nat. Sci., **15**: 21–181.

CAIRNS, JOHN, JR., AND ARTHUR SCHEIER. 1957. The effects of temperature and hardness of water upon the toxicity of zinc to the common bluegill (*Lepomis macrochirus* Raf.). Notulae Naturae, Acad. Nat. Sci. Philadelphia, No. 299, 12 p.

CAIRNS, JOHN, JR., AND ARTHUR SCHEIER. 1958. The effects of temperature and hardness of water upon the toxicity of zinc to the pond snail, *Physa heterostropha* (Say). Notulae Naturae, Acad. Nat. Sci. Philadelphia, No. 308, 11 p.

CARPENTER, J. H. 1957. A study of some major cations in natural waters. Chesapeake Bay Inst., Tech. Rept. 15 (Ref. 57-7): 1–80.

———. 1960a. Tracer for circulation and mixing in natural waters. Pub. Works Mag., **91**: 110–112.

———. 1960b. The Chesapeake Bay Institute study of the Baltimore Harbor. Proc. Maryland-Delaware Water Sewage Assoc., 33rd Ann. Conf.: 62–78.

CLAASSEN, P. W. 1931. Plecoptera nymphs of America (north of Mexico). Thomas Say Foundation, Publ. No. 3: 1–199.

———. 1940. A catalogue of the Plecoptera of the world. Cornell Univ. Agr. Expt. Sta., Mem. No. 232: 1–235.

CLARKE, A. H., JR., AND C. O. BERG. 1959. The freshwater mussels of central New York. Cornell Univ. Agr. Expt. Sta., Mem. No. 367: 1–79.

CLOVIS, J. F. 1955. A new record for *Cladophora* balls. Amer. Midland Nat., **54**: 508–509.

CONGER, P. S. 1943. Ebullition of gases from marsh and lake waters. Chesapeake Biol. Lab., Contrib. No. 59, 42 p.

COOK, A. H., AND C. F. POWERS. 1958. Early biochemical changes in the soils and waters of artificially created marshes in New York. New York Fish & Game J., **5**: 9–65.

COOPER, E. L. 1959. Trout stocking as an aid to fish management (a review). Pennsylvania Agr. Expt. Sta., Bull. 663, 21 p.

CROCKER, D. W. 1957. The crayfishes of New York State. New York State Museum, Bull. 355, 97 p.

CROWELL, R. M. 1961. Catalogue of the distribution and ecological relationships of North American Hydracarina. Canadian Entomol., **93**: 321–359.

CUSHMAN, R. V. 1953. The ground-water resources of Washington County, New York. Bull. GW-33, State Dept. Conserv., Water Power and Control Comm., Albany, 65 p.

DAVIS, C. C. 1948. Studies of the effects of industrial pollution in the Lower Patapsco area. 2. The effects of copper as pollution on plankton. Chesapeake Biol. Lab., Contrib. No. 72, 12 p.

DEKAY, J. E. 1842–44. Natural history of New York, Zoology of New York, or the New-York Fauna. Carroll and Cook, Albany. 5 v.

DELAWARE BASIN SURVEY COORDINATING COMMITTEE. 1959. State of Delaware intrastate water resources survey. W. N. Cann, Wilmington. Various pagination.

DENCE, W. A., AND D. F. JACKSON. 1959. Changing chemical and biological conditions in Oneida Lake,

New York. School Sci. & Math., Apr. 1959: 317–324.

DROUET, FRANCIS, AND W. A. DAILY. 1956. Revision of the coccoid Myxophyceae. Butler Univ. Botan. Studies, **12**: 1–218.

DUGDALE, R. C., AND V. A. DUGDALE. 1961. Sources of phosphorus and nitrogen for lakes on Afognak Island. Limnol. Oceanogr., **6**: 13–23.

EGGLETON, F. E. 1956. Limnology of a meromictic, interglacial, plunge-basin lake. Trans. Amer. Microscop. Soc., **75**: 324–378.

EIPPER, A. W. 1959. Effects of five herbicides on farm pond plants and fish. New York Fish & Game J., **6**: 46–56.

FAIRCHILD, H. L. 1909. Glacial waters in central New York. New York State Museum, Bull. 127: 5–62.

———. 1925. The Susquehanna River in New York and evolution of western New York drainage. New York State Museum, Bull. 256: 5–95.

FELT, E. P. 1904. Mosquitos or Culicidae of New York. New York State Museum, Bull. 79, 164 p.

FLINT, O. S., JR. 1960. Taxonomy and biology of Nearctic limnephelid [*sic*] larvae (Trichoptera), with special reference to species in eastern United States. Entomol. Amer., **40**: 1–120.

FLINT, R. F. 1947. Glacial geology and the Pleistocene epoch. John Wiley & Sons, New York. 589 p.

FOOTE, B. A. 1961. Biology and immature stages of the snail-killing flies belonging to the genus *Tetanocera* (Diptera: Sciomyzidae). Ph.D. Thesis, Cornell Univ. (L.C. Card No. Mic 62-105), 190 p. Univ. Microfilms. Ann Arbor, Mich. (Dissertation Abstr. 22: 3302).

FORNEY, J. L. 1957. Chemical characteristics of New York farm ponds. New York Fish & Game J., **4**: 202–212.

FREY, D. G. 1953. The teaching of limnology in the United States. Sci. Month., **76**: 290–296.

GARLAND, C. F. 1952. A study of water quality in Baltimore Harbor. Chesapeake Biol. Lab., Contrib. No. 96, 132 p.

GOJDICS, MARY. 1953. The genus *Euglena*. Univ. Wisconsin Press, Madison. 268 p.

GRIFFITH, R. E. 1961. Phytoplankton of the Chesapeake Bay—an illustrated guide to the genera. Chesapeake Biol. Lab., Contrib. No. 172, 78 p.

HARMIC, J. L. 1952. Fresh water fisheries survey. Delaware Board, Game Fish. Comm., Fish. Publ. 1, 154 p.

———. 1954a. Fisheries investigations of the Christina Watershed. Delaware Board, Game Fish. Comm., Fish. Publ. 2, 53 p.

———. 1954b. Delaware lake and pond survey. Delaware Board, Game Fish. Comm., Fish. Publ. 3, 56 p.

———. 1955. Delaware lake and pond survey. Delaware Board, Game Fish. Comm., Fish. Publ. 4, 55 p.

HARTMAN, R. T., AND J. H. GRAFFIUS. 1960. Quantitative seasonal changes in the phytoplankton communities of Pymatuning Reservoir. Ecology, **41**: 333–345.

HARTMAN, R. T., AND C. L. HIMES. 1961. A study of phytoplankton from Pymatuning Reservoir in downstream areas of the Shenango River. Ecology, **42**: 180–183.

HATCH, R. W., AND D. A. WEBSTER. 1961. Trout production in four central Adirondack Mountain lakes. Cornell Univ. Agr. Expt. Sta., Mem. No. 373: 1–81.

HAWKINS, E. T., FREDERICK TRESSELT, W. T. BOSTON, E. N. CORY, AND B. H. WILLIER. 1961. Final report. Maryland Comm. Research Educ., 21 p.

HENSON, E. B. 1954. The profundal bottom fauna of Cayuga Lake. Ph.D. Thesis, Cornell Univ. (L.C. Card No. Mic A 54-3231), 140 p. Univ. Microfilms. Ann Arbor, Mich. (Dissertation Abstr. 14: 2163).

———. 1959. Evidence of internal wave activity in Cayuga Lake, New York. Limnol. Oceanogr., **4**: 441–447.

HENSON, E. B., A. S. BRADSHAW, AND D. C. CHANDLER. 1961. The physical limnology of Cayuga Lake, New York. Cornell Univ. Agr. Expt. Sta., Mem. No. 378: 1–63.

HESS, A. D., 1940. A preliminary study of the annual temperature cycle in Cayuga Lake, 7 p. (Unpublished.)

HINMAN, E. H. 1930. A study of the food of mosquito larvae (Culicidae). Amer. J. Hyg., **12**: 238–270.

HOAK, R. D. 1954. Fundamental research in water pollution abatement at Mellon Institute. Mellon Institute, Pittsburgh, 17 p. (Paper read at Pittsburgh Regional Tech. Meeting, Amer. Iron and Steel Inst., 14 Oct. 1954.)

———. 1957. Origins of tastes and odors in drinking water. Pub. Works, **88**(3): 83–85.

———. 1959. Physical and chemical behavior of suspended solids. Sewage & Ind. Wastes, **31**: 1401–1408.

HULL, C. H. J. 1959a. Bibliography on biochemical oxygen demand. Johns Hopkins Univ., Dept. Sanit. Engr. Water Resources, Low-flow Augmentation Project, Rept. No. 5, 27 p.

———. 1959b. Bibliography on the effects of impoundments on water quality. Johns Hopkins Univ., Dept. Sanit. Engr. Water Resources, Low-flow Augmentation Project, Rept. No. 2, 14 p.

HUNGERFORD, H. B. 1919. The biology and ecology of aquatic and semi-aquatic Hemiptera. Kansas Univ., Sci. Bull. No. 11: 3–341.

HUTCHINSON, G. E. 1957. A treatise on limnology. I. Geography, physics, and chemistry. John Wiley & Sons, New York. 1015 p.

JACKSON, D. F., AND W. A. DENCE. 1958. Primary productivity in a dichothermic lake. Amer. Midland Nat., **59**: 511–517.

JOHANNSEN, O. A. 1934. Aquatic Diptera. I. Nemocera, exclusive of Chironomidae and Ceratopogonidae. Cornell Univ. Agr. Expt. Sta., Mem. No. 164: 1–70.

———. 1935. Aquatic Diptera. II. Orthorrhapha-Brachycera and Cyclorrhapha. Cornell Univ. Agr. Expt. Sta., Mem. No. 177: 1–62.

———. 1937a. Aquatic Diptera. III. Chironomidae:

Subfamilies Tanypodinae, Diamesinae, and Orthocladiinae. Cornell Univ. Agr. Expt. Sta., Mem. No. 205: 1–84.

———. 1937b. Acquatic Diptera. IV. Chironomidae: Subfamily Chironominae; V. Ceratopogonidae (by Lillian C. Thomsen). Cornell Univ. Agr. Expt. Sta., Mem. No. 210: 1–80.

JONES, J. D., AND J. R. VALLENTYNE. 1960. Biogeochemistry of organic matter. I. Polypeptides and amino acids in fossils and sediments in relation to geothermometry. Geochim. et Cosmochim. Acta, **21**: 1–34.

KELLER, J. M. 1954. Study of the periodicity of fresh-water algae in the vicinity of New Brunswick, N.J. Ph.D. Thesis, Rutgers Univ.

KINSMAN, BLAIR. 1960. Surface waves at short fetches and low wind speeds—a field study. Chesapeake Bay Inst., Tech Rept. 19 (Ref. 60-1): 1–145.

KOOB, D. D. 1959. A limnological study of some sub-alpine lakes in Colorado. Ph.D. Thesis, Cornell Univ. (L.C. Card No. Mic 60–188), 279 p. Univ. Microfilms. Ann Arbor, Mich. (Dissertation Abstr. 20: 4499).

KORMONDY, E. J. 1959. The systematics of *Tetragoneuria*, based on ecological life history, and morphological evidence (Odonata: Corduliidae). Univ. Mich. Museum Zool., Misc. Publ. No. 107: 1–79.

LANGMUIR, IRVING. 1938. Surface motion of water induced by wind. Science, **87**: 119–123.

LAUFF, G. H. 1953. The design and application of a multiple sample plankton trap. Ph.D. Thesis, Cornell Univ., 40 p.

LEA, A. O., J. B. DIAMOND, AND D. M. DeLONG. 1956. A chemically defined medium for rearing *Aedes aegypti* larvae. J. Econ. Entomol., **49**: 313–315.

LEATHEN, W. W. 1953. Bacteriologic aspects of bituminous coal mine effluents. Proc. Pennsylvania Acad. Sci., **27**: 37–44.

LEHIGH UNIVERSITY, Institute of Research. 1960–61. Research project on effects of condenser discharge water on aquatic life. Progr. Rept. 1956–59; 1960. [Bethlehem.] Loose leaf. Various pagination.

LETSON, E. J. 1905. Check list of the Mollusca of New York. New York State Museum, Bull. No. 88: 1–112.

LIVINGSTONE, D. A. 1955. Some pollen profiles from arctic Alaska. Ecology, **36**: 587–600.

LIVINGSTONE, D. A., KIRK BRYAN, JR., AND R. G. LEAHY. 1958. Effects of an arctic environment on the origin and development of freshwater lakes. Limnol. Oceanogr., **3**: 192–214.

LLOYD, J. T. 1921. The biology of the North American caddis fly larvae. Lloyd Library Botan., Pharm., Materia Med., Bull. No. 21: 1–124.

McMANUS, L. R. 1960. Some ecological studies of the Branchiobdellidae (Oligochaeta). Trans. Amer. Microscop. Soc., **79**: 420–428.

MACIOLEK, J. A. 1961. Quantitative dichromate oxidation—a basic analytical technique for organic limnology. Ph.D. Thesis, Cornell Univ. (L.C. Card No. Mic 61–6832), 147 p. Univ. Microfilms. Ann

Arbor, Mich. (Dissertation Abstr. 22: 2565).

MAGUIRE, BASSETT, JR. 1959. Passive overland transport of small aquatic organisms. Ecology, **40**: 312.

MANSUETI, ROMEO. 1955. Maryland natural resource bibliography, a guide to key works dealing with zoology, botany, geology and related subjects. Chesapeake Biol. Lab., Research Study Rept. No. 7, 27 p.

MARSHALL, W. B. 1895. Geographical distribution of New York Unionidae. New York State Museum, 48th Ann. Rept.: 47–99.

MARTIN, R. C., G. S. BIRKHEAD, JESSE BURKHEAD, AND F. J. MUNGER. 1960. River basin administration and the Delaware. Syracuse Univ. Press, Syracuse. 390 p.

MASON, C. P. 1961. The ecology of *Cladophora* in farm ponds. Ph.D. Thesis, Cornell Univ., 184 p.

MATTINGLY, A. L. 1961. Chemical and physical quality of water resources in the St. Lawrence River basin, New York State (1955–56). New York State Dept. Com., and U.S. Geol. Surv. [Albany], 96 p.

MOORE, EMMELINE. 1915. The potamogetons in relation to pond culture. Bull. U.S. Bur. Fish., **33**: 249–291.

MORGAN, A. H. 1930. Field book of ponds and streams. G. P. Putnam's Sons, New York. 448 p.

MORGAN, P. V., AND CHARLES GAINOR. 1960. A survey of the heterotrophic bacteria in Sanctuary Lake of the Pymatuning Reservoir. Ecology, **41**: 715–721.

MORSE, D. C. 1947. Some observations on seasonal variations in plankton population Patuxent River, Maryland, 1943–45. Chesapeake Biol. Lab., Contrib. No. 65, 31 p.

MOZLEY, AL.N. 1954. An introduction to molluscan ecology. H. K. Lewis, London. 71 p.

MUENSCHER, W. C. 1928. Plankton studies of Cayuga, Seneca and Oneida lakes, p. 140–157. *In* A biological survey of the Oswego River system, N.Y. State Conserv. Dept., Suppl. to Ann. Rept. 17 (1927).

———. 1944. Aquatic plants of the United States. Comstock Publ. Co., Ithaca. 374 + x p.

NASH, C. B. 1947. Environmental characteristics of a river estuary. J. Marine Research, **6**: 147–174.

NEEDHAM, J. G. 1946. The lengthened shadow of a man and his wife. I and II. Sci. Month., **62**: 140–150, 219–229.

NEEDHAM, J. G., AND CORNELIUS BETTEN. 1901. Aquatic insects in the Adirondacks. New York State Museum, Bull. No. 47: 383–612.

NEEDHAM, J. G., AND P. W. CLAASSEN. 1925. A monograph of the Plecoptera or stoneflies of America north of Mexico. Thomas Say Foundation, Publ. No. 2: 1–397.

NEEDHAM, J. G., AND H. B. HEYWOOD. 1929. A handbook of the dragonflies of North America. Chas. C Thomas, Springfield and Baltimore. 378 p.

NEEDHAM, J. G., AND J. T. LLOYD. 1916. The life of inland waters. Comstock Publ. Co., Ithaca. 438 p.

NEEDHAM, J. G., A. D. MACGILLIVRAY, O. A. JOHANNSEN, AND K. C. DAVIS. 1903. Aquatic insects in New York State. New York State Museum. Bull. No. 68: 199–517.

NEEDHAM, J. G., K. J. MORTON, AND O. A. JOHANNSEN. 1905. May flies and midges of New York. New York State Museum, Bull. No. 86: 1–352.

NEEDHAM, J. G., AND P. R. NEEDHAM. 1962. A guide to the study of freshwater biology. 5th ed. Holden-Day, San Francisco.

NEEDHAM, J. G., J. R. TRAVER, AND YIN-CHI HSU. 1935. The biology of mayflies. Comstock Publ. Co., Ithaca. 759 p.

NEEDHAM, J. G., AND M. J. WESTFALL. 1955. A manual of the dragonflies of North America (Anisoptera). Univ. California Press, Berkeley and Los Angeles. 615 + xii p.

NEFF, S. E. 1960. Natural history and immature stages of certain species of *Sepedon, Hoplodictya* and *Protodictya* (Diptera: Sciomyzidae). Ph.D. Thesis, Cornell Univ. (L.C. Card No. Mic 60–6491), 201 p. Univ. Microfilms. Ann Arbor, Mich. (Dissertation Abstr. 21: 2056).

NEWCOMBE, C. L., AND H. F. BRUST. 1940. Variations in the phosphorus content of estuarine waters of the Chesapeake Bay near Solomons Island, Maryland. J. Marine Research, **3**: 76–88.

NEWCOMBE, C. L., W. A. HORNE, AND B. B. SHEPHERD. 1939. Studies on the physics and chemistry of estuarine waters in Chesapeake Bay. J. Marine Research, **2**: 87–116.

NEWCOMBE, C. L., AND A. G. LANG. 1939. The distribution of phosphates in the Chesapeake Bay. Proc. Amer. Phil. Soc., **81**: 393–420.

NEW JERSEY DEPARTMENT OF CONSERVATION AND ECONOMIC DEVELOPMENT, Division of Fish and Game. 1950. Fisheries survey report, lakes and ponds. Trenton. No. 1, 189 p. + 28 p. suppl.

———. 1951. Fisheries survey report, lakes and ponds. Trenton. No. 2, 199 p. + 31 p. suppl.

———. 1957. Fisheries survey report, lakes and ponds. Trenton. No. 3, 198 p. + 43 p. suppl.

NEW YORK STATE CONSERVATION DEPARTMENT. 1927–40. Biological survey. Nos. 1–16. Suppls. to Ann. Repts. 16–29. Albany. Various pagination.

NEW YORK STATE WATER POLLUTION CONTROL BOARD. 1950———. Drainage basin survey report. [A continuing series] Albany. Various pagination.

———. 1957. Eight years of water pollution control progress in New York State, by A. F. Dappert, Exec. secy. [Albany], 33 p.

———. 1959–60. Research report. Nos. 1–7. Albany. Various pagination.

NEW YORK TEMPORARY STATE COMMISSION ON WATER RESOURCES PLANNING. 1960. Progress report (Legislative document, 1960, No. 24), Albany, 260 p.

OANA, SHINYA, AND E. S. DEEVEY, JR. 1960. Carbon 13 in lake waters, and its possible bearing on paleolimnology. Amer. J. Sci., **258A** (Bradley vol.): 253–272.

ODUM, H. T. 1957. Trophic structure and productivity of Silver Springs, Florida. Ecol. Monogr., **27**: 55–112.

OGDEN, E. C. 1953. Key to the North American species of *Potamogeton*. New York State Museum, Circ. 31, 11 p.

OLSON, R. A., H. F. BRUST, AND W. L. TRESSLER.

1941. Studies of the effects of industrial pollution in the Lower Patapsco area. I. Curtis Bay region. Chesapeake Biol. Lab., Contrib. No. 43, 40 p.

ORR, H. D. 1954. Quantitative studies of protozoan populations from two areas of Pymatuning Lake, Pennsylvania. Ecology, **35**: 332–334.

PALMER, R. S. 1953. History of the Zoology Section, New York State Museum and State Science Service. 12 p. (Unpublished.)

PARKER, B. W., J. A. FREEBURG, AND S. B. BARBER. 1960. Automatic system for monitoring water quality. J. Sanit. Engr. Div., Proc. Amer. Soc. Civil Engr., **86**(SA 4): 25–40.

PATRICK, RUTH. 1949. A proposed biological measure of stream conditions based on a survey of Conestoga Basin, Lancaster County, Penna. Proc. Acad. Nat. Sci. Philadelphia, **101**: 277–341.

———. 1959. Bacillariophyceae, p. 171–189. *In* H. B. Ward and G. C. Whipple, Fresh-water biology. 2nd ed. (Ed. by W. T. Edmondson). John Wiley & Sons, New York.

———. 1961. A study of the numbers and kinds of species found in rivers in eastern United States. Proc. Acad. Nat. Sci. Philadelphia, **113**: 215–258.

PATRICK, RUTH, AND L. R. FREESE. 1960. Diatoms (Bacillariophyceae) from northern Alaska. Proc. Acad. Nat. Sci. Philadelphia, **112**: 129–293.

PATRICK, RUTH, M. H. HOHN, AND J. H. WALLACE. 1954. A new method for determining the pattern of the diatom flora. Notulae Naturae, Acad. Nat. Sci. Philadelphia, No. 259, 12 p.

PATTEN, B. C., JR. 1954. *Myriophyllum spicatum* L., in Lake Musconetcong, N.J., its ecology and biology with a view toward control. M.S. Thesis, Rutgers Univ.

———. 1961a. Negentropy flow in communities of plankton. Limnol. Oceanogr., **6**: 26–30.

———. 1961b. Plankton energetics of Raritan Bay. Limnol. Oceanogr., **6**: 369–387.

PAULMIER, F. C. 1905. Higher Crustacea of New York City. New York State Museum, Bull. No. 91, 78 p.

PAUSZEK, F. H. 1959. Chemical quality of surface waters in the Allegheny, Genesee, and Susquehanna River basins New York, 1953–56. New York State Dept. Com., and U.S. Geol. Surv. [Albany], 94 p.

PENNSYLVANIA SANITARY WATER BOARD. 1951. A pilot-plant study of the neutralization of acid drainage from bituminous coal mines. A study made under an Industrial Fellowship of the Sanitary Water Board, Commonwealth of Pennsylvania, by Mellon Institute of Industrial Research. Pennsylvania Dept. Health, Harrisburg, 13 p.

PENNSYLVANIA WATER SUPPLY COMMISSION. 1917a. Water resources inventory report. III. Gazetteer of streams. Harrisburg. 657 p.

———. 1917b. Water resources inventory report. IV. Gazetteer of lakes and ponds. Harrisburg. 214 p.

PETTERSSEN, SVERRE. 1960. Some weather influences due to warming of the air by the Great Lakes in winter. Univ. Mich., Great Lakes Research Div., Proc. 3rd Conf. Great Lakes Research: 9–20.

PHILLIPS, A. M., JR., H. A. PODOLIAK, D. L. LIVINGSTON, R. F. DUMAS, AND G. L. HAMMER. 1961.

Fisheries Research Bulletin No. 24 (Cortland Hatchery Rept. No. 29). New York State Conserv. Dept., Albany, 76 p.

PIERCE, M. E. 1961. A study of the effect of the weed-killer, 2,4-D aqua granular, on six experimental plots of Long Pond, Dutchess County, N.Y. Proc. 15th Ann. Meeting, Northeastern Weed Control Conf.: 539–544.

POTASH, MILTON. 1956. A biological test for determining the potential productivity of water. Ecology, **37**: 631–639.

PRITCHARD, D. W. 1958. Dams affect water properties. Elec. World, **150**(6): 49, 52.

———. 1959. Problems related to disposal of radioactive wastes in estuarine and coastal waters. Trans. 2nd Seminar Biol. Problems Water Pollution, U.S. Pub. Health Serv., Robt. A. Taft Sanit. Engr. Center, 11 p.

PRITCHARD, D. W., AND J. H. CARPENTER. 1960. Measurements of turbulent diffusion in estuarine and inshore waters. Proc. Symposium on Tidal Rivers, Intern. Union Geodesy Geophys., XII Gen. Assembly, Helsinki, Finland: 37–50.

RAFTER, G. W. 1905. Hydrology of the state of New York. New York State Museum, Bull. No. 85: 1–902.

REID, G. K. 1961. Ecology of inland waters and estuaries. Reinhold, New York. 375 p.

REIMER, C. W. 1959a. The diatom genus *Neidium*. I. New species, new records and taxonomic revisions. Proc. Acad. Nat. Sci. Philadelphia, **111**: 1–35.

———. 1959b. Some new United States distribution records for the diatom genus *Navicula* (Bacillariophyceae). Proc. Acad. Nat. Sci. Philadelphia, **111**: 77–89.

RENLUND, R. N. 1953. Study of the net plankton of the Delaware and Raritan Canal. Ph.D. Thesis, Rutgers Univ.

ROBACK, S. S. 1953. Savannah River tendipedid larvae [Diptera: Tendipedidae (= Chironomidae)]. Proc. Acad. Nat. Sci. Philadelphia, **105**: 91–132.

———. 1957. The immature tendipedids of the Philadelphia area. Monogr. Acad. Nat. Sci. Philadelphia, No. 9, 152 p.

SCHOFIELD, C. L., JR. 1962. Water quality in an acidotrophic lake of the Adirondack Mountains in relation to survival of hatchery reared brook trout, *Salvelinus fontinalis* (Mitchill). M.S. Thesis, Cornell Univ., 148 p.

SCHWARTZ, F. J. 1960. Bibliography of Maryland fisheries (including published and unpublished papers on the fisheries and related fields of tidewater Maryland). Chesapeake Biol. Lab., Contrib. No. 144, 35 p.

———. 1961. A bibliography; effects of external forces on aquatic organisms. Chesapeake Biol. Lab., Contrib. No. 168, 85 p.

SHAPIRO, JOSEPH. 1957. Chemical and biological studies on the yellow organic acids of lake water. Limnol. Oceanogr., **2**: 161–179.

———. 1960. The cause of a metalimnetic minimum of dissolved oxygen. Limnol. Oceanogr., **5**: 216–227.

SHEPPS, V. C., G. W. WHITE, L. B. DROSTE, AND

R. F. SITLER. 1959. The glacial geology of northwestern Pennsylvania. Pennsylvania Geol. Surv., Bull. G 32, 64 p.

SHUSTER, C. N., JR. 1959. A biological evaluation of the Delaware River estuary. Univ. Delaware Marine Lab., Inform. Ser., Publ. No. 3, 77 p.

SINGEWALD, J. T., JR. 1945. Maryland stream flow records. Maryland Board Nat. Resources, Dept. Research Educ., Solomons Island, Educ. Ser. No. 9, 16 p.

SINGH, K. R. P., AND D. W. MICKS. 1958. Effects of growth of *Aedes aegypti* L. larvae on a chemically defined medium. Mosquito News, **18**: 59–63.

SMITH, R. F. 1960. An ecological study of an acid pond in the New Jersey Coastal Plain. Ph.D. Thesis, Rutgers Univ. (L.C. Card No. Mic 60–4262), 197 p. Univ. Microfilms. Ann Arbor, Mich. (Dissertation Abstr. 21: 1303).

STONE, ALAN, AND H. A. JAMNBACK. 1955. The black flies of New York State (Diptera: Simuliidae). New York State Museum, Bull. No. 349, 144 p.

STROSS, R. G., AND A. D. HASLER. 1960. Some lime-induced changes in lake metabolism. Limnol. Oceanogr., **5**: 265–272.

TAYLOR, W. R. 1960. Some results of studies on the uptake of radioactive waste materials by marine and estuarine phytoplankton organisms using continuous culture techniques. Chesapeake Bay Inst., Tech. Rept. 21 (Ref. 60–3): 1–49.

THOMPSON, R. H. 1947. Fresh-water dinoflagellates of Maryland. Chesapeake Biol. Lab., Contrib. No. 67, 31 p.

TOTH, S. J., AND R. F. SMITH. 1960. Soil over which water flows affects ability to grow fish. New Jersey Agr., **42**(6): 5–11.

TOWNES, H. K. 1945. The Nearctic species of Tendipedini [Diptera, Tendipedidae (= Chironomidae)]. Amer. Midland Nat., **34**: 1–206.

TRAGER, WILLIAM. 1936. The utilization of solutes by mosquito larvae. Biol. Bull., **71**: 343–352.

TRAMA, F. B., G. W. SAUNDERS, AND R. W. BACHMANN. 1961. Investigations in lake metabolism—photosynthesis: Chlorophyll *a* in Grand Traverse Bay with reference to its use as an index of primary productivity. Univ. Mich., Great Lakes Research Div., Proc. 4th Conf. Great Lakes Research: 163–164. (Abstract.)

TRESSLER, W. L. 1939. The zooplankton in relation to the metabolism of lakes, p. 79–93. *In* Problems in lake biology. Amer. Assoc. Advance. Sci. Science Press, Lancaster.

TRESSLER, W. L., AND RUBY BERE. 1938. A limnological study of Chautauqua Lake. New York State Conserv. Dept., Suppl. to Ann. Rept. 27 (1937): 196–213.

TRESSLER, W. L., AND E. M. SMITH. 1948. An ecological study of seasonal distribution of Ostracoda, Solomons Island, Maryland, region. Chesapeake Biol. Lab., Contrib. No. 71, 61 p.

TRESSLER, W. L., L. G. WAGNER, AND RUBY BERE. 1940. A limnological study of Chautauqua Lake. II. Seasonal variation. Trans. Amer. Microscop. Soc., **59**: 12–30.

TRYON, C. A., JR., AND R .T. HARTMAN (eds.). 1960. The ecology of algae. Univ. Pittsburgh, Pymatuning Lab. Field Biol., Spec. Publ. No. 2, 96 p.

TRYON, C. A., JR., AND D. F. JACKSON. 1952. Summer plankton productivity of Pymatuning Lake, Pennsylvania. Ecology, **33**: 342–350.

TRYON, C. A., JR., AND M. A. SHAPIRO (eds.). 1956. Man and the waters of the upper Ohio basin. Univ. Pittsburgh, Pymatuning Lab. Field Biol., Spec. Publ. No. 1, 100 p.

UNIVERSITY OF DELAWARE, Marine Laboratory, 1954. Biennial report. Marine Lab., Publ. 2, 83 p.

U.S. DEPARTMENT OF AGRICULTURE. 1941. Climate and man. Yearbook of agriculture. U.S. Govt. Printing Office, Washington. 1248 + xii p.

U.S. DEPARTMENT OF AGRICULTURE, Northeast Postwar Planning Committee. 1943. Northeast agricultural atlas. Duplicated by Bur. Agr. Econ., Upper Darby. Various pagination.

VALLENTYNE, J. R. 1957. Carotenoids in a 20,000 year old sediment from Searles Lake, California. Arch. Biochem. Biophys., **70**: 29–34.

VALLENTYNE, J. R., AND Y. S. SWABEY. 1955. A reinvestigation of the history of Lower Linsley Pond, Connecticut. Amer. J. Sci., **253**: 313–340.

VAN DEUSEN, R. D. 1954. Maryland freshwater stream classification, by watersheds. Chesapeake Biol. Lab., Contrib. No. 106, 30 p.

VISHER, S. S. 1954. Climatic atlas of the United States. Harvard Univ. Press, Cambridge. 403 + xii p.

VON ENGELN, O. D. 1961. The Finger Lakes region: Its origin and nature. Cornell Univ. Press, Ithaca. 156 p.

WEBSTER, D. A. 1954. Smallmouth bass, *Micropterus dolomieui*, in Cayuga Lake. Cornell Univ. Agr. Expt. Sta., Mem. No. 327: 1–39.

———. 1961. An unusual lake of the Adirondack Mountains, New York. Limnol. Oceanogr., **6**: 88–90.

WHALEY, R. C. 1960. Physical and chemical limnology of Conowingo Reservoir. Chesapeake Bay Inst., Tech. Rept. 20 (Ref. 60–2): 1–140.

———. 1961. Conowingo Reservoir sedimentation and transparency. (Mimeographed summary of data and observations). Chesapeake Bay Inst., 14 p.

WHIPPLE, G. C. 1898. Classifications of lakes according to temperature. Amer. Nat., **32**: 25–33.

WHITFORD, L. A., AND G. J. SCHUMACHER. 1961. Effect of current on mineral uptake and respiration by a fresh-water alga. Limnol. Oceanogr., **6**: 423–425.

WOLFE, P. E. 1953. Periglacial frost-thaw basins in New Jersey. J. Geol., **61**: 133–141.

WOODS, W. J. 1960. An ecological study of Stony Brook, New Jersey. Ph.D. Thesis, Rutgers Univ. (L.C. Card No. Mic 60–4270), 365 p. Univ. Microfilms. Ann Arbor, Mich. (Dissertation Abstr. 21: 1676).

WURTZ, C. B., AND THOMAS DOLAN. 1960. A biological method used in the evaluation of effects of thermal discharge in the Schuylkill River. Proc. 15th Ind. Waste Conf., Purdue: 461–472.

7 | *Shelby D. Gerking*

Central States

The development of limnology in the Central States began just before the turn of the century in the glacial lake region of northern Indiana and Ohio. The development was closely related to the founding of two freshwater biological stations by Dr. Carl H. Eigenmann of Indiana University and Dr. David S. Kellicot of the Ohio State University. The Indiana University Biological Station began its activities in 1895 in a boathouse on Lake Wawasee, a 2600-acre lake in the northern part of the state. The Ohio State University Biological Station, first called the Lake Laboratory and later named the Franz Theodore Stone Laboratory, also had humble beginnings. Operations were initiated in 1896 in a building of the State Fish Hatchery on Sandusky Bay of Lake Erie. Both stations were established primarily for the purpose of research, but teaching soon became an important function. Students from both establishments were largely responsible for the early progress of limnology in the Central States, and their influence was felt in other parts of the country as well.

The research in the glacial lake region has followed the pattern inherited from the European progenitors of limnology. Identification of the aquatic fauna and flora and studies of the formation, distribution, and morphometry of the lakes were characteristic of the early period. Attention soon turned to more specific problems concerning the plankton, benthos, fishes, and physico-chemical conditions. Nearly all of the classical

Contribution No. 710 of the Department of Zoology, Indiana University.

aspects of the science have been applied to the glacial lakes during the past 70 years.

Aquatic environments in other areas were explored as interest in limnology broadened and more trained workers entered the field. Streams began to be investigated in the Central States in the 1930's. The activities of the Tennessee Valley Authority and the Reelfoot Lake Biological Station in Tennessee, established during the same decade, added significantly to the completeness of the record of regional limnology. The Tennessee Valley Authority had the foresight to employ a group of biologists to study the first great network of flood-control reservoirs in the United States. Reelfoot Lake is one of the few bodies of water in the region with cypress trees. The Biological Station has been active in describing the flora and fauna of the lake and its surroundings.

The research on streams and reservoirs characterizes the limnology of the region better than does the lake work. Streams and reservoirs are spread over a much wider area than are the glacial lakes and are more sensitive to the variable seasonal rainfall characteristic of the region. Fluctuating water levels are the rule, and the chemistry and biology of these environments are highly variable as a result. For this reason the limnology of streams and reservoirs occupies an important part of the following discussion. This section is followed by two topics—sedimentation and bottom fauna—selected from the research on glacial lakes. They were chosen as examples of the type of contributions made to limnology by Central States biologists. The work of the Stone Laboratory was not included here since it will be reviewed in the chapter on the limnology of the St. Lawrence Great Lakes.

Fishery research has been very active in the region, and again it has not been possible to give complete coverage to this subject. The broad concept of fish production has been used to bring together a variety of material. This last major topic is followed by short sections on centers of limnological research and on the specialized environments of caves and strip-mine drainage.

Water resources

Rainfall and topography control the water resources in the Central States of West Virginia, Ohio, Indiana, Kentucky, and Tennessee. The Allegheny Mountains form the eastern boundary of this section of the country, and the western section borders on the prairie. The Wisconsin glacier, which covered the northern two-thirds of Ohio and Indiana, influenced stream flow and left some kettle-hole lakes as reminders. Equal in importance with topography is the continental climate with widely fluctuating seasonal temperature and rainfall. Temperatures range from freezing or below in the winter to humid heat in the summer, which often reaches 38° C. Sudden temperature changes are frequently experienced, and the weather can vary as much as 16° C in a 24-hour period during the spring and fall.

A comparatively heavy annual rainfall ranging between 102 and 127 cm is concentrated in the cool months of the year. As much as 203 cm have been recorded in the mountains of eastern Tennessee. Seasonal fluctuations are the rule, and, as a result, alternating periods of floods and drought are commonplace. Many streams flow intermittently, drying up in summer and becoming raging torrents in winter and spring. For example, in 1948 the flow of the Harpeth River, a comparatively small stream in central Tennessee, varied from 3182 cfs in February to 1.3 cfs in September. Year-to-year variations are great as well. In 1950 the Harpeth averaged 879 cfs per day and only 137 cfs per day in 1941, representing the extremes in a 14-year period of observations (Tennessee Dept. Conserv., 1961).

Streams are the greatest surface water resource and with few exceptions in this region drain westward into the Mississippi River. Clear, cold, torrential streams cascade from the Allegheny Mountains of eastern West Virginia, Kentucky, and Tennessee to the lower elevations where they become the warm, murky waters of the Ohio and Mississippi valleys. Warm-water streams dominate cold-water streams by a large margin.

The Ohio River cuts the Central States into two nearly equal parts (Fig. 7.1). The major tributaries arising north of the river are the Muskingum, Scioto, and Miami rivers of Ohio and the Wabash River of Indiana. To the south, West Virginia contributes the Kanawha River, and through Kentucky and Tennessee flow the Licking, Kentucky, Green, Cumberland, and Tennessee rivers. A few small streams of western Kentucky and Tennessee enter the Mississippi River directly.

The exceptions to the Mississippi drainage are found on the eastern and northern borders. A continental divide in West Virginia separates the eastward-flowing Potomac drainage from the upper reaches of the Ohio River. A few Ohio streams, such as the Maumee, Sandusky, and Cuyahoga rivers, flow northward into Lake Erie of the Great Lakes drainage, and northern Indiana contributes some of its stream flow to Lake Michigan. None of these streams compares in size with the great rivers of the Ohio Valley.

The Central States have been cursed with flooding. Huge reservoirs have been constructed to regulate stream flow and reduce the danger to lives and property. The dams often serve several purposes: regulate stream flow, create a source of hydroelectric power, and provide uninterrupted navigation on the larger rivers. The Tennessee Valley Authority (TVA) and the U.S. Army Corps of Engineers are responsible for a unique and priceless source of water in Kentucky and Tennessee. Development on the Tennessee River basin began in 1936 with Norris Dam, and now 22 dams are located on the main stream and its tributaries (Fig. 7.2). In addition, seven dams are located in the Cumberland River basin, one on the Kentucky River, and another in the Big Sandy drainage. There are about 532,000 acres of water in these large reservoirs. The largest is Kentucky Lake which extends nearly through the north-south dimension of western Kentucky into the northwestern portion of its neighboring state, Tennessee. The Corps of Engineers is actively continuing its work. Five major dams are under construction in Kentucky, and flood-control planning is active in West Virginia, Ohio, and Indiana where several structures have already been installed.

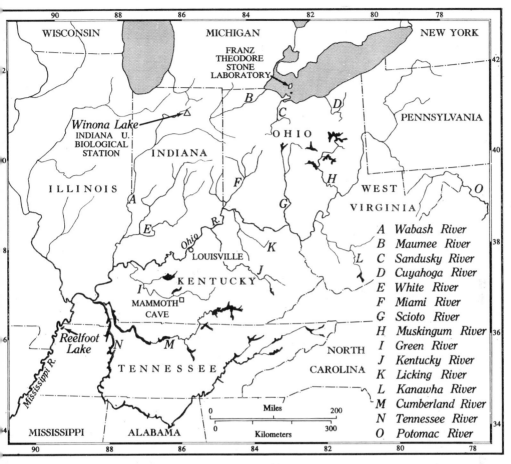

ig. 7.1.—Map of the Central States showing the *rincipal* rivers. Prepared by the University of Wis-*onsin* Cartographic Laboratory.

The same purpose has been served by a differ-*nt* agency in Ohio. A unique Water Conservancy *w* allows a basin-wide program of water man-*gement* to be initiated on petition of landowners *r* political subdivisions. The law was passed in *913* after the state suffered disastrously from *oods* the previous year. There are now 22 water *onservancy* districts and subdistricts, and the *reation* of reservoirs has been one of their major *ctivities.*

Summer drought is a continual threat. It is *articularly* serious in rural areas where a de-*endable* water supply is vital for sheep and *attle.* Literally thousands of farm ponds have *een* built to prevent a shortage of water in late *ummer.* Records of these small ponds, which *ary* from about 0.25 to 5.0 acres, are incom-

plete, but there are an estimated 110,000 in the Central States. Ponds have great practical im-portance because they are also used for recrea-tional fishing and may offer a water supply for the home. The role of these small bodies of water in the limnology of the region is described in the chapter on farm ponds.

The limnological importance of the glacial lakes far outweighs the area they occupy. Until reservoir building gained popularity, they were the only important source of standing water in the Central States. Repeated readvances of the Wisconsin glacier left about 1000 kettle-hole lakes in northern Indiana and additional ones scattered in northwestern Ohio and along the southern border of Lake Erie. Oxbows, abandoned chan-nels of the major rivers, are the only other nat-

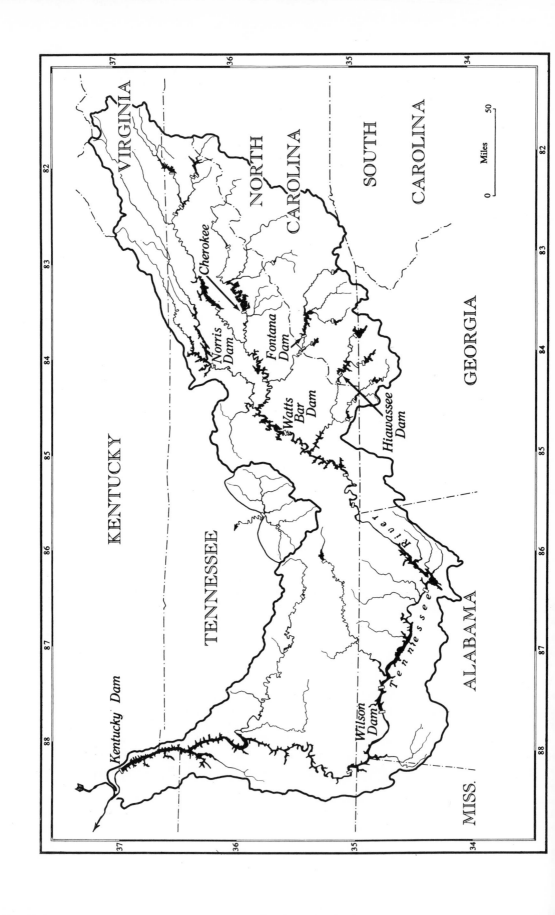

ural lakes in the area. They are comparatively few in number and have not received the attention they deserve.

Karst topography is an unusual feature of the landscape of southern Indiana, Kentucky, Tennessee, and western West Virginia. Solution of the limestone bedrock has resulted in extensive systems of underground streams and caverns, of which Mammoth Cave, Kentucky, is the best known. The roofs of the caverns sometimes collapse from the weight of the overlying soil, forming sinkholes which pock-mark the countryside. The drainage holes may become plugged on occasion and may form ponds known as solution ponds. The underground streams contain a unique aquatic fauna devoid of sight and pigmentation which has excited the interest of limnologists and evolutionists alike.

Fluctuating water levels

Reservoirs

Physicochemical conditions.—The operation of a multipurpose storage reservoir (Figs. 7.3 and 7.4) is designed to take advantage of the seasonal cycle in rainfall. By the first of each year the reservoir is drawn to its lowest level to provide space for flood storage. The flood pool is gradually filled during the cold, rainy season in winter and spring. The summer drawdown provides water for navigation and electric power production, and by the end of the year the minimum storage capacity is again reached.

The wide fluctuation in water volume from season to season is responsible for radical departures from the ordinary thermal and chemical stratification observed in glacial lakes which, by comparison, have small inflows and outflows. From November to April there is nearly complete vertical mixing of a homothermous water mass in the TVA reservoirs. Thermal stratification takes place during summer, but the causes are somewhat different from those described for natural lakes. The surface water warms by insolation and is reinforced by large volumes of warm water from tributary streams. This water, less dense than the colder hypolimnion, remains near the surface. A rather thin thermocline stratum develops. Water temperature of the hypolimnion is in the neighborhood of 10° C and has no oxygen by late summer. Water is discharged from the reservoir from below the upper limit of the hypolimnion. This general description will be supplemented with detailed observations on the development of massive density currents.

The entrance of flood waters into the reservoirs creates density currents, which vary in size and position according to the volume and tempera-

Fig. 7.3. Watts Bar Dam is a main-stream reservoir operated primarily for maintaining proper depth for navigation. Watts Bar is on the Tennessee River, in Meigs and Rhea counties, Tennessee (see Fig. 7.2). It is 112 ft high, 2960 ft long, and impounds a lake of 38,600 acres. Length of the lake is 72.4 mi. Published by permission of the Tennessee Valley Authority.

Fig. 7.4.—Fontana Dam is a storage reservoir of the TVA system. It is the highest dam east of the Rocky Mountains, towering 146 m. Fontana is on the Little Tennessee River in North Carolina and borders the Great Smoky Mountains Park (see Fig. 7.2.). Published by permission of the Tennessee Valley Authority.

ture of the incoming water mass and the conditions in the reservoir. Density currents were first detected by the presence of a layer of water with a low dissolved oxygen content interposed between strata with much higher concentrations. This was called the "D.O. dip." Wiebe (1938, 1939, 1940, 1941) described this and associated phenomena in Norris Reservoir, Tennessee. On 16 August 1937 oxygen was 8.7 ppm in the surface waters near the dam, and between 7 and 8.5 m it decreased precipitously to 2.0 ppm. After another maximum of 6.0 ppm at 23 m, the oxygen content declined gradually to 4.0 ppm at the maximum depth of 67 m. The oxygen-deficient stratum was also characterized by distinctive methyl orange alkalinity, free CO_2, pH, and turbidity. The atypical sheet of water extended the entire width of the reservoir and was traced for 20 mi toward the headwaters. The condition persisted in the face of a typical thermal stratification until November 4 when it disappeared. The distribution of oxygen and temperature on 7 September was typical of conditions prevailing in the reservoir while it was under the influence of the density current (Fig. 7.5).

The factors responsible for the sheet of intrusion water were uncovered by taking vertical series of oxygen measurements the entire length of the reservoir during the summer and autumn. Stagnation developed rapidly at the head of the reservoir where the warm, turbid Clinch River entered with a high oxygen demand, while the oxygen content of the hypolimnial water near the dam was still high. As the summer progressed, the hypolimnion was gradually removed by drawdown at the dam, creating a tendency for the incoming water to move downstream at its density level. The identity of the intrusion sheet was lost in November when it merged with the hypolimnial water that still remained. Similar density currents were observed in Hiawassee Reservoir, North Carolina, Herrington Lake, Kentucky, and Wilson Reservoir, Alabama.

An even more dramatic example of the formation of density currents was reported by Lyman (1944) for Cherokee Reservoir, Tennessee (Figs. 7.6 and 7.7). The Holston River above Cherokee flooded in May 1942, and a huge mass of turbid water poured into the reservoir in a period of a week. The Holston River's average flow is 4270 cfs, but on May 22 it was 21,000 cfs. The volume of the reservoir rose 26% above its mid-May capacity. The river water entered as a wedge-shaped mass, which met its greatest thermal resistance at 5–10 m and spread out fan-like across the reservoir at approximately the center of this interval. It "stepped over" the thermocline, depressing it 10 m in the process. The hypolimnion was entirely undisturbed. The net result of the flood was a thickening of the epilimnion by 5–7

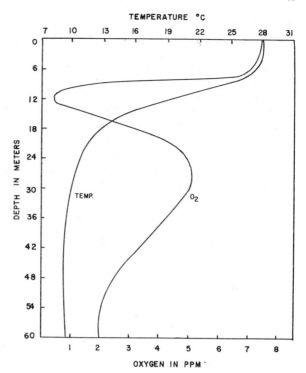

Fig. 7.5.—Oxygen and temperature distribution of Norris Lake, Tennessee, on 7 Sept. 1937. The low oxygen concentration at 12 m indicates the presence of a density current. Copied from Wiebe, 1938.

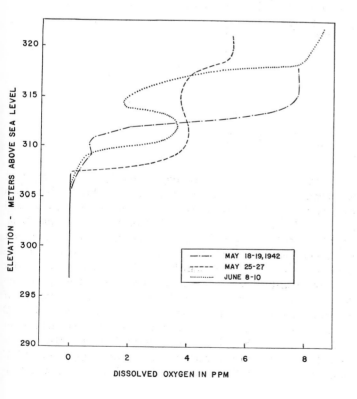

Fig. 7.6.—Oxygen distribution in Cherokee Reservoir, Tennessee, in 1942. The peculiar changes are due to a massive density current caused by stream floods entering the reservoir. Copied from Figure 3 of Lyman, 1944.

m because of a drop in the upper limit of the thermocline and a reduction in the thickness of that layer.

Density currents with their typically low oxygen content and high turbidity could be expected to influence aquatic life. There have been no critical studies of the plankton, but the reactions of the fish to stagnant sheets of intrusion water are well documented in Norris Reservoir (Dendy, 1945, 1946). Gill nets were set in 1943 and 1944 extending from the shoreline to deep water, and a record was kept of the depth at

water above (Fig. 7.8). Several other species reacted in the same manner as the sauger.

Dendy made it clear that the influence of the density layer on fish distribution was secondary in importance to temperature. Each species had a temperature preference, which was expressed by the depth at which the majority of individuals were found (Fig. 7.9). The largemouth bass (*Micropterus salmoides*) was found most often at temperatures above 27° C, and the majority of the sauger were distributed at depths where the temperature ranged between 18 and 22° C.

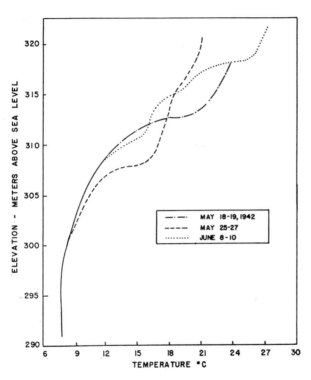

Fig. 7.7.—Temperature profile of Cherokee Reservoir, Tennessee, during a period when a massive density current entered the reservoir (compare with Fig. 7.5). Copied from Figure 4 of Lyman, 1944.

which each individual was captured. The depth of capture was influenced by the temperature of the water and a density current which made its appearance in late June 1943 at a depth of 7 m with 0.4 ppm oxygen. The current gradually made its way toward the dam and sank as a result of drawdown. The intrusion water was 11.5 m deep in mid-August and 13 m by the first week in September. Sauger (*Stizostedion canadense*) were distributed below the density current when it was first noticed in July. They remained there until the oxygen was almost completely exhausted. The fish were then forced to move through the stagnant layer to reach the aerated

The outpouring of the hypolimnial water at the discharge gates has a profound effect upon the character of water downstream (Dendy and Stroud, 1949). Construction of Fontana Dam, North Carolina, completely changed the habitat of the downstream reservoirs, Cheoah and Calderwood, which preceded it in time. The latter lakes were much smaller and warmer than Fontana. The 1938 August surface temperature of Calderwood was 30° C and at 7 m was 27° C before the influence of Fontana was felt. After the closure of Fontana Dam in 1944, Calderwood's surface temperature dropped to 21° C and at 7 m was 13.5° C. Discharge into Fon-

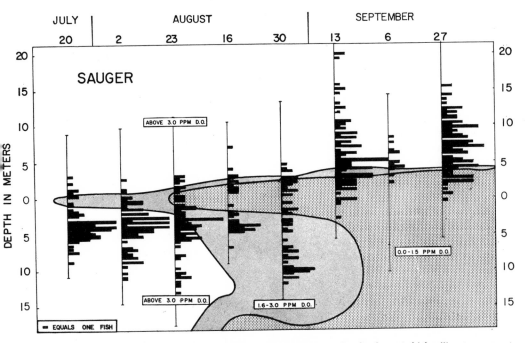

Fig. 7.8.—Distribution of sauger in relation to oxygen depletion in Norris Reservoir, Tennessee, in 1943 during the time when a density current was flowing through the reservoir. The position of the density current is represented as being at a constant level, and all other variables are related to it. The vertical lines represent the depths at which gill nets were set. The upper end of these lines is at the surface of the water and the lower end is at the maximum depth at which the nets were set. The histograms indicate the number of sauger caught at each depth. Graph slightly modified from Dendy, 1945.

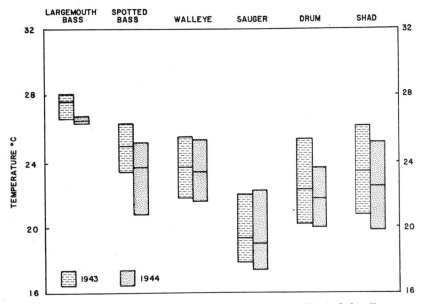

Fig. 7.9.—Temperature distribution of six species of fish in Norris Lake, Tennessee. The horizontal line indicates the average temperature preference of each species, and the vertical distance represents the range in temperature over which the fish was distributed. Copied from Dendy, 1946.

tana's sluices and turbines is drawn from the hypolimnion where the August temperature is 13° C and oxygen content is 6 ppm. Thick density currents pass through Cheoah Reservoir and thence into Calderwood with little change in either temperature or oxygen content. The Little Tennessee River, below the last in this series of dams, was once a warm-water stream, but under the dominating influence of Fontana's water it has been converted into a cold-water stream where trout have been stocked successfully.

Successional changes in benthos and plankton. —The construction of reservoirs offers a unique opportunity to study successional changes that take place as streams change suddenly to lakes. Limnologists of the Central States have not taken full advantage of this opportunity; much research is required to appreciate the magnitude of the changes and the amount of time needed to make the shift from a lotic to a lenitic environment.

There have been no complete "before and after" investigations of successional changes in bottom fauna among the large reservoirs of the region. Roach (1933) sampled the zooplankton, phytoplankton, and bottom fauna in the pools formed by low dams on three streams in Ohio and in the normally flowing sections upstream from the impoundments. Phytoplankton was the same or greater in the natural portions of streams than in the impoundments, but this relation did not hold for the zooplankton or benthos. In two of three cases the zooplankton was more numerous in the impounded areas, and there was no consistent difference in the quantity of benthos between the natural stream and the impoundment. The species composition of the two habitats was not reported.

Lyman (1943) and Lyman and Dendy (1945) made pre-impoundment bottom fauna studies of the Tennessee River and Holston River near the points where they were to be dammed to create Watts Bar and Cherokee reservoirs, respectively. These rivers contrasted in their physical characteristics; the first was predominantly a deep-water habitat with a mud-sand bottom, and the second was principally a shallow, riffle area over limestone and shale. It was to be expected that the benthos would be strikingly different, and this was the case.

In the deep water (10 m) of the Watts Bar area, Ephemeroptera, Diptera, Oligochaeta, and

Anisoptera made up practically all of the fauna. Trichoptera made their appearance in water about 0.5 m deep accompanied by the above-named groups. The mud bottom was the most productive, and *Hexagenia bilineata,* a burrowing mayfly, was the dominant component of this habitat (*ca.* 60% by numbers and by volume). The benthic population was 238 organisms per m^2 in July 1941 and progressively increased to 1004 per m^2 in December. This seasonal pattern of abundance was reproduced in the Cherokee area, although the area was much more productive; 497 organisms per m^2 were found in August and 6836 per m^2 in November. Domestic sewage and industrial waste pollution accounted for at least a part of the difference between sites. Trichoptera, Diptera, and Megaloptera were the dominant insect groups in this riffle environment, comprising 90% of the total number of organisms collected and from 70 to 90% by volume.

The authors predicted that the riffle forms of neither area would survive impoundment because of their lack of adaptability to standing water. Watts Bar was thought to be in a particularly advantageous position because of its large *Hexagenia* population, which would be likely to thrive under the new conditions. Certain members of the Diptera which have a wide range in tolerance gave promise of "seeding" both lakes quickly. There has been no follow-up to confirm these predictions, but no one will deny that "before and after" studies under a variety of conditions would be exceedingly interesting. O'Connell and Campbell's (1953) work on the Black River, Missouri, showed that the time lag can be expected to be very short between a typical lotic fauna and the development of a lenitic fauna.

The species composition of the planktonic entomostraca changes rapidly after a reservoir is built. Yeatman (1954) acquired an intimate knowledge of the copepod fauna of the Elk River and ponds in its valley before it became the 5000-acre Woods Reservoir in Franklin County, Tennessee. *Diaptomus pallidus, Tropocyclops prasinus,* and *Mesocyclops leuckarti* occurred in the river before the dam was built, and *Mesocyclops edax* inhabited a nearby pond which was later flooded. *D. pallidus* and *M. leuckarti* were both found in the reservoir, but they became scarcer during the sampling period from June 1953 to November 1954. The other species increased in abundance during the same time.

Diaptomus pallidus bloomed soon after the reservoir began to fill in June but became scarce by August and made an insignificant appearance the following year. Yeatman attributed this change to competition by *Diaptomus reighardi*, which was not collected before impoundment but which became a dominant form during the first 18 months of the reservoir's life. *Daphnia longispina galeata* was a brief member of the cladoceran population in June and July 1953 but was not collected thereafter. Yeatman points out that his results are similar to changes in the copepod fauna of Reelfoot Lake, Tennessee, reported by Eddy (1930) and Hoff (1944a). Four species were found by the former and nine by the latter. Only *Cyclops vernalis* was listed by both. Apparently the species composition of this lake had changed considerably in 14 years.

Streams

Physicochemical conditions.—The flow of a typical small stream of the Central States varies enormously with the seasonal rainfall. During the autumn it may become intermittent with pools separated by gravel bars, or it may dry up entirely. The rains of winter and spring swell the stream to the point where it often spills over its banks. Localized heavy rains during summer produce "flash floods" nearly every year. Such large variations in stream flow cause constantly changing physicochemical conditions and a variable flora and fauna.

Mountain streams on the eastern border are in the minority and have not been studied extensively. Powers (1929) undertook a survey of the West Fork of the Little Pigeon River and the East Prong of the Little River in Smoky Mountain National Park. His most interesting results centered around measurements of pH, temperature, and alkalinity from an altitude of about 1300 m to the broad valleys of the foothills. Each of these factors increased with decreasing altitude. The streams were largely acid in character, ranging from pH 5.92 to 7.42, and poorly buffered with carbonates and bicarbonates. Shoup (1940) also studied the streams of eastern Tennessee and found the total alkalinity, expressed as carbonate, to be very low, ranging from 2 to 45 ppm and averaging about 12 ppm.

Shoup's (1947, 1950) studies of mountain and lowland streams in Tennessee led to the recognition of ten different regions of the state on the basis of water quality. Total alkalinity, expressed as carbonate, ranged from about 11 ppm in streams originating in crystalline rocks of granites, gneisses, and schists to 140 ppm in streams arising in magnesium limestones. There was a notable agreement between the geological description of the formations and the chemistry of the water flowing over them. Shoup cautioned against interpreting the chemistry of certain rivers as reflecting the geology of the immediate area. For example, the mainstream of the Cumberland River has a total carbonate alkalinity of 65 ppm while flowing over relatively soluble Ordovician limestones. Adjacent tributaries have 150 ppm carbonate alkalinity. The Cumberland arises in mountainous regions of insoluble rocks, and its water dilutes that of its tributaries. The nature of the geologic formation is shown to best advantage by the chemistry of a small stream which flows in a single stratum.

Intermittent streams have made some unusual contributions to stream limnology (Neel, 1951; Schneller, 1955; Slack, 1955). One of the most interesting is the reciprocal relationship between photosynthesis and decomposition in alternating riffles and pools. Neel made careful analyses of carbonates and bicarbonates in Boone Creek near Lexington, Kentucky, a stream which originates in spring-fed brooks of the bluegrass pastures of that region and cuts through 130 m of Ordovician limestone on its way to the Kentucky River. Photosynthesis had its greatest effect in the spring when benthic algae were abundant in the riffles. Decomposition dominated when the stream pooled up in the fall and deciduous leaves began to decay. In times of normal flow carbonates were greatest over the riffles where photosynthesis by the periphyton removed the CO_2 from the bicarbonates. The reverse occurred in the pools. Monocarbonates snapped up the free CO_2 as soon as it formed from decay of organic matter which accumulated there. Regeneration of bicarbonates in pools permits relatively constant amounts to be maintained in solution. Oxygen and pH levels depend upon the outcome of the struggle between the two mutually counteracting forces, photosynthesis and decomposition.

On rare occasions there is insufficient carbonate to remove the CO_2 being produced, and carbonic acid reacts slightly with the limestone stream bed to increase the methyl orange alkalinity to a small degree. Neel, Slack, and Schneller all agree that acid action of stream water is of minor importance in erosion. Most of the carbonates and other mineral salts are brought into the stream by the flow of ground water, pollution excepted.

Thermal stratification was noticed by both Neel and Slack when intermittent streams were in low stages. Density currents may form in pools of as little as 0.7 m in depth. Warm water may flow over a stationary bottom layer after a warm, summer rain. Conversely, cold water may pass under a warm surface layer if the riffle water drops to a lower temperature than the pool at night.

Schneller and Slack were both impressed by the "black-water" condition that develops with considerable regularity in Indiana streams when low stages of stream flow coincide with the autumnal fall of leaves. Slack describes the water as first becoming brown, then gradually changing to opaque, purplish-black. The color is so intense that it cannot be read with a U.S. Geological Survey water color outfit. During these periods free CO_2 concentration as great as 49 ppm has been observed in the Styx-like water, and oxygen is either extremely low or nil. Schneller did not find evidence that organisms suffered unduly from the "black water" in Salt Creek, Indiana, but the conditions were not so severe as in nearby Brummetts Creek where Slack worked. Slack made direct observations at a time when both fish and invertebrates were suffocating.

Each pool and riffle acquires distinct physico-chemical characteristics during the middle and low stages of stream flow. At these stages the stream water is very sensitive to changes in the intensity of solar radiation, and the chemical conditions are exaggerated. Individuality of riffles is due to (1) variation in amount of surface exposed per unit volume of water, (2) the degree of exposure, which is governed by the relative amount of shade provided by trees, (3) nature of the bottom, and (4) chemical conditions prevailing in the pool above. Individuality of pools is attributed to (1) conditions prevailing in the riffle above, (2) extent of decomposition, (3) depth and area, and (4) degree of exposure.

Plankton and bottom fauna.—Studies of the plankton of the Hocking River in southeastern Ohio have contributed substantially to this phase of stream limnology (Roach, 1932; Hutchison,

1939). Roach took samples of zooplankton with a Foerst trap and samples of phytoplankton by centrifugation in October, November, January, and April. The fall and winter collections were made at an exceptionally low stage of the river after a severe drought in the summer of 1930. Just before the spring samples were taken, the river had risen over 4 m as a result of heavy rain. These conditions affected the plankton populations considerably, as would be expected.

The population of all plankters averaged about 5 billion /m³ in the autumn, 2¼ billion/m³ in the winter, and 600 million/m³ in the spring. Diatoms were the dominant form of phytoplankton, represented by nine genera. Seven genera of rotifers were the most numerous of the zooplankters. Vertical stratification was lacking, and no difference was found in the size of the population between the center and edge of the stream. Roach's results confirmed Kofoid's (1903) conclusions "that the plankton of the channel is not immediately derived from the tributaries, but comes in large part from the impounding backwaters, and at low-water stages is almost exclusively indigenous in the channel itself."

The effect of the spring flood was to flush the plankton from the river. Only 20 genera were found at this time, compared with 33 in winter and 42 in autumn. Five days after the flood subsided, small plankters appeared in substantial numbers, and ten days later a well-balanced association was evident, although the populations were small. Apparently stream plankton recovers quickly from the effects of flooding.

Hutchison concentrated his efforts on the zooplankton and confirmed several of Roach's findings. For example, a November 1935 sample taken a day after the first heavy precipitation for a month yielded an unusually high population. Hutchison attributed this result to the flushing of organisms from the tributaries, since the winter population in subsequent months was low and compared favorably with the October sample of the year following. Year-to-year variability in zooplankton populations is so great that some caution must be exercised in accepting Hutchison's interpretation without further substantiating evidence. Zooplankton was more abundant in the fall than at any other time of year (Fig. 7.10), again confirming Roach's results, and Hutchison concluded that the greatest productivity occurred when hydrographic conditions were most stable.

The headwaters of the Hocking River had a lower plankton population than any other portion. Lackey *et al.* (1943) also found in Four Mile Creek, Ohio, an increase in plankton downstream in number of individuals but not of species. Hutchison also learned that the slowly flowing water of the lower portion of the river stimulated no greater plankton populations than did the more swiftly flowing water of the mid-portion. Fifty-two genera of zooplankton were col-

of this subject, and it is not intended to discuss the subject extensively here. It is sufficient to say that a large amount of research on the subject has been done in the Central States. Lackey (1938a) discussed the possibility of using protozoan plankton as indicators of pollution in his study of the Scioto River, Ohio. These remarks were extended in a detailed appraisal of the pollution of the Scioto by Kehr *et al.* (1941) and in a monograph on the ecological factors af-

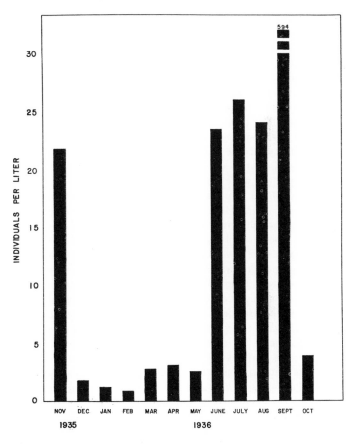

Fig. 7.10.—Monthly distribution of zooplankton in the Hocking River, Ohio. The November sample was collected a day after the first heavy precipitation in a month. Copied from Hutchison, 1939.

lected. *Paramecium, Stentor, Euplotes, Vorticella,* and *Philodina* were characteristic of the headwaters, while *Arcella, Eudorina, Pandorina, Keratella, Brachionus, Noteus, Polyarthra,* copepods, and insect larvae appeared more often in the lower portions of the stream.

Pollution cannot be disregarded in dealing with the biology of the streams of the Central States, and the Hocking River is no exception. Domestic pollution and mine wastes entering the stream were taken into account by both Hutchison and Roach. They attempted no definitive treatment

fecting the distribution of Protozoa (Lackey 1938b). Lackey (1938c, 1942a, 1942b) has also made several other studies of the effects of domestic pollution and industrial wastes upon the plankton. The White River in Indiana is one of the best documented streams in the United States in this respect (Palmer, 1932; Coffing, 1937; Denham, 1938; Brinley, 1942; Hupp, 1943; Lackey and Hupp, 1956).

The Hocking River has also played an important part in the development of studies on bottom fauna productivity. Ludwig (1932) made detailed investigations of the influence of substrate on benthic populations, seasonal variation, depth distribution, and the relative size of the standing crops in riffles and pools. The bottom fauna was unaffected by the depth of the water up to 50 cm, but beyond 100 cm a decrease was evident. Riffles were more heavily populated than pools, generally speaking, but there were exceptions. The total numbers and kinds of insect larvae were smaller in April than in autumn, whereas the size of populations of other forms was greater. Ludwig attributed the low insect population to the short time that elapsed between the close of winter conditions and the time the samples were taken.

The results on seasonal variation in benthic productivity were confirmed by Stehr and Branson (1938), who included summer and winter samples as well as those taken during spring and autumn in their work on Rock Riffle, a headwater tributary of the Hocking River. Spring samples contained 180 and fall samples had 777 organisms per m², while summer and winter collections had 39 and 12 per m², respectively. Rock Riffle, as well as the Hocking itself, had a fluctuating water level during the sampling period. Up to 7-m floods swept the former stream, and benthic counts were always low after such catastrophes. Repopulation was accounted for by egg-laying of insects from neighboring bodies of water and by immigration of some of the larger forms from the Hocking. Crustacea, Mollusca, and annelids were replenished for the most part by reproduction of the survivors.

Considerable portions of Rock Riffle dry up during the late summer and fall. Crustacea, worms, and mollusks withstand the drought by burrowing below the surface of the stream bed where moisture is present. Many of these and other forms either perish from the dry conditions or are subject to heavy predation by terrestrial animals which move into the dry stream bed to feed. The predators were observed to feed actively throughout the length of the stream at night.

Denham (1938) also observed the effect of fluctuating water levels on the bottom fauna of White River, Indiana. Sand bars were populated during a rise in water level, and the organisms were left stranded when the water receded. He observed burrowing by certain forms and migration back to the main channel by others. By setting up conditions resembling a receding water level in the laboratory, he demonstrated that midges and oligochaetes burrowed, while *Heptagenia, Tricorythrus, Caenis, Baetis,* and *Hydropsyche* migrated toward a receding water line. Apparently many organisms can survive such violent changes in the habitat.

All of the authors mentioned above have been struck by the exceedingly great variation among samples of benthos taken in different parts of streams, regardless of the sampling methods employed. This fact has directed effort toward studies of substrate preference by bottom organisms. Uniformly, sand was the poorest environment (Wene, 1940; Murray, 1938; Ludwig, 1932; and Denham, 1938). Other substrates produced greater quantities of benthos, and the results depended upon the types of bottom the investigator chose to study. Clay-loam contained the greatest number of chironomid larvae among a variety of bottom types examined by Wene. Murray found gravel more productive than mud, gravel-sand, or sand bottoms. Shockley (1949) and Murray both observed that vegetated areas contained more organisms than barren ones. Hunt (1930), Shockley, and Ludwig pointed out the species differences that occur on different bottom types. Chance provides isolated environmental conditions which are especially desirable compared with closely adjacent areas. Shockley described a great abundance of Trichoptera larvae in a small clump of leaves that had accumulated on the upstream side of rocks, and Ludwig cited similar examples.

The quantitative sampling of stream benthos leaves much to be desired because of the many variables that control population density. Nevertheless, average populations may be of some value for comparison. In addition to the figures quoted above, Ludwig counted 836 organisms/m² in the Hocking River; Murray reported an average of 2101/m² in 33 northern Indiana streams, and Denham collected 1437/m² in White River. All values were computed after excluding samples that were affected by pollution. Slack (1955) found 1909/m² in Jacks Defeat Creek in June compared with 506/m² in Brummetts Creek during the same month. When the creeks became low in July, the organisms were more concentrated, but the difference between the creeks remained the same, 3411/m² in Jacks Defeat compared with 2071/m² in Brummetts. The first-named

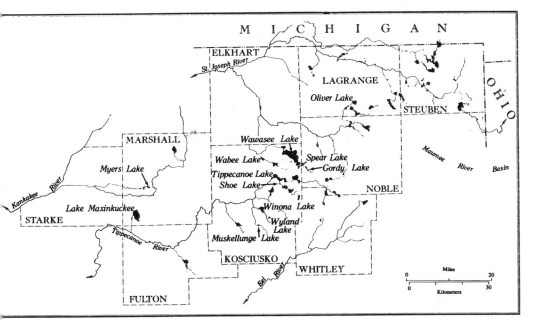

Fig. 7.11.—Lake district of northeastern Indiana. Lakes which are referred to in the text are identified. Prepared by the University of Wisconsin Cartographic Laboratory.

stream had greater quantities of carbonate, nitrate, nitrite, phosphate, and chloride than the second. Mollusks were virtually absent in Brummetts Creek, but its quantity of benthos was below that of Jacks Defeat even though snails were excluded from the computation. Shoup (1943) has also shown that mollusks are less abundant in streams with low concentrations of dissolved salts. The quantitative and qualitative differences between Slack's streams were a true reflection of differences in the supply of dissolved nutrient materials together with the effects of various physical factors.

Glacial lakes

Sedimentation

The origin, rate of accumulation, and composition of sediment in the bottom of lakes is of fundamental importance with respect to the process of eutrophication. Some of the pioneer work in this field of limnology was initiated on the northern Indiana lakes (Wilson, 1936, 1938; Scott and Miner, 1936; Wilson and Opdyke, 1941). The research was done by making borings through the sediments to the original basin, by collecting sediment samples in jars suspended at intervals from the surface to the bottom, and by analyzing sediments for carbonates, silicates, and organic matter. From the considerable body of data it has been possible to formulate a theory to account for the deposition of materials, to reconstruct the history of two lakes from glacial times to the present, and to predict the fate of these lakes.

Before launching the discussion of sedimentation, some comment about the formation of the lakes is in order (Scott, 1916, 1931). The principal belt of glacial lakes in Indiana extends from the northeastern corner of the state for about 75 mi in a southwesterly direction (Fig. 7.11). Three lobes of the Wisconsin glacier projected into the state during the late stages of the Pleistocene period, the Michigan lobe from the northwest, the Saginaw from the north, and the Huron-Erie from the northeast. The Michigan lobe left relatively few lakes as it retreated, compared with the number formed in the interlobate region between the Saginaw and Huron-Erie. Some of the lakes were termed "channel lakes" in the early literature since they were interpreted as having been formed in glacial outwash channels. This interpretation has been chal-

TABLE 7.1

Comparison of sedimentation in Winona and Tippecanoe lakes, Indiana. From Wilson, 1938.

	Winona Lake	Tippecanoe Lake
Area of original basin (m²)	3,244,000	3,630,000
Area of present basin (m²)	2,030,000	2,870,000
% of area obliterated	37	21
Volume of original basin (m³)	33,925,000	48,300,000
Volume of present basin (m³)	19,100,000	32,900,000
% of basin filled with sediment	44	32
Average depth of sediment (m)	4.55	4.26

lenged by the sedimentation studies, and the lakes are presently accepted as typical "kettle-hole" lakes left by melting blocks of ice.

All of the lakes exhibit thermal stratification, and a wide variety of oxygen conditions prevails (Frey, 1955). One of the most interesting conditions in this regard is a metalimnetic oxygen maximum, which has been found on several occasions and has been described in detail for Myers Lake (Eberly, 1959). By far the majority are eutrophic, but a few can be regarded as mesotrophic since oxygen is present throughout the summer in the hypolimnion.

Wilson made 75 borings in Winona Lake and 103 borings in Tippecanoe Lake to chart the depth and composition of the sediment. The borings were made by driving a 4.3-cm iron pipe casing into the bottom from an anchored float. Tubing of 1.2-cm diameter was placed inside. Water was forced into the tubing, thereby flushing sediment upward between the casing and tubing to the surface. Plugs of sediment were collected at selected depths by forcing the tubing into undisturbed bottom deposits. Scott and Miner suspended collecting jars on a float-anchor arrangement in the same pair of lakes for as long as five years.

The cores were taken in such a manner that the form of the original basin could be mapped and compared with that of the present basin. The bottom was extremely irregular just after it was formed; Tippecanoe Lake, for example, had ten depressions originally but now has three. Sedimentation has been responsible for evening out the irregularities. Deep water contained

thicker deposits than the shore zone. Wilson accounted for this by assuming that the sediments suspended by wave action along shore were evenly distributed over the whole lake by currents and mixed with particles originating in the open water. Much of the material found its way into the deepest portions of the lake, and less remained on knobs, ridges, or slopes. The differential thickness of bottom deposits can be explained on the basis of currents. Wave action and currents have a greater opportunity to pick up and resuspend fine sediments on slopes and exposed areas on the bottom than in the basins when the lake is in complete circulation. Several areas in Winona Lake had accumulated no deposits where the slope was 7–8°. The greatest regions of accumulation were in the basins and the edges of shelves on the shore side of the "drop-off." Tippecanoe sediments were 6.4, 4.3, 5.5, and 2.5 m in deep water, slopes, shelves, and littoral zone, respectively, in one cross section of the lake.

Evidence of climatic fluctuation and an explanation of the occurrence of "marl islands" were revealed by the borings. Alternating layers of sand and marl in the inlets of both lakes implied that more sand was carried by the streams and carried further into the lake in wet periods than in dry periods when deposits more characteristic of present-day conditions were laid down. Marl islands are mounds rising from the bottom to within one or two meters of the lake surface. Heavy deposition occurred on the knobs that were high enough to be in the photic zone and support the growth of higher plants. The plants not only contributed sediments to the knobs at a rapid rate but also furnished protection from currents which would ordinarily tend to dislodge the accumulations.

The average depth of sediment in Winona and Tippecanoe (4.55 and 4.26 m, respectively) is the same (Table 7.1), but since Winona is the smaller of the two, the results imply that its productivity per unit area is greater than that of Tippecanoe. Scott and Miner (1936), using collecting jars, had the same impression. Winona produced an average of 2.32 kg/m² per year of sediment compared with 1.4 kg in Tippecanoe. The area outside the 7-m contour, the near-shore zone, is nearly alike in the two lakes, 45.9% of the total in Winona and 47.0% in Tippecanoe, but there are some interesting differences in the formation and distribution of the sediment from this region. Winona Lake littoral zone has a greater average deposition per unit area of littoral area than Tippecanoe, which suggests that the shore of the first lake produces more sediment than that of the second. The results of Scott and Miner again supported Wilson's conclusion. The fact that Tippecanoe Lake has a less obliterated shore zone than Winona, but has the same proportion of area outside the 7-m contour, is explained on the assumption that Tippecanoe, being larger, has greater wave energies which more effectively erode the sediment from the littoral zone and transport it to deeper water.

The carbonate, silicate, and organic matter analyses of the Tippecanoe sediments by Wilson and Opdyke (1941) revealed that at least 80% was derived from autochthonous sources (Table 7.2). There was a lesser relative amount of carbonate in the deep water than in shallower water, since re-solution occurs in the hypolimnion because of the accumulations of CO_2 and the consequent formation of carbonic acid. This also explained the high percentage of silicates which are not so readily attacked by the acid. Re-solution of carbonates may also account for the relatively high proportion of organic matter in the deep water, but another factor may be responsible as well. Dead algae and other forms which reach the hypolimnion probably have a greater chance of falling intact to the bottom than the same organisms which die in the epilimnion where bacteria and fungi are more active. The first silicates deposited in the basin of the lake were derived largely from sand which had been washed out from the barren shores. Later deposits were largely made up of diatom shells and some sponge spicules. The increase in organic matter in the surface sediments (10.7%) compared with those first deposited (4.0%) is probably due to

an increase in plant and animal life as the lake ages.

The fate of the lakes can be described in Wilson's words.

With the persistence of the filling of the middle of the various basins more rapidly than the areas along shore are being obliterated and the filling on the outer edges of shelves (outside the "drop off") faster than on steep slopes, it can be predicted that a condition will be reached eventually where the lake basin will have the form of a broad flat emerged zone with a steep drop-off to a body of shallow water of uniform depth in the former deepest part of the basin. From this point on it can be predicted that the rate of filling in the center will be less rapid than the obliteration of the area around the edges, because as the lake becomes older, the rate of filling in the center will decelerate, due to less effective abrasion and circulation. This would be expected since, as the lake grows smaller, the waves become smaller. Also, with less wave action, accumulation at the edges would be expected to accelerate. The final shallow remnant of the lake would be expected to be obliterated by the typical encroaching mat-forming association of plants characteristic of bogs.

The description of the physical displacement and deposition of sediments has provided enormous help in reconstructing the developmental history of lakes, but the biologist would be more satisfied if successional stages could be correlated with changes in the aquatic flora and fauna. The study of animal microfossils shows promise of yielding important data on this question. Frey (1958, 1960a, 1960b) has recently begun intensive work on the cladoceran fauna of lake sediments. The first step was to identify to species the fragments of head shields, shells, postabdomens, postabdominal claws, and ephippia. This formidable task has proven successful, and his first effort was made on the sediments of Wallensen in north Germany. Microfossils proved to be very abundant, and the species in the sediments were the same as present-day European species. The number of species and the population density increased from the time of the pond's origin in the Older Dryas period into the Alleröd, indicating that the pond was undergoing progressive eutrophication.

The work has continued in this country with a study of the cladoceran remains in four lakes near Madison, Wisconsin, in which for many years Birge had worked over the fauna and listed 23 species of chydorids. Frey, with comparatively little effort, collected fragments of all of Birge's species in surface sediments and added six addi-

TABLE 7.2

Organic and inorganic composition of the sediments of Tippecanoe Lake, Indiana. From Wilson and Opdyke, 1941.

Depth zones of cores m	No. of samples	% carbonates	% silica	% organic matter
0 – 1.7	37	77.2	11.8	8.9
1.7–11.7	99	83.2	10.5	6.4
>11.7	148	65.5	27.4	7.8
Entire lake	284	72.8	19.1	7.4

tional forms to the list. The abundance of the cladoceran remains corresponded with the rank order of the four lakes in terms of phytoplankton and zooplankton standing crops. Thus, the quantitative changes of microfossil populations with time in a single lake may be expected to reflect real changes in the rates of production of Cladocera and their food organisms. Microfossil remains may ultimately contribute to lake typology by correlating the species composition with the limnological characteristics of their environment. Experimental studies will be required to learn the factors limiting the development of cladoceran species populations. Frey maintains a cladoceran microfossil reference collection in his laboratory at Indiana University.

Bottom fauna

Investigations of the benthos of the Indiana lakes have progressed concurrently with the interest in sedimentation. Initially these studies were independent of one another, but recently they have been integrated by the description of dipteran microfossils from cores (Stahl, 1959). Two papers by Scott *et al.* (1928, 1938) on lakes Wawasee and Tippecanoe were among the first published on the benthos of North American lakes. Of necessity they were largely descriptive in nature since the fauna was not well known at the time. Nevertheless, the authors keenly appreciated the quantitative approach and made estimates of the standing crops of the benthos in all parts of the lake.

Their contribution to methodology was the use of a hoe dredge, the first specialized instrument designed to sample the littoral zone. As its name implies, the dredge was pulled along the bottom with a long handle. Sediments and plants were collected in a trailing cloth bag. For quantitative work it was drawn through a metal frame of standard dimensions which was placed over the sampling site. The hoe dredge was an effective device for recovering the total littoral invertebrate fauna. It did not, however, separate the benthos from the phytomacrofauna, and the relative contribution of the bottom and the plants could not be ascertained. For this purpose Gerking (1957a) designed a scheme which allows this separation. The sampler consists of two square "shells" 77 cm high, one fitting inside the other. Plants enclosed by the sampler are cut at the base, a sliding door is inserted in the base of the inner shell, and this part of the sampler is removed. A hand-operated Ekman dredge collects a sample of mud from inside the outer shell. The phytomacrofauna has been successfully differentiated from the benthos in beds of three species of aquatic plants. The quantity of phytomacrofauna varied with the amount of leaf dissection, and the quantity of benthos varied with the degree of development of the root system.

The work on Wawasee and Tippecanoe lakes produced a comparative study which demonstrated that the two lakes could be differentiated on the basis of their benthic standing crops. Wawasee had a benthic population four times greater than Tippecanoe. Scott attributed the difference in benthic fauna to a difference in the slope of the bottom in the two lakes: Wawasee averaged 3.7% slope and Tippecanoe 7.2%. He felt that the slope influenced the quantity of aquatic plants, thereby affecting the habitat and food of insect larvae and other benthic organisms.

Slope, of course, is only one factor affecting the abundance of bottom-dwellers. Wohlschlag (1950) pointed out the complexity of this broad problem in his work on Wabee Lake, in which the benthos was significantly smaller than in either Tippecanoe or Wawasee (Table 7.3). A sizable portion of this lake has a marl bottom and is nearly devoid of plants. Weedy areas had a

TABLE 7.3

A comparison of benthic populations in Wawasee, Tippecanoe, and Wabee lakes, Indiana. The first two lakes were investigated by Scott *et al.* (1928, 1938) and the last by Wohlschlag (1950). The densely weeded Wabee stations have populations comparable with the averages for the other lakes, but this habitat is rare in Wabee. Values apply to collections made at depths less than two meters and are rounded to the nearest hundred.

			Wabee		
	Wawasee	Tippecanoe	Mixed vegetation	Chara	Barren marl
Number/m^2	2,100	1,400	2,000	5,900	500
Weight in mg/m^2	12,000	6,700	4,500	13,400	1,200

greater benthos than barren areas. Since plants played such a dominant role in the productivity of the fauna, experiments on the growth of plants in different soils were performed. Four soils were used: light gray marl, dark gray marl, sand, and peat. The last was more effective in promoting growth than were the other three. Sand had a negative interaction when mixed with either marl or peat. Wohlschlag was the first to employ the factorial experimental design to delineate effects of aquatic soils on plant growth.

Scott maintained an interest in the important subject of insect emergence over a period of

The emergence traps of Scott and Opdyke captured mostly midges and *Chaoborus* with caddis flies a poor second. The peak Diptera emergence took place between 6 and 12 P.M. with a smaller peak at 4–6 A.M. More caddis flies were taken between 6 and 10 A.M. than at other hours. Yearly variations were pronounced, but no significant variations were encountered between June and September. Perhaps the most interesting contribution involved a comparison of the number of larvae in the mud with the number of emerging imagines (Fig. 7.12). Emergence was much greater than would be expected on the

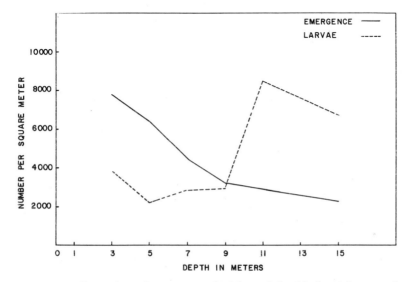

Fig. 7.12.—Comparison of emergence of adults and benthic insect larvae and pupae in Winona Lake, Indiana. Copied from Scott and Opdyke, 1941.

years. He and Opdyke (1941) completed one of the first papers on emergence. They captured the insects in a 50 cm × 50 cm pyramidal floating trap. The sides were covered with white muslin protected by chicken wire. They encountered several difficulties with their collectors, and in the course of their work they demonstrated that the muslin-covered traps collected more efficiently than those with opaque sides. Since the muslin itself allowed only a small proportion of the light to enter, it was probable that their collections were minimal. Wohlschlag (1950) borrowed the idea of emergence traps for his work on Wabee Lake but altered their design and operation. The traps were covered with translucent plastic for greater light penetration and were submerged below the surface for greater collecting efficiency.

basis of the number of larvae, and the number of adults captured over different depths did not correspond with the larval populations at the same depths. The greatest larval population was found at 11 m, but the greatest emergence occurred at a depth of 3 m. In fact, the ratio of emergence to number of larvae decreased progressively with depth. These results are still unexplained. Faulty sieving techniques, inshore migration of larvae or pupae, emergence at times of year not covered by the study, and different generation times for shallow and deep water forms were suggested as possibilities, and each suggestion offers fruitful ideas for further research.

As mentioned before, Stahl (1959) brought together information on benthos and sedimentation by identifying dipteran microfossils from a deep-water core of Myers Lake, Indiana. He identified the head capsules of *Sergentia coracina* in the lowermost section of the core (27.7 m) up to 21.8 m where it was the dominant profundal midge. Above that level it disappeared and was replaced by other forms. A survey of 16 other lakes in the vicinity brought to light the fact that this species survives only in those that have the greatest hypolimnial oxygen concentration. It seems reasonable to presume that *Sergentia* requires more oxygen than other species and lived in Myers Lake during its early history while the hypolimnion enjoyed at least a moderate supply of oxygen. As sedimentation reduced the volume of the hypolimnion, oxygen became a limiting factor and the species disappeared.

Fishery studies

Quantitative research on fish populations in the Central States has developed rapidly in the past twenty years and has contributed to practical and theoretical problems associated with the higher trophic levels of aquatic environments. There is a heavy emphasis on the production problem in limnology at the present time, and the research in the Central States has progressed to the point where fish production can be measured with reasonable accuracy. The computation of production of an organism, or the total quantity formed during a stated period of time regardless of whether or not all of the organisms survive to the end of that time, depends upon knowledge of the weight of the population at some point in time, the growth rate, and the survival rate. There are inherent problems in measuring each of the three facets of the overall problem, and each has received a share of attention. Production is, of course, largely governed by the food supply, and research is just beginning to bear fruit on this relationship.

Abundance

The problem of measuring the abundance of fish populations in natural waters has been intriguing, since direct counts are possible only in unique situations such as a spawning run. Mark-and-recapture methods have been devised by which a known number of marked fish are released, and the proportion of marked to unmarked individuals is determined in the catch. Two general kinds of abundance estimates have been made in the Central States. The Petersen

(1896) type of population estimate involves marking as large a group of fish as possible in a small interval of time and attempting to recapture them at a later time. The Schnabel (1938) method employs the recovery of marked fish while marking is in progress. The second is essentially the same as the first except that progressively more accurate estimates are made as the marked fish accumulate in the population. Shumacher and Eschmeyer (1943) designed another method, based on a modification of the Schnabel method, to estimate the fish population of Yellow Creek Pond in Tennessee. Their mathematical formulation is theoretically more sound in cases where the proportion of marked fish to the total population is high (0.25 or above), whereas Schnabel's is applicable to the more usual case where the proportion is low. In actual practice the differences between Schumacher and Schnabel estimates are small compared with the rather broad confidence limits associated with each.

Mark-and-recapture experiments are subject to a number of limitations. Ricker (1948, 1958) has reviewed these thoroughly, and they will not be repeated here. It is sufficient to say that estimates can now be made with a reasonable degree of confidence in situations where the entire population cannot be censused by direct observation, if these limitations are taken into account. In addition to Schumacher and Eschmeyer's work in Tennessee, several population studies have been done in the northern Indiana lakes. Ricker (1942, 1945a, 1955) reported on Shoe, Muskellunge, and Spear lakes, and Gerking (1950, 1953) reported on Oliver Lake and Gordy Lake. Lagler and Ricker (1942) prepared population estimates of the fishes in Foots Pond, an oxbow lake near the Wabash River. Perhaps the greatest lesson to be learned from this work is that each situation must be treated individually; unexpected behavior on the part of the fish or their captors requires adjustment of the mathematical model.

The last point is emphasized especially well by Krumholz's (1956) work on White Oak Lake, Tennessee. Six separate estimates of the fish populations were made by the Schnabel method, followed by killing the entire stock with rotenone. The actual count after the rotenone treatment did not agree in many respects with the estimates. The estimates for three species agreed reasonably well with the counts, but those for three other species failed to correspond. In all such studies the limits of confidence are usually wide. Krumholz's research was much more extensive than can be treated here, but one of its most interesting features involved the uptake of radioactive isotopes by the fish. White Oak Lake receives the radioactive waste effluent from the Oak Ridge National Laboratory. Radiostrontium and radiophosphorus were selectively concentrated in the hard tissues. The soft tissues selectively concentrated cesium and the rare earths. Exposure to radiation may have had deleterious effects on the fish as manifested by a shortened life span, slowed growth rate, and decreased fertility.

Survival rates

Ricker's greatest contributions in the field of fish populations are in the measurement and analysis of survival rates. Two papers (Ricker, 1940, 1944) lay the theoretical background, and several others apply the findings to specific problems. His initial approach was to erect hypothetical situations in which human exploitation and natural mortality affect the population either separately or concurrently. The nature of the problem forced the adoption of instantaneous rates to express rates of change. These rates can be added or subtracted without introducing error in contrast to other fractional expressions. Although instantaneous rates had been used in earlier fishery literature, Ricker should be given credit for popularizing their use.

Three ways of expressing mortality rates have emerged from Ricker's work, and each has practical utility in expressing population change. An-

nual instantaneous rates express changes which occur during the year if recruitment and total mortality are balanced day by day. An annual mortality rate, such as that from natural causes, is the fraction of fish present at the beginning of a year which would die if no competing cause of death existed. Thus, it is possible to learn the "primitive" natural mortality rate that existed in a population before man began to take his toll. An annual mortality rate is distinguished from an annual expectation of death in that the latter is the fraction of fish at the start of the year that actually die from either fishing or natural causes during the year.

It is rare to find a body of water that does not regularly feel the effect of the rod or net. Total mortality consists, therefore, of deaths from fishing and from natural causes, such as predation, disease, parasitism, and senility. The fish that die a so-called natural death are rarely seen; they are presumably eaten quickly by scavengers. As a result, the expectation of natural death is obtained by subtracting the rate of exploitation from the total expectation of death, the only two vital statistics that can be measured conveniently. The rate of exploitation is measured by a marking experiment of the Petersen type, explained above, where the fisherman's catch provides the recaptures. An intensive census of the creel or commercial catch is required. The total mortality rate can be measured in one of two ways. Either a marking experiment covering at least two years can be conducted, or the rate of disappearance can be computed from the age-frequency distribution of a large sample of the catch. The latter has been the most commonly adopted method, and the study of "catch curves"

TABLE 7.4

The annual expectations of death and the annual natural mortality of bluegills (*Lepomis macrochirus*) above 123 mm fork length in several Indiana lakes. The data have been taken from sources mentioned in the text.

Lake	Year studied	Total expectation of death %	Expectation of death from fishing %	Expectation of death from natural causes %	Natural mortality rate %
Muskellunge	1942	60	19	41	49
Muskellunge	1943	60	17	43	48
Shoe	1941	76	32	44	56
Shoe	1942	71	24	47	56
Shoe	1943	70	21	49	57
Oliver	1947	89	39	50	71
Spear	1944–45	78	32	46	59
Spear	1947–49	83	44	39	56
Gordy	1950	73	35	38	49
Wyland	1955–56	80	13	67	74

has been of great value in interpreting the past history of a population and the future course of a fishery.

Using the concepts and methods of measurement previously explained, Ricker (1945b) was able to conclude that the annual natural mortality rate of bluegills (*Lepomis macrochirus*) was about 50% in northern Indiana lakes (Table 7.4). There was evidence that larger and older fish had a greater mortality rate than smaller ones. On this basis, plus the fact that the natural mortality rate was of a high order and could not be accounted for by predation, emigration, parasitism, or disease, Ricker concluded that senescence is an important cause of death, overtaking fish of each year-class over a wide range of ages and sizes. This point of view has received support from studies which show that mortality rate increases with age in non-exploited populations (Gerking, 1957b).

The work in Tennessee and Indiana brought about some rather revolutionary changes in sport fishing regulations. When it became apparent that the rate of exploitation was below the expectation of death from natural causes for certain species, seasonal restrictions in fishing were lifted, and what is popularly known as the "year-round open season" has been in effect for nearly 15 years.

Growth

Growth studies are so numerous they cannot be reviewed here. All the major species have been studied. Comparisons have been made from year to year and from place to place. Hile (1931) was one of the first to study the growth of fishes in the Midwest by the scale method, and his work occupies a prominent place in the development of this field of research. Studies by Stroud (1948) are examples of the modern work in the field. Carlander's (1950, 1953) handbook of freshwater fishery biology may be referred to for a complete bibliography on growth.

Production

Ricker (1944, 1946) foresaw the possibility of making a direct estimate of fish production from measurements of abundance, survival rates, and growth rates but did not put the method to a test until he and Foerster (1948) used data on the early life history stages of the sockeye salmon for the purpose. Some years earlier they had made a direct count of sockeye at traps in an outlet stream as the fish migrated from Cultus Lake, British Columbia, to the sea. Seasonal survival rates were based on the release of marked fish at various times of the year, and growth was computed from the increase in weight of specimens recovered from the stomachs of predaceous fishes. Instantaneous rate of growth was compared with the instantaneous mortality rate to learn whether or not the population was exhibiting a net increase or a net decrease in weight at different times of year. The average biomass on hand during half-month intervals was multiplied by the rate of growth during the same period to obtain the production. The sum of the half-monthly production values over the whole year gave the annual production rate. This was the first time that fish production in the technical sense had ever been measured.

Sockeye production varied greatly from year to year between 1925 and 1936, reaching a maximum of 6.6 metric tons per km². Young sockeye of age-group 0 were responsible for a high proportion of the production. Sockeye normally migrate at the end of their first year in the lake, but a few delay their exit until the year following. The production of these group-I fish was negligible by comparison. Growth and, therefore, production ceased during the winter months.

Food turnover

Ricker and Foerster estimated the amount of food consumed by the young sockeye during their freshwater life by making some "educated guesses" about the daily ration and the efficiency of food conversion. They reported that the mean stock of fish consumed 6.5 times their own weight in entomostraca. This is, of course, the first step in determining the ecotrophic coefficient, or the fraction of production of the food supply that is consumed by the predator. If this coefficient were known, the second and third trophic levels could be linked together, and it would be possible to judge how efficiently a fish population crops off its food supply.

The efficiency of food utilization for growth is essentially a physiological measure, and it may be influenced by several factors. Two have been investigated—age or size of fish and the amount of food consumed (Gerking, 1952, 1954, 1955). This work was done in the laboratory by feeding different quantities of food to three species of sunfishes of various sizes. Mealworms (*Tenebrio molitor* larvae) were used as food, since they could easily be cultured in the laboratory, and they simulated the insect larvae that serve as a natural source of energy. Protein retention was used as a criterion of growth. Protein utilization varied with the size of the fish used in the experiments. In bluegills nearly 40% was used for growth by small fish of about 8 g and about 20% by fish weighing approximately 100 g. The decrease in efficiency of food utilization with increasing size has been confirmed by other investigators using different species, and it is apparently a general phenomenon among fishes.

The results of the laboratory experiments were applied to the bluegill population of Gordy Lake (Gerking, 1954). This population was characterized by rapid growth, which compared favorably with that achieved by the specimens in the laboratory. At least 156 kg of protein were consumed during the growing season of about 150 days. In terms of live weight this amounts to 1635 kg (142 kg/ha) of benthos and entomostraca, the bluegills' principal source of natural food. The average efficiency of the Gordy Lake bluegills in converting their food to body flesh was 26%.

The laboratory work was continued by feeding different protein rations to fish of the same size. The maximum conversion values were confirmed at high rates of feeding, but as lower rations were fed, efficiency declined to a point where protein intake balanced protein catabolism. The variables of both age and food consumption can now be incorporated into the computation of the food turnover. This has been done for a population in Wyland Lake, Indiana, with exceptionally slow growth and a low efficiency of food utilization of 16%. The production of benthos was estimated at the same time, and it was learned that the ecotrophic coefficient was in the neighborhood of 50% (Gerking, 1962). The fish population is efficient in cropping off its principal source of food.

Specialized environments

Caves

Cave streams are potentially one of the most interesting aquatic environments in the Central States, but their limnology is practically un-

touched. Southern Indiana, Kentucky, Tennessee, and western West Virginia are honeycombed with limestone caverns. Many of them are dry, but a large number are "wet caves," to use the vernacular. Troglobites have been described which are so modified that they are unable to live in the light, but unfortunately little is known about their ecology. Vertebrates and invertebrates alike are eyeless and exhibit a loss of pigment. Water chemistry has not been systematically investigated, although there should be interesting comparisons to be made with surface streams in the same region. Under normal conditions cave water temperature is close to air temperature, about 12° C. Drainage of warm water from the surface may cause flooding of cave streams in summer with consequent rise in water temperature considerably above 12°, however, and by the same process the temperature may be lowered in winter.

Cave streams should be particularly advantageous for community trophic research. The community is composed of few species, the food chain is short, there are few "side chains" to complicate the analysis as there are in more highly developed communities, and there is no opportunity for photosynthesis in the total darkness. Energy for community-metabolism must originate outside the cave. Organic matter is washed in during periods of high water. Excrements of bats and infrequent animal visitors may contribute food for the obligate cave inhabitants.

Two studies of plankton comprise the only work on cave limnology in the strict sense (Kofoid, 1900; Scott, 1909). C. H. Eigenmann made a towing net collection of plankton in Echo River of Mammoth Cave in 1898 and sent it to Kofoid for identification. Two genera of algae, several Protozoa, one nematode, one rotifer, one ostracod, one Diptera larva, and five copepods were present, all of which were typical surface species. Kofoid concluded that the plankton had been recently derived from epigean waters.

Scott made an intensive study of the caves near Mitchell, Indiana, a small town named for the Mitchell limestone, which is unusually pervious and subject to solution. Scott confirmed Kofoid's interpretation of the origin of the plankton and brought considerably more evidence to bear on the question. A total of 49 forms was identified, and all proved to be surface-water species. Scott (1910) supplemented these findings

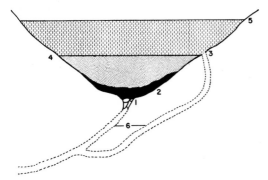

Fig. 7.13.—Diagram of a sinkhole whose opening has been plugged. A secondary sink forms on the slope of the original one and receives flow from the pond when the water level rises. (1) Original opening with obstruction; (2) impervious layer of clay; (3) secondary opening; (4) original water level; (5) flood water level; (6) subterranean passages. Copied from Scott, 1909.

by studying the plankton of a surface solution pond. The plankton in the caves had apparently been derived from sinkhole ponds of a special nature (Fig. 7.13). The ordinary sinkhole is funnel-shaped and drains into an underground passage at its deepest point. Occasionally a secondary sink may arise on the slope of an older one, and its drainage point lies some distance above the original opening. The opening at the lower elevation may become plugged with clay which caves in from the sides. A small solution pond then forms which overflows into the secondary sink when the water level rises.

The history of cave faunistic studies has indeed been a brilliant one. J. DeKay, R. E. Call, T. A. Tellkampf, A. S. Packard, and E. D. Cope were among the most able of the early naturalists to discover the fauna in the middle to late 1800's and theorize about its origin. C. H. Eigenmann saw the possibilities of investigating what he termed "degenerate evolution" among the cave vertebrates. His many studies of the eyes and other sense organs were summarized in a monograph in which mammals, salamanders, reptiles, and fishes were considered (Eigenmann, 1909). Cave research was neglected for many years after Eigenmann's time, but recently there has been a renewed interest. Woods and Inger (1957) have reviewed the family Amblyopsidae which contains the typical cave fish, *Amblyopsis spelea,* first described by DeKay in 1842. Barr *et al.* (1960) presented a symposium on speciation and raci-

ation in caverniculous planarians, crayfish, arachnids, and several groups of insects. A check list of all the troglobitic organisms in the United States with reference to the original species description, type locality, and range is given in an appendix to the symposium.

Strip-mine drainage

Coal is mined in all of the Central States by stripping off the overlying soil with huge shovels and exposing the coal seams. The excavation is below the water table, and ponds are formed by seepage, frequently with outlets into streams. The ponds are very acid in their early history but gradually neutralize as they age. In this latter condition they become popular recreational areas for picnicking, boating, and fishing. The reason for raising the question of the "strip pits" in this chapter is that they provide an unusual habitat for aquatic life and that the chemical change from an acid condition to neutrality has not been adequately studied. Results of both theoretical and practical importance are promised for investigators who decide to tackle the problem.

Acid mine drainage has become a favorite habitat for the salt-marsh mosquito, *Aedes sollicitans.* This species is successful in waters with high concentrations of dissolved salts. Dixon (1957) presents a chemical analysis of a typical habitat in the western coal fields of Kentucky as follows: pH, 2.9–3.1; chlorides, 5–16 ppm; calcium, 180–270 ppm; iron, 4.5–45 ppm; magnesium, 19–120 ppm; sulfates, 100–3500 ppm.

An acid stream or pond in a strip-mine area appears to be barren of life. A few *Isoetes* and cattails may be growing on the banks, the water is crystal clear, and there are usually heavy deposits of iron oxide on the bottom. Many groups of aquatic animals are absent such as sponges, flatworms, mollusks, and vertebrates, but more careful examination discloses a few organisms in unusual abundance. Lackey (1938c) observed a hatch of mosquitoes, several beetles, and mayfly larvae in an acid pool in West Virginia with a pH of 2.4. In other places in that state and southern Indiana, *Gammarus,* caddis flies, and *Chaoborus* were seen on a few occasions, and species of *Chironomus* were frequent. Microscopic organisms were extremely numerous in some habitats at pH 3.9 or lower. Protozoa were represented by eleven genera of flagellates, seven rhizopods, and twelve ciliates. *Euglena mutabilis* was an especially tolerant species in highly acid streams, coating the surfaces of sticks, leaves, and stones. Lackey remarked that he had never encountered the ten most common species in such numbers elsewhere.

These acid-tolerant organisms can provide the first link in a more complex food chain when the water becomes suitable for other forms of life. The successional stages are incompletely known but could be investigated by selecting strip pits of different ages and comparing their chemistry and aquatic life.

Centers of limnological research

Indiana University

Virtually all of the interest in aquatic science in the Central States can be traced to David Starr Jordan who came in 1871 to Indiana to teach in an Indianapolis high school and left in 1891 as President of Indiana University. Seldom has there been a more influential man on the American educational scene, and modern-day ichthyology has him to thank for much of the popularity it enjoys. Students were drawn to him. Even his colleagues on the faculty caught his enthusiasm and studied fishes. Charles H. Gilbert, Oliver P. Jenkins, Amos Butler, Albert B. Ulrey, Stephen A. Forbes, Oliver P. Hay, Barton Warren Evermann, Willis Blatchley, Seth E. Meek, Samuel Hildebrand, and John Otterbein Snyder either received tutelage under Jordan or were stimulated to work on Indiana fishes by him. Obviously one of Jordan's great talents was to attract superior men and bring them to full flower. From Jordan's famous walking trips to the South resulted the first systematic survey of the ichthyological fauna of the Central States. "Partial synopsis of the fishes of Upper Georgia with supplementary papers on fishes of Tennessee, Kentucky, and Indiana" (Jordan, 1877) is a good example of the results of these trips to the Smokies.

In Jordan's wake there followed another preeminent ichthyologist, Carl H. Eigenmann. He is chiefly known for two great pieces of research— studies on the cave vertebrates and the taxonomy of South American fishes. Eigenmann authored or co-authored 225 papers on these subjects. Limnologists will remember him as the founder of the Indiana University Biological Station, one of the first biological stations to be located on a freshwater lake. The station was established on Wawasee Lake in 1895 and later moved to Winona Lake in 1899. Eigenmann's objective in founding the station was to stimulate research on evolutionary problems. The lakes in northern Indiana were ideal for collecting material in quantity for studies on variation. A paper by Moenkhaus (1898) on the variation in two percid fishes is an example of the pioneer work done in this field. Some of the highlights of the station's program have been chronicled in the preceding discussion, dating from the time Will Scott became active in aquatic research. The early history of the study of fishes in Indiana has been written by Gerking (1957c).

There has not been an opportunity to mention the two-volume work, *Lake Maxinkuckee, a Physical and Biological Survey* (Evermann and Clark, 1920). This treatise stands as one of the most complete ecological surveys ever conducted. The U.S. Fish Commission sponsored the project from 1899 to 1908, and the treatise was finally published by the Indiana Department of Conservation. The list of people associated with the survey reads like a "Who's Who" of American limnology.

University of Kentucky

While a student at the Indiana University Biological Station, the late William Ray Allen of the Department of Zoology of the University of Kentucky began a fine series of papers on the ecology of mussels. He reported on their food, feeding habits, distribution, and movement (Allen, 1914, 1921a, 1921b, 1923). Although not limnology in the strict sense, such thorough life-history studies are invaluable for understanding the role such organisms play in the aquatic environment. Allen was a close associate of Eigenmann and traveled to South America on two collecting expeditions. The results of these expeditions were published in the last paper bearing Eigenmann's name, *The Fishes of Western South America* (Eigenmann and Allen, 1942).

University of Louisville

Gerald A. Cole and one of his students produced four papers on a 2.3-ha artificial lake, called Tom Wallace Lake, near Louisville during his stay at the University of Louisville (Cole, 1953, 1954, 1957; Neff, 1955). They deal primarily with the plankton. Cole and Krumholz

TABLE 7.5

Selected references from the literature on the flora and fauna of Reelfoot Lake, Tennessee

Organisms	Reference
Plants	
Local flora	Eyles and Eyles, 1943
Aquatic plants	Davis, 1937
Crustacea	
Cladocera and ostracoda	Hoff, 1943; Eddy, 1930
Crayfish	Hobbs and Marchand, 1943
Insects	
Anisoptera	Wright, 1938
Hemiptera	Green, 1937
Trichoptera	Edwards, 1956
Other invertebrates	
Hydracarina	Hoff, 1944b
Gastropoda	Byrd, Norton, and Denton, 1940
Turbellaria	Bolen, 1938
Protozoa	Bevel, 1938
Microdrili	Collins, 1937
Vertebrates	
Fishes	Baker, 1939
Amphibia and reptilia	Parker, 1939

(1959) collaborated on a study of the heat budget and chemical changes during an unusually cold winter when the lake underwent three intermittent ice covers in January and February. The alternate warming and cooling of the water plus inflow from the drainage produced complex thermal and chemical gradients. Both vertical and horizontal turbulence was pronounced. The Tom Wallace Lake work represents the most complete limnological study on an artificial pond in the Central States.

Recently the Pomatological Institute, under the direction of W. M. Clay and D. H. Jackson, has been established by the University of Louisville on the banks of the Ohio River. The institute is in its initial stage, and it can be expected to make unique contributions to the limnology of large rivers in the near future.

Reelfoot Lake Biological Station

Reelfoot Lake is a large body of water located in western Tennessee on which the Tennessee Academy of Science operates a biological station. The origin of the lake has never been carefully documented to my knowledge. Some accounts claim that it was formed by the New Madrid earthquake in 1811. White settlers were so scarce that no report was written at the time, and geological evidence is apparently not conclusive. A low dam raised the water level, but it

still averages less than three meters deep. The Tennessee General Assembly granted a plot of land on the lake to the state's Academy of Sciences in 1931 for the purpose of establishing a biological station. The station opened its doors in 1932 and has been operating ever since.

Tennessee scientists as well as those from other parts of the country were immediately attracted to the station. Over the years they have produced a virtually complete faunistic and floristic treatment of the lake and its environs. This work has never been summarized, and it is necessary here to present the findings in a tabular listing (Table 7.5). The list is by no means complete, and the writer admits to having chosen the entries in a somewhat arbitrary fashion. The latitudinal variation in species composition in the Central States can be made by comparing the Reelfoot Lake fauna and flora with that of Lake Maxinkuckee.

Ohio State University

Since a chapter in this book is being written on the limnology of the St. Lawrence Great Lakes, research on Lake Erie has been deliberately omitted. But it would not be fair to leave unmentioned the splendid contributions of the Franz Theodore Stone Laboratory of The Ohio State University on Gibraltar Island and South Bass Island in western Lake Erie. The laboratory was founded in 1896 on Sandusky Bay and moved in step-wise fashion from Sandusky and Cedar Point on the mainland to its location among the off-shore islands. Thomas H. Langlois (1949) has written a detailed history of the laboratory from its inception to 1949. Needless to say, knowledge of Lake Erie would be scanty indeed without the research of the limnologists working at the Stone Laboratory.

It would be an equally great oversight to fail to call attention to Milton B. Trautman's (1957) monograph, *The Fishes of Ohio*. Without question, this is the finest documentation of the fish fauna of any state.

References

ALLEN, W. R. 1914. The food and feeding habits of freshwater mussels. Biol. Bull., **27**(3): 127–141.

———. 1921a. Studies of the biology of freshwater mussels. I. Experimental studies of the food relations of certain Unionidae. Biol. Bull., **40**(4): 210–241.

———. 1921b. Studies of the biology of freshwater mussels. III. Distribution and movements of Winona

Lake mussels. Proc. Indiana Acad. Sci., **37**: 227–238.

———. 1923. Studies of the biology of freshwater mussels. II. The nature and degree of response to certain physical and chemical stimuli. Ohio J. Sci., **23**(2): 57–82.

BAKER, C. L. 1939. Key to the Reelfoot Lake fishes. J. Tennessee Acad. Sci., **14**: 41–45.

BARR, T. C., *et al.* 1960. Symposium: Speciation and raciation in cavernicoles. Amer. Midland Nat., **64**: 1–160.

BEVEL, NELL. 1938. Some notes on the protozoa of Reelfoot Lake. J. Tennessee Acad. Sci., **13**: 137–159.

BOLEN, H. R. 1938. Planarians of the Reelfoot Lake Region in Tennessee. J. Tennessee Acad. Sci., **13**: 164–165.

BRINLEY, F. J. 1942. The effect of pollution upon the plankton population of the White River, Indiana. Invest. Indiana Lakes and Streams, **2**: 137–143.

BYRD, E. E., E. M. NORTON, AND J. F. DENTON. 1940. Studies on the gastropod fauna of the Reelfoot Lake region. J. Tennessee Acad. Sci., **15**: 157–162.

CARLANDER, K. D. 1950. Handbook of freshwater fishery biology. Wm. C. Brown Co., Dubuque, Iowa. 281 + iii p.

———. 1953. First supplement to handbook of freshwater fishery biology. Wm. C. Brown Co., Dubuque, Iowa. 152 + vi p.

COFFING, CHARLENE. 1937. A quantitative study of the phytoplankton of the White River Canal, Indianapolis, Indiana. Butler Univ. Botan. Studies, **4**: 13–31.

COLE, G. A. 1953. Notes on the calanoid and cyclopoid Copepoda of the Louisville region. Trans. Kentucky Acad. Sci., **14**: 6–9.

———. 1954. Study on a Kentucky Knobs Lake. I. Some environmental factors. Trans. Kentucky Acad. Sci., **15**: 31–47.

———. 1957. Studies on a Kentucky Knobs Lake. III. Some qualitative aspects of the net plankton. Trans. Kentucky Acad. Sci., **18**: 88–101.

COLE, G. A., AND L. A. KRUMHOLZ. 1959. Studies on a Kentucky Knobs Lake. IV. Some limnological conditions during an unusually cold winter. Limnol. Oceanogr., **4**: 367–385.

COLLINS, D. S., JR. 1937. The aquatic earthworms (Microdrili) of Reelfoot Lake. J. Tennessee Acad. Sci., **12**: 188–205.

DAVIS, J. H., JR. 1937. Aquatic plant communities of Reelfoot Lake. J. Tennessee Acad. Sci., **12**: 96–103.

DENDY, J. S. 1945. Fish distribution in Norris Reservoir, Tennessee, 1943: Depth distribution of fish in relation to environmental factors. J. Tennessee Acad. Sci., **20**: 114–135.

———. 1946. Further studies of depth distribution of fish, Norris Reservoir, Tennessee. J. Tennessee Acad. Sci., **21**: 94–104.

DENDY, J. S., AND R. H. STROUD. 1949. The dominating influence of Fontana Reservoir on temperature and dissolved oxygen in the Little Tennessee River and its impoundments. J. Tennessee Acad. Sci., **24**: 41–51.

DENHAM, S. C. 1938. A limnological investigation of the West Fork and Common Branch of the White River. Invest. Indiana Lakes and Streams, 1(5): 17–71.

DIXON, ELBERT. 1957. Analyses of water containing *Aedes sollicitans* in Kentucky. J. Tennessee Acad. Sci., **32**: 147–151.

EBERLY, W. R. 1959. The metalimnetic oxygen maximum in Myers Lake. Invest. Indiana Lakes and Streams, **5**: 1–46.

EDDY, SAMUEL. 1930. The plankton of Reelfoot Lake, Tennessee. Trans. Amer. Microscop. Soc., **49**: 246–251.

EDWARDS, S. W. 1956. The Trichoptera of Reelfoot Lake with descriptions of three new species. J. Tennessee Acad. Sci., **31**: 7–19.

EIGENMANN, C. H. 1909. Cave vertebrates of America; a study in degenerative evolution. Publ. Carnegie Inst., **104**: 1–241.

EIGENMANN, C. H., AND W. R. ALLEN. 1942. The fishes of western South America. The University of Kentucky, Lexington. 494 + xv p.

EVERMANN, B. W., AND H. W. CLARK. 1920. Lake Maxinkuckee, a physical and biological survey. Indiana Dept. Conserv., Indianapolis, Indiana. 2 v.

EYLES, M. S., AND D. E. EYLES. 1943. A local flora of the Reelfoot Lake region of West Tennessee. J. Tennessee Acad. Sci., **18**: 108–136.

FREY, D. G. 1955. Distributional ecology of the cisco (*Coregonus artedii*) in Indiana. Invest. Indiana Lakes and Streams, **4**: 177–228.

———. 1958. The late-glacial cladoceran fauna of a small lake. Arch. Hydrobiol., **54**: 209–275.

———. 1960*a*. The ecological significance of cladoceran remains in lake sediments. Ecology, **41**: 684–699.

———. 1960*b*. On the occurrence of cladoceran remains in lake sediments. Proc. Natl. Acad. Sci. U. S., **46**: 917–920.

GERKING, S. D. 1950. Populations and exploitation of fishes in a marl lake. Invest. Indiana Lakes and Streams, **2**: 47–72.

———. 1952. The protein metabolism of sunfishes of different ages. Physiol. Zoöl., **25**: 358–372.

———. 1953. Vital statistics of the fish population of Gordy Lake, Indiana. Trans. Amer. Fish. Soc., **82**: 48–67.

———. 1954. The food turnover of a bluegill population. Ecology, **35**: 490–498.

———. 1955. The influence of the rate of feeding on the body composition and the protein metabolism of the bluegill sunfish. Physiol. Zoöl. **28**: 267–282.

———. 1957*a*. A method of sampling the littoral macrofauna and its application. Ecology, **38**: 219–226.

———. 1957*b*. Evidence of aging in natural populations of fishes. Gerontologia, **1**: 287–305.

———. 1957*c*. A history of the study of fishes in Indiana. Proc. Indiana Acad. Sci., **66**: 275–285.

———. 1962. Production and food utilization in a bluegill sunfish population. Ecol. Monogr., **32**: 31–78.

GREEN, S. C. 1937. Aquatic Hemiptera of Reelfoot Lake. J. Tennessee Acad. Sci., **12**: 154–162.

HILE, R. 1931. The rate of growth of fishes of Indiana. Invest. Indiana Lakes and Streams, **1**(2): 8–55.

HOBBS, H. H., JR., AND L. J. MARCHAND. 1943. A contribution towards a knowledge of the crayfishes of the Reelfoot Lake area. J. Tennessee Acad. Sci., **18**: 6–34.

HOFF, C. C. 1943. The Cladocera and Ostracoda of Reelfoot Lake. J. Tennessee Acad. Sci., **18**: 49–107.

———. 1944a. The Copepoda, Amphipoda, Isopoda, and Decapoda (exclusive of the crayfishes) of Reelfoot. J. Tennessee Acad. Sci., **19**: 16–28.

———. 1944b. A preliminary study of the hydracarina of Reelfoot Lake, Tennessee. J. Tennessee Acad. Sci., **19**: 45–69.

HUNT, J. S. 1930. Bottom as a factor in animal distribution in small streams. J. Tennessee Acad. Sci., **5**: 11–18.

HUPP, E. R. 1943. Plankton and its relationship to chemical factors and environment in White River Canal, Indianapolis, Indiana. Butler Univ. Botan. Studies, **6**: 30–53.

HUTCHISON, LYNN. 1939. Some factors influencing zooplankton distribution in the Hocking River. Ohio J. Sci., **39**: 259–273.

JORDAN, D. S. 1877. A partial synopsis of the fishes of upper Georgia; with supplementary papers on fishes of Tennessee, Kentucky and Indiana. Ann. New York Lyc. Nat. Hist. 1874–77, **11**: 307–377.

KEHR, R. W., W. C. PURDY, J. B. LACKEY, O. R. PLACAK, AND W. E. BURNS. 1941. A study of the pollution and natural purification of the Scioto River. Pub. Health Bull., **276**: 1–153.

KOFOID, C. A. 1900. The plankton of Echo River, Mammoth Cave. Trans. Amer. Microscop. Soc., **21**: 113–126.

———. 1903. The plankton of the Illinois River, 1894–99, with introductory notes on the hydrography of the Illinois River and its basin. I. Quantitative investigations and general results. Bull. Illinois State Lab. Nat. Hist. (Urbana), **6**: 95–629.

KRUMHOLZ, L. A. 1956. Observations on the fish population of a lake contaminated by radioactive wastes. Bull. Amer. Museum Nat. His., **110**: 227–368.

LACKEY, J. B. 1938a. Protozoan plankton as indicators of pollution in a flowing stream. Pub. Health Rept. (U.S.), **53**: 2037–2058.

———. 1938b. A study of some ecological factors affecting the distribution of protozoa. Ecol. Monogr., **8**: 502–527.

———. 1938c. The flora and fauna of surface waters polluted by acid mine drainage. Pub. Health Rept. (U.S.), **53**: 1499–1507.

———. 1942a. The plankton algae and protozoa of two Tennessee rivers. Amer. Midland Nat., **27**: 191–202.

———. 1942b. The effects of distilling wastes and waters on the microscopic flora and fauna of a

small creek. Pub. Health Rept. (U.S.), **57**: 253–260.

LACKEY, J. B., AND E. R. HUPP. 1956. Plankton populations in Indiana's White River. J. Amer. Water Works Assoc., **48**: 1024–1036.

LACKEY, J. B., ELSIE WATTIE, J. F. KACHMAR, AND O. R. PLACAK. 1943. Some plankton relationships in a small unpolluted stream. Amer. Midland Nat., **30**: 403–425.

LAGLER, K. F., AND W. E. RICKER. 1942. Biological fisheries investigations of Foots Pond, Gibson County, Indiana. Invest. Indiana Lakes and Streams, **2**: 47–72.

LANGLOIS, T. H. 1949. The Biological Station of the Ohio State University. Franz Theodore Stone Lab., Contrib. No. 11: 1–55.

LUDWIG, W. B. 1932. The bottom invertebrates of the Hocking River. Bull. 26, Ohio Biol. Surv., **5**: 223–249.

LYMAN, F. E. 1943. A pre-impoundment bottom-fauna study of Watts Bar Reservoir area (Tennessee). Trans. Amer. Fish. Soc., **72**: 52–62.

———. 1944. Effects of a flood upon temperature and dissolved oxygen relationships in Cherokee Reservoir, Tennessee. Ecology, **25**: 70–84.

LYMAN, F. E., AND J. S. DENDY. 1945. A pre-impoundment bottom-fauna study of Cherokee Reservoir area (Tennessee). Trans. Amer. Fish. Soc., **73**: 194–208.

MOENKHAUS, W. J. 1898. Material for the study of the variation of *Etheostoma caprodes* Rafinesque and *Etheostoma nigrum* Rafinesque in Turkey Lake and Tippecanoe Lake. Proc. Indiana Acad. Sci., **11**: 278–296.

MURRAY, M. J. 1938. An ecological study of the invertebrate fauna of some northern Indiana streams. Invest. Indiana Lakes and Streams, **1**(8): 102–110.

NEEL, J. K. 1951. Interrelations of certain physical and chemical features in a headwater limestone stream. Ecology, **32**: 368–391.

NEFF, S. E. 1955. Studies on a Kentucky Knobs Lake. II. Some aquatic Nematocera (Diptera) from Tom Wallace Lake. Trans. Kentucky Acad. Sci., **16**: 1–13.

O'CONNELL, T. R., AND R. S. CAMPBELL. 1953. The benthos of Black River and Clearwater Lake, Missouri. Univ. Missouri Studies, **26**: 25–41.

PALMER, C. M. 1932. Plankton algae of White River in Marion County and Morgan County, Indiana. Butler Univ. Botan. Studies, **2**: 125–131.

PARKER, M. V. 1939. The amphibians and reptiles of Reelfoot Lake and vicinity with a key for the separation of species and subspecies. J. Tennessee Acad. Sci., **14**: 72–100.

PETERSEN, C. G. J. 1896. The yearly immigration of young plaice into the Limfjord from the German Sea. Rept. Danish Biol. Sta. for 1895, **6**: 1–48.

POWERS, E. B. 1929. Fresh water studies. I. The relative temperature, oxygen content, alkali reserve, the carbon dioxide tension and *p*H of the waters of certain mountain streams at different altitudes in the Smoky Mountain National Park. Ecology, **10**: 97–111.

RICKER, W. E. 1940. Relation of "catch per unit effort" to abundance and rate of exploitation. J. Fish. Research Board Canada, **5**: 43–70.

———. 1942. Creel census, population estimates, and rate of exploitation of game fish in Shoe Lake, Indiana. Invest. Indiana Lakes and Streams, **2**: 215–253.

———. 1944. Further notes on fishing mortality and effort. Copeia, 1944: 23–44.

———. 1945*a*. Abundance, exploitation and mortality of the fishes of two lakes. Invest. Indiana Lakes and Streams, **2**: 345–448.

———. 1945*b*. Natural mortality among Indiana bluegill sunfish. Ecology, **26**: 111–121.

———. 1946. Production and utilization of fish populations. Ecol. Monogr., **16**: 373–391.

———. 1948. Methods of estimating vital statistics of fish populations. Indiana Univ. Studies, Sci. Ser., **15**: 1–101.

———. 1955. Fish and fishing in Spear Lake, Indiana. Invest. Indiana Lakes and Streams, **4**: 117–161.

———. 1958. Handbook of computations for biological statistics of fish populations. Bull. Fish. Research Board Canada, **119**: 7–300.

RICKER, W. E., AND R. E. FOERSTER. 1948. Computation of fish production. Bull. Bingham Oceanogr. Coll., **11**: 173–211.

ROACH, L. S. 1932. An ecological study of the plankton of the Hocking River. Bull. 26, Ohio Biol. Surv., **5**: 253–279.

———. 1933. Some physical, chemical, and biological studies of impounded waters in Ohio. Trans. Amer. Fish. Soc., **63**: 265–270.

SCHNABEL, Z. E. 1938. The estimation of the total fish population of a lake. Amer. Math. Monthly, **45**: 348–352.

SCHNELLER, MYRTLE. 1955. Oxygen depletion in Salt Creek, Indiana. Invest. Indiana Lakes and Streams, **4**: 163–175.

SCHUMACHER, F. X., AND R. W. ESCHMEYER. 1943. The estimate of fish population in lakes or ponds. J. Tennessee Acad. Sci., **18**: 228–249.

SCOTT, WILL. 1909. An ecological study of the plankton of Shawnee Cave, with notes on the cave environment. Biol. Bull., **17**(6): 386–406.

———. 1910. The fauna of a solution pond. Proc. Indiana Acad. Sci., **26**: 395–442.

———. 1916. Report on the lakes of the Tippecanoe Basin (Indiana). Indiana Univ. Studies, **31**: 3–39.

———. 1931. The lakes of northeastern Indiana. Invest. Indiana Lakes and Streams, 1(3): 61–145.

SCOTT, WILL, R. O. HILE, AND H. T. SPEITH. 1928. A quantitative study of the bottom fauna of Lake Wawasee (Turkey Lake). Invest. Indiana Lakes and Streams, 1(1): 5–25.

SCOTT, WILL, R. O. HILE, AND H. T. SPEITH. 1938. The bottom fauna of Tippecanoe Lake. Invest. Indiana Lakes and Streams, 1(4): 3–16.

SCOTT, WILL, AND D. H. MINER. 1936. Sedimentation in Winona Lake and Tippecanoe Lake, Kosciusko County, Indiana. Proc. Indiana Acad. Sci., **45**: 275–286.

SCOTT, WILL, AND D. E. OPDYKE. 1941. The emergence of insects from Winona Lake. Invest. Indiana Lakes and Streams, **2**: 5–15.

SHOCKLEY, C. H. 1949. Fish and invertebrate populations in an Indiana bass stream. Invest. Indiana Lakes and Streams, **3**: 247–270.

SHOUP, C. S. 1940. Biological and chemical characteristics of the drainage of the Big South Fork of the Cumberland River in Tennessee. J. Tennessee Acad. Sci., **15**: 76–105.

———. 1943. Distribution of fresh-water gastropods in relation to total alkalinity of streams. Nautilus, **56**: 130–134.

———. 1947. Geochemical interpretation of water analyses from Tennessee waters. Trans. Amer. Fish. Soc., **74**: 223–239.

———. 1950. Field chemical examination of the waters in Tennessee streams. J. Tennessee Acad. Sci., **25**: 4–55.

SLACK, K. V. 1955. A study of the factors affecting stream productivity by the comparative method. Invest. Indiana Lakes and Streams, **4**: 3–47.

STAHL, JOHN. 1959. The developmental history of The chironomid and *Chaoborus* faunas of Myers Lake. Invest. Indiana Lakes and Streams, **5**: 47–102.

STEHR, W. C., AND J. W. BRANSON. 1938. An ecological study of an intermittent stream. Ecology, **19**: 294–310.

STROUD, R. H. 1948. Growth of the basses and black crappie in Norris Reservoir, Tennessee. J. Tennessee. Acad. Sci., **23**: 31–99.

TENNESSEE DEPARTMENT OF CONSERVATION, Division of Water Resources. 1961. Tennessee's Water Resources: 1–128.

TRAUTMAN, M. B. 1957. The fishes of Ohio. The Ohio State Univ. Press, Columbus, Ohio. 638 p.

WENE, GEORGE. 1940. The soil as an ecological factor in the abundance of aquatic chironomid larvae. Ohio J. Sci., **40**: 193–199.

WIEBE, A. H. 1938. Limnological observations on Norris Reservoir with especial reference to dissolved oxygen and temperature. Trans. N. Amer. Wildl. Conf., **3**: 440–457.

———. 1939. Density currents in Norris Reservoir. Ecology, **20**: 446–450.

———. 1940. The effect of density currents upon the vertical distribution of temperature and dissolved oxygen in Norris Reservoir. J. Tennessee Acad. Sci., **15**: 301–308.

———. 1941. Density currents in impounded waters —their significance from the standpoint of fisheries management. Trans. N. Amer. Wildl. Conf., **6**: 256–264.

WILSON, I. T. 1936. A study of sedimentation of Winona Lake. Proc. Indiana Acad. Sci., **45**: 234–253.

———. 1938. The accumulated sediment in Tippecanoe Lake and a comparison with Winona Lake. Proc. Indiana Acad. Sci., **47**: 234–253.

WILSON, I. T., AND D. F. OPDYKE. 1941. The distri-

bution of the chemical constituents in the accumulated sediment of Tippecanoe Lake. Invest. Indiana
Lakes and Streams, 2: 16–43.

WOHLSCHLAG, D. E. 1950. Vegetation and invertebrate life in a marl lake. Invest. Indiana Lakes
and Streams, 3: 321–372.

WOODS, L. P., AND R. F. INGER. 1957. The cave,
spring and swamp fishes of the family Amblyop-

sidae of central and eastern United States. Amer.
Midland Nat., 58: 232–256.

WRIGHT, MIKE. 1938. Notes on dragonflies of Reelfoot Lake, Tennessee. J. Tennessee Acad. Sci.,
13: 104–108.

YEATMAN, H. C. 1954. Plankton studies on Woods
Reservoir, Tennessee. J. Tennessee Acad. Sci., 31:
32–53.

8 | *James L. Yount*

South Atlantic States

Limnological resources and historical notes

The physiography of a region is of fundamental importance to its limnology, for elevation, composition of soil (and agricultural management of the soil), and rainfall are directly influential in determining the nature of its streams and lakes. The South Atlantic seaboard states comprise three principal physiographic regions (Fig. 8.1) that thus largely determine the form and type of the water therein (see Fenneman, 1938). Extending northerly and westerly, there is a relatively narrow Mountain Zone with altitudes up to 6700 ft, forming generally small, clear, and rapid streams. Easterly and southerly of the mountains these streams join on the wide and lower Piedmont region to form large and more slowly flowing rivers that are usually rather turbid because of runoff from agricultural lands. The Piedmont ranges in elevation from about 1600 ft in the west to about 250 ft at its eastern edge, where the "fall line" delimits it from the low-lying Coastal Plain. The fall line is so named because a more or less abrupt reduction of elevation in this region produces waterfalls on the rivers traversing it; in the larger rivers, it originally represented the point beyond which shipping no longer could move up the rivers (Russell,

Contribution No. 117, Florida State Board of Health, Entomological Research Center, Vero Beach. This investigation was supported in part by Public Health Service Grant WP-216 (C1), from the Division of Water Supply and Pollution Control.

1898). The Coastal Plain occupies the greatest area of the three physiographic regions, including the eastern portions of Virginia and the Carolinas, the southern portion of Georgia, and the whole of Florida. The Coastal Plain is characterized by broad, slowly flowing, and relatively siltless rivers and by numerous lakes, chiefly solution lakes (especially in Florida) and bay lakes (especially in the Carolinas). The rivers and lakes of the Coastal Plain are usually highly colored from extensive marsh and swamp drainage.

The South Atlantic region was first investigated from a limnological point of view by John Bartram (1942) and later by his son, William Bartram (1791, 1942; Harper, 1958; Cruickshank, 1961), who traveled through the Carolinas, Georgia, and Florida during the late 18th century, making numerous interesting observations on the natural history of the region as well as of the inhabitants. William Bartram, in particular, observed various facts of interest to limnologists; for example, in his *Travels* he described an artesian spring near Lake George, Florida, in beautiful prose, some of which follows (pp. 149–151): ". . . just under my feet, was the inchanting and amazing crystal fountain, which incessantly threw up, from dark, rocky caverns below, tons of water every minute, forming a bason, capacious enough for large shallops to ride in, and a creek of four or five feet depth of water, and nearly twenty yards over, which meanders six miles through green meadows, pouring its limpid waters into the great Lake George, where they seem to remain pure and unmixed,"

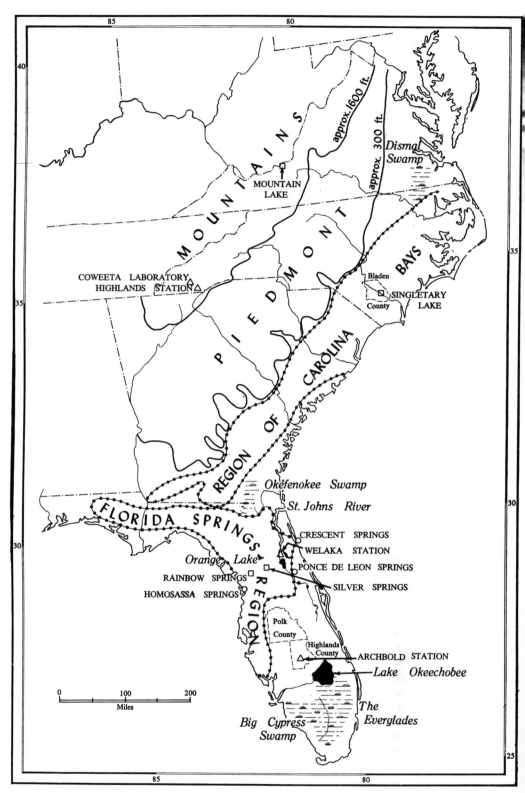

Fig. 8.1.—Outline map of the South Atlantic states, showing major physiographic provinces. Location of frequent Carolina bays taken from Prouty (1952); location of frequent Florida springs taken from Ferguson *et al.* (1947). Map prepared by the University of Wisconsin Cartographic Laboratory.

and "behold . . . a vast circular expanse before you, the waters of which are so extremely clear as to be absolutely diaphanous or transparent as the ether; the margin of the bason ornamented with a great variety of fruitful and floriferous trees, shrubs, and plants, the pendant golden Orange dancing on the surface of the pellucid waters, the balmy air vibrating with the melody of the merry birds, tenants of the encircling aromatic grove." He noted the presence of various marine and freshwater fish together in the spring, a subject that is discussed further later. In this same book, he noted the tremendous numbers of emerging mayflies on the St. Johns river, which today has problems from an abundance of chironomids. His ecological perception was as acute as his aesthetic, as can be seen (p. 89) in his reference to mayfly larvae being created for the food of fish.

In addition to the Bartrams, early reports by Brinton (1859) and LeConte (1861; see Odum 1957a) were made on visits to Silver Springs, chiefly regarding the great clarity of the water and describing the *Sagittaria* and its moss-like Aufwuchs, and observations on temperature and discharge were made by Brinton.

Two other early naturalists contributed observations on limnology in the South Atlantic states, Smyth (1784) and Bailey (1851). Smyth noted how lake beds in the Dismal Swamp were formed by immense fires during the dry summer and later filled with water. In one case that he observed, a lake was formed that was 1½ mi broad and 3 mi long and from 4 to 12 ft deep (see Wright and Wright, 1932). J. W. Bailey traveled in the south during 1849–50 to the Carolinas, Georgia, and Florida and reported microscopic studies on various algae, chiefly from fresh waters, with the hope this would stimulate further studies (see Silva, 1948). It was not until the present century, however, that hydrobiology has been investigated to a considerable extent in this area, and limnology only in recent decades.

Centers of activity in limnology in the South Atlantic states are few. At the Mountain Lake Biological Laboratory in Virginia, Hutchinson and Pickford (1932), Shoup (1948), and Platt and Shoup (1950) have carried out limnological studies. Highlands Biological Station in North Carolina has served since 1932 as a center of activity in algal and aquatic insect ecology as well as in other fields (Anon., 1946). Some outstanding hydrobiologists have worked in the universities in the Carolinas, Georgia, and Florida, such as R. E. Coker and D. G. Frey (University of North Carolina), H. T. Odum (University of Florida and Duke University), L. A. Whitford (North Carolina State), and D. A. Livingstone (Duke University). The majority of studies from this area, however, have been faunistic or floristic rather than limnological in scope. An Institute of Radiation Ecology was recently established at the University of Georgia in cooperation with the Savannah River Plant of the Atomic Energy Commission at Aiken, South Carolina. E. P. Odum is director of the institute, with F. P. Golley serving as resident director at the Savannah River Plant. It is expected that limnological studies of significance will soon come from this institute. Three other stations that should be mentioned are the Welaka Conservation Reserve of the University of Florida, the Archbold Biological Station at Lake Placid, Florida, and the Everglades National Park in southern Florida. These all offer excellent opportunity for the person interested in subtropical limnology. Other studies of interest from a subtropical point of view on central Florida lakes are being conducted by the Midge Research Project of the Florida State Board of Health, by G. K. Reid of Florida Presbyterian College, and by D. G. Frey of Indiana University.

Major habitats

Rivers

The rivers of the South Atlantic states begin as small swift streams in the mountains to the west and terminate as broad, slowly-flowing streams in the east, where extensive marshes, both salt and fresh, adjoin them. The discussion here attempts to describe some of their more important limnological aspects.

Personnel of the Coweeta Hydrologic Laboratory of the United States Forest Service have conducted extensive research since 1934 to determine the effects of forest and land management practices on the water regime in the Mountain and Piedmont regions of North and South Carolina and Georgia, particularly aimed at rehabilitation of eroded logging and agricultural land. This program promises to have far-reaching effects on the long-neglected waters of the mountain areas as well as on those of the Piedmont and of the Coastal Plain. Travelers and natives have long noticed the muddy cast of the rivers in these regions, particularly in the wet winter and spring period. Four major fields of study have gradually developed over the years at Coweeta involving the behavior of water in the soil, the plant, the atmosphere, and the stream channels (Hewlett and Metz, 1960).

The effect on the watersheds of different types of vegetation is being studied to determine the relative value of different plant covers in reducing runoff, i.e., native hardwood, white pine, grass, and shrub. The use of entire watersheds for erosion studies has led to new management insights. Cutting forest cover in whole or in part showed that vegetation largely controlled runoff, erosion, and turbidity in receiving streams —and the logger or farmer, through mismanagement, literally destroyed his own farm. This is illustrated by stream turbidities measured at Coweeta (Dils, 1957): in undisturbed forest streams, turbidities during non-storm periods are usually less than 2 ppm, during storms less than 11 ppm, whereas under farming or logging conditions turbidities have been produced up to 80 ppm.

To illustrate the effect of "old time" farming, a small 23-acre farm was established near the laboratory and farmed for corn and cattle by conventional methods. Before the farm was established, erosion was minimal; some 1.8 tons of matter was eroded from the farm in one year. After 13 years of farming, the year's accumulation was greater than 200 tons of eroded matter. Moreover, infiltration of water was greatly reduced in the farmed area, the stream channel cut away its banks, and flooding was a common occurrence. Dils also reported on rehabilitation of the farm by planting with oats and lespedeza (and later with coniferous trees). "After one season of rehabilitation, a 6-inch storm in December 1954 moved only 3 tons of sediment from the area, as contrasted with 1-inch storms of the previous winter which consistently carried off 20 to 30 tons each" (p. 22). The effect of logging by outdated as well as by modern methods also was reported by Dils; turbidity in an area stream was 1200 ppm during a storm, compared to a control site turbidity of only 25 ppm. In this case log skidways and roads were the principal source of increased turbidity.

Perhaps the best known study at the Coweeta station is that in which all woody vegetation was cut down and recut yearly during a 14-year period. There was a large early increase in water yield of more than 17 in. from the area. This leveled off, with invasion of herbaceous plants, to an increase of about 11 in. through the remainder of the experiment. There were, of course, corresponding increases in streamflow.

Tebo (1955) and Hassler and Tebo (1958) have reported the effects of logging operations in the Coweeta Forest on stream fauna, especially on bottom organisms and trout. They found that silt and sand resulting from the logging were highly destructive to bottom organisms, particularly in time of floods. The trout populations were adversely affected also, since their food is made up largely of the bottom forms.

In connection with the high turbidities reported above, Hoskin (1959) studied some North Carolina streams, including Mountain, Piedmont, and Coastal Plain portions. He concluded from the constant excess of respiration over productivity that the communities of these streams receive more organic matter than they produce and are, therefore, largely heterotrophic.

Clarke (1924) showed that rivers located in regions of high rainfall and fertile soil are generally dominated by calcium and carbonate. The rivers of the South Atlantic states, he reported, are largely of this type. Where organic matter is abundant, carbonic acid is also abundant, and this is the primary solvent of limestone, the rock most abundant in the region. This relationship is especially well shown in Florida springs, as we shall see later. There are significant quantities of substances of marine origin in areas of recent elevation above the sea, however, and this has resulted in marine invasion or marine relicts existing in nearly fresh waters.

The invasion of inland rivers and their smaller tributaries by marine animals has received considerable attention from hydrobiologists in Florida, beginning with W. Bartram (1791), who noted (p. 150) that in a spring adjacent to Lake George on the St. Johns River both freshwater fish (gar, bream, trout, and catfish) and saltwater fish (sting ray, skate, flounder, sheepshead, and drum) occurred together. Oligohaline and even fresh waters in Florida are inhabited at present by numerous other marine organisms, including crabs and other marine invertebrates as well as fish and marine plants (Odum, 1953b; McLane, 1955). One of the large springs of Florida

Fig. 8.2.—Underwater photograph of marine fish, chiefly snappers *(Lutjanus)*, in Homosassa Springs. Photo courtesy of the management, Homosassa Springs, Florida.

(Homosassa, Fig. 8.2) has its underwater viewing area especially designed to reveal the mixture of freshwater and saltwater fish to tourists.

Cooke (1939) considered that the salt of Salt Springs (2–3 ‰ salinity) originated from the underlying salt water that contaminated the very deep springs. The oligohaline nature of many of Florida's waters below 20 ft elevation was considered by Odum (1953*b*) to originate from salt deposits held in sediments. In some instances large areas that were once arms of the sea retain a limited salinity and a population of marine organisms, e.g., various waters adjoining the St. Johns River (McLane, 1955).

The St. Johns River is interesting from various points of view, being one of the few rivers that has a marine fauna in its headwater areas and that, because of its slight gradient, shows a tidal effect as far as 145 mi inland (the mean tidal range 103 mi inland is ½ ft according to McLane, 1955; cf. Pierce, 1947). The salinity of some of its headwater lakes has been reported by McLane as high as 10.7 ‰, although the main river is fresh. Sea cows still spend the winter in one of the springs tributary to the St. Johns as in Bartram's day.

Lakes

The lakes of the South Atlantic states are of two principal types—the bay lakes of the Carolinas and Georgia (Fig. 8.1) and the solution

lakes of Florida. A type of lake that is rare in the South Atlantic states was described by Hutchinson and Pickford (1932): Mountain Lake, Virginia, was formed as a result of landslides in this relatively highly elevated region. In its low quantity of dissolved substances, deep Secchi disc readings, and other limnological characteristics, this lake resembles oligotrophic alpine lakes. There are also lakes formed as sea bottom depressions during earlier periods, e.g., Lake Okeechobee, Florida.

The Carolina bays* are elliptical or ovoid depressions oriented generally in a northwest-southeast direction in the Coastal Plain region and are estimated to number in the hundreds of thousands (Prouty, 1935, 1952). The few remaining lakes are shallow (mostly less than 15 ft) with peat and sand bottoms. The former lake basins characteristically have very thin sediment layers (Frey, 1949, 1951*a*, 1953). These lakes are usually acidic, with pH ranges between 4 and 5, and have a rather low productivity; nevertheless, they have quite extensive fish faunas (Frey, 1951*b*). The bay lakes are especially interesting because, in contradistinction to the normal evolution of lakes, they apparently have been expanding in area during the last 500 years, as evidenced chiefly by studies on cypresses in the lakes (Frey, 1954).

In a study of pollen from sediment cores taken from some of the bay lakes in North Carolina, Frey (1953) concluded that there have been major changes in the vegetation of the Coastal Plain during the late Pleistocene; in fact, the present type of southeastern evergreen forest has been in existence for only a relatively brief period, contrary to the commonly accepted opinion that it has existed for a much longer period. These major changes were tentatively correlated with advances and retreats of the Wisconsin ice sheet in the north.

Numerous theories have been advanced concerning the origin of these lakes; the major ones are that the lakes are the result of meteorite showers (Melton and Schriever, 1933; Prouty, 1935, 1952), the result of deflation (Shand, 1946; Odum, 1952), or the result of solution (Johnson, 1942; Le Grand, 1953). According to the mete-

---

* This discussion follows Hutchinson, who reviewed the subject recently in detail (1957, pp. 151–156). I wish to thank D. G. Frey for furnishing additional references.

oritic theory, the bays are thought to have received their elliptical form from the shock wave accompanying the meteorite. With regard to deflation, wind is thought to have excavated the lakes when climatic conditions were very different from the present, during the Pleistocene. Le Grand (1953) postulated that artesian limestone aquifers underlying near-surface clays produced sinks by solution of the limestone and subsidence of the clay. Ground-water flow around the impervious clay plugs then led to increased rate of solution and to subsidence in the down-gradient side of the sink. Ultimately this would produce an ovoid bay, with its more pointed end at the down-gradient side. Frey (1955) reported evidence that the presently elliptical bay lake, Lake Singletary, was formed from three older irregular depressions, a fact that may be difficult to explain by the meteoritic theory of origin. This subject represents an interesting field for future research.

Solution lakes are also numbered in the thousands, ranging in size from tiny ponds to lakes many square miles in area. They are characteristic of lands recently elevated above the sea and consisting chiefly of carbonate rocks (Russell, 1895; Sellards, 1914; Cooke, 1939) and are thus most frequent in Florida of the South Atlantic states. One Florida lake, Okeechobee, is very large (730 mi²), although it is a comparatively shallow lake; its normal depth, according to Cooke, is only 20.5 ft. Parker and Cooke (1944) consider it to have originated not as a solution lake but as a slight depression in the sea bottom during Pliocene time.

Solution lakes and basins or sinks are particularly abundant in regions where the limestone lies near the surface. The carbonate is dissolved by the action of carbonic acid, resulting in a karst topography, the sinks being connected underground with the water table or with underground conduits cutting from one sink to another (Stubbs, 1940). To illustrate an extreme depth of these sinks, the "Devil's Mill-hopper," a sink near Gainesville, was reported by Cooke to be 115 ft deep. Sinks may fill with organic debris to such an extent that they retain water, even though shallow. Usually sinks have no inflow or outflow on the surface. In other instances they may be "perched" above the general ground-water level by an impermeable underlying clay deposit: a large region may be perched, having

sinks, solution lakes, streams, and its own perched water table many feet above the ground-water table of the region, as is the case in northeastern Alachua County (H. K. Brooks, personal communication; see Pirkle and Brooks, 1959). Occasionally, one reads in local newspapers about a surface collapse, producing a sink that may be large enough to take large trees into its bottom (cf. Stubbs, 1940). Bartram (1791, pp. 201–203) described such an occurrence as related to him by a trader. Disappearing lakes are also a striking phenomenon of this region (Sellards, 1914; Stubbs, 1940).

An interesting fact about central and southern Florida lakes is that whereas some of them are strongly alkaline, others are acid and have very soft water. According to Frey (personal communication), the lakes in Highlands County usually have a pH of less than 7 and methyl orange alkalinity values of less than 10 ppm (as $CaCO_3$). The present writer has found some lakes in Polk County to be acidic, but the majority studied have relatively high pH values, although the alkalinity is usually less than 30 ppm.

The sinks that are permanently filled with water are frequently thickly covered with duckweed (*Lemna*, etc.) and occasionally other plants, such as water hyacinths (*Eichornia*), water lettuce (*Pistia*), or *Salvinia*, the water fern. The duckweed-covered sinks may have a very thick mat so that light is excluded from the water beneath, and on windless days oxygen may be completely lacking a few centimeters below the surface. Minnows, chiefly *Gambusia affinis*, are, however, common inhabitants, apparently being able to gulp air during unfavorable periods, as Odum and Caldwell (1955) showed they do in anaerobic springs. Turtles and alligators are frequent inhabitants of these interesting ponds.

Because of their shallowness most lakes in Florida do not possess a typical thermocline in Birge's sense (a temperature gradient of 1° C/m depth) but, rather, have thermoclines depending on stability from high temperatures (cf. Yount, 1961). Lake Mize in northern Florida, however, possesses a typical thermocline, generally between 8 and 9 m, for it is in a small cone-shaped basin and is some 24 m deep. It is anaerobic in summer below about 4 m (Harkness and Pierce, 1940). According to Frey (personal communication), several small lakes in Highlands

County 15 to 20 m deep also exhibit Birgean thermoclines.

Because of their frequency in Florida, the effect of hurricanes on lakes has been investigated to some extent. Bartram (1791; pp. 131–133) described the tremendous destruction of a hurricane to trees and buildings, noting that the water on the shore opposite him on Lake Beresford was raised several feet above the level of the near-shore water. Douglas (1947, pp. 340–346) described the devastating effect of a hurricane in 1926, as a result of which more than 300 people were killed, and one in 1928 when 1800 people were killed near Lake Okeechobee. Since then great improvements have been made to protect lives and property around the lake. Haurwitz (1951) described the effect of the August 26–27, 1949, hurricane on Lake Okeechobee, showing the combined effect of seiche influence and hurricane winds. The water piled up so that there was more than a 3-m difference in lake level between one end of the lake and the other. As the hurricane wind direction changed, large areas of bottom were exposed, and elsewhere marshes and the lake margin were inundated. Some lakes in the vicinity of Winter Haven, Florida, were studied before and after the hurricane of September 10–11, 1960, by vertical temperature and oxygen measurements (Yount, 1961). In these shallow lakes (less than 30 ft), overturn was complete after the hurricane. It was also complete after a much weaker storm on July 27–28, 1960, at which time, however, deep lakes in Highlands County maintained their thermal stability (Frey, personal communication).

The problem of cyclomorphosis has been investigated in North Carolina, chiefly by Coker (1939), who reviewed the subject on *Daphnia*. These organisms, as well as a number of others, may undergo structural changes from generation to generation under the influence of various environmental factors. To illustrate, in a North Carolina lake all *Daphnia* taken in January had round heads. In March and April round heads and pointed heads occurred in about equal numbers, whereas from May until July only pointed heads occurred. It is interesting that in Florida lakes, *Daphnia* commonly have pointed heads the year round. Various explanations for this cyclomorphosis have been advanced, the most satisfactory being that cyclomorphic changes are not the simple result of either external or hereditary factors but, rather, are due to a combination of these, and that temperature alone acting on the embryo is an important factor. It was later shown by J. L. Brooks (1946) that turbulence also is important, in that larger helmets are produced under more turbulent conditions than under less turbulent.

Swamps

The term swamp is used here generically, to include swamp forests, marshes of shrubs, grasses, or herbs, etc. The South Atlantic states probably possess the most extensive body of swamps of any region in the United States, considering that the Dismal Swamp of North Carolina and Virginia, Okefenokee in Georgia and Florida, and Big Cypress and the Everglades in Florida are only a small part of the total swamp area present. Particularly in Florida, huge inland areas are intermittently or continuously flooded. Although they are outside the scope of this article, salt marshes are very extensive along the coastline of the whole South Atlantic region and are receiving considerable attention at North Carolina State College, the University of Georgia Marine Laboratory at Sapelo Island, and the Entomological Research Center of the Florida State Board of Health at Vero Beach. For such a prominent feature of the landscape, however, swamps have received relatively little attention from limnologists.

As in the case of every other major habitat, Bartram (1791) reported observations on swamps, including descriptions of Alachua savanna (Payne's Prairie) near Gainesville (p. 165 ff.) and Okefenokee (pp. 47–48), although Bartram did not visit the latter. Even before Bartram, Smyth (1784) visited Dismal Swamp in Virginia and North Carolina and, as previously mentioned, described lakes formed by conflagrations.

Swamp waters are characteristically brown colored from the great amounts of humus arising from breakdown of various plant substances. The Dismal Swamp is notably dark colored (Hesse *et al.*, 1951, p. 350). Apparently the number of larger inhabitants is relatively small (Teale, 1951, p. 254), a fact that also seems to apply to the fishes (Roseberry and Bowers, 1959). The Dismal Swamp is only about 10 to 20 ft above sea level (Ekblaw, 1961).

The Okefenokee is a large swamp (660 mi²) chiefly in Georgia, forming the headwaters of the tea-colored Suwanee River draining to the Gulf, as well as of the St. Mary's River draining to the

Atlantic. Its elevation is some 125 ft above sea level (Wright and Wright, 1932). These authors described its chief habitats, such as prairie (shallow open marsh), hammock, bay, etc., from the point of view of the vegetation and physical characteristics; in addition they reported on the frogs and reptiles in an earlier article. The "trembling land" of Okefenokee reminds one of the famous floating islands of Orange Lake in Florida (Teale, 1951, p. 73 ff.). Carr (1940) and Davis (1943, p. 250 ff.) regard these great mats of floating vegetation as an important means of filling up lake basins, and the mats apparently are far more important in this respect than the ordinary accumulation of organic matter, at least in Florida. Large pieces of peat-like bottom material floating at the surface are a common sight in ponds and lakes in the spring; they are apparently buoyed up by decomposition gases. Most floating islands, however, have sizable plant growths on them, including even small trees such as buttonbush (*Cephalanthus occidentalis*).

A type of swamp characteristic of the Coastal Plain of the South Atlantic states is the cypress swamp, dominated by the deciduous conifer, the bald cypress (*Taxodium distichum*). This tree characteristically possesses a swollen, fluted base and "knees," which are growths from the roots projecting up above the swamp water. According to Oosting (1953, p. 176), the formation of buttressed bases, plank roots, and knees is apparently a response to alternate inundation and exposure to air. Whitford (1956a) postulated that exposure of a root area to increased aeration stimulates a much greater growth in that area than where the root remains submerged. This greater growth produces, after some time, a knee that may grow to a height of six feet. Cooke (1939) felt that the sandy soil of Big Cypress Swamp might account for the great abundance of trees there, while the limestone base of the Everglades might account for its relative lack of trees; he pointed out inconsistencies, however, and this remains an unsolved problem. It is well known that because cypress seedlings require atmospheric oxygen for initial establishment, cypress forests occur only where water is lacking at least some of the year; a similar wet-dry alternation also seems to be favorable for the saw grass of the Everglades (Davis, 1943, pp. 179–253).

The Big Cypress Swamp occupies the major part of Collier County, Florida, adjoining the western margin of the even larger Everglades. Cypress trees in this swamp grow on intermittently flooded soils. Different parts of this region support various other large trees in addition to the bald cypress; in fact, sizable areas of the region are seldom inundated (Davis, 1943, p. 175 ff.). Cypress domes or hammocks have a distinctive form, with the largest trees occurring in the center, along with the deepest and most permanent water. The reason for this relationship is not clear, although it undoubtedly is based on environmental factors, for the so-called pond cypress (*T. ascendens*) seems to dominate the fringes, whereas the bald cypress dominates the center. Davis feels that these may be the same species showing minor variations related to different environmental factors (p. 183).

The Everglades is the most famous marsh in the United States. It is also one of the largest marshes in the world, comprising some 5000 mi^2, a portion of which is now set aside as the Everglades National Park. (The park also includes vast mangrove swamps and a considerable portion of Florida Bay with its numerous islands.) The Everglades is dominated by various grasses, sedges, reeds, and rushes as well as larger plants in the various areas. The most conspicuous plant, however, is the saw grass (*Mariscus jamaicensis*), which dominates a vast region of more than one million acres (Davis, 1943; Loveless, 1959).

Cooke (1939) pointed out that the Everglades differs from most marshes in the scarcity of trees and the relative lack of mud and clay. It also differs from most South Atlantic marshes in the relative lack of color in the water and the possession of a moderately strong to very weak current. The Everglades is aptly called the "river of grass." The lack of color customary in Everglades water is in striking contrast to the coffee color typical of swamp water; in fact, in places, the water reminds one of that of Silver Springs in both clarity and lack of color.

The Everglades is underlain by limestone rocks of the Pliocene and Pleistocene epochs, chiefly oolitic limestone, which have been covered by peat to more than 15 ft in places. (Detailed discussion of the geology can be found in Parker and Cooke, 1944, and Jones, 1948.) According to Davis (1943, p. 248), there are two principal peat types—that originating in deeper water areas from aquatic plants and that originating in the intermittently exposed saw grass marsh. (A detailed study of peat in Florida was published by Davis in 1946.) Various Everglades plant growths have filled the inequalities in the limestone base with peat, so that the whole Everglades basin has become a gently sloping plain carrying overflow water toward the south and southwest from Lake Okeechobee. Under present conditions, the inflow to Lake Okeechobee from the Kissimmee River watershed varies from about 750,000 to 2,200,000 acre-feet annually; much of this flowed into the Everglades before canal construction. Moreover, rainfall over the Everglades averages about 50 in. per year, producing a large quantity of water for the Everglades under primeval conditions, even considering that evapotranspiration averaged 40.3 in. per year during 1940, 1941, and 1942.

Saw grass grows well only where soils are wet during most of the year. Under present conditions of drainage of much of the Everglades region for cultivation and other purposes, however, the overflow from Lake Okeechobee is minimal. The soils are, consequently, dry for long periods, and this drought may penetrate deeply, resulting in oxidation of peat in addition to poor growth of saw grass and, therefore, relatively little soil formation. Fires are frequent and widespread during dry years. Subsidence of the soils takes place at a rapid rate in non-cultivated as well as in cultivated soils even without the fires, but fires can burn all soil away to the ground-water level in a few days or weeks. The recorded subsidence, where fires have not been influential, is tremendous: Davis reported 1.5 ft during the first 10 years after putting the soil in cultivation and an average of 1 in. per year thereafter. Another important result of the changed character of the Everglades brought about by drainage is the change in natural vegetation. Saw grass is being replaced extensively by various other species, especially shrubs (Davis, 1943; Loveless, 1959). Whether this effect will be favorable is not known. Proper regulation of the drainage is, therefore, one of the most important functions of the Everglades Drainage and Canal authorities.

An apparent peculiarity of the fish populations in these drainage canals is the tremendous population of gars (*Lepisosteus platyrhincus*), a fact that seems odd because of their obvious carnivorous nature. Hunt (1960) found that the digestion rate of these fish is very slow compared to that of other carnivores in the canals. He noted also that they tend to be sedentary and have a low food consumption. This means that a population of gars $2\frac{1}{2}$ or more times as large as the population of other carnivores can be supported on the same amount of food.

Marshes are being investigated in North Carolina by E. O. Beal (personal communication) and colleagues. During the past five years a project concerned with the floristic composition and gross ecological relationships (pH, chloride, organic matter, etc.) of marsh and aquatic areas has been under way. The inadequacy of our taxonomic knowledge of some aquatic plant groups (e.g., Sparganiaceae and Alismataceae) has necessitated critical taxonomic revisions. In one genus, *Nuphar,* the gross ecology of two subspecies seemed to warrant an extensive investigation into their ecological and genetical relationships from a speciation point of view.

Springs

One of the most interesting aquatic habitats, which is especially well represented in Florida among the South Atlantic states, is that of artesian springs. The fabled fountain of youth that Ponce de Leon discovered in 1512 is the present day Ponce de Leon Springs located near DeLand. Springs were described by Bartram, as mentioned previously, and have long been outstanding attractions to tourists as well as to naturalists. Some of them are of such large size that glass-bottomed boats permit easy observation of their flora and fauna through the very clear water (Figs. 8.2 and 8.6).

The existence of these great springs depends directly on the regional geology of the area where they occur: sufficient rainfall, in addition to limestone near the surface that can be dissolved by carbonic acid, permits the formation of complex sinks, conduits, and artesian water that rushes out at a lower elevation (Ferguson *et al.,* 1947). The present artesian springs of Florida are presumed to be remnants of sinks connected to other sinks by underground rivers that were hollowed out during an earlier epoch when the water table was at the level of the present underground rivers (Cooke, 1939). The water table has since risen above these underground rivers, permitting the springs to flow. In the case of Silver Springs, the old water table is thought by Cooke to have stood at least 80 ft below its present position. Therefore, if the present water table were lowered

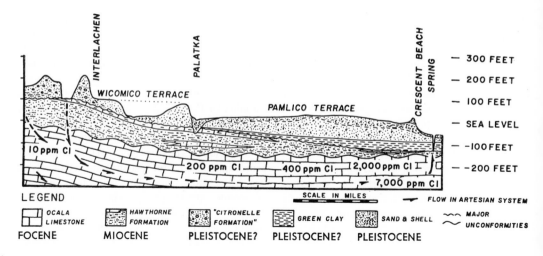

Fig. 8.3.—Structural diagram through Interlachen, Palatka, and Crescent Beach, Florida. The stratigraphy and hydrology of the Floridan aquifer (Ocala limestone) as related to the submarine spring are portrayed. Reprinted by courtesy of Professor H. K. Brooks.

below its mouth, the spring would cease to flow, reverting to a sink. This relationship is strikingly shown in the case of Crescent Springs located in the ocean a few miles south of St. Augustine (H. K. Brooks, 1961).

The crater at the bottom of Crescent Springs, from where the water "boils" up to the surface of the ocean 2½ mi offshore, is 126 ft below sea level. The water that produces this spring originates as rainfall on the area west of Interlachen, more than 40 mi west of the spring (Fig. 8.3). The rainfall passes 100 to 200 ft below the sur-

face into the limestone, from where it flows eastward. An interesting legend has developed that mariners have used this spring to obtain a supply of fresh water at sea, but Brooks has shown that the water that boils up to the surface is almost as salty as the sea water around it (Fig. 8.4). The quantity of water in the surface boil is very large, about 1500 cfs, but because of quick mixing near the bottom, it is salty by the time it rises to the surface. The amount of water actually discharged from the crater is estimated by Brooks to be about 40 cfs. This mixes with the sea

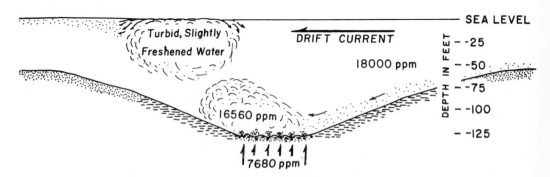

Fig. 8.4.—Diagram of Crescent Spring, Florida, drawn northwest to southeast across the crater, showing size, slopes, and hydrographic conditions observed on June 16, 1960. Reprinted by courtesy of Professor H. K. Brooks.

water and accumulates in the crater until it rises upward rapidly somewhat like a large bubble. There is a large amount of suspended matter in this spring, shutting out light below 90 ft, but at depths below 120 ft the water is clear, except on the bottom where mixing of fresh and sea water produces a refraction "such that only vague forms could be seen in a turbulent translucent fog" (H. K. Brooks, 1961, p. 125). An interesting finding of Brooks' study is that no freshwater organisms were observed in the spring; the bottom has no life, while the higher slopes bear large numbers of sea anemones, sea urchins, and marine mollusks.

To give some idea of the nature of the inland springs, a few facts are cited here from Ferguson *et al.* (1947). The discharge of the two largest, Silver Springs and Rainbow Springs, averages more than 700 cfs, the temperature of all the major springs is about 70° F throughout the year, and the waters of most of the springs are hard, varying little seasonally in the same spring. Although most springs resemble one another chemically, a few are distinctly different. For example, a few springs are anaerobic and have an unusually high sulfur content. Odum and Caldwell (1955) described how certain fish have adapted to an anaerobic spring, where the water picks up oxygen as it flows downstream. Most of the fish found in the spring were limited to that part of the run (the stream formed by the boil) where the oxygen content was at least 1.3 ppm. *Gambusia* and *Mollienesia* were able to live in water with an oxygen content as low as 0.2 ppm, however, and *Lepomis, Lucania,* and *Heterandria* lived in water with only slightly higher oxygen content. By experimenting with these fish in cages, Odum and Caldwell demonstrated that gulping is necessary for them to live in such an environment.

Silver Springs has received the most detailed study of all of the Florida springs, chiefly by Odum from 1951 to 1957, with other studies by some of his associates at the University of Florida and elsewhere. His monograph (Odum, 1957a) doubtless will be considered a classic aquatic study, because it is concerned with many facets of the spring ecosystem, and it represents the principal basis for our present knowledge of productivity of flowing aquatic environments. The following discussion is based largely on his work.

Silver Springs is a remarkably constant ecosystem. Although it has an average flow of about 80,000 m³/hr, it is in a steady state, meaning that chemical factors, temperature, and organisms as a whole are constant both in quantity and species. The principal factor showing annual variation is light, and this, of course, effects variations in dependent processes such as reproduction, productivity, etc. For example, productivity is two to three times as great in the spring season as in the winter. The principal factor showing diurnal variation is also light, and this has major consequences on the ecosystem. Even with these variations, however, there is a striking biological and physicochemical stability as evidenced by Odum's plant map of the spring, which had hardly changed from 1951 to 1955 in either quantity or species of larger plants over the years, by algal populations (Whitford, 1956b), by fish populations, by snail populations, by insect populations in various springs (Sloan, 1956), by other invertebrate populations, by bacterial populations, by productivity, and by the constancy of various physicochemical factors.

The energy relationships in Silver Springs were described thoroughly (Odum, 1956a, 1957a), the results of which are reproduced here as Figure 8.5. The loss of energy as heat is large as required by the second law of thermodynamics. Because of the relatively large insolation, however, there is a very high production. Gross annual productivity in Silver Springs averaged 6390 g/m², while the daily production varied from about 10 g/m² in the winter to more than 30 g/m² in the summer. Odum's method of measuring productivity is a simple one. An upstream-downstream oxygen or carbon dioxide difference curve is taken over a 24-hour period and plotted on a graph. Production is then determined from the area under the resulting curve from sunrise to the evening value equivalent to the sunrise value. Respiration, diffusion, and accrual (addition by seepage from outside the run) are estimated and accounted for in the final figure, which then is multiplied by the average depth, giving an estimate of the gross primary production of the measured portion of the stream in grams of oxygen or carbon dioxide per square meter per day. By this method Odum has determined the productivity of a number of Florida springs to range from less than 1 to more than 59 g oxygen/m² per day and has used the technique with success

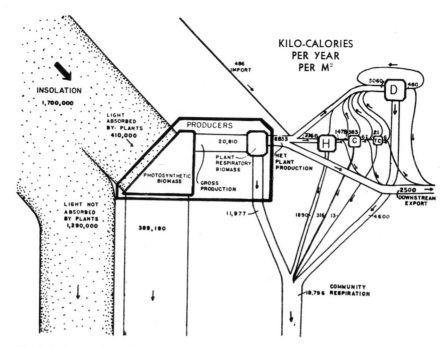

Fig. 8.5.—Energy flow diagram with estimates of energy flows in kilocalories per square meter per year in the Silver Springs community: *H*, herbivores; *C*, carnivores; *TC*, top carnivores; *D*, decomposers. After Odum, 1957*a*.

in various marine environments as well, such as turtle grass flats and coral reefs (Odum, 1956*a*, 1957*b*; Odum and Odum, 1955).

It is evident that the presence of the current in Silver Springs is an important factor in bringing about its high productivity, inasmuch as the productivity in one stillwater basin of the spring was about one-fifth that in the running water part. This, however, is probably due to the lesser total nutrient volume in the basin as well as to the reduced current, as Odum points out. Whitford (1960), in studying the effect of current on algae, showed that the current produces a steep diffusion gradient at the cell surface, thereby increasing exchange of materials between the alga and its environment. Odum considered that the current acts as an auxiliary energy source because of this relationship, and Odum and Hoskin (1957) verified its important role.

The trophic structure of Silver Springs also was analyzed by Odum. The primary producers were chiefly *Sagittaria lorata* and the small Aufwuchs growing on them (Fig. 8.6). As can be seen in Figure 8.7, the biomass of *Sagittaria* is far greater than that of the Aufwuchs, about 70% of the total producer biomass. Photosynthetic pro-

duction of the Aufwuchs, however, amounted to about 70% of the total production, whereas *Sagittaria* only produced 30%. Moreover, the dominant character of the Aufwuchs is reflected in the relatively huge amount (878 g/m² per yr) of small particulate matter exported downstream as compared to the insignificant amount (25 g/m² per yr) of *Sagittaria* exported. A similar relationship is shown by the bacteria, which are small in biomass (bacterial biomass was 0.3 to 0.6 g/m²) but large in metabolic activity. The oxygen use by bottom bacteria was measured as 270 mg/g bacteria dry weight per hour (0.079 g O₂/ m² per hr). Odum (1956*b*) made a special report on this relation of size to metabolism as well as the relationship between efficiency and production. From his Silver Springs and other data, he concluded that a moderately low efficiency would be expected to be developed by competitive communities of high production. For a discussion of this concept, see Odum and Pinkerton, 1955.

Miscellaneous habitats

Although the locality (Jamaica) is outside the area of discussion, the microlimnologic study of bromeliads by Laessle (1961) is of interest in a discussion of South Atlantic states limnology, since these plants are abundant in southern Florida. These interesting air plants retain water in the basal area between the tightly adjacent leaves, and this water contains many organisms, including crabs and frogs. The total amount of water in a large specimen was estimated conservatively to be two liters, so that microlimnologic methods were necessarily used for the study.

By measuring oxygen, carbon dioxide, pH, and temperature diurnally, Laessle determined that exposure to wind and to light were of major importance in development of chemical properties. The well-lighted water reservoirs of the leaves of one plant, for example, showed a diurnal variation in oxygen from less than 1 ppm at night to more than 8 ppm during the day, and in carbon dioxide from about 10 ppm during the day to about 45 ppm at night. These chemical relationships varied considerably among the reservoirs of different leaves of the same plant, depending chiefly on exposure to light and wind.

The surface-volume ratio in the reservoirs of these plants varies according to the differing leaf-axil angles of the various species and according to the age of the leaves, the younger and more erect leaves holding water to a greater depth than the older ones, thereby exposing less water surface.

Fig. 8.6.—Underwater photograph in Silver Springs, showing the large plant, *Sagittaria,* with its Aufwuchs especially clearly shown in upper left. The clarity of the water is evident. The fish are shiners and bluegill sunfish. Photo courtesy of the management, Silver Springs, Florida.

This ratio, as well as exposure to wind and sunlight, is of importance in determining the physicochemical relationships in, and indirectly the biotic constitution of, the reservoirs. Where the plant is

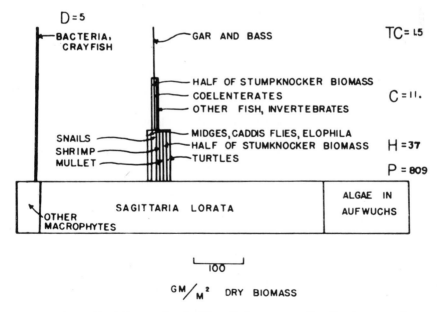

Fig. 8.7.—Pyramid of biomass for the Silver Springs community. *P,* primary producers; *H,* herbivores; *C,* carnivores; *TC,* top carnivores; *D,* decomposers. After Odum, 1957a.

well exposed to light, algal populations are large, and chironomid populations are also large; however, the outer leaves of these exposed plants which are shaded by the inner leaves have few algae and no chironomids. The reservoirs have various fauna so that they are a sort of microcosm with a fully developed trophic structure. In plants that are shaded, the diurnal variation in physicochemical factors is small, as is the biomass.

Laessle postulated an interesting adaptation for the frog, *Hyla brunnea*, the larvae of which chiefly eat eggs from their own egg mass and from egg masses laid later by other adult females. "It seems likely then that succeeding batches of eggs, not necessarily from the same female, serve the same function as milk in mammals, supporting the larvae until they are able to transform and forage for themselves."

Impoundments have become a major habitat in the South Atlantic region and deserve a great deal of limnological study. For example, Weiss and Oglesby (1960) reported a study of University Lake, an impoundment used for the water supply of Chapel Hill, North Carolina. Here there was an odor problem in the city water, which was untreatable by conventional methods. They localized the layer of odor production by limnological techniques and recommended that water be tapped from a different layer where there was no odor. Their study described seasonal variation in temperature and oxygen and also iron and chlorophyll distribution. In this case, peak odors were associated with chlorophyll minima so that green plants were not the direct cause of the odor.

A field of peculiar interest to the South Atlantic and Gulf states is that of ecological relations of the organisms of the water hyacinth community and of the ecologically analogous communities of water lettuce, duckweed, and water fern. The vertebrate fauna of the water hyacinth community was studied by Goin (1943), who found among other things that the hyacinth roots develop directly in proportion to the depth of the water down to three feet. There appears also to be a relationship between extent of surface growth–root growth and the nutrients available to the hyacinths (J. E. Burgess, personal communication).

There have been numerous primarily taxonomic studies on aquatic organisms from the South Atlantic region that have not been discussed in this report, many of which consider ecological relationships of interest to limnologists. The interested student should examine, in addition to the better known journals, publications from the various universities (e.g., *University of Florida Publications, Biological Science Series*) and laboratories (e.g., *Highlands Biological Station Bulletin*).

Limnological potential

An area of potential in the South Atlantic states is the study of subtropical waters from the point of view of their relatively high rate of metabolism. Lakes in the southern part of this region occasionally have surface temperatures higher than 35° C, and the bottom waters may be as high as 30° C, at least in shallow lakes. This results in great stability, so that overturn may be infrequent even where the difference from top to bottom of a lake or even a river is very small (cf. Dickinson, 1949; McLane, 1955; Yount, 1961), and undoubtedly has effects on the general rate of metabolism that would give interesting results.

Studies on marine invasion represent an area of possible great potential in the Southeast, where waters may be oligohaline far inland, in considering migration of animals into fresh water from the sea (Pearse, 1950; Odum, 1953b; McLane, 1955). Because of the extensive swamps in the region, there is also the possibility of learning means of invasion of the aerial environment by animals from both the sea and fresh waters.

Saltwater intrusion has become an important problem to Florida in recent decades because of the tremendous increase in water use by an expanding population and industry (Black et al., 1953; Kohout, 1960). In some extensive coastal areas drinking water in wells has been polluted to such an extent that the water must be treated for general use. What effect this is having on marine invasion is undetermined but may be of importance.

Whitford (1959) summarized knowledge of the ecological distribution of algae, pointing out many areas where study is needed. Among these are studies on algae as indicators of limnological conditions, the need for studies on light, temperature, and current effects and time of appearance of different species in spring and fall, the need for studies on seasonal distribution of algae, and precise identification of the microhabitats of the various species. His report, combined with the historical summary by Silva (1948), leaves one with the impression that no satisfactory system of community classification will be possible until much more fundamental work is carried out.

The problem of factors controlling the diversity of species in communities was considered in Silver Springs. Yount (1956) studied the species diversity of diatoms collected over a year on microscope slides suspended in a high production and a low production station in Silver Springs. He postulated that species diversity was an inverse function of community productivity and was dependent on density of individuals; that is, the greater the number of individuals per habitat, the fewer the species. Hohn (1961), however, studying the same slides by a different method, concluded that density of the diatoms did not affect the species diversity; in fact "the species diversity may be 'masked' by the over-abundance of one or a few species so that the false impression of a reduced species complex seems apparent." This is a field of interest that deserves further investigation, particularly in Florida springs because of their steady-state nature.

The large quantities of nutrients in many of the waters of the South Atlantic states pose a number of problems of great potential, for example, ways of reducing the ill effects of high organic pollution (cf. Odum, 1953a). The obvious aim of studies in this field is to provide means of reducing nutrients flowing into these waters from agricultural leachings and industrial and domestic wastes. The most efficient way is to remove the wastes before they get to the water. This, so far, is not economically feasible, and the present approach is largely to attempt to handle nutrients already in the waters. Treatment plants not only release dissolved nutrients into receiving waters but also release large quantities of nutrients in the bodies of the organisms from the treatment, so that there may not be an actual nutrient reduction resulting from treatment.

Reduction of nutrients in treatment plants can probably most efficiently be performed by using filtered organisms, settled sewage, etc., directly as fertilizer by farmers. In order to make this practicable, however, this "sludge" must be cheaper than it now is, thus probably requiring government subsidy, which would mean competing with fertilizer companies. Perhaps a more practicable, but wasteful, method would be to burn the sludge; that is, filter the fully "bloomed" sewage water over fine sand to remove all organisms possible, and dry and burn the residue in the filter bed so that only ash remains. Moreover, the same filter bed probably could be used many times over before the sand would have to be replaced, and the sand finally removed would be a concentrated fertilizer for which farmers would be willing to pay more money. In this way, the water released into receiving waters would contain a minimum of nutrients instead of the near maximum that the usual present methods release.

An attempt to induce oligotrophication by artificial aeration of lakes is being performed by the writer and his associates. Anaerobic conditions are common in summer in central Florida lakes receiving quantities of nutrients. If some nutrients are precipitated under conditions of oxidation in nature, and nutrients are released under anaerobic conditions, then artificial aeration should "lock" these nutrients in the bottom muds where they would be largely unavailable for phytoplankton production.

By reversing one's thoughts from an aquicultural point of view, another possible way of reducing nutrients becomes obvious (based on discussion with J. E. Burgess), as has been mentioned in the text by Hynes (1960). Since aquiculture began, the object has been to increase production of fish by adding fertilizer to the pond. Oligotrophication, thus, possibly can be induced by removing nutrients from the water in the form of fish and other organisms, even plants in some cases. The greater the rate of removal, the greater the results should be, even with considerable continuous inflow of nutrients. Obviously where nutrients are being added continuously, a dynamic equilibrium would arise between the inflow nutrients and the nutrients being removed as fish bodies. It appears from the various viewpoints (sewage plant, agriculture, industry, sport fishery) that the best method of forcing this equilibrium towards oligotrophy is to permit commercial fishermen to operate in lakes and rivers and require them to remove all captured fish. This would probably meet with considerable opposition from sport fishermen but in the long run would probably favor production of sport fish.

A field of increasing interest is that of identification of the extent of pollution in waters by using the biotic community as indicators (Beck, 1954; Lackey, 1956). The problem with this method is that professional biologists are required to carry out the stream survey. Nevertheless, it is possible for a biologist to learn the fauna well enough in a short time to do this, and the technique of Beck, who uses macroorganisms, will probably become used more generally. Beck approaches the identification of the pollution extent of a stream from the unusual point of view that the organisms more or less intolerant of pollution are the ones most useful for detection and measurement of pollution.

Acknowledgment

The author wishes to express special appreciation to the following individuals for their help: L. A. Whitford, D. G. Frey, S. E. Neff, R. A. Crossman, Jr., J. E. Burgess, H. M. Frisch, and J. D. Hewlett. The author also wishes to thank Duke University Press for permission to reproduce Figures 8.5 and 8.7.

References

ANONYMOUS. 1946. A review for 1931–46. Bull. Highlands Biol. Lab., 14 p.

BAILEY, J. W. 1851. Microscopical observations made in South Carolina, Georgia and Florida. Smithsonian Inst. Publ., Contrib. to Knowledge, 2: 1–48.

BARTRAM, JOHN. 1942. Diary of a journey through the Carolinas, Georgia and Florida, from July 1, 1765, to April 10, 1766. Annotated by Francis Harper. Trans. Amer. Phil. Soc., 33: 1–120.

BARTRAM, WILLIAM. 1791. Travels through North and South Carolina, Georgia, East and West Florida. . . . Reprint ed. [1950]. Dover Publications, New York. 414 p.

———. 1942. Travels in Georgia and Florida, 1773–74. A report to Dr. John Fothergill. Annotated by Francis Harper. Trans. Amer. Phil. Soc., 33: 121–242.

BECK, W. M., JR. 1954. Studies in stream pollution biology. I. A simplified ecological classification of organisms. Quart. J. Florida Acad. Sci., 17: 211–227.

BLACK, A. P., EUGENE BROWN, AND J. M. PEARCE. 1953. Salt water intrusion in Florida—1953. Florida Water Surv. and Research, 9: 1–38.

BRINTON, D. G. 1859. The Silver Spring, p. 101–104. In D. G. Brinton, Notes on the Floridian Peninsula. John Salim, Philadelphia.

BROOKS, H. K. 1961. The submarine spring off Crescent Beach, Florida. Quart. J. Florida Acad. Sci., 24: 122–134.

BROOKS, J. L. 1946. Cyclomorphosis in Daphnia. Ecol. Monogr., 16: 409–447.

CARR, A. F. 1940. A contribution to the herpetology of Florida. Univ. Florida Publ., Biol. Sci. Ser., 3: 1–118.

CLARKE, F. W. 1924. The data of geochemistry. U.S. Geol. Surv., Bull. No. 770: 1–841.

COKER, R. E. 1939. The problem of cyclomorphosis in Daphnia. Quart. Rev. Biol., 14: 137–148.

COOKE, C. W. 1939. Scenery of Florida. Florida Geol. Surv., Geol. Bull. No. 17: 1–118.

CRUICKSHANK, H. G. (ed.). 1961. John and William Bartram's America. Nat. Hist. Library, Doubleday and Co., Garden City, New York. 378 p.

DAVIS, J. H., JR. 1943. The natural features of southern Florida. Florida Geol. Surv., Geol. Bull. No. 25: 1–311.

———. 1946. The peat deposits of Florida. Florida Geol. Surv., Geol. Bull. No. 30: 1–247.

DICKINSON, J. C., JR. 1949. An ecological reconnaissance of the biota of some ponds and ditches in northern Florida. Quart. J. Florida Acad. Sci., 11: 1–28.

DILS, R. E. 1957. A guide to the Coweeta Hydrologic Laboratory. U.S. Dept. Agr. Forest Serv., Southeastern Forest Expt. Sta.: 1–40.

DOUGLAS, M. S. 1947. The Everglades, River of Grass. Rinehart and Co., New York. 406 p.

EKBLAW, W. E. 1961. Dismal Swamp, p. 422–423. In Encyclopaedia Britannica, 7.

FENNEMAN, N. M. 1938. Physiography of eastern United States. McGraw-Hill, New York. 714 p.

FERGUSON, G. E., C. W. LINGHAM, S. K. LOVE, AND R. O. VERNON. 1947. Springs of Florida. Florida Geol. Surv., Geol. Bull. No. 31: 1–196.

FREY, D. G. 1949. Morphometry and hydrography of some natural lakes of the North Carolina coastal plain: The bay lake as a morphometric type. J. Elisha Mitchell Sci. Soc., 65: 1–37.

———. 1951a. Pollen succession in the sediments of Singletary Lake, N.C. Ecology, 32: 518–533.

———. 1951b. The fishes of North Carolina's bay lakes and their intraspecific variation. J. Elisha Mitchell Sci. Soc., 67: 1–44.

———. 1953. Regional aspects of the late-glacial and post-glacial pollen succession of southeastern North Carolina. Ecol. Monogr., 23: 289–313.

———. 1954. Evidence for the recent enlargement of the "bay" lakes of North Carolina. Ecology, 35: 78–88.

———. 1955. Stages in the ontogeny of the Carolina bays. Verh. intern. Ver. Limnol., 12: 660–668.

GOIN, C. J. 1943. The lower vertebrate fauna of the water hyacinth community in northern Florida. Proc. Florida Acad. Sci., 6: 143–154.

HARKNESS, W. J. K., AND E. L. PIERCE. 1940. The limnology of Lake Mize, Florida. Quart. J. Florida Acad. Sci., 5: 96–116.

HARPER, F. (ed.). 1958. The travels of William Bartram. Yale Univ. Press, New Haven. 732 p.

HASSLER, W. W., AND L. B. TEBO, JR. 1958. Fish management investigations on trout streams. North Carolina Wildl. Resources Comm., Fish Div., Raleigh, N. C.: 1–118. (Mimeo.)

HAURWITZ, B. 1951. The slope of lake surfaces under variable wind stresses. Tech. Mem. U.S. Army Erosion Board, 25: 1–23.

HESSE, R., W. C. ALLEE, AND K. P. SCHMIDT. 1951.

Ecological animal geography. John Wiley & Sons, New York. 715 p.

HEWLETT, J. D., AND L. J. METZ. 1960. Watershed management research in the Southeast. J. Forestry, 58: 269–271.

HOHN, M. H. 1961. The relationship between species diversity and population density in diatom populations from Silver Springs, Florida. Trans. Amer. Microscop. Soc., 80: 140–165.

HOSKIN, C. M. 1959. Studies of oxygen metabolism of streams of North Carolina. Publ. Inst. Marine Sci., 6: 186–192.

HUNT, B. P. 1960. Digestion rate and food consumption of Florida gar, warmouth and largemouth bass. Trans. Amer. Fish. Soc., 89: 206–211.

HUTCHINSON, G. E. 1957. A treatise on limnology. Vol. I. John Wiley & Sons, New York. 1015 p.

HUTCHINSON, G. E., AND G. E. PICKFORD. 1932. Limnological observations on Mountain Lake, Virginia. Intern. Rev. Hydrobiol. Hydrogr., 27: 252–264.

HYNES, H. B. N. 1960. The biology of polluted waters. Liverpool Univ. Press, Liverpool. 202 p.

JOHNSON, D. W. 1942. Origin of the Carolina bays. Columbia Univ. Press, New York. 341 p.

JONES, L. A. 1948. Soils, geology and water control in the Everglades region. Univ. Florida Agr. Expt. Sta., Bull. 442: 1–168.

KOHOUT, F. A. 1960. Cyclic flow of salt water in the Biscayne aquifer of southeastern Florida. J. Geophys. Research, 65: 2133–2141.

LACKEY, J. B. 1956. Stream enrichment and microbiota. Pub. Health Repts., 71: 708–721.

LAESSLE, A. M. 1961. A micro-limnological study of Jamaican bromeliads. Ecology, 42: 499–517.

LE CONTE, J. L. 1861. On the optical phenomena presented by the Silver Springs in Marion Co., Fla. Amer. J. Sci., Ser. 2, 31: 1–12.

LE GRAND, H. E. 1953. Streamlining of the Carolina bays. J. Geol., 61: 263–274.

LOVELESS, C. M. 1959. A study of the vegetation in the Florida Everglades. Ecology, 40: 1–9.

McLANE, W. M. 1955. The fishes of the St. Johns' River System. Ph.D. Dissertation, Univ. Florida, Gainesville, 362 p.

MELTON, F. A., AND W. SCHRIEVER. 1933. The Carolina bays—are they meteorite scars? J. Geol., 41: 52–66.

ODUM, H. T. 1952. The Carolina bays and a Pleistocene weather map. Amer. J. Sci., 250: 263–270.

———. 1953a. Dissolved phosphorus in Florida waters. Florida Geol. Surv., Rept. 9: 1–40.

———. 1953b. Factors controlling marine invasion into Florida fresh waters. Bull. Marine Sci. Gulf & Caribbean, 3: 134–156.

———. 1956a. Primary production in flowing waters. Limnol. Oceanogr., 1: 102–117.

———. 1956b. Efficiencies, size of organisms and community structure. Ecology, 37: 592–597.

———. 1957a. Trophic structure and productivity of Silver Springs, Florida. Ecol. Monogr., 27: 55–112.

———. 1957b. Primary production measurements in eleven Florida springs and a marine turtle grass community. Limnol. Oceanogr., 2: 85–97.

ODUM, H. T., AND D. K. CALDWELL. 1955. Fish respiration in the natural oxygen gradient of an anaerobic spring in Florida. Copeia, 1955: 104–106.

ODUM, H. T., AND C. M. HOSKIN. 1957. Metabolism of a laboratory stream microcosm. Publ. Inst. Marine Sci., 4: 115–133.

ODUM, H. T., AND E. P. ODUM. 1955. Trophic structure and productivity of a windward coral reef community on Eniwetok Atoll. Ecol. Monogr., 25: 291–320.

ODUM, H. T., AND R. C. PINKERTON. 1955. Times speed regulator, the optimum efficiency for maximum power output in physical and biological systems. Amer. Scientist, 43: 331–343.

OOSTING, H. J. 1953. The study of plant communities. W. H. Freeman Co., San Francisco. 389 p.

PARKER, G. G., AND C. W. COOKE. 1944. Late Cenozoic geology of southern Florida, with a discussion of the ground water. Florida Geol. Surv., Geol. Bull. 27: 1–119.

PEARSE, A. S. 1950. The emigrations of animals from the sea. Sherwood Press, Dryden, New York. 210 p.

PIERCE, E. L. 1947. An annual cycle of the plankton and chemistry of four aquatic habitats in northern Florida. Univ. Florida Publ., Biol. Sci. Ser., 4: 1–67.

PIRKLE, E. C., AND H. K. BROOKS. 1959. Origin and hydrology of Orange Lake, Santa Fe Lake, and Levys Prairie Lakes of north-central peninsular Florida. J. Geol., 67: 302–317.

PLATT, R. P., AND C. S. SHOUP. 1950. The use of a thermistor in a study of summer temperature conditions of Mountain Lake, Virginia. Ecology, 31: 484–488.

PROUTY, W. F. 1935. The Carolina bays and elliptical lake basins. J. Geol., 43: 200–207.

———. 1952. Carolina bays and their origin. Bull. Geol. Soc. Amer., 63: 167–224.

ROSEBERRY, D. A., AND R. B. BOWERS. 1959. Under the cover of Lake Drummond. Virginia Wildl., 13: 1–3.

RUSSELL, I. C. 1895. Lakes of North America. Ginn and Co., Boston. 125 p.

———. 1898. Rivers of North America. G. P. Putnam & Sons, New York. 327 p.

SELLARDS, E. H. 1914. Some Florida lakes and lake basins. Florida Geol. Surv., Rept. 6: 115–159.

SHAND, S. J. 1946. Dust devils? Parallelism between the South African salt pans and the Carolina bays. Sci. Monthly, 62: 95.

SHOUP, C. S. 1948. Limnological observations on some streams of the New River watershed in the vicinity of Mountain Lake, Virginia. J. Elisha Mitchell Sci. Soc., 64: 1–12.

SILVA, HERMANN. 1948. A review of freshwater phycological research in southeastern United States. Castanea, J. Southern Appalachian Botan. Club, 13: 133–141.

SLOAN, W. C. 1956. The distribution of aquatic

insects in two Florida springs. Ecology, **37**: 81–98.

SMYTH, J. F. D. 1784. A tour in the United States of America. G. Robinson, London. 2 v.

STUBBS, S. A. 1940. Solution a dominant factor in the geomorphology of peninsular Florida. Quart. J. Florida Acad. Sci., **5**: 148–167.

TEALE, E. W. 1951. North with the spring. Dodd, Mead & Co., New York. 358 p.

TEBO, L. B., JR. 1955. Effects of siltation, resulting from improper logging, on the bottom fauna of a small trout stream in the southern Appalachians. Progr. Fish-Cult., **17**: 64–70.

WEISS, C. M., AND R. T. OGLESBY. 1960. Limnology and quality of raw water impoundments. Pub. Works Mag., Aug., 1960: 97–101.

WHITFORD, L. A. 1956a. A theory on the formation of cypress knees. J. Elisha Mitchell Sci. Soc., **72**: 80–83.

―――. 1956b. The communities of algae in the springs and spring streams of Florida. Ecology **37**: 433–442.

―――. 1959. Ecological distribution of fresh-water algae. Pymatuning Symposia in Ecol., Spec. Publ. **2**: 1–10.

―――. 1960. The current effect and growth of fresh-water algae. Trans. Amer. Microscop. Soc., **79**: 302–309.

WRIGHT, A. H., AND A. A. WRIGHT. 1932. The habitats and composition of the vegetation of Okefenokee Swamp, Georgia. Ecol. Monogr., **2**: 109–232.

YOUNT, J. L. 1956. Factors that control species numbers in Silver Springs, Florida. Limnol. Oceanogr., **1**: 286–295.

―――. 1961. A note on stability in central Florida lakes, with discussion of the effect of hurricanes. Limnol. Oceanogr., **6**: 322–325.

9 | Walter G. Moore

Central Gulf States and the Mississippi Embayment

Limnological resources

Physiography and climate

The Central Gulf States of Alabama, Mississippi, Louisiana, and Arkansas lie predominantly within the Coastal Plain Province (see Fig. 9.1). Northeastern Alabama is dominated by the Appalachian Highlands; northwestern Arkansas, by the Ozark Plateau and Ouachita Provinces. Between these the Mississippi Embayment, a vast low plain which owes its existence in part to a structural trough, extends inland to the Missouri-Illinois region. For much of its history the trough was submerged; after late Pliocene uplift the Mississippi River followed its axis to the sea.

Details of physiography and drainage will be found in Fenneman (1928, 1938) and Shelford (1926). In general, the eastern and western sections of the Coastal Plain are given a belted character by successive Cretaceous and Eocene outcrops. The Alluvial Plain, consisting of three great flood basins (Yazoo, St. Francis, and Tensas: see Fig. 9.2) and the Delta, occupies the central part of the Mississippi Embayment. The uplands of Alabama and Arkansas include both folded systems and dissected plateaus.

The climate of the Central Gulf States (U.S. Dept. Agr., 1941) is influenced strongly by the land mass to the north and by the tempering waters of the Gulf of Mexico to the south. Average annual temperatures range between 60° and 70° F. Mean annual precipitation (mostly in the form of rain) varies from 50 to 60+ in., the Gulf border being within the area of maximum precipitation east of the Rocky Mountains. In general the climate of the area north of latitude 33° (including the whole state of Arkansas) is controlled by alternating cyclones and anticyclones, the centers of their paths usually lying to the north. There is a transition zone to latitude 31° 30′, south of which the climate is largely subtropical and markedly influenced by the Gulf of Mexico.

Throughout most of the area the summers are long and hot, the winters short and mild. Freezing temperatures and snow are infrequent and usually of short duration, although in the mountainous sections of Arkansas zero temperatures are common in January and February and snow cover may persist for two or three weeks.

Types of aquatic habitats

Lying outside the area of Pleistocene glaciation and being virtually unaffected by tectonic or volcanic activity, basins in the Central Gulf States all fall within the Hutchinsonian categories of lakes of fluviatile origin, coastline lakes, and man-made basins. While no comprehensive surveys of the limnology of the area can be cited, brief characterization of the major aquatic resources of each of the four states follows.

Alabama.—A detailed inventory of Alabama water areas, by counties, was prepared by Byrd and Moss (1952). A more recent summary (Byrd,

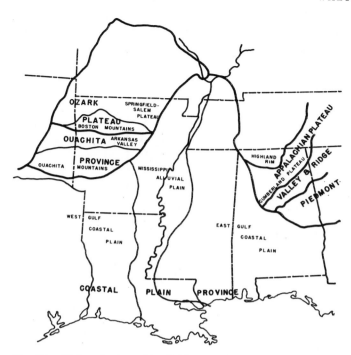

Fig. 9.1.—Major physiographic divisions of the Central Gulf States. After Fenneman, 1928.

1958) of the freshwater fishing areas of Alabama cites 50 rivers, 250 creeks, 19 large impoundments, and 15,000 ponds with a total area of 459,000 acres. More than half of this water area is included in major impoundments on the Tennessee, Coosa, Tallapoosa, and other large rivers. Farm fish ponds are very numerous and are being constructed at the rate of over 1,000 per year. Much of the limnological work in the state relates to the farm pond program and has been carried out by H. S. Swingle and co-workers at Auburn University; this subject is considered in another chapter. Estuarine areas, mainly in the Mobile River Basin and Bay Area in the southwestern part of the state, add another 500,000 acres (Beshears and Byrd, 1959) to Alabama's aquatic resources.

Mississippi.—The state lies almost entirely in the East Gulf Coastal Plain; this fact, the altitude range to only 800 ft, and an average annual rainfall approximately uniform for all sections would suggest little diversity of soils, topography, and aquatic habitats. Within limits this is indeed the case.

The major river systems draining to the Gulf include the Pascagoula on the east with its tributaries the Chickasawhay and the Leaf, the Pearl

River which drains 6,800 mi^2 of the central part of the state, and the Mississippi River, including almost the entire area of the Yazoo Basin, on the west. Within the Yazoo Basin much of the land is swampy, and the streams are meandering with numerous bayous, cut-offs, and sloughs. Crescent-shaped lakes, which were originally old stream beds, are numerous. The lower courses of the Pearl and Pascagoula rivers cross the Long Leaf Pine Region and the Coastal Pine Meadows (Lowe, 1921) and are frequently bordered by peaty, acid swamps and marshes. The Pearl divides into five distributaries in the St. Tammany Parish (Louisiana) region; the main flow is through the West Pearl River. Both the Pearl and Pascagoula rivers are brackish near their mouths.

The Mississippi Game and Fish Commission (1961) has listed and briefly characterized over 200 fishing localities in the state. Among them are several major flood-control reservoirs constructed in north Mississippi since 1940. Four of these (Sardis, Arkabutla, Enid, and Granada) make up the Yazoo Basin Headwater Project with a total surface area (at spillway level) of over 154,000 acres. They utilize dams of the earth-fill type (Towery, 1958).

Louisiana.—An excellent survey of the various

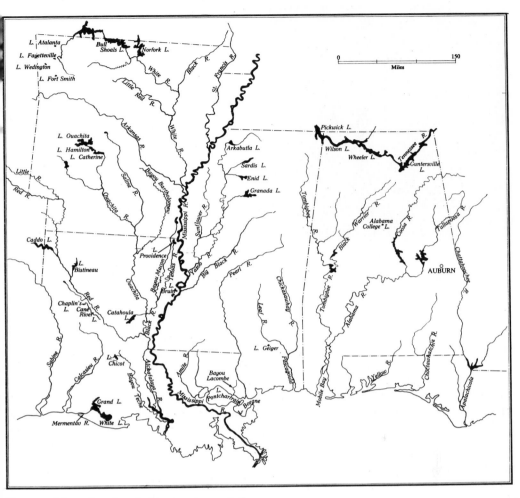

Fig. 9.2.—Map of major drainage systems of the Central Gulf States. Prepared by the University of Wisconsin Cartographic Laboratory.

types of aquatic habitats in Louisiana will be found in the publications of Viosca (1928, 1933). Gunter (1952, 1956) and Gunter and Shell (1958) provide additional details on the Mississippi River and the coastal lakes. In general terms, the drainage of the northern part of the state is dominated by the Mississippi River with a broad flood plain extending along the eastern border in a belt about 50 mi wide and 400 mi long. Joining the Mississippi, midway between the Arkansas and the Gulf, is the Red River which flows diagonally across the state from its northwest corner. Paralleling the Mississippi alluvial plain in the north is another broad valley, that of the Ouachita River, which merges with the valleys of the Mississippi and the Red rivers east of Alexandria.

Accompanying each of these master streams of north Louisiana are two long chains of lakes, more or less surrounded by swamps. Bayous, a term derived from the Choctaw "bayuk" meaning "creek" (Read, 1931) and applied quite generally to sluggish streams, enter these lakes on the north and emerge on the south where they join the main rivers. Water levels thus fluctuate with those of the rivers since the bayous, swamps, and lakes are flooded by backwaters when the rivers are high.

Below the mouth of the Red River there are no major tributaries of the Mississippi, but there are numerous important distributaries on the fan-shaped alluvial plain which terminates in the delta. Except for the passes at the mouth and

Fig. 9.3.—Lake Providence, an oxbow in East Carroll Parish, Louisiana. The Mississippi River is in the lower right corner. Photo courtesy U.S. Army, Corps of Engineers.

the Atchafalaya, which carries one-fifth of the Mississippi's water at flood stage, these distributaries have all been dammed. Along the main river and its distributaries, meanders and cut-offs have produced a large series of oxbow lakes (Fig. 9.3), which are especially numerous in the upper or older parts of the valleys.

Where the level of the "back lands" between the levees and the escarpment dips below the mean water table, swamps form. These differ from the swamps of the chain lakes of the Red and Ouachita valleys in that they do not drain back into the main streams and are not flooded by backwaters. Since drainage is away from the main channels, they serve merely as catch-basins for overflow water (when the artificial levees give way) and for precipitation. The swamp bayou, a type of bayou not of alluvial origin, develops within these catch-basin swamps. These are sluggish streams which carry little material in suspension and which have insignificant natural levees.

Adjacent to the coastal region there are treeless marshes and many lagoons or lakes at or near sea level which have resulted from the surrounding of arms of the sea by deltaic ridges. In the coastal region proper the lakes and marshes are generally saline or brackish, although the transition from fresh water is usually gradual. Separating these marshes from the sea in most places are wave-and-wind–built barrier beaches

which act as dikes against intrusion by the sea water.

Arkansas.—Because of the extremes of topography and climate, the aquatic habitats of the state of Arkansas are perhaps the most diversified of the Central Gulf States. The entire state slopes to the south and east, and practically all the drainage reaches the Mississippi River through the St. Francis, White, Arkansas, Ouachita, and Red rivers. Oxbows, sloughs, and catch-basin swamps, as described for Mississippi and Louisiana, are numerous on the flood plains of the Mississippi and Arkansas rivers.

In 1960 Arkansas had 21 storage reservoirs with a capacity of 5,000 acre-feet or more. Of these, by far the largest were Bull Shoals Lake on the White River, Ouachita Lake on the Ouachita, and Norfork Lake on the Norfork River, all maintained by the U.S. Army Corps of Engineers. Bull Shoals Lake is particularly noteworthy since discharge of cold water from low-level outlets at Bull Shoals Dam has altered the character of the White River from a warm-water to a cold-water stream, which now supports an extensive trout fishery for at least 35 mi below the dam (Baker, 1959).

It was estimated by the Arkansas Game and Fish Commission (1955) that there were over 453,000 acres of fishing waters in the state (excluding farm ponds) and 9,700 mi of fishable streams.

Major areas of limnological activity

Limnological investigations in the Central Gulf States area have been few and mostly of a general reconnaissance character. The extensive publications and maps of the Mississippi River Commission, U.S. Army Corps of Engineers, deal in detail with navigation and flood-control projects on the Mississippi River and its tributaries. The program of the U.S. Fish and Wildlife Service, whose river basin studies were inaugurated in 1945, has been reviewed by Johnson (1959). Since passage of the Dingell-Johnson Act in 1950, the various state fish and game departments have also been active in survey work. Much of the limnological data accumulated under these programs remains unpublished, being available, if at all, chiefly in the form of mimeographed progress reports. Some more intensive basic surveys of selected sites have been carried out by biologists associated with colleges and universities; again much of this is in the form of unpublished Masters' and Doctors' dissertations and hence not readily available.

In the following review, lake studies will be grouped, as far as possible, into categories based on basin origin following Hutchinson (1957), whose type numbers will be used to designate specific examples. Stream studies will be separately considered as will certain investigations of estuarine habitats. The limits of these categories are, in many cases, virtually indistinguishable, and certain habitats are assigned only provisionally to the indicated categories.

Lake Studies

Lateral lakes (Type 52).—A most important type of fluviatile lake is formed when deposited sediments of a rapidly aggrading main stream cause water to back up into tributary streams, producing drowned valleys. This mode of formation has been suggested as the source of the numerous lakes in the side valleys of the Red River in northwest Louisiana (Fig. 9.4). Veatch (1906) proposed a different method of origin (subsequently criticized by Vernon, 1942) which involved the formation of obstructive log jams. The famous "Great Raft" of the Red River at its greatest extent attained a length of 160 mi and reached almost to the Arkansas boundary. After its removal in 1873, the channel began to degrade and the lakes to shrink. Certain of them (Bistineau, Black) still persist as shallow bodies of water; others (Poston, Bayou Pierre) have been reduced to swamps or bayous. An extensive contemporary account will be found in Veatch (1899).

Caddo Lake, a shallow backwater on the Louisiana-Texas boundary, occupies part of the old bed of Ferry and Sodo lakes (see Fig. 9.4). With an area of 32,000 acres, the lake has a mean depth of only about 6 ft. It has been studied by Fuss (1959) and Geagan and Allen (1961) who found that severe wave action precluded the development of summer thermal stratification, except of a temporary nature near the dam at the outlet.

A somewhat similar lake type found on the flood plains of the major rivers is the "backwater lake" which, during periods of high water, receives backwater from nearby streams. The standing crop of fishes in several such lakes in Louisiana was determined by rotenone sampling

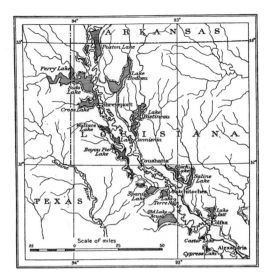

Fig. 9.4.—Lakes in the tributary valleys of the Red River at their fullest recorded development. From Veatch, 1906.

by Lambou (1959b). As a general index of productivity these data are compared with standing crops, similarly determined, for two other lake types (see Table 9.1). Lambou attributed the high productivity of the backwater lakes to the fertility of the alluvial flood plains on which they are found and to the influence of periodic high water levels during spawning periods.

Deltaic levee lakes (Type 53).—Hutchinson (1957) has cited Lake Pontchartrain (Fig. 9.2) as "a very fine example of a lake held between the levee of an outgrown distributary, Bayou Sauvage, and the higher country north of the flood plain of the Mississippi." Steinmeyer (1939) described its origin from a remnant of an arm of the Gulf of Mexico which was impounded by deltaic deposits and gradually freshened, while Russell (1940) emphasized the importance of downwarping in the formation of the whole chain of lakes extending westward from Mississippi Sound.

Although essentially an estuarine habitat, the lake is considered here because of the importance of the freshwater elements in its community composition, and because it is one of the few localities in the Central Gulf States where an extensive and detailed study of an aquatic community has been carried out. The results have appeared in the form of processed reports (Suttkus *et al.*, 1953–56) and a continuing series of publications

TABLE 9.1

Comparison of standing crops of fishes in Louisiana freshwater lakes

| Habitat type | No. of examples | Standing crop (lbs/acre) | | Reference |
		Mean	Range	
Impoundments (over 500 acres)	8	73	13–146	Lambou, 1959a
Oxbows	7	202	156–267	Lambou, 1960
Backwater lakes	7	297	142–651	Lambou, 1959b

(Darnell, 1954, 1958, 1959, 1961; Suttkus, 1954, 1956).

Lake Pontchartrain has a surface area of 635 mi^2, a shoreline length of ca. 100 mi, and an average depth of only 11 ft. The physical environment is characterized by an annual temperature range of 9° to 34° C, generally low salinity (1.2 to 18.6 ‰ with an average of less than 6.0 ‰), and high turbidity. Stratification is observed in summer, particularly when temperature-related density differences are reinforced by differential salinity currents.

The zooplankton of Lake Pontchartrain (Suttkus et al., 1953, 1954) consists of a large population of a few brackish-water species (dominated by the calanoid copepod, Acartia tonsa) and low densities or localized populations of many freshwater and littoral marine forms. The major elements of the phytoplankton include the freshwater genus Anabaena and two typical marine diatoms, Chaetoceros and Coscinodiscus. A large population of a few species survive and thrive under the conditions in this habitat; many freshwater and marine species are swept passively into the lake and do not reproduce.

In a quantitative study of the food habits of 35 of the more important species of fishes and invertebrates, Darnell (1958) found that most were omnivorous; organic detritus was prominent in the diet of most species; and many exhibited a definite ontogenetic progression of food stages. Two primary food chains (planktonic and benthonic) were found to support the top predators, but distinct "trophic levels" among the consumers were not recognizable.

A recent study (Darnell, 1961) attempted to interpret the preceding findings in the context of the total community. The author concluded that the Lake Pontchartrain estuarine community is a broadly open system exchanging nutrients, producers, and consumers with adjacent freshwater, saltwater, and neighboring marsh and swamp areas. The consumers apparently depend in great measure upon primary production which takes place outside the lake, and hence the community may be trophically unbalanced. Figure 9.5 presents a model of the trophic relations in the community, emphasizing the relatively little utilization of phytoplankton, vascular plants, and zooplankton and the heavy dependence upon detritus, benthos, and fishes.

Oxbows or isolated loops of meanders (Type 54).—"Oxbow lakes are extremely common in the flood plain of the lower Mississippi and its tributaries; hundreds of examples must exist in Arkansas, Mississippi, and Louisiana" (Hutchinson, 1957, p. 122). Except for certain of the larger impoundments, they are the only deep lakes (15 m or more) to be found on the Coastal Plain; yet they have received almost no attention from limnologists. Investigations at Lake Providence, Louisiana, by Moore (1950) established that the general nature of the annual thermal cycle of such bodies is characterized by free circulation in winter and direct stratification in summer, i.e., the "warm monomictic" category of Hutchinson. Other Louisiana oxbows (e.g., Lake Bruin) have been shown to exhibit similar thermal properties (Geagan and Fuss, 1959).

Located on the fertile alluvial soils of river flood plains, these lakes typically produce high standing crops of plankton, benthos, and fishes (Geagan and Allen, 1961; Lambou, 1960). Rooted aquatic vegetation tends to be scanty because of steep slopes, minimal shoal areas, and abundant phytoplankton, especially blue-green algae.

The Louisiana oxbows studied have all been separated from the parent river by levees. Scattered observations on a number of oxbow lakes in the state of Mississippi which still communicate by chutes with the Mississippi River at high water stages have been made by Coleman (1960).

Lakes in abandoned channels (Type 57).—Al-

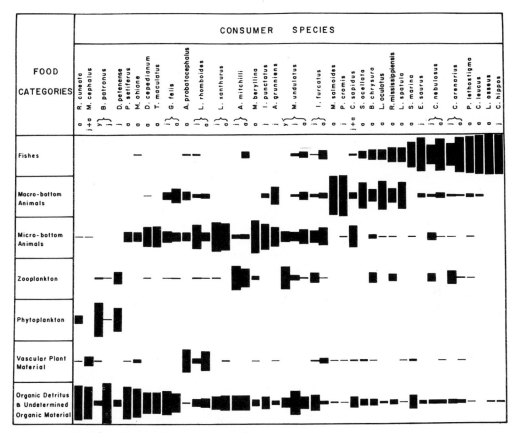

Fig. 9.5.—Trophic spectra for important consumer species of the Lake Pontchartrain community. From Darnell, 1961.

though differing markedly from the "meander scrolls" cited as illustrating lakes of this category, both Cane River Lake and Chaplin's Lake in Natchitoches Parish, Louisiana, will be considered here. Both represent old channels of the Red River, isolated after the removal of the "Great Raft" and subsequently confined by artificially constructed earthen dams at the end. Their origin is evidenced by long, narrow basins, precipitous shore slopes, and meandering form.

Sublette and Sublette (1957) reported only transitory thermal stratification in Chaplin's Lake during midsummer and incomplete oxygen depletion at the lower levels. They attributed this to the shallow nature of the basin and lack of protection from wind. Geagan and Allen (1961) found thermally stratified conditions at the deeper, lower end of Cane River Lake and no marked oxygen depletion. Buckley (1958), on the other hand, found a strong tendency to thermal

stratification in upper Cane River Lake from April to September and virtually complete oxygen exhaustion in the lower strata persisting through the summer months. He made a special study of Chironomidae emergence and found it to be greater from the littoral zone than from the sublittoral and profundal combined. Thirty-three species, of a lake total of forty-five, were taken on emergence from aquatic vegetation, chiefly alligator weed (*Alternanthera*) and cutgrass (*Zizaniopsis*).

Lateral levee lakes (Type 58).—An interesting lake type which has received almost no attention from limnologists is that which may collect between a levee and a scarp defining the flood plain. Catahoula Lake on the course of the Little Red River in LaSalle Parish, Louisiana, is such a lake (Fisk, 1938). A scarp on the northwest delimits the flood plain, while a series of levees delimits the lake on the southeast. Like most such lakes,

Catahoula is extremely variable in area and depth; the larger streams either drain or fill the lake according to the water height in their drainage systems. At low-level stages Little Red River is the principal outlet of Catahoula Lake; at high water the back pressure reverses the flow, and it becomes an inlet. At its maximum extent the lake is 12 mi long, 3-4 mi wide, 40 ft deep, and has an area of 40 mi²; at other times it may disappear completely. These variations in level are reflected in the zonation of vegetation around the basin (Brown, 1943). The lake has been described as "a place to hunt ducks in winter, to fish in spring, and to graze cattle in summer" (Yancey, 1952).

Maritime coastal lakes (Type 64).—According to Hutchinson (1957), some of the saline lakes on the Gulf Coast have been formed by bars building up across irregularities or indentations of the shoreline. When the building was sufficiently vigorous, a new drainage pattern parallel to the coast might develop, giving rise to a series of lakes which corresponded, in most cases, to old bays and estuaries.

The Pleistocene history of Cameron Parish, Louisiana, appears to have been one of alluviation by deltaic deposits of the Mississippi, Calcasieu, and Sabine rivers, followed in recent times by subsidence caused in part by a worldwide rise in sea level (Gunter and Shell, 1958) along with settling from compaction (Russell, 1936). The confinement of the major rivers to fixed channels by artificial levee systems developed since the early 1700's has resulted in subsidence, erosion, and drowning dominating over the processes of alluviation which now occur chiefly as a result of westward littoral drift. As a result, Gulf waters are encroaching upon the coastal marshland.

Studies of certain aspects of the limnology of these coastal lakes, especially Grand and White lakes of the Mermentau River Basin, have been made by Gunter (1956), Gunter and Shell (1958), and Smith (1959). Gunter reported salinities varying from 0.08 to 4.05 ‰ with the fauna a mixture of freshwater and marine species, the latter dominant. He concluded that animals do distribute themselves over definite salinity ranges and appear to be quite sensitive to salinity differences near the lower end of their range. Upper salinity limits are seldom exceeded, since most estuarine animals can tolerate full sea-

water salinity. Smith made a special study of the Chironomidae in these and other water bodies in western Cameron Parish. She found the salinities of most to fluctuate between the alpha and beta mesohaline ranges of Redeke (1922). An inverse, straight-line relationship was demonstrated between midge emergence and salinity, and a direct relationship with pH. Some emergence took place even from water approaching one-half sea strength. In areas of almost constant and complete oxygen depletion, midges emerged from floating aquatic vegetation.

Anthropic (man-made) basins (Types 73 and 74).—Probably the greatest number of basins falls into the category of those formed by the damming of streams or in excavations made by man. Farm ponds and major reservoirs, both of which fall within this class, are treated in more detail in other chapters. The impoundments on the Tennessee River are excellent examples of reservoirs. These T.V.A. lakes, the "Great Lakes of the South" as they have been called, comprise 180,000 acres of water area in four major reservoirs in north Alabama: Guntersville, Wheeler, Wilson, and Pickwick lakes (Byrd, 1958). The impoundments serve several primary purposes (Baker, 1950), including flood control, navigation, and electric power production. Biological resource development is a secondary objective, although investigations of sport and commercial fisheries are actively conducted. Bryan and White (1958) report that, in 1956, 372 licensed commercial fishermen harvested over 3,900,000 lbs of rough fish (catfish, buffalo, and carp, with lesser numbers of spoonbill, drum, and carpsucker) from the T.V.A. lakes of Alabama.

In Table 9.2 there is a list of representative studies of man-made lakes of the Central Gulf States. The annual thermal cycle of most of these —a summer stratification period and free circulation throughout the rest of the year—conforms to the general pattern described for Texas reservoir lakes by Harris and Silvey (1940). Normal summer stratification is frequently modified by local conditions; thermocline instability has been reported for shallow (maximum depth: 12 ft) Lake Chicot, Louisiana (Moore, 1952; Geagan and Allen, 1961), and for Lake Fort Smith, Arkansas (Hoffman, 1952). Brief periods of thermal stratification during winter have been noted in Lakes Atalanta, Hindsville, and Fort Smith, Arkansas (Tatum, 1951; Nelson, 1952; Hoffman

TABLE 9.2

Representative studies of man-made lakes in the Central Gulf States

State	Impoundments studied	References
Alabama	Alabama College Lake, Shelby Co.	Nelson, 1958
Mississippi	Lake Geiger, Forest Co. Sardis Reservoir, Panola and Lafayette counties Sardis, Arkabutla, Enid, and Granada reservoirs	Grantham, 1958 Hanebrink, 1955 Towery, 1958
Louisiana	Lake Chicot, Evangeline Parish	Penfound, 1949; Moore, 1952; Geagan & Fuss, 1959; Geagan, 1960; Geagan & Allen, 1961
	Holloway's Pond, Tangipahoa Parish (an excavation lake)	Geagan & Fuss, 1959
Arkansas	Lake Wedington, Washington Co. Lake Fort Smith, Crawford Co.	Allman, 1952; Owen, 1951 Hoffman, 1951, 1952; Hoffman & Causey, 1952; Nelson, 1952
	5 impoundments in northwest Arkansas Lake Fayetteville, Washington Co. Lakes Ouachita, Hamilton, and Catherine, west- central Arkansas Lake Atalanta, Benton Co.	Hoffman et al., 1954 Hulsey, 1956 Stevenson & Hulsey, 1958 Tatum, 1951

et al., 1954), and multiple thermoclines for Sardis Reservoir in Mississippi (Towery, 1958). In the latter body hypolimnetic waters are periodically discharged during summer from outlets at the base of the dam, resulting in a gradual elimination of first the hypolimnion and then the thermocline.

Several valuable studies of the plankton of these impoundments have been made, some of them as yet unpublished. Hanebrink (1955), for example, studied the origin, development, and fate of Sardis Reservoir (in the Yazoo headwaters) plankton and concluded that it did not develop from plankton carried into the reservoir by tributary streams but from species indigenous to the reservoir. Grantham (1958) and Woodmansee and Grantham (1961) investigated the vertical migration patterns of certain plankters in Lake Geiger, a 320-acre impoundment in south-central Mississippi. The lake is an old stream valley in the Black Creek drainage, a tributary of the Pascagoula River. The copepod, *Mesocyclops edax,* and the larval dipteran, *Chaoborus albatus,* exhibited marked diurnal decrease in planktonic numbers, the diurnal planktonic populations being only 25% and 32%, respectively, of the maximum nocturnal populations. A majority of the populations of both species occurred in the oxygen-deficient hypolimnion during most of the day, moving at night into the upper oxygenated waters.

Stream studies

Limnological investigations of the streams of the Central Gulf States have been concerned primarily with fisheries and pollution problems. Hancock and Sublette (1957), however, have published an account of the fishes of the Upper Kisatchie drainage of west-central Louisiana in which they briefly characterized some general limnological features of the streams studied.

Sublette (1956) has also published an account of the seasonal changes in the bottom fauna of an Ozark headwater stream in the limestone area of northwestern Arkansas. He found the bottom fauna was dominated by insects; the standing crop reached a maximum in late winter and was abruptly reduced by the erosional effects of spring flood waters.

A stream of a very different type is Bayou Lacombe in southeastern Louisiana, studied by Bick *et al.* (1953). This is a brown-water, acid stream rising in a black-gum slough, flowing across longleaf pine flats, and discharging into Lake Pontchartrain. About one-third of its 36-mi channel was drastically altered by dredging and clearing in 1952, virtually denuding it of all macroscopic life. Geagan (1959) restudied the biota of the stream five years later and reported a very considerable degree of recovery in the disturbed area; however, certain clinging forms (Plecoptera, Megaloptera) remained scarce probably because logs, brush, and other suitable substrates had been eliminated.

Sources of stream pollution vary widely throughout the area. Domestic sewage is undoubtedly the most widespread pollutant, with industrial wastes from paper mills and chemical manufacturers contributing to the problem in certain areas. Oil and gas fields are a source of heavy salt concentrations in many places, and the increasing use of toxic organic insecticides has aggravated the problem in agricultural areas in recent years.

The detrimental effect of domestic pollution on plankton was demonstrated in Black Warrior River near Tuscaloosa, Alabama, by Farmer (1960). Swingle (1954) studied the fish populations of this and other Alabama streams and found both lower and higher standing crops in polluted sections, depending on circumstances, but with a consistent trend toward unbalanced populations in such areas. Grantham (1959, 1960) investigated the effects of organic pollution, chiefly sewage and wastes from poultry and livestock processing plants, on the fishes and benthos of the Pearl River (Mississippi). The qualitative and quantitative composition of the fish population was seriously affected by these pollutants; the benthos, in areas of heavy pollution, was dominated by enormous numbers of a few forms such as Tubificidae.

Louisana pollution studies include those of Lafleur (1956) on the Calcasieu River and of Davis (1960) on the Ouachita system. One of the first accounts of fish-kills resulting from the use of agricultural insecticides was that of Young and Nicholson (1951) on several streams in the Tennessee River Valley of Alabama. Recent tabulations of pollution-caused fish-kills (U.S. Dept. Health, Education, and Welfare, 1961) have included numerous instances from the Central Gulf States area.

Estuarine waters

Estuarine habitats have been considered to some extent in the foregoing discussions of Lake Pontchartrain and the maritime coastal lakes. Although numerous estuaries are found along the Central Gulf Coast, they have not been studied extensively and, in any event, constitute a habitat that does not properly lie within the scope of this review. An interesting study of Loesch (1960) might be mentioned, however, on mass shoreward migrations of fish and crustaceans in Mobile Bay, Alabama. These "jubilees," as they

are called locally, occur sporadically but not infrequently; 35 occurrences were reported from 1946 to 1956. They always take place in summer and involve enormous numbers of demersal species. Loesch attributed the phenomenon to a coincidence of factors which results in an inshore movement of oxygen-deficient water, made so by decomposition of organic detritus deposited by the Tensas River. Demersal animals apparently move inshore ahead of the water mass, and the jubilee is terminated when winds, tides, etc., re-aerate the water.

Biotal studies

There exists a substantial body of literature dealing with the biota of the Central Gulf States, including studies of many groups of limnological importance. Unfortunately almost no bibliographic treatment of this literature has been published, and consequently much of it remains little known. One of the few such lists is that of Bick (1954) which deals with Louisiana zoology and includes most of the published references pertaining to the fauna of the state to the time of publication.

Aquatic plants

The algal flora of the south and southeast has been the subject of an extensive series of publications by Prescott and co-workers, of which Prescott (1942) and Prescott and Scott (1942, 1952) are representative.

Most of the floristic and plant ecology studies of limnological interest deal with wetlands rather than the purely aquatic environment. One of the older, but still widely quoted, studies on cypress germination and survival under various conditions of submergence in Reelfoot Lake, Tennessee, and the lower St. Francis River, Arkansas, is that of Demaree (1932). Penfound (1952) reviewed the literature on southern swamps and marshes, and he and co-workers have contributed a long series of phytosociological studies of tupelo gum, cypress, and marshland communities (Hall and Penfound, 1939, 1943; Penfound and Hall, 1939; Penfound and Hathaway, 1938; Penfound and Schneidau, 1945).

Penfound has also studied the biology of a number of vascular aquatics including the water hyacinth (Penfound and Earle, 1948). The long frostless season (322 days in the New Orleans area) allows continuous growth of this species from at least March 15 through November 15 and results in the development of a thick floating mat, even in the deeper watercourses. This mat builds downward, providing a platform for the ecesis of other species and eventually forming a floating marsh (flotant). Anaerobic or near-an-aerobic conditions prevail in the water under the mat to the detriment of animal life (Lynch *et al.*, 1947). In this and a subsequent paper (Pen-found, 1956) comparison of primary production in vascular aquatics with that of several terrestrial communities emphasized the high productivity of the former. Penfound reported, for example, the total wet weight of material in an eight-year-old hyacinth mat to vary from 123 tons per acre in winter to 184 tons per acre in summer.

Aquatic animals

Taxonomic and ecological studies of freshwater invertebrates have included the sponges (Moore, 1953) of the New Orleans area and a number of crustacean groups including the Anostraca (Moore, 1955, 1959), the Cladocera (Jones, 1958), and the Copepoda which have been treated at length (M. S. Wilson, 1954, 1958; Wilson and Moore, 1953). G. W. Penn has published a long series of investigations dealing with the crawfishes of Louisiana and the South; a recent paper in the series (1959) provides a comprehensive bibliography. Hedgpeth (1949) has reviewed the distribution of the river shrimps (genus *Macrobrachium*) of the area.

The aquatic insects have received rather spotty attention. Only the Odonata (Bick, 1950, 1957), the Hemiptera (C. A. Wilson, 1958), and the chironomid Diptera (Dendy and Sublette, 1959) have been treated comprehensively.

The molluscan fauna of the area has long been known to be varied and abundant. The gastropods of Alabama have been accorded especially detailed study (Goodrich, 1922, 1936, 1941, 1944; Clench and Turner, 1956). Clench remarks (1959) on the remarkable endemic molluscan fauna of the Coosa River, Alabama, in which no less than six genera and a multitude of species are known to occur.

Acknowledgments

Many persons have made substantial contributions to this review by supplying literature citations, copies of technical reports, and by critical reading of the manuscript. The responsibility for omissions and for the evaluation of materials is, of course, my own. Among those whose assistance has been especially helpful, I should like to name the following: I. B. Byrd, Alabama Department of Conservation; R. M. Darnell, Marquette University; B. O. Freeman, Mississippi Game and Fish Commission; A. H. Hulsey, Arkansas Game and Fish Commission; H. E. Schafer, Louisiana Wild Life and Fisheries Commission; J. E. Sublette, Eastern New Mexico University; and R. A. Woodmansee, Mississippi Southern College.

References

ALLMAN, J. F. 1952. Phytoplankton studies of Lake Wedington. M.S. Thesis, Univ. Arkansas, Fayetteville.

ARKANSAS GAME AND FISH COMMISSION. 1955. Map of Arkansas Fishing Waters. Arkansas Game and Fish Comm., Little Rock.

BAKER, R. F. 1959. Historical review of the Bull Shoals Dam and Norfork Dam tailwater trout fishery. Proc. 13th Ann. Conf. Southeastern Assoc. Game and Fish Comm.: 229–236.

BAKER, W. M. 1950. Fish and wildlife in the Tennessee valley. Div. of Forestry Relations, Tennessee Valley Authority, 18 p.

BESHEARS, W., AND I. B. BYRD. 1959. Alabama's estuarine areas. Alabama Conserv., **30**: 6–15.

BICK, G. H. 1950. The dragonflies of Mississippi. Amer. Midland Nat., **43**: 66–78.

———. 1954. A bibliography of the zoology of Louisiana. Proc. Louisiana Acad. Sci., **17**: 5–48.

———. 1957. The Odonata of Louisiana. Tulane Studies Zool., **5**: 71–135.

BICK, G. H., L. E. HORNUFF, AND E. N. LAMBREMONT. 1953. An ecological reconnaissance of a naturally acid stream in southern Louisiana. J. Tennessee Acad. Sci., **28**: 221–231.

BROWN, C. A. 1943. Vegetation and lake level correlations at Catahoula Lake, Louisiana. Geograph. Rev., **33**: 435–445.

BRYAN, PAUL, AND C. E. WHITE. 1958. An economic evaluation of the commercial fishing industry in the T.V.A. lakes of Alabama during 1956. Proc. 12th Ann. Conf. Southeastern Assoc. Game and Fish Comm.: 128–132.

BUCKLEY, B. R. 1958. The limnology of upper Cane River Lake, Natchitoches Parish, Louisiana, with particular reference to the emergence of Tendipedidae. M.S. Thesis, Northwestern State Coll., Natchitoches, 45 p.

BYRD, I. B. 1958. An inventory of Alabama's fishing waters. Alabama Conserv., **29**: 4–5.

BYRD, I. B., AND D. D. MOSS. 1952. Public lake and stream investigations in Alabama. Alabama Dept. Conserv., Div. Game and Fish, Montgomery, 167 p.

CLENCH, W. J. 1959. Mollusca, p. 1117–1160. *In* H. B. Ward and G. C. Whipple, Fresh-water biology, 2nd ed. (W. T. Edmonson, ed.). John Wiley & Sons, New York.

CLENCH, W. J., AND R. D. TURNER. 1956. Freshwater mollusks of Alabama, Georgia, and Florida from the Escambia to the Suwannee River. Bull. Florida State Museum, 1 : 97–220.

COLEMAN, E. W. 1960. State-wide lake and stream survey. F–8–R–3 Project Rept., Mississippi Game and Fish Comm., Jackson, 83 p.

DARNELL, R. M. 1954. An outline for the study of estuarine ecology. Proc. Louisiana Acad. Sci., 27 : 52–59.

———. 1958. Food habits of fishes and larger invertebrates of Lake Pontchartrain, Louisiana, an estuarine community. Inst. Marine Sci., 5 : 353–416.

———. 1959. Studies of the life history of the blue crab, Callinectes sapidus Rathbun, in Louisiana waters. Trans. Amer. Fish. Soc., 88 : 294–304.

———. 1961. Trophic spectrum of an estuarine community, based on studies of Lake Pontchartrain, Louisiana. Ecology, 42 : 553–568.

DAVIS, J. T. 1960. Fish populations and aquatic conditions in polluted waters in Louisiana. Louisiana Wildl. and Fish. Comm., New Orleans, 121 p.

DEMAREE, DELZIE. 1932. Submerging experiments with Taxodium. Ecology, 13 : 258–262.

DENDY, J. S., AND J. E. SUBLETTE. 1959. The Chironomidae of Alabama with descriptions of six new species. Ann. Entomol. Soc. Amer., 52 : 506–519.

FARMER, J. A. 1960. The effects of industrial and domestic pollution of the Black Warrior River on the net plankton production. J. Alabama Acad. Sci., 31 : 447–458.

FENNEMAN, N. M. 1928. Physiographic divisions of the United States. Ann. Assoc. Amer. Geograph., 18 : 261–353.

———. 1938. Physiography of eastern United States. McGraw-Hill, New York. 714 p.

FISK, H. N. 1938. Geology of Grant and LaSalle Parishes. Dept. Conserv., Louisiana Geol. Surv., Geol. Bull. No. 10, 239 p.

FUSS, C. M. 1959. A limnological reconnaissance of three Louisiana lakes. M.S. Thesis, Univ. Southwestern Louisiana, Lafayette, 46 p.

GEAGAN, D. W. 1959. An ecological survey of a disturbed, naturally acid stream. M.S. Thesis, Loyola Univ., New Orleans, 31 p.

———. 1960. A report of a fish kill in Chicot Lake, Louisiana, during a water level drawdown. Proc. Louisiana Acad. Sci., 23 : 39–44.

GEAGAN, D. W., AND T. D. ALLEN. 1961. An ecological survey of factors affecting fish production in Louisiana waters. Dingell-Johnson Project F–6–R, Louisiana Wildl. and Fish. Comm., New Orleans, 100 p.

GEAGAN, D. W., AND C. M. FUSS. 1959. Thermal and chemical stratification of some Louisiana lakes. Proc. Louisiana Acad. Sci., 22 : 32–43.

GOODRICH, CALVIN. 1922. The Anculosae of the Alabama River drainage. Museum Zool., Univ. Michigan Misc. Publ. No. 7 : 1–57.

———. 1936. Goniobasis of the Coosa River, Alabama. Museum Zool., Univ. Michigan Misc. Publ. No. 31 : 1–60.

———. 1941. Distribution of the gastropods of the Cahaba River, Alabama. Museum Zool., Univ. Michigan Occasional Papers, No. 428 : 1–30.

———. 1944. Certain operculates of the Coosa River. Nautilus, 58 : 1–10.

GRANTHAM, B. J. 1958. The seasonal variation of the plankton of Lake Geiger. M.S. Thesis, Mississippi Southern Coll., Hattiesburg.

———. 1959. Preliminary report of pollution in the Pearl River Basin. F–9–R Project Rept., Mississippi Game and Fish Comm., Jackson, 23 p.

———. 1960. Detection of sources of stream pollution and its effect upon bottom organisms, fishes, and chemical qualities of the water. F–9–R Project Rept., Mississippi Game and Fish Comm., Jackson, 45 p.

GUNTER, GORDON. 1952. Historical changes in the Mississippi River and the adjacent marine environment. Inst. Marine Sci., 2 : 119–139.

———. 1956. Land, water, wildlife and flood control in the Mississippi Valley. Proc. Louisiana Acad. Sci., 19 : 5–11.

GUNTER, GORDON, AND W. E. SHELL. 1958. A study of an estuarine area with water level control in the Louisiana marsh. Proc. Louisiana Acad. Sci., 21 : 5–34.

HALL, T. F., AND W. T. PENFOUND. 1939. A phytosociological study of a Nyssa biflora consocies in southeastern Louisiana. Amer. Midland Nat., 22 : 369–375.

HALL, T. F., AND W. T. PENFOUND. 1943. Cypressgum communities in Blue Girth Swamp near Selma, Alabama. Ecology, 24 : 208–217.

HANCOCK, C. D., AND J. E. SUBLETTE. 1957. A survey of the fishes in the upper Kisatchie drainage of west central Louisiana. Proc. Louisiana Acad. Sci., 20 : 38–52.

HANEBRINK, E. L. 1955. Origin, development, and fate of Sardis Reservoir plankton. M.S. Thesis, Univ. Mississippi, University.

HARRIS, B. B., AND J. K. G. SILVEY. 1940. Limnological investigations on Texas reservoir lakes. Ecol. Monogr., 10 : 112–143.

HEDGPETH, J. W. 1949. The North American species of Macrobrachium. Texas J. Sci., 1 : 28–38.

HOFFMAN, C. E. 1951. Limnological studies in Arkansas. Temperature and turbidity records for Lake Fort Smith. Proc. Arkansas Acad. Sci., 4 : 91–95.

———. 1952. Limnological studies in Arkansas. The effect of intense rainfall on the abundance and vertical distribution of plankton in Lake Fort Smith, Arkansas. Proc. Arkansas Acad. Sci., 5 : 83–89.

HOFFMAN, C. E., AND DAVID CAUSEY. 1952. Limnological studies in Arkansas. Physico-chemical and net-plankton studies of Lake Fort Smith in its fourth year of impoundment. Proc. Arkansas Acad. Sci., 5 : 55–72.

HOFFMAN, C. E., A. HULSEY, C. NELSON, B. OWEN, AND B. TATUM. 1954. An annual temperature study of five northwest Arkansas lakes. Proc. Arkansas Acad. Sci., 8 : 144–148.

HULSEY, A. H. 1956. Limnological studies in Arkansas. Physical, chemical, and biological features of Lake Fayetteville in its first year of impoundment. M.S. Thesis, Univ. Arkansas, Fayetteville.

HUTCHINSON, G. E. 1957. A treatise on limnology. Vol. I: Geography, physics, and chemistry. John Wiley & Sons, New York. 1015 p.

JOHNSON, W. J. 1959. A portrait of river basin studies in the Southeast. Proc. 13th Ann. Conf. Southeastern Assoc. Game and Fish Comm.: 181–192.

JONES, W. H. 1958. Cladocera of Louisiana. Proc. Louisiana Acad. Sci., **21**: 50–55.

LAFLEUR, R. A. 1956. A biological and chemical survey of the Calcasieu River. M.A. Thesis, Louisiana State Univ., Baton Rouge, 45 p.

LAMBOU, V. W. 1959a. Louisiana impoundments, their fish populations and management. Trans. 24th N. Amer. Wildl. Conf.: 187–200.

———. 1959b. Fish populations of backwater lakes in Louisiana. Trans. Amer. Fish. Soc., **88**: 7–15.

———. 1960. Fish populations of Mississippi River oxbow lakes in Louisiana. Proc. Louisiana Acad. Sci., **23**: 52–64.

LOESCH, H. 1960. Sporadic mass shoreward migrations of demersal fish and crustaceans in Mobile Bay, Alabama. Ecology, **41**: 292–298.

LOWE, E. N. 1921. Plants of Mississippi. Mississippi State Geol. Surv. Bull. No. 17, 293 p.

LYNCH, J. J., J. E. KING, T. K. CHAMBERLAIN, AND A. L. SMITH. 1947. Effects of aquatic weed infestations on the fish and wildlife of the Gulf States. U.S. Dept. Interior, Spec. Sci. Rept. No. 39, 71 p.

MISSISSIPPI GAME AND FISH COMMISSION. 1961. Mississippi angler's guide, 12 p.

MOORE, W. G. 1950. Limnological studies of Louisiana lakes I. Lake Providence. Ecology, **31**: 86–99.

———. 1952. Limnological studies of Louisiana lakes. II. Lake Chicot. Proc. Louisiana Acad. Sci., **15**: 37–49.

———. 1953. Louisiana fresh-water sponges, with ecological observations on certain sponges of the New Orleans area. Trans. Amer. Microscop. Soc., **72**: 24–32.

———. 1955. The life history of the spiny-tailed fairy shrimp in Louisiana. Ecology, **36**: 176–184.

———. 1959. Observations on the biology of the fairy shrimp, *Eubranchipus holmani*. Ecology, **40**: 398–403.

NELSON, C. W. 1952. Limnological studies in Arkansas. Chemical, physical, and biological features of Lake Fort Smith during its 15th and 16th years of impoundment. M.S. Thesis, Univ. Arkansas, Fayetteville, 55 p.

NELSON, G. E. 1958. The limnology of a small, artificial impoundment in Alabama. J. Alabama Acad. Sci., **30**: 39–50.

OWEN, B. G. 1951. Limnological studies in Arkansas. Chemical, physical, and biological features of Lake Wedington in its 13th and 14th years of impoundment. M.S. Thesis, Univ. Arkansas, Fayetteville.

PENFOUND, W. T. 1949. Vegetation of Lake Chicot, Louisiana, in relation to wildlife resources. Proc.

Louisiana Acad. Sci., **12**: 47–56.

———. 1952. Southern swamps and marshes. Botan. Rev., **18**: 413–446.

———. 1956. Primary production of vascular aquatic plants. Limnol. Oceanogr., **1**: 92–101.

PENFOUND, W. T., AND T. T. EARLE. 1948. The biology of the water hyacinth. Ecol. Monogr., **18**: 447–472.

PENFOUND, W. T., AND T. F. HALL. 1939. A phytosociological analysis of a tupelo gum forest near Huntsville, Alabama. Ecology, **20**: 358–364.

PENFOUND, W. T., AND E. S. HATHAWAY. 1938. Plant communities in the marshlands of southeastern Louisiana. Ecol. Monogr., **8**: 1–56.

PENFOUND, W. T., AND J. D. SCHNEIDAU. 1945. The relation of land reclamation to aquatic wildlife resources in southeastern Louisiana. Trans. 10th N. Amer. Wildl. Conf.: 308–318.

PENN, G. H. 1959. An illustrated key to the crawfishes of Louisiana with a summary of their distribution within the state. Tulane Studies Zool., **7**: 3–20.

PRESCOTT, G. W. 1942. The fresh-water algae of southern United States. II. The algae of Louisiana, with descriptions of some new forms and notes on distribution. Trans. Amer. Microscop. Soc., **61**: 109–119.

PRESCOTT, G. W., AND A. M. SCOTT. 1942. The fresh-water algae of southern United States. I. Desmids from Mississippi, with descriptions of new species and varieties. Trans. Amer. Microscop. Soc., **61**: 1–29.

PRESCOTT, G. W., AND A. M. SCOTT. 1952. The algal flora of southeastern United States. V. Additions to our knowledge of the desmid genus *Micrasterias*. Trans. Amer. Microscop. Soc., **71**: 229–252.

READ, W. A. 1931. Louisiana-French. Louisiana State Univ. Studies, No. 5: 1–253.

REDEKE, H. C. 1922. Zür biologie der Niederländischen Brackwassertypen. Bijdr. Dierk., **22**: 329–335.

RUSSELL, R. J. 1936. Physiography of the lower Mississippi delta. Louisiana Dept. Conserv., Bull. No. 8, 199 p.

———. 1940. Quaternary history of Louisiana. Bull. Geol. Soc. Amer., **51**: 1199–1234.

SHELFORD, V. E. (ed.). 1926. Naturalists' guide to the Americas. Williams and Wilkins Co., Baltimore. 761 p.

SMITH, R. F. 1959. General limnology of selected water bodies in the western part of Cameron Parish, Louisiana, and its relationship to the emergence of Tendipedidae. M.S. Thesis, Northwestern State Coll., Natchitoches, 115 p.

STEINMEYER, R. A. 1939. Bottom sediments of Lake Pontchartrain, Louisiana. Bull. Amer. Assoc. Petrol. Geol., **23**: 1–23.

STEVENSON, JAMES, AND A. H. HULSEY. 1958. Appraisal and management recommendations resulting from a three-year comparative fishery study of Lake Catherine, Lake Hamilton, and Lake Ouachita, Arkansas. Proc. 12th Ann. Conf. Southeastern Assoc. Game and Fish Comm.: 183–198.

SUBLETTE, J. E. 1956. Seasonal changes in bottom

fauna of an Ozark headwater stream (Clear Creek, Washington County, Arkansas). Southwestern Nat., 1: 148–156.

SUBLETTE, J. E., AND M. S. SUBLETTE. 1957. The physicochemical features and bottom fauna of Chaplin's Lake, Natchitoches Parish, Louisiana. Proc. Louisiana Acad. Sci., 20: 85–94.

SUTTKUS, R. D. 1954. Seasonal movements and growth of the Atlantic croaker (*Micropogon undulatus*) along the Louisiana coast. Proc. Gulf and Caribb. Fish. Inst., 7th Ann. Session: 1–7.

———. 1956. Early life history of the Gulf menhaden *Brevoortia patronus* in Louisiana. Trans. 21st N. Amer. Wildl. Conf.: 390–407.

SUTTKUS, R. D., R. M. DARNELL, AND J. H. DARNELL. 1953–56. Biological study of Lake Pontchartrain. Research Progr. Repts. Submitted to Commercial Seafoods Div., Louisiana Wildl. and Fish. Comm., New Orleans. (Multilithed.)

SWINGLE, H. S. 1954. Fish populations in Alabama rivers and impoundments. Trans. Amer. Fish. Soc., 83: 47–57.

TATUM, B. L. 1951. Limnological studies in Arkansas. Lake Atalanta. M.S. Thesis, Univ. Arkansas, Fayetteville, 62 p.

TOWERY, B. A. 1958. Mississippi flood control reservoirs. Chemical, biological and physical data. F–6–R Project. Mississippi Game and Fish Comm., Jackson, 15 + xxxiii p.

U.S. DEPARTMENT OF AGRICULTURE. 1941. Climate and man: 1941 yearbook of agriculture. U.S. Govt. Printing Office, Washington. 1248 p.

U.S. DEPARTMENT OF HEALTH, EDUCATION AND WELFARE. 1961. Pollution-caused fishkills in 1960. Pub. Health Serv., Publ. No. 847, 20 p.

VEATCH, A. C. 1899. The Shreveport area. Spec. Rept. No. 2, p. 149–208. *In* G. D. Harris and A. C.

Veatch, A preliminary report on the geology of Louisiana. Louisiana Geol. Surv. Rept. for 1899.

———. 1906. Geology and underground water resources of northern Louisiana and southern Arkansas. Profess. Papers, U.S. Geol. Surv., No 46, 422 p.

VERNON, R. O. 1942. Tributary valley lakes of western Florida. J. Geomorph., 5: 303–311.

VIOSCA, PERCY. 1928. Louisiana wet lands and the value of their wildlife and fishery resources. Ecology, 9: 216–229.

———. 1933. Louisiana out-of-doors. Published by the author, New Orleans, Louisiana. 187 p.

WILSON, C. A. 1958. Aquatic and semi-aquatic Hemiptera of Mississippi. Tulane Studies Zool., 6: 113–170.

WILSON, M. S. 1954. A new species of *Diaptomus* from Louisiana and Texas with notes on the subgenus *Leptodiaptomus*. Tulane Studies Zool., 2: 51–60.

———. 1958. The copepod genus *Halicyclops* in North America, with description of a new species from Lake Pontchartrain, Louisiana, and the Texas coast. Tulane Studies Zool., 6: 176–189.

WILSON, M. S., AND W. G. MOORE. 1953. New records of *Diaptomus sanguineus* and allied species from Louisiana, with the description of a new species. J. Washington Acad. Sci., 43: 121–127.

WOODMANSEE, R. A., AND B. J. GRANTHAM. 1961. Diel vertical migrations of two zooplankters (*Mesocyclops* and *Chaoborus*) in a Mississippi lake. Ecology, 42: 619–628.

YANCEY, R. K. 1952. Catahoula Lake. Louisiana Conserv., 4: 10–12.

YOUNG, L. A., AND H. P. NICHOLSON. 1951. Stream pollution resulting from the use of organic insecticides. Progr. Fish-Cult., 13: 193–198.

10 | *Samuel Eddy*

Minnesota and the Dakotas

Minnesota, North Dakota, and South Dakota make up an area of considerable variety in geology, soils, topography, and climate. Consequently, chemical, physical, and biological conditions in lakes and streams show a great range. The lakes vary from deep soft-water (low carbonate), oligotrophic lakes in northeastern Minnesota, through hard-water (high carbonate), eutrophic lakes, to the shallow (high sulfate) and saline (high chloride) lakes of the prairies.

Most of the deeper lake basins are depressions formed in various ways by Pleistocene glaciation (Figs. 10.1 and 10.2). The topography of much of this area has been shaped by four continental glaciers. The areas covered by deposits of the older ice sheets, extending from Minnesota westward into the Dakotas, have developed better drainage systems and contain only shallow prairie lakes.

The geological character and origin of the lakes in Minnesota have been described by Zumberg (1952). Some lakes occupy depressions left in the ground moraine, others occupy valleys dammed by glacial moraines, and many lie in depressions formed by melting of buried ice blocks. A few lakes occupy depressions in the drained basins of ancient glacial lakes. Thus, Lake of the Woods and the Red lakes occur in the basin of Glacial Lake Agassiz and the Des Lacs lakes of North Dakota in the basin of Glacial Lake Souris.

The largest and deepest lakes of this entire area are in Minnesota, where there are more than 10,000 well-defined lakes not including several hundred thousand ponds and many bogs and swamps which represent remains of senescent

lakes (Moyle and Hotchkiss, 1945). About 5,000 lakes are larger than 16 ha. The largest of these are the Red lakes, covering 111,333 ha. These lakes range from 2 m to over 60 m in maximum depth.

The chemical nature of the water, which is largely determined by the nature of the glacial drift, greatly influences the type and abundance of the aquatic life present. The glacial subsoils of Minnesota are generally either the gravelly red drift or the clayey gray drift (Fig. 10.3) of the late Wisconsin ice sheet. The red drift covers most of east-central and northeastern Minnesota, and the gray drift covers the rest as far west as the Missouri River except for that covered by older ice sheets in southwestern Minnesota and eastern South Dakota. West of the Missouri River, the region is largely unglaciated and consists of older eroded soils usually rich in soluble salts such as sulfates and chlorides.

Four major drainage systems occur in this area. The upper Mississippi River drains the north-central and south-central portions of Minnesota. The northeastern part of Minnesota drains into Lake Superior. The extreme northern and northwestern part of Minnesota and the northeastern and north-central part of North Dakota drain into the Arctic Ocean. The southwestern half of North Dakota, almost all of South Dakota, and a small part of southwestern Minnesota are drained by the Missouri River.

Many types of natural lakes occur within this wide area. Each region is characterized by certain types of lakes, and within each region most of the successional stages of these types may be

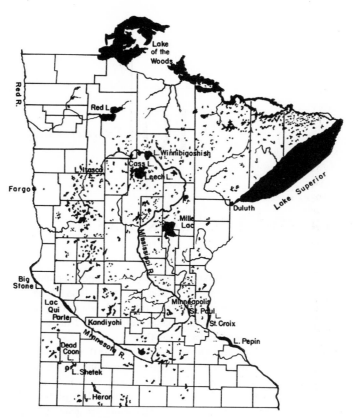

Fig. 10.1.—General distribution of lakes and major streams in Minnesota.

found. The lakes of this area may be classified generally according to their trophic conditions as indicated by their dissolved salts and characteristic organisms. Moyle (1945a, 1945b) defined the grosser aspects of regional water chemistry for Minnesota on the basis of the distribution of aquatic floras and later (1946) pointed out that total alkalinity and total phosphorus are useful indices of lake productivity. In Minnesota there is a general increase in the total alkalinity (as $CaCO_3$) of surface waters from northeast southward and westward (Fig. 10.4) and a similar increase in the total phosphorus (Fig. 10.5) of summer surface water (Moyle, 1956). There are softwater (low carbonate), hard-water (high carbonate), alkaline (high sulfate), and saline (high chloride) lakes, the waters of which range in total concentration of dissolved salts from less than 40 ppm in northeastern Minnesota to 62,929 ppm for Devils Lake, North Dakota, as reported by Young (1924). Although the composition of the lake water in any part of the region is generally similar, because of both soils and climate

there is much local variation. For example, occasional soft-water lakes occur in typically hard-water regions. Likewise, the chemical composition of the prairie lakes may vary considerably with climatic conditions, the concentrations of dissolved salts increasing with the drop in water levels caused by drought.

Flood-plain lakes, mostly quite shallow, occur along many of the major rivers. These have never been studied to any extent. Natural lakes, except for a few flood-plain lakes and sloughs, are practically absent from the extreme southwestern corner of Minnesota and the southern part of South Dakota. Natural lakes are mostly absent from the unglaciated plains region of North Dakota and South Dakota west of the Missouri River (Fig. 10.2) except for several in the Black Hills of South Dakota.

Most of the limnological studies in this region have been made in Minnesota, and only a few studies have been made in the Dakotas. In 1909 a biological laboratory was established at Devils Lake, North Dakota, to study the conditions as-

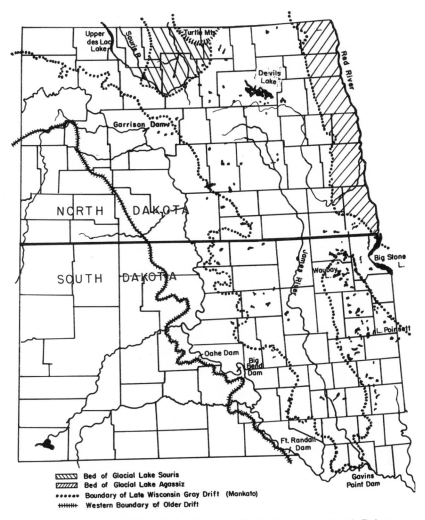

Fig. 10.2.—Larger lakes and glacial drift of North Dakota and South Dakota.

sociated with its extreme salinity. South Dakota has maintained a State Geological Survey since 1894, but very few of their investigations can be considered limnological.

Aside from the unreliable reports of early explorers and the brief reconnaissance of the Lake Superior region by Louis Agassiz (1850), no attempt was made to study the waters of Minnesota until the establishment of the Minnesota Geological and Natural History Survey in 1872. Prof. N. H. Winchell, a geologist at the University of Minnesota, was the first director and for several years not only carried on most of the burden of the extensive basic geological surveys but also found time to collect much faunal material as shown by the specimens in the university collections.

Most of the investigations made by the Minnesota Geological and Natural History Survey were faunal surveys, and little work was done on the water chemistry and physics of lakes and streams. Several zoologists were added to the staff. Prof. C. L. Herrick joined the staff in 1876, and until 1885 he studied the distribution of mammals and Crustacea (Herrick, 1884; Herrick and Turner, 1895). Ulysses S. Grant was employed from 1885 until 1888 as conchologist and geologist, and his extensive collections of mollusks remain at the university although no reports have ever been published.

Prof. H. F. Nachtrieb of the University of Minnesota was appointed state zoologist in 1887

Bed of Glacial Lake Agassiz
Area of Precambrian Rock
Boundary of Late Wisconsin Red Drift
Boundary of Late Wisconsin Gray Drift

Fig. 10.3.—Glacial drift of Minnesota.

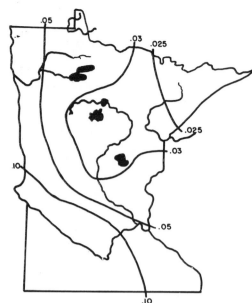

Fig. 10.5.—Isolines for mean concentration of total phosphorus in ppm for surface waters of Minnesota. After Moyle, 1954.

and assumed charge of the zoological studies of the survey. Under his direction a long program of faunal studies, mostly on the aquatic fauna, was initiated. Temporary laboratories were es-

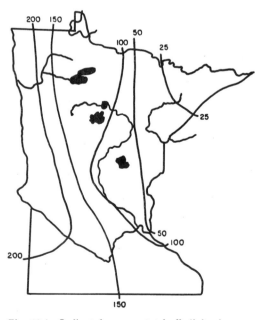

Fig. 10.4.—Isolines for mean total alkalinity in ppm for surface waters of Minnesota. After Moyle, 1954.

tablished at Gull Lake and at Leech Lake for the purpose of surveying the fauna of the northern waters. A floating laboratory was maintained on the Mississippi River below Minneapolis until 1910. Various specialists collaborated in the study of their particular taxonomic groups. Most outstanding of these was Cox (1897) who made a detailed survey of the fishes of the state. Moore (Nachtrieb *et al.*, 1912) studied the leeches. Interest in the biological investigations ceased about 1910, and in 1911 the Geological and Natural History Survey became the Geological Survey.

Aside from the studies of trout streams by Thaddeus Surber (1922) in the period 1918–20, no limnological investigations in the modern sense were made in Minnesota until 1925 when Philip (1927), a graduate student at the University of Minnesota, studied the diurnal fluctuations of the hydrogen-ion concentrations in Crystal Lake near Minneapolis. Later Oosting (1933) made a study of the physicochemical variables during 1928–29 in Ham Lake, Anoka County. Investigations of regional limnology in Minnesota, initiated at the University of Minnesota in 1928 by Johnson (1933), have been continued since 1929 by Samuel Eddy and his students to the present time. The initial investigations consisted largely of quantitative surveys of the organisms and conditions affecting life in the lakes of Minnesota. Beginning with the lakes and streams in the vicinity of Minneapolis, the studies later included waters in all parts of the state. Many surveys were made in the years after 1935 following the establishment of the Emergency Conservation Works program and the Civilian Conservation Corps, both of which contributed much manpower for such work. Surveys, including contour maps, were made of several hundred lakes annually. Much of the basic knowledge of the limnological conditions of Minnesota lakes and of the regional limnology of this region has come from these surveys.

A fishery research laboratory was established at the University of Minnesota in 1936, in collaboration with the Minnesota Department of Conservation, for the purpose of continuing basic and applied research on the waters of the state. This laboratory was transferred from the university to the Department of Conservation in 1940 where it has expanded its activities and is now part of the Section of Research and Planning. Since 1940 this laboratory and staff has operated successively under the direction of Dr. Lloyd L. Smith, Jr., Dr. Raymond E. Johnson, and Dr. John B. Moyle. Lake and stream surveys have been pursued vigorously, and the files now contain basic limnological data on more than 2,000 Minnesota lakes and many streams. Much of the limnological research in these surveys has been on the relationship of the chemical conditions of lake waters to fishes and plants (Moyle, 1945a, 1946, 1956) and on limnology as related to the production of fish in ponds (Dobie *et al.*, 1948; Dobie and Moyle, 1956).

The development of limnological studies in Minnesota made it necessary to provide more courses in basic limnology and in related field studies. Consequently, the Lake Itasca Forestry Station at Itasca State Park was modified in 1935 to the present Lake Itasca Forestry and Biological Station. This station, developed as part of the training program of the University of Minnesota, provides an excellent opportunity for limnological research.

In the early 1930's a forest area 32 mi north of Minneapolis became a favorite study area for field classes and for graduate research at the University of Minnesota. This area included Cedar Bog Lake which was studied by Lindeman (1941a, 1941b, 1942a, 1942b, 1942c). Through the aid of many generous people, the Fleischmann Foundation, and the Minnesota Academy of Science, the University of Minnesota gradually acquired 4,250 acres which now constitutes the Cedar Creek Natural History Area. A large modern laboratory was constructed in 1958. The area includes Fish Lake, Cedar Bog Lake, and several smaller lakes as well as excellent bog forest. In recent years, this area has been used by geologists who have become interested in limnological conditions as applied to the study of sedimentation and the chemistry of lake sediments (Swain and Prokopovich, 1954; Swain, 1961).

Soft-water (low carbonate) lakes

Moyle (1945a, 1945b), on the basis of the distribution of aquatic plants, classified the lakes in Minnesota with a total alkalinity ($CaCO_3$) of less than 40 ppm (Fig. 10.4) as soft-water lakes. He found that these ranged from pH 6.8 to 7.4 and usually had a sulfate-ion concentration less than 5 ppm (Fig. 10.6). Within this series, however, there are many with a total alkalinity of less than 20 ppm, and these are quite unproductive.

The soft-water lakes of this area lie mostly in the bedrock basins of northeastern Minnesota

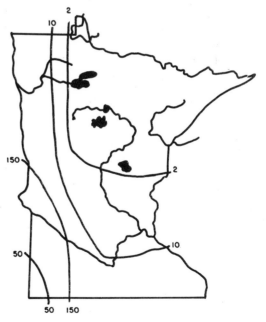

Fig. 10.6.—Isolines for mean concentrations for sulfate ions in ppm for surface waters of Minnesota. After Moyle, 1954.

(Fig. 10.3). The pre-Cambrian rocks of this region are covered by a thin layer of red drift, and together they supply very little nutrient material to the waters. In many lakes the steep bedrock basins further reduce the productivity by allowing only a small littoral area, sometimes less than 15% of the total area of the lake. Many of these lakes are quite deep, with maximum depths ranging from 20 to over 60 m. Well-defined summer stratification is usual in most of the lakes over 9 m in depth. The hypolimnion of the deeper lakes shows little oxygen depletion in summer. Because precipitation on the lake surface exceeds evaporation, most of the lakes have active outlets, a condition that prevents accumulation of dissolved salts.

The limnological surveys of the deeper lakes showed them to be typically oligotrophic. Only the more shallow soft-water lakes with maximum depths less than 15 m showed much evidence of eutrophication. The summer plankton of the deeper lakes was usually scanty and was characterized by the scarcity of blue-green algae and by an abundance of diatoms, mostly species of *Tabellaria*, *Fragilaria*, and *Asterionella*, and by the presence of such copepods as *Limnocalanus*. *Mysis relicta* occurred in several of the deepest lakes. The dry weight of the standing crop of summer plankton from nine of these lakes with maximum depths from 20 to 50 m averaged 0.201 g/m^3. The turbidity was very low, and Secchi disc readings of 7 m were common.

The profundal bottoms of these deeper lakes supported large numbers of the amphipod *Pontoporeia affinis*, but the littoral bottoms supported only a sparse fauna mainly of insect larvae, the amphipod *Hyallela azteca*, and a few mollusks. Mollusks were usually not abundant in these soft-water lakes and were represented by only a few species of snails and sphaeriid clams. In some lakes there were a few very thin-shelled unionid clams, *Anodonta marginata*.

The standing crop of summer bottom fauna of these nine northeastern lakes averaged 0.190 g/m^2 (dry weight) for the littoral area and 0.137 g/m^2 for the profundal area. The average summer standing crop for the bottom fauna for the nine lakes was 0.161 g/m^2. The standing summer crop of fishes in these waters was low—perhaps 35 kg/ha.

A typical oligotrophic lake investigated in this region was Lake Winchell in Cook County. This is one of the many long and narrow lakes found here that occupy steep bedrock basins. Lake Winchell has a maximum depth of 54 m. No summer oxygen depletion was noted in the hypolimnion. The water was quite soft (calcium 4.5 ppm and magnesium 1.4 ppm), and the *p*H ranged from 6.2 to 6.9. The lake contained a typical oligotrophic fauna. About 79% of the area could be considered profundal. The standing crop of summer bottom fauna of the littoral area averaged 0.078 g/m^2 and was less than that of the profundal area which averaged 0.102 g/m^2.

These deeper lakes are suitable for cold-water fishes and are characterized by lake trout (*Salvelinus namaycush*), ciscoes (*Coregonus artedi*) and whitefish (*Coregonus clupeaformis*). These lakes were classified as "lake trout type" by Eddy (1938). Northern pike (*Esox lucius*), yellow perch (*Perca flavescens*), burbot (*Lota lota*), and walleye (*Stizostedion vitreum*, mostly introduced) also are found in such soft-water lakes.

Often the more shallow soft-water lakes do not have sufficient oxygen in their hypolimnions in summer to allow survival conditions for cold-water fishes, but, instead, support such fishes as northern pike, walleye, and yellow perch. Such lakes show some eutrophication. Since they usually have a larger percentage of littoral area, they are more productive than the deeper lakes. The standing summer crop of littoral bottom fauna for 12 of these lakes with maximum depths from 3 to 18 m averaged 0.458 g/m^2, and the profundal bottom fauna averaged only 0.141 g/m^2 dry weight. The average standing summer crop of bottom fauna for the 12 lakes was 0.310 g/m^2 dry weight. The standing crop of summer plankton averaged 0.203 g/m^3 dry weight. The warm-water centrarchid and ictalurid fishes are not common in these lakes and occur mostly where they have been introduced.

Many small, acid bog lakes and ponds occur in this region. The bog lakes are usually small and typically surrounded by floating sedge mats. Many of these lakes have accumulated ten meters or more of flocculent bottom deposits. The water of the several bog lakes that have been studied ranged from *p*H 6.2 to 6.8. These small lakes are quite dystrophic. Some support perch and northern pike, but several have been found which had no fishes. Small, acid bog lakes also occur in the red drift area along the eastern border of Minnesota as far as Pine County.

Hard-water lakes

Most of the thousands of lakes on gray glacial till in central and northern Minnesota were classified as hard-water lakes by Moyle (1945b). Moyle considered as hard-water lakes those with total alkalinities ($CaCO_3$) ranging from 40 to 250 ppm (Fig. 10.4). Their summer pH range was 8.0 to 8.8, and their sulfate-ion concentration usually ranged as high as 50 ppm (Fig. 10.5). These lakes are quite eutrophic. The gray drift supplies an abundance of calcium carbonate and other nutrient materials to these lakes, rendering them quite fertile. Some lakes in the eastern part of the state that are on deep red drift also fall into this category.

Many of the lakes in central and northern Minnesota are large, covering thousands of hectares. Some of these have maximum depths of over 30 m, and at least one has a maximum depth of over 60 m. Many of these lakes range from 9 to 12 m in depth. Many other lakes throughout the region are less deep, partly because the depths of their original basins were less and also because they have had a more rapid rate of sedimentation. Oosting (1933) pointed out in a study of Ham Lake that vegetation played a very significant part in the filling of the original basin, building up layers of sediments 3 to 7 m thick. The high fertility of the hard-water lakes is responsible for the high rates of sedimentation and has resulted in many senescent lakes and swamps. Core samples made from some of these lakes by several graduate students have shown profundal deposits ranging from 3 to 10 m in thickness. Chemical analyses of the sediments of several of these lakes have been made by Swain (1956). He has pointed out that there is a difference in types of sediments from lakes in various stages of trophication. The sediments contain many fossilized lipids and other organic compounds.

A few of the largest lakes such as Mille Lacs, Lake Winnibigoshish, and Leech Lake (Fig. 10.1) show little thermal stratification because their great widths (15 to 32 km) offer much exposed area to wind which keeps the water in circulation.

In the smaller and deeper lakes summer oxygen depletion is characteristic of the hypolimnion. The profundal bottoms support a meager population mainly of anaerobic chironomids and oligochaetes. Such lakes usually have extensive littoral areas which support an abundant biota. The dry weight of the summer bottom fauna from 32 of these lakes with maximum depths over 8 m ranged from 0.170 to 5.84 g/m² and averaged 1.078 g/m². The profundal bottoms were low in production. The standing crop of the summer littoral bottom fauna of these 32 lakes averaged 1.84 g/m² (about 10 times that of the soft-water lakes), and the profundal bottom fauna averaged 0.655 g/m² (about 6 times that of the soft-water lakes). In most lakes the littoral area covered a greater part of the lake (average 54%).

The large hard-water lakes with little or no summer stratification were much more productive than the smaller lakes. The littoral portions ranged from 27 to 51% of the total area of these lakes. An average of the standing crops of summer bottom fauna for Mille Lacs, Lake Winnibigoshish, Cass Lake, and Leech Lake was 3.260 g/m². The dry weight of the standing crops of summer bottom fauna averaged 4.110 g/m² for the littoral areas and 2.521 g/m² for the profundal areas.

These hard-water lakes supported a rich summer plankton characterized by an abundance of blue-green algae. The standing crop of summer plankton of the 32 lakes surveyed ranged from 0.106 to 1.01 g/m² dry weight and averaged 0.313 g/m² for all 32 lakes. The more shallow lakes had a larger standing crop of summer plankton than the deeper lakes. Klak (1937) made a study of the summer plankton in 21 hard-water lakes and ponds in the vicinity of St. Paul and Minneapolis.

The hard-water lakes usually supported a large fish population. Eddy (1938) classified these lakes into three different types on the basis of their dominant fishes. The larger lakes were considered to be walleye types because the walleye (*Stizostedion vitreum*) was the dominant fish, thriving best in those lakes with lengths of several kilometers or more. The second type consisted of the bass-crappie lakes, which were the smaller lakes where the largemouth bass (*Micropterus salmoides*), the crappies (*Pomoxis* spp.), and other centrarchids seemed to thrive. In addition to the fishes mentioned, the walleye and bass-crappie lakes usually contained many other species including perch (*Perca flavescens*), white sucker (*Catostomus commersoni*), and northern pike (*Esox lucius*). The lake trout (*Salvelinus namaycush*) was practically unknown in these lakes, occurring in only several very deep lakes where they had been introduced. Ciscoes (*Coregonus artedi*) and whitefish (*Coregonus clupeaformis*) occurred in a few of the larger lakes but were apparently survivors of earlier colder stages since extensive summer-kills were common (Eddy and Surber, 1947). Attempts to determine the standing summer crop of fishes in these lakes have shown that the weights varied from 90 to over 160 kg/ha.

The third type of hard-water lake was the bullhead type, consisting of shallow lakes from 2 to 3 m in depth, which suffer from winter oxygen depletion during those winters with heavy snowfall. Only the more hardy fishes such as bullheads (*Ictalurus* spp.) occurred in some of the more southern lakes. Carp (*Cyprinus carpio*) have invaded many of these lakes in the central and southern part of this region. The productivity is very high in these shallow lakes, which sometimes contained more than 400 kg of fishes per hectare.

Many of these shallow lakes are the result of increased sedimentation caused by their high fertility and by the morphometry of their original basin. Thomas (1959), in a four-year study of the origin of the sediments in Horseshoe Lake, a late eutrophic lake in Isanti County, attempted to determine the present rate of sedimentation. The sediments had accumulated to a maximum depth of 10.8 m and filled 57% of the original basin. Thomas estimated that from 60% to 80% of the sediments were of autochthonous origin, mainly from plankton and higher plants. The total annual production of plankton was estimated at 602 kg/ha dry weight, but only about 133 kg/ha became incorporated into the permanent sediments. The average annual production of higher plants was 1,765 kg/ha, from which Thomas concluded that the higher plants were the major contributors to the sediments, especially in the late stages of eutrophication.

Although the final senescent stages of eutrophication frequently resulted in swamps filling up the original basin, many senescent stages of the hard-water lakes have resulted in bog lakes surrounded by sedge mats and bog forests. The water in most of these bog lakes is quite alkaline; the total alkalinity of several that have been investigated ranged as high as 160 ppm (as $CaCO_3$). The sediments under the sedge mats were rich in marl which sometimes constituted

50% of the sediments. These lakes occupied the basins of ancient and sometimes large lakes which have filled with sediments from 10 to 18 m deep. Although the water in these lakes is quite fertile, these lakes were usually low in productivity. The bottom fauna was quite sparse, because the soft bottoms and unstable marginal areas offered a poor substrate for bottom fauna. They often supported a rather rich plankton. Many of them contained a few fishes such as perch (*Perca flavescens*), largemouth bass (*Micropterus salmoides*), species of sunfish (*Lepomis* spp.), mud minnows (*Umbra limi*), and brook sticklebacks (*Eucalia inconstans*).

Several students at the University of Minnesota have investigated the productivity and trophic dynamics of small lakes and ponds in central Minnesota. One of the most outstanding studies was that made by Lindeman in 1936–40 on Cedar Bog Lake, now included in the Cedar Creek Natural History Study Area. Lindeman (1941a) traced the developmental history of the bog lake through a study of the ancient deposits of the surrounding bog. A later study of the composition of the deposits in the bog was made in 1953–54 by Swain and Prokopovich (1954). In a still later investigation Swain et al. (1959) traced the postglacial history of Cedar Creek Bog through a study of the amino acids of the sediments.

Because the present lake is small, covering only 1.48 ha, Lindeman (1941b) was able to determine the productivity and food-cycle dynamics of the lake, which later formed the basis for his study of trophic dynamic principles (Lindeman, 1942c). He was able to demonstrate that the efficiency of energy utilization increased from 0.10% in the producers to 22.3% in the secondary consumers. Two other studies appeared in relation to this investigation (Lindeman, 1942a, 1942b).

Hooper (1951) studied the productivity of Demming Lake in Itasca State Park in 1946. This was a small lake, 5.19 ha in area, with a maximum depth of 16.5 m. The lake was permanently stratified chemically and was without a permanent inlet or outlet. It differed greatly from other lakes in that region because it was low in fertility and productivity. It supported a meager fish population which by poisoning was estimated at 22.4 kg/ha.

Dineen (1953) studied the trophic dynamics of

a small pond north of St. Paul in 1948–50. This pond was shallow, and during the study it froze to the bottom, thereby eliminating all the fishes. This allowed other predators to assume the top consumer role, thus causing a readjustment of the other trophic levels. Dineen found that the dynamics of the pond community indicated that the exchange of energy, as measured by the production of organic materials, from one trophic level to the next was low even though the pond community was fertile and productive.

Other limnological studies on lakes at the University of Minnesota have resulted in 15 graduate theses, many of which have not been published (Hanson, 1932; Wood, 1938; Hellberg, 1948; Hendricks, 1949).

Alkaline (sulfate) and saline (chloride) lakes

In southwestern and extreme western Minnesota and extending westward through the Dakotas are many bodies of water that are higher in dissolved salts than the carbonate waters already discussed. In these the concentration of sulfate salts (as sulfate ions) often exceeds the concentration of carbonates (as total alkalinity). Such waters, which are characteristic of arid regions, have been variously designated as "sulfate" waters, "alkaline" waters, "saline" waters and sometimes are called locally "alkali" waters. The latter is the term used for them by Moyle (1945a) who points out that in Minnesota such waters show a range in total alkalinity (as $CaCO_3$) from 150 to 376 ppm (Fig. 10.4) and typically have a sulfate-ion concentration greater than 150 ppm (Fig. 10.5). They range in pH from 8.4 to 9.0 in Minnesota where the associated metallic ions are principally calcium and magnesium. They are characterized by such brackish-water plants as *Ruppia occidentalis* and *Naias marina*. Where otherwise suitable, such waters are highly productive of fish, especially rough fish, and waterfowl.

The high concentration of salts in these waters reflects both the influence of the underlying salt-rich Cretaceous formations which are incorporated into the gray glacial drift and the excess of evaporation from the water surface over the precipitation. Many of these prairie lakes are shallow, mostly with maximum depths less than 3 m although a few are deeper, ranging to 15 m. Many of these lakes are dry in periods of drought.

In others which still retain water in periods of drought, the concentration of dissolved salts greatly increases, in one instance as much as 50 times.

Metcalf (1931) studied many of these lakes in North Dakota in relation to their production of duck food. He cited all sorts of variations in salt content often in the same vicinity where saline lakes were interspersed with lakes of varying alkalinities. Most of these lakes were much higher in total alkalinity than those of Minnesota. He considered those with a salt concentration of less than 1,000 ppm as relatively fresh; those with salt concentrations of 1,000 to 1,500 ppm he designated as alkaline; and those with salt concentrations, mainly of sodium chloride and sodium sulfate, of over 1,500 ppm he called saline. He reported some waters with salt concentrations as high as 91,529 ppm. Many of these saline lakes had their bottoms and shores covered with heavy, white salt deposits. None of these lakes has been studied in detail except those of the Devils Lake region.

The Devils Lake region in Ramsey and Benton counties contains some of the more saline lakes reported from North Dakota. The lakes in this area were studied in detail by Young (1924) and were also included by Metcalf (1931) in his survey of lake conditions for aquatic plants. Young found that the area of Devils Lake had receded from 401.5 km² in 1883 to 180–200 km² at the time of his investigations. The lake had become divided into a complex of small shallow lakes, the deepest of which had a maximum depth of 7–8 m in 1918. The salt concentration had increased with the decrease in area. Young reported a salt concentration of 15,210 ppm for part of the complex but stated that one portion had a salt concentration of 62,929 ppm in 1920. Metcalf reported salt concentrations in 1917 ranging from 20,774 to 36,045 ppm.

Young presented data on the seasonal periodicity of the various plankters and other organisms in the various parts of the Devils Lake complex. The waters supported a plankton composed of a mixture of freshwater and brackish water species, but many of the freshwater plankters common to other saline lakes in the region were absent. Some aquatic insects occurred in the littoral areas. The amphipod *Hyalella azteca* was common wherever vegetation grew. Mollusks, freshwater sponges, bryozoans, and coelenterates were absent. The ooze covering the deeper parts

TABLE 10.1

Average summer standing crops of benthos and plankton in various types of Minnesota lakes

	No. of lakes	Benthos (g/m²)			Plankton (g/m³)
		Entire lake	Littoral	Profundal	
Soft-water lakes, 20–60 m depth	9	0.161	0.190	0.137	0.201
Soft-water lakes, 3–18 m depth	12	0.310	0.458	0.141	0.203
Hard-water lakes, >8 m depth	32	1.078	1.840	0.655	0.313
Very large hard-water lakes	4	3.260	4.110	2.521	0.471
Alkaline prairie lakes, shallow	4	0.531	0.531	—	5.426

was anaerobic and supported only a few species of chironomids. The only fish present was the brook stickleback (*Eucalia inconstans*).

Prairie lakes and sloughs, some covering several thousand hectares, are quite common in central North Dakota. Many of these are quite alkaline. Some which are deep enough and do not dry up in summer support a few fishes, mainly bullheads. A group of lakes less alkaline than those of the neighboring prairie region are located in the Turtle Mountain region along the Canadian boundary in north-central North Dakota.

A few of the prairie lakes of South Dakota were studied briefly by Over and Churchill (1927) and by Tschetter (1942). The larger and deeper lakes lie in the northeastern part of the state in an area not covered by the gray drift (Fig. 10.2). Although many of the lakes are less than 3 m in maximum depth, several are quite deep, such as Pickerel Lake in Day County with a maximum depth of 18 m. Some are quite large, Lake Poinsett and Lake Thompson each covering about 19,000 ha. Although the waters are quite alkaline, they are less alkaline than many of the lakes farther north in North Dakota. Tschetter reported that the water ranges from pH 7.2 to 9.5. Not much information is available about the plankton and bottom fauna of these lakes. The deeper lakes support a wide variety of fishes such as northern pike (*Esox lucius*), perch (*Perca flavescens*), largemouth bass (*Micropterus salmoides*), black crappies (*Pomoxis nigromaculatus*), and several species of sunfish (*Lepomis* spp.). Bullheads (*Ictalurus* spp.), white suckers (*Catostomus commersoni*), and carp (*Cyprinus carpio*) are characteristic of the more shallow lakes.

Westward to the Missouri River, the lakes of South Dakota tend to become more shallow and alkaline. Lakes are practically absent west of the Missouri River except for several in the Black Hills and a few artificial impoundments.

Some of the prairie lakes of southwestern Minnesota in the region classified as alkaline by Moyle (1945b) have been surveyed by the University of Minnesota and by the Department of Conservation. Four of these lakes were studied by Wilson (1958). These lakes are only slightly alkaline when compared to the strongly alkaline lakes of the Dakotas. These lakes are shallow, and many are subject to frequent winter oxygen depletion. Eddy (1938) considered all of these capable of supporting fish as bullhead-type lakes.

Wilson investigated Dead Coon Lake, Lake Shetek, Lake Kandiyohi, and Heron Lake in 1937–38 when water levels were low following the drought of the early 1930's. Some of these lakes had lost their fish populations. The total alkalinity varied considerably with the seasons and in the various parts of the lakes, ranging from 125 to 338 ppm (as $CaCO_3$). The total dissolved solids ranged from 335 to 1,991 ppm.

The plankton of these lakes was characterized by heavy blooms of blue-green algae. The plankton production was heavier than that for most of the deeper hard-water lakes, the standing summer crops for the four lakes averaging 5.427 g/m³. At the time of the low water levels, the entire bottoms of these lakes could be considered as littoral. The bottom fauna was sparse on the soft ooze bottoms and consisted mostly of several species of chironomids and annelids. The production of bottom fauna was less than that for most of the deeper hard-water lakes, the standing summer crops for the four lakes averaging 0.531 g/m². All of these lakes had or were supporting populations of bullheads, and at the present time some of the deeper lakes with increased water levels are supporting game fish populations with the aid of fish management.

The estimates in Table 10.1 for benthos and plankton production of Minnesota waters may be considered representative averages showing the magnitude of summer standing crops. The averages for each lake represent several summer samples. All are expressed in dry weight.

Natural river lakes

Several large natural river lakes occur in this area. In Minnesota prominent river lakes are Lake Pepin on the Mississippi River, Lake St. Croix on the St. Croix River, and Lac Qui Parle and Big Stone lakes (Fig. 10.1) on the Minnesota River. The three Des Lacs lakes on the Des Lacs River in northern North Dakota are river lakes which drain northward through the Souris River into the Assiniboine River of the Arctic drainage. Some of these lakes are over 30 km long and 1 km wide. These are lake-like expansions of rivers in which river and lake conditions are combined. Only two river lakes have been studied. Lake St. Croix and Lake Pepin, both because of their proximity to the University of Minnesota and because they have been included in Mississippi River surveys.

Lake Pepin is an enlargement of the Mississippi River formed by a natural dam caused by the outwash of the Chippewa River from Wisconsin (Zumberg, 1952). It is 35 km long and about 1.6 km wide. The average depth is about 12 m. It has a total alkalinity (CaCO$_3$) ranging from 110 to 142 ppm.

Lake St. Croix is a lake-like expanse of the St. Croix River, 24 km long and 1 km wide. It was formed by a natural dike thrown across the mouth of the St. Croix River by the Mississippi River. The water of Lake St. Croix is somewhat softer than that of Lake Pepin, the total alkalinity ranging from 85 to 95 ppm. Although lake-like in extent and in the reduction of currents, these lakes retain their river characters. They are deep enough for thermal stratification, but sufficient current exists to prevent the formation of a thermocline.

The surveys have shown that the deeper bottoms of these two river lakes supported an abundant population of sphaeriids, annelids, chironomids, and burrowing mayflies (*Hexagenia* spp.). Many species of unionid clams occurred in Lake Pepin and at one time formed very large populations. Dawley (1947) pointed out that 35 species of clams existed in Lake Pepin, and 14 species occurred in Lake St. Croix, whereas in lakes with little or no stream connections, only a total of 4 species occurred, and usually only 2 or 3 species of these ever occurred in a single lake.

The fishes in these lakes were the same species found in the large rivers and included some not commonly found in lakes. The paddlefish (*Polyodon spathula*), the shovelnose sturgeon (*Scaphirhynchus platorynchus*), the flathead catfish (*Pylodictis olivaris*), and several others which are not commonly found in lakes are quite characteristic of these two river lakes.

The plankton of these river lakes is more lake-like than are any of the other characters. Although the larger rivers have developed a plankton similar in quality to that of the lakes, it is not so abundant except where impounded. In these river lakes the plankton is much more abundant than that of the river and shows the same heavy abundance of blue-green algae as appears in the nearby lakes.

Flood-plain lakes

Flood-plain lakes and river sloughs are numerous along parts of the Mississippi and the Missouri rivers. A few occur along some of the larger tributaries such as the Minnesota River. Many of these lakes are shallow, and some dry up in the summer. Many of them are connected with the channel during high water, and some are now permanently connected by channels caused by high water levels produced by recent impoundments. None of these flood-plain lakes and sloughs has been investigated to any extent.

Artificial impoundments

In recent years numerous artificial impoundments have been constructed on the major rivers of the area (Fig. 10.2). Because most of these are relatively new, no extensive limnological studies have been completed on them.

In the past 15 years, the construction of the Garrison Dam in North Dakota and the Oahe, the Big Bend, the Fort Randall, and the Gavins Point dams in South Dakota have virtually changed the Missouri River into a continuous pool for its entire course through the Dakotas. This has created an enormous area for limnological research in a region formerly rather deficient in limnological opportunities. Many impoundments have been created on various tributaries of the Missouri River, forming large lakes in the formerly lakeless region of the western Dakotas and elsewhere (see chapter on reservoirs for further details). Impoundments have been constructed on the Souris River and on several tributaries of the Red River in North Dakota.

These lakes are created on smaller streams and seem to have lake conditions predominating over the river conditions.

The Mississippi River has been greatly altered during the past 25 years by the development of the nine-foot channel. This was formed by the construction of seven dams from Minneapolis southward to the Iowa border and has created practically continuous pool conditions over this entire stretch, although the river conditions prevail over most of the river.

Rivers

The large rivers of this area have become so modified by artificial impoundments that very few natural large river environments remain undisturbed. Prior to the creation of the various impoundments, a number of investigations had been made of the Mississippi and the Missouri rivers.

The Mississippi River rises as a small stream draining Lake Itasca, 449.7 m above sea level, and flows 738 km northward, eastward, and southward to St. Anthony Falls at Minneapolis. The river drops 266.2 m between its source and the base of St. Anthony Falls, which is more than the change in elevation between St. Anthony Falls and the Gulf of Mexico. The river flows through both gray and red drift in this upper portion (Fig. 10.3), and the chemical condition of its water is very similar to that of the numerous lakes it drains.

An investigation of the upper portion of the Mississippi River from Minneapolis to Crosby, Minnesota, was made in 1939 by survey crews under the direction of Dr. John B. Moyle. The total alkalinity (as $CaCO_3$) ranged from 90 to 125 ppm and the sulfate-ion concentration from 1.0 to 22.0 ppm. Some of the tributaries draining from the west had much higher alkalinities, ranging up to 252 ppm, with sulfate-ion concentrations as high as 63 ppm.

In the upper part of the river, swift-water areas separated by long pool-like stretches were common. The bottom fauna was abundant: 123 collections made by survey crews in 1939 averaged 9.24 g/m^2 dry weight. The bottom fauna at comparable depths for 69 lakes in this area averaged only 2.05 g/m^2. Considerable plankton production occurred behind the dams in the lower stretches of this portion of the river. The river plankton resembled that of the hard-water lakes

of this region. Blue-green algae and typical lake diatoms such as species of *Asterionella, Fragilaria, Tabellaria,* and *Melosira* predominated. Zooplankters were usually not abundant.

St. Anthony Falls acts as an effective natural barrier for many animals and has caused a number of characteristic river species to be absent from the river above the falls. Only nine species of unionid clams occurred above the falls, although the numbers of species in the river below the falls has been estimated at 38 by the Van der Schalies (1950). Many of the fishes characteristic of the lower river such as the paddlefish (*Polyodon spathula*), the lake sturgeon (*Acipenser fulvescens*), the several species of *Carpiodes,* and many others have not passed over the barrier of the falls.

Below St. Anthony Falls, the Mississippi River is greatly enlarged by the entrance of the Minnesota River from the west and the St. Croix River from the north. It now becomes a wide and rather placid stream occupying a rocky, preglacial valley which it follows throughout the rest of its course in Minnesota. About 112 km below Minneapolis it widens out into Lake Pepin (Fig. 10.1). Below Lake Pepin, it continues in its narrow rocky valley until it leaves the state at 186.6 m above sea level and 2,912 km above its mouth. Its total length in Minnesota is 1,053 km.

Several surveys have been made of the Mississippi River below Minneapolis prior to 1930 partly to determine the distribution of freshwater clams or mussels (Grier, 1922; Grier and Mueller, 1922–23; Ellis, 1931a, 1931b) and partly to determine the conditions produced by pollution from the sewage of Minneapolis and St. Paul. At that time, the river was not greatly altered by impoundments, but gross pollution had modified the conditions for life for nearly 112 km below Minneapolis.

Galtsoff (1924), in a study of the plankton from Hastings, Minnesota, to Alexandria, Missouri, in 1921, found that the river carried a moderate amount of plankton which greatly increased in the quiet waters of Lake Pepin. Wiebe (1927) made a biological survey of the river from Minneapolis to Winona, Minnesota, in 1926 to determine the changes in the biota caused by pollution. He found that the pollution had affected the biota to such an extent that the normal biota did not appear until 112 km downstream at Lake Pepin. Although the plankton was not greatly changed by the gross pollution, he found oxygen depletion and other conditions unfit for normal bottom fauna and for fishes as far as 112 km downstream. The conditions have since been somewhat alleviated by treatment of the metropolitan sewage.

Reinhard (1931) made a study of the plankton of the Mississippi River between Minneapolis and La Crosse, Wisconsin, in 1928. He attempted to make a quantitative study of the various plankters to determine their seasonal distribution in relation to the environmental factors at various points of the river. Because he used only small centrifuged samples, his data on much of the macroplankton are unreliable.

The Missouri River, prior to 1950, occupied a shallow meandering bed throughout most of its course in North Dakota and South Dakota, but at present most of its original channel has been obliterated by recent impoundments. It was a turbid stream wandering through numerous sand bars and over shifting sand bottoms.

A study made by Damann (1951) of the Missouri River and its plankton in 1950–51, before most of the impoundments were filled, showed the river to be relatively barren of plankton. Some of the tributaries carried considerable plankton and probably contributed whatever scanty plankton was noted in the river. During high waters the river was unusually turbid, reaching values as high as 600 (SiO_2) ppm. The nutrient materials were abundant in the water: the total phosphorus (PO_4) ranged from 0.092 to 3.89 ppm and the total nitrogen from 0.53 to 0.98 ppm. The water was alkaline, with a total alkalinity (as $CaCO_3$) ranging from 202 to 268 ppm and with a sulfate-ion concentration ranging from 172 to 230 ppm.

Gastler and Moxon (1948) found that the total alkalinity of the Missouri River at Fort Pierre, South Dakota, ranged from 235 to 312 ppm. They found the sulfate-ion concentration to range from 181 to 268 ppm. One of the main tributaries, the James River, draining much of the central South and North Dakota was much more alkaline, with a total alkalinity ranging from 250 to 741 ppm and with a sulfate-ion concentration ranging from 141 to 849 ppm.

The swift current and the high turbidity of the Missouri River have been important factors limiting the development of plankton. The bottom fauna has also been limited in its development by

these same factors and by the shifting and unstable bottom sands. Unionid clams were rare. The fishes were the same species common to the Mississippi, except for the presence of certain species characteristic of the turbid streams of the great plains such as *Hybopsis gracilis* and *Hybognathus placita*. Personius and Eddy (1955), studying the fishes of some of the tributaries, especially the Little Missouri River, noted that there were distinct differences in the species of fishes in the tributary streams entering from the western side of the river as compared with those entering from the eastern side.

There are numerous small rivers throughout these three states, but very few have been investigated. Several limnological studies have been made in Minnesota on small streams. Six unpublished Masters' theses on limnological conditions in small streams are on file in the University of Minnesota Library. Many of the small cold-water streams of the state have been surveyed by the Minnesota Department of Conservation to determine the fishes suitable for fisheries management programs. Some of the other small rivers of Minnesota have been surveyed by the Minnesota Department of Health, particularly in relation to stream pollution. Relatively few of these investigations have been published.

The most outstanding of the small stream investigations was that by Smith and Moyle (1944) on 30 of the Minnesota streams draining into Lake Superior. Although the purpose of the survey was to determine the extent of stream improvement needed for fish production, many limnological data were obtained. These streams were rather immature, and in many cases their channels were on pre-Cambrian bedrock or on the scanty red drift characteristic of that region.

The bottoms of these streams ranged from bedrock and boulders to soft ooze. Rapids and waterfalls were common. Starting northeastward from Duluth, the total alkalinity ($CaCO_3$) of these streams dropped from 85.1 ppm to 20–35.6 ppm in the pre-Cambrian area near the Canadian border. Many of these streams maintained temperatures low enough for trout. The average bottom production (wet weight) was estimated to range from 0.96 g/m^2 on sand and gravel bottoms to 9.57 g/m^2 on boulder and rubble bottoms. In the rich ooze of the pools, the bottom fauna averaged 1.00 g/m^2.

The waters of Minnesota and the Dakotas offer an unusually wide variety of limnological types. In this area there is almost every known type of lake, pond, and stream. This area properly includes part of the very large and deep Lake Superior which is discussed elsewhere. The magnitude of some of the lakes and the vast number of many types of ponds, lakes, and streams in this area offer practically inexhaustible opportunities for almost every kind of limnological research.

References

AGASSIZ, LOUIS. 1850. Lake Superior: Its physical character, vegetation, and animals, compared with those of other and similar regions. Gould, Kendall, and Lincoln, Boston. 428 p.

COX, U. O. 1897. A preliminary report on the fishes of Minnesota. Geol. Nat. Hist. Surv. Minnesota, Ser. 3, 93 p.

DAMANN, K. E. 1951. Missouri River Basin plankton study. Fed. Security Agency, Pub. Health Serv., Environmental Health Center, Cincinnati, Ohio. 100 p.

DAWLEY, CHARLOTTE. 1947. Distribution of aquatic mollusks in Minnesota. Amer. Midland Nat., **38**: 671–697.

DINEEN, C. F. 1953. An ecological study of a Minnesota pond. Amer. Midland Nat., **50**: 349–376.

DOBIE, J. R., O. L. MEEHEAN, AND G. N. WASHBURN. 1948. Propagation of minnows and other bait species. U.S. Fish and Wildl. Serv., Circ. No. 12: 1–113.

DOBIE, J. R., AND JOHN MOYLE. 1956. Methods used for investigating productivity of fish-rearing ponds in Minnesota. Minnesota Dept. Conserv., Fish. Research Unit, Spec. Publ. No. 5: 1–54.

EDDY, SAMUEL. 1938. A classification of Minnesota lakes for fish propagation. Progr. Fish Cult., No. 41: 9–13.

EDDY, SAMUEL, AND THADDEUS SURBER. 1947. Northern fishes with special reference to the Upper Mississippi Valley. Rev. ed. Univ. Minnesota Press, Minneapolis, 276 p.

ELLIS, M. M. 1931a. A survey of conditions affecting fisheries in the Upper Mississippi River. U.S. Bur. Fish., Circ. No. 5: 1–18.

———. 1931b. Some factors affecting the replacement of the commercial fresh-water mussels. U.S. Bur. Fish., Circ. No. 7: 1–10.

GALTSOFF, P. S. 1924. Limnological observations in the Upper Mississippi, 1921. Bull. U.S. Bur. Fish., **39**: 347–438.

GASTLER, G. F., AND A. L. MOXON. 1948. Composition of Missouri River water samples taken at monthly intervals from May 15 to Sept. 15, 1947. Proc. South Dakota Acad. Sci., **27**: 32–35.

GRIER, N. M. 1922. Final report on the study and appraisal of mussel resources in selected areas of the Upper Mississippi River. Amer. Midland Nat., **8**: 1–33.

GRIER, N. M., AND J. F. MUELLER. 1922–23. Notes on the naiad fauna of the Upper Mississippi. II. The Naiades of the Upper Mississippi Drainage. Nautilus, **36**: 46–94, 96–103.

HANSON, H. A. 1932. A study of winter conditions and the effect on fish life of certain Minnesota lakes. M.A. Thesis, Univ. Minnesota.

HELLBERG, J. M. 1948. A study of the vertical distribution of the plankton in Lake Itasca, Minnesota, during August, 1947. M.A. Thesis, Univ. Minnesota.

HENDRICKS, H. A. 1949. The microscopic fauna of the sandy beaches of three Minnesota lakes. M.A. Thesis, Univ. Minnesota.

HERRICK, C. L. 1884. A final report on the Crustacea of Minnesota included in the orders Cladocera and Copepoda. Geol. Nat. Hist. Surv. Minnesota, 1884. 191 p.

HERRICK, C. L., AND C. H. TURNER. 1895. Synopsis of the Entomostraca of Minnesota. Geol. Nat. Hist. Surv. Minnesota, Zool. Ser. 2, 525 p.

HOOPER, F. F. 1951. Limnological features of a Minnesota seepage lake. Amer. Midland Nat., **46**: 462–481.

JOHNSON, M. S. 1933. Preliminary report on some Minnesota lakes and their productiveness of fish food. Univ. Minnesota Agr. Expt. Sta., Tech. Bull. No. 90: 1–31.

KLAK, G. E. 1937. A comparative study of summer plankton in the vicinity of Minneapolis and St. Paul, Minnesota. Trans. Amer. Microscop. Soc., **56**: 196–202.

LINDEMAN, R. L. 1941a. The developmental history of Cedar Creek Bog. Amer. Midland Nat., **25**: 101–112.

———. 1941b. Seasonal food-cycle dynamics in a senescent lake. Amer. Midland Nat., **26**: 636–673.

———. 1942a. Experimental simulation of winter anaerobiosis in a senescent lake. Ecology, **23**: 1–13.

———. 1942b. Seasonal distribution of midge larvae in a senescent lake. Amer. Midland Nat., **24**: 428–444.

———. 1942c. The trophic-dynamic aspect of ecology. Ecology, **23**: 399–418.

METCALF, F. P. 1931. Wild duck foods of North Dakota lakes. U.S. Dept. Agr., Tech. Bull. No. 221: 1–72.

MOYLE, J. B. 1945a. Some chemical factors influencing the distribution of aquatic plants in Minnesota. Amer. Mildland Nat., **34**: 402–420.

———. 1945b. Classification of lake waters upon the basis of hardness. Proc. Minnesota Acad. Sci., **13**: 8–12.

———. 1946. Some indices of lake productivity. Trans. Amer. Fish. Soc., **76**: 322–334.

———. 1954. Some aspects of the chemistry of Minnesota surface waters as related to game and fish management. Minnesota Dept. Conserv., Invest. Rept. No. 151, 36 p.

———. 1956. Relationships between chemistry of Minnesota surface waters and wildlife management. J. Wildl. Mgmt., **20**: 303–320.

MOYLE, J. B., AND NEIL HOTCHKISS. 1945. The aquatic and marsh vegetation of Minnesota and its value to waterfowl. Minnesota Dept. Conserv., Tech. Bull. No. 3 : 1–122.

NACHTRIEB, H. F., E. E. HEMINGWAY, AND J. P. MOORE. 1912. The leeches of Minnesota. Geol. Nat. Hist. Surv. Minnesota, Zool. Ser. 5, 150 p.

OOSTING, H. J. 1933. Physical-chemical variables in a Minnesota lake. Ecol. Monogr., 3 : 493–534.

OVER, W. H., AND E. P. CHURCHILL. 1927. A preliminary report of a biological survey of the lakes of South Dakota. South Dakota Geol. Nat. Hist. Surv., Circ. No. 29 : 1–18.

PERSONIUS, R. G., AND SAMUEL EDDY. 1955. The fishes of the Little Missouri River. Copeia, 1955(1) : 41–43.

PHILIP, C. B. 1927. Diurnal fluctuations in the hydrogen ion activity of a Minnesota Lake. Ecology, 8 : 73–89.

REINHARD, E. G. 1931. The plankton ecology of the Upper Mississippi, Minneapolis to Winona. Ecol. Monogr., 1 : 395–464.

SMITH, L. L., JR., AND J. B. MOYLE. 1944. A biological survey and fishery management plan for the streams of the Lake Superior north shore watershed. Minnesota Dept. Conserv., Tech. Bull. No. 1 : 1–228.

SURBER, THADDEUS. 1922. A biological reconnaissance of streams tributary to Lake Superior, Baptism River to Devil Track River. Manuscript Rept., Minnesota Dept. Conserv., 153 p.

SWAIN, F. M. 1956. Stratigraphy of lake deposits in central and northern Minnesota. Bull. Amer. Assoc. Petrol. Geol., 40 : 600–653.

SWAIN, F. M. 1961. Limnology and amino-acid content of some lake deposits in Minnesota, Montana, Nevada, and Louisiana. Bull. Geol. Soc. Amer., 72 : 519–546.

SWAIN, F. M., A. B. BLUMENTHALS, AND R. MILLERS. 1959. Stratigraphic distribution of amino acids in peats from Cedar Creek Bog, Minnesota, and Dismal Swamp, Virginia. Limnol. Oceanogr., 4 : 119–127.

SWAIN, F. M., AND N. PROKOPOVICH. 1954. Stratigraphic distribution of lipoid substances in Cedar Creek Bog, Minnesota. Bull. Geol. Soc. Amer., 65 : 1183–1198.

THOMAS, B. O. 1959. The biodynamics of sedimentation in Horseshoe Lake, Isanti County, Minnesota. Ph.D. Thesis, Univ. Minnesota.

TSCHETTER, P. G. 1942. A study of certain lakes in Waubay Migratory Waterfowl Refuge with special emphasis on acidity and its relation to plants and animals. Proc. South Dakota Acad. Sci., 22 : 88–89.

VAN DER SCHALIE, HENRY, AND ANNETTE VAN DER SCHALIE. 1950. The mussels of the Mississippi River. Amer. Midland Nat., 44 : 448–466.

WIEBE, A. H. 1927. Biological survey of the Upper Mississippi River with special reference to pollution. Bull. U.S. Bur. Fish., 43 : 137–167.

WILSON, J. N. 1958. The limnology of certain prairie lakes in Minnesota. Amer. Midland Nat., 59 : 418–437.

WOOD, EVELYN. 1938. An ecological study of lower Lake Minnetonka. M.A. Thesis, Univ. Minnesota.

YOUNG, R. T. 1924. The life of Devils Lake, North Dakota. Publ. North Dakota Biol. Sta., 114 p.

ZUMBERG, J. H. 1952. The lakes of Minnesota, their origin and classification. Bull. Minnesota Geol. Surv., 35 : 1–99.

11

Kenneth D. Carlander
Robert S. Campbell
William H. Irwin

Mid-Continent States

Most of the area included in the mid-continent states (Fig. 11.1) is in two physiographic provinces known as the Great Plains and the Central Lowlands (Fenneman, 1931, 1938). The general features of the two provinces are fairly similar, both being flat to somewhat rolling. The dividing line between them is set at about the 1,500-ft elevation contour. In general, rainfall is 18 to 30 in. per year on the Great Plains and 30 to 50 in. in the Central Lowlands. In the Central Lowlands mean annual evaporation from water surfaces about equals the mean annual precipitation, but in the western area of the Central Lowlands evaporation rate from a water surface greatly exceeds mean rainfall. An escarpment or a range of eroded hills in some places marks the boundary between the two provinces. The Great Plains Province is a fluviatile plain deposited in late Tertiary time, sloping eastward from the Rocky Mountains. In western Nebraska and Oklahoma the highest plains are at 5,260 and 3,750 ft above sea level. All streams eventually flow into the Mississippi River, which is 230 ft above sea level as it leaves southeastern Missouri. The Red River, where it leaves southeastern Oklahoma, is at about 280 ft above sea level.

The Central Lowland in the states of Oklahoma, eastern Kansas, and west-central Missouri was never glaciated and is a plain of low relief, mature topography, sometimes referred to as redbed plains because of the red clays. Glaciers once covered most of the area north of the Missouri River, and the topography here is of well-dissected till plains. A small section of north-central Iowa that was covered more recently by glaciers still retains the "pot and kettle" terrain

of young drift and terminal moraines.

In southern Missouri and eastern Oklahoma the Ozark Plateaus, Boston Mountains, and Ouachita Mountains comprise a third physiographic province of rather rugged, dissected topography with peaks at 1,700 to 2,800 ft (Collier, 1953, 1955).

The climate of the mid-continent states is characterized by an abundance of radiant energy, strong winds, warm summers, arid periods, and floods from excessive and deluge-type rainfall (Blair, 1942). Lying directly east of the Rocky Mountains uplift, the prairie land slopes toward the southeast and receives a prevailing westerly wind that has lost its moisture before the high altitudes it attained over the four Western uplifts. What moist air reaches the states does so by way of the southern winds from the Gulf of Mexico. Precipitation is triggered by cold fronts from masses of cold air moving southeastwardly and southerly from the mountains and the Arctic (Kendrew, 1961). Even in areas where mean annual rainfall is less than 20 in., each year one or more localities will receive 12 to 18 in. within a two-week period. In June 1946 the area around Hydro, Oklahoma, had 19 in. of rain in 18 hours (Linsley *et al.*, 1958; also see Garrett, 1951).

Lakes and streams are frozen about five months each winter in the northern part of the region but have only occasional skim ice in the southern areas.

The mid-continent states are largely agricultural, and much of the land is under cultivation. The major limnological features, which are limited in comparison to much of the rest of the country, can be considered under four headings:

(Text continued on page 320)

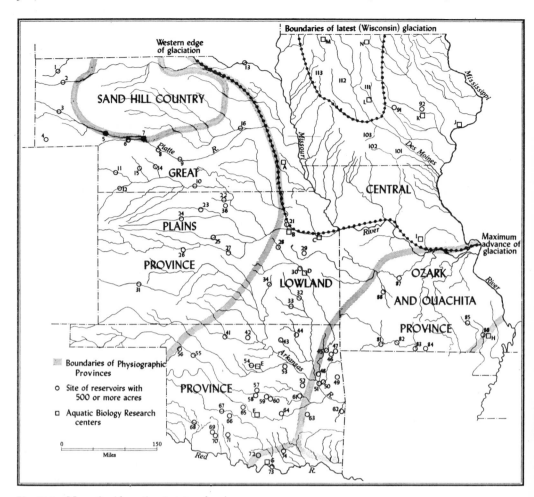

Fig. 11.1.—Map of mid-continent states showing major physiographic areas, extent of glaciation, major rivers, reservoirs of over 500 acres (numbered), and aquatic biology research centers (indicated by letters). Prepared by the University of Wisconsin Cartographic Laboratory.

Aquatic biology research centers

A. Nebraska Game, Forestation and Parks Commission. Dr. O. E. Orr, Project Leader; University of Nebraska, Lincoln. Dr. W. Coil.

B. Kansas State University, Manhattan. Drs. O. W. Tiemeier and Robert J. Robel.

C. University of Kansas, Lawrence. Drs. K. B. Armitage, F. B. Cross (Ichthyology), and H. B. Hungerford (Entomology).

D. Kansas State Teachers College, Emporia. Drs. T. F. Andrews and R. J. Boles.

E. Oklahoma State University, Stillwater. Graduate research in aquatic biology since 1940. Special laboratory for pollution and bioassay studies set up in 1959. Drs. W. H. Irwin, Troy Dorris, and G. A. Moore.

F. University of Oklahoma, Norman. Drs. H. P. Clemens, W. T. Penfound (aquatic plants), C. D. Riggs (fisheries). The Oklahoma Fishery Research Laboratory, sponsored by the Oklahoma Wildlife Conservation Department and the University of Oklahoma Biological Survey, is also at Norman.

G. University of Oklahoma Biological Station, Lake Texoma, Willis, Oklahoma. Established 1949. Summer sessions for teaching and research. Staff from University of Oklahoma and other schools.

H. Gaylord Wildlife Research Laboratory, Puxico, Missouri. Research laboratory and field base with resident director, Dr. John P. Rogers, of the staff of University of Missouri. The laboratory is a cooperative arrangement between University of Missouri and the Missouri Conservation Commission.

I. University of Missouri, Columbia. The Missouri Cooperative Research Unit, sponsored by the State University, the Missouri Conservation Commission, Wildlife Management Institute, and the U.S. Fish and Wildlife Service, carries on research and an undergraduate-graduate training program in aquatic biology (Drs. R. S. Campbell and A. Witt, Jr.). Drs. W. C. Curtis, G. Lefevre, and M. M. Ellis of the Mississippi River studies were at the university. The Fisheries Section of the Missouri Conservation Commission is also at Columbia. Management and research in fishery biology (Chief biologist John L. Funk and staff).

J. Site of Fairport Biological Laboratory of the U.S. Bureau of Fisheries, 1909–1932 (Coker, 1916; Carlander, H. B., 1954). Dr. R. E. Coker, A. F. Shira, P. L. Barney, Dr. A. H. Wiebe, and Dr. H. S. Davis were directors. It is now a warm-water fish culture station of the U.S. Fish and Wildlife Service.

K. State University of Iowa, Iowa City. Dr. R. V. Bovbjerg.

L. Iowa State University of Science and Technology, Ames. Graduate studies in aquatic biology since 1939. The Iowa Cooperative Fisheries Research Unit, sponsored by the Iowa State Conservation Commission and Iowa State University, was established in 1941 (Carlander, 1949). Drs. K. D. Carlander and R. B. Moorman.

M. Iowa Lakeside Laboratory, Milford, Iowa. Established 1909. Summer sessions for teaching and research. Staffed from State University of Iowa, Iowa State University, and State College of Iowa (Cedar Falls). Nearby in Spirit Lake, Iowa, is the Biology Laboratory of the Iowa State Conservation Commission, with responsibilities in fishery investigations and management.

N. Clear Lake, Iowa, a field research station of Iowa Cooperative Fisheries Research Unit.

Data on a few reservoirs over 500 acres

5. McConaughy: completed 1940; 35,200 acres; 140 ft deep (Kiener, 1952).

27. Kanopolis: completed 1948, 3,550 acres; Secchi disc, 9–33 in.; blue-green algae dominant (Tiemeier, 1951).

45. Grand Lake (Lake o' the Cherokees): completed 1939; 46,300 acres; dissolved solids, 158 ppm; pH 7.3–8.4; chlorides 8 ppm; sulfates 34 ppm; bicarbonates 87 ppm; fishes (Jenkins, 1953; Thompson, 1950).

46. Spavinaw Lake: completed 1923; 1,637 acres; municipal water supply; fishery (Jackson, 1958).

48. Ft. Gibson Lake: completed 1952; 19,000 acres; food of fishes (Clemens, 1954); fishery (Houser and Heard, 1958).

50. Tenkiller Lake: completed 1952; 20,800 acres; 130 ft deep; stratified (Finnell, 1953); food of fishes (Clemens, 1954); fishes (Hall, 1955; Jenkins *et al.*, 1952).

54. Lake Carl Blackwell: 3,300 acres; completed 1937; somewhat stratified; pH 7.6–8.4; turbidity 25–94 ppm; fishes (Loomis and Irwin, 1954).

55. Canton Lake: 5,400 acres; Secchi disc, few inches to 3 ft; total alkalinity 145 ppm; pH 7.5–8.6; unstratified except for short periods; fisheries (Hancock, 1954; Buck and Cross, 1952).

62. Wister Lake: fishes (Hall and Latta, 1952).

71. Duncan Lake: fishes (Ward, 1951).

73. Lake Texoma: completed 1944; fishes (Bonn, 1953; Martin, 1954; Riggs and Smithpeter, 1954; Riggs and Dowell, 1956; Weese, 1951); fishery (Houser, 1957).

82. Taneycomo Lake: completed 1913; oldest in Missouri; hydroelectric; 2,432 acres; 44 ft deep; unstratified; 83–160 ppm total alkalinity; pH 7.2–7.8 (Witt and Campbell, research in progress).

85. Clearwater Lake: completed 1948; flood control; 1,660 acres; 48 ft deep; 25–154 ppm total alkalinity; pH 7.2–8.2 (Campbell and Funk, 1953; O'Connell and Campbell, 1953; Martin and Campbell, 1953).

86. Wappapello Lake (Wappello): completed 1941; flood control; 5,700 acres; 15 ft maximum depth (Patriarche, 1953).

87. Lake of the Ozarks: completed 1931; hydroelectric; 58,900 acres; 1,372 mi of shoreline; 130 ft deep; stratified; 50–251 ppm total alkalinity; pH 7.1–8.4 (Borges, 1950; Witt, research in progress).

Data on a few reservoirs under 500 acres

101. Lake Wapello: completed 1933; 287 acres; recreation (Aitken, 1935a, 1936).

102. Red Haw Hill Lake: completed 1935; 72 acres; recreation; stratified (Lewis, 1949b, 1950a, 1950b).

103. Lake Ahquabi: completed 1935; 130 acres; recreation (Hennemuth, 1955).

Data on a few natural lakes

111. Little Wall Lake: 273 acres; less than 6 ft deep except where dredged (Catlin and Hayden, 1927; Carlander and Sprugel, 1955; Sprugel, 1955).

112. North Twin Lake: 569 acres; less than 8 ft deep except where dredged (Collier, 1959; Kutkuhn, 1955, 1958a, 1958b, 1958c; Owen, 1956, 1958).

113. Storm Lake: 3,080 acres; less than 9 ft deep except where dredged (Rose, 1954b, 1949b).

TABLE 11.1

Some chemical characteristics of some mid-continent streams. Most values are means for several seasons; daily figures show much wider ranges. All figures are parts per million.

Location and citation	Total dissolved solids	Bicarbonates	Sulfates	Chloride	Calcium	Sodium-potassium	Turbidity	Specific conductance mho×10⁻⁶ at 25° C
Niobrara R., Nebraska[a]	177–269	69–111	0–10	0.1–2.9	28–49	21–37	52–56	—
Platte R., Nebraska[a]	295–437	165–186	66–152	6–14	46–63	30–48	307–379	—
Smoky Hill R., Kansas[a]	867	256	237	191	114	161	247	—
Saline R., Kansas[a]	2,908	323	479	1,012	132	760	180	—
Other Kansas R. tributaries[a]	320–534	258–334	15–108	9–67	67–92	33–86	304–920	—
Osage R., Kansas[a]	267–270	222–251	35–36	5–10	67–81	23–28	22–356	—
Medicine Lodge R., Kansas[a]	1,054	226	455	98	163	106	118	—
Cimmaron R., Kansas[a]	1,324	308	157	498	85	356	811	—
Other tributaries of Arkansas R.[a]	255–445	139–312	29–131	7–23	64–102	23–38	52–388	—
Kansas streams[b]	—	76–230	—	—	—	—	5–200	—
Arkansas R., Kansas[a]	990–1,571	230–253	193–826	72–292	95–186	167–243	2,227–3,359	—
Arkansas R., Oklahoma[c]	1,175	216	—	379	107	—	—	1,941
Canadian R., Oklahoma[c]	1,929	147	—	1,049	133	—	—	3,426
Neosho-Verdigris R., Oklahoma[c]	268–271	123–128	—	23–58	42–47	—	—	408–436
Rock Creek, Sulphur, Oklahoma[c]	449	336	—	58	94	—	—	762
Red River, Oklahoma[a]	561	135	140	121	74	90	790	—
Ouachita streams, Oklahoma[c]	40–88	14–70	—	3–6	3–22	—	—	34–155
Ozark streams, Missouri[d,e]	—	52–225	—	—	—	—	7–85	—
Missouri R.[a]	346–454	178–203	104–168	9–13	52–65	36–49	1,726–1,931	—
Missouri R., Missouri[f]	—	83–185	—	—	—	—	1,700–8,000	434[h]
Iowa and Northern Missouri tributaries to Missouri R.[a]	140–886	59–249	10–378	1–40	26–164	9–33	—	—
Des Moines R., Iowa[g]	323–414	235–298	55–90	3–10	70–79	8–18	—	50–65
Tributaries to Mississippi R., Iowa[a]	157–312	90–216	6–71	2–5	41–58	5–17	64–542	383–1,510[h]
Mississippi R.[a]	179–269	152–175	24–56	3–10	33–44	10–21	117–858	—
Mississippi R.[h]	—	51–135	0–51	2–5	24–54	—	50–1,880	200–470

[a] Clarke, 1924
[b] Andrews and Brenkelman, 1952.
[c] Unpublished, U.S. Geological Survey.
[d] Campbell and Funk, 1953.
[e] Unpublished, Univ. Missouri.
[f] Berner, 1951
[g] Starrett and Patrick, 1952
[h] Platner, 1946.

river systems, reservoirs, prairie lakes, and glacial lakes. A fifth section includes smaller limnological habitats and limnological methods developed in the region.

River systems

The paucity of natural lakes in most of the area is evidence of a well-developed drainage system. The western part of the region is arid, and most of the streams and rivers are subject to violent water level changes, many being dry during the late summer. The larger rivers originate in the mountains to the west, but even in these the water may be utilized for irrigation before reaching the mid-continent states. Impoundments have been built in recent years in all these states and will be reviewed later.

Most of the streams, particularly the larger ones (Missouri, Arkansas, and Red rivers), are old ecologically with broad flood plains and shallow depths and are continuously turbid (Table 11.1; Fig. 11.2). Some smaller streams are clear except for short periods following severe storms, some are clear intermittently, and some are clear only at rare intervals (Fig. 11.3).

During the dry periods (which occur almost

yearly) many of the streams cease to flow at least above the river beds and exist as separated pools and ribbons of deposition, which is blown into clouds of dust along the entire river bed. A week or a few days later with the advent of a cold front, precipitation may have swollen the streams beyond their banks, inundating the bottomlands to flood conditions. The stream channels may show considerable meandering (Hussey and Zimmerman, 1954).

The ability of a species to withstand crowding and low oxygen is an important factor in determining the fauna of the streams most often intermittent (Starrett, 1950b). Paloumpis (1957, 1958a) called attention to the importance of the isolated pools as havens for fish and other aquatic organisms in intermittent streams. Although the pools were isolated, flow of water through the sands in the stream channel kept the pool waters from stagnation. Tributary streams were also found to serve as havens for fish during floods. Palmer (1919) found a mixed population of fish maintaining themselves in the spring-fed headwaters of Dry Run, a stream which was usually dry in the lower two miles of its course. The water ran to the Cedar River through the sands of the stream bed.

Starrett (1951) pointed out that spawning of most species of fishes in the Des Moines River, Iowa, occurred at relatively low water stages, and that since floods were most common in June, species spawning at this time were less abundant (Fig. 11.4). The more successful species spawned later in the summer or were intermittent spawners with a prolonged spawning season. When there was suitably low water in June, the early-spawning species filled the habitat, thereby reducing the success of late-spawning species.

Fig. 11.3.—Typical stream of eastern prairie region, showing effects of frequent erosion and silting. Courtesy Missouri Conserv. Comm. Photo by Don Wooldridge.

Hornuff (1957) found primary production in four streams in Oklahoma to be largely benthic, with very little plankton growth. The bottom ooze in quiet waters of Des Moines River, Iowa, comprised mostly of diatoms (Starrett and Patrick, 1952), was a principal food of several species of minnows (Starrett, 1950a). Other minnows and

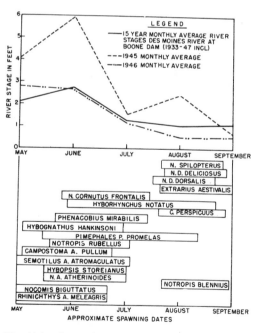

Fig. 11.4.—Comparison of the approximate spawning dates of the Des Moines River minnows with monthly average river stages in Boone County, Iowa. The minnows are arranged in order of their abundance in the Des Moines River. From Starrett, 1951.

Fig. 11.2.—Missouri River, Decatur Bend, Iowa, showing broad flood plain and meanders. Courtesy Iowa State Conserv. Comm.

other river fishes show little specialization in feeding and adjust their feeding habits to seasonal abundance of various food items (Starrett, 1950a; Bailey and Harrison, 1948).

The prairie streams mostly have moderate to high amounts of electrolytes (Table 11.1). Several of the streams in west and central Kansas have average values of 800 to 2,900 ppm total solids. The Saline and Canadian rivers have over 1,000 ppm chlorides. Sulfates are higher than either chlorides or carbonates in a number of other streams of the area. In general the streams east of the Missouri River are low in chlorides (<10 ppm) and fairly low in sulfates (<100 ppm). Sodium and potassium concentrations exceed calcium concentrations in several Kansas and Oklahoma streams (Smoky Hill, Saline, Cimmaron, Arkansas, and Red rivers) but are much lower in most other sections.

Jewell (1927) pointed out that the Iowa and Missouri streams and those in eastern Kansas and Nebraska are not really prairie streams, because their valleys are wooded, and the streams receive much organic matter from the banks and overhanging trees. The true prairie streams to the west, on the other hand, are usually quite barren, with gravel, sand, or clay soils practically free of organic matter. This condition is also partly the result of the greater gradient of these streams (an average drop of 7.5 ft/mi, west to east across Kansas) and of the fluctuations in water flow.

Streams in the Ozark and Ouachita Highlands in southern Missouri and eastern Oklahoma are relatively low in electrolytes (Table 11.1). They are spring-fed clear-water streams with steep gradients and stream beds of chert and exposed limestone. Flash floods follow heavy rains. The Black River is a characteristic smallmouth bass stream draining the Ozark Highland (Campbell and Funk, 1953). The river and Clearwater Lake, a reservoir in the system, had 75 species of fishes (Martin and Campbell, 1953; Funk and Campbell, 1953), of which 20 were minnows (Cyprinidae). The benthos (O'Connell and Campbell, 1953) of Black River resembled closely that of trout streams. Baetidae, Chironomidae, and Parnidae made up 70% by number and 40% by weight of the standing crop of 455 mg dry weight/m². Substrates of rubble or gravel were the most productive. Sullivan (1929) classified the Niangua River as a mayfly stream.

Linton (1959) and Fajen (1959) followed the movement of green sunfish and smallmouth bass by marking and transplanting them in Ozark tributary streams less than 10 mi in overall length. Home range was estimated at 190 ft for the green sunfish and at least 600 ft for bass. In stable pools 67% of the bass and 86% of the green sunfish tagged were recaptured there. In homing experiments 66% of the displaced green sunfish and 42% of the bass returned to their home pools. In a detailed behavioral–life history study of the black redhorse (*Moxostoma duquesni*) Bowman (unpublished, University of Missouri) reported that the size of the territory defended by the male was dependent upon the size of the spawning area and the density of spawning males, and it varied from 9 to 18 in. in diameter. The spawning sequence was discussed. The spawning period lasted only 4 days.

Observations of fish behavior by SCUBA divers Poole (1961) and Kuester (1961) showed clearly that game fishes were less wary and more curious of diving activity than were rough fishes. The relation of these fishes to cover and their distribution in deeper water was also recorded. Average underwater visibility was reported as 4 ft in the more turbid north-flowing Ozark streams, 11 ft in clear south-flowing Ozark streams, and as low as 2 ft and in excess of 9 ft in different reservoirs.

The streams in northeastern Iowa, where there are several limestone outcroppings and where the streams are short and with relatively steep gradient, are more like the Ozark streams than those of the prairie. This area, like the Ozarks, also has a number of spring-fed streams cold enough to maintain trout. Application of standard channel improvements to improve the habitat for trout failed because the structures silted in or were washed out at high water (Aitken, 1935b).

Limnological information on springs in Missouri is largely flow data (Beckman, 1927; Beckman and Hinchey, 1944). The largest, Big Springs, has an average discharge of 252 million gallons per day (390 cfs). The Missouri Ozark region has more than 10,000 springs, and of these, 98 have a daily flow in excess of a million gallons each. The average temperature of water in the large springs seldom varies more than one degree from the average of 58° F (Wood and Short, 1950).

In general spring water is not highly mineralized and is of moderate hardness. The following are selected values (as ppm) from chemical anal-ses of 103 springs (Beckman and Hinchey, 944):

Alkalinity		Sodium	
as CaCO₃	105.0–282.9	and potassium	0.0–3,990
Silicates	2.4–35.8	Sulfates	0.0–1,112.0
Iron	0.17–1.87	Chloride	1.0–6,398
Calcium	19.8–452.0	Nitrates	0.0–15.62
Magnesium	0.8–100.0		

Even the prairie regions have some springs. Schoewe (1953) lists several in Kansas. The Waconda or Great Spirit Spring in Mitchill County (Swineford and Frye, 1955) has a 35-ft high travertine core. The chemical content of the spring waters includes 213 ppm calcium, 413 ppm magnesium, 6,233 ppm sodium, 1,718 ppm bicarbonates, 3,372 ppm sulfates, and 7,700 ppm chloride.

The Missouri River is 2,600 mi long, and it drains almost 1/6 of the area of the 48 contiguous states (U.S. War Dept., 1935). Its average discharge was about 59,000 cfs from 1928 to 1939 (Beckman, 1940), which is about one-half that of the upper Mississippi which it joins. Mean current velocities in the lower Missouri are from 2 to 7 mi/hr. Turbidity is probably the principal factor limiting productivity in the Missouri River (Ellis, 1937a). During high water periods it may exceed 8,000 ppm, and it averages 4,500 ppm (Berner, 1951). The Secchi disc often disappeared at one-half inch. With such high turbidity dissolved oxygen content is often below the levels favorable to fish and other aquatic organisms. Berner (1951) found an average of only 67 plankters per liter during a 7-month survey, about 0.0001 of that reported for the Illinois River by Kofoid (1908). The benthos was also low (0.4–0.7 kg/ha). Syrton (drifting organisms and organic matter) was the most important fish food.

Prior to improvement by the Corps of Engineers, the river meandered through the valley and it has not been uncommon for the wild river to erode and carry away a whole farm in the course of a day or, by avulsion, to shift several farms from one side of the river to the other. Between the rock bluffs the river in its natural state built itself high banks, easily erodible, which contained the normal high water but were overtopped by floods These banks were from 1,500 feet to a mile apart, covered with willows, cottonwoods, and hardwoods. In general, the river followed a meandering course of bends and reaches impeded by soft and shifting bars, shoals, snags, and debris which frequently caused the formation of two or more shallow channels. Smoothly-curved bends in a single fixed channel now characterize the river after improvement work. The river is no longer uncon-

Fig. 11.5.—Missouri River, Snyder Bend area, showing re-aligning of main channel. Unless protected, the old channel will silt in and become a mud and sand flat. Courtesy Delmar Robinson.

trolled and the danger that large areas of farm land might be eroded overnight has been eliminated almost entirely [U.S. War Dept., 1946].

To provide a more stable channel for navigation and to reduce flood damage, the engineers have used revetments and permeable pile dikes and soon expect to have the channel straightened and controlled to the South Dakota border (Fig. 11.5). Very few backwaters or oxbow lakes are left (Fig. 11.6). Upstream from this point many large reservoirs have been built for flood control and for storage of water to maintain flows for navigation. These reservoirs serve as settling basins, and as a result the silt and turbidity is no longer so characteristic of the Missouri River, which was often described earlier as too thick to drink but too thin to plow. Downstream from the Platte River, however, the Missouri River remains very turbid.

The Mississippi River, with a drainage basin of over 1.24 million mi² (3 million km²) (Reid, 1961), is the third largest river system of the world (exceeded only by the Amazon and the Congo). It carries 400 million tons of soil to the Gulf of Mexico each year (Russell, 1944). The mid-continent states are entirely within its watershed. At the northeastern corner of Iowa, where the river first forms the eastern border of the states under consideration, the river is already 693 mi from its source at Lake Itasca and has a mean discharge of about 30,000 cfs (U.S. War Dept., 1948, 1958). Where it leaves southeastern Missouri, 803 mi farther downstream and 835 mi from the Gulf of Mexico, the mean discharge is

Fig. 11.6.—Lake Manawa, an old oxbow lake, near Council Bluffs, Iowa. Courtesy Iowa State Conserv. Comm.

about 460,000 cfs. At this point the watershed totals 923,500 mi². Both the Missouri and Ohio rivers enter the Mississippi River between these two points. The average drop in this 803-mi stretch of the river is 0.48 ft/mi, and the only areas where this drop is exceeded are the rapids at Rock Island, Keokuk, and Chain of Rocks (near St. Louis). In the channel, current velocities are from 1 to 5 mi/hr and may be as high as 8 mi/hr at Chain of Rocks.

In its original condition the Mississippi River consisted of a series of relatively deep pools separated by shoal bars and rapids (Fig. 11.7). The channel was obstructed by rocks and snags, and during low water the flow through the shoals was divided into several chutes with narrow widths and depths as little as 30 in. At higher stages the river was navigable to St. Paul, Minnesota. Hus (1908) described the plant communities across the valley below St. Louis, including the river, its islands, sloughs, and banks. Galtsoff (1924, p. 348) noted: "A peculiar characteristic of the river is the great number of islands. Between St. Paul and the mouth of the Missouri, 658 miles, there are about 540 big enough to be marked and enumerated on the map. Many of these are more than 10 miles long and of irregular shape. They split the river into many sloughs and form many bays and channels, most of which are too shallow to be reached even in a small flat-bottomed river launch." The flood plain also had, and still has, many lakes. Dorris (1958) described conditions in four permanent flood-plain lakes in which further succession is slowed by wind action and fish predation.

Many ponds became isolated from the river and dried up in late summer, stranding fish and other aquatic organisms. Several of the state fish commissions and the U.S. Bureau of Fisheries

carried on extensive "fish-rescue" operations by seining the fish and restocking them in the river or in other waters within the region (H. B. Carlander, 1954). This rescue work was started in 1876 and reached its peak in the 1920's. The 1921 records list 176 million fish rescued that year. There has been little fish rescue work in recent years since impoundment and stabilization of the river.

About 1889, the abundant mussel or clam populations were recognized as a resource which could be exploited for the manufacture of pearl buttons, and within 10 years there were 60 button factories employing 1,917 persons (not counting the thousands who fished for the clams). Muscatine, Iowa, became the "Pearl Button Capitol of the World." One bed near New Boston, Illinois, yielded 10,000 tons of shells in three years. The bed was about 1.5 mi long and 60 rods wide. Many areas were showing signs of depletion by 1898. Most of the clams require 10 to 15 years to reach a harvestable size, and the clamming was faster than replenishment. Increased propagation was attempted through large scale infection of fish from the "fish-rescue" operations with glochidia of the clams (Lefevre and Curtis, 1908;

Fig. 11.7.—Mississippi River near McGregor, Iowa, showing islands and backwaters. Courtesy Iowa State Conserv. Comm. Photo by James Sherman.

Howard, 1914; Coker *et al.*, 1921).

Artificial propagation of the clams without the glochidial attachment to fish was achieved by M. M. Ellis in 1926. However, silting of the river by this time had destroyed most of the habitat for clams suitable for pearl buttons (Ellis, 1931*a*). More recent surveys indicate a lower abundance and number of species in the river (the van der Schalies, 1950).

In an attempt to save the mussel fisheries, the U.S. Commission of Fisheries established a biological laboratory at Fairport, Iowa, in 1908. In addition to work on clam propagation, this laboratory became an important limnological research center. Scientists from colleges and universities who came to Fairport during the summers to work on their own research included C. B. Wilson on parasitic copepods, H. S. Davis, H. B. Bigelow, E. P. Churchill, Emmeline Moore, and A. S. Pearse. The laboratory also served as a training center for many Fish Commission employees, e.g., A. H. Wiebe, P. S. Galtsoff, T. K. Chamberlain, A. D. Howard, R. A. Muttkowski, and T. Surber. The main laboratory was destroyed by fire in 1917, but a new laboratory was dedicated on October 7, 1920, with talks by E. A. Birge, Hugh M. Smith, S. A. Forbes, J. G. Needham, R. E. Coker, V. E. Shelford, F. A. Stromsten, and A. S. Pearse. Many scientific papers came from the work at Fairport, but the research activities were discontinued in 1933 after the nine-foot river channel was established and hopes for return of the mussel resources were largely abandoned. The station is now run as a warm-water fish culture station (H. B. Carlander, 1954).

Navigation on the Mississippi has been important from the time of first settlement and in the days of the paddlewheels was particularly colorful. Mark Twain and several others have written about life on the river boats. As early as 1820 the U.S. Army Corps of Engineers was directed to remove snags and to maintain a boat channel in the Mississippi. In 1878 work was begun to establish a 4.5-ft channel between Minneapolis and the Missouri River. The channel was then deepened to 6, 8, and finally 9 ft. Wing dams were built to speed the current and to promote sedimentation in the back waters, but these dams plus dredging of the channel were not entirely successful, and in 1930 Congress authorized dams and locks. There are now 26 dams between Minneapolis and the Missouri River, converting the

Fig. 11.8.—Mayflies (*Hexagenia bilineata*) weighting down branches of a tree near Keokuk, Iowa. From Fremling, 1960*b*.

river into a series of lakes. One of the effects of the dams has been an increase in permanent water area. The impoundment above the Keokuk Dam covers 60 mi^2 compared to 36 mi^2 prior to the dam. Differences between the area at low and high water are also reduced. Coker (1929, 1930) reported that Keokuk Lake had only 4 mi^2 more water area at high water than at low, compared to 18 mi^2 difference before impoundment. The reduced current also resulted in settling out of the silt which covered sand and gravel bars essential for some fish, mollusks, and other aquatic organisms. Mayfly larvae, particularly *Hexagenia* spp., thrive in the mud bottoms of the lake-like areas and at emergence may be abundant enough to interfere with barge and bridge traffic (Fig. 11.8). Fremling (1960*a*) found evidence of simultaneous emergence over 500 mi of stream. Chironomid larvae are abundant in other stretches of the river (Leathers, 1922; Dorris, 1956). The swift water and clean-swept rock surfaces at the dams provide excellent habitat for the net-building caddis fly larvae. At Keokuk, Iowa, where the main street starts near the base of the dam (Fig. 11.9), the lights attract myriads of emerging

Fig. 11.9.—Dam and locks at Keokuk, Iowa, showing proximity of town to swift waters which produce caddis flies. From Fremling, 1960a.

adults of *Hydropsyche orris*, *Cheumatopsyche campyla*, and *Potamyia flava* (Fremling, 1960b; Ross, 1944). *H. orris* larvae build rigid catching nets in the fastest current; *C. campyla* and *P. flava* build loose, voluminous nets where current is somewhat moderated. Mayfly naiads appear to be important in the diet of most river fishes, whereas few fish feed extensively upon the above species of caddis larvae (Hoopes, 1960). The impounded lakes are more productive of plankton than is the river (Galtsoff, 1924; Coker, 1930).

The first (completed 1913) and highest dam (53 ft) on the Mississippi, at Keokuk, was built not by the Army Engineers but by a private electric company. There is no fishway in the dam, and Coker (1930) found that fish did not use the boat lock effectively for upstream passage since it developed little current. He found evidence of interference with upstream movement of paddlefish (*Polyodon spathula*), eel (*Anguilla bostoniensis*), skipjack (*Alosa chrysochloris*), Ohio shad (*A. ohiensis*), buffalo (*Ictiobus* spp.), drum (*Aplodinotus grunniens*), shortnose gar (*Lepidosteus platostomus*), carp (*Cyprinus carpio*), shovelnose sturgeon (*Scaphirhynchus platyrhynchus*), and catfishes (*Ictalurus* spp.). The interference was of greatest importance in the case of the skipjack, because this species was the specific host of the glochidia of the important "niggerhead" mussel, valuable to the button industry. No skipjacks have been collected upstream at Keokuk since 1930. Paddlefish and eel also have decreased greatly in this time (Barnickol and Starrett, 1951), but the paddlefish has increased in abun-

dance again (Meyer 1960). Purkett (1961) has recently found eggs and larvae (these stages not previously described) of this species in the lower Missouri River.

Several of the states require fishways on all dams blocking streams. The University of Iowa hydrology laboratories studied several fishways designed for the relatively low dams used in prairie streams (Nemenyi, 1941; McLeod and Nemenyi, 1940). Since the more important game fishes do not use the fishways in Iowa streams as much as do the rough fishes (Harrison, 1950), fishways are not now in operation in Iowa.

The Upper Mississippi River Conservation Committee was established in 1943 to coordinate research and management of the fish and wildlife resources of the Mississippi River. It is comprised of representatives of the Conservation Commissions of Minnesota, Wisconsin, Illinois, Iowa, and Missouri and the U.S. Fish and Wildlife Service (H. B. Carlander, 1954).

Silt is the most characteristic pollutant in streams of the mid-continent states. The prairie soils are mostly fine and readily eroded by wind or water. In the more arid regions the grasses are too sparse to prevent considerable erosion. Plowing and intensive agriculture have accelerated erosion in moisture areas. Floods may redistribute tremendous quantities of soil (e.g., Carlson and Runnels, 1952). Coker (1930) and Ellis (1931b, 1936) consider silt to be the major pollution problem even in the Mississippi River itself.

Industrial pollution and municipal sewage present serious pollution problems on many streams, particularly below large population centers (e.g., Ellis, 1937a; Luebbers, 1959; Wiebe, 1928, 1931a; Crohurst, 1932; Petry, 1936; U.S. Dept. Health, Education and Welfare, 1953; Federal Security Agency, 1951).

Quantitative data from limnological examination of the Missouri and Mississippi rivers to evaluate the extent of water pollution from sewage and industrial wastes are being collected and reported in mimeographed Transcripts of Hearings and Conferences by the U.S. Department of Health, Education and Welfare and in annual compilations of data from the National Water Quality Network. Ellis *et al.* (1946) reviewed the determination of water quality for fishes and other aquatic organisms.

In Oklahoma oil refinery wastes and brine from

oil wells affect many streams (Clemens and Jones, 1954; Clemens and Finnell, 1957). A laboratory at Oklahoma State University, under the direction of Drs. W. H. Irwin and T. C. Dorris and partially financed by the oil companies, is testing a variety of fishes for bioassay of these wastes.

In Missouri, eastern Kansas, eastern Oklahoma, and southern Iowa, coal near the surface is mined by stripping off the overlying soils. Investigations which are in part published (J. D. Parsons, 1956, 1957) describe factors that influence excessive flows of coal strip-mine effluents into a Missouri stream and the effects of these acid effluents on the biota. In the upstream section of Cedar Creek the species of plankton and benthos were markedly reduced, and fishes were excluded. The numbers of each persistent species were large, however, so that the standing crop was approximately equal to that of the usually unpolluted downstream section. Fish were killed in the lower section during periods of excessive flow when the pH range was 4.0–4.5, and the average titratable acid was 100 ppm (as $CaCO_3$). Repopulation of the stream by fishes is from unpolluted tributaries or the Missouri River. Parsons (1957) itemized the literature pertaining to formation and effects of acid mine wastes.

The Iowa Natural Resources Commission (1953, 1955a, 1955b, 1956a, 1956b, 1957, 1958a, 1958b, 1959) prepared summaries of water supply and pollution for eight watersheds. Similar inventory and planning is going on in all the states.

Water resource planning can, of course, be traced back for centuries, but in the United States it was stimulated by the droughts and floods in the 1930's (Paul, 1935; Elam, 1946; Anon., 1954; Metzler, 1956; van Orman, 1956; McCallum, 1960). A documentary motion picture, "The River," depicts the influences of the Mississippi River on our civilization (script available in Lorentz, 1938).

Reservoirs

Man-made impoundments are the most prominent and abundant limnological features of much of the mid-continent area. Impoundments with areas from less than 1 to more than 110,000 acres have been built in the region to store water for flood control, municipal and industrial use, irrigation, power, soil erosion control, livestock and farm use, and recreation. While some of these reservoirs are over a hundred years old, most have been built in recent years, and the construction rate seems to be still increasing, particularly for larger reservoirs. Whereas the "dust bowl" conditions in Oklahoma and Kansas in the 1930's were most spectacular, almost eliminating the cattle industry, the more severe 1952–56 drouth had less disastrous effects because of the much greater amounts of stored water in large and small reservoirs.

It is customary to speak of impoundments smaller than 5–10 acres as farm or ranch ponds and to consider them separately. Most of the larger impoundments (Fig. 11.1) are in the western prairie section, where they are subject to open wind and are seldom thermally or chemically stratified even when more than 50 ft deep. Reservoirs and ponds in wooded valleys in the eastern part of the region (Fig. 11.10) are thermally stratified (Lewis, 1949b; Sprugel, 1951a, 1951b; Wallen, 1950; Finnell, 1953; Moen, 1956), and oxygen may be depleted in late summer to within 6 ft of the surface.

Because the reservoirs inundate crop and forested land, they early display such eutrophic features as oxygen depletion, high temperatures, plankton blooms, warm-water fish populations, and stratification. It must be emphasized that while chemical and thermal stratification is usually found June through August in the deepest sections of the reservoirs, yet even here there may be occasional overturn. In shallower and more exposed areas mixing may persist for long periods. This instability with respect to stratification in summer is related to depth, degree of exposure of the reservoir arm to winds, duration

Fig. 11.10.—Table Rock Reservoir, in Ozark region, showing extreme irregularity of shoreline typical of such impoundments. Courtesy Missouri Conserv. Comm. Photo by Don Wooldridge.

and force of the wind, and frequent variations in lake level. Water level fluctuations of 1 to 5 ft from rapid drawdown and inflow are common, and major fluctuations of 20 to 40 ft may persist over several weeks during the period of spring rainfall.

Ellis (1936, 1937b, 1942) refers to chemical conditions in the Lake of the Ozarks and describes definite stratification of the erosion silt load where a warm, muddy stratum flows over a cold, clear hypolimnion.

Red Haw Hill Lake in southern Iowa is much more strictly stratified than East Lake in the valley below it, even though both lakes are about 80 acres in area (Lewis, 1949b). Red Haw is more protected by high forested banks. East Lake is also periodically treated with copper sulfate which keeps down algal production and reduces fungus growth on fish injured during spawning (Lewis, 1950a). White crappies (*Pomoxis annularis*) are more abundant than black crappies (*P. nigromaculatus*) in East Lake, which has a greater clay turbidity than Red Haw, where the species are reversed in abundance (Lewis, 1950b). This difference in tolerance of the two species has been noted elsewhere (e.g., Hall *et al.*, 1954).

The vertical distributional pattern of fishes in the Niangua arm of the Lake of the Ozarks was closely correlated with thermal stratification (Borges, 1950). During June fishes were rather evenly distributed from surface to bottom; in late July and August most species avoided the midwater stagnant stratum, concentrating in the epilimnion and in a deep stratum of cold, oxygen-bearing spring water; in September fishes re-entered the middle stratum but were more concentrated in the deepest water at 15–27 ft depth. Loomis and Irwin (1954) found little evidence of an effect of temperature on fish distribution in Blackwell Lake, Oklahoma, which is only partially stratified.

Sprugel (1951a) found that bluegills frequently foraged into the oxygen-depleted hypolimnion of a small impoundment in Iowa and suffocated if detained there in traps. Sprugel (1951b) also noted that a large green ciliate protozoan, *Stentor coeruleus*, remained mostly in water with 0.1 to 2.0 ppm dissolved oxygen.

Most of the research on reservoirs of the region has dealt with the fisheries and with the fish and other biota, pre- and post-impoundment (e.g., Kathrein, 1953; Lane, 1954; Lewis, 1950a, 1950b; Ward, 1951; Patriarche, 1953; Weyer,

1940; Witt, 1957; Hancock, 1954; Heaton and Orr, 1956; Buck and Cross, 1952; Cross, 1950). The Oklahoma Fisheries Research Laboratory has a long list of papers on these topics (e.g., Clemens, 1954; Finnell, 1956; Hall, 1955; Hall and Latta, 1952; Houser, 1957, 1959; Jackson, 1958; Jenkins, 1951, 1953, 1956a, 1956b; Jenkins and Leonard, 1954; Jenkins *et al.*, 1952; McCoy, 1955; Martin, 1954; Sandoz, 1960; Summers, 1954; Thompson, 1950, 1951, 1955). While there are many variations, the usual picture is one of good growth of fishes and good fishing success while the populations are expanding into the new environment. Usually a few species become over-abundant, and growth rates and fishing success drop off as the reservoirs reach five or more years of age.

Changes in the biota of a clear, spring-fed river as a result of impoundment are documented in a series of papers on Black River and Clearwater Lake, Missouri. Major changes in the benthos (O'Connell and Campbell, 1953) evident within three months of flooding included (1) dominant families of mayflies, midges, and riffle beetles replaced by midges, mosquitoes, and oligochaetes and (2) a marked decrease in the variety of benthic organisms. Total standing crops were similar. Minnows formed 77% of the small-fish population in the river (Martin and Campbell, 1953). The dominant fishes of Clearwater Lake, namely brook silversides (*Labidesthes sicculus*), bluntnose minnow (*Pimephales notatus*), bluegill (*Lepomis macrochirus*), and longear sunfish (*Lepomis megalotis*), were species that had been inhabitants of river pools. The authors discuss the ecological factors influencing spawning success and species assortment. Smallmouth bass (*Micropterus dolomieui*) and rock bass (*Ambloplites rupestris*), the two principal predacious fishes in Black River (Funk and Campbell, 1953), failed to establish in Clearwater Lake (Patriarche and Campbell, 1958). The dominant successful species six years after impoundment, namely gizzard shad (*Dorosoma cepedianum*), bluegills, longear sunfish, white crappie, bullheads (*Ictalurus* spp.), and golden redhorse (*Moxostoma erythrurum*), were all either prolific spawners or omnivorous species. Largemouth bass (*Micropterus salmoides*), the most numerous large predators in the lake, were never abundant. The authors concluded that the carrying capacity of Clearwater Lake with reference to the fish populaion was reached five years after impoundment.

Temporary filling of Table Rock Reservoir, Missouri, affected the fish population of the inundated upper White River, resulting in a marked increase in gizzard shad, black bullheads (*Ictalurus melas*), and centrarchids and a sharp decrease in minnows and darters (Knapp, 1958).

A continuing study (Witt, research in progress) begun in 1950 on the comparative growth of the white crappie (*Pomoxis annularis*) in five major Missouri impoundments has shown (1) the most rapid growth occurred during the first year of impoundment, and (2) the best growth occurred in the newer reservoirs, Clearwater and Norfork, poorer growth in the older lakes, Taneycomo and Wappapello, and poorest growth in the Lake of the Ozarks as a result of tremendous numbers of young fish. Witt suggests that populations of white crappie were (in 1952) still approaching the carrying capacity of the newer reservoirs but had reached the asymptote in the older impoundments.

Some of the early work on improving impoundments for fish through the addition of shelters and gravel beds was on Lake Wapello, Iowa (Aitken, 1935a, 1936; Aitken and Salyer, 1938), and some of the early cooperative studies were in Oklahoma (Aldrich, 1947; Duck, 1949).

Fish populations in midwestern impoundments averaged almost 400 lbs per acre and ranged from 71 to 1,235 lbs per acre (K. D. Carlander, 1955). There was a suggestion of increased standing crop per acre with increased acreage of the impoundment, no evidence of relationship with mean depth, and a definite increase associated with increased methyl orange alkalinity. There is also an increase in standing crop as the number of species of fishes in the reservoir is increased, hence as more of the niches are filled. High total standing crop does not necessarily result in favorable fishing success or fish production, however.

The smaller ponds are usually built to detain water, to prevent soil erosion, or to store water for livestock and other farm use (Fig. 11.11). The state conservation departments all have ponds for rearing fish for stocking in natural waters and impoundments, and there are a few privately owned fish hatcheries in the region, the largest devoted to raising goldfish for aquaria and bait fish for sport fishermen. The number of farm ponds has been estimated at over 300,000 for Oklahoma (Anon., 1960a), 100,000 for Kansas

Fig. 11.11.—A typical 2-acre farm pond in central Oklahoma. Area fenced to exclude livestock, which are watered from a tank below the dam (not shown). Terraces to regulate water flow into the pond. Watershed well grassed. Courtesy W. H. Irwin.

(Anon., 1960b), 90,000 for Missouri (Barnickol and Campbell, 1952), and 3,400 for Iowa (K. D. Carlander, 1952), but the numbers are only approximate since many more are being built each year, and some are not long maintained. These small ponds, when protected from wind, may exhibit pronounced thermal and chemical stratification. Generally they are quite eutrophic (Wiebe, 1931b; Wallen, 1955; Tiemeier and Elder, 1957; Tiemeier and Moorman, 1957) and may have abundant algal growth (Wiebe, 1930; Wallen, 1949). At times the water blooms, particularly those of *Microcystis aeruginosa* and *Anabaena flos-aquae*, may result in conditions toxic to animals. Other toxic blue-green algae that sometimes occur but are not important components are *Aphanizomenon flos-aquae*, *Coelosphaerium kuetzingianum*, and *Gleotrichia echinulata* (B. D. Vance, personal communication). Burris (1954) found 20 genera of insects established in the bottom fauna of a pond in its first year. Some experiments have been carried on to increase fish production by adding fertilizing substances (Barnickol and Campbell, 1952), by maintaining population "balance" (Carlander and Moorman, 1957; Fessler, 1950), and by other methods (Dyche, 1914; Schneberger and Jewell, 1928; K. D. Carlander, 1952; Moorman, 1957a; Aldrich et al., 1944; Ward et al., 1954; Anon., 1953).

Comparison of limnological data on fertilized and unfertilized Missouri farm ponds (Zeller, 1953, 1955) suggests that soluble phosphate was a limiting factor in productivity. Significant amounts of nitrogen were shown to enter ponds from watersheds planted to the legume *Lespedeza cuneata* (sericea lespedeza). Walker (1959) de-

scribes techniques for application of more effective soluble fertilizers, limited results of herbicide
treatment on flora and bottom fauna, and use
of the plastic barrier to facilitate replication in
pond studies.

An overabundance of rooted vegetation, which
is fairly common in ponds, interferes with harvest
of the fish and with maintenance of the proper
balance between predators and forage fish. In
Iowa winter-kill from oxygen depletion under the
ice is one of the major causes of poor fish production (Moorman, 1957a).

Standing crops of bass and bluegills in Iowa
farm ponds ranged from 28 to 653 lbs per acre
(Carlander and Moorman, 1956). Standing crops
in 11 Oklahoma ponds averaged 287 lbs per acre,
with a range of 90 to 845 (Sandoz, 1958). Standing crops of over 300 lbs per acre were the
result of abundance of bullheads.

Fish populations in 30 unmanaged Missouri
farm ponds 5 to 73 years of age (1) contained
no predatory species, (2) contained less than 5%
by weight of keeper-size fish, (3) were dominated
by green sunfish and black bullheads, and (4)
averaged 319 lbs per acre for 9 ponds (Bauman,
1946).

The effects of high density of bluegill populations in both fertilized and unfertilized farm ponds
(Burress, 1949) were evident in (1) reduced
growth rate, (2) starvation accompanied by scale
resorption in older year classes, and (3) a lowered
frequency of false annulus formation. Growth
rates were poorest in the most turbid ponds.

Sprugel (1954) found that growth of bluegills
in a new pond slowed down abruptly by the time
bluegills from a second spawning were a year old.

In an unpublished analysis of the effect on carp
on the limnology of ponds, Hendricks (1955)
demonstrated that the major effects, exclusive of
benthos reduction, were the results of increased
turbidity. These could be duplicated by mechanical disturbance of the pond bottom. In a mixed
population of carp and buffalo in farm ponds, only
buffalo increased in weight (Hendricks, 1956).

Hydrophylidae, Odonata, Dytiscidae, and Belostomatidae comprised 16.8% by volume of the
total diet of bullfrogs (*Rana catesbiana*) in Missouri farm ponds. Snails, crayfish, fish, amphibia,
and turtles made up an additional 55.8%
(Korschgen and Moyle, 1955).

Siltation and turbidity cause serious problems
in many impoundments of all sizes. Turbidities
reduce the productivity of the water by reducing
the penetration of light (Ellis, 1936, 1937a, 1944,
Prescott, 1939; Chandler, 1940, 1942a, 1942b
1944; Irwin, 1945; Claffey, 1955). Turbidity also
unfavorably affects the growth and survival of
fish and other aquatic organisms (Buck, 1956;
Wallen, 1951). Soil conservation measures on
the watershed decreased turbidity in Lake Ahquabi, Iowa, a 130-acre reservoir, and this was
followed by increased growth of the fish (Hennemuth, 1955).

The large deposits of clay in the plains states
furnish a continuous supply of colloidal particles
to the waters of the area. These colloids usually
have negative electrical charges and hence can
be coagulated and made to settle out if these
charges are neutralized (Irwin and Stevenson
1951). Positive ions from green manure (Irwin
1945, 1946), gypsum (Anon., 1953), and oil field
brine (Keeton, 1959) have been effectively used
to clear pond waters in the area.

Siltation records on Ashland Lake, a 17-acre
eutrophic reservoir with a drainage area of 2,345
acres, show a storage depletion of 27% in 14
years. Lateral siltation in Lake Taneycomo on the
White River has restricted the open water area
to a narrow channel with a conspicuous flow. As
a result of this and controlled flow from Table
Rock reservoir immediately upstream, the lake
no longer stratifies as it did earlier in its life. The
metabolism of Ashland Lake has been described
by Parsons and Campbell (1961). It is recognized
that many of the reservoirs, particularly on watersheds not under effective erosion control, are
relatively short-lived. With increasing water needs
it is expected that reservoirs will be larger and
even more abundant in the next few years.

Prairie lakes

The Great Plains region has few permanent natural lakes (Jewell, 1927). The largest is Inman
Lake in central Kansas, which has an area up to
about 200 acres in wet years and an average depth
of about 4 ft. The bottom is fine, hard clay, and
the water is turbid and rather unproductive. There
are numerous depressions that retain water for
a few days or even for a few years between drier
spells. Many of these with built-up rims are
known as "buffalo wallows" and were used by
the bison, once abundant. Through evaporation,
total dissolved solids are increased sometimes
to very high levels in some of these prairie lakes.

The salts may leave a white crust around the margin of these drying "playa" lakes. True playa lakes are more abundant to the west than they are in the mid-continent states here considered. These temporary prairie lakes have been little studied but often have abundant populations of phyllopods and spadefoot toads (*Scaphiopus* spp.). In permanent pools the top minnow (*Fundulus kansae*) is commonly found. Such lakes are at times very important as waterfowl nesting and resting areas.

A particularly interesting area is the Sandhill Country of Nebraska (Fig. 11.1). The Sandhill area is a plains region of about 24,000 mi² modified by wind. The area has not been glaciated, and the soils, which are of Pleiocene Age, have been reworked by the wind, leaving dunes and sandy basins and valleys. The altitude ranges from 2,000 ft in the southeast to 3,500 ft in the northwest. Four major river systems transverse the area: Elkhorn, Niobrara, North-Middle-South Loops, and Dismal rivers. All but the Niobrara arise in the sandhills.

The Sandhill area includes 1,640 lakes varying in size from 10 to 2,300 acres, plus about 850 smaller lakes or ponds, with a combined surface area of 65,800 acres (McCarraher *et al.*, 1961). All of the lakes are comparatively shallow, the deepest being Blue Lake, 13.8 ft, and none is thermally stratified. Evaporation losses are from 3 to 5 ft annually. Total dissolved solids range from 150 to 448,000 ppm (Table 11.2). The lakes usually have a northwest to southeast axis (Fig. 11.12).

Most of the lakes are alkaline eutrophic, but some high in potassium salts are classed as alkaline dystrophic. Entomostraca are abundant but as yet have been little studied. Phytoplankton is predominately blue-green algae (Anderson and Walker, 1920; McCarraher *et al.*, 1961). There is a distinct decrease in abundance of submerged aquatic plants when the alkalinity reaches 600 ppm and again around 800 ppm. All species of fish, except the fathead minnow (*Pimephales promelas*), disappear when bicarbonate values exceed 900 ppm. This minnow has been found at bicarbonate levels of 1,500 ppm.

Glacial lakes

The last advance of the glaciers, the late Wisconsin, 35,000 to 14,000 years ago, extended into northern Iowa, leaving terminal moraines and a

Fig. 11.12.—Typical sandhill lake. Courtesy D. B. McCarraher and O. E. Orr.

small extension of the lake region typical of Minnesota and Wisconsin. Harlan and Speaker (1956) list 52 glacial lakes in Iowa, ranging in size from 13 to 5,684 acres, most of which are shallow. Many other marshes and shallow lakes in the same region (Fig. 11.13) have been lost through drainage and development of the land for agriculture (Shimek, 1924). Some lakes, like Little Wall Lake, have fluctuated from almost complete dryness to lakes with well-established fish populations (Catlin and Hayden, 1927; Carlander and Sprugel, 1955). Several of the lakes are silting in rather rapidly, and only four have maximum depths of 15 ft or more. The Iowa State Conservation Commission has attempted to maintain and improve some of the lakes through hydraulic dredging (Fig. 11.14). The bottom fauna of Lizard Lake, once scheduled for dredging, was studied (Tebo, 1955) and compared with that of dredged and undredged areas of nearby North Twin Lake (Owen, 1956). *Chaoborus* sp. replaced tendipedids in the dredged area. The dredged area served as a silting basin, permitting a wider, cleaner erosion littoral zone than in the undredged end of North Twin Lake (Owen, 1958).

Algal production is often high in these shallow lakes (Kutkuhn, 1958a, 1958b), and concentrations of blue-green algae have resulted in toxic conditions killing mammals, birds, and fish (Prescott, 1948; Rose, 1954a, 1954b). At North Twin Lake algal problems were greatly reduced during years when there was a high population of gizzard shad (*Dorosoma cepedianum*) feeding on the algae (Kutkuhn, 1958b). The young gizzard shad in turn provided most of the food for

predatory fishes in the lake (Kutkuhn, 1955, 1958c).

Oxygen depletion during the period of ice cover from late November to mid-April often results in mortality of invertebrates and fish (Sprugel, 1955; Carlander and Sprugel, 1955; Collier, 1959). Such mortality may bring about a thinning of the fish population, resulting in increased growth of the remaining fish (Sprugel, 1955), elimination of overpopulations of gizzard shad as at North Twin Lake (Collier, 1959), or more commonly the elimination of all fishes, sometimes leaving only black bullheads (*Ictalurus melas*) and fathead minnows (*Pimephales promelas*), which are able to survive by gulping air at holes in the ice or at burrows maintained by muskrats (Carlander and Sprugel, 1955). A strong 1941 year-class of bullheads resulting from the few adults that survived the 1940–41 winter-kill in Lost Island Lake was so crowded that the fish showed little growth from 1942 to 1945 (Rose and Moen, 1951). Bottom fauna organisms were rare in 1946, probably as a result of overuse by bullheads and carp. Removal of 160 lbs of carp (*Cyprinus carpio*) and 190 lbs of bullheads per

Fig. 11.13.—Aerial photographs of South and North Twin Lakes at normal high water (*A*) and after a heavy rain (*B*), showing pothole condition typical of region before widespread tiling and draining. From Owen, 1958.

TABLE 11.2

Some characteristics of lakes in the Nebraska Sandhills Area. From McCarraher *et al.*, 1961.

	Lakes with fish	Borderline lakes	Lakes with no fish
*p*H	7.8–9.2	9.2–9.5	9.0–10.8
Total dissolved solids, ppm	150–1,402	2,200–3,800	654–448,000
Total alkalinity, ppm	50–825	640–840	500–55,000
Sulfate, ppm	1–94	94–3,200	120–24,700
Potassium, ppm	9–189	180–200	22–96,000
Sodium, ppm	13–300	320–2,100	650–89,000
Gastropods	Common to abundant		Scarce to absent; often only *Physa*
Aquatic vegetation	Common to abundant	Includes *Potamogeton pectinatus* and/or *Ruppia maritima*	Absent or restricted to *Potamogeton pectinatus* and *Ruppia maritima*

Fig. 11.14.—Hydraulic dredging of lake in Iowa, showing silting basin at top of picture, Courtesy Iowa State Conserv. Comm. Photo by James Sherman.

acre in 1946–48 resulted in increased growth of the bullheads and in some build-up of bottom fauna.

Spirit, West Okoboji, and East Okoboji lakes, the three deepest Iowa lakes, are connected, with the first two flowing into East Okoboji (1,875 acres; maximum depth, 24 ft). Flowage continues from East Okoboji through a series of shallower lakes to the Little Sioux River and thence to the Missouri River. East Okoboji is a rich eutrophic lake with an abundance of aquatic vegetation. Heavy populations of carp, buffalo (*Ictiobus* spp.), and sheepshead (*Aplodinotus grunniens*) apparently suppressed the vegetation in the early 1940's, because the vegetation expanded after removal of 2,726 lbs of these fish per acre in 1940–45 (Rose and Moen, 1953). Game fish populations also increased as the rough fish populations were reduced.

Spirit Lake is a roughly circular lake, 5,684 acres in area, with boulder and sandy beaches and a maximum depth of 25 ft. Numerous small lakes and marshes are connected with the lake, but the lake itself has only a moderate amount of aquatic vegetation, mostly *Potamogeton* spp. and *Chara contraria* (Sigler, 1948). Most of the fishery management is directed toward maintain-

Fig. 11.15.—Air view of West Okoboji Lake in winter, showing small houses used by sport fishermen. Courtesy Iowa State Conserv. Comm.

ing walleye (*Stizostedion vitreum*) fishing (Rose, 1949a, 1955). During the period 1942 to 1946, white bass (*Roccus chrysops*) was the dominant sport fish as the result of a very successful 1941 year-class (Sigler, 1949).

West Okoboji (Fig. 11.15), 3,939 acres in area,

is a particularly interesting lake with a maximum depth of 132 ft. No other lake over 30 ft deep is within a hundred miles. The water is clearer than that of other lakes in the region. Taylor and Jahn (1940) report 30% light transmission per meter for the upper 10 m in West Okoboji compared to 0.0002% per meter in East Lake. Weber (1958) found photosynthetic activity using the carbon-14 method, at 9 m in West Okoboji, whereas photosynthesis did not occur below 2 to 3 m in East Okoboji or in Clear Lake (Weber, 1960). *Ceratophyllum demersum* was found growing to the depth of 9 m in West Okoboji (E. N. Jones, 1925). On the west side of the lake is Lakeside Laboratory, established in 1909 by the University of Iowa for summer instruction and research. Since 1947 the laboratory has been run as a summer station of the State University of Iowa (at Iowa City), Iowa State University (at Ames), and State College of Iowa (at Cedar Falls).

Birge and Juday (1920) spent several days at Lakeside Laboratory in 1919 working particularly on thermal conditions, which studies have been continued by many other scientists. In years when June is cold and windy, thermal stratification may be fairly incomplete, with water down to at least 30 m reaching 17° C (Birge and Juday, 1920; Tilton, 1916; Stromsten, 1926, 1927; Jahn and Taylor, 1940; Bardach, 1955). In 1936 the epilimnion temperatures reached 29° C, and the annual heat income was calculated as 24,000 ca/cm^2, compared to 18,000-21,000 cal/cm^2 in previous years. In years of late or incomplete thermal stratification, yellow perch (*Perca flavescens*) and concentrations of *Tendipes* larvae were found at greater depths in midsummer than in years of early thermal stratification (Bardach, 1955). Dissolved oxygen is depleted at the bottom in both types of years, but concentrations at 20 m averaged 2.2 ppm in years of late stratification compared to a mean of 0.7 ppm in years of early stratification. Bardach (1954) found internal seiches with amplitudes of 4 to 5 m, which affected chironomid distribution.

Most of the aquatic work at Lakeside Laboratory has been of floristic and faunistic nature: aquatic plants (Shimek, 1897; Wylie, 1920; E. N. Jones, 1925); algae (Smith, 1926; Tiffany, 1926; Prescott, 1931); protozoans (Bishop and Jahn, 1941); zooplankton (McDonald, 1940a); rotifers (Ensign, 1920); hydracarinids (Marshall, 1926);

leeches (Mathers, 1948); entomostracans (Stromsten, 1917, 1920a, 1920b); mollusks (Shimek, 1915, 1935; Bovbjerg and Ulmer, 1960); bottom fauna (Bardach et al., 1951; Clampitt et al., 1960); fishes (Larrabee, 1926). While the lakes in the Okoboji region are all relatively hard-water eutrophic lakes, they differ considerably in some of their chemical constituents (Adamson and Jahn, 1940; Hayden, 1948).

On Clear Lake, with an area of 3,643 acres and a maximum depth of 20 ft in north-central Iowa, fishery investigations have been carried on since 1941 by the Iowa Cooperative Fishery Research Unit, sponsored by the State Conservation Commission and Iowa State University (e.g., Bailey and Harrison, 1945; Carlander and Cleary, 1949; Carlander and Ridenhour, 1955; Carlander and Whitney, 1961; Carlander et al., 1960; Di Costanzo and Ridenhour, 1957; English, 1952; Forney, 1955; McCann, 1959; J. W. Parsons, 1950; Ridenhour, 1957; Sieh and Parsons, 1950; Whitney, 1958). Strictly limnological observations have been rather limited (Pearcy, 1953). The lake is usually thoroughly mixed by winds and seldom shows thermal or chemical stratification.

The period of fishery investigations includes a series of years of below normal rainfall during which the water level dropped to 2.5 ft below the outlet, thereby exposing about 300 acres of shore (McCann, 1960). The watershed is only about twice the surface area of the lake. Much of the rooted vegetation was unable to maintain itself at the lowered water levels. Secchi disc readings in the summer of 1950, when water levels were high, averaged 58 in. but were only 22 to 24 in. in 1957–59 when water levels were low. Increased stirring of the bottom muds by wind and increased plankton growth are believed to have been responsible for the lesser transparency. White crappies (*Pomoxis annularis*), known to be more tolerant of turbid waters, largely replaced the black crappies (*P. nigromaculatus*) with the change in turbidity (Neal, 1962). In 1959 all the photosynthesis of plankton algae was found to take place within one to two meters of the surface, and primary production was estimated at 1.95 g carbon/m^2 per day (Weber, 1960). Very little difference in vertical distribution of the plankton could be demonstrated, but pronounced concentrations of surface plankton were sometimes found in certain areas associated with wind direction and stress or on very calm days caused by local reproduction and growth (Small, 1961a).

Yellow bass (*Roccus mississippiensis*), introduced into Clear Lake in the early 1930's, first became abundant in the 1940's. The 1941 year-class grew rapidly, but growth since then has been much slower. At the end of the second year yellow bass were 8.9 in. long in 1939, 5.3 in. in 1950, and 4.6 in. in 1958 (Carlander *et al.*, 1953; Bucholz, 1960). After reaching a length of 6–7 in., they did not grow enough in the mid-1950's to add annuli, and some yellow bass with only 5 annuli on their scales were known to have been over 8 years old (Buchholz, 1958).

There is one small sphagnum bog lake a few miles northwest of Clear Lake, in Pilot Knob State Park. The 2.5-acre acid bog (*p*H 4.5–6.0) is contiguous with a 2.7-acre neutral pool with a typical marsh margin (Grant and Thorne, 1955; Smith and Bovbjerg, 1958). A few other small bogs without much open water are located in the glaciated area of Iowa (Carter, 1939; Hempstead and Jahn, 1940).

Miscellaneous

Limnological work on a few other waters does not fit well into the above categories. Some impoundments form where gravel, stone, or coal have been removed. Gravel pits may be found in all parts of the region and in many ways are similar to farm ponds. They may be less fertile and are often left unmanaged. The fish population of one gravel pit, which had been managed for fishing but had been flooded by the Iowa River three years earlier thereby introducing carp, buffalo, and several other unwanted fishes, had a standing crop of 1,235 lbs per acre when treated with rotenone (Carlander, 1951).

In a few areas abandoned rock quarries have formed relatively infertile, usually clear ponds somewhat deeper and steeper-sided than other impoundments of their area.

Water accumulating among spoil banks on land strip-mined for coal is initially highly acid and with high concentration of iron and sulfates (Fig. 11.16). These lakes are scattered on some 65,000 acres of strip-mined land in Arkansas, Oklahoma, Kansas, Missouri, and Iowa (Rogers, 1951).

Parsons (1956, 1957) has shown that strip-mine lakes in the watershed of Cedar Creek, Missouri, must contribute their acid water overflow to the acid runoff from spoil banks before

Fig. 11.16.—Strip mine pond, showing spoil banks and outlet to Cedar Creek, Missouri. Courtesy Missouri Conserv. Comm. Photo by Don Wooldridge.

the flow will be of such volume and intensity as to move the length of the creek and cause a severe fish-kill throughout. Neighboring lakes may differ quite significantly in chemical composition and biota (Table 11.3), perhaps partly because of ecological succession (Table 11.4). One area in Iowa had several pools with *p*H values of 4.0–4.5, low alkalinity, and Secchi disc readings at 9–18 ft and several others with *p*H values of 7.0–7.5, 70–120 ppm alkalinity, and Secchi disc readings of 2–7 ft (Mayhew, 1959).

Investigations in Kansas have emphasized the highly restricted biota associated with acid waters of strip-mine lakes (Burner and Leist, 1953; Stockinger and Hays, 1960; Maupin *et al.*, 1954). *Chara* was reported growing in May in clear water at depths of 12 ft or more in strip pits where the chemical conditions were *p*H range, 4.0 to 8.2; carbonates, 54 to 432 ppm; sulfates, 3,176 to 6,424 ppm (Schoonover and Coates, n.d.). Simpson (1961) has completed a detailed chemical analysis of three strip-mine lakes in southeast Kansas.

A 4.9-acre mining pit lake in Iowa received drainage from cultivated land as well as spoils pile. With a *p*H ranging from 6.5 to 7.8, it had a fish population and other biological conditions quite similar to other reservoirs (Ruhr, 1952).

In the Ozarks, Ouachitas, and in northeast Iowa there are a number of limestone caves

TABLE 11.3

Physical and chemical aspects of succession in aging strip-mine lakes in Missouri. From unpublished data at University of Missouri by John D. Parsons.

	Chemically young	Chemically older	Chemically mature
Apparent color of water	red	blue	grey
Cause of color	reddish black iron oxides	no turbidity	suspended organic and inorganic material
Thermal character spring and summer	stratification	homothermous	stratification
pH	1.5–2.5	3.0–4.0	>4.0
Titratable acid, ppm	816–6,870	250–6,360	low
O_2, ppm	0.0–5.8	0.1–9.9	—
SO_4, ppm	1,905–11,820	1,234–10,885	—
Fe^{++}, ppm	0.3–15	0.5–11	low
Fe^{+++}, ppm	40–349	0.8–28	low

with streams or pools and characteristic endemic salamanders (S. C. Bishop, 1943), fish (Woods and Inger, 1957), crayfish (Wells and Witt, 1957), and other aquatic organisms (Garman, 1889; Drouet, 1933).

Ratzlaff (1952) studied the limnology of some roadside ditches in Kansas, with particular reference to the ecology of Cladocera and copepods.

Proctor (1957) noted that *Haematococcus pluvialis,* a motile green alga, occurs in temporary rain-water pools but not in permanent ponds. Using media prepared with unautoclaved pond water, he showed that the pond water was usually toxic to *Haematococcus* and proposed that this effect was due to inhibiting substances associated with algal blooms in the ponds. Pure cultures of *Chlamydomonas* and *Scenedesmus* produced extra-cellular substances toxic to *Haematococcus.*

It would be difficult and beyond the scope of this book to list all the faunistic and floristic research related to aquatic organisms of the region. Even though it is recognized that equally significant papers are probably hereby neglected, a few in addition to those mentioned earlier should be cited, as, for example, the extensive work on aquatic Hemiptera by Hungerford (e.g., 1919, 1922, 1933, 1948) and his associates (Anderson, 1931; Bare, 1926; Cummings, 1933; Gould, 1931; Griffith, 1945).

Mention might be made of other work on aquatic Hemiptera (Drake and Harris, 1934), Coleoptera (Sanderson, 1938; Wilson, 1923*a*, 1923*b*), Odonata (Wells, 1917; Wilson, 1920), and Diptera (Leathers, 1922; Dorris, 1956); on crayfish (Steele, 1902; Williams, 1952; Minckley and Deacon, 1959), ostracods (Danforth, 1948), amphipods (Mackin, 1935), phyllopods (Mackin, 1939), entomostracans (Mackin, 1931; McDonald, 1940*b*; Prophet, 1957; Prophet *et al.,* 1959; Ratzlaff, 1952; Willis, 1959), and Crustacea in general (Leonard and Ponder, 1949).

In addition to the papers mentioned when referring to the Fairport Station and the Mississippi River, mention should be made of the following papers on mollusks: Coker (1914*a*, 1914*b*, 1919), Fitch and Lokke (1956), Isely (1914), D. T. Jones (1941), Surber (1913, 1915), Utterback (1914). Moen (1951) and Harbaugh (1937) make reference to Hydrozoa, and Geiser (1937) to a bryozoan. A few papers on free-living Protozoa include Edmondson (1906), Johnson (1944), and Shawhan *et al.* (1947).

TABLE 11.4

Biological aspects of succession in an aging strip-mine lake in the Carrington Strip-Mine Area, Missouri. From Crawford (1942) and Heaton (1955).

	1940–41	1949–50
pH	3.8	6.6
Higher plants	3 species	10 species
Plankton	17 genera	52 genera
Benthos	3 genera	17 genera
Fishes	none (?)	6 species

Moreover, there are other papers on algae (Elmore, 1921; Gier and Johnson, 1954; Leake, 1945; Myers, 1898; Prescott and Andrews, 1955; Showalter, 1952; Taft, 1934; Thompson, 1938; Vinyard, 1955; Vivian, 1932) and on higher aquatic plants (Gilly, 1946; Gruchy, 1938; Penfound, 1953).

Among the many studies dealing with fish distribution in the area may be mentioned Cross (1954), Cross and Moore (1952), Harlan and Speaker (1956), Minckley (1956, 1959), Moore and Buck (1955), Moore and Paden (1950), Ortenburger and Hubbs (1926).

While many fishery investigations have been mentioned, a few more may give a better picture of the research in this area: Funk (1953, 1957), Moen (1954, 1959), Moorman (1957b), Muncy (1958), J. W. Parsons (1951), Patriarche and Lowry (1953), Purkett (1958a, 1958b), Witt and Marzolf (1954).

Some mention should also be made of several papers from this region contributing to methodology in limnology and associated fields. Stromsten (1923) described an early application of the platinum wire thermocouple for measuring water temperatures. Sigler and Moen (1947) developed a shallow-water diving rig. Fremling (1961) improved a screening pail for separating bottom fauna from soils. Hungerford et al. (1955) and Fremling (1960b) used subaquatic light traps for insects and other aquatic organisms. Kutkuhn (1958d) and Small (1961b) worked on methods of increasing plankton sampling efficiency.

Comparisons of gear for the collection of fish have been made by Carlander (1953, 1957), Cleary and Greenbank (1954), Clemens (1952), Funk (1958), Paloumpis (1958b), Ridenhour and Di Costanzo (1956), Ridenhour (1960), and Starrett and Barnickol (1955). Some improvements in the use of electrical shockers for collecting fish were described by Funk (1949), Riggs (1955), and Witt and Campbell (1959). Rose (1951) described a light-weight engine for pulling seines. Methods of estimating fish populations by marking and recovery were discussed by Carlander and Lewis (1948) and Fredin (1950). H. Bishop (1958) described experiments in marking white bass with spaghetti tags. Some aspects of the use of rotenone in removing fish from a body of water were investigated by Hamilton (1941) and Clemens and Martin (1953). Improved creel census methods were discussed at a

Symposium at Iowa State University (Carlander, 1956b; Carlander et al., 1958).

Fish growth studies have an important role in the fisheries investigations of this region, and a number of papers contributing to its methodology have appeared (Campbell and Witt, 1953; Carlander, 1956a, 1961; English, 1952; Leonard and Sneed, 1951; Lewis 1949a; Lewis and Carlander, 1949; Lowry, 1951; Marzolf, 1955; Sneed, 1951; Whitney and Carlander, 1956).

Improvement of fishing through manipulation of fish populations and the selective removal of some of the fish for the benefit of others is practiced throughout the area (e.g., Carlander, 1958a, 1958b; Jenkins, 1959; Rose and Moen, 1951, 1953; Sandoz, 1959). Sneed and Clemens (1956, 1959, 1960a, 1960b) have made considerable progress in the spawning of catfish and other warm-water fishes through the use of hormones.

Witt (1960), using otoliths of freshwater drum (*Aplodinotus grunniens*) from ancient Indian middens and mounds, was able to demonstrate smaller average size of these fish about 7000 years ago when the glaciers extended further south, an interesting technique in paleolimnology.

In summary it might be stressed that most of the limnological research in the mid-continent states is of a floristic or faunistic nature or is associated with practical fisheries problems. Much of the work has not been published but is in files at the colleges and universities or the state conservation and natural resources commissions. In addition to the research centers mentioned, many biologists at other colleges in the region carry on research in aquatic biology, and biologists associated with the state fish and game and public health organizations contribute regularly to limnological knowledge.

Acknowledgments

The authors wish to express special thanks for help in preparing this chapter to Dr. Orty E. Orr and D. McCarraher of the Nebraska Game Forestation and Parks Commission, to Roy Schoonover of the Kansas Forestry, Fish and Game Commission, to Dr. Arthur Witt, Jr., of the University of Missouri, and to John Funk of the Missouri Conservation Commission. For providing photographs for the illustrations, thanks are due Dr. Orty E. Orr, D. McCarraher, D. Robinson, Public Relations Section of the Iowa State

Conservation Commission, and the Missouri Conservation Commission.

References

ADAMSON, A. G., AND T. L. JAHN. 1940. The oxidizable organic matter and organic nitrogen content of the Okoboji lakes. Proc. Iowa Acad. Sci., 46: 407–411.

AITKEN, W. W. 1935a. Iowa's artificial lakes. Proc. Iowa Acad. Sci., 42: 189–197.

————. 1935b. Iowa stream improvement work. Trans. Amer. Fish. Soc., 65: 322–323 + 6 fig.

————. 1936. Introduction of aquatic plants into artificial lakes of Iowa. Proc. Iowa Acad. Sci., 43: 133–137.

AITKEN, W. W., AND J. C. SALYER, II. 1938. Improvement of artificial lakes. Michigan Inst. Fish. Research, Bull. 2: 175–201.

ALDRICH, A. D. 1947. Impoundments utilized to the advantage of fishery-management studies. Progr. Fish-Cult., 9: 82–85.

ALDRICH, A. D., F. M. BAUMGARTNER, AND W. H. IRWIN. 1944. Fish production in farm ponds. Oklahoma Agr. Expt. Sta., Circ. C-115: 1–8.

ANDERSON, E. N., AND E. R. WALKER. 1920. An ecological study of the algae of some sandhill lakes. Trans. Amer. Microscop. Soc., 39: 51–85.

ANDERSON, L. D. 1931. A monograph of the genus Metrobates (Hemiptera, Gerridae). Univ. Kansas Sci. Bull., 20: 297–311.

ANDREWS, T. F., AND JOHN BRENKELMAN. 1952. Studies in Kansas limnology. I. Survey of the Kansas State Lakes. Trans. Kansas Acad. Sci., 55: 315–329.

ANONYMOUS. 1953. Ponds for fish and wildlife production. 4th ed. Missouri Conserv. Comm., 32 p.

————. 1954. Water in Kansas. Report to 1955 legislature, Topeka, Kansas, 216 p.

————. 1960a. Oklahoma's water resources. Oklahoma Water Resources Board, 44 p.

————. 1960b. Report to the 1961 Kansas legislature concerning state water policy and program needs. Kansas Water Resources Board, 48 p.

BAILEY, R. M., AND H. M. HARRISON, JR. 1945. The fishes of Clear Lake, Iowa. Iowa State Coll. J. Sci., 20: 57–77.

BAILEY, R. M., AND H. M. HARRISON, JR. 1948. Food habits of the southern channel catfish (Ictalurus lacustris punctatus) in the Des Moines River, Iowa. Trans. Amer. Fish. Soc., 75: 110–138.

BARDACH, J. E. 1954. Effects of the wind on water movements in Lake West Okoboji, Iowa. Proc. Iowa Acad. Sci., 61: 450–457.

————. 1955. Certain biological effects of thermocline shifts. Hydrobiologia, 7: 309–324.

BARDACH, J. E., J. MORRILL, AND F. GAMBONY. 1951. Preliminary report on the distribution of bottom organisms in West Lake Okoboji. Proc. Iowa Acad. Sci., 58: 405–414.

BARE, C. O. 1926. Life histories of some Kansas "backswimmers." Ann. Entomol. Soc. Amer., 19: 93–101.

BARNICKOL, P. G., AND R. S. CAMPBELL. 1952. Summary of selected pond studies in Missouri. J. Wildl. Mgmt., 16: 270–274.

BARNICKOL, P. G., AND W. C. STARRETT. 1951. Commercial and sport fishes of the Mississippi River. Bull. Illinois. Nat. Hist. Surv., 25: 257–350.

BAUMAN, A. C. 1946. Fish populations in unmanaged impoundments. N. Amer. Wildl. Conf., 11: 426–433.

BECKMAN, H. C. 1927. Water resources of Missouri 1857–1926. Missouri Geol. Mines, Ser. 2, No. 20, 424 p.

————. 1940. Surface waters of Missouri (streamflow records, 1927–39). Missouri Geol. Surv. Water Resources, Ser. 2, No. 26, 900 p.

BECKMAN, H. C., AND N. S. HINCHEY. 1944. The large springs of Missouri. Missouri Geol. Surv. Water Resources, Ser. 2, No. 29, 141 p.

BERNER, L. M. 1951. Limnology of the lower Missouri River. Ecology, 32: 1–12.

BIRGE, E. A., AND CHANCY JUDAY. 1920. A limnological reconnaissance of West Okoboji. Univ. Iowa Studies Nat. Hist., 9(1): 3–56.

BISHOP, E. L., JR., AND T. L. JAHN. 1941. Observations on colonial peritrichs (Ciliata: Protozoa) of the Okoboji region. Proc. Iowa Acad. Sci., 48: 417–421.

BISHOP, H. 1958. Marking white bass with spaghetti tags. Proc. Oklahoma Acad. Sci., 38: 68–70.

BISHOP, S. C. 1943. Handbook of salamanders. Comstock Publ. Co., Ithaca, New York. 555 p.

BLAIR, T. A. 1942. Climatology, general and regional. Prentice-Hall, Inc., New York. 484 + xvi p.

BONN, E. W. 1953. The food and growth rate of young bass (Morone chrysops) in Lake Texoma. Trans. Amer. Fish. Soc., 82: 214–221.

BORGES, H. M. 1950. Fish distribution studies, Niangua Arm of the Lake of the Ozarks, Missouri. J. Wildl. Mgmt., 14: 16–33.

BOVBJERG, R. V., AND M. J. ULMER. 1960. An ecological catalogue of the Lake Okoboji gastropods. Proc. Iowa Acad. Sci., 67: 569–577.

BUCHHOLZ, M. M. 1958. Failure of some yellow bass to form annuli in later years of life. 20th Midwestern Wildl. Conf., Columbus, Ohio, 2 p. (Mimeo.)

————. 1960. Ecological relationships associated with decreasing growth rate of Clear Lake yellow bass. Ph.D. Dissertation, Iowa State Univ., Ames, 115 p.

BUCK, D. H. 1956. Effects of turbidity on fish and fishing. Trans. N. Amer. Wildl. Conf., 21: 249–261.

BUCK, D. H., AND F. CROSS. 1952. Early limnological and fish population conditions of Canton Reservoir, Oklahoma. Oklahoma Agr. and Mech. Coll. (Mimeo.)

BURNER, C. C., AND C. LEIST. 1953. A limnological study of the College Farm Strip-Mine Lake. Trans. Kansas Acad. Sci., 56: 78–85.

BURRESS, R. M. 1949. The growth rates of bluegills and largemouth black bass in fertilized and unfertilized ponds in Central Missouri. M.A. Thesis, Univ. Missouri.

BURRIS, W. E. 1954. The bottom fauna development of a newly constructed pond in central Oklahoma. Proc. Oklahoma Acad. Sci., 33: 129–136.

CAMPBELL, R. S., AND J. L. FUNK. 1953. The Black River basin in Missouri. Univ. Missouri Studies, 26(2): 11–21.

CAMPBELL, R. S., AND A. WITT, JR. 1953. Impressions of fish scales in plastic. J. Wildl. Mgmt., 17: 218–219.

CARLANDER, H. B. 1954. A history of fish and fishing in the Upper Mississippi River. Publ. Upper Mississippi River Conserv. Comm., 96 p.

CARLANDER, K. D. 1949. The Iowa Cooperative Fisheries Research Program. Proc. Iowa Acad. Sci., 56: 325–331.

——. 1951. An unusually large population of fish in a gravel pit lake. Proc. Iowa Acad. Sci., 58: 435–440.

——. 1952. Farm fish pond research in Iowa. J. Wildl. Mgmt., 16: 258–261.

——. 1953. Use of gill nets in studying fish population, Clear Lake, Iowa. Proc. Iowa Acad. Sci., 60: 621–625.

——. 1955. The standing crop of fish in lakes. J. Fish. Research Board Canada, 12: 543–570.

——. 1956a. Fish growth rate studies: Techniques and role in surveys and management. Trans. N. Amer. Wildl. Conf., 21: 262–274.

—— (ed.). 1956b. Symposium on sampling problems in creel census. Iowa Coop. Fish. Research Unit, Ames, Iowa. 80 p.

—— (ed.). 1957. Symposium on evaluation of fish populations in warm-water streams. Iowa Coop. Fish. Research Unit, Ames, Iowa. 118 p.

——. 1958a. Disturbance of the predator-prey balance as a management technique. Trans. Amer. Fish. Soc., 87: 34–38.

——. 1958b. Some simple mathematical models as aids in interpreting the effect of fishing. Iowa State Coll. J. Sci., 32: 395–418.

——. 1961. Variations on rereading walleye scales. Trans. Amer. Fish. Soc., 90: 230–231.

CARLANDER, K. D., AND R. E. CLEARY. 1949. The daily activity patterns of some freshwater fishes. Amer. Midland Nat., 41: 447–452.

CARLANDER, K. D., C. J. DI COSTANZO, AND R. J. JESSEN. 1958. Sampling problems in creel census. Progr. Fish-Cult., 20: 73–81.

CARLANDER, K. D., AND W. M. LEWIS. 1948. Some precautions in estimating fish populations. Progr. Fish-Cult., 10: 134–137.

CARLANDER, K. D., W. M. LEWIS, C. E. RUHR, AND R. E. CLEARY. 1953. Abundance, growth and condition of yellow bass, *Morone interrupta* Gill, in Clear Lake, Iowa, 1941 to 1951. Trans. Amer. Fish. Soc., 82: 91–103.

CARLANDER, K. D., AND R. B. MOORMAN. 1956. Standing crops of fish in Iowa ponds. Proc. Iowa Acad. Sci., 63: 659–668.

CARLANDER, K. D., AND R. B. MOORMAN. 1957. Some experiments in changing population balance in farm ponds. Progr. Fish-Cult., 19: 92–94.

CARLANDER, K. D., AND R. L. RIDENHOUR. 1955. Dispersal of stocked northern pike in Clear Lake, Iowa. Progr. Fish-Cult., 17: 186–189.

CARLANDER, K. D., AND GEORGE SPRUGEL, JR. 1955. Fishes of Little Wall Lake, Iowa, prior to dredging. Proc. Iowa Acad. Sci., 62: 555–566.

CARLANDER, K. D., AND R. R. WHITNEY. 1961. Age and growth of walleyes in Clear Lake, Iowa, 1935–57. Trans. Amer. Fish. Soc., 90: 130–138.

CARLANDER, K. D., R. R. WHITNEY, E. B. SPEAKER, AND K. MADDEN. 1960. Evaluation of walleye fry stocking in Clear Lake, Iowa, by alternate-year planting. Trans. Amer. Fish. Soc., 89: 249–254.

CARLSON, W. A., AND R. T. RUNNELS. 1952. A study of silt deposited by the July 1951 flood, Central Kansas River Valley. Trans. Kansas Acad. Sci., 55: 209–213.

CARTER, C. 1939. Observations upon bogs of northern Iowa. Proc. Iowa Acad. Sci., 46: 223–224.

CATLIN, L. A., AND ADA HAYDEN. 1927. The physiographic ecology of a Wisconsin drift lake. Proc. Iowa Acad. Sci., 34: 165–190.

CHANDLER, D. C. 1940. Limnological studies of Lake Erie. I. Plankton and certain physical-chemical data of the Bass Islands region from September, 1938, to November, 1939. Ohio J. Sci., 40: 291–336.

——. 1942a. Limnological studies of western Lake Erie. II. Light penetration and its relation to turbidity. Ecology, 23: 41–52.

——. 1942b. Limnological studies of western Lake Erie. III. Phytoplankton and physical-chemical data from November, 1939, to November, 1940. Ohio J. Sci., 42: 24–44.

——. 1944. Limnological studies of western Lake Erie. IV. Relation of limnological and climatic factors to the phytoplankton of 1941. Trans. Amer. Microscop. Soc., 63: 203–236.

CLAFFEY, F. J. 1955. The productivity of Oklahoma waters with special reference to relationships between turbidities from soil, light penetration and the populations of plankton. M.S. Thesis, Oklahoma Agr. and Mech. Coll., 102 p.

CLAMPITT, P. T., E. L. WAFFLE, AND R. V. BOVBJERG. 1960. An ecological reconnaissance of the bottom fauna, Miller's Bay, Lake Okoboji. Proc. Iowa Acad. Sci., 67: 553–568.

CLARKE, F. W. 1924. The composition of the river and lake waters of the United States. U.S. Geol. Surv., Profess. Paper 135, 199 p.

CLEARY, R. E., AND J. GREENBANK. 1954. Estimating fish populations in streams. J. Wildl. Mgmt., 18: 461–476.

CLEMENS, H. P. 1952. Cove selection and use of gill nets in fish population surveys in large impoundments. J. Wildl. Mgmt., 16: 393–396.

——. 1954. Pre-impoundment studies of the summer food of three species of fishes in Tenkiller and Fort Gibson Reservoirs, Oklahoma. Proc. Oklahoma Acad. Sci., 33: 72–79.

CLEMENS, H. P., AND J. C. FINNELL. 1957. Biological conditions in a brine-polluted stream in Oklahoma. Trans. Amer. Fish. Soc., 85: 18–27.

CLEMENS, H. P., AND W. H. JONES. 1954. Toxicity

of brine waters from oil wells. Trans. Amer. Fish. Soc., **84**: 97–109.

CLEMENS, H. P., AND M. MARTIN. 1953. Effectiveness of rotenone in pond reclamation. Trans. Amer. Fish. Soc., **82**: 167–177.

COKER, R. E. 1914*a*. Water power development in relation to fishes and mussels of the Mississippi. U.S. Bur. Fish. Document 805: 1–28.

———. 1914*b*. The protection of fresh-water mussels. U.S. Bur. Fish. Document 793: 1–23.

———. 1916. The Fairport Fisheries Biological Station: Its equipment, organization, and functions. Bull. U.S. Bur. Fish., **34**: 383–406.

———. 1919. Fresh-water mussels and mussel industries of the United States. Bull. U.S. Bur. Fish., **36**: 15–89.

———. 1929. Keokuk Dam and the fisheries of the Upper Mississippi. Bull. U.S. Bur. Fish., **45**: 87–139.

———. 1930. Studies of common fishes of the Mississippi River at Keokuk, 1930. Bull. U.S. Bur. Fish., **45**: 141–225.

COKER, R. E., A. R. SHIRA, H. W. CLARK, AND A. D. HOWARD. 1921. Natural history and propagation of fresh-water mussels. Bull. U.S. Bur. Fish., **37**: 77–181.

COLLIER, JAMES E. 1953. Geography of the northern Ozark border region in Missouri. Univ. Missouri Studies, **26**(1), 105 p.

———. 1955. Agricultural atlas of Missouri. Univ. Missouri Agr. Expt. Sta., Bull. 645, 75 p.

COLLIER, JOE E. 1959. Changes in fish populations and food habits of yellow bass in North Twin Lake, 1956–58. Proc. Iowa Acad. Sci., **66**: 518–522.

CRAWFORD, B. T. 1942. Ecological succession in a series of strip-mine lakes in central Missouri. M.A. Thesis, Univ. Missouri.

CROHURST, H. R. 1932. A study of the pollution and natural purification of the upper Mississippi River: Surveys and laboratory studies. U.S. Pub. Health Bull. 203, U.S. Govt. Printing Office, Washington, D.C.

CROSS, F. B. 1950. Effects of sewage and of a headwaters impoundment on the fishes of Stillwater Creek in Payne Co., Oklahoma. Amer. Midland Nat., **43**: 128–145.

———. 1954. Fishes of Cedar Creek and the South Fork of the Cottonwood River, Chase County, Kansas. Trans. Kansas Acad. Sci., **57**: 303–314.

CROSS, F. B., AND G. A. MOORE. 1952. The fishes of the Poteau River, Oklahoma and Arkansas. Amer. Midland Nat., **47**: 396–412.

CUMMINGS, C. 1933. The giant water bugs (Belostomatidae: Hemiptera). Univ. Kansas Sci. Bull., **21**: 197–220.

DANFORTH, W. A. 1948. A list of Iowa ostracods with description of three new species. Proc. Iowa Acad. Sci., **55**: 351–359.

DI COSTANZO, C. J., AND R. L. RIDENHOUR. 1957. Angler harvest in the summers of 1953 to 1956 at Clear Lake, Iowa. Proc. Iowa Acad. Sci., **64**: 621–628.

DORRIS, T. C. 1956. Limnology of the middle Mississippi River and adjacent waters. II. Observations on the life histories of some aquatic Diptera. Trans. Illinois Acad. Sci., **48**: 27–33.

———. 1958. Limnology of the middle Mississippi River and adjacent waters. Lakes on the leveed floodplain. Amer. Midland Nat., **59**: 82–110.

DRAKE, C. J., AND H. M. HARRIS. 1934. The Gerrinae of the Western Hemisphere (Hemiptera). Ann. Carnegie Museum, **23**: 179–240.

DROUET, F. 1933. Algal vegetation of the large Ozark Springs. Trans. Amer. Microscop. Soc., **52**: 83–101.

DUCK, L. G. 1949. Cooperative management of fish and wildlife resources of large impoundments in Oklahoma. Trans. N. Amer. Wildl. Conf., **14**: 313–319.

DYCHE, L. L. 1914. Ponds, pond fish and pond fish culture. Kansas State Dept. Fish and Game, Bull. 1, 208 p.

EDMONDSON, C. H. 1906. The Protozoa of Iowa. Proc. Davenport Acad. Sci., **11**: 1–124.

ELAM, W. E. 1946. Speeding floods to the sea, or The evolution of flood control engineering on the Mississippi River. Hobson Book Press, New York, 173 p.

ELLIS, M. M. 1931*a*. Some factors affecting the replacement of the commercial fresh-water mussels. U.S. Bur. Fish., Fish. Circ. 7, 10 p.

———. 1931*b*. A survey of conditions affecting fisheries in the Upper Mississippi River. U.S. Bur. Fish., Fish. Circ. 5, 18 p.

———. 1936. Erosion silt as a factor in aquatic environments. Ecology, **17**: 29–42.

———. 1937*a*. Detection and measurement of stream pollution. Bull. U.S. Bur. Fish., **48**: 365–437.

———. 1937*b*. Some fishery problems in impounded waters. Trans. Amer. Fish. Soc., **66**: 63–71.

———. 1942. Fresh-water impoundments. Trans. Amer. Fish. Soc., **71**: 80–93.

———. 1944. Water purity standards for fresh-water fishes. U.S. Fish and Wildl. Serv., Spec. Sci. Rept. No. 2, Fish. Ser., 16 p.

ELLIS, M. M., B. A. WESTFALL, AND M. D. ELLIS. 1946. Determination of water quality. U.S. Fish and Wildl. Serv., Research Rept. 9, 122 p.

ELMORE, C. J. 1921. The diatoms (Bacillariodeae) of Nebraska. Univ. Nebraska Studies, **21**: 22–214.

ENGLISH, T. S. 1952. Growth studies of the carp, *Cyprinus carpio* Linnaeus, in Clear Lake, Iowa. Iowa State Coll. J. Sci., **24**: 527–540.

ENSIGN, D. C. 1920. The Rotatoria of the Lake Okoboji region. Proc. Iowa Acad. Sci., **27**: 271–286.

FAJEN, O. F. 1959. Movement and growth of smallmouth bass in small Ozark streams. M.A. Thesis, Univ. Missouri.

FEDERAL SECURITY AGENCY, Public Health Service. 1951. Summary report on water pollution. Missouri River Drainage Basin. Water pollution series No. 3, 212 p.

FENNEMAN, N. M. 1931. Physiography of western United States. McGraw-Hill Book Co., New York. 334 p.

———. 1938. Physiography of eastern United States. McGraw-Hill Book Co., New York. 714 p.

FESSLER, F. R. 1950. Fish populations in some Iowa farm ponds. Progr. Fish-Cult., **12**: 3–13.

FINNELL, J. C. 1953. Dissolved oxygen and temperature profiles of Tenkiller Reservoir and tailwaters. Proc. Oklahoma Acad. Sci., **34**: 65–72.

———. 1956. Comparison of growth-rates of fishes in Stringtown Sub-prison Lake prior to and three years after draining and restocking. Proc. Oklahoma Acad. Sci., **35**: 30–36.

FITCH, H. S., AND D. H. LOKKE. 1956. The molluscan record of succession on the University of Kansas Natural History Reservation. Trans. Kansas Acad. Sci., **59**: 442–454.

FORNEY, J. L. 1955. Life history of the black bullhead, *Ameiurus melas* (Rafinesque), of Clear Lake, Iowa. Iowa State Coll. J. Sci., **30**: 145–162.

FREDIN, R. A. 1950. Fish population estimates in small ponds using the marking and recovery technique. Iowa State Coll. J. Sci., **24**: 363–384.

FREMLING, C. R. 1960a. Biology of a large mayfly, *Hexagenia bilineata* (Say), of the Upper Mississippi River. Iowa State Agr. and Home Econ. Expt. Sta., Research Bull. 482: 842–852.

———. 1960b. Biology and possible control of nuisance caddisflies of the Upper Mississippi River. Iowa State Agr. and Home Econ. Expt. Sta., Research Bull. 483: 856–879.

———. 1961. Screened pail for sifting bottom-fauna samples. Limnol. Oceanogr., **6**: 96.

FUNK, J. L. 1949. Wider application of the electrical method of collecting fish. Trans. Amer. Fish. Soc., **77**: 49–61.

———. 1953. Management and utilization of the fishery of Black River, Missouri. Univ. Missouri Studies, **26**(2): 113–122.

———. 1957. Movement of stream fishes in Missouri. Trans. Amer. Fish. Soc., **85**: 39–57.

———. 1958. Relative efficiency of gear used in fish population studies. Trans. N. Amer. Wildl. Conf., **23**: 236–248.

FUNK, J. L., AND R. S. CAMPBELL. 1953. The population of larger fishes in Black River, Missouri. Univ. Missouri Studies, **26**(2): 69–82.

GALTSOFF, P. S. 1924. Limnological observations in the Upper Mississippi, 1921. Bull. U.S. Bur. Fish., **39**: 347–438.

GARMAN, S. 1889. Cave animals from southwestern Missouri. Bull. Museum Comp. Zool. Harvard, **17**(6): 225–240.

GARRETT, R. A. 1951. Kansas flood producing rains of 1951. Trans. Kansas Acad. Sci., **54**: 346–355.

GEISER, S. W. 1937. *Pectinatella magnifica* Leidy an occasional river-pest in Iowa. Field and Lab., **5**: 65–76.

GIER, L. J., AND MARTHA JOHNSON. 1954. Algae of Missouri. Trans. Kansas Acad. Sci., **57**: 78–80.

GILLY, C. L. 1946. The Cyperaceae of Iowa. Iowa State Coll. J. Sci., **21**: 55–151.

GOULD, G. E. 1931. The *Rhagovelia* of the Western Hemisphere with notes on world distribution (He-

miptera, Veliidae). Univ. Kansas Sci. Bull., **20**: 5–61.

GRANT, M. L., AND R. F. THORNE. 1955. Discovery and description of a sphagnum bog in Iowa, with notes on the distribution of bog plants in the state. Proc. Iowa Acad. Sci., **62**: 197–210.

GRIFFITH, M. E. 1945. The environment, life history, and structure of the water boatman, *Ramphocorixa acuminata* (Uhler) (Hemiptera, Corixidae). Univ. Kansas Sci. Bull., **30**: 241–365.

GRUCHY, J. H. B. DE. 1938. A preliminary study of the larger aquatic plants of Oklahoma with special reference to their value in fish culture. Oklahoma Agr. and Mech. Coll., Agr. Expt. Sta., Tech. Bull. 4, 31 p.

HALL, G. E. 1955. Preliminary observations on the presence of stream-inhabiting fishes in Tenkiller Reservoir, a new Oklahoma impoundment. Proc. Oklahoma Acad. Sci., **34**: 34–40.

HALL, G. E., R. M. JENKINS, AND F. C. FINNELL. 1954. The influence of environmental conditions upon the growth of white crappie and black crappie in Oklahoma waters. Oklahoma Fish. Research Lab., Rept. 40, 56 p. (Mimeo.)

HALL, G. E., AND W. C. LATTA. 1952. Pre- and postimpoundment fish populations in the silting basin below Wister Dam. Proc. Oklahoma Acad. Sci., **32**: 1–6.

HAMILTON, H. L., 1941. The biological action of rotenone on fresh-water animals. Proc. Iowa Acad. Sci., **48**: 467–479.

HANCOCK, H. M. 1954. Investigations and experimentation relative to winter aggregations of fishes of Canton Reservoir, Oklahoma. Oklahoma Agr. and Mech. Coll., Research Foundation Publ. No. 58, 104 p. (Mimeo.)

HARBAUGH, M. J. 1937. On the occurrence of freshwater medusae in Kansas. Trans. Amer. Microscop. Soc., **56**: 116.

HARLAN, J. R., AND E. B. SPEAKER. 1956. Iowa fish and fishing. 3rd ed. State of Iowa, Des Moines. 377 p.

HARRISON, H. M. 1950. Use by fish of the modified Denil fishway in the Des Moines River. Proc. Iowa Acad. Sci., **57**: 449–456.

HAYDEN, A. A. 1948. A quarterly standard mineral analysis of the waters of four Iowa lakes in the Ruthven area. Proc. Iowa Acad. Sci., **55**: 171–177.

HEATON, J. R. 1955. The ecology and succession of a group of acid and alkaline strip-mine lakes in Central Missouri. M.A. Thesis, Univ. Missouri.

HEATON, J. R., AND O. E. ORR. 1956. Preliminary surveys of public power and irrigation reservoirs in Nebraska with special reference to the fish populations. 18th Midwestern Wildl. Conf., Lansing, Michigan, 23 p. (Mimeo.)

HEMPSTEAD, D. R., AND T. L. JAHN. 1940. The Protozoa of Silver Lake bog. Proc. Iowa Acad. Sci., **46**: 413–416.

HENDRICKS, L. J. 1955. The effect of carp (*Cyprinus carpio*) on the limnology of central Missouri farm ponds. Ph.D. Thesis, Univ. Missouri.

———. 1956. Growth of the smallmouth buffalo in carp ponds. Progr. Fish-Cult., **18**: 45–46.

HENNEMUTH, R. C. 1955. Growth of crappies, bluegill, and warmouth in Lake Ahquabi, Iowa. Iowa State Coll. J. Sci., **30**: 119–137.

HOOPES, D. T. 1960. Utilization of mayflies and caddisflies by some Mississippi River fishes. Trans. Amer. Fish. Soc., **89**: 32–34.

HORNUFF, L. E. 1957. A survey of four Oklahoma streams with reference to production. Oklahoma Fish. Research Lab., Rept. 62, 22 p.

HOUSER, A. 1957. A study of the commercial fishery of Lake Texoma. Oklahoma Fish. Research Lab., Rept. 63, 1–32.

———. 1959. Fish population estimates in Crystal Lake, Cleveland County, Oklahoma. Proc. Oklahoma Acad. Sci., **39**: 191–195.

HOUSER, A., AND W. R. HEARD. 1958. A one-year creel census on Fort Gibson Reservoir. Proc. Oklahoma Acad. Sci., **38**: 137–146.

HOWARD, A. D. 1914. Experiments in propagation of fresh-water mussels of the Quadrula group. U.S. Bur. Fish. Document 801: 1–52.

HUNGERFORD, H. B. 1919. The biology and ecology of aquatic and semiaquatic Hemiptera. Univ. Kansas Sci. Bull., **11**: 3–341.

———. 1922. The Nepidae in North America north of Mexico. Univ. Kansas Sci. Bull., **14**: 425–469.

———. 1933. The genus *Notonecta* of the world. Univ. Kansas Sci. Bull., **21**: 5–195.

———. 1948. The Corixidae of the Western Hemisphere. Univ. Kansas Sci. Bull., **32**: 1–827.

HUNGERFORD, H. B., P. J. SPANGLER, AND N. A. WALKER. 1955. Subaquatic light traps for insects and other animal organisms. Trans. Kansas Acad. Sci., **58**: 387–407.

HUS, H. T. A. 1908. An ecological cross section of the Mississippi River in the region of St. Louis, Missouri. Ann. Rept. Missouri Botan. Garden, **19**: 127–258.

HUSSEY, K. M., AND H. L. ZIMMERMAN. 1954. Rate of meander development as exhibited by two streams in Story County, Iowa. Proc. Iowa Acad. Sci., **60**: 390–392.

IOWA NATURAL RESOURCES COUNCIL. 1953. An inventory of water resources and water problems, Des Moines River Basin, Iowa. Bull. 1: 1–63.

———. 1955a. An inventory of water resources and water problems, Nishnabotna River Basin, Iowa. Bull. 2: 1–61.

———. 1955b. An inventory of water resources and water problems, Iowa-Cedar River Basin, Iowa. Bull. 3: 1–94.

———. 1956a. An inventory of water resources and water problems, Floyd-Big Sioux River basins, Iowa. Bull. 4: 1–56.

———. 1956b. Report of the Iowa Study Committee of water rights and drainage laws. State of Iowa, State House, Des Moines. 30 p.

———. 1957. An inventory of water resources and water problems, Skunk River Basin, Iowa. Bull. 5: 1–65.

———. 1958a. An inventory of water resources and

water problems, Southern Iowa River Basins. Bull. 6: 1–70.

———. 1958b. An inventory of water resources and water problems, Northeastern Iowa River Basins. Bull. 7: 1–74.

———. 1959. An inventory of water resources and water problems, Western Iowa River Basins. Bull 8: 1–86.

IRWIN, W. H. 1945. Methods of precipitating colloidal soil particles from impounded waters of central Oklahoma. Bull. Oklahoma Agr. and Mech. Coll., **42**(11), 16 p.

———. 1946. Some successful methods of clearing impounded waters of turbidities due to silt. Proc. Texas Acad. Sci., **29**: 241–243.

IRWIN, W. H., AND J. H. STEVENSON. 1951. Physiochemical nature of clay turbidity with special reference to clarification and productivity of impounded waters. Bull. Oklahoma Agr. and Mech. Coll., **49**(3), 54 p.

ISELY, F. B. 1914. Experimental study of the growth and migration of fresh-water mussels. U.S. Bur. Fish. Document 792: 1–24.

JACKSON, S. W., JR. 1958. Summary of a three-year creel census on Lake Eucha and Spavinaw Lake, Oklahoma, with comparisons of other Oklahoma reservoirs. Proc. Oklahoma Acad. Sci., **38**: 146–154.

JAHN, T. L., AND A. B. TAYLOR. 1940. The temperature cycle in Okoboji lakes. Proc. Iowa Acad. Sci., **46**: 403–406.

JENKINS, R. M. 1951. A fish population study of Claremore City Lake. Proc. Oklahoma Acad. Sci., **30**: 84–93.

———. 1953. Growth histories of the principal fishes in Grand Lake (O' the Cherokees), Oklahoma, through thirteen years of impoundment. Oklahoma Fish. Research Lab., Rept. 34: 1–87.

———. 1956a. An estimate of the fish population in a fifty-five-year-old Oklahoma pond. Proc. Oklahoma Acad. Sci., **35**: 69–76.

———. 1956b. The effect of gizzard shad on the fish population of a small Oklahoma lake. Trans. Amer. Fish. Soc., **85**: 58–74.

———. 1959. Some results of the partial fish population removal technique in lake management. Proc. Oklahoma Acad. Sci., **37**: 164–173.

JENKINS, R. M., AND E. M. LEONARD. 1954. Initial effects of impoundment on the growth rates of channel catfish in two Oklahoma reservoirs. Proc. Oklahoma Acad. Sci., **33**: 79–86.

JENKINS, R. M., E. M. LEONARD, AND G. E. HALL. 1952. An investigation of the fisheries resources of the Illinois River and pre-impoundment study of Tenkiller Reservoir, Oklahoma. Oklahoma Fish. Research Lab., Rept. 26, 136 p. (Mimeo.)

JEWELL, M. E. 1927. Aquatic biology of the prairie. Ecology, **8**: 289–298.

JOHNSON, L. P. 1944. Euglenae of Iowa. Trans. Amer. Microscop. Soc., **63**: 97–135.

JONES, D. T. 1941. Mollusks in the vicinity of Ames, Iowa. Iowa State Coll. J. Sci., **15**: 183–188.

JONES, E. N. 1925. *Ceratophyllum demersum* in West

Okoboji Lake. Proc. Iowa Acad. Sci., **32**: 181–188.

KATHREIN, J. W. 1953. An intensive creel census on Clearwater Lake, Missouri, during its first four years of impoundment, 1949–52. Trans. N. Amer. Wildl. Conf., **18**: 282–295.

KEETON, DEE. 1959. Limnological effects of introducing oil field brine into farm ponds to reduce the turbidity. Oklahoma Fish. Research Lab., Rept. 72: 1–47.

KENDREW, W. G. 1961. The climates of the continents. Oxford Univ. Press, London. 608 p.

KIENER, W. 1952. Concise review of eleven years fishing in the reservoir system of the Platte River in Nebraska. 14th Midwestern Wildl. Conf. (Mimeo.)

KNAPP, L. W. 1958. A distributional study of the fishes of the upper White River, Missouri. M.A. Thesis, Univ. Missouri.

KOFOID, C. A. 1908. The plankton of the Illinois River, 1894–99, with introductory notes upon the hydrography of the Illinois River and its basin. II. Bull. Illinois State Lab. Nat. Hist., **8**: 1–361.

KORSCHGEN, L. J., AND D. L. MOYLE. 1955. Food habits of the bullfrog in central Missouri farm ponds. Amer. Midland Nat., **52**: 332–341.

KUESTER, D. R. 1961. A creel census of underwater spearfishermen in Missouri Ozark Streams. M.A. Thesis, Univ. Missouri.

KUTKUHN, J. H. 1955. Food and feeding habits of some fishes in a dredged Iowa lake. Proc. Iowa Acad. Sci., **62**: 576–588.

———. 1958a. The plankton of North Twin Lake, with particular reference to the summer of 1955. Iowa State Coll. J. Sci., **32**: 419–450.

———. 1958b. Utilization of plankton by juvenile gizzard shad in a shallow prairie lake. Trans. Amer. Fish. Soc., **87**: 80–103.

———. 1958c. Utilization of gizzard shad by game fishes. Proc. Iowa Acad. Sci., **65**: 71–579.

———. 1958d. Notes on the precision of numerical and volumetric plankton estimates from small-sample concentrates. Limnol. Oceanogr., **3**: 69–83.

LANE, C. E., JR. 1954. Age and growth of the bluegill, *Lepomis m. macrochirus* (Rafinesque), in a new Missouri impoundment. J. Wildl. Mgmt., **18**: 358–365.

LARRABEE, A. P. 1926. An ecological study of the fishes of the Lake Okoboji region. Univ. Iowa Studies Nat. Hist., 11(12): 1–35.

LEAKE, D. B. 1945. The algae of Crystal Lake, Cleveland County, Oklahoma. Amer. Midland Nat., **34**: 750–768.

LEATHERS, A. L. 1922. Ecological study of aquatic midges and some related insects with special reference to feeding habits. Bull. U.S. Bur. Fish., **38**: 1–61.

LEFEVRE, G., AND W. C. CURTIS. 1908. Experiments in the artificial propagation of fresh-water mussels. Bull. U.S. Bur. Fish., **28**: 617–626.

LEONARD, A. B., AND L. H. PONDER. 1949. Crustacea in eastern Kansas. Trans. Kansas Acad. Sci., **52**: 168–204.

LEONARD, E. M., AND K. E. SNEED. 1951. Instrument

to cut catfish spines for age and growth determinations. Progr. Fish-Cult., **13**: 232.

LEWIS, W. M. 1949a. The use of vertebrae as indicators of the age of the northern black bullhead, *Ameiurus m. melas* (Rafinesque). Iowa State Coll. J. Sci., **22**: 209–218.

———. 1949b. Fisheries investigations on two artificial lakes in southern Iowa. I. Limnology. Iowa State Coll. J. Sci., **23**: 355–361.

———. 1950a. Fisheries investigations on two artificial lakes in southern Iowa. II. Fish populations. Iowa State Coll. J. Sci., **24**: 287–324.

———. 1950b. Fisheries investigations on two artificial lakes in southern Iowa. III. History and creel census. Iowa State Coll. J. Sci., **24**: 405–420.

LEWIS, W. M., AND K. D. CARLANDER. 1949. A simple method of mounting scales. Progr. Fish-Cult., **11**: 263.

LINSLEY, R. K., JR., M. A. KOHLER, AND J. L. H. PAULHUS. 1958. Hydrology for engineers. McGraw-Hill, New York. 340 + xvi p.

LINTON, J. R. 1959. A study of a stream population of green sunfish. M.A. Thesis, Univ. Missouri.

LOOMIS, R. H., AND W. H. IRWIN. 1954. A report of a study designed to determine the depth distribution of fishes in relation to vertical temperature. Oklahoma Agr. and Mech. Coll., Research Foundation Publ. No. 56, 20 p. (Mimeo.)

LORENTZ, P. 1938. The river. Stackpole & Sons, New York. 64 p.

LOWRY, E. M. 1951. A nomograph for rapid back-calculation of fish lengths. Progr. Fish-Cult., **13**: 199–204.

LUEBBERS, R. H. (ed.). 1959. Proceedings of the fifth annual air and water pollution conference. Univ. Missouri Engr. Expt. Sta., Bull. 47, 54 p.

McCALLUM, G. E. 1960. The role of water quality. Proc. Iowa Acad. Sci., **67**: 55–65.

McCANN, J. A. 1959. Life history studies of the spottail shiner of Clear Lake, Iowa, with particular reference to some sampling problems. Trans. Amer. Fish. Soc., **88**: 336–343.

———. 1960. Estimates of the fish populations of Clear Lake, Iowa. Ph.D. Dissertation, Iowa State Univ., Ames, 163 p.

McCARRAHER, D. B., O. E. ORR, C. P. AGEE, G. R. FOSTER, AND M. O. STEEN. 1961. Sandhill lake survey. Job No. 2, Dingell-Johnson F-4-R, Nebraska Game, Forest., and Parks Comm., Lincoln, Nebraska, 83 p. (Mimeo.)

McCOY, H. A. 1955. The rate of growth of flathead catfish in twenty-one Oklahoma lakes. Proc. Oklahoma Acad. Sci., **34**: 47–52.

McDONALD, MALCOLM. 1940a. The distribution of zooplankton in Lake Okoboji. Proc. Iowa Acad. Sci., **46**: 455–456.

———. 1940b. A key to species of *Cyclops* in Iowa. Proc. Iowa Acad. Sci., **46**: 373–381.

McLEOD, A. M., AND P. NEMENYI. 1940. An investigation of fishways. Univ. Iowa Studies Engr., Bull. No. 24: 1–72.

MACKIN, J. G. 1931. V. Studies on the Crustacea of

Oklahoma: Notes on the cladoceran fauna. Proc. Oklahoma Acad. Sci., 11: 22–28.

———. 1935. Studies on the Crustacea of Oklahoma. III. Subterranean amphipods of the genera *Niphargus* and *Boruta*. Trans. Amer. Microscop. Soc., 54: 41–51.

———. 1939. Key to the species of Phyllopoda of Oklahoma and neighboring states. Proc. Oklahoma Acad. Sci., 19: 45–47.

MARSHALL, RUTH. 1926. Water mites of the Okoboji region. Univ. Iowa Studies Nat. Hist., 11(9): 28–35.

MARTIN, M. 1954. Age and growth of the goldeye, *Hiodon alosoides* (Rafinesque), of Lake Texoma, Oklahoma. Proc. Oklahoma Acad. Sci., 33: 37–49.

MARTIN, R. G., AND R. S. CAMPBELL. 1953. The small fishes of Black River and Clearwater Lake, Missouri. Univ. Missouri Studies, 26(2): 45–66.

MARZOLF, R. C. 1955. Use of pectoral spines and vertebrae for determining age and rate of growth of the channel catfish. J. Wildl. Mgmt., 19: 243–249.

MATHERS, C. K. 1948. The leeches of the Okoboji region. Proc. Iowa Acad. Sci., 55: 397–425.

MAUPIN, J. K., J. R. WELLS, JR., AND C. LEIST. 1954. A preliminary survey of food habits of the fish and physicochemical conditions of the water of three strip-mine lakes. Trans. Kansas Acad. Sci., 57: 164–171.

MAYHEW, J. 1959. The use of toxaphene as a fish poison in strip mine ponds with varying physical and chemical characteristics. Proc. Iowa Acad. Sci., 66: 513–517.

METZLER, D. F. 1956. Use, misuse and future use of water in Kansas. Trans. Kansas Acad. Sci., 59: 111–117.

MEYER, F. P. 1960. Life history of *Marsipometra hastata* and the biology of its host, *Polyodon spathula*. Ph.D. Dissertation, Iowa State Univ., Ames, 145 p.

MINCKLEY, W. L. 1956. A fish survey of the Pillsbury Crossing Area, Deep Creek, Riley County, Kansas. Trans. Kansas Acad. Sci., 59: 351–357.

———. 1959. Fishes of the Big Blue River Basin, Kansas. Univ. Kansas Publ. Museum Nat. Hist., 11: 401–442.

MINCKLEY, W. L., AND J. E. DEACON. 1959. New distributional records for three species of Kansas crayfish. Trans. Kansas Acad. Sci., 62: 165.

MOEN, T. 1951. Hydra in an Iowa nursery lake. Proc. Iowa Acad. Sci., 58: 501–506.

———. 1954. Food habits of the carp in northwest Iowa lakes. Proc. Iowa Acad. Sci., 60: 665–686.

———. 1956. Stratification of Iowa artificial lakes. Proc. Iowa Acad. Sci., 63: 714–720.

———. 1959. Sexing channel catfish. Trans. Amer. Fish. Soc., 88: 149–150.

MOORE, G. A., AND D. H. BUCK. 1955. The fishes of the Chikaskia River in Oklahoma and Kansas. Proc. Oklahoma Acad. Sci., 34: 19–27.

MOORE, G. A., AND J. M. PADEN. 1950. The fishes of the Illinois River in Oklahoma and Arkansas. Amer. Midland Nat., 44: 76–95.

MOORMAN, R. B. 1957a. Some factors related to success of fish populations in Iowa farm ponds. Trans. Amer. Fish. Soc., 86: 361–370.

———. 1957b. Reproduction and growth of fishes in Marion County, Iowa, farm ponds. Iowa State Coll. J. Sci., 32: 71–88.

MUNCY, R. J. 1958. Movements of channel catfish in Des Moines River, Boone County, Iowa. Iowa State Coll. J. Sci., 32: 563–571.

MYERS, P. C. 1898. Preliminary report on the diatoms of Iowa. Proc. Iowa Acad. Sci., 6: 47–52.

NEAL, R. A. 1962. White and black crappies in Clear Lake, summer, 1960. Proc. Iowa Acad. Sci., 68: 247–253.

NEMENYI, P. 1941. An annotated bibliography of fishways. Univ. Iowa Studies Engr., Bull. No. 23: 1–72.

O'CONNELL, T. R., JR., AND R. S. CAMPBELL. 1953. The benthos of Black River and Clearwater Lake, Missouri. Univ. Missouri Studies, 26(2): 25–41.

ORTENBURGER, A. I., AND C. L. HUBBS. 1926. A report on the fishes of Oklahoma, with descriptions of new genera and species. Proc. Oklahoma Acad. Sci., 6: 123–141.

OWEN, J. B. 1956. Invertebrate fish food from dredged and undredged portions of North Twin Lake. Ph.D. Dissertation, Iowa State Univ., Ames, 168 p.

———. 1958. The erosion-littoral zone of North Twin Lake, and its relation to dredging. Iowa State Coll. J. Sci., 33: 91–102.

PALMER, E. L. 1919. An ecological study of Dry Run, a typical prairie stream. I. Fishes. Proc. Iowa Acad. Sci., 26: 111–124.

PALOUMPIS, A. A. 1957. The effects of drought conditions on the fish and bottom organisms of two small oxbow ponds. Trans. Illinois Acad. Sci., 50: 60–64.

———. 1958a. Responses of some minnows to flood and drought conditions in an intermittent stream. Iowa State Coll. J. Sci., 32: 547–561.

———. 1958b. Measurement of some factors affecting the catch in a minnow seine. Proc. Iowa Acad. Sci., 65: 580–586.

PARSONS, J. D. 1956. Factors influencing excessive flows of coal strip-mine effluents. Trans. Illinois Acad. Sci., 49: 25–33.

———. 1957. Literature pertaining to formation of acid-mine wastes and their effects on the chemistry and fauna of streams. Trans. Illinois Acad. Sci., 50: 49–59.

PARSONS, J. D., AND R. S. CAMPBELL. 1961. Metabolism of a eutrophic reservoir. Proc. Intern. Assoc. Limnol., 14: 613–618.

PARSONS, J. W. 1950. Life history of the yellow perch, *Perca flavescens* (Mitchill), of Clear Lake, Iowa. Iowa State Coll. J. Sci., 25: 83–97.

———. 1951. Growth studies of the yellow perch, *Perca flavescens* (Mitchill), in three northwest Iowa lakes. Iowa State Coll. J. Sci., 25: 495–500.

PATRIARCHE, M. H. 1953. The fishery in Lake Wappapello, a flood-control reservoir on the St. Francis River, Missouri. Trans. Amer. Fish. Soc., 82: 242–254.

PATRIARCHE, M. H., AND R. S. CAMPBELL. 1958. The development of the fish population in a new flood-control reservoir in Missouri, 1948 to 1954. Trans. Amer. Fish. Soc., 87: 240–258.

PATRIARCHE, M. H., AND E. M. LOWRY. 1953. Age and rate of growth of five species of fish in Black River, Missouri. Univ. Missouri Studies, 26(2): 85–109.

PAUL, C. H. 1935. Inventory of the water resources of the Mississippi River drainage area. Nat. Resources Board, Washington, D.C., 64 p. (Abstract)

PEARCY, W. G. 1953. Some limnological features of Clear Lake, Iowa. Iowa State Coll. J. Sci., 28: 189–207.

PENFOUND, W. T. 1953. Plant communities of Oklahoma lakes. Ecology, 34: 561–583.

PETRY, E. J. 1936. The biota of the Cedar River as related to odor and taste production. Proc. Iowa Acad. Sci., 43: 123–126.

PLATNER, W. S. 1946. Water quality studies of the Mississippi River. U.S. Fish and Wildl. Serv., Spec. Sci. Rept. No. 30, 77 p. (Multilith.)

POOLE, R. L. 1961. A creel census of underwater spearfishermen in two Missouri reservoirs. M.A. Thesis, Univ. Missouri.

PRESCOTT, G. W. 1931. Iowa algae. Univ. Iowa Studies Nat. Hist., 13(6): 1–235.

———. 1939. Some relationships of phytoplankton to limnology and aquatic biology. Amer. Assoc. Advance. Sci., Publ. No. 10: 65–78.

———. 1948. Objectionable algae with reference to the killing of fish and other animals. Hydrobiologia, 1: 1–13.

PRESCOTT, G. W., AND T. F. ANDREWS. 1955. A new species of *Anabaenopsis* in a Kansas lake with notes on limnology. Hydrobiologia, 7: 60–63.

PROCTOR, V. W. 1957. Some controlling factors in the distribution of *Haematococcus pluvialis*. Ecology, 38: 457–462.

PROPHET, C. W. 1957. Seasonal variations and abundance of Cladocera and Copepoda of the Fall and Verdigris rivers in Wilson and Montgomery counties, Kansas. Emporia State Research Studies, 5(3): 5–29.

PROPHET, C. W., T. F. ANDREWS, AND C. E. GOULDEN. 1959. Annotated check list of the Cladocera and Copepoda of Lyon County, Kansas. Southwestern Naturalist, 4: 185–194.

PURKETT, C. A., JR. 1958a. Growth of the fishes in the Salt River, Missouri. Trans. Amer. Fish. Soc., 87: 116–131.

———. 1958b. Growth rates of Missouri stream fishes. Fed. Aid Fish Restoration Program, D-J Proj. No. Mo. F-1-R, 46 p.

———. 1961. Reproduction and early development of the paddlefish. Trans. Amer. Fish. Soc., 90: 125–129.

RATZLAFF, W. 1952. The limnology of some roadside ditches in Chase and Lyon counties, Kansas. Emporia State Research Studies, 1(1): 1–32.

REID, G. K. 1961. Ecology of inland waters and estuaries. Reinhold Publ. Corp., New York. 375 p.

RIDENHOUR, R. L. 1957. Northern pike, *Esox lucius* L., population of Clear Lake, Iowa. Iowa State Coll. J. Sci., 32: 1–18.

———. 1960. Development of a program to sample young fish in a lake. Trans. Amer. Fish. Soc., 89: 185–192.

RIDENHOUR, R. L., AND C. J. DI COSTANZO. 1956. Nylon vs. linen gill nets at Clear Lake, Iowa. Proc. Iowa Acad. Sci., 63: 700–704.

RIGGS, C. D. 1955. Collecting fish by combined use of a seine and an electric shocker. Proc. Oklahoma Acad. Sci., 34: 30–32.

RIGGS, C. D., AND V. E. DOWELL. 1956. Recent changes in the fish fauna of Lake Texoma. Proc. Oklahoma Acad. Sci., 35: 37–39.

RIGGS, C. D., AND R. SMITHPETER. 1954. The fish population of a small, periodically inundated island pond in Lake Texoma, Oklahoma. Proc. Oklahoma Acad. Sci., 33: 49–55.

ROGERS, N. F. 1951. Strip-mined lands of the Western Interior Coal Province. Univ. Missouri Agr. Expt. Sta., Research Bull. 475, 55 p.

ROSE, E. T. 1949a. The population of yellow pike-perch (*Stizostedion v. vitreum*) in Spirit Lake, Iowa. Trans. Amer. Fish. Soc., 77: 32–42.

———. 1949b. A fish population study of Storm Lake. Proc. Iowa Acad. Sci., 56: 385–395.

———. 1951. A lightweight pulling engine for seines. Progr. Fish-Cult., 13: 99–100.

———. 1954a. Toxic algae in Iowa lakes. Proc. Iowa Acad. Sci., 60: 738–745.

———. 1954b. Bluegreen algae control at Storm Lake. Proc. Iowa Acad. Sci., 61: 604–614.

———. 1955. The fluctuation in abundance of walleyes in Spirit Lake, Iowa. Proc. Iowa Acad. Sci., 62: 567–575.

ROSE, E. T., AND T. MOEN. 1951. Results of increased fish harvest in Lost Island Lake. Trans. Amer. Fish. Soc., 80: 50–55.

ROSE, E. T., AND T. MOEN. 1953. The increase in game-fish populations in East Okoboji Lake, Iowa, following intensive removal of rough fish. Trans. Amer. Fish. Soc., 82: 104–114.

ROSS, H. H. 1944. The caddis flies, or Trichoptera, of Illinois. Bull. Illinois Nat. Hist. Surv., 23 (Article 1): 1–326.

RUHR, C. E. 1952. Fish population of a mining pit lake, Marion County, Iowa. Iowa State Coll. J. Sci., 27: 55–77.

RUSSELL, R. J. 1944. The Mississippi River. Univ. Social Studies Ser., Louisiana State Univ., Baton Rouge, Louisiana: 1–120.

SANDERSON, M. W. 1938. A monographic revision of the North American species of *Stenelmis* (Dryopidae: Coleoptera). Kansas Univ. Sci. Bull., 25: 635–717.

SANDOZ, O'R. 1958. Fish population studies on three Wichita Mountains Wildlife Refuge lakes. Proc. Oklahoma Acad. Sci., 38: 173–177.

———. 1959. Changes in the fish population of Lake Murray following the reduction of gizzard shad numbers. Proc. Oklahoma Acad. Sci., 37: 174–181.

———. 1960. Suggestions for conducting pre-impoundment fishery surveys. Proc. Oklahoma Acad. Sci., **40**: 144–147.

SCHNEBERGER, E., AND M. E. JEWELL. 1928. Factors affecting pond fish production. Kansas Forest., Fish and Game Comm., Bull. **9**: 5–14.

SCHOEWE, W. H. 1953. The geography of Kansas. III. Hydrogeography. Trans. Kansas Acad. Sci., **56**: 131–190.

SCHOONOVER, R. E., AND J. L. COATES. n.d. Southeastern Kansas strip-pit study. Kansas Forest., Fish and Game Comm., 16 p. (Mimeo.)

SHAWHAN, F. M., L. JOHNSON, AND T. JAHN. 1947. Protozoa of Iowa. Proc. Iowa Acad. Sci., **54**: 353–368.

SHIMEK, B. 1897. Notes on aquatic plants from northern Iowa. Proc. Iowa Acad. Sci., **4**: 77–81.

———. 1915. The Mollusca of the Okoboji region. Bull. Univ. Iowa, **7**: 70–88.

———. 1924. Drainage in Iowa. Proc. Iowa Acad. Sci., **31**: 149–155.

———. 1935. The effect of pollution on mollusks in Iowa. Nautilus, **48**: 104–111.

SHOWALTER, W. V. 1952. *Placosphaera opaca:* Its morphology and life history. Trans. Kansas Acad. Sci., **55**: 113–119.

SIEH, J. G., AND J. PARSONS. 1950. Activity patterns of some Clear Lake, Iowa, fishes. Proc. Iowa Acad. Sci., **57**: 511–518.

SIGLER, W. F. 1948. Aquatic and shore vegetation of Spirit Lake, Dickinson County, Iowa. Iowa State Coll. J. Sci., **23**: 103–124.

———. 1949. Life history of the white bass, *Lepibema chrysops* (Rafinesque), of Spirit Lake, Iowa. Iowa State Coll. Agr. Expt. Sta., Research Bull. **366**: 203–244.

SIGLER, W. F., AND T. MOEN. 1947. A shallow-water diving rig. Copeia, 1947(2): 85–88.

SIMPSON, G. M. 1961. Chemical composition of strip-mine lakes waters. M.A. Thesis, Pittsburgh State Coll., Pittsburgh, Kansas, 98 p.

SMALL, L. F. 1961a. Some aspects of plankton population dynamics in Clear Lake, Iowa. Ph.D. Dissertation, Iowa State Univ., Ames.

———. 1961b. An optical density method of measuring phytoplankton standing crop. Iowa State Coll. J. Sci., **35**: 343–354.

SMITH, G. M. 1926. The plankton algae of the Okoboji region. Trans. Amer. Microscop. Soc., **45**: 156–233.

SMITH, P. E., AND R. V. BOVBJERG. 1958. Pilot Knob bog as a habitat. Proc. Iowa Acad. Sci., **65**: 546–553.

SNEED, K. E. 1951. A method for calculating the growth of channel catfish, *Ictalurus lacustris punctatus.* Trans. Amer. Fish. Soc., **80**: 174–183.

SNEED, K. E., AND H. P. CLEMENS. 1956. Survival of fish sperm after freezing and storage at low temperatures. Progr. Fish-Cult., **18**: 99–103.

SNEED, K. E., AND H. P. CLEMENS. 1959. The use of human chorionic gonadotrophin to spawn warmwater fishes. Progr. Fish-Cult., **21**: 117–121.

SNEED, K. E., AND H. P. CLEMENS. 1960a. Use of fish pituitaries to induce spawning in channel cat-

fish. U.S. Fish and Wildl. Serv., Spec. Sci. Rept. No. 329, Fish. Ser.: 1–12.

SNEED, K. E., AND H. P. CLEMENS. 1960b. Hormone spawning of warm-water fishes: Its practical and biological significance. Progr. Fish-Cult., **22**: 109–113.

SPRUGEL, GEORGE, JR. 1951a. An extreme case of thermal stratification and its effect on fish distribution. Proc. Iowa Acad. Sci., **58**: 563–566.

———. 1951b. Vertical distribution of *Stentor coeruleus* in relation to dissolved oxygen levels in an Iowa pond. Ecology, **32**: 147–149.

———. 1954. Growth of bluegills in a new lake, with particular reference to false annuli. Trans. Amer. Fish. Soc., **83**: 58–75.

———. 1955. The growth of green sunfish (*Lepomis cyanellus*) in Little Wall Lake, Iowa. Iowa State Coll. J. Sci., **29**: 707–719.

STARRETT, W. C. 1950a. Food relationships of the minnows of the Des Moines River, Iowa. Ecology, **31**: 216–233.

———. 1950b. Distribution of the fishes of Boone County, Iowa, with special reference to the minnows and darters. Amer. Midland Nat., **43**: 112–127.

———. 1951. Some factors affecting the abundance of minnows in the Des Moines River, Iowa. Ecology, **32**: 13–27.

STARRETT, W. C., AND P. G. BARNICKOL. 1955. Efficiency and selectivity of commercial fishing devices used on the Mississippi River. Illinois Nat. Hist. Surv. Bull., **26**: 325–366.

STARRETT, W. C., AND RUTH PATRICK. 1952. Net plankton and bottom microflora of the Des Moines River, Iowa. Proc. Acad. Nat. Sci., Philadelphia, **54**: 219–243.

STEELE, M. 1902. The crayfish of Missouri. Univ. Cincinnati Bull., **10**: 1–53.

STOCKINGER, N. F., AND H. A. HAYS. 1960. Plankton, benthos, and fish in three strip-mine lakes with varying *p*H values. Trans. Kansas Acad. Sci., **63**: 1–11.

STROMSTEN, F. A. 1917. A list of Entomostraca from the Okoboji region. Proc. Iowa Acad. Sci., **24**: 309–310.

———. 1920a. Cladocera of the Okoboji region. Proc. Iowa Acad. Sci., **27**: 265–268.

———. 1920b. Copepoda of the Okoboji region. Proc. Iowa Acad. Sci., **27**: 269–270.

———. 1923. A new apparatus for measuring deep water temperatures. Proc. Iowa Acad. Sci., **30**: 139–142.

———. 1926. Temperature studies of Lake Okoboji for 1925. Proc. Iowa Acad. Sci., **33**: 299–302.

———. 1927. Lake Okoboji as a type of aquatic environment. Univ. Iowa Studies Nat. Hist., **12**(5): 1–52.

SULLIVAN, K. C. 1929. Notes on the aquatic life of the Niangua River, Missouri, with special reference to insects. Ecology, **10**: 322–325.

SUMMERS, P. B. 1954. Some observations on limnology and fish distribution in the Illinois River below Tenkiller Reservoir. Proc. Oklahoma Acad. Sci., **35**: 15–20.

SURBER, T. 1913. Notes on the natural hosts of fresh-water mussels. Bull. U.S. Bur. Fish., **32**: 103–116.

———. 1915. Identification of the glochidia of fresh-water mussels. U.S. Bur. Fish. Document 813: 1–9.

SWINEFORD, ADA, AND J. C. FRYE. 1955. Notes on Waconda or Great Spirit Spring, Mitchell County, Kansas. Trans. Kansas Acad. Sci., **58**: 265–270.

TAFT, C. E. 1934. Desmids of Oklahoma. Trans. Amer. Microscop. Soc., **53**: 95–101.

TAYLOR, A. B., AND T. L. JAHN. 1940. Absorption of light in the Okoboji lakes. Proc. Iowa Acad. Sci., **46**: 458–459.

TEBO, L. B., JR. 1955. Bottom fauna of a shallow eutrophic lake, Lizard Lake, Pocahontas County, Iowa. Amer. Midland Nat., **54**: 89–103.

THOMPSON, R. 1938. A preliminary survey of the fresh-water algae of eastern Kansas. Univ. Kansas Sci. Bull., **25**: 1–83.

THOMPSON, W. H. 1950. Investigation of the fisheries resources of Grand Lake. Oklahoma Game and Fish Dept., Fish. Mgmt. Rept. 18, 46 p. (Mimeo.)

———. 1951. The age and growth of white bass, *Lepibema chrysops* (Rafinesque), in Lake Overholser and Lake Hefner, Oklahoma. Proc. Oklahoma Acad. Sci., **30**: 101–110.

———. 1955. Problems of reservoir management. Trans. Amer. Fish. Soc., **84**: 39–46.

TIEMEIER, O. W. 1951. Studies on Kanopolis Reservoir in 1950. Trans. Kansas Acad. Sci., **54**: 175–189.

TIEMEIER, O. W., AND J. B. ELDER. 1957. Limnology of Flint Hills farm ponds for 1956 and preliminary report on growth studies of fishes. Trans. Kansas Acad. Sci., **60**: 379–392.

TIEMEIER, O. W., AND R. B. MOORMAN. 1957. Limnological observations on some Flint Hills farm ponds. Trans. Kansas Acad. Sci., **60**: 167–173.

TIFFANY, L. H. 1926. The filamentous algae of northwestern Iowa with special reference to the Oedogoniaceae. Trans. Amer. Microscop. Soc., **45**: 69–132.

TILTON, J. R. 1916. Records of oscillations in lake level, and records of lake temperature and meteorology secured at the MacBride Lakeside Laboratory, Lake Okoboji, Iowa, July, 1915. Proc. Iowa Acad. Sci., **23**: 91–102.

U.S. DEPARTMENT OF HEALTH, EDUCATION, AND WELFARE, Division of Water Pollution Control. 1953. A comprehensive program for control of water pollution in the Missouri River Drainage Basin. 123 p.

U.S. WAR DEPARTMENT CORPS OF ENGINEERS. 1935. Missouri River. 73rd Congress, 2nd Session.

———. 1946. Improvements of the Missouri River for navigation. 4th revision. Kansas City, Missouri.

———. 1948. The middle and upper Mississippi River. U.S. Govt. Printing Office, Washington, D.C.

———. 1958. Stages and discharges of the Mississippi River and its outlets and tributaries. Mississippi River Comm., Vicksburg, Mississippi, 278 p.

UTTERBACK, W. I. 1914. Mussel resources in Missouri. U.S. Bur. Fish., Econ. Circ. 10: 1–6.

VAN DER SCHALIE, HENRY, AND ANNETTE VAN DER SCHALIE. 1950. The mussels of the Mississippi River. Amer. Midland Nat., **44**: 448–466.

VAN ORMAN, C. R. 1956. Surface water—its control and retention for use. Trans. Kansas Acad. Sci., **59**: 105–110.

VINYARD, W. C. 1955. Epizoophytic algae from mollusks, turtles, and fish in Oklahoma. Proc. Oklahoma Acad. Sci., **34**: 63–65.

VIVIAN, E. L. 1932. Report on the Myxophyceae of Nebraska. Trans. Amer. Microscop. Soc., **51**: 79–128.

WALKER, C. R. 1959. Control of certain aquatic weeds in Missouri farm ponds. Weeds, **7**: 310–316.

WALLEN, I. E. 1949. The plankton population of a small fertile pond in central Oklahoma. Trans. Amer. Microscop. Soc., **68**: 200–205.

———. 1950. Thermal stratification in some eastern Oklahoma waters. Proc. Oklahoma Acad. Sci., **31**: 57–64.

———. 1951. The direct effect of turbidity on fishes. Oklahoma Agr. Bull., **48**(2): 1–27.

———. 1955. Some limnological considerations in the production of Oklahoma farm ponds. J. Wildl. Mgmt., **19**: 450–462.

WARD, H. C. 1951. A study of fish populations, with special reference to the white bass, *Lepibema chrysops* (Rafinesque), in Lake Duncan, Oklahoma. Proc. Oklahoma Acad. Sci., **30**: 69–84.

WARD, H. C., E. M. LEONARD, AND J. M. MARTIN. 1954. Farm ponds for fish in Oklahoma. Oklahoma Game and Fish Dept., 31 p.

WEBER, C. I. 1958. Some measurements of primary production in East and West Okoboji lakes, Dickinson County, Iowa. Proc. Iowa Acad. Sci., **65**: 166–173.

———. 1960. The measurement of carbon fixation in Clear Lake, Iowa, using carbon-14. Ph.D. Dissertation, Iowa State Univ., Ames, 65 p.

WEESE, A. O. 1951. Age and growth of *Lepibema chrysops* in Lake Texoma. Proc. Oklahoma Acad. Sci., **30**: 45–48.

WELLS, LLOYD. 1917. Odonata of Iowa. Proc. Iowa Acad. Sci., **24**: 327–333.

WELLS, P. H., AND A. WITT, JR. 1957. Recent collections of the albinistic cave crayfish, *Cambarus hubrichti*. Anat. Record, **128**: 640.

WEYER, A. E. 1940. The Lake of the Ozarks: A problem in fishery management. Progr. Fish-Cult., **51**: 1–10.

WHITNEY, R. R. 1958. Numbers of mature walleyes in Clear Lake, Iowa, 1952–53, as estimated by tagging. Iowa State Coll. J. Sci., **33**: 55–79.

WHITNEY, R. R., AND K. D. CARLANDER. 1956. Interpretation of body-scale regression for computing body length of fish. J. Wildl. Mgmt., **20**: 21–27.

WIEBE, A. H. 1928. Biological survey of the upper Mississippi River, with special reference to pollution. Bull. U.S. Bur. Fish., **43**: 137–167.

———. 1930. Investigations on plankton production in fish ponds. Bull. U.S. Bur. Fish., **46**: 137–176.

———. 1931*a*. Dissolved phosphorus and inorganic nitrogen in the water of the Mississippi River. Science, **73**: 652.

————. 1931b. Diurnal variation in amount of dissolved oxygen, alkalinity, and free ammonia in certain fish ponds at Fairport, Iowa. Ohio J. Sci., 31: 120–126.

WILLIAMS, A. B. 1952. Six new crayfishes of the genus Orconectes (Decapoda: Astacidae) from Arkansas, Missouri and Oklahoma. Trans. Kansas Acad. Sci., 55: 330–351.

WILLIS, H. 1959. Some limnological conditions of Turkey Creek and two ponds near Shawnee, Kansas, from June 8, 1957, to August 16, 1957. Trans. Kansas Acad. Sci., 62: 20–28.

WILSON, C. B. 1920. Dragonflies and damselflies in relation to pond culture, with a list of those found near Fairport, Iowa. Bull. U.S. Bur. Fish., 36: 182–264.

————. 1923a. Water beetles in relation to pondfish culture, with life histories of those found in fishponds at Fairport, Iowa. Bull. U.S. Bur. Fish., 39: 231–345.

————. 1923b. Life history of the scavenger water beetle, Hydrous (Hydrophilus) triangularis, and its economic relation to fish breeding. Bull. U.S. Bur. Fish., 39: 9–38.

WITT, A., JR. 1957. Seasonal variation in the incidence of lymphocystis in the white crappie from the Niangua Arm of the Lake of the Ozarks, Missouri. Trans. Amer. Fish. Soc., 85: 271–279.

————. 1960. Length and weight of ancient freshwater drum, Aplodinotus grunniens, calculated from otoliths found in Indian middens. Copeia, 1960(3): 181–185.

WITT, A., JR., AND R. S. CAMPBELL. 1959. Refinements of equipment and procedures in electrofishing. Trans. Amer. Fish. Soc., 88: 33–35.

WITT, A., JR., AND R. C. MARZOLF. 1954. Spawning and behavior of the longear sunfish, Lepomis megalotis megalotis. Copeia, 1954(3): 188–190.

WOOD, H. W., AND J. A. SHORT. 1950. Water resources, p. 58–78. In Missouri: Its resources, people, and institutions. Univ. Missouri.

WOODS, L. P., AND R. F. INGER. 1957. The cave, spring, and swamp fishes of the family Amblyopsidae of central and eastern United States. Amer. Midland Nat., 58: 232–256.

WYLIE, R. B. 1920. The major vegetation of Lake Okoboji. Proc. Iowa Acad. Sci., 27: 91–97.

ZELLER, H. D. 1953. Nitrogen and phosphorus concentrations in fertilized and unfertilized farm ponds in central Missouri. Trans. Amer. Fish. Soc., 82: 281–288.

————. 1955. A modification of the 1-naphthylamine-sulfanilic acid method for the determination of nitrites in low concentration. Analyst, 80(953): 632–633.

Robert W. Pennak

Rocky Mountain States

The five Rocky Mountain States form a region of great contrasts in climate, topography, and geochemistry; consequently it is an area presenting extreme ranges of limnological conditions. Nevertheless, at the outset, it must be admitted that this vast area of 517,000 mi² (1,341,000 km²) is limnologically poorly known, in spite of the fact that the earliest studies were published more than 60 years ago (Jordan, 1889; Evermann, 1891; Elrod, 1901).

Much of the region is traversed by extensive mountain ranges. Montana, with a mean elevation of 3,400 ft (1,037 m), is lowest of the five states, and Colorado, with a mean elevation of 6,800 ft (2,073 m), is highest. The approximate mean elevation of the whole region is 5,220 ft (1,591 m). The eastern halves of Montana, Wyoming, and Colorado, however, consist of relatively flat, semiarid High Plains, having an annual precipitation of only 10 to 18 in. (255 to 458 mm). To the west these plains often give way to foothills areas of varying width, and these, in turn, may rise to the montane and alpine areas still farther west. The Continental Divide runs generally in a northwest-southeast direction (Fig. 12.1), commonly at elevations exceeding 11,000 to 13,000 ft. The high elevations have a progressively greater annual precipitation, up to 30 or 40 in., or more. West of the Continental Divide the topography and climate are confused and heterogeneous. Much of the area is mountainous

Contribution No. 39, Limnology Laboratory, University of Colorado. This paper was organized and written during tenure of a University of Colorado Faculty Fellowship.

with high rainfall, such as northwestern Montana, much of Idaho, northwestern Wyoming, parts of Utah, and parts of the western half of Colorado. Arid and semiarid mesas, sometimes with intervening deep canyons, are common in Utah, southwestern Wyoming, and western Colorado. Extensive, low-lying deserts form a large part of Utah and smaller areas of western Colorado. (The Great Basin section of Utah is discussed in Chapter 13.) Irrigation along the valleys of larger streams and rivers has modified much of the local drainage pattern, ground water, and vegetation.

Mountain lakes

In contrast to such countries as Austria, the mountainous parts of the western United States have relatively few large *natural* lakes, considering the extensive area involved. Great Salt Lake is, of course, the largest body of water in the five states, with an area of about 1,750 mi² (4,533 km²). Other large lakes in Utah are Utah Lake (about 140 mi²) and Bear Lake (about 125 mi²) on the Idaho-Utah border. In Montana, the largest lake is Flathead with an area of 188 mi². In addition, Glacier National Park contains ten narrow, deep lakes, having areas ranging between about 2 and 9 mi² (Fig. 12.2). Northern Idaho contains three large lakes: Priest Lake has an area of about 37 mi², Coeur d'Alene 44 mi², and Pend Oreille is said to have an area of 180 mi² and a maximum depth exceeding 1,100 ft (335 m). In Wyoming there are three large lakes: Yellowstone has an area of 139 mi² (maximum depth 300 ft), Jackson Lake 40 mi², and Shoshone about 8 mi². Essentially all these large natural lakes are more than 60 m deep.

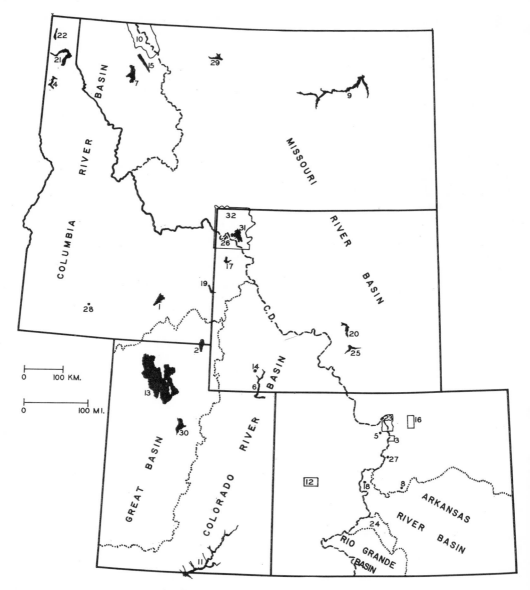

Fig. 12.1.—Reference map for the five states comprising the Rocky Mountain limnological region. *C.D.,* Continental Divide. Dotted lines separate major drainage systems. Numbered locations indicate areas of limnological interest mentioned or discussed in the text, as follows:

1. American Falls Reservoir.
2. Bear Lake.
3. Western portion of Boulder County, Colorado (details in Fig. 12.3).
4. Coeur d'Alene Lake.
5. Location of the main features of the Colorado-Big Thompson Reclamation Project (details in Fig. 12.16).
6. Flaming Gorge Reservoir.

7. Flathead Lake.
8. Location of Florissant lake fossil deposits.
9. Fort Peck Dam and Reservoir.
10. Glacier National Park.
11. Glen Canyon Reservoir.
12. Grand Mesa lake district (details in Fig. 12.5)
13. Great Salt Lake.
14. Center of rich fossiliferous area of Green River shales.

Fig. 12.2.—Waterton Lake, a long, narrow, deep lake
partly in Glacier National Park and partly in Canada.
Photo by the author.

In view of the generally high elevation of all
five states, the term "mountain lake" may have
quite a different meaning from this expression as
used, for example, in New England and Europe.
In our (strict) sense true mountain lakes are
bodies of water lying at elevations exceeding 1,700
m (5,576 ft), and the majority of bodies of water
in the mountainous sections of this region fall
into this category. Most of the lakes listed in
the foregoing paragraph, however, do not actually
qualify under this definition.

The vast majority of natural mountain lakes
have areas of less than 1 mi² (259 ha). The
largest of the many hundreds of mountain lakes
in the state of Colorado has an area of only
about 2.25 mi² (Lower Twin Lake); three others

have areas ranging between 1.0 and 1.6 mi². Indeed, it is probably safe to say that more than
half of our western mountain lakes have areas
of less than 40 acres (16 ha). Also, contrary to
popular opinion, the great majority of natural
mountain lakes have maximum depths of less than
8 m. Few are more than 15 m deep.

If, however, man-made bodies of water are
taken into consideration, the picture becomes
quite different, since many large and deep mountain reservoirs have been constructed, especially
during the past 30 years (e.g., Figs. 12.1, 12.16,
12.17). They function in varying degrees for irrigation, municipal water supplies, hydroelectric
power, more constant stream flow, and recreation.
Many have areas exceeding 10 mi² (2590 ha).

15. Hungry Horse Dam and Reservoir.
16. Typical irrigated plains area (details in Fig.
    12.13).
17. Jackson Lake.
18. Location of Lower Twin Lake.
19. Palisades Reservoir.
20. Pathfinder Reservoir.
21. Pend Oreille Lake.
22. Priest Lake.
23. Rocky Mountain National Park.

24. San Luis Valley, a closed drainage basin.
25. Seminoe Reservoir.
26. Shoshone Lake.
27. Location of Summit Lake.
28. Location of Thousand Springs.
29. Tiber Reservoir.
30. Utah Lake.
31. Yellowstone Lake.
32. Yellowstone National Park.

A typical high altitude drainage pattern is shown in Figure 12.3. Almost all the lakes are valley and gulch drainage lakes, with year-round inflows and outflows. Some of the small bodies of water near the Continental Divide are true "staircase" lakelets and ponds. A few small scattered bodies of water below timberline, e.g., Redrock and Muskee lakes (Figs. 12.3 and 12.4), have been called semidrainage lakes (Pennak, 1945). Limnologically these are quite distinct from drainage lakes, notably in their rich populations of invertebrates, growths of rooted aquatics, and lack of regular inflow and outflow.

Figure 12.5 shows the abundance of lakes occurring on Grand Mesa in west-central Colorado. Here the terrain is different from usual mountain country. It is a large, flat area, mostly between 9,000 and 10,000 ft in altitude and exceptionally

well watered and fertile. The lakes are highly diverse and unusually productive. A few semi-drainage lakes are to be found here also (Pennak, 1950).

In northern Colorado where lakes are numerous and readily accessible, it has been convenient to recognize four limnological zones with reference to altitude (Pennak, 1945, 1958a). The plains zone includes those areas below 1,700 m; the foothills zone extends from 1,700 to 2,500 m; montane zone, from 2,500 to 3,200 m; and alpine zone, above 3,200 m. Comparable altitudinal limnological zones can undoubtedly be recognized in other areas of the Mountain States, but little information is available in the literature. Like most zonal phenomena in mountains, there are several important determining ecological factors in addition to altitude *per se*, especially latitude,

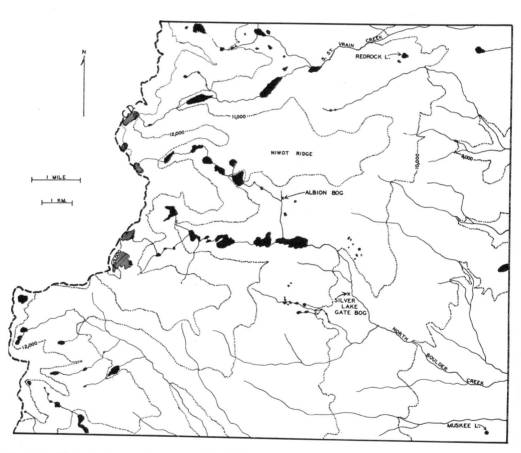

Fig. 12.3.—Major drainage patterns and altitudinal contours (in feet) of the west-central part of Boulder County, Colorado. Five small glaciers are shown by parallel hatching. *C.D.*, Continental Divide. From Pennak, 1963.

Fig. 12.4.—Redrock Lake, Colorado; a typical semi-drainage lake. Location shown in Figure 12.3. Photo by the author. From Pennak, 1963.

substrate, prevailing winds, insolation, temperature, precipitation, geochemistry, and general topography. These factors operate in varying degrees to determine some of the fundamental limnological features of lakes. In general the zones corresponding to the Colorado limnological zones are at lower elevations in higher Rocky Mountain latitudes, and timberline may be taken as a rough index of the relative zonal gradient. In southern Colorado, for example, timberline averages 3,660 m, in northern Colorado 3,500 m, in the Tetons of Wyoming 3,300 m, and in Glacier National

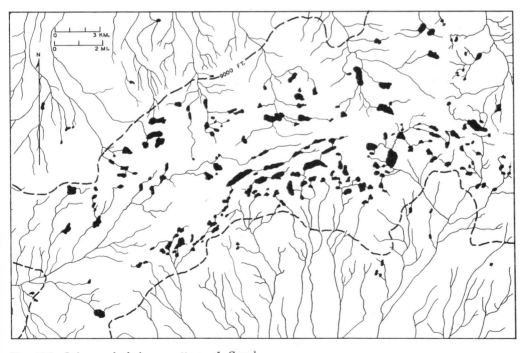

Fig. 12.5.—Lakes and drainage pattern of Grand Mesa, Colorado. Location shown in Figure 12.1. Modified from Pennak, 1950.

Fig. 12.6.—Pass Lake, a typical northern Colorado alpine lake, in early October. Photo by the author.

Park only 2,060 m. For definitive purposes, however, it will be necessary to restrict the discussion immediately following to the northern Colorado lake district and the specific altitudinal zones as indicated.

The alpine zone includes lakes in the upper spruce and fir forests, past timberline at 3,500 m, and through the tundra as high as 3,884 m. This is the altitude of Summit Lake, Colorado (Fig. 12.1: *27*); it is the second highest North American Lake of any size (26.1 acres). About 50 of the lakes and ponds shown in Figure 12.3 are in this zone. The typical alpine lake (Fig. 12.6) is a cold tarn with a rock, rubble, and gravel basin and nearby snowfields and glacierets, even in midsummer. The late-summer snowbanks often have pinkish areas of "watermelon snow" owing to dense populations of *Chlamydomonas nivalis,* a red-pigmented protist. Inflow and outflow are high, so that there is little opportunity for biological or chemical "aging" of the water. Lakes immediately below glacierets sometimes receive large loads of glacial milk, which make the lakes almost biological deserts. Commonly there is a complete or partial ice cover for eight or nine months per year, and the season of productivity is remarkably short and ill-defined. The total plankton is poor, averaging annually fewer than 100,000 phytoplankton cells, 60 rotifers, and 15 immature and adult entomostracans per liter. In exceptionally unproductive alpine lakes these figures may be as low as 10,000 phytoplankton cells, 10 rotifers, and 2 entomostracans. Little definitive published information is available concerning the bottom fauna, but casual studies by the present writer indicate an impoverished situation,

with sparse populations of dipteran larvae and little else. Rooted aquatics are absent. The phytoplankton of mountain lakes is chiefly a diatom plankton, with *Asterionella, Melosira,* and *Synedra* being the dominant genera. Myxophyceae (chiefly Chroococcales) are usually the second most abundant group.

From the standpoint of field studies, there are two major areas deserving special attention. (1) We need to know the nature of plankton populations, as well as physical and chemical conditions, during the long seasons of ice cover; this is virtually an unknown segment of mountain limnology. (2) In view of the simple communities in alpine lakes, we could learn much concerning the fundamental dynamics of community structure and primary and secondary production by means of well-planned field work, especially on a year-round basis. Studies of small tundra ponds (Fig. 12.7) have much to contribute to such basic ecology (Neldner and Pennak, 1955; Schmitz, 1959; Ives, 1941).

The limnetic crustacean zooplankton of alpine lakes is characterized by several "indicator" species, plus a few widely distributed cosmopolitan species, but all present in small numbers. The following copepod indicator species, for example, are generally restricted to cold alpine lakes: *Diaptomus shoshone, D. coloradensis,* and *D. arapahoensis.* No endemic cladoceran indicator species are known from high lakes. Material on altitudinal distribution of entomostraca in Colorado has been summarized by Reed and Olive (1958).

Fig. 12.7.—Colorado tundra pond, photographed on 29 June. Note the large ice blocks. Photo by the author.

Fig. 12.8.—Howard Lake, Colorado, a small montane lake showing thick masses of plankton algae accumulated along the shore in a band 10 m wide and 0.5 m thick. Photo by the author. From Pennak, 1949*b*.

A striking feature of certain species of copepods occurring in alpine habitats is their brilliant coloration. *Diaptomus shoshone,* for example, is a deep scarlet, and other species may be red, orange, or purple. Furthermore, the coloration of a particular euryzonal species is often clearly correlated with altitude. If it is collected in the plains or foothills areas, it is typically gray or gray-brown; in the montane or mid-mountain levels it is likely to be pinkish-gray or orange-brown; and in the highest cold lakes it is apt to be more deeply pigmented. The significance of such coloration has not been satisfactorily explained, but usually it is attributed to lipids and other pigments of phytoplanktonic origin which are stored, unoxidized, in the hemocoel and tissues. The species composition of the phytoplankton food supply does not differ markedly from one altitude to another, and most investigators are inclined to ascribe the accumulation of pigments in copepods to low water temperatures and low metabolic rates rather than to differences in the diet. It is interesting to note that these color phenomena do not occur in the Cladocera.

Maximum midsummer surface temperatures of alpine lakes are usually between 8° and 12° C, but small lakes in protected areas sometimes do not exceed 5° or 7° C. Dissolved oxygen is abundant at all times in the ice-free season, and bottom waters seldom go below 80% saturation. Oxygen conditions are unknown in midwinter and late winter under the thick layer of ice and snow. The higher the altitude, of course, the smaller the quantity of oxygen necessary to produce saturation. At 10° at sea level, for example, a liter of water will contain 10.92 ppm dissolved

oxygen at 100% saturation; at an altitude of 3,200 m the corresponding figure is only 7.32 ppm.

Montane lakes, at elevations of 2,500 to 3,200 m, are limnologically much more variable than alpine lakes but, as a group, are more fertile and have denser plankton populations. Indeed, in many montane lakes the plankton exhibits marked warm-season population bursts, and true algal "nuisances" (Fig. 12.8) are not unknown (Pennak, 1949b, 1955). Depending on local ecological conditions, the bottom fauna varies from poor to rich (Buscemi, 1961), and rooted aquatics often grow densely. Summer warming is sufficient to produce stratification and a definite mesolimnion in the deeper lakes (Pennak, 1955). The more eutrophic lakes develop summer oxygen exhaustion in the bottom waters. Grassy meadows and forests of spruce and pine surround the typical montane lakes (Fig. 12.9), and beaver ponds (Fig. 12.10) are a common part of the montane terrain (Ives, 1942).

The foothills zone of northern Colorado, and, for that matter, foothills areas throughout the mountain states, usually have V-shaped valleys with swift streams and intervening low to high ridges (Fig. 12.11). Consequently, the terrain is not suitable for the formation of lake basins, and most of the few natural bodies of water in such

Fig. 12.9.—Looking east from the Continental Divide in Boulder County, Colorado, showing a typical montane lake (Long Lake). Photo by the author.

Fig. 12.10.—Beaver dam, beaver house, and pond in the montane zone of Rocky Mountain National Park. Photo by the author.

areas are small ponds and lakes located on the tops of the ridges (Fig. 12.12). On the other hand, the foothills zone is ideal for the construction of reservoirs, and such artificial bodies of water are common everywhere in the West.

Fig. 12.11.—Typical Rocky Mountain foothills stream with steep canyon walls. Photo by the author.

Fig. 12.12.—Small foothills pond situated on top of ridge separating two V-shaped valleys. Note the dense growth of rooted aquatics. Photo by the author.

Plains lakes

Originally the rolling plains areas of the five Mountain States contained very few lakes, and the only aquatic habitats of consequence were sluggish rivers and streams arising at higher elevations. With the settlement of the West, however, and beginning in about 1870, the picture became greatly modified. It was soon discovered that the plains soils were fertile in many areas, but that the semiarid climate afforded insufficient moisture for good crops on a dependable year-to-year basis. The outcome was the construction of an extensive system of artificial reservoirs and canals—a region-wide project involving enormous labor and expense and a project which still continues today.

Briefly, western irrigation involves the digging of narrow branching canals, or "ditches," which take water from streams and carry it varying distances laterally along carefully calculated contours to agricultural lands and reservoirs. Plains reservoirs are constructed by selecting a suitable (and accessible) depression and building a stone and earthen dike along one or two sides of the depression in order to obtain a deeper basin. Most plains reservoirs have maximum depths of only

2 to 6 m. Water is brought into each reservoir through a ditch; a reservoir outlet pipe valve or headgate, usually in the bottom of the dam, governs the outflow. A whole system of branching ditches and associated reservoirs is supplied with numerous shut-off and control gates so that the flow in any part of the system can be carefully controlled. The size of main ditches is variable; some may carry a full head of water 1 m deep and 5 m wide; others carry a full head only 10 cm deep and 40 cm wide. Depending on precipitation, season, available supply, and a complicated legal system of "water rights," some parts of an irrigation system receive ample supplies of water each year; others, especially at the ends of ditch systems, receive less dependable quantities. The great majority of plains reservoirs have surface areas ranging between 5 and 60 acres.

The chief role of reservoirs is to receive water in times of good supply, conserve it, and have it available for irrigating fields at critical periods of crop development. Some reservoirs have a relatively constant water level; others may vary from 0 to 100% of capacity during the course of a year. Levels are lowest during autumn months.

The effective portions of an irrigation system are usually confined to a strip 3 to 15 mi outward from the base of a mountain range and 1 to 8 mi on either side of a river bed.

Figure 12.13 shows the irrigation system in a strip of plains zone extending out from the base of the foothills of the Front Range in northern Colorado. The 1700-m contour of the first ridge of the hills appears as dotted lines along the left of this figure. Two small rivers, one creek, and a few insignificant tributaries (indicated by fine lines) are the only natural waters in this figure. Everything else—reservoirs, ponds, and all of the complicated series of ditches—is man-made. Note especially the extensive branching and network pattern of the ditches. Note also that some ditches and small streams appear to cross each other. This is possible because one traverses a conduit pipe at a lower or higher level than the other. Such a diagram cannot, of course, show the the aggregate of thousands of miles of small ditches that carry water to individual fields and farm plots of corn, sugar beets, etc. Neither does it show the hundreds of small artificial farm and ranch ponds.

Limnologically the plains reservoirs cover a wide spectrum. In the more southern states of Colorado and Utah, the climate is sufficiently mild so that plains reservoirs may have a complete ice cover for only a month or six weeks. In Wyoming and Montana, however, the plains winter climate is much more severe, and the ice cover may persist for two to four months. In deeper reservoirs there may be summer oxygen stratification and exhaustion in the bottom waters. Winter-kills of fish populations are not infrequent.

Some plains reservoirs have poor plankton populations; others have rich standing crops the year around (Pennak, 1949a). Some have negligible bottom faunas; others have rich and dense populations. From the standpoint of species composition, these bodies of water are similarly diverse. Much of this biological diversity is thought

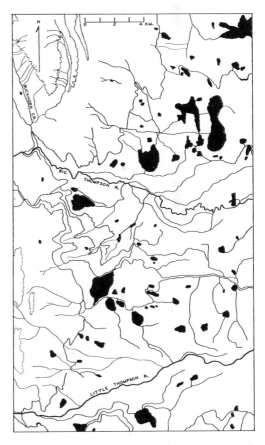

Fig. 12.13.—Strip of plains zone in northern Colorado (number *16* in Fig. 12.1) showing the complex of irrigation canals and reservoirs. See text for further explanation.

Fig. 12.14.—View over the plains from the first ridge of foothills in northern Colorado, showing a typical plains reservoir (Allens Lake) with dike along the east and north shores. Photo by the author.

to be a reflection of chemical conditions. Plains surficial geochemistry is locally heterogeneous and spotty. Some reservoir basins are in areas where the substrate contains little in the way of soluble nutrients (e.g., Allens Lake, Fig. 12.14); the waters of others are especially rich in bicarbonates, phosphates, and nitrates; still other plains reservoirs are built over soils that are so rich in soluble salts that the waters become highly alkaline and are toxic to fishes and most invertebrates (Fig. 12.15). Total dissolved solids in the last group may exceed 2%, and in extreme cases 10%.

Most of the above comments about plains reservoirs apply equally to irrigation and reservoir systems that have been constructed in river valleys and mountain parks everywhere throughout the Rocky Mountain States, e.g., the very extensive irrigation works along the Snake River in southern Idaho.

Large sections of the mesa and plains areas of the Mountain States support an abundance of shallow vernal ponds, which contain water for only two to eight weeks per year. Such ponds have been almost entirely ignored by aquatic biologists, in spite of the fact that their limnology and transient fauna of phyllopods, cladocerans, and copepods undoubtedly comprise a fascinating ecological complex.

Altitude and lake chemistry

Working in the rich limnological area of north-central Colorado, the present writer (1945, 1958a) has demonstrated basic relationships between altitude and certain aspects of lake and reservoir

chemistry. Such data are summarized for 155 bodies of water in Table 12.1, and there is strong evidence to suggest that similar relationships hold for other lake districts in the Mountain States.

Most of the exposed rocks over large sections of the Rocky Mountains are relatively insoluble granites, schists, and gneisses, which are low in carbonates, nitrates, sulfates, phosphates, halogens, etc. As a consequence, the lake waters above the plains zone are typically poor in dissolved salts. Especially in the alpine zone, the small quantities of dissolved materials in lakes are a reflection of the "newness" of their waters, low temperatures, and the insoluble nature of the substrate. As these waters "age" and pass to lower levels through the various drainage channels, however, they take up additional solutes, so that by the time they reach the plains zone, the total load of dissolved solids has increased by 1000%, with bound (methyl orange) carbon dioxide and calcium having comparable increases. (Incidentally, the values in Table 12.1 are averages, and determinations for individual lakes commonly vary ±50% from these averages.) Hydrogen-ion concentration values change accordingly, with high lakes having readings clustered around neutrality and the lower lakes generally being more and more alkaline. A portion of the total organic matter is allochthonous and is washed into lake basins, but a large fraction of the progressive increase at lower altitudes is a reflection of greater production in these waters. The supply of phosphates is very low in alpine lakes, and it is probably an important limiting factor, but the increase at lower elevations is not especially pronounced, the foothills lakes exhibiting only about a twofold increase. The distribution of nitrate nitrogen follows the same general pattern, being lowest in alpine lakes and about twice as abundant at lower levels. Goldman (1961) has found that the shed leaves of alder trees are an important contribution to the total nitrogen picture of Castle Lake, California (a cirque lake at 1,585 m elevation), but the importance of needle- and leaf-fall has not elsewhere been established for mountain lakes. Goldman (1960) has also demonstrated that molybdenum is a limiting factor in the primary production of Castle Lake, but there is no reason to suppose that this element is any more important than a dozen other trace and essential ions that are undoubtedly present in only negligible quantities in alpine and montane lakes. For example, many of these high lakes have a total ash content of less than 15 mg/L. Usually 6 to 12 mg of this quantity consists of silicon compounds, which leaves only 3 to 9 mg of all other inorganic ions! Indeed, if silicon compounds, bicarbonates, and calcium are subtracted from the total ash, all other inorganic ions often total less than 1 mg/L.

Some of the striking differences between montane drainage and semidrainage lakes require comment. In general, the larger quantities of solutes in the latter may be attributed to the fact that these lakes have no regular outlet. Surface drainage from the surroundings contributes sufficient water to these basins to offset evaporation, but at the same time evaporation leaves solutes behind, and the end result is generally greater concentrations of these materials. It should be noted, however, that the calcium and phosphate phosphorus concentrations are similar in both drainage and semidrainage lakes of the montane zone. A logical explanation is not apparent, but perhaps these ions are being lost to the sediments of semidrainage lakes as fast as they are coming into the basins (Pennak, 1963). The striking "nitrogen-accumulator" role of semidrainage lakes has been discussed at length by the present writer (1958a), and this phenomenon is perhaps the most unusual limnological feature of this group of lakes. Since most semidrainage lakes are shallow and relatively rich in organic matter, they often develop oxygen exhaustion during the long winter cover of ice and snow. Although some such lakes are regularly stocked with fish during the open season, populations rarely overwinter to the following year.

Plains lakes exhibit an exceptionally wide range of chemical conditions, depending on the age of the water, its source, and especially the local geochemistry of the substrate. Non-alkali lakes are those that have total residues of less than 500 mg/L, and alkali lakes (Fig. 12.15) are those having residues in excess of this figure. This is a rather arbitrary distinction but a useful one, nevertheless.

It is our observation that the magnitude of the standing crop of bottom invertebrates, zooplankton, and phytoplankton is more closely correlated with the total ash content of lake waters than with any other single ecological factor. And except for highly alkaline lakes, there is a rough linear correlation between number of plankton species and ash content.

TABLE 12.1

Some chemical features of the surface waters of north-central Colorado lakes. Average values for numbers of lakes as indicated. Modified from Pennak, 1958a.

Type of lake and number	Altitude (m)	Ash (mg/L)	Total organic matter (mg/L)	pH (mode)	Bound CO_2 (ppm)	Calcium (mg/L)	Nitrate-nitrogen (mg/L)	Phosphate-phosphorus (mg/L)
Alpine (19)	3,200–3,884	14.90	6.00	6.9	5.0	3.66	0.063	0.0029
Montane	2,500–3,200							
drainage (33)		28.52	10.41	7.1	12.4	7.20	0.168	0.0046
semidrainage (22)		60.23	34.08	7.6	24.4	8.84	1.137	0.0053
Foothills (16)	1,700–2,500	116.61	20.15	7.9	32.7	19.83	0.073	0.0075
Plains	1,480–1,700							
non-alkali (44)		202.96	24.69	8.0	49.6	40.20	0.114	0.0072
alkali (21)		1,729.78	237.20	8.3	110.4	108.07	0.098	0.0143

Major reservoir projects

Especially since 1930 the federal, state, and a few local governments have been engaged in the construction of numerous large multipurpose reservoirs. Some are in the plains zone; others are in the mountains at elevations up to 2,500 m (Figs. 12.1, 12.16, 12.17, 12.18). When completed, the

Fig. 12.15.—Highly alkaline plains lake. Although there is an ice cover, the whitish deposits on the shore in the right foreground are carbonate and sulfate crusts, not snow. Photo by the author. From Pennak, 1949*a*.

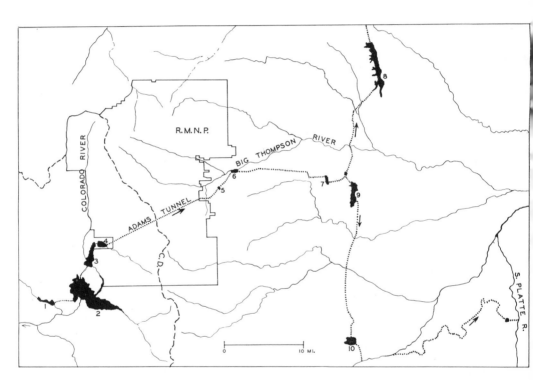

Fig. 12.16.—Schematic plan of the major drainage features of the Colorado-Big Thompson Reclamation Project. (The following features are not shown: dams, hydroelectric plants, natural lakes, and reservoirs relating to other irrigation and reclamation systems.) *R.M.N.P.*, Rocky Mountain National Park; *C.D.*, Continental Divide; heavy dotted lines indicate tunnels, siphons, and canals. Major reservoirs are as follows:

1. Willow Creek Reservoir.
2. Lake Granby (about 65 m deep).
3. Shadow Mountain Lake.
4. Grand Lake (a natural lake, 81 m deep).
5. Marys Lake.

6. Lake Estes (13.7 m deep).
7. Rattlesnake Reservoir.
8. Horsetooth Reservoir (about 60 m deep)
9. Carter Lake.
10. Boulder Reservoir.

Fig. 12.17.—Horsetooth Reservoir, a major unit in the Colorado-Big Thompson project. About 6½ mi long. Photo courtesy U.S. Bureau of Reclamation.

Fig. 12.18.—Lake Estes, Colorado, looking west toward the village of Estes Park and the Continental Divide. A foothills reservoir of the Colorado-Big Thompson Reclamation Project. From Pennak, 1955.

Glen Canyon Dam (Fig. 12.1: *11*), located on the Colorado River just below the Utah border, will back up the river into Utah to form a reservoir having an area of 254 mi². This is to be the second largest reservoir in the United States, with a capacity of 28,040,000 acre-feet of water; it will function in power production, river regulation, and recreation in a large, sparsely populated, arid section of the West. The Fort Peck Dam (Fig. 12.1: *9*) in northeastern Montana is the world's largest earth-fill dam; it backs up the Missouri River to form a reservoir having a capacity of 19,412,000 acre-feet and an area of 383 mi². It functions in flood control, power production, irrigation, river regulation, and recreation. The Flaming Gorge Dam (Fig. 12.1: *6*) (under construction) just below the Wyoming-Utah border will dam the Green River in southwestern Wyoming to make an irrigation and power reservoir having a capacity of 3,789,000 acre-feet. The Hungry Horse Dam (Fig. 12.1: *15*) in Montana on the South Fork of the Flathead River forms a multiple-purpose reservoir having a capacity of 3,468,000 acre-feet. Other reservoirs having capacities in excess of a million acre-feet in the Mountain States (see Fig. 12.1) are American Falls Reservoir on the Snake River in Idaho, Palisades Reservoir on the South Fork of the Snake River in Idaho and Wyoming, Tiber Reservoir on the Marias River in Montana, and the Pathfinder and Seminoe reservoirs on the North Platte River in Wyoming. In addition there are many other large reservoir projects having capacities between 300,000 and 1,000,000 acre-feet.

A complicated reservoir system (the Colorado-Big Thompson Reclamation Project) is shown schematically in Figure 12.16. This system brings large quantities of water from the water-rich Colorado River headwaters of the Western Slope to the (relatively) water-poor areas of the Eastern Slope by means of a 13.1-mi tunnel through the Continental Divide range. The waters are used for flood control, irrigation, municipal supplies, hydroelectric power, and last but not least, for recreational facilities. In spite of dire predictions to the contrary, the creation of the new reservoirs has greatly increased the fishing opportunities and potential throughout the whole project area. The project was essentially completed in 1956. It supplies supplemental irrigation service to 720,000 acres of land in northeastern Colorado

as far as the corner of the state. It consists of the following major facilities: 16 storage reservoirs with an active capacity of 879,500 acre-feet, 7 diversion dams, 130 mi of canals, 15 pumping plants, and 6 power plants with a capacity of 183,950 kw. Figure 12.17 is a general view of the Horsetooth Reservoir unit, looking southeast over the first ridge of foothills and onto the plains. This reservoir is about 6½ mi from north to south and about 200 ft deep. Figure 12.18 is a view of Lake Estes, another unit in the C.B.T. project. It is situated at an altitude of 2,277 m and has a maximum depth of 13.7 m and a volume of 3,104,100 m³; Pennak (1955) has studied this reservoir in some detail.

Most of the C.B.T. reservoirs develop a heavy growth of blue-green algae late in each summer —an usual situation in this general area. Lake Granby and Shadow Mountain Lake, however, are reservoirs that have been created over fertile mountain park grazing land (Fig. 12.16), and it is thought that their nutrient-rich waters are generally responsible for the algal growth problem, since such waters flow eastward through the Divide to supply the Eastern Slope reservoirs.

Many other large western reservoirs present additional major and unexpected limnological problems, especially with reference to silting, fish management, and algal nuisances. A few serious investigations have been carried out, but unfortunately little information has appeared in print. The papers of Wright (1958, 1959, 1960), however, form a notable exception. His thorough studies of Canyon Ferry Reservoir in Montana are among the first to contain quantitative information on plankton standing crops, primary production, and grazing effects in a large American reservoir (35,180 acres).

Running-water habitats

The Rocky Mountain States are the source of most of the major river systems of the United States (Fig. 12.1), and owing to the rugged terrain of mountains and hills, it is a region rich in headwater streams, brooks, and springs. Indeed, few other areas of the world offer such a wide range of accessible running-water habitats, from clear alpine rivulets to broad, sluggish, silted rivers (Fig. 12.19) and massive hot and cold springs (e.g., the spectacular Thousand Springs of southern Idaho). Yet, in spite of fascinating

Fig. 12.19.—South Platte River, a typical silted, sandy river of the plains. Photo by the author.

field opportunities, only a few major investigations have been published on the chemistry, physics, and biology of running waters of this region.

In the area of primary, herbivore, and carnivore productivity, the contribution of McConnell and Sigler (1959) is perhaps most important. Working on the Logan River in Utah, they found that the canyon section of this swift stream had an average of 0.30 g of chlorophyll per m² of bottom and an annual gross primary production of 1.2 kg/m²; the average standing crops of insects and fish were 5% and 1.6% as large, respectively, as the average standing crop of substrate algae. Gaufin (1959) worked out the seasonal and annual abundance of bottom invertebrates along a 72-mi stretch of the Provo River, Utah. Pennak and Van Gerpen (1947) studied the differential distribution of stream invertebrates with reference to substrate type. Figure 12.11 is a typical foothills stream in a V-shaped valley; it is representative of those studies mentioned above and, incidentally, is the type locality of the mountain midge, *Deuterophlebia coloradensis*.

Zoogeographic and ecological problems associated with stream invertebrates are especially abundant, particularly since the mountain fauna is so poorly known. The four pioneer papers of Dodds and Hisaw (1924a, 1924b, 1925a, 1925b) are among the most significant in this field. Armitage (1958) was one of the first to study the effects of temperature on the distribution of insects in a warm stream gradient in Yellowstone National Park.

Other important papers on Rocky Mountain stream biology are listed in the literature section.

Farm ponds

During much of the 19th century the eastern plains of Montana, Wyoming, and Colorado were a part of what newspapers called the "Great American Desert," chiefly because these semiarid grasslands had little water except for a few creeks and rivers. Today, however, especially as one flies over the area, the impression is otherwise, partly because of the role played by irrigation ditches but more importantly because of the abundance of farm and ranch ponds which are associated with almost every piece of property in the area. Essentially all of these ponds have been constructed by man, and their areas usually range between ½ acre and 5 acres. Surface drainage is the main source in some cases, but often the water is pumped into the basins from wells.

The surprising speed with which new farm ponds are colonized by rich invertebrate populations is a major problem of zoogeography and dispersal, and the pertinent literature contains little information and much speculation. As pointed out by Pennak (1958b), however, the whole system of farm and ranch ponds of the Great Plains is serving as a dense series of scattered but closely aligned "stepping stones" for many species of aquatic invertebrates to spread rapidly, especially westward, over an area that is otherwise difficult to traverse owing to the currents, silty qualities, and unstable sandy substrates of most of the plains rivers and intermittent streams.

Aquatic invertebrate fauna of the Mountain States

Within the restrictions of this chapter it is impossible to give an adequate account of the salient features of the aquatic invertebrate fauna of such a large and complex area. Nevertheless, there are a few generalities to be emphasized.

First, there is a large group of species, mostly microscopic, which are cosmopolitan in suitable habitats all over the United States (and world) and which are well represented in the Rocky Mountain States. These include many Protozoa, Turbellaria, Gastrotricha, Rotatoria, Nematoda, Tardigrada, Oligochaeta, Cladocera, Copepoda, Ostracoda, Hydracarina, a few Amphipoda and Odonata, and some Diptera.

In a second category we may list those invertebrate groups in which many species are known to be characteristic of or restricted to various habitats or areas in the Mountain States: Eubranchiopoda, Copepoda, Ostracoda, Hydracarina, Plecoptera, Ephemeroptera, Trichoptera, Diptera, etc.

In a third category we may list those groups whose zoogeographic status and occurrence in the Mountain States are especially poorly known because of lack of field studies. These are the Porifera, Coelenterata, Bryozoa, Hirudinea, and Isopoda.

Several other taxa require special comment. Although a few common species of Amphipoda are everywhere abundant in the Mountain States, careful field studies are necessary in order to tell whether or not the total amphipod fauna is comparable in number of species to that found in the eastern half of the United States.

The Decapoda fauna of the area is impoverished, presumably because the West Coast species and the rich eastern fauna have been confronted with difficult geographic barriers, especially shifting, silted rivers of the plains and valleys and streams with steep gradients at higher elevations. During the past 40 years, however, several Mississippi Valley species have been artificially introduced by man, and these have become so well established that they constitute a nuisance because of their burrowing habits in the lateral slopes of irrigation ditches. Central United States species of *Cambarus* may now be found thriving as high as 2,700 m in some places. Incidentally, they are often an important element in the diet of trout in lakes.

Odonata and aquatic Hemiptera are well represented in swamps, swales, and backwater areas of the plains and low valleys, but few species have been able to colonize areas above 2,500 m, these exceptions being a few Mesoveliidae, Gerridae, Veliidae, Notonectidae, and Corixidae.

Unfortunately little intensive collecting has been done on the aquatic beetles of high altitudes. It is known, however, that a rich fauna of Dryopidae and Elmidae occurs in many mountain streams. The usual assemblage of common Haliplidae, Dytiscidae, Hydrophilidae, etc. occurs in lowland waters, but the list of species is small.

The mountain Diptera are poorly known in this area, only the mosquitoes having been carefully studied.

Compared with the Midwest and eastern states, the Rocky Mountain States have a poor molluscan fauna. To be sure, a few widely distributed and euryokous species of *Lymnaea, Physa, Helisoma,* *Musculium, Sphaerium, Pisidium,* etc. are common, even up to elevations of 2,500 m. On the other hand, the larger bivalves, including a few species of *Anodonta, Margaritifera, Lampsilis,* and *Strophitus,* are becoming increasingly difficult to find, chiefly because of irrigation practices, silting, and river pollution. Fifty or more years ago they were common in the larger lowland rivers of the area. In Colorado only an occasional specimen may now be collected in some of the seepage backwaters of streams near the eastern border of the state. In addition to topography and other ecological barriers, it is probable that the absence of suitable fish hosts for the glochidium stage has also been an important factor in preventing the development of a richer fauna in the area. It is further likely that swift currents and relatively small quantities of carbonates have been important mechanisms in preventing the spread of both univalves and bivalves into the higher altitudes.

Henderson (1924, 1936) has catalogued the mollusks of the Mountain States, but it should be borne in mind that many of his species and subspecies have been synonymized.

The San Luis Valley of Colorado is a small closed drainage basin (Fig. 12.1), the aquatic invertebrates of which are essentially unknown. It is an area which should be rich in distributional problems.

Fish

From the standpoint of the number of native species, the fish fauna of the Rocky Mountain States is by no means rich. The cutthroat or black-spotted trout (*Salmo clarki*) is the only native trout of the area, and it was originally recognizable as several subspecies restricted to various drainage system headwaters. Because of widespread hatchery plantings and crossbreeding during the past 40 years, however, the subspecific characters have been blended and lost so that in only a few high lakes and streams can original subspecies still be distinguished morphologically. In addition, *S. clarki* is not holding up successfully against introduced species of trout except in high, cold lakes where it is more suited to the habitat.

The introduced rainbow trout (*Salmo gairdneri*) is now the dominant trout of the Rocky Mountain States, especially in the southern half of the region, and most hatchery plantings involve this relatively) euryokous species. Brown trout (*S. trutta*) in the warmer trout waters and brook trout (*Salvelinus fontinalis*) have also been widely introduced, but they are much less important to the sportsman than the rainbow. Some other salmonids that have been only locally introduced and established in suitable habitats are kokanee salmon (*Oncorhynchus nerka kennerlyi*), lake trout (*Salvelinus namaycush*), and golden trout (*Salmo aguabonita*).

A few interesting species are peculiar to the Rocky Mountain drainages but have become locally extinct in many places because of pollution, silting, fishing pressure, and competition by introduced species. These include the American grayling (*Thymallus signifer*) in the upper Missouri system, several species of mountain-suckers (*Pantosteus*), Colorado squawfish (*Ptychocheilus lucius*), which is the largest native North American cyprinid, and several species of Rocky Mountain bullheads or sculpins (*Cottus*). The mountain whitefish (*Prosopium williamsoni*), on the other hand, seems to be holding its own.

The majority of introduced species in the Rocky Mountain States are lowland ("warmwater") forms, which have become common in man-made reservoirs everywhere. For the most part they are species typical of the Mississippi Valley drainages and include such familiar fish as the carp (*Cyprinus carpio*), several Ictaluridae, the largemouth bass (*Micropterus salmoides*), several species of *Lepomis*, black and white crappies (*Pomoxis*), yellow perch (*Perca flavescens*), and the walleye (*Stizostedion vitreum*) in a few places.

Most of the species native to the lower elevations of the Rocky Mountain States are Cyprinidae, the remainder being chiefly Ictaluridae, Catostomidae, Cyprinodontidae, and Percidae (darters).

About 90 species and subspecies of fishes are known from the state of Colorado, of which only 54 are native (Beckman, 1953). Twenty-five of the native forms are cyprinids and ten are catostomids. Similar proportions of native and introduced species are found in the other four Mountain States.

Although the number of species occurring in plains and lower mountain areas is relatively large, the high lakes and headwater streams have an impoverished fauna. A day's seining in a plains river or large reservoir, for example, often yields

Fig. 12.20.—Seine-load of fish that has just been taken from a plains reservoir. The technician is holding a largemouth bass, but the tub is filled with "runt" bluegills, crappies, and perch. Photo by the author.

as many as 8 to 15 species, but a mountain lake or stream within 1,500 ft (altitudinally) of timberline usually supports only one or two species of trout and one species of sucker.

Many of the high mountain lakes contain no native fish population because of the barrier effects of falls and torrential outlet streams. Beginning in about 1880, however, essentially all lakes, even the most isolated ones, have been stocked with at least two species of trout.

Standing crops and creel census records vary widely, just as they do in other parts of the continent, depending on the nature of a particular lake or stream. Some plains lakes support more than 200 lbs of fish per acre; unproductive alpine lakes and highly alkaline plains lakes contain less than 5 lbs per acre (occasionally 0 lbs per acre). Many plains lakes have badly managed fish populations, and overcrowding with "runt" perch and bluegills is common (Fig. 12.20), chiefly because of low fishing pressure.

Lack of sufficient food is the factor limiting fish populations in many mountain lakes, and it is the writer's conviction that the situation could be partly remedied by introducing suitable species of forage fishes and crustaceans (e.g., *Mysis* and *Asellus*), especially where such introduced species would be utilizing ecological niches not now occupied.

Research centers

At least some limnological research (in the very broad sense) is being done at about half of the college and university campuses in the Rocky Mountain States, but the situation ranges from an intensive program and regular publication to (commonly) desultory and sporadic efforts and only an occasional publication. The last edition of the Membership List of the American Society of Limnology and Oceanography includes 29 members from this area, but most of these are graduate students, U.S. Public Health Service workers, and applied fisheries biologists. Only about six could be considered senior investigators in "theoretical" limnology. Obviously the Rocky Mountain area is in dire need of active researchers.

None of the five Rocky Mountain States has a summer field station where the emphasis is chiefly in hydrobiology. A partial explanation for this situation is the fact that some of the campuses are geographically ideally situated for lake and stream research, and there is no particular advantage to be gained in establishing a field station elsewhere. One important exception is the Montana State University Flathead Lake Biological Laboratory, established in 1899 on the shore of Flathead Lake (Fig. 12.1: 7). Although not primarily a hydrobiological establishment, this laboratory has been the source of some important papers on the limnology of Flathead Lake and nearby lakes, e.g., the limnological survey of Young (1935), the vertical distribution of bacteria by Potter and Baker (1956, 1961), and Lauff's study (1953) on the relationships between water chemistry and phytoplankton.

A list of all of the Rocky Mountain area workers doing limnological work, however modest, would be out of place in this volume. At the risk of doing injustices, nevertheless, we are listing below those individuals and laboratories which appear to have firmly established and continuing research programs in limnology, especially as measured by regular publication.

At Montana State College (Bozeman) C. J. D. Brown is active in fisheries biology, and John C. Wright is interested chiefly in primary and secondary production in limnetic plankton populations. At Montana State University (Missoula) Royal B. Brunson is a specialist in the Gastrotricha and general limnology.

Arden R. Gaufin at the University of Utah (Salt Lake City) is working on stream pollution, stream bottom faunas, and aquatic insects (especially Plecoptera); George Edmunds is a noted specialist in the Ephemeroptera. At Utah State University (Logan) W. F. Sigler and his associates are interested chiefly in fish productivity and natural history.

The Colorado Cooperative Fishery Research Unit at Colorado State University (Fort Collins) has close ties with the Colorado State Department of Game and Fish and is under the direction of Howard A. Tanner. Investigations are chiefly in applied limnology, including fish food and growth studies, creel censuses, fish hepatoma, lake fertilization, and the use of hexadecanol and allied substances as inhibitors of reservoir evaporation.

Robert W. Pennak and his students at the University of Colorado (Boulder) have been actively publishing for more than 20 years, chiefly in comparative limnology, plankton populations, high-altitude limnology, stream biology, and the biology of freshwater invertebrates.

Considerable limnological work is being done by the staffs of the various state fish and game departments, but such investigations are usually in applied fish biology and are customarily (and unfortunately) issued as mimeographed reports having limited circulation, or as semi-popular articles.

Fossil lake beds

Two of the most famous of all fossil lake beds occur in the Rocky Mountain States. The Green River formation is a very extensive series of middle Eocene sediments from 1,500 to 2,000 ft thick found over an area of 25,000 mi^2 in southwestern Wyoming, east-central Utah, and west-central Colorado. The formation represents sedimentary deposits of several large lakes, the size of which varied greatly depending on long-time climatic changes. It is thought that at high-water level there were only two lakes, one in Wyoming and the other in Utah and Colorado. Many of the Green River deposits are not fossiliferous and the known fossil beds are restricted to small areas, the most famous of which is near the town of Green River in Wyoming (Fig. 12.1: *14*). Here, in varved chalky shales, are vast quantities of perfectly preserved herring-like fishes, as well as an abundance of aquatic and terrestrial insects and plants, some turtles, crocodiles, and crustaceans, and a few terrestrial and aquatic mollusks. Limnologically, it is thought that the lakes were highly productive, with negligible currents and continuously anaerobic hypolimnetic conditions for long periods of time (Bradley, 1948). It has been postulated that unusual climatic conditions occasionally produced complete circulation, and the resulting dispersion of hydrogen sulfide at all depths brought about mass mortality of the fish and aquatic invertebrate populations. In later stages the lakes had no outlet to the sea, and the waters became highly saline and dried up completely. Excellent fossil algal "reefs" are found along the old shorelines.

Another famous Tertiary lake basin is located near the village of Florissant in central Colorado (Fig. 12.1: *8*). During Oligocene times this was an irregular shallow lake in a broad, flat, mountain valley; it had an area of at least 5 mi² but may have been much larger. Sedimentation was relatively rapid, and since the area was one of great volcanic activity, the bottom deposits consisted mostly of volcanic ash, volcanic mud, and some sand. Eventual drainage and destruction of the lake came about by tilting of the whole region so that the lake overflowed its northwestern rim and cut down its barrier at that end. About 50 ft of Florissant shales are fantastically rich in hundreds of species of beautifully preserved insects (mostly terrestrial) and plants (leaves), in addition to many species of spiders and several species of mollusks, birds, and fishes. Judging from the abundance of fossils and the way in which they were deposited, the lake must have been in an area which was subjected to at least a dozen catastrophic volcanic eruptions at more or less widely spaced intervals. The falling ash of each such eruption carried large numbers of organisms to the lake bottom. The association of plant and animal genera is indicative of a climate somewhat similar to that of the Gulf States today.

These two fossil lakes are discussed in greater detail in the chapter on paleolimnology by W. H. Bradley.

National parks and other preserves

From the standpoint of the preservation of our rich aquatic fauna and limnological opportunities, the Rocky Mountain States are in an exceptionally favorable situation. The region contains 7 national parks totaling 6,247 mi² and including such interesting limnological areas as Yellowstone National Park, Glacier National Park, and Rocky Mountain National Park, 17 national monuments aggregating 605 mi², and 47 national forests aggregating nearly 21% of the total area of the five states! Although the national forests are not under such close ecological control as the parks and monuments, they are, nevertheless, large accessible areas having natural or seminatural conditions which are exceptionally favorable for stream and lake research.

Yellowstone National Park, in Wyoming, Idaho, and Montana, is limnologically so unusual it requires special comment. Much of the park is a volcanic plateau with an amazing array of 100 geysers and 3,000 hot springs and pools. Many of the hot springs have thick and brilliantly colored mineral deposits and extensive terraces around their outlets. Because of the many types of chemical and physical gradients between hot mineral springs and the cold streams into which they empty, there are countless problems relating to the ecology of stream invertebrates and algae (Armitage, 1958; Muttkowski, 1929; Brues, 1924).

Pollution

In spite of the low population density and the thousands of square miles of timberland having

Fig. 12.21.—Mountain trout stream showing mine tailings outfall. Two hundred meters downstream from this point the stream is essentially a biological desert. Photo by the author.

essentially natural conditions, the pollution problem is nevertheless important. In some mountainous sections pollution is especially serious owing to excessive erosion and silting resulting from injudicious heavy timber cuttings and mining wastes (Fig. 12.21). The latter, particularly, are sometimes effective in temporarily wiping out the invertebrate and fish faunas in long sections of mountain and hill streams.

In the valleys and plains, pollution is produced by local soil erosion, faulty irrigation practices, industrial wastes, and municipal sewage wastes. Many drastic modifications in the fish and invertebrate faunas have been recorded here, especially during the past 40 or 50 years.

References

A complete hydrobiological bibliography of the Rocky Mountain States would include more than 1,100 titles. However, the great majority of these are brief and preliminary studies, unpublished theses, taxonomic articles, abstracts, unpublished mimeographed reports, and applied fisheries studies. The list of titles below consists primarily of specific references mentioned in the foregoing text and a few other titles of a comprehensive nature or of some especially significant aspect of the Mountain States' limnology.

ARMITAGE, K. B. 1958. Ecology of the riffle insects of the Firehole River, Wyoming. Ecology, 39: 571–580.

BECKMAN, W. C. 1953. Guide to the fishes of Colorado. Univ. Colorado Museum, Leaflet 11: 1–110.

BRADLEY, W. H. 1948. Limnology and the Eocene lakes of the Rocky Mountain region. Bull. Geol. Soc. Amer., 59: 635–648.

BROWN, C. J. D., W. D. CLOTHIER, AND W. ALVORD. 1953. Observations on ice conditions and bottom organisms in the West Gallatin River, Montana. Proc. Montana Acad. Sci., 13: 21–27.

BROWN, C. J. D., et al. 1959. A classification of Montana fishing streams—1959. U.S. Bur. Sport Fish. and Wildl., Missouri River Basin Studies, Billings, Montana, 8 p. and map.

BRUES, C. T. 1924. Observations on animal life in the thermal waters of Yellowstone Park, with a consideration of the thermal environment. Proc. Amer. Acad. Arts Sci., 59: 371–487.

BUSCEMI, P. A. 1961. Ecology of the bottom fauna of Parvin Lake, Colorado. Trans. Amer. Microscop. Soc., 80: 266–307.

CHRISTENSEN, E. M. 1956. Bibliography of Utah aquatic biology. Proc. Utah Acad. Sci. Arts Lett., 33: 91–100.

DODDS, G. S., AND F. L. HISAW. 1924a. Ecological studies of aquatic insects. I. Adaptations of mayfly nymphs to swift streams. Ecology, 5: 137–148.

DODDS, G. S., AND F. L. HISAW. 1924a. Ecological studies of aquatic insects. II. Size of respiratory organs in relation to environmental conditions. Ecology, 5: 262–271.

DODDS, G. S., AND F. L. HISAW. 1925a. Ecological studies on aquatic insects. III. Adaptations of caddisfly larvae to swift streams. Ecology, 6: 123–137.

DODDS, G. S., AND F. L. HISAW. 1925b. Ecological studies on aquatic insects. IV. Altitudinal range and zonation of mayflies, stoneflies and caddisflies in the Colorado Rockies. Ecology, 6: 380–390.

ELROD, M. J. 1901. Limnological investigations at Flathead Lake, Montana, and vicinity, July, 1899. Trans. Amer. Microscop. Soc., 22: 63–80.

EVERMANN, B. W. 1891. A reconnaissance of the streams and lakes of western Montana and northwestern Wyoming. Bull. U.S. Fish Comm., 11: 3–60.

GAUFIN, ARDEN. 1959. Production of bottom fauna in the Provo River, Utah. Iowa State Coll. J. Sci., 33: 395–419.

GOLDMAN, C. R. 1960. Molybdenum as a factor limiting primary productivity in Castle Lake, California. Science, 132: 1016.

———. 1961. The contribution of alder trees (Alnus tenuifolia) to the primary productivity of Castle Lake, California. Ecology, 42: 282–288.

GUMTOW, R. B. 1955. An investigation of the periphyton in a riffle of the West Gallatin River, Montana. Trans. Amer. Microscop. Soc., 74: 278–292.

HENDERSON, JUNIUS. 1924. Mollusca of Colorado, Utah, Montana, Idaho and Wyoming. Univ. Colorado Studies, 13: 65–223.

———. 1936. Mollusca of Colorado, Utah, Montana, Idaho, and Wyoming—Supplement. Univ. Colorado Studies, 23: 81–145.

IVES, R. L. 1941. Tundra ponds. J. Geomorphol., 4: 285–296.

———. 1942. The beaver-meadow complex. J. Geomorphol., 5: 191–203.

JOHNSON, K. R. 1941. Vegetation of some mountain lakes and shores in northwestern Colorado. Ecology, 22: 306–316.

JORDAN, D. S. 1889. A reconnaissance of the streams and lakes of the Yellowstone National Park, Wyoming, in the interest of the United States Fish Commission. Bull. U.S. Fish Comm., 9: 41–63.

LAUFF, G. H. 1953. A contribution to the water chemistry and phytoplankton relationships of Roger's Lake, Flathead County, Montana. Proc. Montana Acad. Sci., 13: 5–19.

McCONNELL, W. J., AND W. F. SIGLER. 1959. Chlorophyll and productivity in a mountain river. Limnol. Oceanogr., 4: 335–351.

MacPHEE, CRAIG. 1961. Bioassay of algal production in chemically altered waters. Limnol. Oceanogr., 6: 416–422.

MILLER, L. R. 1936. Desmids of the Medicine Bow Forest of Wyoming. Univ. Wyoming Publ., 2: 67–120.

MOFFETT, J. W. 1936. A quantitative study of the

bottom fauna in some Utah streams variously affected by erosion. Bull. Univ. Utah, **26**: 1–32.

MUTTKOWSKI, R. A. 1929. The ecology of trout streams in Yellowstone National Park. Roosevelt Wildl. Ann., **2**: 155–240.

NELDNER, K. H., AND R. W. PENNAK. 1955. Seasonal faunal variations in a Colorado alpine pond. Amer. Midland Nat., **53**: 419–430.

OLIVE, J. R. 1953. A bibliography of the limnology and fishery biology of Colorado, 34 p. (Mimeo.)

PENNAK, R. W. 1941. A bibliography of high altitude limnological investigations in the western United States. Univ. Colorado Studies, D, **1**: 225–229.

———. 1943. Limnological variables in a Colorado mountain stream. Amer. Midland Nat., **29**: 186–199.

———. 1945. Some aspects of the regional limnology of northern Colorado. Univ. Colorado Studies, D, **2**: 263–293.

———. 1949a. Annual limnological cycles in some Colorado reservoir lakes. Ecol. Monogr., **19**: 233–267.

———. 1949b. An unusual algal nuisance in a Colorado mountain lake. Ecology, **30**: 245–247.

———. 1950. A limnological reconnaissance of Grand Mesa, Colorado. Univ. Colorado Studies, Ser. Biol., **1**: 15–23.

———. 1955. Comparative limnology of eight Colorado mountain lakes. Univ. Colorado Studies, Ser. Biol., **2**: 1–75.

———. 1958a. Regional lake typology in northern Colorado, U.S.A. Verh. intern. Ver. Limnol., **13**: 264–283.

———. 1958b. Some problems of freshwater invertebrate distribution in the Western States. Zoogeography, Amer. Assoc. Advance. Sci. Publ. No. 51: 223–230.

———. 1963. Ecological and radiocarbon correlations in some Colorado mountain lake and bog deposits. Ecology, **44**. (In press.)

PENNAK, R. W., AND E. D. VAN GERPEN. 1947. Bottom fauna production and physical nature of the substrate in a northern Colorado trout stream. Ecology, **28**: 42–48.

POTTER, L. F., AND G. E. BAKER. 1956. The microbiology of Flathead and Rogers lakes, Montana. I. Preliminary survey of the microbial populations. Ecology, **37**: 351–355.

POTTER, L. F., AND G. E. BAKER. 1961. The microbiology of Flathead and Rogers lakes, Montana. II. Vertical distribution of the microbial populations and chemical analyses of their environments. Ecology, **42**: 338–348.

REED, E. B., AND J. R. OLIVE. 1958. Altitudinal distribution of some entomostraca in Colorado. Ecology, **39**: 66–74.

ROBERTSON, O. H. 1947. An ecological study of two high mountain trout lakes in the Wind River Range, Wyoming. Ecology, **28**: 87–112.

SCHMITZ, E. H. 1959. Seasonal biotic events in two Colorado alpine tundra ponds. Amer. Midland Nat., **61**: 424–446.

SIMON, J. R. 1946. Wyoming fishes. Bull. Wyoming Game and Fish Dept., **4**: 1–129.

U.S. DEPARTMENT OF THE INTERIOR, BUREAU OF RECLAMATION. 1961. Colorado-Big Thompson project. Reclamation Proj. Data: 121–153.

WRIGHT, J. C. 1958. The limnology of Canyon Ferry Reservoir. I. Phytoplankton-zooplankton relationships in the euphotic zone during September and October, 1956. Limnol. Oceanogr., **3**: 150–156.

———. 1959. Limnology of Canyon Ferry Reservoir. II. Phytoplankton standing crop and primary production. Limnol. Oceanogr., **4**: 235–245.

———. 1960. The limnology of Canyon Ferry Reservoir. III. Some observations on the density dependence of photosynthesis and its cause. Limnol. Oceanogr., **5**: 356–361.

YOUNG, R. T. 1935. The life of Flathead Lake, Montana. Ecol. Monogr., **5**: 91–163.

13 | *W. T. Edmondson*

Pacific Coast and Great Basin

The area covered in this chapter is characterized by an extraordinary diversity of climate, geology, and topography. Fully as great extremes that influence limnological characteristics exist within this area as in that covered by any one of the other chapters. Altitudes of the land range from 4,418 m above sea level (Mt. Whitney) to 86 m below (Death Valley). Annual rainfall varies from 371 cm to less than 5 cm, indeed zero over large areas in some summers. The difference between summer and winter weather exhibits a wide range from north to south. The vegetation cover of the land varies from dense rain forest to nothing. Naturally, the lakes within this region show a comparable diversity, ranging from those with very little dissolved material (16 mg/L) to those that are saturated with salt ($>$400,000 mg/L), and the ionic ratios are very diverse. The standing waters vary from temporary playa lakes and ponds to the deepest lake in the United States (Crater Lake, Oregon). The flowing waters vary from small streamlets to one of the largest rivers on the continent (Columbia River). There are hot springs on the one hand and on the other lakes that are unfrozen only briefly in the summer. Within a large region of such great diversity, it is not surprising to find that only a very small fraction of the waters have been studied from a limnological point of view.

State and federal governmental agencies have made extensive studies of water resources and fisheries biology. They have produced a large volume of information of considerable background interest to limnologists, although the results are not appropriate for summary in this volume. The more strictly limnological work reported in the following pages has generally been carried out by members of the faculties of the state universities, although some important contributions have been made by others. An important proportion of the information available stems from research done for advanced degrees at the universities and is still in the form of manuscripts or theses deposited in libraries. An attempt has been made to cite major publications which are widely distributed and which serve as a key to the literature, only part of which can be summarized here. Much information has been distributed in the form of informal mimeographed progress reports circulated chiefly within governmental agencies and available only on request. This material has not been put into the bibliography.

General distribution of lakes

The north-south running course of mountains divides the region (Fig. 13.1), in general, into a western humid section with many streams, lakes, and ponds, and an arid eastern section, parts of which contain lakes and ponds with relatively high concentrations of dissolved solids and many temporary waters in which large populations of branchiopod crustaceans develop. Because of the great chemical diversity that exists, the word *saline* will be used here in a purely descriptive sense for lakes with a relatively high content of any salts, i.e., more than 500 mg/L (Russell, 1895; contrary to Hedgpeth, 1959; Schmitz, 1959). The mountains themselves are dotted with elevated lakes and streams.

The first wide-scale survey of the characteristics of lakes in the region was made by Kemmerer *et al.* (1924). This paper includes quantitative data on various simple chemical properties

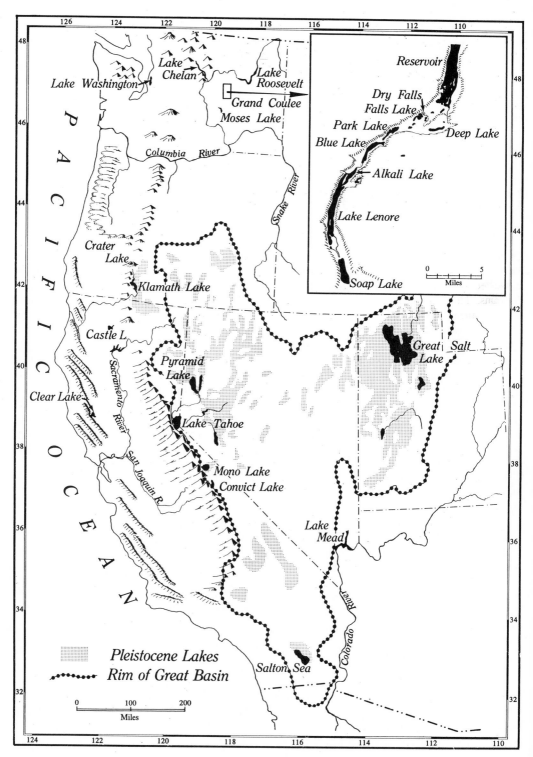

Fig. 13.1.—Map showing the location of most of the lakes discussed in Chapter 13. The inset shows the details of the lakes in the Lower Grand Coulee, Washington (see also Fig. 13.5). The main ranges of mountains are indicated, and the outline of the Great Basin is shown. Prepared by the University of Wisconsin Cartographic Laboratory; based in part on Russell, 1895.

as well as on zooplankton and net phytoplankton. The study was made in the years 1907–1913 and indicates some features of several lakes that have subsequently been highly modified by cultural processes, as Lake Washington and Lake Stevens, Washington. Some of the lakes reviewed in this publication have never again been studied in any detail, as, for instance, the most interesting Lake Chelan, Washington.

The regions in which most limnological work has been done are listed below arbitrarily in geographical order from the north. References are given in this list to papers that will not be discussed further.

Western Washington.—Much of the published work has been devoted to Lake Washington in recent years because of its artificial eutrophication. Other work in the same area has included sedimentation and peat formation (Rigg, 1958; Rigg and Gould, 1957; Gould and Budinger, 1958), the characteristics of meromixis in a small humic lake (Hall Lake), and general studies of a variety of other lakes (Scheffer, 1933; Edmondson *et al.*, 1962). A volcanic explosion of Glacier Peak about 6,700 years ago distributed ash over a large area of the northwest, and the resultant volcanic ash layer in lakes and bogs serves as a convenient time mark (Rigg and Gould, 1957). Results of much morphometric work in western Washington have been presented in the form of bottom contour maps and photographs (Wolcott, 1961), and the origin of some lakes has been discussed by Bretz (1910, 1913).

Central Washington.—The central part of Washington is semiarid, with rainfall in the order of 10 cm per year, and the land is covered with *Artemisia* desert. The region contains a large number of lakes and ponds of varied salinity. An extensive irrigation project supplied with water from Grand Coulee Dam has greatly altered the hydrology of much of the region, and two saline lakes in the Lower Grand Coulee have been greatly diluted in the past decade.

The Columbia River has received considerable study because of the conflict between its salmon fishery and its many hydroelectric projects. The presence of an atomic isotope production plant has stimulated some additional work on the biota of the river.

Oregon.—Crater Lake, visited by thousands of tourists each year, has received thus far a relatively small amount of investigation. Other lakes

and ponds have been surveyed for phytoplankton population density, aquatic vegetation, and nutrient content (Phinney and McLachlan, 1956).

California.—The chief regions of limnological investigation in California are Clear Lake, Castle Lake, a group of lakes in the Convict Creek Basin at altitudes up to 3,338 m, and the Salton Sea below sea level. Information on the bottom fauna of streams and lakes in California has been taken in conection with fishery management programs. Much of this work is summarized in detail in the journal *California Fish and Game*, which is now in its 49th volume of publication.

The Great Basin.—While this region includes a wide variety of geology and climate, it is unified and related to Southern California by the existence of a high degree of aridity and the presence of saline and semi-saline lakes, some of which have been studied in detail. Surprisingly, Great Salt Lake in Utah and Mono Lake and Lake Tahoe in California have received little limnological study relative to their general popular interest.

Colorado River.—The Colorado River which forms the southeastern boundary of the region considered in this chapter has been dammed in several places, providing a series of large lakes. The physical limnology and sedimentation of Lake Mead have been given considerable attention.

The limnological work done in the areas listed will now be summarized in greater detail. Much of it may be regarded as material toward descriptive comparative regional limnology, but some has been directed at more specific limnological problems. Following is a list of the general aspects of limnology to which studies in these regions have contributed most: (1) lake productivity in relation to nutrient supply, (2) relation of salinity to climate, (3) relation of biota to salinity, and (4) character of meromixis.

Western Washington

Lake Washington

Lake Washington lies in an area that has been increasing in human population density rapidly, especially since 1946 (Fig. 13.2). It became of interest to limnologists when it began to repeat the history of changes exhibited by Lake Zürich some sixty years earlier. In 1955 the lake bloomed with *Oscillatoria rubescens*, and earlier than that *Bosmina longirostris* had replaced *B. coregoni* in the plankton (Edmondson *et al.*, 1956). Fortunately, the lake had already been studied in some

Fig. 13.2.—Aerial view of Lake Washington from the south, November 1956. The line connecting the large island with the west shore is a floating concrete bridge. The ship canal connecting the lake with Puget Sound to the west can be seen starting with the bay immediately north of the floating bridge. The lake is 40 km long. For a contour map of the bottom, see Gould and Budinger (1958). Hall Lake is 8 km north of Lake Washington. Photograph by Pacific Aerial Surveys, Inc.

detail by Scheffer and Robinson (1939), Peterson *et al.* (1952), Peterson (1955), and Comita and Anderson (1959). Since 1955 the lake has been sampled frequently, and further changes in plankton and chemical conditions have been defined (Shapiro, 1960; G. C. Anderson, 1961; Edmondson, 1961a, and unpublished).

For many years Lake Washington has been used for the disposal of sewage, and at the present time about 2.45 million m³ of purified effluent from secondary treatment plants enter the lake each day, making an annual contribution to the lake of 47,000 kg of phosphorus and 82,270 kg of nitrogen toward the known annual totals of 104,600 and 741,000 kg, respectively. The purified sewage is very concentrated in phosphorus

(Edmondson, 1961a). The quantity has been increasing over the years as communities around the lake have grown. Public concern that the lake should begin to produce algal nuisances of the kind generated in other parts of the world has led to the development of a metropolitan legislative action to divert sewage from Lake Washington to Puget Sound. Sewage diversion is planned to start in late 1963 and to be 85% completed by the end of 1966. Thus, Lake Washington offers a good opportunity to obtain certain kinds of information about the response of a lake to large changes in nutrient income.

Various properties of the lake connected with productivity have shown large changes over the years. Rates of gross photosynthetic oxygen production in the trophogenic zone have ranged up to 1.36 mg/L per day, which lies within the range of highly productive lakes in Europe and compares well with values obtained in fertilized lakes (Nelson and Edmondson, 1955). Correspondingly, the quantity of phytoplankton has increased. In 1950 the average population density of total phytoplankton in the epilimnion during the summer was 0.6 thousand μ^3/ml and in 1956 was 4.2 thousand μ^3/ml. Corresponding values for chlorophyll were 1.8 and 6.1 μg/L. Population densities of zooplankton have also increased, and in 1958 the maximum population of *Diaptomus ashlandi* was about two times its value in 1950.

Lake Washington has shown a metalimnetic oxygen minimum every year in which it has been adequately studied, and the concentration of oxygen at the minimum decreased between 1933 and 1957 (Fig. 13.3). Calculations by Shapiro (1960) suggest that a large fraction of the oxygen removal in this layer can be attributed to respiratory activities of *Diaptomus ashlandi*, which has its maximum population density in the region of the minimum and apparently migrates little if at all. Transport of oxygen from above by turbulent processes is evidently slow enough to permit development of the minimum.

The net summer accumulation of phosphate in the hypolimnion has increased over the years (Fig. 13.3). In 1961 the accumulation was about twice as great as that for 1957, although the oxygen concentrations were not so low.

The sediments of Lake Washington show clear signs of nutrient enrichment. In one core the P content of the top centimeter layer was 1.56% of the organic matter, and that of the next two centimeter layers was 0.72% and 0.54%, respectively. The role of currents in shaping the floor of the lake is discussed by Gould and Budinger (1958).

Lake Washington is connected to Puget Sound by a ship canal with locks, but under some conditions in dry summers, salt water may fill the intermediate Lake Union to sill level and move into Lake Washington. A mildly saline warm layer then appears in the bottom (Rattray *et al.*, 1954). During winter the lake is mixed to uniformity.

Hall Lake

This soft-water, meromictic lake near Seattle has been studied in great detail, although only a

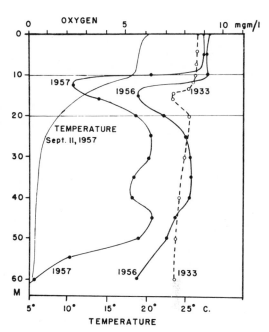

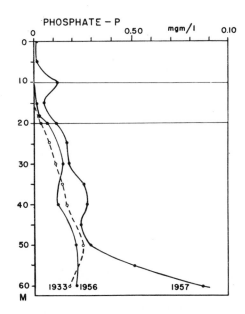

Fig. 13.3.—Vertical distribution of oxygen and phosphate phosphorus in Lake Washington at the end of summer stratification in three years. Temperature for 1957 is also shown. Note the progressive development of the oxygen minimum.

TABLE 13.1

Chemical characteristics of the meromictic lakes in the western United States

Depth (m)	pH	Total dissolved solids (mg/L)	Ions (mg/L)									
			Ca	Mg	Na	K	CO_3	HCO_3	SO_4	H_2S	HS^-	Cl
					1. HALL LAKE 47° 48′ N, 122° 19′ W; area 2.8 ha; 23 Oct. 1952							
0	7.4	69.8	7.5	2.7	4.8	1.9	0	26	13.0	—	—	5.0
14	7.4	90.1	9.2	4.1	4.6	2.4	0	44	7.8	—	—	4.0
16	7.4	105.2	9.2	3.6	4.3	2.4	0	64	3.7	—	—	4.0
					2. HOT LAKE 48° 58′ N, 119° 29′ W; area 1.27 ha; 22 Aug. 1955							
0	8.2	161,200	640	22,838	7,337	891	0	3,148	103,680	—	—	1,668
3	7.8	391,800	720	53,619	16,790	1,564	0	3,062	243,552	—	—	1,882
					3. WANNACUTT LAKE 48° 52′ N, 119° 34′ W; area 180 ha; 18 May 1956							
0	8.3	7,864	256	895	513	84	0	185	5,136	—	—	58
42	7.8	53,740	430	6,722	3,588	563	0	1,891	34,560	—	—	351
					4. BLUE LAKE 48° 39′ N, 119° 46′ W; area 120 ha; 15 July 1958							
0	8.7	3,864	9.0	179	564	88	123	558	1,445	—	—	53
36	8.7	8,284	16	379	1,256	183	224	1,251	3,072	—	—	138
					5. SOAP LAKE (OKANOGAN COUNTY) 48° 14′ N, 119° 39′ W; area 120 ha; 27 Sept. 1955							
0	9.7	26,400	40	205	8,326	688	609	3,965	13,152	—	—	1,509
16	9.0	98,000	20	506	30,475	1,376	594	11,773	51,696	—	—	888
					6. SOAP LAKE (GRANT COUNTY) 47° 23′ N, 119° 30′ W; area 364.5 ha; 20 July 1955							
0	9.8	24,800	16	15.5	8,717	782	3,930	5,063	4,584	—	—	3,245
17.5	9.8	25,600	16	15.5	8,878	899	4,080	5,051	4,666	—	—	3,436
18.5	9.8	38,120	8	14.5	12,765	1,165	6,150	6,588	6,816	1	500	4,828
19.5	9.7	41,280	6.2	13	14,260	1,107	6,330	6,039	7,392	2	1,200	5,467
25.0	9.5	144,400	8	2.4	52,095	4,184	28,530	13,847	27,408	24	6,518	12,425
					7. LOWER GOOSE LAKE 46° 57′ N, 119° 17′ W; area 41.7 ha; 16 Aug. 1955							
0	8.5	458	16	24	101	12	118	306	59	—	—	41
27.5	8.4	41,480	64	625	11,730	6,412	289	5,289	15,646	—	—	6,212
					8. BIG SODA LAKE (NEVADA) 39° 31′ N, 118° 52′ W; area 161.6 ha; 23 July 1933							
0	9.3	—	—	—	—	—	1,800	2,234	—	0	—	8,200
60	9.3	—	—	—	—	—	11,030	12,515	—	786	—	27,300

The table lists all the meromictic lakes in the area known to the author. All are in Washington except Big Soda Lake, Nevada. Hall Lake is the only soft-water lake in the list; it is about 15 km north of Seattle. The other Washington lakes are all in the arid central part of the state. The list is arranged geographically. Lakes 2–5 are in Okanogan County, 6 and 7 are in Grant County, Washington. Note the similar longitude of the saline lakes, 2–8. Note also the confusing fact that there are two meromictic lakes in the state of Washington called Soap Lake, one in the Lower Grand Coulee, which is in Grant County (No. 6), and one in Okanogan County (No. 5). Also No. 4 (Blue Lake) is not the Blue Lake in the Lower Grand Coulee. Analyses of Hall Lake are by C. S. Howard, U.S. Geological Survey, of Big Soda Lake from Hutchinson, 1937, others from U.S. Bureau of Reclamation. The sulfide values of 18.5 and 19.5 given for Soap Lake are interpolated from determinations at slightly different depths on 7 September 1955. Note that the values for carbonate and bicarbonate at depths in Soap Lake have been corrected for interference from sulfide.

few of the results have yet been published (Edmondson, 1956, 1961b, and unpublished; Main, 1953; Foreman, 1953). With an area of 2.8 ha and a maximum depth of about 16 m, it is well protected from the wind by hills and trees, and meromixis apparently is maintained biogenically. The water is humic, with only a moderate amount of dissolved salts (Table 13.1). The lake produces a very dense population of *Oscillatoria agardhii* at a depth of about 4 m, with an observed maximum cell volume of 57.6 million μ^3/ml and a maximum chlorophyll concentration of 48.6 µg/L. Rather large populations of zooplankton develop, including a *Daphnia* maximum of 198 per L. A conspicuous population of *Chaoborus* lives planktonically, descending to the lower levels of the mixolimnion during the day where it is easily sampled with quantitative zooplankton apparatus (maximum about 3 per L, with most values ranging between 0.1 and 0.4).

The chemistry and plankton population of the lake was studied during a three-year period (see Fig. 13.4; see also Oana and Deevey, 1960).

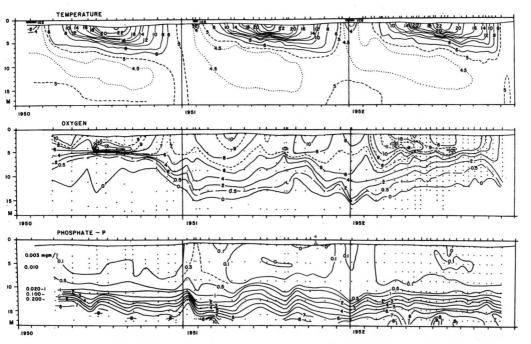

Fig. 13.4.—Distribution of temperature, oxygen, and phosphate in Hall Lake for a three-year period. Isotherms are shown for even degrees in solid lines, for others in broken lines. Lines of equal oxygen distribution are shown for even numbered values of mg/L, for others with broken lines. The line marked 0 shows the upper limit of the anaerobic layer. Note the oxygen maximum at about 4 m in 1950 and 1952. Lines of equal phosphorus concentration are in microgram-atoms/liter. Corresponding values for the first date of collection as mg/L are shown on the scale at the left.

Since the lake level varies, the data are plotted below an arbitrary, fixed level. The dots on the lower two panels show the time and depth of each analysis. The temperatures were read from bathythermograms taken on dates shown by short lines on the upper margin.

Note that early in 1951 relatively high phosphate values appear at the surface, but not in 1952. In the latter year the phytoplankton remained much more abundant all winter than in 1951, and high particulate P values were found.

Central Washington

Lower Grand Coulee

During the Pleistocene the Columbia River was dammed by ice at about the present location of Grand Coulee Dam and flowed to the south (Bretz, 1932). One of the major results of the cutting done by the diverted river is the Grand Coulee, a steep-sided gorge about 300 m deep, 1–2 km wide, and 70 km long (Fig. 13.1). A number of basins were scoured out in the southern half of the Coulee, and they now hold water forming a chain of lakes. The northernmost, Falls Lake, lies against a cliff, Dry Falls, over which

the river was plunging just before it returned to its original bed (photograph in Hutchinson, 1957, Plate 5). Dry Falls divides the Coulee into two approximately equal parts; the northern part was occupied only by temporary waters until about 1952 when it was filled with water to serve as a reservoir. The lakes form a salinity gradient series, with relatively freshwater lakes at the north and two quite saline lakes (Soap and Lenore) at the south (Table 13.2; Fig. 13.5).

Since about 1947 an irrigation project based on Grand Coulee Dam has considerably modified the hydrology of the region with consequent dilution of the lakes. In the late 1940's the water level began rising naturally in a number of closed

Fig. 13.5.—Aerial view up the Lower Grand Coulee, Washington, from the south, 11 October 1950. Soap Lake is in the foreground and Lake Lenore in the upper part. The southern tip of Blue Lake is visible just below the upper right corner. The white lines east and west of Soap Lake are concrete irrigation ditches in process of construction. Note the steep Coulee wall to the west of the lakes; there is a similar one to the east which does not show because of the angle of illumination and view. Photograph by U.S. Bureau of Reclamation.

TABLE 13.2

Analyses of surface water of lakes in Lower Grand Coulee, Washington. Data from Bureau of Reclamation. For location of lakes, see inset of Figure 13.1.

Lake	Date	Total dissolved solids (mg/L)	pH	Ca	Mg	Na	K	CO₃	HCO₃	SO₄	Cl
								Ions (mg/L)			
Soap	29 May 1945	37,112	9.5	9.2	15.4	13,292	1,188.2	7,746	5,613	6,653	4,988
Lenore		16,902	9.6	5.8	14.8	6,274	539.6	3,962	3,812	2,655	1,775
Blue		392	8.4	19.2	29.0	81.4	0.0	18.0	342.8	34.1	17.8
Park		290	8.8	25.0	19.0	54.3	0.0	15.3	241.6	33.1	5.3
Falls		246	8.2	25.6	16.1	32.7	0.0	10.2	183.0	25.9	8.7
Deep		198	8.1	24.8	12.4	25.3	0.0	0.0	181.8	16.8	4.6
Soap	19 April 1955	21,200	9.8	3.2	19.5	7,245	676	3,420	4,588	3,970	2,797
Lenore		8,740	9.6	3.2	20.7	2,990	258	1,029	4,002	1,421	827
Blue		406	8.4	22.4	22.6	54.3	7.8	6.6	267.2	26.4	12.8
Park		248	8.2	26.0	17.2	35.6	5.1	0.0	221.4	25.7	10.6
Falls		256	8.1	25.6	18.5	33.8	5.1	0.0	212.3	26.4	10.3
Deep		312	8.4	24.0	13.4	22.1	3.9	0.6	164.7	23.5	7.1

basins in the arid parts of Washington, but the levels of Soap Lake and Lake Lenore have continued to rise at a rate that cannot be accounted for on natural grounds. It became necessary for the U.S. Bureau of Reclamation to pump water from the two lakes to keep the town of Soap Lake from being flooded (Fig. 13.5). Water from irrigated land appears to work its way through aquifers in the basaltic rock layers of the region and enter the lakes. Since 1946 when Soap Lake had its maximum recorded salinity of 39.4 g/L and Lenore 18.8 g/L, the two lakes have been diluted to 45% and 27% of the original salinity, respectively, and the biota has changed distinctly (Fig. 13.6; Table 13.2). The northern lakes in the series have also changed.

The first indication of the biotal change in response to the decreasing salinity was the appearance in the summer of 1954 in Soap Lake of a bloom of *Chaetoceros elmorei*, a diatom characteristic of moderately saline, alkaline lakes. During 1950 this diatom was abundant in Lake Lenore, but it had not been seen previously in Soap Lake (G. C. Anderson, 1958a). Available field data suggest that this species becomes abundant in a range of about 10–30 g/L total dissolved salts, although it has been found in as little as 0.40 g/L.

Formerly Soap Lake had only three species of metazoa in quantity in the zooplankton—*Moina hutchinsoni* Brehm, *Hexarthra fennica* (Levander), and *Brachionus plicatilis* Müller. Lake Lenore had these and, in addition, *Diaptomus sicilis* S. A. Forbes in large numbers and *Diaptomus nevaden-sis* Light in smaller numbers. These two saline lakes produce very dense zooplankton populations, and for much of the summer the population density of rotifers and Cladocera is so high that it is easily noticeable to a person standing on the shore of the lake. In 1957 *Diaptomus sicilis* became established in Soap Lake, and in the following year *Daphnia similis* Claus appeared in Lake Lenore and has been increasing in population density ever since (Fig. 13.6). In 1961 the large rotifer *Asplanchna sylvestrii* was found in both lakes. Lake Lenore has certain chemical and biotal resemblances to Devil's Lake, North Dakota, including the presence of *Brachionus satanicus* Rousselet, first described from Devil's Lake (Young, 1924; Swenson and Colby, 1955).

The Coulee lakes also produce dense phytoplankton populations, but at times of zooplankton abundance the phytoplankton appears to be kept at a very low level by grazing (G. C. Anderson et al., 1955; G. C. Anderson, 1958a). The rate of reproduction of copepods in Lake Lenore is clearly correlated with phytoplankton abundance (Edmondson et al., 1962).

The bottom fauna of the two lakes has been studied in detail (Lauer, 1959). The benthic population, like the plankton, is rather specialized and limited in number of species. Mollusks and oligochaetes are absent, the larger bottom fauna being limited to insects. Mean standing crops during a 14-month period of study were 29.7 and 28.8 g/m² wet weight with seasonal maxima of 123 and 121 g/m² for Soap and Lenore, respectively. These quantities stand very high relative

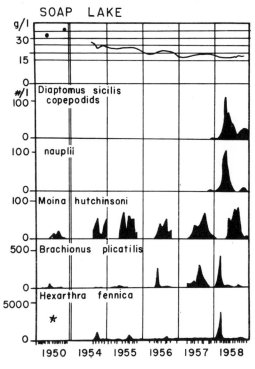

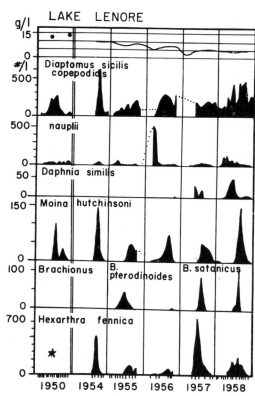

Fig. 13.6.—Population density of zooplankton in Soap Lake and Lake Lenore 1950–58. The top panel shows the salinity. The marks along the bottom show the dates on which collections were made.

* Hexarthra was abundant in both lakes in 1950, but counts are not available.

to other lakes and are minimal estimates because the very active Hemiptera and Coleoptera present in large numbers were hardly sampled by the Ekman dredge. The beetle *Hygrotus masculinus* (Crotch) became established in Soap Lake in 1955 and has become very abundant since. The hemipteran *Cenocorixa expleta* (Uhler) was present in 1950 in small numbers, but apparently has become much more abundant in the past ten years.

Various characteristics of the lakes have been studied throughout the period of changing salinity. Soap Lake is meromictic with a very dense monimolimnion, which has changed little (Fig. 13.7; Table 13.1). The monimolimnion has the highest concentration of total sulfides yet recorded (cf. Big Soda Lake: Hutchinson, 1957). Its meromixis was evidently established long before the present reduction in salinity. Before the reduction, large crystals of mirabilite ($Na_2SO_4 \cdot 10H_2O$) appeared on the bottom of Soap Lake every winter (cf. Little Manitou: Rawson and Moore, 1942). Studies of mixing have been made in the

alkaline upper waters by following clouds of water dusted with powdered phenolphthalein and in the lower water by marking with a quantity of radiorubidium which was then traced by a Geiger probe on the end of a cable. This work, which has not yet been fully published, has been referred to in a preliminary way by Hutchinson (1957). Measurements of isotopes of carbon, hydrogen, and sulfur provide valuable insight to processes of exchange, evaporation, and flow (Deevey *et al.*, 1954; Oana and Deevey, 1960; Redfield, personal communication). Deuterium shows considerable differences among the lakes of the Lower Grand Coulee and at different depths in Soap Lake; the saline lakes and the deep water of Soap Lake are enriched (Friedman and Redfield, personal communication).

The two saline lakes in the Lower Grand Coulee have essentially no rooted vegetation, and the shore regions have rock or gravel bottoms, covered with a thin film of periphyton. The periphytic algae, especially diatoms, of the two saline lakes and two relatively freshwater lakes were studied extensively in 1955 and 1956 by Castenholtz (1960). The population growth rate measured on glass plates as increment of organic material could exceed 500 mg/m² per day during the spring and fall periods, but the maximum rate ever observed, 1,043 mg/m² per day, occurred during the winter in Soap Lake. There appear to be two distinct periods of relatively rapid growth with a summer minimum. Castenholtz suggests that the summer population minimum is the result of a real decrease in growth rate, not of grazing, although special experiments were not carried out to test the point.

Other lakes in the Columbia Basin

In addition to the series of lakes in the Lower Grand Coulee just discussed, there are many other waters varying from temporary ponds with a remarkably rich fauna of Anostraca, Notostraca, and Conchostraca to large lakes distributed throughout the semiarid Columbia Basin. This distribution of Cladocera and Copepoda in 40 lakes of various size and temporary ponds with a range of dissolved salts from 0.170 to 88.0 g/L was studied with special reference to the salinity range of each species. Complete mineral analyses were made (Whittaker and Fairbanks, 1958; additional analyses by Walter and McNeil, 1959). Most saline lakes were dominated by *Moina hutchinsoni* as in Soap Lake, the ponds by *Artemia salina*. Some copepods had their maximum population density at intermediate salinities. *Diaptomus sicilis*, which entered Soap Lake when the salinity became about 19 g/L, was found in a salinity as low as 0.325 g/L, but the largest populations were found at about 4.5 g/L. The mean population density of all species together increased with increasing salinity up to about 10 g/L, but the increase of population density with salinity was much greater in ponds than in lakes, and the maximum population densities achieved were about twice as high in the ponds as in the lakes. A detailed analysis of species groups in relation to salinity was presented. Some of the species have been studied in culture (Parker, 1960, 1961).

Irrigation, which has changed Soap Lake, has brought many new bodies of fresh water into existence and has eliminated many former sites of temporary saline waters, among them the type locality of the remarkable *Branchinecta gigas* Lynch, a fairy shrimp 10 cm long.

An unusual meromictic lake, Hot Lake, north of the Columbia Basin occupies a basin from which magnesium sulfate has been mined (G. C. Anderson, 1958*b*). The deepest water at 3.5 m is saturated with magnesium sulfate with about 400 g/L, while the surface water ordinarily is between 100 and 200 g/L (Table 13.1). The strongly stable salinity stratification and the fact that the anaerobic deep waters were made turbid by bacteria resulted in an accumulation of heat at about 2 m depth and the development of temperatures in excess of 50° C by the middle of summer. Even when the lake was frozen over in winter, temperatures of 25° C were found near the bottom. A breeding population of *Artemia salina* occurred during the entire year, varying in its depth distribution with the temperature. During the spring of 1955 the lake became covered with a layer of relatively fresh water from melting snow, and in this layer a large population of *Branchinecta mackini* Dexter, a relatively freshwater species, developed.

Lake Chelan apparently has not been reinvestigated since the initial survey by Kemmerer *et al.* (1924). This lake, 76 km long, occupies a narrow valley in the Cascade Range. Its upper end lies in the Cascade Mountains and receives water from melting snow. The southeastern end lies in the semiarid Columbia Basin, and thus there is a possibility of rather interesting hori-

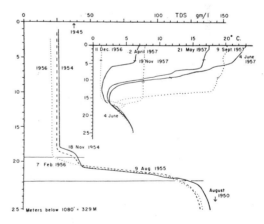

Fig. 13.7.—Salinity and temperature in Soap Lake. The salinity values are based on *in situ* measurements of conductivity at 1-meter intervals (Edmondson, 1956) and are plotted below a fixed elevation because the lake level was variable. The surface value for 1945 and the bottom value for 1950 are shown by vertical arrows. The inset shows bathythermograph data plotted below lake surface. The cross mark on each line indicates Secchi disc transparency.

zontal gradients in various properties of the lake. Kemmerer *et al.* reported a slight temperature inversion, with 5.9° at 458 m and 5.6° at 300 and 450 m in the deepest part of the lake. Whether the lake is meromictic remains to be seen in future investigations. Full meromixis is unlikely since the bottom oxygen was 90% saturated, but mixing may well be incomplete in some years.

Columbia River

One of the major rivers in North America is the Columbia River, which drains an area of about 670,800 km² in southern Canada and northwest United States. Most of the area of the state of Washington lies in the Columbia Basin. The mean annual flow of the river near its mouth is 5,527 m³/second. Because of the commercial importance of the salmon population in this river and its tributaries and because of the great development of hydroelectric and irrigation projects along the Columbia River, it has a great amount of interest (Craig and Hacker, 1940). Studies have been made on certain sites that will be affected by future dams. Several lakes have been artificially created by the dams, the principal one of which is Roosevelt Lake behind Grand Coulee Dam.

The existence of a large installation at Hanford, Washington, for the manufacture of plutonium has led to investigation of the accumulation of isotopes in aquatic organisms (Coopey, 1953; Davis *et al.*, 1959; Davis and Foster, 1958). Zinc-65 is found in the organisms in the Columbia River and in the Pacific Ocean near the mouth of the river (Watson *et al.*, 1961). An elaborate study of phosphorus metabolism in aquarium microcosms was carried out at Hanford using phosphorus-32 (Whittaker, 1961).

The chief sources of information on conditions in the Columbia River (Robeck *et al.*, 1954; Sylvester, 1958) are devoted primarily to chemical and physical conditions but do include data on the kind and quantity of plankton and bottom fauna at several stations in the lower Columbia.

In general in the upstream stations, 400 mi from the mouth, the maximum population densities of total phytoplankton are achieved in May and June, with the increase from January being interrupted by a sharp drop in April. Downstream, at 278 mi, the population densities

achieved are about twice as great as upstream, and the seasonal variation is somewhat different, with dense populations in January being followed by a period of decline to April and an abrupt resurgence to seasonal maxima in July and August with secondary maxima in November. Qualitatively the chief difference among the stations is a very great increase in the number of diatoms downstream, largely *Cyclotella*. *Cyclotella* becomes very abundant in the Snake and Walla Walla rivers during the summer and autumn, and apparently this is the source of the organism in the lower reaches of the Columbia. Myxophyceae are of consequence only in the upstream stations.

The bottom fauna of the Columbia River is rich, with about 37.7 g/m² wet weight (more than 2,875 individual organisms per m²) at the richest station and about half this amount at the least. The population is dominated in numbers by Trichoptera, Diptera, and Ephemeroptera, but on a weight basis, mollusks are important. The major tributaries—Yakima River, Snake River, and Walla Walla River—have rather denser populations on the basis of numbers than do any of the Columbia River stations. The Walla Walla River has a very large population of Trichoptera and Diptera, with a total wet weight of about 140 g/m².

The chemical characteristics of the water are, of course, strongly affected by the lateral tributaries, some of which originate in melting snow fields. After the river comes down to the Oregon border, it passes through the Cascade Mountains and thus enters a climatically very different region, and the tributaries that enter contain water of somewhat lesser dissolved solid content than in the arid region of the state. Roosevelt Lake receives most of its water from tributaries that have arisen from snow fields in mountainous areas, and therefore the water is less rich in dissolved material than the water of tributaries that have come through arid lowlands. The total dissolved solid content in the upper reaches of the lake is 110 mg/L and in the lower reaches is between 40 and 54 mg/L after receiving the dilute water of the Spokane River (Robeck *et al.*, 1954).

Lake Wenatchee is the origin of one of the tributaries to the Columbia. It is a deep (100 m) soft-water lake, with total dissolved salts varying seasonally between 10 and 87 mg/L. The

Fig. 13.8.—Crater Lake showing Wizard Island with Lloa Rock in the background. Photograph courtesy

U.S. National Park Service, Crater Lake National Park.

total settled volume of zooplankton varied between 0.078 and 1.44 ml/m.³ The zooplankton is dominated numerically by rotifers, but the volume is mostly copepods which are an important item of food for the young sockeye salmon. Copepod populations varied between 127 and 1,788 individuals of copepodid stages per m³ (Sylvester and Ruggles, 1958).

Oregon

Crater Lake

One of the most spectacularly beautiful lakes in the area covered in this chapter is Crater Lake, Oregon (Fig. 13.8). Unfortunately, it has not received the limnological study it deserves. The lake is easily accessible to viewing by tourists, but the difficult descent from the rim to the lake surface 300 m below has evidently inhibited investigation. Nevertheless, some interesting information has been obtained (Kemmerer et al., 1924; Pettit, 1936; Utterback et al., 1942; Hasler, 1938). The lake occupies a collapsed caldera, modified by secondary activity to provide a volcanic island. The maximum depth, 608 m (mean 364 m), makes this the deepest lake in the United States and the seventh deepest in

the world. Total dissolved salts are 80 mg/L. Phosphate values are rather high, up to 0.015 mg/L. The water has a rather large amount of minute fragments of suspended volcanic glass, but this has little optical significance, and the Secchi disc transparency is high (25 m: Pettit, 1936; Hutchinson, 1957). *Fontinalis* grows to a depth of 120 m (Hasler, 1938).

The phytoplankton in the single sampling had a maximum at 100 m of 3,250 cells per ml, largely *Anabaena*. The zooplankton appears to be dominated by *Daphnia*. On the basis of the contents of trout stomachs, the bottom fauna includes Diptera (presumably tendipedids), Trichoptera larvae, and *Hyalella*, although no direct evidence exists on the quantity and character of the bottom fauna. Some fish stomachs contained *Daphnia* and, unexpectedly, *Chaoborus*.

Upper Klamath Lake in Oregon has attracted attention because of its naturally high productivity, as manifested by nuisance productions of algae, without evidence of enrichment by human activity (Kemmerer et al., 1924; Phinney and Peek, 1961). The lake is large but shallow (56 km long, a few km wide, 8 m deep) and receives drainage from a very large marshy area south of

Crater Lake. It develops dense standing crops of Myxophyceae, as many as 194,756 filaments of *Aphanizomenon* per L having been observed. The lake is in a region of mineral waters and, as a wildlife refuge, is host to a large population of birds.

California

California is the largest state covered in this chapter, and while it has relatively fewer standing waters than the area to the north, it has a great diversity of lakes from the mountainous, more humid north to the arid south (Foshag, 1926; Davis, 1933). Some of the lakes will be discussed in connection with the Great Basin.

Castle Lake

The productivity of Castle Lake (Fig. 13.9), at present under intensive investigation, has been shown to be strongly influenced by the presence of nitrogen-fixing alder trees (*Alnus tenuifolia*) (Fig. 13.10). Since the trees are limited to the east side of the lake, opportunity existed to detect localized effects of drainage within the lake, the primary production being distinctly higher on the east side and in samples enriched with drainage from alder soil (Goldman, 1961). The annual mean photosynthetic fixation of carbon was 0.098 g/m² per day (range 0.006–0.317; trophogenic zone 8–30 m thick) (Goldman, personal communication). Added molybdenum increased the primary production (Goldman, 1960). The lake has been lightly fertilized in connection with fishery work (Wales, 1946; Wales and German, 1956).

Clear Lake

Clear Lake has attracted attention because of very large emergences of the culicid dipteran *Chaoborus astictopus* (Meigen), locally known as "the Clear Lake Gnat," which creates nuisances by congregating around lights and cooking stoves. How much they inadvertently contribute to the human diet has not been computed. At the height of the emergence season, as many as 3.5 billion individual flies may leave the lake in one night, and the total annual production may be 712 billion, amounting to 324 metric tons live weight.

The number of benthic larvae in a large series of samples through a three-year period varied from about 1,100 to 11,000 per m². The aver-age population approximates 7,000 per m² (Deonier, 1943; Lindquist and Deonier, 1942, 1943). *Chaoborus* larvae are an important item in the diet of many species in the rather rich fish fauna of the lake (Lindquist *et al.*, 1943; Murphy, 1949, 1950, 1951; Coleman, 1930). There is often a high summer mortality of fish. Although the lake is 114 km² in area and only about 9 m deep, on calm summer days the deeper water becomes depleted of oxygen. Clear Lake is very productive; the mean annual photosynthetic fixation of carbon is 0.438 g/m² per day (range 0.002–2.44) (Goldman, personal communication).

Convict Creek Basin

An extensive limnological study has been made of ten clear lakes (Fig. 13.11) in glacial basins at altitudes between 2,311 m and 3,338 m in the Sierra Nevada of California at about latitude 38° N. (Reimers *et al.*, 1955; Reimers and Combs, 1956). The ice-free period varies among the lakes from roughly two to six months. The maximum temperature observed was 19.4° C. The lakes vary in size from 1.8 to 68.0 ha, with maximum depths from 7.6 to 88 m. They lie in a basin of complex geology and mineralogy; most of the drainage comes from rather insoluble rocks.

The total salt content of the lakes varies with the position of the drainage system and character of the basin from 16 to 74 mg/L. Analyses were made of minor elements as well as major ions. The lakes are of the calcium bicarbonate type except for one which has more sulfate than bicarbonate and three others which have rela-

Fig. 13.9.—Castle Lake, California, looking north toward cinder cone. Note the alder trees along the east shore (cf. Goldman, 1961, Fig. 1). Photograph by Charles Goldman.

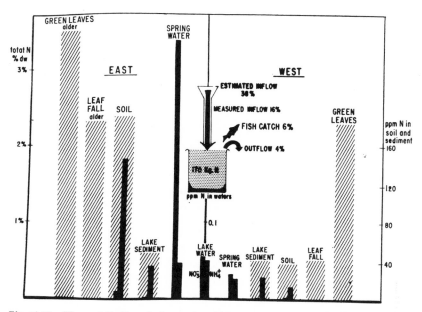

Fig. 13.10.—The contribution of nitrogen by alder trees (*Alnus tenuifolia* Nutt.) to Castle Lake, California, is evident from a comparison of the nitrogen distribution on the east and west sides of the lake. The cross-hatched bars represent the total Kjeldahl nitrogen as per cent dry weight of the alder and other deciduous plant leaves, the soil, and lake sediment. The solid bars are the ppm NO_3^- and NH_4^+ levels in the soil and sediment in accordance with the scale on the right side of the figure, while the lake and spring water values are indicated by the more exaggerated scale in the center of the figure. The average nitrogen content of the 48-acre lake with inflow, outflow, and fish removal as percentages of this average value are also given. Goldman, unpublished.

tively rather high sulfate concentrations.

Two of the lakes showed distinct temperature inversions, and one, Lake Edith, showed a higher dissolved mineral concentration at the bottom than at the surface as indicated by a conductivity of 32 micromhos (at 25° C) as compared to 24 micromhos at the surface. The oxygen, though low, was still about 32% of saturation, and it is unlikely that the lake is permanently stratified.

Settled zooplankton mean crops varied in the series of the lakes from 0.86 ml/m³ to undetectable quantities. The maximum population found at any one level was in Bright Dot Lake in the stratum 50–60 ft deep which had 2.4 ml/m³ (1,270 individuals per m³), mostly Cladocera.

The bottom fauna was generally dominated volumetrically by larvae of Diptera, but in Lake Mildred nearly half was *Gammarus* and in Big Horn Lake more than half was Oligochaeta. The total varied among the lakes from 2.15 to 23.7 g/m³ wet weight averaged for the whole lake,

Fig. 13.11.—Lakes of the Convict Creek Basin. Convict Lake is in the lower left corner. Photograph by Robert F. Symons, Bishop, California; provided by Norman Reimers.

including the rock areas which were not sampled but were presumed to be unpopulated.

The growth of periphyton on artificial substrates varied from 3.5 to 11.5 mg/m² per day of organic matter in Convict Lake, in contrast to the far higher rates obtained by Castenholz in the rich lakes of the lower Grand Coulee. The periphyton increment was closely correlated with the temperature sum calculated above 32° F ($r = 0.966$). Very likely a close correlation would have also been found with solar radiation income had measurements been made.

The object of the investigation was to characterize the lakes for their trout fisheries. Most of the lakes were populated by brook trout (*Salvelinus fontinalis*) which had been planted. As would be expected with single samplings of the food organisms, no correlation existed between the bottom fauna population, zooplankton population, and fish growth and condition. Perhaps the more successful fish populations decreased the bottom fauna to a low level. There is, nevertheless, a distinct tendency for fish growth rate to be correlated with the mineral content of the water, with the most rapid growth occurring in Bright Dot Lake which had the highest mineral content.

Alviso salt ponds

California has a solar salt industry, which evaporates sea water as it flows through a series of ponds of salinity ranging from about 28 to 94‰ (Carpelan, 1957; Gibor, 1956b). The ponds develop a very specialized and dense population of algae and animals of which *Artemia salina* is the most prominent, producing a maximum population of 13 g/m³ dry weight with an annual production of 62 kg/ha. Several species of copepods live in the fresher ponds but not in the two most saline ones where *Artemia* thrives. It is not clear how much the separation depends on salinity tolerance and how much on predatory and competitive interactions. Various insects and crustaceans live on the bottom and in the margins.

The photosynthetic assimilation of carbon, determined by oxygen production in the middle pond, was about 3.9 mg/L per day on the average for the year, giving an annual production of 1,400 mg/L.

In the ponds with *Artemia* a dense population of *Stichococcus bacillaris* exists at the same time (mean 170 mg/L dry weight in one pond), and

it might seem a bit puzzling that this alga could maintain itself in the face of heavy grazing by *Artemia*. Gibor (1956a) showed that *Stichococcus* is not digested by *Artemia* but is filtered and passed through the digestive tract unharmed. On the other hand, *Dunaliella* is digested by *Artemia*.

Salton Sea

One of the more remarkable bodies of saline water in the arid south of California is the so-called Salton Sea, a large lake which today has a salinity approximating that of sea water, although the ionic ratios are different, and has a marine fauna including a polychaete and a barnacle. The present Salton Sea occupies part of the basin of an ancient large freshwater lake near the Gulf of California. Its deepest point is 88.4 m below sea level. At various times in the past it has filled with water naturally and dried again because of the arid climate. The sea was filled most recently by human activity starting in the year 1905, when the Colorado River broke through irrigation works and flowed until 1907, filling the basin to a level of 59.4 m below sea level. At that time, the lake had a maximum depth of 25 m and covered an area of about 1,334 km.²

Subsequently there have been large fluctuations in water level and in concentration of salt. First the level decreased to a minimum of −76.2 m, because evaporation in the area exceeded the delivery of water, and salt became very concentrated. Since 1948, however, increasing flow of waste waters from irrigation has caused the level to rise, reaching −71.6 m in 1956. The waters were diluted to 33‰ from the most concentrated observed 40‰. Salts are derived by evaporation from the river inlets and by solution from the basin. The water of the Salton Sea is proportionally richer than ocean water in sulfate, calcium, carbonate, and bicarbonate, less rich in magnesium, potassium, and chloride.

The Salton Sea has received very extensive limnological study, summarized in detail by Walker et al. (1961; see also MacDougal, 1914; Coleman, 1929b; Blaney, 1955; and Carpelan, 1958). The surface temperature has varied annually between 10° and 36° C. The sea never becomes firmly stratified thermally, and at the most a temperature gradient of about 5° is established. During times of the existence of a temperature gradient during the summer, the deeper waters may become low in oxygen or even depleted while ammonia and phosphate increase, the maximum bottom ammonium nitrogen being about 0.450 mg/L and phosphate phosphorus 0.130 mg/L.

The waste water from irrigation which flows into the lake carries high concentrations of nutrients; two of the inlets average about 0.525 mg/L of N and 0.155 mg/L of P.

The phytoplankton is composed of a variety of species, but the four organisms most important volumetrically were *Nitzschia longissima*, *Cyclotella caspia*, *Glenodinum* sp. and *Exuviella compressa*. The largest population sampled had 123 million μ^3/ml of *Glenodinium* sp., but numerically the largest was 160,000 cells per ml of a minute green organism, possibly *Westella* sp.

Measurements of photosynthetic oxygen production were made at the surface at monthly intervals through a one-year period. The mean oxygen liberation was 2.0 mg/L per day with a range from 0.57 to 2.57. These values are quite high, even relative to artifically enriched lakes, and surely are related to the high nutrient concentration in the water supply. .

The benthic invertebrate fauna is fairly limited in species, but some of the organisms are abundant. The polychaete *Neanthes succinea* (Light) was introduced into the Salton Sea in 1930, had become prevalent by 1936, and is now the most important item of food for fish. Spawning occurs year round with peaks in March-June and October-November, but there appears to be no trace of a lunar periodicity.

A subspecies of the barnacle *Balanus amphitrite* (Darwin) has become very abundant since it was first observed about 1944 and now occupies essentially all of the surfaces within the lake that are hard enough for attachment. Larvae are found widely distributed in the plankton at all times of year except in January-February and part of July, with maxima in spring and autumn. Settling rates and growth rates were measured on glass slides. The growth rate in summer is fast, about ten times that in winter, and results in a maximum basal diameter of 9 mm in a month. Sexual maturity is achieved in about a month after attachment in the summer. The production of barnacles is so great that large shore areas have become covered with a sort of sand resulting from shells crushed by the surf,

and these areas are now usable for recreational purposes, whereas formerly they were too muddy.

The most abundant benthic microorganisms studied in the lake are Foraminifera, which are distributed in correlation with the nature of the sediment (Arnal, 1961). The fauna is rather restricted in species, presumably because the temperature and other features are much more variable than in the ocean. Some of the species show a high degree of malformations particularly in places in the Salton Sea where fresh water enters; apparently, variable salinity affects their development.

The zooplankton, in addition to having larvae of the benthic animals, is dominated by the rotifer *Brachionus plicatilis* (Müller) and the copepod *Cyclops dimorphus* (Kiefer). The maximum populations observed were 998 and 535 per L, respectively. Both have very pronounced seasonal changes in population density, with both the rotifer and the copepod being essentially absent during winter and spring.

Marine fish have been introduced into the Salton Sea, and several species have survived, but only a few have done well. *Bairdiella icistius* (Jordan and Gilbert) has become quite abundant and is an important food item for the one important game fish, *Cynoscion xanthulus* (Jordan and Gilbert).

Other studies in California

Lack of space prevents more discussion of the very scattered literature on Californian waters. The following papers give some data on water chemistry, bottom fauna, and plankton of streams and lakes: Abel (1959), Aldrich (1961), Allen (1920: much quantitative information), Calhoun (1944a, 1944b), Clarke (1924), Cordone and Kelley (1961), Juday (1907), Needham (1934, 1937, 1940), Needham and Jones (1959), Needham and Usinger (1956), Reimers (1957, 1958), Pister (1960), Maciolek and Needham (1952). Lake Tahoe is discussed by Kemmerer *et al.* (1924) and Coleman (1926, 1929a). Mono Lake is described by Putnam (1950) and Dunn (1953). A number of reservoirs in southern California have been studied by McEwen (1941), M. W. Johnson (1949), J. W. Johnson (1948), Munk and Anderson (1948), and Ramsey (1960). A series of salt lagoons, estuaries of small streams in a region 20 mi north of La Jolla, have been studied extensively from an ecological point of view (Carpelan, 1961, and private communication). The lagoons are partly isolated and vary in salinity from nearly fresh to almost fully coastal-oceanic salinity. Studies of events in sewage oxidation lagoons are of interest (Allen, 1955).

The Great Basin

The Great Basin, a large and arid region of internal drainage, contains many saline lakes and many temporary lakes which are occupied with water only in rare rainy periods. The eastern and western parts of the basin became occupied during the Pleistocene with two enormous freshwater lakes, Lake Bonneville and Lake Lahontan, respectively. Lake Bonneville drained to the north through the Snake River, while Lake Lahontan had no outlet. Subsequently, with increasing aridity, water levels fell, leaving behind many lakes (Fig. 13.1). Great Salt Lake is the principal remnant of Lake Bonneville; the more irregular Lake Lahontan has left several smaller lakes. The complex history of geology and climate are summarized in detail in the chapter on paleolimnology by Bradley, and in Russell (1885), Blackwelder (1948), and Antevs (1948). An elaborate discussion of the distribution of fish is given by Hubbs and Miller (1948). Much information on the chemistry of the water is presented by Clarke (1924) and Whitehead and Feth (1961).

The major limnological work in the Great Basin is that of Hutchinson (1937) on five lakes in the Lahontan Basin (see also Summer, 1939). Big Soda is especially interesting since it is meromictic. The lake is 64.2 m deep, with a mixolimnion about 10 m thick (Hutchinson, 1957: Figs. 12, 144). The level of the lake rose by nearly 18 m between 1905 and 1933 as a result of alteration of the water table by irrigation. It appears that the meromixis is of relatively recent origin, probably related to the major rise in water level between 1911 and 1927, which spread relatively fresh water over the saline lake. The deep water had 786 mg/L of H_2S, and the specific gravity was 1.066. As is usual in saline meromictic lakes, there was a strong temperature inversion. Another remarkable lake is Big Washoe, with an area of about 10 km² but a maximum depth of about 0.5 m. Two of the lakes contained a cladoceran named *Moina hutchinsoni* by Brehm, later found to be widely distributed

in the arid regions of western North America. Considerable attention has been given to the fisheries of Pyramid Lake, Walker Lake, and Lake Tahoe.

The lake in the Great Basin that is most familiar to tourists is Great Salt Lake, but it has received surprisingly little limnological study (McDonald, 1956). The lake is saline, having varied between 137.9 and 277.2 g/L total dissolved salts since 1869 (Clarke, 1924) with changes in climatic conditions. The area, over 6,000 km², varies with the level. The lake had a mean depth of 9 m in 1940 when the level was at a minimum; the level had stood 11 m higher in 1873. Recently, diversions of water from the inlets for use by the growing human population of the area have threatened to reduce the level of the lake greatly. The flora and fauna are qualitatively restricted, but some species may become extremely abundant. *Artemia* sometimes occurs so densely in streaks and patches as to be conspicuous from airplanes. Windrows of decaying *Artemia* occasionally reduce the oxygen content of the water to zero. The bottom fauna is dominated by larvae of two species of the dipteran *Ephydra*. The phytoplankton includes a variety of algae, mostly Myxophyceae.

Considerable information has been obtained in the laboratory on feeding and growth of *Artemia* from Mono Lake (Mason, 1961).

The Colorado River and impoundments

The Colorado River, which forms the southeastern border of the region considered in this chapter, flows from origins in the Rocky Mountains to the Gulf of California. Dams on it create large hydroelectric and irrigation operations. The best known of these is Hoover Dam, forming Lake Mead on the Nevada-Arizona border and extending into Nevada.

Lake Mead is the site of one of the major concerted investigations of physical limnology in the country, with special attention to heat and water budgets and flow patterns (Bell, 1942; E. R. Anderson et al., 1950; Gould, 1951; E. R. Anderson and Pritchard, 1951; Smith et al., 1960; Saur and Anderson, 1956). The investigation of Anderson and Pritchard involved monthly cruises to 68 stations for a year with measurements of salinity and temperature on which were based a detailed analysis of flow patterns, evaporation, and energy budget, using in general the techniques and viewpoints of physical oceanography. In winter the Colorado River brings in water with a salinity ranging from about 840 to 1,200 mg/L, which can be traced as a tongue into the depths of the more dilute lake water (Hutchinson, 1957: Fig. 84). During the spring the river water is much more dilute (about 220 mg/L), and the lake acts as a large mixing bowl in which the diversity of the inflowing water is averaged as it flows toward the dam. When the river is carrying a high silt content, tongues of very turbid water flow down into the lake so sharply separated from the lake water that the interface can be clearly seen in a transparent water bottle (Bell, 1942; Gould, 1951). Much sediment has been deposited in Lake Mead since its formation. The newest sediments are very soft, and a bathythermograph may settle 6 m into the sediments before coming to rest. This has permitted observations on the temperature profile within sediments. There is a sharp positive gradient, with temperature increasing, for example, by as much at 4.8° C in less than 2 m of depth. Evidence has been presented that the heat has accumulated from microbial action (ZoBell *et al.*, 1953). The distribution of lead-210, which seems useful as a tracer, has been investigated in Lake Mead and other waters (Rama and Goldberg, 1961).

Summary

The four general topics listed at the end of the introduction of this chapter have been evident in the foregoing discussion. Material pertinent to the relation between nutrient supply and productivity can be found in the studies of Lake Washington, Castle Lake, Salton Sea, and some of the other localities cited. The interrelations of climate, salinity, and biota are included in the work in Central Washington, Salton Sea, and the Great Basin. Several excellent examples of meromictic lakes are found in the region, and to the extent that the study of extreme conditions illuminates the usual, studies of permanent stratification contribute to an understanding of the effect of stratification on limnological processes.

In several of the arid regions of the West, artificial changes in hydrology of large regions by irrigation or by diversion of water have created new lakes and altered the character of existing ones. While some of these alterations are best known for their economic aspects, they present the limnologist with challenging large-scale experiments which can provide valuable opportunities for analysis of complex processes. Similarly, the more familiar problem of artificial enrichment of lakes with various nutrients amounts to a gigantic experiment which no individual limnologist could arrange, but which can provide him with useful material for analysis, especially when, as in Lake Washington, the process of enrichment is reversed.

Acknowledgment

The unpublished data in Figures 13.3, 13.4, 13.6, and 13.7 were obtained with the aid of grants from the National Science Foundation, the National Institutes of Health, and the State of Washington Initiative 171 Fund for Research in Biology and Medicine, to which the author expresses gratitude.

References

ABEL, D. L. 1959. Observations on mosquito populations of an intermittent stream in California. Ecology, **40**: 186–193.

ALDRICH, F. A. 1961. Seasonal variations in the benthic invertebrate fauna of the San Joaquin River Estuary of California, with emphasis on the amphipod, *Corophium spinicorne* Stimpson. Proc. Acad. Nat. Sci., Philadelphia, **113**: 21–28.

ALLEN, M. B. 1955. General features of algal growth in sewage oxidation ponds. California Water Pollution Control Board, Sacramento, Publ. No. 13, 48 p.

ALLEN, W. E. 1920. A quantitative and statistical study of the plankton of the San Joaquin River and its tributaries in and near Stockton, California, in 1913. Univ. California Studies Zool., **22**: 1–292.

ANDERSON, E. R., L. J. ANDERSON, AND J. J. MARCIANO. 1950. A review of evaporation theory and development of instrumentation. U.S. Navy Electronics Lab., San Diego, California, Rept. 159, 62 p.

ANDERSON, E. R., AND D. W. PRITCHARD. 1951. Final report: Physical limnology of Lake Mead. U.S. Navy Electronics Lab., San Diego, California, Rept 258, 152 p.

ANDERSON, G. C. 1958a. Seasonal characteristics of two saline lakes in Washington. Limnol. Oceanogr., **3**: 51–68.

———. 1958b. Some limnological features of a shallow saline meromictic lake. Limnol. Oceanogr., **3**: 259–270.

———. 1961. Recent changes in the trophic condition of Lake Washington, p. 27–33. *In* Algae and metropolitan wastes, Robert A. Taft Sanit. Engr. Center, Cincinnati 26, Ohio, Tech. Rept. W 61-3.

ANDERSON, G. C., G. W. COMITA, AND VERNA ENGSTROM-HEG. 1955. A note on the phytoplankton-zooplankton relationships in two lakes in Washington. Ecology, **36**: 757–759.

ANTEVS, E. 1948. Climatic changes and pre-white

man, p. 168–191. *In* A symposium on the Great Basin with emphasis on glacial and postglacial times. Bull. Univ. Utah, Biol. Ser., 10(7).

ARNAL, R. E. 1961. Limnology, sedimentation, and microorganisms of the Salton Sea, California. Bull. Geol. Soc. Amer., **72**: 427–478.

BELL, H. S. 1942. Stratified flow in reservoirs and its use in prevention of silting. U.S. Dept. Agr., Misc. Publ. 491, 30 p.

BLACKWELDER, E. 1948. The geological background, p. 3–16. *In* A symposium on the Great Basin with emphasis on glacial and postglacial times. Bull. Univ. Utah, Biol. Ser., 10(7).

BLANEY, H. F. 1955. Evaporation from and stabilization of Salton Sea water surface. Trans. Amer. Geophys. Union, **36**: 633–640.

BRETZ, J. H. 1910. Glacial lakes of Puget Sound. J. Geol., **18**: 448–458.

———. 1913. Glaciation of the Puget Sound region. Washington Geol. Surv., Bull. No. 8, 244 p.

———. 1932. The Grand Coulee. Amer. Geograph. Soc., Spec. Publ. 15, 89 p.

CALHOUN, A. J. 1944a. The bottom fauna of Blue Lake, California. California Fish and Game, **30**: 86–94.

———. 1944b. The food of the black-spotted trout (*Salmo clarkii henshawi*) in two Sierra Nevada lakes. California Fish and Game, **30**: 80–85.

CARPELAN, L. H. 1957. Hydrobiology of the Alviso salt ponds. Ecology, **38**: 375–390.

———. 1958. The Salton Sea: Physical and chemical characteristics. Limnol. Oceanogr., **3**: 373–386.

———. 1961. Salinity tolerances of some fishes of a southern California coastal lagoon. Copeia, 1961: 32–39.

CASTENHOLZ, R. W. 1960. Seasonal changes in the attached algae of fresh water and saline lakes in the Lower Grand Coulee, Washington. Limnol. Oceanogr., **5**: 1–28.

CLARKE, F. W. 1924. The data of geochemistry. U.S. Geol. Surv., Bull. No. 770, 841 p.

COLEMAN, G. A. 1926. Conditions of existence of fish in Lake Tahoe and tributary streams. California Fish and Game, **12**: 23–27.

———. 1929a. A biological survey of Lake Tahoe. California Fish and Game, **15**: 99–102.

———. 1929b. A biological survey of the Salton Sea. California Fish and Game, **15**: 218–227.

———. 1930. A biological survey of Clear Lake, Lake County. California Fish and Game, **16**: 221–227.

COMITA, G. W., AND G. C. ANDERSON. 1959. The seasonal development of a population of *Diaptomus ashlandi* Marsh, and related phytoplankton cycles in Lake Washington. Limnol. Oceanogr., **4**: 37–52.

COOPEY, R. W. 1953. Radioactive plankton from the Columbia River. Trans. Amer. Microscop. Soc., **72**: 315–327.

CORDONE, A. J., AND D. W. KELLEY. 1961. The influences of inorganic sediment on the aquatic life of streams. California Fish and Game, **47**: 189–228.

CRAIG, J. A., AND R. L. HACKER. 1940. History and development of the fisheries of the Columbia River. U.S. Bur. Fish., Fish. Bull., **32**: 133–216.

DAVIS, J. J., AND R. F. FOSTER. 1958. Bioaccumulation of radioisotopes through aquatic food chains. Ecology, **39**: 530–535.

DAVIS, J. J., R. W. PERKINS, R. F. PALMER, W. C. HANSON, AND J. F. CLINE. 1959. Radioactive materials in aquatic and terrestrial organisms exposed to reactor effluent water. 2nd U.N. Geneva Conf.: 423–428.

DAVIS, W. M. 1933. The lakes of California. California J. Mines, **39**: 175–236.

DEEVEY, E. S., JR., M. S. GROSS, AND G. E. HUTCHINSON. 1954. The natural C^{14} contents of materials from hard-water lakes. Proc. Natl. Acad. Sci., Washington, **40**: 285–288.

DEONIER, C. C. 1943. Biology of the immature stages of the Clear Lake Gnat. Ann. Entomol. Soc. Amer., **36**: 383–388.

DUNN, J. R. 1953. The origin of the deposits of tufa in Mono Lake. J. Sediment. Petrol., **23**: 18–23.

EDMONDSON, W. T. 1956. Measurement of conductivity of lake water *in situ*. Ecology, **37**: 201–204.

———. 1961a. Changes in Lake Washington following an increase in the nutrient income. Verh. intern. Ver. Limnol., **14**: 167–175.

———. 1961b. Secondary production and decomposition. Verh. intern. Ver. Limnol., **14**: 316–339.

EDMONDSON, W. T., G. C. ANDERSON, AND D. R. PETERSON. 1956. Artificial eutrophication of Lake Washington. Limnol. Oceanogr., **1**: 47–53.

EDMONDSON, W. T., G. W. COMITA, AND G. C. ANDERSON. 1962. Reproductive rate of copepods in nature and its relation to phytoplankton population. Ecology, **43**. (In press.)

FOREMAN, M. H. 1953. A limnological study of the population of *Daphnia dentifera* (Cladocera) in Hall Lake, Washington. M.S. Thesis, Univ. Washington.

FOSHAG, W. F. 1926. Saline lakes, Mojave Desert, California. Econ. Geol., **21**: 56–64.

GIBOR, AARON. 1956a. Some ecological relationships between phyto- and zooplankton. Biol. Bull., **111**: 230–234.

———. 1956b. The culture of brine algae. Biol. Bull., **111**: 223–229.

GOLDMAN, C. R. 1960. Molybdenum as a factor limiting primary productivity in Castle Lake, California. Science, **132**: 1016–1017.

———. 1961. The contribution of alder trees (*Alnus tenuifolia*) to the primary productivity of Castle Lake, California. Ecology, **42**: 282–288.

GOULD, H. R. 1951. Some quantitative aspects of Lake Mead turbidity currents. Soc. Econ. Paleontol. Mineral., Spec. Publ. No. 2: 34–52.

GOULD, H. R., AND T. F. BUDINGER. 1958. Control of sedimentation and bottom configuration by convection currents, Lake Washington, Washington. J. Marine Research, **17**: 183–198.

HASLER, A. D. 1938. Fish biology and limnology of Crater Lake, Oregon. J. Wildlife Mgmt., **2**: 94–103.

HEDGPETH, J. W. 1959. Some preliminary considerations of the biology of inland mineral waters. Arch. Oceanogr. Limnol. Suppl., **11**: 111–141.

HUBBS, C. L., AND R. R. MILLER. 1948. The zoological evidence, p. 18–166. *In* A symposium on the Great Basin with emphasis on glacial and postglacial times. Bull. Univ. Utah, Biol. Ser., **10**(7).

HUTCHINSON, G. E. 1937. A contribution to the limnology of arid regions. Trans. Connecticut Acad. Arts Sci., **33**: 1–132.

——. 1957. A treatise on limnology. Vol. I. John Wiley & Sons, New York.

JOHNSON, J. W. 1948. The characteristics of wind waves on lakes and protected bays. Trans. Amer. Geophys. Union, **29**: 671–681.

JOHNSON, M. W. 1949. Relation of plankton to hydrographic conditions in Sweetwater Lake. J. Amer. Water Works Assoc., **41**: 347–356.

JUDAY, C. 1907. Studies on some lakes in the Rocky and Sierra Nevada mountains. Trans. Wisconsin Acad. Sci. Arts Lett., **15**: 780–793.

KEMMERER, G., J. F. BOVARD, AND W. R. BOORMAN. 1924. Northwestern lakes of the United States: Biological and chemical studies with reference to possibilities in production of fish. Bull. U.S. Bur. Fish., **39**: 51–140.

LAUER, G. J. 1959. The bottom fauna of two saline lakes in Washington. M.S. Thesis, Univ. Washington, 147 p.

LINDQUIST, A. W., AND C. C. DEONIER. 1942. Emergence habits of the Clear Lake gnat. J. Kansas Entomol. Soc., **15**: 109–120.

LINDQUIST, A. W., AND C. C. DEONIER. 1943. Seasonal abundance and distribution of larvae of the Clear Lake gnat. J. Kansas Entomol. Soc., **16**: 143–149.

LINDQUIST, A. W., C. C. DEONIER, AND J. E. HANCEY. 1943. The relationship of fish to the Clear Lake gnat in Clear Lake, California. California Fish and Game, **29**: 196–202.

MCDONALD, D. B. 1956. The effects of pollution upon Great Salt Lake, Utah. M.S. Thesis, Univ. Utah, 42 p.

MACDOUGAL, D. T., *et al.* 1914. The Salton Sea: A study of the geography, the geology, the floristics, and the ecology of a desert basin. Carnegie Inst. Washington, Publ. No. 193, 182 p.

MCEWEN, G. F. 1941. Observations on temperature, hydrogen ion concentration and periods of stagnation and overturning in lakes and reservoirs of San Diego County, California. Bull. Scripps Inst. Oceanogr., **4**: 219–259.

MACIOLEK, J. A., AND P. R. NEEDHAM. 1952. Ecological effects of winter conditions on trout and trout foods in Convict Creek, California, 1951. Trans. Amer. Fish. Soc., **81**: 202–217.

MAIN, R. A. 1953. A limnological study of *Chaoborus* (Diptera) in Hall Lake, Washington. M.S. Thesis, Univ. Washington, 106 p.

MASON, D. T. 1961. The growth response of *Artemia salina* (L.) Leach to various feeding regimens. M.A. Thesis, Univ. California, Davis.

MUNK, W. H., AND E. R. ANDERSON. 1948. Notes on a theory of the thermocline. J. Marine Research, **7**: 276–295.

MURPHY, G. I. 1949. The food of young largemouth black bass (*Micropterus salmoides*) in Clear Lake, California. California Fish and Game, **35**: 159–163.

——. 1950. The life history of the greaser blackfish (*Orthodon microlepidotus*) of Clear Lake, Lake County, California. California Fish and Game, **36**: 119–133.

——. 1951. The fishery of Clear Lake, Lake County, California. California Fish and Game, **37**: 439–483.

NEEDHAM, P. R. 1934. Quantitative studies of stream bottom foods. Trans. Amer. Fish. Soc., **64**: 238–247.

——. 1937. A biological survey of Lake Arrowhead, California. California Fish and Game, **23**: 310–328.

——. 1940. Quantitative and qualitative observations on fish foods in Waddell Creek Lagoon. Trans. Amer. Fish. Soc., **69**: 178–186.

NEEDHAM, P. R., AND A. C. JONES. 1959. Flow, temperature, solar radiation, and ice in relation to activities of fishes in Sagehan Creek, California. Ecology, **40**: 465–474.

NEEDHAM, P. R., AND R. L. USINGER. 1956. Variability in the macrofauna of a single riffle in Prosser Creek, Calfornia, as indicated by the Surber sampler. Hilgardia, **24**: 383–409.

NELSON, P. R., AND W. T. EDMONDSON. 1955. Limnological effects of fertilizing Bare Lake, Alaska. U.S. Fish and Wildl. Serv., Fish. Bull., **56**(102): 413–436.

OANA, SHINYA, AND E. S. DEEVEY. 1960. Carbon-13 in lake waters, and its possible bearing on paleolimnology. Amer. J. Sci. (Bradley Volume), **258A**: 253–272.

PARKER, R. A. 1960. Competition between *Simocephalus vetulus* and *Cyclops viridis*. Limnol. Oceanogr., **5**: 180–189.

——. 1961. Competition between *Eucyclops agilis* and *Daphnia pulex*. Limnol. Oceanogr., **6**: 299–301.

PETERSON, D. R. 1955. An investigation of pollutional effects in Lake Washington. Washington Pollution Control Comm., Tech. Bull. 18: 1–18.

PETERSON, D. R., K. R. JONES, AND G. T. ORLOB. 1952. An investigation of pollution in Lake Washington. Washington Pollution Control Comm., Tech. Bull. 14, 29 p.

PETTIT, E. 1936. On the color of Crater Lake water. Proc. Natl. Acad. Sci., Washington, **22**: 139–146.

PHINNEY, H. K., AND J. L. MCLACHLAN. 1956. Aquatic weed survey of Oregon. Agr. Expt. Sta., Oregon State Coll., 85 p.

PHINNEY, H. K., AND C. A. PEEK. 1961. Klamath Lake, an instance of natural enrichment, p. 22–29. *In* Algae and metropolitan wastes, Robert A. Taft Sanit. Engr. Center, Tech. Rept. W 61–3.

PISTER, E. P. 1960. Some limnological factors influencing the trout fishery of Crowley Lake, California. California Dept. Fish and Game, Inland Fish Admin., Rept. No. 60–11, 20 p.

PUTNAM, W. C. 1950. Moraine and shoreline relationships at Mono Lake, California. Bull. Geol. Soc. Amer., 61 : 115–122.

RAMA, M. KOIDE, AND E. D. GOLDBERG. 1961. Lead-210 in natural waters. Science, 134 : 98–99.

RAMSEY, W. L. 1960. Dissolved oxygen in Sweetwater Lake. Limnol. Oceanogr., 5 : 34–42.

RATTRAY, MAURICE, JR., G. R. SECKEL, AND C. A. BARNES. 1954. Salt budget in the Lake Washington ship canal system. J. Marine Research, 13 : 263–275.

RAWSON, D. S., AND J. E. MOORE. 1942. The saline lakes of Saskatchewan. Canadian J. Research, D, 22 : 141–201.

REIMERS, NORMAN. 1957. Some aspects of the relation between stream foods and trout survival. California Fish and Game, 43 : 43–69.

———. 1958. Conditions of existence, growth, and longevity of brook trout in a small, high-altitude lake of the eastern Sierra Nevada. California Fish and Game, 44 : 319–333.

REIMERS, NORMAN, AND B. D. COMBS. 1956. Method of evaluating temperature in lakes with description of thermal characteristics of Convict Lake, California. U.S. Fish and Wildl. Serv., Fish. Bull., 56 : 535–553.

REIMERS, NORMAN, J. A. MACIOLEK, AND E. P. PISTER. 1955. Limnological study of the lakes in Convict Creek Basin, Mono County, California. U.S. Fish and Wildl. Serv., Fish. Bull., 56 : 437–503.

RIGG, G. B. 1958. Peat resources of Washington. Dept. Conserv., Div. Mines and Geol., State of Washington, Bull. No. 44, 262 p.

RIGG, G. B., AND H. R. GOULD. 1957. The age of Glacier Peak eruption and chronology of postglacial peat deposits in Washington and surrounding areas. Amer. J. Sci., 255 : 341–363.

ROBECK, G. R., C. HENDERSON, R. C. PALANGE. 1954. Water quality studies on the Columbia River. U.S. Dept. Health, Educ., Welfare, Robert A. Taft Sanit. Engr. Center, Cincinnati, Ohio, 81 p.

RUSSELL, I. C. 1885. Geological history of Lake Lahontan. Monogr. U.S. Geol. Surv., 11, 287 p.

———. 1895. Lakes of North America. Ginn, Boston and London. 125 p.

SAUR, J. T. F., AND E. R. ANDERSON. 1956. The heat budget of a body of water of varying volume. Limnol. Oceanogr., 1 : 247–251.

SCHEFFER, V. B. 1933. Biological conditions in a Puget Sound lake. Ecology, 14 : 15–30.

SCHEFFER, V. B., AND R. J. ROBINSON. 1939. A limnological study of Lake Washington. Ecol. Monogr., 9 : 95–143.

SCHMITZ, W. 1959. Zur Frage der Klassifikation der binnenländischen Brackwässer. Arch. Oceanogr. Limnol., 11 (suppl.) : 179–226.

SHAPIRO, JOSEPH. 1960. The cause of a metalimnetic minimum of dissolved oxygen. Limnol. Oceanogr., 5 : 216–227.

SMITH, W. O., et al. 1960. Lake Mead comprehensive survey of 1948–49. 3 v. U.S. Geol. Surv., Profess. Papers, 295 p.

SUMNER, F. H. 1939. The decline of the Pyramid Lake fishery. Trans. Amer. Fish. Soc., 69 : 216–224.

SYLVESTER, R. O. 1958. Water quality studies in the Columbia River Basin. Bur. Commercial Fish., Spec. Sci. Rept., Fish., No. 239, 134 p.

SYLVESTER, R. O., AND C. P. RUGGLES. 1957. A water quality and biological study of the Wenatchee and middle Columbia Rivers prior to dam construction. Univ. Washington, Dept. Civil Engr., p. 1–147, 1–50.

UTTERBACK, C. L., L. D. PHIFER, AND R. J. ROBINSON. 1942. Some chemical, planktonic and optical characteristics of Crater Lake. Ecology, 23 : 97–103.

WALES, J. H. 1946. Castle Lake trout investigation. First phase : Interrelationships of four species. California Fish and Game, 32 : 109–143.

WALES, J. H., AND E. R. GERMAN. 1956. Castle Lake investigation. Second phase : Eastern brook trout. California Fish and Game, 42 : 93–108.

WALKER, B. W. (ed.). 1961. The ecology of the Salton Sea, California, in relation to the sport-fishery. California Dept. Fish and Game, Fish Bull., 113 : 1–204.

WALTER, W. M., AND C. W. MCNEIL. 1959. Chemical composition of natural and irrigation waters in Central Washington. Northwest Science, 33 : 19–42.

WATSON, D. G., J. J. DAVIS, AND W. C. HANSON. 1961. Zinc-65 in marine organisms along the Oregon and Washington coasts. Science, 133 : 1826–1828.

WHITEHEAD, H. C., AND J. H. FETH. 1961. Recent chemical analyses of waters from several closed-basin lakes and their tributaries in the western United States. Bull. Geol. Soc. Amer., 72 : 1421–1425.

WHITTAKER, R. H., AND C. W. FAIRBANKS. 1958. A study of plankton copepod communities in the Columbia Basin, southeastern Washington. Ecology, 39 : 46–65.

WOLCOTT, E. E. 1961. Lakes of Washington. State of Washington, Dept. of Conserv., Olympia Water Supply Bull. No. 14, 619 p.

YOUNG, R. T. 1924. The life of Devil's Lake, North Dakota. Publ. North Dakota Biol. Sta. : 1–116.

ZOBELL, C. E., F. D. SISLER, AND C. H. OPPENHEIMER. 1953. Evidence of biochemical heating in Lake Mead mud. J. Sediment. Petrol., 23 : 13–17.

Addendum to References

CASTENHOLZ, R. W. 1960. The algae of saline and freshwater lakes in the Lower Grand Coulee, Washington. Research Studies (Washington State Univ.), 28 : 125–155.

KISER, R. W., J. R. DONALDSON, and P. R. OLSON. 1963. The effect or rotenone on zooplankton populations in freshwater lakes. Trans. Amer. Fish. Soc., 92 : 17–24.

SHAPIRO, J. 1958. Yellow acid-cation complexes in lake water. Science, 127 : 701–704.

14 | *Gerald A. Cole*

The American Southwest and Middle America

The American Southwest (Fig. 14.1) and Middle America, covered in this chapter, is probably the most heterogeneous geographic region considered in this book. The area covers about 25° of latitude and 42° longitude and amounts to more than 3.8 million km². Altitudes range from sea level to 5,500 m above sea level, and extremes in climate, edaphic factors, and biotic zones are the rule.

Lakes of this vast area owe their origins to many processes. There is no such thing as one lake district to be considered here. The phrase lake district is used loosely; pond district is the proper terminology in many instances. Furthermore, the region contains unique aquatic habitats: thermal springs, extremely saline waters, lava-collapse ponds, the cenotes of Yucatan, water-containing caves, and ephemeral ponds, to mention a few.

Yet the southwestern states and republics of Middle America are not separate natural entities. They are related climatically and geologically. The Colorado Plateau is shared in part by New Mexico and northern Arizona, and the Texas coastal plain continues far southward into Mexico. The Basin and Range physiographic province is common to Trans-Pecos Texas, southern New Mexico and Arizona, and the northern portion of Mexico to about latitude 18° N. Similarly, Middle American republics share Caribbean and Pacific coastal lowlands, mountain chains, and other geologic features.

Some areas are practically unknown limnologically. Many published data exist for other regions. For this reason, it seems advisable to treat some lakes on an artificial, political basis, and others on the basis of districts of similar origin or location within the same physiographic province. Lack of published studies or exploration of any kind in many areas leaves no alternative except to point out, in such cases, the existence of water bodies and the opportunities for future original research there.

One of the most important single papers on the limnology of the Southwest and Middle America is that of Deevey (1957), who reported on waters from Texas to El Salvador. His publication, though based on hurried visits to the area and a few data from pre-existing literature, is the most valuable summary and synthesis of southwestern and Middle American limnology. To be rewarding, future work in this area should be on a systematic regional and natural basis, concerned with individual lake districts.

Superficially it appears that the arid Southwest has remained practically unchanged since settlement by European man. This is true to a relative extent, but disturbances are far greater than expected. Miller (1961) discussed the modifications of aboriginal aquatic habitats in the Southwest with particular emphasis on the effects on fish faunas. Since 1900, six or seven species have become extinct, and at least 13 additional forms are seriously threatened. Many streams which were permanent during the latter part of the 19th century now flow intermittently, carrying heavy

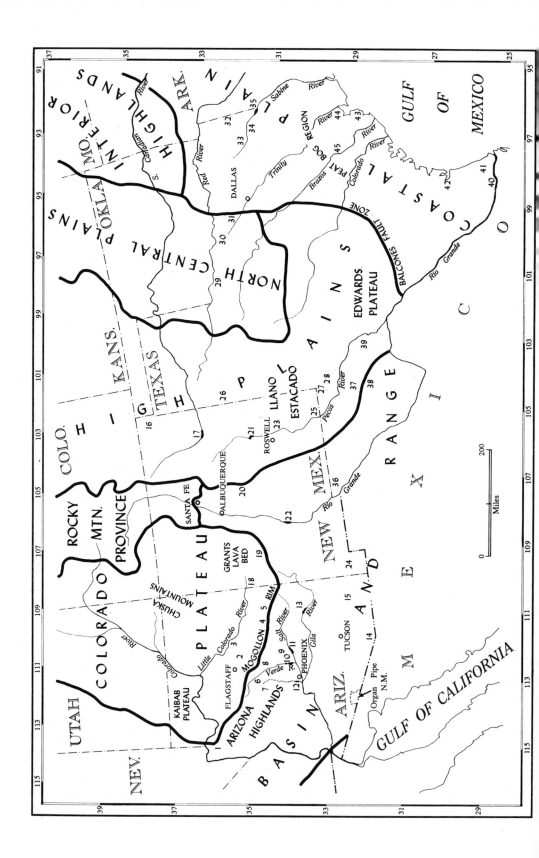

Fig. 14.1.—The American Southwest. Prepared by the University of Wisconsin Cartographic Laboratory.

Arizona

1. Red Lake Playa.
2. Mormon Lake and the Arizona volcanic lake district.
3. Meteor Crater at Coon Butte.
4. Woods Canyon Lake.
5. Big Lake and others of the Show Low–Springerville region.
6. Peck Lake.
7. Castle Hot Springs.
8. Montezuma Well.
9. Verde Hot Springs.
10. Horseshoe and Bartlett reservoirs, Verde River.
11. The reservoirs on the Salt River.
12. Lake Carl Pleasant, Agua Fria River.
13. San Carlos Lake, Gila River.
14. Peña Blanca Lake.
15. Willcox Playa.

New Mexico

16. Clayton Lake, Seneca Creek.
17. Conchas Reservoir, South Canadian River.
18. Zuñi Salt Lake.
19. San Augustin Plains.
20. Estancia Valley and Playa.
21. Alamogordo Reservoir, Pecos River.
22. Elephant Butte Reservoir, Rio Grande.
23. The Bottomless Lakes and Lander Springbrook.
24. Playas Valley.
25. Willow Lake, Black River.

Texas

26. Goose Lake.
27. The Monahans Dunes.
28. Odessa Crater.
29. Lake Wichita, Big Wichita River.
30. Lakes Worth, Dallas, Eagle Mountain, and Bridgeport, Trinity River Basin.
31. White Rock Lake, Trinity River Basin.
32. Caddo Lake, Cypress Creek.
33. Upper Ellis Lake, Sabine River Basin.
34. Striker Creek Reservoir, Neches River Basin.
35. Murvaul Lake, Sabine River Basin.
36. Grable's Salt Works.
37. Toyah Playa Lake.
38. Balmorhea Lake.
39. Fort Stockton Lake.
40. La Sal del Rey.
41. La Sal Vieja.
42. Ponds of Kleberg County.
43. Small depressions near Houston (descr. by Deevey, 1957).
44. Small depressions near Houston (descr. by Deevey, 1957).
45. Minter Spring.

silt loads in flash floods through deeply entrenched arroyos. Many smaller streams and springs are gone, and the freshwater marshy areas known as cienegas have virtually disappeared. Over-grazing, lumbering, pollution, river impoundment, dredging, ditching, pumping ground water, and the introduction of exotic species have been extremely important factors in habitat modification and the resultant alteration of faunas. These factors were combined with the onset of a natural erosional cycle, probably related to increased summer rainfall (Martin *et al.*, 1961). Disturbances in Middle America also have been great because of plantations, lumbering activities, charcoal manufacture, and subsequent erosion.

Texas

Texas, ranging in altitude from sea level to 2,612 m, contains parts of at least four main physiographic provinces, for which numerous subdivisions have been proposed. The low Coastal Plain, the North Central Plains, the Great Plains, and the Trans-Pecos area (part of the Basin and Range province) are the prominent physiographic features. Of particular interest are the subdivisions of the Great Plains: first, the Southern High Plains or the Llano Estacado, which lies in the panhandle area, extending into eastern New Mexico; and, second, the Edwards Plateau which is south of the Llano Estacado and east of the Pecos River.

On the basis of precipitation, Texas can be divided into zones separated by north-south lines. The most eastern region is characterized by a mean annual rainfall of 109 cm and a low evaporation rate. At the other extreme, precipitation is less than 25 cm in some places west of the Pecos River—the so-called Trans-Pecos area. Water quality of the state can be correlated roughly with these east-to-west regions. There are relatively few permanent natural bodies of water except for rivers, but there are hundreds of man-made ponds and large reservoirs, the latter covering a total area of more than 283,000 ha (Thomas and Harbeck, 1956). Many more are planned (Texas Board of Water Engineers, 1961.) In general artificial impounds are the best-known aquatic habitats in Texas.

Much of the work done in Texas has been concerned with estuaries, lagoons, and the littoral marine environments, and there are relatively few published data in the realm of limnology, although ichthyologists have collected for a period of many years from Texas waters. Preliminary investigations by Wiebe (1934) on some impoundments represented the beginning of Texas limnology. One of the first comprehensive studies was that of Harris and Silvey (1940), concerned with four reservoirs in the northeastern part of the state. This was followed by the paper of Cheatum *et al.* (1942) on another impoundment farther east. Students of these men have investigated many aspects of Texas fisheries and reservoir limnology since the 1930's. Titles of graduate theses on fishery biology and related subjects in Texas compiled by the Sport Fishing Institute (1959) are abundant, particularly unpublished Masters' theses from North Texas State University. Patterson (1942) includes titles of two other theses in the bibliography of her paper on the plankton of White Rock Lake, Texas.

Furthermore, the Texas Game and Fish Commission, under the direction of Marion Toole, has prepared a series of reports concerning basic investigations of many Texas lakes and streams. Monthly field chemical analyses have been made on most of the big impoundments in the state.

Deevey (1957) briefly reconnoitred some ponds of the Texas coastal plain and the arid Trans-Pecos region. Most other studies of Texas lakes, especially those on the Llano Estacado, have been carried out by geologists and paleoecologists and will be mentioned in a later section.

There is still much to be learned about the lacustrine fauna and flora of Texas, although the lack is not as great as in New Mexico and Arizona. Examples are the paper of Tressler (1954) on ostracods in Texas and reports by several workers, including Comita (1951), on copepods. Comparable papers do not exist for the other southwestern states. Of particular interest are the many papers of Silvey and Roach on the aquatic actinomycetes of Texas (e.g., Roach and Silvey, 1958; Silvey and Roach, 1959).

New Mexico

Four physiographic provinces are represented in New Mexico: the Rocky Mountains extend into the north-central portion; the Great Plains, including a part of the Llano Estacado, lie along the eastern margin; the Colorado Plateau extends across the northwest; and a portion of the

Basin and Range province occupies the southwestern third of the state. Because elevations range from 1,000 to 4,600 m above sea level, biotic regions include such extremes as the Chihuahuan desert in the south and the cool, coniferous forest at higher altitudes in the north. More than half the state receives less than 37.5 cm precipitation per annum, and, in the United States, only Connecticut has a smaller total area covered by lakes, ponds, and streams. The most arid region is the southwestern half, although a tongue of aridity extends up the Rio Grande Valley almost to the Colorado state line.

In the Sangre de Cristo Mountains in north-central New Mexico are some small natural lakes which may be the only glacial lakes in the entire area treated in this chapter. Most of these are at elevations between 2,100 m and 3,350 m and seem to be intermediate between cirque and moraine lakes (Koster, personal communication). The formative montane glaciers were small in these mountains. This small lake district is in the headwaters of the South Canadian, Rio Grande, and Pecos rivers.

The largest body of water in New Mexico is Elephant Butte Reservoir, a long, narrow impoundment on the Rio Grande. In general, the most important lakes of the state are man-made.

Many New Mexican waters are characterized by a high sulfate content, a reflection of the widespread and commercially-important gypsum. Some exceptions are seen in the soft waters of the small lake district on the crest of the Chuska Mountains (Megard, 1961) and in the mineralized spring water of Ojo Caliente near Taos. The latter was cited as an example of carbonate water in the classification devised by Clarke (1924), and the dominant cation is sodium. Also, the small trout lakes cursorily surveyed by Gersbacher (1935) in the mountains of north-central New Mexico seem to be soft-water lakes.

One important biological effect, ultimately ascribed to high sulfates, was described by Clark and Greenbank (1936) who investigated the recurring catastrophic fish-kills in Park Lake at an elevation of about 1,430 m near Santa Rosa. The reduction of SO_4 to H_2S following the death and decay of an abundant algal growth was succeeded by sudden strong winds which mixed the waters. Results were disastrous. Those authors compared Park Lake with the nearby Club Lake in which fish-kills had not occurred. Both lakes are fed by underground water high in CaSO₄ and are similar in their border vegetation, transparency, and hydrogen-ion concentration. The main differences are morphometric. Park Lake has an area of 3.5 or 4 ha and is no deeper than 4 m, while Club Lake is 20 m deep and has twice the surface area. Profiles from Club Lake show sharp temperature stratification and a marked thermoclinal minimum in dissolved oxygen at about 6 m. There is limited evidence that this corresponded to a level where benthic algae were decaying and H_2S was being produced. The possibility of sudden, wind-generated circulation with resultant fish-kills in such a lake is unlikely.

The history of New Mexican limnology begins in the 1930's when the names of John D. Clark, Lillard L. Smith, John Greenbank, and others appeared on a few University of New Mexico Bulletins concerned with public water supplies. Also, in 1935 Gersbacher's report of a summer's survey of lakes and streams in northern New Mexico was prepared.

The study of Elephant Butte Reservoir (Ellis, 1940) is particularly worthy of note, and the New Mexico Department of Game and Fish has contributed a series of reports on impoundments and streams with emphasis on fishes (Navarre, 1958, 1959, 1960; Little, 1961; Jester, 1960). Wright (1956), Bent (1960), and Megard (1961) have begun what may become a series of reports on the geology, limnology, and paleoecology of a natural lake district in the Chuska Mountains in northwestern New Mexico. Such unusual habitats as saline springbrooks and the water-filled depressions and caves of the Grants Lava Bed have received attention and will be mentioned later.

Other studies largely in the realm of geology and paleoecology will be discussed in a following section. Extinct Lake San Augustin and the deflation basins in the western flank of the Llano Estacado have been under investigation by several people, and there are numerous geological studies of ground-water resources of the state.

Although C. L. Herrick lived briefly in Albuquerque during the latter part of the 19th century and performed some taxonomic work on copepods in New Mexico (Herrick, 1895), we know almost nothing about the aquatic invertebrates of the state. Koster (1957) has summarized the status of ichthyology in New Mexico in his *Guide to the Fishes of New Mexico.*

Arizona

Arizona is characterized by two main physiographic provinces with a fairly distinct intermediate area worthy of mention. A section of the Colorado Plateau is in the northern third of the state, its southern boundary marked abruptly in the central area by the Mogollon Rim. Part of the Basin and Range province occupies roughly the southern third of the state and is usually termed the Sonoran desert in this region. Between the two lies a varied mountainous area, sometimes called the Arizona Highlands. Many physical geographers will not agree with the boundaries set forth here.

Altitudes in the state range from about 30 m in the southwest to 3,862 m at the top of the San Francisco Mountains—volcanic cones on the Colorado Plateau above the Mogollon Rim. Extremes in temperature from $-36°$ C to $+53°$ C have been recorded from the state. In the extreme southwest of Arizona precipitation may be as low as 7.6 cm per annum. In the intermediate mountainous area in some places it is ten times greater. Above the Mogollon Rim summer showers and winter snows are common, but precipitation is somewhat less than in the mountainous area below.

Very little limnological work has been done in Arizona if we exclude reports on Lake Mead, which is largely in Nevada. No studies which approach completeness have been made. Some mimeographed summaries of lake and stream surveys by Madsen (1935*a, b, c, d,*) contribute generalities concerning a few physicochemical data and the aquatic life in the National Forests in Arizona. These reports, although sketchy, constitute the most extensive surveys in the state. Hydrographic and water-quality data are being accumulated by various agencies in Arizona, and there are several U.S. Geological Survey publications with information. An example is U.S. Geological Survey Water-Supply Paper No. 1523. These are slanted toward irrigation needs and municipal usage. The Arizona drainage map prepared by Miller (1954) is of merit. Also, the Arizona Game and Fish Department has begun to assemble limnological data, and their publication (1958) includes bathymetric maps and other data for ten important fishing lakes in the state. Work is under way on a desert lake, Peña Blanca, by William J. McConnell (personal communication), with particular emphasis on primary productivity. Martin *et al.*

(1961) and Hevly and Martin (1961) have studied the sediments of Pluvial Lake Cochise, a playa in southeastern Arizona.

The scarcity of papers dealing with some taxonomic groups of Arizona plants and animals which make up important segments of freshwater communities is apparent in the ensuing discussion. Several phyllopod crustaceans have been recorded (see Dexter, 1959). Edmondson (1935) discussed rotifers from seven ponds and lakes near Flagstaff. Until very recently only three species of calanoid copepods, from a total of seven locations, had been reported (Marsh, 1929; Kincaid, 1953; Wilson, 1955). Now a minimum of seven species is known to occur in Arizona (Cole, 1961). Marsh (1910) described a new cyclopoid from southern Arizona, probably the only one reported from the state. No records of Arizona harpacticoid copepods have been published. Brooks (1957), in a detailed monograph on the genus *Daphnia* in North America, reported three species from two localities in Arizona. There may be no other records of Cladocera from the state. Only one species of the modern ostracod fauna of Arizona is represented in published papers (Dobbin, 1941). Other aquatic crustaceans such as the Amphipoda, Isopoda, and decapods have been neglected completely. There are a few papers on the ichthyofauna of Arizona. Most of these are cited by Miller (1961) in a paper emphasizing the changes wrought by man in the Southwest. Taylor and Colton (1928) published on pond phytoplankton in northern Arizona, and Wien (1958, 1959) studied algae and aquatic seed plants present in irrigation canals near Phoenix. Hevly (1961a, 1961b) has summarized and added to our knowledge of Arizona's aquatic flora. Although there may be omissions in the above, in general we know much more about the general limnology and aquatic flora and fauna of Mexico than of Arizona.

Mexico

Mexico, ranging over more than 18° of latitude and 31° of longitude and from sea level to 5,500 m in altitude, is a land of extreme diversity. The physiographic complexity of this republic is surpassed only by variation in climatic and biotic zones, which vary from humid tropical forests to arctic-alpine conditions with perpetual snow cover. It seems advisable to describe the country in the simplest terms to set the stage for dis-

cussion of its limnology.

First, a great interior plateau, continuous from the Basin and Range areas of Texas, New Mexico, and Arizona, stretches between the high Sierra Madre Occidental in the west and a shorter, less magnificent range, the Sierra Madre Oriental, on the east (Fig. 14.2). The coastal plain, so conspicuous in South Texas, continues along the Gulf of Mexico, merging into the broad, flat plain which makes up the entire Yucatan Peninsula. On the Pacific side, the coastal plain is narrower and occasionally interrupted by mountain spurs. The State of Baja California is a narrow peninsula bearing a single mountain range which extends nearly its entire length.

We know little about limnology over much of this vast country. Ichthyologists and herpetologists have collected throughout the streams and ponds of Mexico, but limnological exploration have been limited. The lakes of the Río Lerma system at the southwestern edge of the Mexican plateau have been studied, but on the eastern coastal plain we have information only on the sinks, or cenotes, of Yucatan. On the Pacific coastal plain a very few lagoons have been investigated from a limnological approach.

Summarizing the status of knowledge in Mexico seems to be popular with biologists of that country. Osorio Tafall (1944a) wrote a historical résumé of hydrobiology up to that time, including littoral marine investigations. Alvarez (1949) summarized freshwater ichthyology in Mexico and several people have assembled historical data on our knowledge of various invertebrate groups, for example, the freshwater sponges (Rioja, 1953) and planktonic rotifers (Osorio Tafall, 1942). One of the most important summarizing documents appeared very recently and too late to be utilized in the preparation of this report. This is a bibliography of Mexican investigations on aquatic biology, oceanography, fish, and related subjects, prepared by the Instituto Mexicano de Recursos Naturales Renovables (Alvarez et al., 1961). This publication contains a bibliography of 1,831 titles and historical summaries of the various subjects. A recent paper by Darnell (1962) has an extensive bibliography of Mexican ichthyology with emphasis on publications relating to the Río Tamesí drainage and the Tampico Embayment in the east-central part of the country. In summary, there is an extensive literature on the freshwater fauna of Mexico

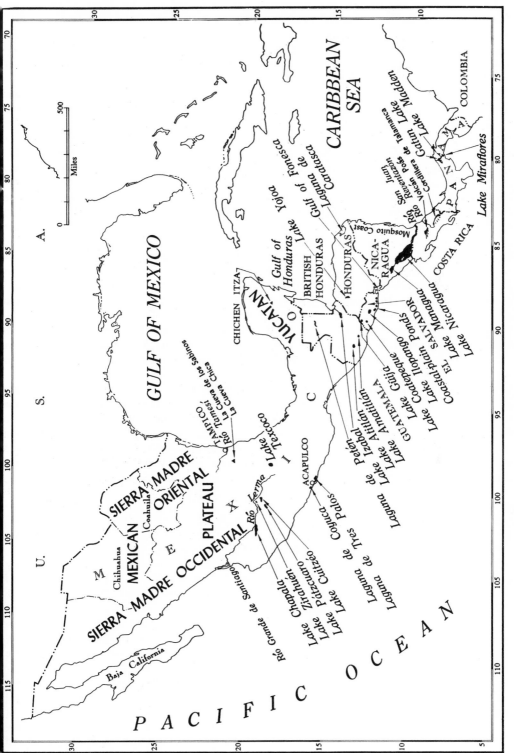

Fig. 14.2.—Middle America. Prepared by the University of Wisconsin Cartographic Laboratory.

quite in contrast to the paucity of information concerning the southwestern United States and the Middle American republics south of Mexico.

Serious Mexican limnological endeavor began with the establishment of the Estación Limnológica de Pátzcuaro on the shores of Lake Pátzcuaro in 1938. In October 1939 Fernando de Buen began directing research there, and within a few years a large number of papers had appeared in the *Informes,* the *Trabajos,* and the *Investigaciones* published by the station. By 1940, a group of taxonomic papers published in Volume 11 of the *Anales del Instituto de Biologia* of the Universidad Nacional de México included more than 80 titles concerned with Lake Pátzcuaro. Also, limnologists from the Pátzcuaro station have made at least reconnaissance investigations of other lakes of the Lerma Valley. Their contributions will be considered later. Deevey's (1957) discussion of Pátzcuaro and Chapala, although based on a relatively short period of study, is meritorious. Two classical papers in Mexican limnology concern the caves and cenotes of Yucatan (Pearse *et al.*, 1936, 1938).

Pioneer work on palynology far south of the limits of continental glaciation began in Mexico with Deevey's (1944) study of Pátzcuaro sediments. Further work on Deevey's cores was performed by Hutchinson *et al.* (1956). Inferences about Pleistocene climate from these studies agree with the results of several investigations from the Valley of Mexico, somewhat farther south (Sears, 1952; Sears and Clisby, 1955; Clisby and Sears, 1955; Foreman, 1955). The pluvial lake which covered this basin lay perhaps 3,000 km beyond the border of continental glaciation.

The peninsula of Baja California in Mexico, with its extensive latitudinal and altitudinal ranges and varied climatic patterns, should be a rewarding area for future regional freshwater studies. The littoral marine faunas indicate a climate ranging from mild temperate to tropical (Soule, 1960). Lacustrine habitats are rare, however, and abrupt escarpments along the eastern coast have worked against the formation of lagoons. Some streams, hot springs, and sloughs are present, from which there have been several ichthyological studies (see Follett, 1960).

Guatemala

Some limnological features of Guatemalan lakes have been reported by Meek (1908), Juday (1916), Holloway (1950), and Deevey (1957), although Meek and Holloway were especially concerned with fish. In addition, there have been occasional plankton studies (Clark, 1908; Tilden, 1908; Peckham and Dineen, 1953).

Lake Amatitlán and the deeper Atitlán stand out as the best-known bodies of water in Guatemala, and bathymetric maps are available for both in Deevey's (1957) paper. Probably the most important contributions to tropical limnology in Middle America have come from study of these lakes.

The large Lake Izabal, at an altitude of 10 m above the Gulf of Honduras and connected to it by the Río Dulce, is an entirely different type of lake. Some data and an incomplete bathymetric map were supplied by Holloway (1950). Calculations made from the map suggest an area of more than 63,700 ha, a maximum length of 46.5 km, a mean breadth of 13.7 km, and a mean depth of about 8–9 m. As is true of many Middle American lakes, Lake Izabal is subjected to strong, daily wind action and is isothermal at these times. Dissolved oxygen values range from 60% of saturation at the bottom to 100% one meter below the surface. Bicarbonate alkalinity data show 76 mg/L at the upper end of the lake and 100 mg/L at the lower.

The Laguna de Petén is a large compound limestone sink, isolated to a great extent, and showing resultant speciation in its fish fauna (Hubbs and Miller, 1948).

El Salvador

The Republic of El Salvador consists of a volcanic highland, which is a southeast continuation of the mountains of Guatemala, bounded by lowlands on either side. This highland is relatively low, and, as a result, most of the country is of the climatic *tierra caliente*. There has been much destruction of the original forests, followed by floods, soil erosion, and dought. The country is well supplied with streams, hot springs, and numerous lakes, but there have been no complete studies of any of them.

For many years the paper of Juday (1916), which contained information on lakes Coatepeque and Ilopango, was the only good account of El Salvador lakes. Since then Deevey (1957) published on these and also, in greater detail, on Lake Güija. Armitage (1958) visited these three

nd several other volcanic lakes in the highlands.
Ie also investigated ponds in the Pacific coastal
lain (Armitage, 1957) and prepared a report
Fassett and Armitage, 1961) on the aquatic
nacrophytes of both lake regions, using the
osthumous notes of Dr. Norman C. Fassett with
vhom he worked. Bathymetric maps of at least
lopango, Coatepeque, and Güija are available
Williams and Meyer-Abich, 1953, 1954; Deevey,
957).

Ionduras

Γhe largest Honduran body of water is the
_aguna Caratasca, connected to the Caribbean
y a narrow passageway. Until information is
vailable on the salinity and biota of this lagoon
n the northeastern coastal plain, it must be
onsidered outside the scope of limnology.

The only other major body of water is Lake
'ojoa, a solution lake in east-central Honduras at
n elevation of 610 m. Along the precipitous
astern shore a massive Cretaceous limestone is
xposed. The area of the lake is about 135 km².
'arr (1950) writes of incredibly rich avian popu-
ations in the shoreline marshes at the northern
nd southern margins of Lake Yojoa. In spite of
he high altitude, many aquatic birds typical of
he lowland marshes of Florida are present.

Other aquatic habitats in Honduras are best
onsidered marshes or swamps. On both coastal
owland areas, saline mangrove swamps grade into
reshwater marshes. The fresh tidal swamp is a
ransitional type and offers peculiar habitat con-
litions. Another lowland habitat mentioned by
'arr is the peat swamp composed of gamalote
grass (*Paspalum*). At high altitudes (*ca.* 1,830 m)
ear the cloud forest margins, micromarshes dom-
nated by *Juncus* are present.

Iritish Honduras

Iritish Honduras, a small lowland country, ex-
iibits features typical of neighboring Guatemala
ind the Yucatan Peninsula. There are several
arge lagoons near the coast and a few farther
nland in the valleys of sluggish rivers. Beard
'1953) mentions the "lakes, wooded swamps, un-
lrained sinkhole ponds or aguadas" of that coun-
ry, but no limnological reports are available.

Iicaragua

Γhe Republic of Nicaragua is a land of volcanoes
ind lakes, yet little can be said about its limnol-

ogy. The country consists of three major regions:
the highlands through the center of the country,
reaching elevations no greater than 2,134 m; the
Mosquito Coast along the Caribbean Sea, with
many lagoons and slowly flowing rivers and an
annual rainfall of 762 cm, hardly to be surpassed
anywhere in the world; and the Nicaraguan lowlands, running south from the Gulf of Fonesca
along the Pacific coast and then cutting across to
the Caribbean at the Costa Rican border. Only
the lakes of the third region can be discussed.

The largest lake to be found between Lake
Titicaca in South America and the North American Great Lakes of the St. Lawrence drainage
is Lake Nicaragua, 19 km from the Pacific and
34 m above it. Unfortunately, little is known
concerning the limnology of this body of water
or of the closely related and nearby Lake Managua, except for hydrographic data (Davis, 1900),
studies of the remarkable fish fauna (Meek,
1907), and a mimeographed summary of work
done by Dr. W. H. Shuster and Dr. S. Yen Lin
in 1956 and 1960, respectively. The last was
supplied by the Ministerio de Agricultura y
Ganaderia, Managua, and contains a summary of
chemical data from the two lakes which was used
to produce Table 14.1.

Geologically the lakes are young, probably
formed when post-Tertiary eruptions isolated an
elongate basin of the Pacific. Originally, they
were a single lake, but marginal erosion and drainage separated the two basins. Today Managua
drains into Nicaragua, about 7 m below it, by
way of the 26-km Río Tipitata. Lake Nicaragua
has a surface area of more than 7,700 km² and
a maximum depth of about 60 m. Thus, the bottom of the lake lies some 26 m below sea level.
Managua is only 1,295 km² and has a maximum
depth of 30 m, although much of the lake is approximately 8 m deep. The volcanism that originally impounded the lakes reversed the existing
hydrographic pattern, so they do not drain toward
the nearby Pacific but, by way of the San Juan
River, into the distant Caribbean. The salinity
of these well-drained lakes, lying in a region
where precipitation exceeds evaporation, is greatly
reduced, so that in spite of the marine origin of
the waters, the lakes are freshwater bodies, especially Lake Nicaragua (Table 14.1).

The surface elevation of Lake Managua varies
from 1 to 2.5 m between the dry season (Novem-
ber-April) and the rainy season (May-October)

TABLE 14.1

Comparison of the waters of Lake Nicaragua and Lake Managua. All values except pH are in mg/L.

	Managua	Nicaragua
pH	8.7	7.0
Total dissolved solids	747	151
SiO_2	7	16
Ca	9.4	19
Mg	22.1	3.5
Na	230.8	17.7
K	35.9	3.9
CO_3	30	0
HCO_3	470	82.4
SO_4	30.3	9.1
Cl	132.9	15.9
F	0.95	0.76
B	1.31	0.08
NO_3	trace	0.62

Extensive marginal flats are exposed to direct solar radiation during the dry months, and some years the lake is so low that it does not drain into the Río Tipitata. This probably accounts for the greater salinity in Managua than in the well-drained Nicaragua.

The surface temperature of Lake Managua is 26° C in the early hours of the day, warming to 30° C by noon if the lake is calm. However, during the months from January to May, winds varying from 13 to 16 km/hour destroy stratification, and the lake is uniformly 28° C. These winds bring about the suspension of bottom sediments, and this, coupled with high plankton production, results in a low Secchi disc transparency from 0.5 to 2.0 m.

Puzzling fish-kills occasionally occur in Lake Managua. These have not been explained, but in that region subsurface volcanism might be involved.

The two lakes are extremely rich. About 375 professional fishermen, lacking modern methods and equipment, harvest about 810,000 kg of fish per year. Surveys have suggested, however, that the total annual production of all types of fish is in the neighborhood of 91,370,000 kg.

Lake Nicaragua is remarkable for its landlocked marine fishes, although it is less saline than Managua which lacks them. These include two elasmobranchs and the Atlantic tarpon. One elasmobranch is a dangerous shark, attaining weights of 68 kg and lengths of 2 m or more. The other, a sawfish, grows to more than 300 kg. These animals probably entered the lake by way of the Río San Juan long before earthquakes created extensive rapids in the river some 300 years ago. The euryhaline shark of the Caribbean, *Carcharhinus leucas*, is undoubtedly the ancestor of the form in Lake Nicaragua. The same three fish species are present also in Lake Izabal, Guatemala (Holloway, 1950).

In both lakes several bizarre cichlids occur. Many are golden-red with strangely humped foreheads. The red fish are sold in the market as *mojarras coloradas* and are also found in some of the other lakes nearby, especially those in deep calderas.

One of the most remarkable lakes in Nicaragua is Lake Apoyo occupying a caldera depression and with a cryptodepression of 110 m. There are many lakes in Nicaraguan calderas, but probably few if any attain this depth.

Armitage (1961) reported some unusual chemical data from a shallow volcanic lake about 5 km west of the city of Managua. This is Lake Nejapa which occupies a closed caldera depression. When visited in December, the lake was only one meter deep, although exposed mud flats implied higher levels during the rainy season. Water temperature was 28.5° C, and the turbidity so great that Secchi disc transparency was only 10 cm. A strong odor of H_2S prevailed, although no tests were performed for sulfur compounds. The pH was in excess of 10, the carbonate alkalinity was 10,440 mg/L, and the bicarbonate alkalinity was 4,390 mg/L. No zooplankters were present, but a bloom of blue-green algae was evident, with species of *Arthrospira, Spirulina,* and *Oscillatoria* predominating.

Costa Rica

The limnology of Costa Rica, "the Switzerland of Central America," is practically unknown. Some notes on high-altitude bogs, to be discussed in another section, are present (Reark, 1952; Martin, 1960). Also unexplored volcanic-crater lakes occur. Reark (personal communication) has stated that in the gorge of the Río Reventazón there are a number of oxbow lakes in various successional stages. No detailed studies have been made of these, but they contain fish, aquatic plants, and probably the invertebrate fauna typical of subtropical ponds.

Panama

The Republic of Panama is a narrow isthmus covering a small area, but it has varied ecological conditions. Altitudes range from sea level to 3,850 m, and the Pacific side of the Continental Divide differs climatically from the Atlantic. There is little limnological history to report. The major lakes—Gatun, Madden, and Miraflores—were pooled by construction of the Panama Canal. Gatun Lake is one of the world's largest artificial bodies of water, covering an area of about 423 km². Annual temperatures in its waters vary from about 26° to 29° C.

Prescott (1951) found significant differences between the algal floras of Gatun and Lake Miraflores. Gatun is in the Atlantic drainage, whereas Miraflores is close to the Pacific Ocean. Prescott suggested that waters draining into the Atlantic reaches of the Panama Canal may differ chemically from those west of the Divide.

Extinct lake basins

Bogs

Many extinct lakes are present in southwestern United States, adjacent Mexico, and perhaps far more than suspected in the mountainous areas of the other republics of Middle America. In arid regions they are conspicuous as ephemeral playas or extensive salt flats. In forested regions they are either rare or have escaped attention. With the relatively recent interest in past climatic conditions south of the limits of continental glaciation, research literature is accumulating rapidly. The bulk of recent limnological work in the Southwest has been geological or in the realm of paleolimnology.

Bog lakes and large accumulations of peat are associated most often with formerly glaciated regions, although a few have been reported from the Southwest and Middle America. Several acid peat bogs occur in east-central Texas, in a southwest-northeast strip from Guadalupe and Gonzales counties to Polk and Houston counties (Chelf, 1941; Plummer, 1941, 1945; Shafer, 1941). Many of these peat accumulations occupy various poorly drained depressions such as old meander scars, impounded tributary valleys, and closed basins near ancient natural levees. Others are not fluviatile in origin but owe their existence to perched-water conditions. Water seeping from sands and gravels spreads over impermeable clay areas, collecting in depressions not subjected to frequent flooding and drainage which would preclude peat accumulation. Some of these depres-

sions in Texas are surrounded by trees and shrubs and are called "bay galls." Sphagnum is present in many of the bogs, some of which are domed. The occurrence of sphagnum in Gonzales County, Texas, may mark its southwestern limit in the United States. In general, this is a moist, relict area characterized by disjunct floral and faunal elements (Raun, 1959). Several ericaceous plants around the bay galls are rather far from their normal range, and Raun considered that more than 50% of the vertebrates in the peat bogs of Gonzales County show eastern affinities.

Some Texas peat bogs in three different counties were studied by Potzger and Tharp (1943, 1947, 1954), and pollen profiles were presented. On the basis of palynological data, they proposed a four-phase climatic oscillation for that part of Texas. Since then commercial peat mining has destroyed their bogs, except for the lower 1.5 m of Gause Bog in Milam County. Graham and Heimsch (1960) reinvestigated the peat remnants in this bog and studied the pollen fossils in a fourth, Soefje Bog. Their data show essentially unmodified vegetation throughout the entire history of the 4.7-m deep sediments, and radiocarbon dating places the age of the bog at about 8,000 years. Probably the lower level of Soefje Bog correlates with the 3-m level in Gause Bog. Below this the sediments of the latter contain some *Picea* pollen, implying a moister and cooler climate, but Graham and Heimsch see no evidence above this for climatic oscillations. The age of these bottom sediments in Gause Bog is estimated to be a little more than 12,000 years.

A case of incipient bog formation may have been described in Texas by Cheatum *et al.* (1942). In a shallow, artificial reservoir, 160 km east of Dallas, there is an encroaching mat of *Zizania* and *Typha*, on which *Cephalanthus, Alnus, Hypericum, Salix,* and some ferns grow. The open-water pH is from 6.4 to 7.0, but in the marginal mats it is 6.1 or 6.2. The lake is partly fed by acid springs.

Some solution basins below the limits of continental glaciation contain peat, but none has been reported from Texas. In the Arizona sink, Montezuma Well,* some well-defined peat has

---

* Studies on Montezuma Well, Arizona, have been made possible by National Science Foundation Grant G 1316 and the cooperation of the National Park Service.

accumulated near a marginal stand of *Scirpus*. This is brown, fibrous material extending below the water surface to some depth. The full extent of this peat bed is not known, but there is a slant to it which suggests it has slipped into deeper water over a period of years and may not imply a rising water level. Further investigation is needed before much can be said, because the plugging of former, lower outlets could have occurred. Montezuma Well is not a closed system and does not seem conducive to peat formation. The peat is not widespread, however, and although the daily flow of water is on the order of one-tenth of the total volume, there may be stagnant conditions where the peat forms at the shore opposite the outlet.

Many montane bogs occur at elevations of 2,300 m and above in the granitic Cordillera de Talamanca of Costa Rica (Reark, 1952; Martin, 1960). Reark (personal communication) has noted at least one below 1,640 m and has theorized the bogs were formed by landslides damming valleys above the elevation of continuous stream flow. In this region of both high precipitation and high relative humidity, slides are common, and the year-long growing season effects rapid stabilization of dams formed across intermittent tributaries. The bogs are found in at least two climatic belts, the upper being characterized by páramo conditions with mean annual temperatures of 6° to 12° C. From the palynological study of a 13-m core, Martin (1960) inferred that two-thirds of the core represented colder climate, and that páramo conditions formerly extended 600–800 m below their present altitudinal limits.

There is a North American aspect to these bogs because of the presence of such familiar genera as *Sphagnum, Vaccinium,* and *Xyris.* The most conspicuous plants show Andean affinities, however, and the bogs have been designated *Puya-Lomaria* types on the basis of the two dominant species, which reach their northern limits here.

Successional stages are probably present among the bogs. The one observed at the lowest elevation by Reark had steep sides, was water filled, and most of the typical plants were missing. Most other bogs had only a little surface water above the peat upon which the *Puya* and *Lomaria* grew. Many of these active bogs are in forests of the huge oak, *Quercus copeyensis,* but older sediments are covered by typical cloud forest species, which seem to be playing an ecological role similar to that of certain spruces, cedars, and tamaracks of northern United States and Canada.

In the volcanic Cordillera Central, to the north of the Talamanca range, there are no such bogs (Reark, personal communication). Topographic and edaphic factors, perhaps combined with the relative frequency of eruptions, have acted against bog formation. The craters of Volcán Irazú, V. Turrialba, V. Barba, and V. Poás, however, contain cold lakes bordered by oozy margins with sparse plant growth.

Basin and Range playas

The Basin and Range physiographic province is widespread, ranging from far to the north of the area covered by this report to about 18° N latitude in Mexico. Typically it is a region of block faulting, with broad structural valleys and isolated mountain ranges. The valleys are debris-filled basins called bolsons. Much of the Basin and Range province in Arizona, New Mexico, and Trans-Pecos Texas is actually a continuation of the Mexican Plateau, bordered in Mexico by the Sierra Madre Occidental and the Sierra Madre Oriental. Many bolsons have no exterior drainage and contain ephemeral, saline playas, often overlying the sediments of ancient pluvial lakes. Meinzer (1922) mapped many of these Pleistocene lakes, and Hubbs and Miller (1948) discussed and located all the important ones.

New Mexico has more of these ancient lakes than either Arizona or Texas. One of the principal ones is Lake Estancia, 96 km southeast of Albuquerque, which was once 1,166 km² in area and 46 m deep. The lake bed is one of the most commercially important sources of NaCl in the state (Phalen, 1919).

Few bolsons in Arizona are closed, with a resulting scarcity of playa lakes. In northwestern Arizona there is an ephemeral lake, 9.6 km in diameter, called Red Lake, which may have been more or less permanent during the Pleistocene. The most important in Arizona is the Willcox Playa in the southeast at an elevation of 1,245 m. This is the site of Pluvial Lake Cochise, which had an area of 311 km² and a depth of 14 m. The extremely mineralized waters of Croton Springs, arising from the western edge of the playa, contain a great deal of sodium, chloride, and sulfate. Interesting mounds, some as high as 3 m, are found at the shores of the playa.

These were considered of recent origin by Meinzer and Kelton (1913), who postulated trapping of lake-bed deflation materials by aquatic vegetation at artesian seeps. Hevly and Martin (1961) have shown by pollen analyses that the knolls are of pluvial age and probably represent erosional remnants.

Most studies on bolson playas have been in the realm of geologic, ground-water, or salt-resource reports. The papers of Hevly and Martin (1961) and Martin *et al.* (1961) on Lake Cochise and other sites are largely palynological. For data on the modern limnology of bolson lakes, we must turn to Deevey's (1957) short discussion of playas in the so-called Salt Basin of Trans-Pecos Texas. This is an extensive graben bounded on the east by the Guadalupe Mountains and extending north into New Mexico. Deevey's discussion makes it plain that Grable's Salt Works and Fort Stockton Lake are greatly modified, but Toyah Lake appears to be a good example of a playa. The waters of Toyah are about 3‰ total salinity. Grable's Salt Works is extremely concentrated and very high in chloride. Fort Stockton and Toyah have relatively more sulfate, but in all three magnesium is surprisingly low, and the dominant cation is sodium.

One feature of these lakes, which may apply generally to turbid waters in arid regions, is the high percentage (*ca.* 85%) of phosphorus in sestonic form. Total phosphorus is not especially high, and the N/P ratio is normal.

The Valley of Mexico is a bolson which contained a large, but shallow, pluvial lake, much of which remained until early 16th century when drainage operations began. Seven remnants are present now, the largest of which is saline Lake Texcoco. Apparently this bolson was closed by volcanic mountain building. Deevey (1957) gives a good account of the known history of the lake, including Aztec usage. Osorio Tafall (1942) classified Texcoco as a brackish habitat and *Brachionus pterodinoides* as a rotifer typical of it.

Lake San Augustin

Sediments derived from former pluvial lakes, now entirely dry or, at the most, ephemeral in nature, have been studied by several workers in the Southwest. Most of these playa basins lie within the Basin and Range physiographic province, but an important exception is extinct Lake San Augustin now represented by the San Augustin Plains in west-central New Mexico. This is an intermontane basin, probably a graben (Stearns, 1956), within the Colorado Plateau physiographic province. It lies at elevations from 2,050 to 2,100 m, with surrounding mountains 1,000 m higher. Powers (1939) described the lake as having been 50 m deep with a surface area of 660 km². Descriptions of the modern aspect of the San Augustin Plains and evidence for the relatively recent existence of the lake have been published by Potter (1957) and Potter and Rowley (1960). Core studies by Clisby, Foreman, and Sears (1957) have suggested that the rate of deposition was about 30 cm per 1,000 years, and below a depth of 165 m the sediments are probably Pliocene. Recent drillings to a subsurface level of 600 m are probably well into the Pliocene. A new 15-m core collected for radiocarbon dating contains *Pediastrum* microfossils between 1.3 and 10 m depth (Clisby, personal communication). This implies a freshwater lake, perhaps high enough to overflow, thus precluding marked accumulation of salts. The levels of *Pediastrum* abundance coincide roughly with the *Picea* pollen maximum first shown by Clisby and Sears (1956).

Basins of meteoritic origin

Some of the now-extinct pluvial lakes of the Southwest are known to have had their origins in meteoritic impact and explosion. They are, at present, anomalous basins in lake districts of entirely different genesis. The most famous of these is the dry crater at Coon Butte on the Colorado Plateau in Arizona. The crater lies in a region of volcanism, and Darton (1910) believed it was formed by volcanic explosion. Blackwelder (1946) seems to have established clearly the meteoritic origin. Barringer (1905) wrote that the floor of the crater contains about 30 m of lacustrine sediments.

In Ector County, Texas, there are several meteoritic pits. At least one of these, Odessa Meteor Crater, 16 km east of the Monahans Dunes, contains 20 m of eolian and lacustrine deposits, representing former pond stages (Green, 1961). The crater is a small, flat-bottomed depression, its impact ring rising 4 m above the floor. It is situated in a district of deflation basins at the southern edge of the Llano Estacado.

High-altitude lakes of Arizona and New Mexico

Volcanic lakes of the Colorado Plateau

In a strip 120 km long from Williams, Arizona, southeast past Flagstaff, on the southern edge of the Colorado Plateau, are many small lakes which are volcanic in origin. An exception is Lake Mary, near Flagstaff, which occupies a limestone valley and is artificially impounded. Probably none is deeper than 7 or 8 m, and all are above 2,135 m in elevation. The lakes of this district are worthy of study, but few data have been assembled concerning them.

Most of these lakes have no permanent source of water, and only seasonal runoff fills them. During dry periods many are empty. The natural lakes of this district are characterized by a rich and varied flora and fauna, with luxuriant emergent vegetation bounding their shallows in spite of fluctuations in water level. Taylor and Colton (1928) pointed out that the natural tanks and lakes of northern Arizona are much more likely to have rich algal flora than are the artificial ones, and the occurrence of a varied green-alga and diatom population is practically limited to natural bodies of water. This seems to apply to the emergent and submerged aquatics also, for most man-made impoundments on Arizona rivers have barren shores. Of course this may be caused by morphometric features. Lakes on large Arizona rivers were formed within steep-walled canyons, while natural lakes above the Mogollon Rim occupy relatively shallow, saucer-like depressions. Fluctuations in water level are probably more drastic in the large, dammed lakes because of irrigation requirements.

Mormon Lake, the largest natural lake in Arizona (2,590 ha), lies in an intercone basin dammed by lava flows and Mormon Mountain. At least one spring enters the lake, but during periods of reduced precipitation the lake is dry (Colton, personal communication). Madsen (1935a) reported accounts of Mormon Lake's having been formed by the trampling of cattle and sheep. According to ranchers, the lake was originally a grassy meadow surrounded by dry hills, into which livestock was turned to graze. Trampling made the basin watertight and created the lake. One is inclined to believe a longer lacustrine history with only occasional interruptions.

Stoneman Lake occupies a small caldera (Colton, 1957), and this is probably true also of Crater Lake and Walker Lake. Five small springs feed Stoneman Lake, but in spite of this it has been dry occasionally in recent years. It is especially rich in aquatic macrophytes. Others such as Kinnikinick, Ashurst, Marshall, and Vail lakes occupy depressions in Pliocene or early Pleistocene lava flows (Colton, personal communication). Some of these lakes have been deepened by dams to increase their fishing potential. Thus, Kinnikinick formerly had a maximum depth of 5 m. This shallowness, combined with strong winds and the volcanic-ash sediments, resulted in extreme turbidity. A dam constructed in 1956 raised the level 3 m, and the lake now covers 54.6 ha with a total volume of 3.1 million m³. There is some summertime thermal stratification, but oxygen is abundant at all depths. Because of the altitude and low winter temperatures, this is a dimictic lake. Water chemistry data are scarce, but all these volcanic, high-altitude lakes are probably remarkably soft for closed-basin waters. They are characterized by high pH values and a mean methyl orange alkalinity of about 57 mg/L (as $CaCO_3$). An exception is the caldera lake, Stoneman, with recorded alkalinity values from 210 to 280 mg/L.

An interesting volcanic lake, quite different from those in Arizona, lies to the east in New Mexico, 67 km south by east from the Pueblo of Zuñi (Darton, 1905). This is Zuñi Salt Lake, which Darton considered of solution origin, but which Hutchinson (1957) classified as a caldera basin. According to Darton, the lake is 1.6 km in diameter surrounded by high walls of Cretaceous sandstone capped by lava and volcanic ejecta. The floor contains some water with marginal flats of mud and a white saline evaporite which the Indians collect. In the main basin are two secondary volcanic cones, one of which contains a pool of water 50 m in diameter and has a NaCl percentage of 26.

Chuska Mountain lake district

A small lake district may be seen in the Chuska Mountains, which extend for 95 km across the northern portion of the Arizona-New Mexico border, attaining elevations from 2,700 to 3,000 m. The mountains are capped by Tertiary sandstones of eolian origin (Wright, 1956). This

Chuska sandstone contains hundreds of small basins, some of which contain water permanently, others only temporarily. All are shallow and occupy closed basins. In spite of poor drainage, they are rather low in salt content and can be characterized as calcium carbonate-bicarbonate waters with little sulfate and chloride. The permanent ponds contain luxuriant growths of aquatic macrophytes. Cores to a depth of 8 m from Deadman Lake, one of the largest of these ponds (*ca.* 11 ha), have been studied by Bent (1960). Apparently all the sediment was deposited during the Pleistocene except for the uppermost 20 or 30 cm. Remains of *Pediastrum* are absent in the upper strata but are common throughout the core below 60 cm. The disappearance of *Pediastrum* is not easily reconciled with the present water quality of the lake which is neither hard nor saline. Perhaps morphometric changes and the great increase in macrophytes, implied by Bent's pollen diagram, were related in some way to the *Pediastrum* decline. Megard (1961) demonstrated the formation of a daytime microstratification which is destroyed by nocturnal density currents in Deadman and in the larger (21 ha) Whiskey Lake. Both are less than 1.5 m deep. Also, Megard estimated rates of carbon fixation during summer days in the two lakes on the basis of dissolved oxygen and apparent CO_2 changes uncorrected for atmospheric exchanges. Mean net productivity was 364 mg O_2/m^2 per hr or approximately 1 g C/m^2 per day.

Other high-altitude and sub-Mogollon Arizona lakes

In the eastern mountainous area of Arizona in an area bounded roughly by Springerville, St. Johns, and Show Low, there are several artificial impoundments, some of which occupy basins which may have been cienegas. Most of these lakes are over 2,000 m in elevation. They are soft-water lakes with calcium and bicarbonate the principal ions. One of the most important of these is Big Lake, 40 km southwest of Springerville and originally impounded in the 1930's. Trout growth in this lake has been excellent, but the shallowness of the basin, coupled with luxuriant vegetation and ice cover, resulted in an almost annual winter-kill. The dam was raised later to make a lake of 228 ha with a capacity of more than 11 million m^3.

Just below the Mogollon Rim in Arizona there are several small, shallow lakes in addition to abundant stock tanks. Many of these are 1,500 m above sea level in rolling grassland dotted with junipers and pinyon pines. Most are characterized by high summer pH values. An anomalous lake in this region is Peck Lake at about 1,000 m in the Verde Valley. It is a shallow oxbow relict of the Verde River receiving its waters from a spring and from a conduit from the river. Its area of 36 ha is almost compeleły choked with *Myriophyllum,* and pH values up to 10 have been recorded from the surface waters.

Stehr Lake, elevation 1,586 m, in Yavapai County, is a 10-ha body of water with a maximum depth of 4 m. All but 2.5 ha are grown with aquatic macrophytes. The lake was impounded for power generation and receives its water ultimately from several sources known collectively as Fossil Springs. Their flow approaches constancy at about 75 $m^3/$ minute. These are mineralized waters high in bicarbonates, and as they splash on nearby objects, incrustations form, creating the appearance of fossils. These waters flow into Fossil Creek and hence via flume to Stehr Lake. Methyl orange alkalinities up to 375 mg/L (as $CaCO_3$) have been determined in its waters, a reflection of its rheocrene source. However, apparently much carbonate is lost from the creek water before it reaches the lake.

A few small, isolated, man-made lakes are found at high altitudes on peaks of the Basin and Range province in Arizona and in the mountainous area. These serve as trout lakes. Two are Riggs Flat Lake at 2,623 m on Mount Graham in the Pinaleno Mountains and Rose Canyon Lake at 2,135 m on Mount Lemmon.

An interesting artificial lake above the Mogollon Rim, southeast of the Arizona volcanic lakes, is dimictic Woods Canyon Lake, impounded in 1956. It is an elongate lake of 20.6 ha, with a maximum depth of about 11 m. It occupies a basin in a narrow canyon bordered by mature stands of ponderosa pine, fir, and aspen at an altitude of 2,272 m. At present the total solids are only about 51 mg/L, and methyl orange alkalinity is usually under 20 mg/L.

Deflation basins

Wind is a major erosional agent in arid regions, and therefore many Southwestern lake basins are believed to be of eolian origin. Along the Texas coastal plain there are ponds which may be of this type. Deevey (1957) has discussed a possible series, starting with small depressions seldom deeper than 0.3–0.6 m, in the Beaumont Clay formation of the humid coastal plain near Houston, and terminating in large salt lakes, La Sal Vieja and La Sal del Rey, in the semiarid southern extreme of the Texas coastal plain 480 km away. Although these basins seem unrelated, the occurrence of a group of ponds in Kleberg County, intermediate in character and geographic position, suggested to Deevey a transitional series and a common origin for the three districts.

Launchbaugh (1955) has described the microtopography of the San Antonio Prairie, a little more than 160 km northwest of the small depressions on the coastal plain near Houston and at a mean elevation of about 100 m. The majority of the fields studied by Launchbaugh exhibited an undulating surface relief in the form of what he called "hog wallows." These are depressions 3 to 10 m wide and 0.3 to 0.5 m deep, which seem similar to the dimple basins near Houston that Deevey discussed. About 480 km northwest of the San Antonio depressions, the lakes of the Llano Estacado begin. Although several theories have been advanced for the origin of the High-Plains basins, the consensus is that they are deflation products, with assistance rendered by ungulates not ruled out. A description of basins geographically intermediate between the San Antonio Prairie "hog wallows" and the so-called playa lakes of northwestern Texas was published by Van Siclen (1957). East of the Llano Estacado in the Osage Plains of Texas are many shallow basins. However, in Van Siclen's opinion there is no reason to believe them of eolian origin, and he considered them sinkholes formed by solution of calcareous Pleistocene sediments and underlying beds. Thus, the basins of the Llano Estacado are the best examples of a deflation-lake district in the Southwest.

There are thousands of these basins, ranging in size from the small, shallow type called "buffalo wallows" to large, deep lakes extending down through several formations and 115 m below the surface of the surrounding area. In Potter County, Texas, 238 km² are covered by playa lakes. This represents one-tenth of the total county area. Cedar Lake, one of the largest, has some puzzling islands near the southeast margin. These are probably composed of windblown materials, because prevailing winds are from the west. Parker and Whitfield (1941) have described three distinct parts to the larger lakes: a central

low flat making up one-fourth to one-half the total area; a surrounding, concentric, and poorly drained flat known as the "second bottom"; and an outer somewhat eroded slope 0.2–0.4 km wide. Germond (1939) described Guthrie Lake as typical, composed of a large shallow basin and a modern, smaller, deeper one, the latter definitely eolian. In this lake there are 6 m of lacustrine sediments overlying Edwards limestone which shows no evidence of displacement, as would be the case if the lake occupied a solution basin.

The larger lakes have a lunette of sand on the leeward side which is of lesser volume than the basin. Parker and Whitfield (1941) described a lake of 20 ha near Amarillo with a shore 5 m higher on the side opposite prevailing winds. This is a region where winds attain a velocity of 30 or 40 mph nearly every month and a mean annual velocity from 12 to 15 mph. These salt lakes, or alkali lakes as they are often termed, extend from northwestern Texas into eastern New Mexico (Judson, 1950), and similar lakes are known from the Northern High Plains. Hutchinson (1957) has pointed out the great similarity between many of these depressions and the "pans" of the Transvaal. There is little evidence of active deflation today, and most geologists (e.g., Germond, 1939; Evans and Meade, 1945) believe the basins of the Llano Estacado were wind-excavated during drier periods of the Pleistocene. The best source of information concerning late Pleistocene environmental changes in this region, the Southern High Plains, is the series of papers compiled by Wendorf (1961). Among the exposed deflation basins there are many extinct lakes and ponds no longer recognizable except when dissected (Evans, 1943). These are represented now by diatomite sediments up to 23 m thick deposited in freshwater lakes and ponds. Some pond basins were buried by the sands of the Monahans Dunes which lie across a part of the southwest margin of the Llano Estacado.

Probably all but the largest of the playas in northwestern Texas and eastern New Mexico are ephemeral, although many are always moist from ground-water sources. When dry, many are dazzling with a white evaporite, and some are of commercial importance as sources of brine. Reed (1930) listed analyses of the dry lake-bed material which showed NaCl and $MgSO_4$ the most abundant compounds. Meigs et al. (1922) considered the brine to be derived from underlying sediments of Permian seas, and they found marked differences in pump-water brine concentrations from different lakes.

The origin of the salt in the waters of La Sal Vieja and La Sal del Rey, on the coastal plain, is more of a problem. Deevey (1957) suspects the salt is derived, via summer trade winds, from salt flats surrounding Laguna Madre about 48 km away. Percentages of chloride, sodium, and potassium in La Sal Vieja and La Sal del Rey are relatively higher than in sea water. This could be explained by selective enrichment during evaporation, transport, and redeposition.

Published limnological studies of the ephemeral eolian lakes of the Llano Estacado are scarce. Reed (1930) mentioned that algae were scanty in them. Mitchell (1956) reported on winter invertebrates from a modified basin, Goose Lake in Bailey County, a playa lake which has been dammed so that it dries up only in extremely arid years. The fauna, therefore, may be somewhat different from those basins which have at least one annual dry period. Unfortunately Mitchell presented very few physicochemical data. The lake has an area of less than 4.5 ha and a maximum depth of 1.5 m. It lies in a gypsum basin, and the mean winter pH values are 8.34. Floating blue-green algae flourish, and diatoms are present. *Brachionus rubens* and *Keratella valga* are common planktonic rotifers, and blood-red tendipedid larvae abound in the sediments. The fauna contains *Diaptomus clavipes, D. siciloides,* a daphnid, and *Cyclops vernalis.* This is a combination one might expect in some large stock tanks in Arizona, and it may be a widespread association in the arid West. Comita (1951) reported it from a turbid pond in Trans-Pecos Texas.

The life of the saline deflation basins of the southern Texas coastal plain is known only through Deevey's (1957) contributions. Because of their high salinity, their faunas and floras are probably rather specialized, although not necessarily endemic, even though Deevey collected an undescribed species of blue-green alga. Fiddler crabs referable to *Uca subcylindrica* (Stimpson) were found at the margins of both La Sal Vieja and La Sal del Rey. Tendipedid larvae and some gastropods were present in the bottom sediments of La Sal Vieja, but in the more saline La Sal del Rey only ephydrid fly larvae occurred.

Solution basins

Cenotes and Montezuma Well

The northern part of the Yucatan Peninsula in Mexico is characterized by a lack of surface drainage and a number of limestone sinks, termed cenotes, which in many instances connect with ground waters. Thirty cenotes ranging from 0.5 to 54 m in depth were studied by Pearse *et al.* (1936). More recently Cárdenas Figueroa studied the hydrology and fauna of the cenotes and caves of Yucatan as well as the epigean fauna in that region. His results are published in a monograph edited by De la O Carreño (1950). Surfaces of the large cenotes near Chichen Itza lie 20 m below the ground level. Nearer the coast the water is closer to the land surface, and the cenotes are shallow. Some cenotes are cavelike; others are open with steep vertical walls. Eroded and presumably older cenotes occupy saucer-like depressions. Thus, the cenotes grade into two other Yucatan aquatic habitats: water-containing caves and shallow water holes called aguadas.

Several cenotes show evidence of circulation probably brought about by water entering and leaving through subsurface porous fissures of some sort. Others are stagnant and presumably have lost connection with the ground water. The role of water flow in circulation is emphasized by the following data. Although Scan Yui cenote is 54 m deep and bounded by steep cliffs rising 20 m above the surface, its temperature, pH, CO_2, alkalinity, and dissolved oxygen are practically uniform from top to bottom. By contrast, Xtolok and Xanaba II are relatively shallow, 15.4 m and 20.7 m, respectively, and yet exhibit stratification. The thermal gradients from top to bottom involve a difference of about 5° C. Below 6 m there is no detectable oxygen, and H_2S is present. Similarly, pH, CO_2, and bicarbonates are stratified. Maximum surface temperature of the cenotes was found to be 28.5° C, minimum bottom temperature 21.9° C, and the mean temperature was 25.45° C. Each cenote has its own characteristic temperature, varying little during the summer months at least. The oxygen tension in the cenote waters is about one-half of saturation. Highest pH values are associated with the presumed isolation from ground water and are found in Xtolok and Xanaba II. The pH of most cenotes is circumneutral, 6.8 being the lowest. Similarly, surface waters of Xtolok and Xanaba II contain the lowest concentration of CO_2, with the exception of two cenotes less than 2 m deep. Sodium chloride ranged from 70 to 560 mg/L, and $CaCO_3$ from 144 to 460 mg/L. However, although physicochemical conditions are similar in all the cenotes, the variations show no correlation with geographic position. Thus, the highest concentration of NaCl is found in Scan Yui at Chichen Itza, and the lowest in Pisté cenote which is about 5 km away. Chemical analyses of "Lake Chichen-Kanab, Yucatan" shown by Clarke (1924) presumably refer to a cenote. These show a relatively high sulfate content, and, although a carbonate value is not given, Clarke classified it as an example of sulfato-chloride water.

Pearse emphasized the successional aspect, from cave to aguada, of the cenotes and their included biota. The fauna of young, steep-walled cenotes is relatively impoverished, but it increases until in an old cenote it becomes aguada-like. The young cenotes contain some animals found also in the Yucatan caves, but these are gone by the time the old cenotes approach the aguada stage. Catfishes referable to *Rhamdia* are present in all caves and natural cenotes. Cichlid fishes are present in many cenotes, but there is evidence that in many cases these do not survive and are continuously replaced from ponds near the coast. *Macrocyclops albidus, Tropocyclops prasinus,* and *Mesocyclops tenuis* are widely distributed cyclopoid copepods in the cenotes. In Yucatan caves cirolanid isopods, two species of blind shrimps, and a schizopod crustacean are found. These animals, suggestive of marine ancestry, do not extend into the cenotes. However, the leech, *Cystobranchus,* probably with marine relationships, is found in caves and young cenotes. Two other leeches are found only in older cenotes. Dragonflies and damselflies appear in young, open cenotes, although one species, *Telebasis salva,* is limited to old cenotes and aguadas. Similarly, among the cenote mollusks one gastropod is restricted to older cenotes. Aquatic hemipterans and coleopterans are common in older cenotes, although the corixids are represented by only two species, and no members of *Notonecta* are present. The reported chironomid fauna of the cenotes consists of only three species. Only one taxonomic group, the Ostracoda, seems to be well represented by many species in the Yucatan sinks.

The plankton of some cenotes is rather abundant. Several cladocerans and cyclopoids and two species of *Diaptomus* are present. Although several new species have been described from the cenotes, there is little or no evidence of endemism. On the whole, Yucatan aquatic fauna consists of widely distributed species, which occur also to the

south and west and to a lesser extent in the islands to the north.

A habitat which is best compared with the Yucatan cenotes is Montezuma Well (Fig. 14.3) in Yavapai County, Arizona (Cole, unpublished). This is a limestone sink much like the young, open-type cenote. It is surrounded by vertical walls 21 m high, and the maximum water depth is 17 m, except for at least two deep fissures through which water enters, which have been sounded to about 40 m. The well is very nearly circular in outline with a diameter of about 100 m. However, Montezuma Well combines features of a cenote and a warm spring and is essentially a limnocrene habitat. There is a well-marked subterranean outlet through which water leaves at an approximate rate of 5,600 m^3/day, emerging outside the cliffs which bound the well. The entering water approaches physical and chemical constancy throughout the year at about 23.7° C, although the entire body of water cools and warms with the seasons. There is a lack of stratification in the well, reminiscent of Scan Yui cenote, and this lends strength to the theory that gentle currents are circulating through the latter. Chemically Montezuma Well differs from the cenotes. The pH ranges from 6.2 at night and on some cloudy days to 6.9 on bright sunny days. The total alkalinity, which is due entirely to bicarbonate, varies from 565 to 600 mg/L. There is no residual acidity, and aeration of samples raises the pH to 8.3 or more. This indicates a free CO_2 content far higher than that found in any of the Yucatan cenotes and accounts for the absence of fishes. Dissolved oxygen is from 70% to 98% of saturation and is usually uniform throughout. There is usually no detectable turbidity in Montezuma Well waters, and the euphotic zone extends to approximately 9.5 or 10 m. Secchi disc readings average about 3 m.

The fauna of Montezuma Well is represented by relatively few species, although total numbers are high. The absence of fish may account for the extreme abundance of the amphipod, *Hyalella azteca,* in the plankton as well as in the marginal weedbeds and to a lesser extent in the benthos. Only three of the Yucatan cenotes contain this crustacean. Surprisingly, there are no chironomids in the soft organic sediments of the deeper parts, although a few species are found in its weedbeds. The commonest benthic animals are oligochaetes which are present in numbers up

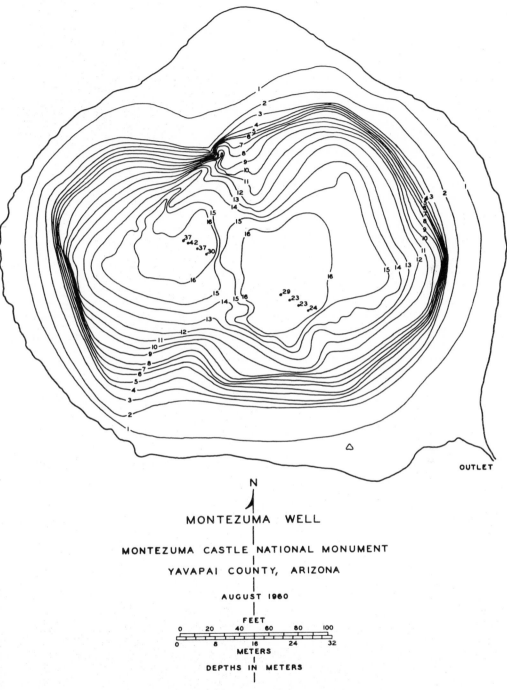

N

MONTEZUMA WELL

MONTEZUMA CASTLE NATIONAL MONUMENT

YAVAPAI COUNTY, ARIZONA

AUGUST 1960

FEET

0   20   40   60   80   100

0   8   16   24   32

METERS

DEPTHS IN METERS

Fig. 14.3.—Bathymetric map of Montezuma Well, Arizona, a large limnocrene and solution-basin environment.

to 10,000 per m². The more abundant of the two oligochaetes is an undetermined species. Leeches, probably referable to *Erpobdella punctata annulata,* are present in some numbers in the benthos but are more typical of the plankton. *Tropocyclops prasinus mexicanus* is an extremely abundant plankter; presumably this is the same subspecies present in the cenotes. *Macrocyclops albidus* is also present in the plankton. There are no calanoid copepods and no planktonic Cladocera or rotifers. The only other crustaceans are some cosmopolitan ostracods, an undetermined species of harpacticoid copepod from *Chara* beds in the shallows, and chydorid cladocerans in the extensive marginal stand of *Potamogeton illinoensis.*

Diurnal migration is conspicuous in the plankton of Montezuma Well. During bright days more than 90% of the plankton is found between 3 and 8 m below the surface. At night, however, the leeches, amphipods, and copepods rise to the surface.

In addition to the lack of calanoids, rotifers, and cladocerans in the plankton of Montezuma Well, there is another unique feature: there are almost no net phytoplankters; the holophytic members of the plankton must be classed as nannoplankton.

The molluscan fauna includes two gastropods and at least the shells of the sphaeriid, *Pisidium.* Hemipterans in the well are represented abundantly, but almost exclusively, by the water scorpion (*Ranatra quadridentata*), *Abedus breviceps,* and microveliid water striders. The beetles are *Cybister, Hydrophilus,* and *Hydroscapha natans. Telebasis salva* is probably the only member of the Odonata which reproduces in the well, although several other damselflies and dragonflies from adjacent Beaver Creek oviposit there.

Bottomless Lakes, New Mexico

East of the Pecos River about 16 km from Roswell, New Mexico, is an interesting group of solution lakes. They lie in a chain along the base of gypsum bluffs at an elevation of 1,054 m and are called the Bottomless Lakes. Seven of these which are within the boundaries of Bottomless Lakes State Park have been studied by the New Mexico Department of Game and Fish. Their report (Navarre, 1959) includes good bathymetric maps (Fig. 14.4). Apparently these lakes are all monomictic, although certain morphometric and chemical features suggest the possi-

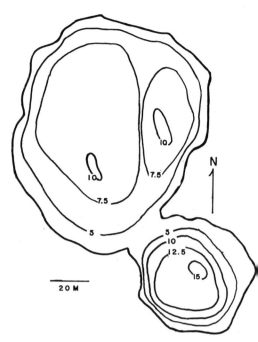

Fig. 14.4.—Bathymetric map of Mirror Lake, Bottomless Lakes State Park, New Mexico, a compound sink in gypsum deposits. Modified from Navarre, 1959.

bility of meromixis. Total depletion of summer oxygen occurs in the deeper waters of some lakes, but the data are not uniform, and it is impossible to state conditions in all of them.

The deepest is Lea Lake with a maximum depth of about 30 m. The largest is No Name Lake, 10.6 ha in area and with a maximum depth of 21 m. The smallest is Devil's Inkwell, 10 m deep, with an area of 0.145 ha. This lake is reminiscent of some Yucatan cenotes and Montezuma Well, for it has vertical banks, and the water surface lies 6.1 m below the surrounding terrain. The same may be said to a lesser degree of nearby Cottonwood Lake which is surrounded by vertical cliffs and lies more than 3 m below the adjacent land.

The dissolved solids in the waters of the Bottomless Lakes are extremely high, with estimates of 25,538 mg/L; conductivities are as high as $2,850 \times 10^{-5}$ mhos at 25° C. They are best characterized as sulfato-chloride waters. Very few analyses of sodium are available, but it appears to be the dominant cation even though calcium values approach 1,000 mg/L. An unusually high fluoride content of 9.5 mg/L was found in one of the lakes. Their silica values are not available.

It is not surprising that such hard-water plants as *Ruppia maritima* and *Chaetophora incrassata* thrive here, and that fish-kills commonly decimate introduced game species, although *Cyprinodon* populations maintain themselves in several of the lakes.

The linear orientation of this group of lakes may be typical of solution basins lying in gypsum deposits. Olive (1955) described many narrow subsidence troughs in the Castile anhydrite south of the Bottomless Lakes. The troughs run parallel to the dip, about 3° E in this case. Sinkholes as deep as 10 m occur in and near the troughs.

Kaibab Plateau of Arizona

A small lake district in the Colorado Plateau province of Arizona is seen in the Kaibab Plateau north of the Grand Canyon. Rasmussen (1941) has discussed the general ecology of this area, which covers 2,980 km² and reaches altitudes of 2,800 m. It is surprisingly level and composed of a thick layer of Permian sediment, the Kaibab limestone, in which there are many solution basins. Some are sealed and permanent, ranging in size from 3 m in diameter to those, such as Jacob Lake and three or four others, which cover areas greater than a hectare. The fauna of many of the sinks include anostracan crustaceans, reflecting their ephemeral nature. Also, one high-altitude copepod of the West, *Diaptomus shoshone*, is present in these temporary ponds. In both permanent and temporary sinks, *D. nudus* occurs. This calanoid is typical of the lakes and ponds of Arizona north of the Mogollon Rim (Cole, 1961).

Lakes of the Río Lerma System, Mexico

A series of related lakes occurs at the southwestern edge of the Mexican Plateau in the states of Guanajuato, Michoacán, and Jalisco. They range in elevation from 2,120 to 1,525 m in a region typified by marked summer rains and winter drought. The important lakes of this system are Zirahuén, Pátzcuaro, Cuitzéo, and the largest in Mexico, Chapala. The first three seem to be successive compartments of a river system in the Lerma basin separated by volcanic materials. Lake Chapala is a relic of an extensive Tertiary or Pleistocene lake. De Buen (1943) considered the lakes fragmented from the Río Lerma system to be a series showing relative degrees of aging. Zirahuén, the youngest, is at the highest elevation and about 46 m deep; Pátzcuaro follows at a lower level, and with a maximum depth of 15 m; Cuitzéo, at a still lower elevation, De Buen termed decadent. Chapala is only 1,525 m above sea level and is probably no deeper than 9.8 m. The extreme shallowness of this large lake has precluded the preservation of a Tertiary fauna, and it may not have had a continuous lacustrine history. Characin fishes, others referable to the Goodeidae, and atherinids of the genus *Chirostoma* are present in these lakes and the Río Lerma. Zirahuén has the fewest, while the river and Chapala have the greatest number of species. A basic similarity among Lerma basin lakes may be reflected in Osorio Tafall's (1942) attempt to relate the brachionid rotifer fauna of Mexico with physicochemical factors. Chapala, Pátzcuaro, and Zirahuén he considered typical of the *habitat alcalino*, with similar faunas. Chemical data approaching completeness are available only from the first two lakes, however, and no bathymetric maps exist.

The Estación Limnológica was established on the shores of Pátzcuaro in 1938, and subsequently numerous publications were concerned with that lake and others of the Lerma system. Both Mexicans and foreigners have contributed studies, and, as a result, Pátzcuaro is one of the best-known lakes in Mexico—perhaps in all Middle America. Many of the data from adjacent waters, even those from lagoons and streams, have been compared with conditions in Lake Pátzcuaro (De Buen, 1945).

Lake Pátzcuaro, elevation 2,035 m, is a C-shaped body of water with an area of 111 km² and a maximum depth of 15 m. There is no outlet, and the water level fluctuates about a meter during the year, the rise occurring during summer months when precipitation exceeds evaporation. Suspended volcanic materials impart extreme turbidity to the lake; the mean monthly Secchi disc transparencies are between 1 and 2 m. The temperature data presented by De Buen (1944) and Deevey (1957) for winter and summer indicate a lack of permanent stratification throughout the year.

Pátzcuaro is much like Lake Chapala chemically, although Deevey's (1957) analyses of inorganic constituents show some differences. The chief discrepancies between the two are a total concentration of dissolved solids in Pátzcuaro more than 1.6 times greater than Chapala, much more sulfate and less carbonate in Chapala, and almost four times as much silica in Chapala. Diatoms are the predominant phytoplankters in Pátzcuaro (Osorio Tafall, 1944b). Both are essentially carbonate lakes with an unusually high concentration of sodium for such a type, Deevey reporting 41% Na+K for each. Calcium and magnesium values, on the other hand, are extremely low, being less than 2% of the principal ions. Surface chlorophyll values determined by Deevey in the summer of 1941 were about the same for both lakes (12.5 to 15 mg/m³), but certain nutrient substances were quite different. Total phosphorus was four times greater in Chapala, although the seston fraction was roughly 50% in both. Nitrates have not been assayed, but without these the N/P ratio is 61.7 in Pátzcuaro and 5.9 in Chapala.

The fauna and flora of Lake Pátzcuaro are well known. The biological survey of the lake published in Volume 11 of *Anales del Instituto de Biologia*, 1940, as "Prospecto Biológico del Lago de Pátzcuaro," is one of the major references, but there have been other contributions. A few animal species have been described originally from the lake, although they are not necessarily endemic. Osorio Tafall (1944b) published a paper on the biodynamics of Lake Pátzcuaro following Lindeman (1941) with emphasis on the central position of the ooze. No quantitative data were presented, but the list of plants and animals with their presumed trophic roles is extensive.

Deevey (1957) examined eleven Ekman-dredge samples from Pátzcuaro and five from Chapala. The total weights were rather low, 1.77 g/m² in the former and 0.472 g/m² in Chapala. An unusual feature was the presence of hirudineans in the deeper areas of these lakes. Deevey found this to be true for Lake Amatitlán in Guatemala also, and the occurrence of many leeches in the cenotes of Yucatan and in the deep sediments of Montezuma Well is worthy of note. To the limnologist familiar with the profundal benthos of temperate lakes, this is an anomalous situation.

Lake Chapala has been described by De Buen (1945) and Deevey (1957). It is a shallow lake with the deepest known point 9.8 m near the western end and a surface area of 1,685 km². It circulates throughout the year. The lake is extremely turbid as evidenced by Secchi disc transparencies as low as 25 cm. The Río Lerma enters

its eastern tip, where it has built a broad delta, and the Río Grande de Santiago drains the lake from a nearby point. De Buen's (1945) paper describes the method by which limnologists under his direction have studied the lakes near the Pátzcuaro station. In April 1943 a concerted attack was made on Chapala. The lake was divided into sectors, and concurrent samples were taken by different teams. The data from this synoptic approach showed the western end of the lake characterized by nearly horizontal isotherms and some degree of regularity in the oxygen and, particularly, pH profiles. This region which is not under the influence of currents of external origin De Buen called the *zona eulimnica*. At the eastern end of the lake the influences of the entering Río Lerma and the effluent Río Santiago were clearly shown. River water, denser, more highly oxygenated, and with a high pH, caused much more irregularity in the various profiles. This region of the lake De Buen termed the *zona pseudolimnica*.

At least exploratory work has been performed on Lake Zirahuén, the deepest in the Lerma system (De Buen, 1943). The waters are clear and blue, with a color of VII on the Forel-Ule scale. The profiles constructed from synoptic temperature and oxygen analyses show considerable influence of currents from the Arroyo de la Palma. De Buen considered the lake almost totally *pseudolimnica* because of the irregularity of these profiles. De Buen's temperature profiles, however, suggest some degree of stability in Zirahuén, and it may be a monomictic lake.

Zirahuén is not rich in plankton. The phytoplankers make up from 87 to 98% of total numbers and are predominantly of the Chlorophyceae, with *Staurastrum* and other desmids particularly abundant.

Lakes Amatitlán and Atitlán, Guatemala

Atitlán and Amatitlán lie in a tropical humid region on the Pacific slope of the Guatemalan highlands, the former at 1,555 m elevation, the latter at 1,189 m. Both are impounded by volcanic dams. The maximum depth of Amatitlán is about 34 m, and Atitlán is 10 times deeper. The areas are a little more than 8 km² for Amatitlán and 136.8 km² for Atitlán. Amatitlán is composed of two quite distinct basins and probably should be considered two lakes.

Lake Atitlán seems to occupy a closed basin.

It has no visible outlet, although there are reasons to suspect subterranean exits. At least one small hot spring enters it from the north, but its influence is not great in such a large lake. On the other hand, the Río Lobos entering Amatitlán brings in much silt which has built a large delta at the north and northeast end. Numerous saline, thermal springs along the south shore have influenced the water quality of Amatitlán markedly. It is drained by the Río Michatoya.

The threefold greater silica content and eight times higher chlorinity in Amatitlán waters when compared with those of Atitlán can be attributed to influent river and saline-spring water in a relatively small lake. The lake water has a greater salinity than the Río Lobos, and probably most of it is derived from the springs. No significant increase in the salinity of the water occurred during the 40 years separating Meek's (1908) and Deevey's (1957) analyses. Apparently a rough equilibrium exists between the influent sources. Meromixis has not occurred in the lake because of the high temperatures of the spring water. Although extremely saline, the water does not flow immediately to the bottom but spreads out over the surface and is gradually mixed as it cools and sinks.

Sulfate values are not available, but it would appear that Lake Atitlán is surprisingly fresh for a closed system and is probably a carbonate lake. In Amatitlán, however, chlorides are sub-equal to the carbonates.

Deevey assayed phosphorus in the two lakes, finding the totals to be not unusual and in a mesotypic range. This is true of the lakes of other Middle American republics with the exception of Ilopango in El Salvador, a special case. The proportion of sestonic phosphorus appeared normal, although somewhat low in Atitlán. An interesting comparison here is the difference between Amatitlán and Lake Güija, El Salvador, and two similar shallow, turbid lakes to the north, Chapala and Pátzcuaro. The two Mexican lakes have a higher percentage of sestonic phosphorus than the two to the south. Deevey attributed the lack of association between turbidity and relatively high seston phosphorus in the latter to more intense metabolism under more nearly tropical conditions. One peculiarity of the lakes of Guatemala and those of El Salvador is the unusually low N/P ratio, supposedly caused by a terrestrial nitrogen deficiency.

Some thermal calculations, based on available morphometric and temperature data, were made by Deevey (1957) for Amatitlán and Atitlán. Probably both lakes are monomictic, but because the stability is not great in Amatitlán, occasional summer isothermy cannot be ruled out. The stability of Atitlán is great, however. A most remarkable feature is the high summer heat income in Atitlán, which is far greater than expected for a tropical lake. Hutchinson (1957) has pointed out that the winter heat content above 4° C in Atitlán is of the same order as in deep lakes of tropical Sumatra, but at the same time Atitlán exhibits an annual heat budget comparable to those of temperate dimictic lakes. Daily high-velocity winds sweep on Atitlán, and the work of the wind in distributing an average calorie is 0.169 g·cm.

Atitlán data contradict the generalization that all tropical lakes have small heat budgets, but the inference that such lakes should be unusually productive was confirmed by Deevey (1957). Dark-light bottle experiments in Amatitlán indicated a primary-productivity rate of 0.514 mg O_2/cm^2 per day and a probable yearly mean two or three times that of such productive temperate lakes as Mendota. Calculated hypolimnetic oxygen deficits in Atitlán suggest the same magnitude.

The summer plankton of Amatitlán consists largely of green algae, particularly desmids (Peckham and Dineen, 1953), but surface scums of blue-green algae are present at times (Clark, 1908). During February Juday (1916) found diatoms, especially *Melosira,* to be predominant in both Amatitlán and Atitlán. There is nothing unusual about the zooplankton in these lakes, although, inexplicably, no calanoid copepods were collected from Atitlán by either Juday or Deevey.

The Amatitlán bottom fauna sampled from various depths had a mean weight of 3.9 g/m^2, which is relatively low when compared to productive temperate lakes (Deevey, 1957). This is probably an outcome of intense metabolism and nutrient regeneration in upper waters, as would be expected in a tropical lake, thus in part depriving sediments of an energy source. Deevey's samplings revealed what may have been an atypical "azoic" zone below 25 m and the familiar concentration zone of tendipedid larvae at about 15 m.

The fauna of Lake Amatitlán contains two common decapod crustaceans: a large prawn and a brachyuran crab. This emphasizes one aspect of Middle American aquatic biology that is unique to the North American limnologist—the presence of large crustaceans in what seem most unlikely habitats. For example lobster-like shrimps called *camarones* occur in rocky, freshwater streams on the eastern slopes of Honduran mountains, and, in the mountainous cloud forests of the same country, crabs are found in small turbulent streams. An inland shrimp fishery is present here (Mercado Sánchez, 1961) as in many other tropical countries.

Volcanic lakes of El Salvador

Volcanic activity, tectonic events, and combinations of these forces produced many lakes which lie in the humid highlands of El Salvador. This is still a region of marked geologic activity, and some of the lakes were formed relatively recently, while others have been destroyed in late years. The large Lake Güija, lying in the Department of Santa Ana on the Guatemalan boundary at an elevation of 426 m, has been estimated to be less than 500 years old. It occupies a valley obstructed by a lava flow, and recent volcanism has produced several small craters nearby. By contrast Lake Zapotitlán has been drained by the Río Sucio and now consists of marsh and saline pools (Armitage, 1958). Formerly it may have been as large as Coatepeque, now the second largest lake of El Salvador. Also, a body of water known formerly as Las Ranas and occupying a crater depression has drained through its eroded walls and contained no water when visited by Armitage in 1953.

The lakes vary in their aspect, some with precipitous margins and little vegetation, others with extensive shallow areas choked with hyacinths and water lilies. Human activity has modified the shores of many. Others are relatively undisturbed. At least one, Lago Verde de Metapán, lying in a small crater at an altitude of 450 m, is so isolated it contains a population of caimans (Armitage, 1958).

At higher altitudes the lakes occupying volcanic basins have a northern aspect, on the basis of their aquatic plants, and appear to be more typical ecologically of temperate regions than of the tropics (Fassett and Armitage, 1961). This is true, for example, of Lago Las Ninfas and Lago Verde de Apaneca, at altitudes of 1,670 and 1,650 m, respectively. Their November surface temperatures were 18° C, which is about 10° lower than that of the other lakes. Certain aquatic macrophytes reach the southern limits of their range in Middle America in these lakes, of which *Nymphaea odorata*, *Proserpinaca palustris*, *Potamogeton pusillus*, and *Brasenia schreberi* are examples. Conversely, *Eleocharis sellowiana* is a South American species that attains its northern limit in these high-altitude lakes of El Salvador.

Continuous temperature data are lacking for the volcanic lakes of El Salvador, but probably most of them are monomictic with circulation occurring during January and February. In some cases polymixis may apply. Temperature profiles from Ilopango and Coatepeque were obtained during February by Juday (1916) and in October by Armitage (1958). Lake Güija temperatures were recorded in January or February by Hildebrand (1925), in October by Deevey (1957), and in October and November by Armitage (1958). In addition, Armitage presented single temperature profiles for six other lakes. Thus, only enough data exist to calculate the thermics of Lake Güija which is relatively shallow (maximum depth 26 m). Unfortunately, seasonal temperature changes in lakes Coatepeque and Ilopango, with depths of 120 m and 248 m, respectively, are little known, although bathymetric maps are available for both. Deevey (1957) calculated some thermal properties of Lake Güija, which show it to be not unlike the similarly shallow Amatitlán in Guatemala.

Temperature data presented by Juday (1916) for lakes Coatepeque and Ilopango during February show a very weak thermal stratification. Armitage's (1958) October data reveal a curve very similar to Juday's for Ilopango, but Coatepeque's is sharper. Deevey's (1957) October profile for Güija shows pronounced stratification, and this is also true of Armitage's temperature curve for this lake. Some profiles from the six other volcanic lakes, which Armitage graphed, show marked thermoclines between temperatures of 29° and 24° C, which imply considerable changes in density.

In the El Salvador lakes studied, deep-water oxygen deficiencies usually occurred, with total depletion in some cases. An exception was Coatepeque: Juday observed only a slight decrease in the dissolved oxygen between the surface and 110 m, with a slight, and perhaps insignificant, increase at 10 m. Armitage (1958) analyzed only surface and 15-m water in this lake; dissolved oxygen amounted to 6.6 mg/L at the surface and 8.0 at 15 m. The latter value he considered questionable, but it may have been valid.

There are conspicuous variations in certain physical features of the volcanic lakes of El Salvador. Some are extremely turbid, while others are relatively clear. Lake Güija and several of the smaller lakes are turbid, while the two largest, Ilopango and Coatepeque, have reported Secchi disc values of 10.5 and 12.5 m, respectively. Seasonal variations occur within individual lakes, however. For example, following summer rains, the waters of Ilopango carry suspended substances derived from severe erosive activity of the Río Guaye. At those times Secchi disc transparencies are reduced to 6.5 m.

Analyses approaching completeness are not available for the volcanic lakes of El Salvador, but chemically the lakes are not unusual and are similar with certain exceptions. Chloride content varies from 5 to 50 mg/L in most of them, but in Ilopango and Coatepeque this ion concentration was 635 and 494 mg/L, respectively, in 1953 (Armitage, 1958). Coatepeque owes much of its salinity to a hot spring influent, and there appears to have been a chloride increase since Renson's 1910 report (Juday, 1916) of 301.5 mg/L. By contrast, Deevey (1957) found that the hot, saline springs entering Lake Amatitlán, Guatemala, did not raise the chlorides appreciably in 40 years, probably a reflection of the fact that this lake has an outlet, whereas Coatepeque occupies a closed basin. Combining the data of Renson and Armitage, one may conclude that, in terms of Clarke's (1924) classification, Coatepeque is a *triple* lake, with chloride slowly gaining ascendancy over carbonate and sulfate. The principal cation is sodium. This is probably not true of the other lakes, with the possible exception of Ilopango. In most of the others carbonates are well ahead of chlorides, but no data are available for sulfates. Much of the salinity of Ilopango is caused by materials brought in by streams, but it is also significant that subsurface eruptions have occurred in this lake, which may have added much. Certainly the unusually high phosphorus content of 646 mg/m³ reported by Deevey (1957) for Ilopango suggests a contribution from underwater volcanic activity. Calcium is low, however, in both Ilopango and Coatepeque. One would expect high acidity in Ilopango, and, on

the basis of what would be considered improper analyses today, Juday reported its waters to show an acid reaction at all depths in 1910. Armitage in 1953, however, found a pH of 8.4 at the surface and 8.3 at a depth of 15 m.

Of the 18 volcanic lakes studied by Armitage (1958), only the nearly extinct Zapotitlán approached Ilopango and Coatepeque in chlorinity. However, Lago Chanmico had more than twice the chloride content of the remaining 15 lakes, with 51 mg/L, and its flora was considered halophytic by Fassett and Armitage (1961). The importance of sulfate must not be overlooked, although no data are available on the concentration of this ion. Fish-kills in Chanmico are said to be an annual event, usually in January, because of sulfurous gases. Parenthetically, Chanmico is of interest because it is a good example of a parasitic maar on the flank of Volcán de San Salvador (Hutchinson, 1957, p. 28).

Najas marina, Ruppia maritima, Chara zeylanica, and *Potamogeton pectinatus,* plants typical of brackish waters, are present only in the four lakes with the highest chlorides mentioned above. These, except for the *Chara* species, are common at North American latitudes, but their presence in the El Salvador lakes from 470 to 750 m elevation and their absence in the less saline high-altitude lakes points to salinity as a very important factor in their distribution.

An interesting lake, from a chemical viewpoint, is Laguna de Alegría situated in a crater at an altitude of 1,220 m in the center of the Department of Usulután. Several sulfurous fumaroles and springs situated along the shore have brought the pH of this lake down to values as low as 2.0, and the only aquatic macrophyte present is *Eleocharis sellowiana.* The other lakes are circumneutral or slightly alkaline.

Some net plankton collections from lakes Ilopango and Coatepeque were studied by Juday (1916). Deevey (1957) reported on collections from Ilopango, Güija, and a small, closed pond near Chalchuapa. Phytoplankters seemed to be scarce, especially in Ilopango. Traces of chlorophyll were found at a 12-m depth in Güija by Deevey, although surface values were only about 12 mg/m³. The zooplankton does not appear unusual and, with the possible exception of the rotifer *Keratella stipitata,* consists of species found in many North American lakes, if we are to rely on lists presented by Juday. However, the taxonomic status of *K. stipitata* is confused (Edmondson, 1959), and it may well be *K. americana* Carlin (*gracilienta* Ahlstrom), which is not rare in the United States.

Ponds and lagoons of Pacific coastal lowlands

The Pacific lowlands of Middle America contain many lagoons and shallow ponds of varied origins, but there are few limnological data concerning them. Nine shallow lakes situated in the coastal lowlands of El Salvador have been studied by Armitage (1957), and the aquatic plants of these and two additional lakes by Fassett and Armitage (1961). Armitage considered none of these basins volcanic in origin, but lava flows partially bound some of them. They share several features: all occupy closed basins; none is deeper than 2.5 m, although fluctations in level are marked; they are wind-swept and turbid; their temperatures are about 30° C; their floras are relatively poor in species and characterized by floating types. Salinities are low in spite of the closed basins; chloride values obtained by Armitage ranged from 8 to 81 mg/L and total alkalinities 36 to 244 mg/L. All were circumneutral with the exception of the only one which showed phenolphthalein alkalinity and had a pH of 9.4.

Two lagoons on the Pacific Coast of Mexico near Acapulco were studied by Ramírez Granados (1952) who presented bathymetric maps and some data on physicochemical and biotic factors. These bodies are quite different from the lakes of the El Salvador coastal plain. They are shoreline lakes, each separated from the sea by a barrier sand bar and fed by a freshwater stream. One of these, Laguna de Tres Palos, has an area of 5,500 ha and a maximum depth of about 5 m. The other, Laguna de Coyuca, is only 2,800 ha but is 18 m deep. Ramírez Granados found Secchi disc transparencies of less than a meter, water temperatures of 28°–29° C, and chloride values ranging from near zero by the influent Río Coyuca up to 900 mg/L in Tres Palos. Although these data imply the lagoons are oligohaline, Osorio Tafall (1942) stated that Laguna de Coyuca's salinity surpasses that of the sea during dry periods, and he classed it as a saline, rather than brackish, habitat. The rotifer, *Brachionus plicatilis*, is found abundantly throughout the year in this lagoon, and Osorio Tafall considered it an indicator species for this type water. Rawson and Moore (1944) found it in only the most saline

of Saskatchewan lakes they studied and mentioned literature reports of it in other extremely saline bodies of water.

Although Ramírez Granados was especially concerned with fish in the two lagoons, he also reported luxuriant aquatic vegetation, a phytoplankton predominantly myxophycean, and a varied invertebrate fauna which included such unrelated forms as green tendipedid larvae, cladocerans, and the brachyuran decapod, *Callinectes*.

Unusual habitats
Irrigation ditches

To quote Pennak (1958), the West is "densely crisscrossed with an extensive system of irrigation ditches" which have been important in changing distribution patterns of many aquatic organisms. Despite the ubiquity of the ditches, they have not attracted attention of limnologists, and there are few studies to report. In Mexico, the official organ of the National Commission of Irrigation, *Irrigacion en Mexico*, contains material on the hydrology, including some biological data, of canals as well as of artificial impoundments, lakes, and rivers.

Irrigation canals in the Salt River Valley in the Phoenix region of Arizona were studied by Wien (1958, 1959). Some of these ditches carried water from the diversion dam below the confluence of the Verde and Salt rivers; others carried pump water from underground sources; one contained water from Lake Carl Pleasant, an impoundment on the Agua Fria River north of Phoenix. Chemical data from the canals receiving their waters from the Verde and Salt rivers reflect the mixture. The chlorides, derived largely from the Salt River, range from 300 to 400 mg/L, and the bicarbonates originating mainly, although not exclusively, from the Verde River range from 250 to 300 mg/L. In the Salt River the mean chloride is about five times the bicarbonate.

Marine or brackish-water affinities are shown by the flora and fauna of these irrigation canals. For example, two red algae, *Compsopogon coeruleus* (Balbis) and *Thorea ramosissima* Bory, and the green alga, *Enteromorpha intestinalis* (L.), are present. Also, the introduced oriental clam *Corbicula fluminea* (O.F.M.), first reported from the Phoenix area by Dundee and Dundee (1958), is abundant. Some species of *Corbicula* show brackish-water affinities, but this may not apply to *C. fluminea*. The plants and mollusk mentioned above, are also present in some canals which carry mineralized, subsurface pump water, but they do not occur in a canal deriving its water from Lake Carl Pleasant. It is tempting to attribute this to lower salt content. Of the principal anions in the lake, bicarbonate is about 74%, sulfate 17%, and chloride 9%. Total soluble salts are only 374 mg/L. Another factor must be considered, however: because of water shortages, releases to the main canal from Carl Pleasant have been made only during the summer in recent years, and the canal is dry most of the time.

Lying below certain Salt-Verde River canals are a series of small, artificial ponds, termed the Papago Ponds. They have been used as experimental ponds for rearing fish and can be considered permanent for all practical purposes. These ponds and others nearby make up a small, but unique, lake district. Chlorides have accumulated in them from canal influents and evaporation. Their chloride content is about 950 mg/L and conductivity values are 1,900 micromhos at 25° C. *Najas marina,* a plant typical of salt springs and brackish waters, is here. Also, in these ponds the calanoid copepods are represented only by *Diaptomus dorsalis* Marsh. This marks the known western limit for this species, which is essentially a West Indies form. It has not been collected in any other bodies of water in Arizona.

Irrigation "drains" from the Rio Grande in New Mexico at altitudes from 1,360 to 1,556 m are somewhat different (Clark and Mauger, 1932; Clark and Smith, 1935). Few biological data are available, but physicochemical assays have been made. In these canals carbonates are only slightly in excess of sulfates, but the relative chlorinity is about the same as in the canals from Lake Carl Pleasant, Arizona. Mean total solids are near 500 mg/L. At such altitudes there might be a possibility of trout survival if drains were shaded, because periods of high water temperatures are brief.

Stock tanks

Pennak (1958) pointed out the rich invertebrate fauna to be found in the stock tanks of the arid West and emphasized the fact that these habitats have been neglected by aquatic biologists. In Arizona earthen tanks are common in all physiographic provinces. Most of them are probably not permanent and exhibit environmental extremes. Many shallow tanks above the Mogollon Rim freeze completely. All are characterized at times by extreme turbidity. High temperatures are pronounced in those at low altitudes in the Sonoran desert. It would seem that real contributions to population ecology could be made through studies of these tanks, because their faunas and floras appear simple. A few comments concerning the planktonic microcrustaceans of Arizona tanks will illustrate this.

In most stock ponds one species of calanoid copepod is present, although in rare instances two occur (Cole, 1961). There is some evidence that congeneric coexistence is a feature of new tanks, but that one species will disappear in time. There are usually one or two species of *Daphnia* and one cyclopoid copepod, the latter most often being *Cyclops vernalis.* Some remarks concerning a Texas pond by Comita (1951) imply the above situation may apply rather generally. In late summer, notonectid nymphs become prevalent, and crustacean populations are decimated. Anomalous situations prevail at times: some tanks have been found to contain tremendous populations of ostracods, referable to *Cyprinotus,* and diaptomids are absent. In some short-lived, shallow tanks various species of *Moina* occur, and *Daphnia* and *Diaptomus* are rare or absent.

An interesting situation was observed in a small Arizona tank that contained *Daphnia pulex* as the sole member of the genus. Immediately below the dam was a small, water-filled depression fed by seepage from the tank. In this pool *Daphnia similis* was abundant, and only a few *D. pulex* occurred.

These preliminary observations suggest excellent opportunities for studying the dynamics of interspecific competition and for answering some questions concerning indicator species. Moreover, it should be emphasized that problems of sampling environmental factors are insignificant compared to the situation in a large lacustrine habitat.

Natural ephemeral waters

Ponds.—Small, ephemeral ponds of the arid Southwest have been neglected to a great extent. They are characterized by extremes of turbidity and temperatures. Many species of phyllopod crustaceans occur in such habitats, the notostracan, *Triops longicaudatus,* being one of the most interesting forms. Large populations of these can be found occasionally in muddy puddles no deeper than 5 cm. Cladocerans of the genus *Moina* and ostracods referable to *Cyprinotus* are also typical inhabitants of seasonal desert pools.

Weise (personal communication) studied a small, desert depression filled by summer showers near Phoenix, Arizona (altitude *ca*. 333 m). The entire life span of this pond was 12 days, during which time a large population of conchostracans hatched and matured. Chemical data were sketchy but suggested that sequential changes in relative anions occurred similar to those which take place over many years in closed basins of arid regions (cf. Hutchinson, 1957, pp. 566–567).

Tinajas.—An interesting aquatic microhabitat in the mountainous areas of the Southwest is the tinaja. This is a cylindrical pothole worn in the rocks of steep washes. Hensley (1954) mentions some in Organ Pipe National Monument in southwestern Arizona. Schwarz (1914) described the "Four Tanks" in a steep, rocky gorge above Castle Hot Springs, Arizona. These are typical, being from 1 to 2 m deep and lying in series one above the other. It is possible that some protected tinajas contain some water throughout the year, although most are not permanent. It is tempting to postulate meromixis in those which approach permanency, but no studies have been made on them. Many contain abundant algal and microcrustacean elements. The ostracod, *Cyprinotus*, is common in some almost inaccessible tinajas of Arizona canyons.

A diminutive counterpart of the tinaja, although of different origin, is the "etched pothole" described by Udden (1925) in calcareous Texas rocks. Some of these tinajitas contain water at times but must be considered extremely ephemeral.

Springs and springbrooks

Permanent limnocrene habitats in the Southwest are relatively common, but there are few data concerning them. Listing the many known springs is prohibitive, but there are tremendous opportunities for future study among them.

Some of the most conspicuous of these are the Big Springs of Texas arising along the Balcones fault line at the southern and eastern border of the Edwards Plateau. Edwards limestone is over 90% $CaCO_3$, affecting the quality of the water issuing from the springs.

Some bolsons have large springs. Balmorhea Springs, south of Pecos, Texas, is one of these, yielding great quantities of water from a porous limestone. In general, the many springs in the Basin and Range physiographic province of Texas, New Mexico, and Arizona are located near or in ancient lake beds and are extremely mineralized. In the United States the water table has been lowered drastically in such areas, but in parts of northern Mexico, particularly in Coahuila and Chihuahua, there are many closed bolsons with high water tables. The bodies of water in these are marked by a high degree of endemism in their faunas and warrant increased attention by biologists.

Springs that would be most appealing to limnologists and other aquatic biologists are those isolated oases in extremely arid areas. Quitobaquito Springs in Organ Pipe National Monument, Arizona, is such a habitat. It flows at the rate of 163 L per minute and has been impounded, covering an area of 0.1 ha (Hensley, 1954). In it occurs a distinct subspecies of *Cyprinodon macularius,* probably endemic to the spring and the Sonoyta River, a recently disrupted segment of the Colorado River drainage (Hubbs and Miller, 1948).

Abbott and Hoese (1960) attempted a study of energy flow in a small, brick spring chamber, Minter Spring, in Brazos County, Texas. The poorly oxygenated and acid water, probably from Pliocene strata, had a mean flow of 7 L a minute, and other physical and chemical conditions approached constancy. Because the chamber had a volume of only about 1,100 L, the mean flushing time was 2.6 hr, precluding establishment of a plankton community. Primary productivity appeared to be derived entirely from encrusting mats of filamentous green algae, but no satisfactory method of measuring it could be devised. Trophic relations were simple, with ostracods and snails serving as primary consumers. Dytiscid larvae were the tertiary consumers. The chlorophyll A content of the entire system during mid-December was 0.53 g/m^2.

Springbrooks of the Southwest have received little attention, although they are another of the unusual aquatic environments of the region. Noel (1954) reported a year's investigation of Lander Springbrook, arising from a rheocrene spring in the Roswell Artesian Basin of New Mexico. The water was extremely mineralized, with a total residue of 4,400 mg/L, and best characterized as sulfato-chloride in quality. Temperatures were nearly constant throughout the year at about 18° C. There were no sphaeriids, isopods, trichopterans, simuliids, hirudineans, or water cress, which are species typical of many springbrook communities. Presumably these were absent because of the high salinity. Although the fauna was depauperate, a few species were abundant, predominantly *Gammarus*, coleopterans referable to *Zaitzevia parvula* (Horn), gastropods, flatworms, tendipedids, and tubificids.

Similar springbrooks, differing mainly in water quality, found in other parts of the Southwest would lend themselves to comparative study. Fossil Creek in Arizona is one such habitat. Another is the ancient Indian canal which carries the effluent from Montezuma Well, Arizona. Within the first kilometer there are conspicuous changes in the water chemistry, resulting chiefly from loss of CO_2 to the atmosphere with ensuing precipitation of $CaCO_3$ and relative enrichment of other ions.

Schwarz (1914) commented on the fauna of Castle Hot Springs, Yavapai County, Arizona. The springs are at an elevation of 600 m near the southern edge of the Wickenburg Mountains. Water temperature is 46° C at the source, cooling to 35° C at the bottom of the gorge. At the source Schwarz collected a mite and two beetles, including the unusual coleopteran *Hydroscapha natans*.

The stream issuing from Verde Hot Springs in Arizona represents another opportunity for study of a western springbrook. It is 41° C and may differ chemically from the last.

Grants Lava Bed, New Mexico

The Grants Lava Bed in west-central New Mexico contains unique aquatic habitats which have been described by Lindsey (1949, 1951). These are lava sinkhole ponds and lava-tube caves which contain water. According to Lindsey, this is the only American lava flow containing permanent water. More than 100 such ponds in collapse depressions and caves exist in an extensive region of 570 km². They receive their waters from Zuñi Mountain and from several large springs at Horace, New Mexico. As is true of so many New Mexican waters, these are high in calcium sulfate.

The ponds are at altitudes of more than 1,800 m. As a result, they freeze over during winter.

At that time stored heat in the lava accounts for unusual circulation and temperature relations. In some cases water 77 cm below the ice is 6° C.

Lindsey (1951) described a plant succession in these bodies of water, starting with a floating film of *Chlorella* and culminating in a shrubby swale. Of particular interest is the optical effect produced by *Chlorella* cells in the dim cave pools, as they orient their chloroplasts opposite the light (Lindsey, 1949). Many pools are lavender-colored because of the presence of the sulfur bacterium, *Lamprocystis roseo-persicina* (Kutz). Of special biogeographical interest is a relict population of an arctic-alpine moss, *Homomallium incurvatum* (Schrad.), on northeast facing walls in some of the ice caves.

Caves

Water-containing caves in the Southwest and Middle America include lava-tube caves and many solution caverns in calcareous regions. The caves of the Yucatan Peninsula grade into open cenotes but were considered in a separate report by Pearse *et al.* (1938). Some other caves in Mexico are relatively well known; these are La Cueva Chica and La Cueva de los Sabinos in the state of San Luis Potosí. Breder (1942) described the ecology of the former with particular emphasis on the blind characin, *Anoptichthys*. Osorio Tafall (1943) recorded 37 species of aquatic animals from the two caves but considered only the following to be typical troglophiles: *Anoptichthys*, a cirolanid isopod, and, surprisingly, the calanoid copepod *Diaptomus cokeri* which he had described previously. Both caves contain ostracods assigned to the genus *Candona* and an harpacticoid possibly referable to *Attheyella pilosa* Chappuis. Probably Osorio Tafall should have included these with the true cave species.

A series of escarpments and faults, known as the Balcones fault zone, forms a curve from southwest to north-central Texas. To the north and west of the fault line lies the Edwards Plateau containing remarkably pure limestone. There are water caves in the Edwards limestone near the faults. They have been little studied, although probably they contain a unique fauna (Maguire, 1961).

Reservoirs of southwestern United States

The impounds of the arid Southwest are similar in many respects to natural lakes, but

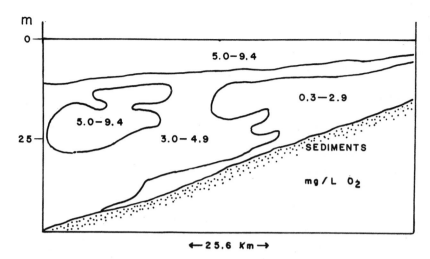

Fig. 14.5.—Mid-channel section of Elephant Butte Reservoir, New Mexico, showing unusual distribution of dissolved oxygen, July 13–17, 1938. Modified from Ellis, 1940.

there are some important departures from natural conditions which preclude accurate calculations of oxygen deficits and heat budgets. At unpredictable intervals, flash floods suddenly introduce turbid waters which profoundly alter existing thermal and oxygen relations. In Elephant Butte Reservoir, New Mexico, a large area of shallow water in the upper part of the lake is either much warmer or much colder than the main body of water, depending on the season. Intrusions of this water mass into the lower lake following floods strikingly alter pre-existing conditions (Ellis, 1940).

Ellis diagrammed some unusual oxygen conditions in Elephant Butte where draw-off for irrigation demands also complicates the normal course of physicochemical events (Fig. 14.5). Moreover, in many impounded waters of the West, such as Elephant Butte, there are unusual subsurface contours, which complicate the flow patterns of density currents. Also stratification in the adclaustral region, which is the term Ellis applied to the portion of lake near the dam, is modified by the interaction of the perpendicular dam surface and wind-generated currents.

Such a problem confronted McConnell (personal communication), who could find no reliable method of measuring the flash-flood import of organic material which entered Peña Blanca Lake in southern Arizona but estimated roughly more than 300 thousand kg a year, which is on the order of 15,000 kg/ha per year. These floods, therefore, not only alter temperature stratifica-

tion and hypolimnion oxygen concentrations but interfere seriously with a compete assay of the lake's economy.

Arizona

Four large impoundments are present on the Salt River of Arizona, formed from tributaries arising in the mountainous areas to the east. The largest and oldest of these is Roosevelt Lake, impounded 50 years ago at an altitude of a little more than 635 m. Below it lie Apache, Canyon, and Saguaro lakes, the last with a spillway crest about 450 m above sea level. Apache Lake is about 80 m deep, and the rest are at least 30 m deep. They have a combined area of 8,979 ha. Except for Roosevelt Lake, they occupy basins bounded abruptly by steep cliffs. Fluctuations in water level are pronounced, and their shores are bare and rocky.

A few data kindly supplied by members of the Arizona Game and Fish Department, the Salt River Valley Water Users' Association, and the Maricopa Water District make possible a sketchy limnological appraisal of these bodies of water. They are warm monomictic lakes which stratify from, at latest, early July until November. Annual surface temperatures range from 31° to 11° C. There is some evidence of density currents entering the upper ends of these lakes and flowing beneath the surface in summer months, but this is not conspicuous in winter. This could be a reflection of the almost daily summer rains in the highlands to the north and east, as opposed to winter months when precipitation in the watershed is largely snow. More reasonably, however, much of the turbidity in the lower lakes is caused by letdown from lake to lake to supply increased irrigation and power demands at this time.

Few chemical data are available for these lakes, although water quality of the Salt River above Roosevelt Lake is well known. This river has salt beds along its course, and this is reflected in its high chloride content which ranges from 330 mg/L, when diluted in early spring, to well over 1,000 mg/L during the low water periods. Sodium is usually the dominant cation, although sometimes calcium surpasses it during periods of high runoff. The lakes themselves are dilute chloride waters, with bicarbonate the second most abundant anion. Sulfates probably attain values up to 100 mg/L at times, and a strong odor of H_2S is present at the outlet of each lake during summer stagnation.

Summer oxygen depletion is complete in the lower waters of the four lakes. Total alkalinities range from 75 to 192 mg/L (as $CaCO_3$) and pH from 6.2 to 9.2.

Plankton usually is scanty in all the lakes, although conspicuous blooms of *Ceratium hirundinella* have been noted occasionally during late summer. There is a similarity in the dominant zooplankters from each lake. *Diaptomus clavipes* and *D. siciloides* are present, and this coexistence is probably typical also of the low-altitude impoundments on the Verde, Gila, and Agua Fria rivers. *Daphnia ambigua* is the common cladoceran, although *Diaphanosoma brachyurum, Ceriodaphnia lacustris,* and *Bosmina* also occur. Large spongillid colonies are found on rocks in the shallows.

Horseshoe and Bartlett lakes are impoundments on the Verde River at elevations of 610 and 533 m, respectively. Waters leaving Bartlett Lake enter the Salt River below Saguaro Lake and are diverted into large canals serving the Phoenix-Mesa area. There are several data available for Bartlett Lake but few for Horseshoe. The former is more than 30 m deep, but summer thermal stratification is not pronounced as it is in the Salt River lakes. Summer records show surface temperatures of about 29° C and 23° C at 24 m, the sharpest clines being 0.5°/m. In spite of this, waters at 15 m and below lack oxygen during the summer months.

Total alkalinities in Bartlett Lake and the Salt River impoundments reflect differences in the drainage systems of the Verde and Salt rivers. In Bartlett Lake methyl orange alkalinities are higher, ranging from 138 to 266 mg/L (as $CaCO_3$), and annual pH values range from 6.8 to 8.9 at the surface. The Salt River arises largely in igneous rocks, whereas most of the Verde River flow originates in the Verde Valley and the calcareous Verde Formation. The dominant compound in the Verde River is calcium bicarbonate; chloride is relatively low.

Lake Carl Pleasant, northwest of Phoenix on the boundary of Yavapai and Maricopa counties, was formed by the impoundment of the Agua Fria River. The headwaters of the Agua Fria lie east of Prescott, Arizona, and the river flows approximately parallel to the Verde River in a different valley. The lake has a maximum depth of 52 m. However, water shortages are common, and these dimensions were attained several years ago. It is a warm monomictic lake, stratifying in summer months, with oxygen depletion occurring in the hypolimnion. Some chemical analyses are available for the waters of this lake, and they show sulfates (50 mg/L) and bicarbonates (202 mg/L) as principal anions. Chlorides are 24 mg/L. Sodium (45 mg/L) and calcium (38 mg/L) are the dominant cations. Plankton has been scanty in collections from the lake.

San Carlos Lake, a large impound on the Gila River at an elevation of 790 m, has been at low levels in recent years. It owes its high chloride and sulfate content at least in part to Clifton Hot Springs which empties into a tributary of the Gila River. The daily contribution of salt from these springs ranges from 22 to 63 thousand kg.

New Mexico

The large reservoirs of New Mexico, like those of Arizona, are warm monomictic bodies of water even though situated at higher elevations. The Arizona impoundments are somewhat warmer than their New Mexican counterparts. There are smaller New Mexican lakes, however, which are dimictic. For example, Clayton Lake (Navarre, 1960) in the northeastern corner of the state at about 36° 30′ N latitude and at an elevation of 1,570 m is dimictic. The lake covers only 31.6 ha and is usually no deeper than 15 m, although a maximum depth of 21 m is possible.

The largest body of water in New Mexico is

Elephant Butte Reservoir, a long narrow impoundment on the Rio Grande which covers a maximum of 15,783 ha with a depth of more than 30 m. The lake lies in a region of semi-desert flora with piñon pine, juniper, cactus, and mesquite. The fishes are typically warm-water fauna, although trout are found below the dam. Like most impoundments of the Southwest, the water level fluctuates considerably, and much of the shoreline is bare of aquatic plants. During summer stagnation complete oxygen depletion is rare. Greenbank (1937), Clark (1938), and Ellis (1940) have contributed papers on this impoundment making it one of the best known in the Southwest.

Willow Lake in southeastern New Mexico originally occupied a solution depression in bedrock of Permian gypsum (Navarre, 1958). In 1920, however, the first of two dams was built to enlarge the lake, and water from the Black River was diverted by canal to fill the basin. The lake covers 145.7 ha but is only 6.5 m deep. In spite of this it stratifies effectively at high temperatures during the summer when bottom waters become as warm as 26°, and there is no dissolved oxygen below 4.8 m. Mean total solids in the lake are 3,465 mg/L, and pH values are usually above 8. The category *apatotrophic,* proposed by Swain and Meader (1958) for alkaline lakes with high total dissolved solids and relatively low sedimentary nitrogen and carbon, does not apply to Willow Lake. Analyses of its hydrosoils show a high nitrogen content.

The fishes of Willow Lake show a higher rate of growth than those of most other New Mexican reservoirs. In all of these lakes benthic production seems to be low, but it is difficult to make comparisons. Data are presented in numbers and volume per unit area, but no weights are given. In Willow Lake the means of Ekman-dredge samples are about 92 organisms per m² having a total volume of 0.86 cm³/m². In New Mexican impoundments plankton feeders such as *Dorosoma* are used as forage fish. In Arizona the similar thread-fin shad *Signalosa* has proven a successful forage species (Haskel, 1959).

Texas

In most reports on Texas reservoirs either there are incomplete chemical analyses or morphometric details are lacking. Most investigation has been concerned largely with fish inventory.

Limnological information is incidental. Harris and Silvey (1940) reported unpublished generalizations from A. H. Wiebe which seem to apply. East Texas reservoirs have a pH varying from 5.8 to 7.1 and are low in total alkalinity. Some of these lakes, for example those in the Cypress Creek Basin such as the natural Caddo Lake, have highly stained waters. That region of Texas bears forests of pine and cypress. Reservoirs of northeastern Texas farther west, where Harris and Silvey worked, have pH values from 7.0 to 8.4, while still farther west many waters show phenolphthalein alkalinity much of the time.

Edaphic and climatic factors interact to bring about these contrasts. Rainfall decreases and evaporation rate increases from east to west. The geologic formations in the state are such that, as one moves from east to west, bedrock changes coincide with precipitation-evaporation changes.

Along the upper half of the eastern border of Texas, reservoirs lie in Eocene sediments and contain relatively high chloride content. In Lake Murvaul, Panola County (Dorchester, 1959), the mean bicarbonate/chloride ratio during the first year following impoundment was about 1.6, the concentrations being 44 mg/L of bicarbonate and 27.56 mg/L of chloride. In Striker Creek Reservoir, Rusk County (Dorchester, 1960), chlorides are higher, and the same ratio is 0.14, the chlorinity being 170 mg/L in contrast to 26 mg/L of bicarbonate. The increased chlorinity in Striker Lake, which lies to the west of Murvaul, might be attributed to subterranean waters derived from the Woodbine Sand, which does not extend eastward into Panola County (Plummer and Sargent, 1931). Although this Cretaceous formation is found farther west in Texas, the chloride content of its waters increases markedly in an eastward direction. Nearby shallow Upper Ellis Lake in Wood County, lying in similar Eocene sediments, was studied by Cheatum *et al.* (1942). Chlorides were not assayed, but surface methyl orange alkalinity was usually less than 20 mg/L (as $CaCO_3$) although concentrations up to 54 mg/L occurred at lower levels during summer. Because this lake is fed in part by acid springs, it rarely attains a pH as high as 7.0. A mat of littoral vegetation is encroaching upon the lake. Apparently, sphagnum is not involved in its formation. Parts of this mat break off and float about during summer. These drifting islands sink during winter but reappear in spring.

TABLE 14.2

Comparison of four Texas reservoir lakes. From Harris and Silvey, 1940.

Name	Year impounded	Number of macro-phyte species	Organic material total plankton (mg/L)	(kg/ha)
Lake Worth	1914	54	3.956	126.5
Dallas Lake	1927	52	5.035	167.2
Eagle Mountain	1934	16	2.935	134.9
Bridgeport Lake	1935	9	4.603	276.2

Harris and Silvey (1940) published on four shallow reservoirs of the Trinity River basin in Jack, Wise, Tarrant, and Denton counties. All lie in Cretaceous sediments, except for Lake Bridgeport located farther west in Pennsylvanian deposits. The report includes excellent data on the plankton, aquatic plants, and physicochemical factors. There is no information on the benthos, and morphometric details also are incomplete. The lakes are usually monomictic, but the authors cite weather bureau records that two of them froze the winter of 1929. These were Lake Dallas and Lake Worth. The former is 12 m deep, 160 m above sea level, and at 33° 20′ N latitude. Lake Worth is 9 m deep, 180 m above sea level, and at 32° 47′ N latitude. Also Harris and Silvey (1948) described thick ice on Lake Dallas during February 1939. This may represent one of the lowest latitudinal limits for dimictism at such altitudes in North America.

The four reservoirs are typical freshwater bodies with bicarbonates making up about 75% of the principal anions and calcium the most abundant cation. Summation of chemical analyses shows the lakes have a mean total salinity of about 240 mg/L. Lake Dallas has a slightly higher chloride content, perhaps because its basin lies in the Woodbine Sand.

In the same drainage system, but farther east in Dallas County, is White Rock Lake (Patterson, 1942). Chemical analyses are incomplete, but this reservoir seems to be similar to those studied by Harris and Silvey. It lies in Cretaceous sediments, and total alkalinities range from 70 to 121 mg/L.

Harris and Silvey approached their study of artificial lakes with an eye to the effects of aging on productivity. They found a direct correlation between age and the number of aquatic macrophyte species present in each lake, but most other data did not show the same relationship. Perhaps the most instructive data were in gravimetric determinations, based on ignition, of the organic content of mean total seston, which are shown in Table 14.2.

Lake Wichita, about 80 km northwest of Lake Bridgeport in Archer and Wichita counties, is 60 years old at this time (Lewis and Dalquest, 1957). Its drainage area is within the Red Beds of the Texas Permian. These marine sediments are high in NaCl and $CaSO_4$, and this is reflected in the water quality. The waters contain more sodium than calcium, and the relative anions are $Cl > SO_4 > CO_3$. According to Lewis and Dalquest, plankton is "extremely rich." No quantitative data are given, but the benthos also "is rich, especially in *Chironomus* larvae."

Small, turbid reservoirs, largely used for irrigation and stock watering, are present in the Salt Basin of Trans-Pecos Texas. These are quite different from the impoundments farther east. Deevey's (1957) account of Fort Stockton Lake and Balmorhea Lake may typify many of them. Both are sulfato-chloride waters with a total salinity of about 2,000 mg/L. Magnesium is remarkably low in these lakes, especially when compared to many of the saline lakes of New Mexico. A further feature which may prove typical of desert lakes is the high percentage of sestonic phosphorus, although there are no comparable data on others outside Trans-Pecos Texas.

Deevey examined one Ekman-dredge sample from Balmorhea Lake, but this does not warrant generalizing about the benthic productivity of desert impoundments. It contained only tendipedid larvae and tubificids in amounts implying 78.58 kg/ha. This is six times less than the mean crop for productive Lake Mendota but about twice the value reported from the lakes of Connecticut's Eastern Highland (Deevey, 1941).

Thermics

In most lakes of the American Southwest the temperature regime is not unusual. Warm monomictic lakes are common, but at high altitudes in New Mexico and Arizona dimixis occurs regularly. The possibility of intermittent ice cover is great, however, and there may be more polymixis than suspected.

A feature of deep Middle American lakes is the considerable stability despite small temperature gradients. This is, of course, consistent with

TABLE 14.3

Thermics of Southwestern and Middle American lakes

	Lat. (N)	Alt. (m)	Area (ha×10⁻²)	Depth (m)		Heat incomes (g·cal/cm²)		
				Max. (z_m)	Mean ($\bar{z}$)	Summer (θ bs)	Winter (θ bw)	Annual heat budget (θ ba)
Dimictic lakes								
Clayton Reservoir, New Mexico	36° 37′	1,569	0.315	15	6	10,475		
Woods Canyon, Arizona	34° 18′	2,294	0.206	11	6.1	7,714		
Monomictic lakes								
Conchas Reservoir, New Mexico	35° 23′	1,289	64.87	50	14		+ 1,871	
Alamogordo Reservoir, New Mexico	34° 39′	1,300	18.82	23	13	16,686	0	16,686
Apache Lake, Arizona	33° 31′	576	10.75	77	28		− 21,600	
Elephant Butte, New Mexico	33° 20′	1,341	148.81	47	18		− 7,246	
Peña Blanca Lake, Arizona	31° 22′	1,219	0.198	18.3	6.6	8,386	− 3,056	8,386
Lake Atitlán, Guatemala[a]	14° 40′	1,555	13,686	341	183	22,110	−288,300	22,110
Lake Amatitlán, Guatemala[a]	14° 25′	1,189	822.6	33.6	18.8	8,510	− 29,670	8,510
Lake Güija, El Salvador[a]	14° 13′	426	4,475	26	16.5	5,410	− 32,090	5,410

[a] From Hutchinson, 1957, Table 53. The symbols for depth and heat income are those proposed by Hutchinson.

the high temperatures that prevail. The gradient from 29° C to 24° C in some lakes of El Salvador (Armitage, 1958) represents a change in density roughly equal to that between 19° and 9.3° C. Some large impoundments of Arizona, New Mexico, and Texas attain surface temperatures comparable to those of Middle American lakes and perhaps higher at times. Harris and Silvey (1948) report an August temperature of 37° C from Lake Dallas, for example. The main differences are in hypolimnion temperatures, which are reflections of winter conditions. Elephant Butte, New Mexico, is 8° C in winter, while Apache Lake, Arizona, at an altitude 765 m lower, has winter temperatures from 11° to 12° C. The Guatemalan and El Salvadoran lakes have winter temperatures near 20° C.

Calculations for Atitlán, Amatitlán, and Güija show large negative winter heat budgets as expected in tropical lakes (Hutchinson, 1957, Table 53). Because of incomplete data, comparisons with reservoirs of the Southwest have to be made on the basis of this parameter. In many of the dimictic lakes the minimum winter temperatures are not known, and in such large lakes as Apache, summer records are available only to a depth of 24 m, which is more than 50 m above the bottom. Therefore, it is impossible to calculate maximum

summer heat content, even though adequate morphometric data exist for Apache. Moreover, many reservoirs are drastically altered during summer by the release of large subsurface volumes and the disturbances caused by density currents.

In Table 14.3 some thermal data are presented for a few Southwestern and Middle American lakes. These are not all valid, because flash floods dramatically change such small lakes as Peña Blanca (McConnell, personal communication).

Chemistry

Several generalizations about the chemistry of Southwestern and Middle American waters have been made in this chapter. Most of these have come from Deevey's (1957) paper, because since its publication there has been almost no other comparable research. However, the unusually low magnesium content Deevey found in some ponds of Trans-Pecos Texas is certainly not typical of many Basin and Range waters.

Silica is high throughout the region. Some summaries and comparative data are presented in Table 14.4. The East Texas reservoirs and the dilute Chuska Mountain lakes are low in silica. Also, the two most saline lakes Deevey studied, La Sal del Rey and Grable's Salt Works, had a small silica content. Most Southwestern lakes and springs of intermediate salinity are moderately high in silica, but the content of the Mexican, Guatemalan, and El Salvadoran lakes averages about 43 mg/L.

Graphic representations of relative concentrations of the three major anions in Texan, New Mexican, and Arizona waters are shown in Figures 14.7, 14.8, and 14.9. The method employed in plotting these by triangular coordinate diagram is explained by Figure 14.6 and its legend.

Arizona waters are the least varied (Fig. 14.7). Most are essentially the carbonate type, even when fairly concentrated. Sulfate is not important, although the issue from Croton Springs is best described as triple water in the classification of Clarke (1924). The Salt River impoundments contain chloro-carbonate waters.

An interesting trend is seen in New Mexican waters (Fig. 14.8). The high-altitude lakes and springs are carbonate waters. With increasing salinity, sulfato-carbonate waters develop, as shown by the three large impoundments on New Mexican rivers—Elephant Butte on the Rio Grande, Conchas on the South Canadian, and Alamogordo on the Pecos River. Most lakes lying in gypsum deposits can be categorized as sulfato-chloride waters. The most concentrated of these, No Name, is a chloro-sulfate lake.

There are no sulfato-carbonate waters plotted for Texas (Fig. 14.9). The playas of Trans-Pecos Texas can be classified as sulfato-chloride waters, and the saline lakes of the South Texas coastal plain fall into the chloride category.

The Mexican lakes, Chapala and Pátzcuaro, plotted in Figure 14.9, appear to be typical carbonate waters, but their dominant cation is sodium. Thus, they are quite different from the reservoirs of eastern Texas, which, although plotted nearby, are calcium lakes.

Productivity

Knowledge of productivity in Southwestern and Middle American waters is based almost entirely on Deevey's (1957) work. This leaves important areas for future investigations in these regions.

High primary productivity in Amatitlán and the hypolimnetic oxygen deficit in Atitlán have been discussed. Here productivity is high, but benthic fauna production is low, a characteristic which may be typical of tropical and semi-tropical lakes. Other data from Deevey apply to

TABLE 14.4

Amounts of silica present in some Southwestern and Middle American waters, with comparative data

Water	Authority	mg/L
Ojo Caliente, New Mexico	Clarke, 1924	60.2
Verde Hot Springs, Arizona	USGS, Phoenix	60.0
Lake Amatitlán, Guatemala	Deevey, 1957	58.7
Lake Chapala, Mexico	Deevey, 1957	50.0
Lake Güija, El Salvador	Deevey, 1957	50.0
Rio Grande Drains, New Mexico (mean)	Clark and Mauger, 1932	39.0
Owl Spring, New Mexico	Megard, 1961	35.0
La Sal Vieja, Texas	Deevey, 1957	25.0
Lake Atitlán, Guatemala	Deevey, 1957	25.0
Bartlett Lake, Verde River, Arizona	Salt R. Valley Water Users' Assoc.	25.0
Montezuma Well, Arizona	Cole, unpublished	22.0
Lake Carl Pleasant, Agua Fria River, Arizona	Maricopa County, Water District No. 1	20.0
Reservoirs on Salt River, Arizona (mean)	Salt R. Valley Water Users' Assoc.	19.0
Eight Trans-Pecos Texas lakes (mean)	Deevey, 1957	18.1
Soda Springs, Arizona	USGS, Phoenix	18.0
Fossil Springs, Arizona	USGS, Phoenix	14.0
Lake Pátzcuaro, Mexico	Deevey, 1957	14.0
Four northeastern Texas reservoirs (mean)	Harris and Silvey, 1940	5.13
La Sal del Rey, Texas	Deevey, 1957	4.0
Chuska Mountains lakes (mean)	Megard, 1961	3.4
Five most saline lakes, Saskatchewan (mean)	Rawson and Moore, 1944	21.0
Sea water	Clarke, 1924	ca. 4.0
Geysers, Yellowstone National Park, Wyoming (mean)	Clarke, 1924	356.0

benthic standing crops and chlorophyll values in Texas waters as well. Neither is high, but of course turnover rates are not known.

Numbers of benthic organisms reported in fisheries surveys from New Mexican reservoirs and the Bottomless Lakes are even smaller. Also, a scanty plankton in the big Arizona impoundments is implied by data supplied by the Arizona Game and Fish Department.

The only adequate data on primary productivity in desert lakes are those supplied by McConnell (personal communication), who studied gross primary productivity in Peña Blanca Lake, Arizona. This is a warm monomictic lake impounded in a narrow canyon in the Pajarito Mountains. It is 1,220 m above sea level and 9.6 km north of Nogales and the Mexican border. Peña Blanca was formed in 1957 and has a total solids content of about 130 mg/L. McConnell estimated the

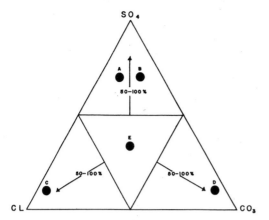

Fig. 14.6.—Triangular coordinate method of portraying relative composition of major anions in natural waters.

Circle	CO_3	SO_4	Cl
A	10%	70%	20%
B	20	70	10
C	5	10	85
D	85	10	5
E	33.3	33.3	33.3

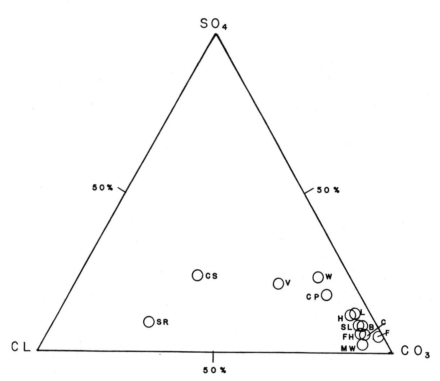

Fig. 14.7.—Relative anionic composition of some Arizonan lakes and streams. Figure following name is sum of principal anions in mg/L.

Large impoundments on rivers

SR	Lakes on the Salt River	520
CP	Lake Carl Pleasant, Agua Fria River	276
H	Horseshoe Lake, Verde River	205

Springs

CS	Croton Springs, Willcox Playa	1066
F	Fossil Springs	513

MW	Montezuma Well	640
V	Verde Hot Springs	2604

Small lakes on southeastern rim of Colorado Plateau

B	Big Lake	67
C	Concho Lake	106
FH	Fools Hollow Lake	133
L	Luna Lake	121
SL	Show Low Lake	120
W	Woods Canyon Lake	25.6

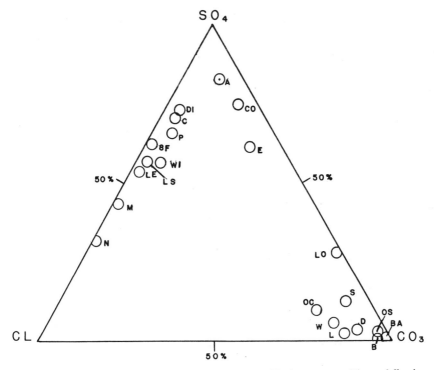

Fig. 14.8.—Relative anionic composition of some New Mexican waters. Figure following name is sum of principal anions in mg/L.

Large impoundments on rivers

A	Alamogordo Reservoir, Pecos River	941
CO	Conchas Reservoir, South Canadian River	590
E	Elephant Butte Reservoir, Rio Grande	286

Waters of the Chuska Mountains

B	Boot Lake	122
BA	Basalt Lake	127.4
D	Deadman Lake	54
L	Landslide Lake	48.1
LO	Long Lake	75
W	Wide Lake	50.9
OS	Owl Spring	234.9

Waters in gypsum deposits of southeast N.M. (Bottomless Lakes)

C	Cottonwood Lake	2900
DI	Devils Inkwell	2939
LE	Lea Lake	4866
M	Mirror Lake	8578
N	No Name Lake	16532
P	Pasture Lake	2798
8F	Figure Eight Lake	8183

Waters in gypsum deposits of southeast N.M. (others)

WI	Willow Lake	1282
LS	Lander Springbrook	2782

Springs of the Rocky Mountain Province of N.M.

OC	Ojo Caliente	1478.3
S	Spring, 1.6 km west of Santa Fe	162.4

rather high mean daily oxygen production by pelagic algae of 0.31 mg/cm². This was based on analyses of diurnal oxygen changes in a mean water column. Further calculations, based on a chlorophyll-photosynthesis ratio, yielded a higher figure, 0.41 mg/cm². The mean assimilation number, 3.12, was used for this, following a few simultaneous measurements of chlorophyll and oxygen.

Megard's (1961) data for the Chuska Mountain lakes apply largely to the productivity of littoral macrophytes. His values, which he considered net productivity, are equivalent to 0.29 mg O_2/cm² per day.

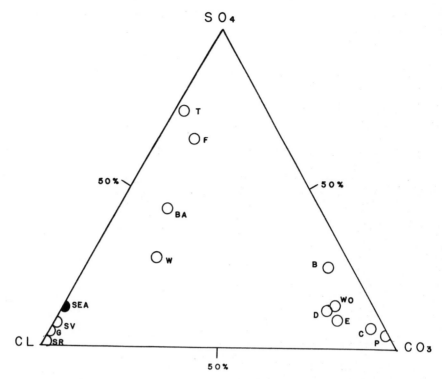

Fig. 14.9.—Relative anionic composition of some Texan lakes and Lake Pátzcuaro and Chapala, Mexico, compared with sea water. Figure following name is sum of principal anions in mg/L.

Mexican lakes		
C	Lake Chapala	471
P	Lake Pátzcuaro	276

Northeastern Texas reservoirs		
B	Bridgeport Lake	141
D	Lake Dallas	183
E	Eagle Mountain Lake	171
WO	Lake Worth	168

North-central Texas		
W	Lake Wichita	669

Lakes and playas of Trans-Pecos Texas		
BA	Balmorhea Lake	1270
F	Fort Stockton Lake	1479
G	Grable's Salt Works	41752
T	Toyah Playa Lake	2078

Salt lakes of south Texas coastal plain		
SV	La Sal Vieja	14238
SR	La Sal del Rey	108325
SEA	Sea Water	*ca.* 22000

Data for calculating areal oxygen deficits are either lacking for most Southwest lakes or are rendered meaningless by flash-flood import and/or drawdown for irrigation. The small, soft-water Woods Canyon Lake, Arizona, however, is relatively undisturbed. The Arizona Game and Fish Department has supplied some temperature and oxygen values for a period from May 27 to June 13. The rate of oxygen decrease below 4.8 m during this time was 0.057 mg O_2/cm² per day, which puts the lake in a low eutrophic category.

References

ABBOTT, WALTER, AND H. D. HOESE. 1960. Ecological observations on Minter Spring, Brazos County, Texas. Texas J. Sci., **12**: 24–35.

ALVAREZ, JOSÉ. 1949. Ictiologia dulceacuicola Mexicana. I. Resumen histórico de los estudios ictiológicos. Rev. Soc. Mexicana Hist. Nat., **10**: 309–327.

ALVAREZ, JOSÉ, PEDRO AVILA, GRACIELA CALDERÓN, AND HÉCTOR CHAPA. 1961. Los recursos naturales de Mexico. III. Estado actual de las investigaciones de hidrobiologia y pesca. Inst. Mex. Recurs. Nat. Renov., Mexico City. 421 p.

ARIZONA GAME AND FISH DEPARTMENT. 1958. Toward better fishing in Arizona. Phoenix, 26 p.

ARMITAGE, K. B. 1957. Lagos de la planicie costera de El Salvador. Comun. Inst. Trop. Invest. Cient., **6**: 5–10 + 10 fig.

——. 1958. Lagos volcánicos de El Salvador. Comun. Inst. Trop. Invest. Cient., **7**: 39–48 + 18 fig.

——. 1961. A highly alkaline lake in Nicaragua. Unpublished manuscript, 2 p.

BARRINGER, D. M. 1905. Coon Mountain and its crater. Proc. Acad. Nat. Sci., Philadelphia, **57**: 861–886.

BEARD, J. S. 1953. The savanna vegetation of northern Tropical America. Ecol. Monogr., **23**: 149–215.

BENT, ANNE M. 1960. Pollen analysis of Deadman Lake, Chuska Mountains, New Mexico. M.S. Thesis, Univ. Minnesota, 22 p.

BLACKWELDER, ELIOT. 1946. Meteor Crater, Arizona. Science, **104**: 38–39.

BREDER, C. M., JR. 1942. Descriptive ecology of "La Cueva Chica," with special reference to the blind fish, *Anoptichthys*. Zoologica, **27**: 7–15.

BROOKS, J. L. 1957. The systematics of North American *Daphnia*. Mem. Connecticut Acad. Arts Sci., **13**: 1–180.

CARR, A. F., JR. 1950. Outline for a classification of animal habitats in Honduras. Bull. Amer. Museum Nat. Hist., **94** (Article 10): 563–594 + pl. 12–33.

CHEATUM, E. P., MAYNE LONGNECKER, AND ALVIN METLER. 1942. Limnological observations on an East Texas lake. Trans. Amer. Microscop. Soc., **61**: 336–348.

CHELF, CARL. 1941. Peat bogs in Gonzales County. Univ. Texas, Mineral Resource Surv., Circ. No. 34, 12 p. (Mimeo.)

CLARK, H. W. 1908. The holophytic plankton of lakes Atitlan and Amatitlan, Guatemala. Proc. Biol. Soc. Washington, **21**: 91–106.

CLARK, J. D. 1938. Chemical and biological studies of the waters of Elephant Butte Reservoir as related to fish culture. Univ. New Mexico Bull., Chem. Ser. 2, No. 6, 39 p.

CLARK, J. D., AND JOHN GREENBANK. 1936. A cause of death of fish in the Southwest. Univ. New Mexico Bull., Chem. Ser. 2, No. 4, 22 p.

CLARK, J. D., AND HARRY MAUGER. 1932. The chemical characteristics of the waters of the Middle Rio Grande Conservancy District. Univ. New Mexico Bull., Chem. Ser. 2, No. 2, 35 p.

CLARK, J. D., AND H. L. SMITH. 1935. A chemical study of the waters of the Middle Rio Grande Conservancy District as related to fish culture. Univ. New Mexico Bull., Chem. Ser. 2, No. 3, 37 p.

CLARKE, F. W. 1924. The data of geochemistry. 5th ed. U.S. Geol. Surv., Bull. 770: 1–841.

CLISBY, K. H., FRED FOREMAN, AND P. B. SEARS. 1957. Pleistocene climatic changes in New Mexico, U.S.A. Veröffentl. Geobotan. Inst. Rübel in Zürich, **34**: 21–26.

CLISBY, K. H., AND P. B. SEARS. 1955. Palynology in southern North America. III. Microfossil profiles under Mexico City correlated with the sedimentary profiles. Bull. Geol. Soc. Amer., **66**: 511–520.

CLISBY, K. H., AND P. B. SEARS. 1956. San Augustin Plains—Pleistocene climatic changes. Science, **124**: 537–539.

COLE, G. A. 1961. Some calanoid copepods from Arizona with notes on congeneric occurrences of *Diaptomus* species. Limnol. Oceanogr., **6**: 432–442.

COLTON, H. S. 1957. Stonemans Lake. Plateau, **29**: 56–58.

COMITA, G. W. 1951. Studies on Mexican copepods. Trans. Amer. Microscop. Soc., **70**: 367–379.

DARNELL, R. M. 1962. Fishes of the Río Tamesí and related coastal lagoons in east-central Mexico, with notes on their distribution, ecology, and zoogeographic relations. Publ. Inst. Marine Sci., Univ. Texas, **8**. (In press.)

DARTON, N. H. 1905. The Zuni Salt Lake. J. Geol., **13**: 185–193.

——. 1910. A reconnaissance of parts of northwestern New Mexico and northern Arizona. U.S. Geol. Surv., Bull. 435, 88 p.

DAVIS, A. P. 1900. Hydrography of Nicaragua. U.S. Geol. Surv., 20th Ann. Rept. 1898–99, Part IV. Hydrography: 563–637.

DE BUEN, FERNANDO. 1943. Los Lagos Michoacanos. I. Carácteres generales. El Lago de Zirahuén. Rev. Soc. Mexicana Hist. Nat., **4**: 211–232.

——. 1944. Los Lagos Michoacanos. II. Pátzcuaro. Rev. Soc. Mexicana Hist. Nat., **5**: 99–125.

——. 1945. Resultados de una campaña limnológica en Chapala y observaciones sobre otras aguas exploradas. Rev. Soc. Mexicana Hist. Nat., **6**: 129–144.

DEEVEY, E. S., JR. 1941. Limnological studies in Connecticut. VI. The quantity and composition of the bottom fauna of thirty-six Connecticut and New York lakes. Ecol. Monogr., **11**: 413–455.

——. 1944. Pollen analysis and Mexican archaeology: An attempt to apply the method. Amer. Antiquity, **10**: 135–149.

——. 1957. Limnological studies in Middle America with a chapter on Aztec limnology. Trans. Connecticut Acad. Arts Sci., **39**: 213–328 + 4 pl.

DE LA O CARREÑO, A. (ed.). 1950. Los recursos naturales de Yucatán. Bol. Soc. Mexicana Geograf. Estadist., **59**: 1–377.

DEXTER, R. W. 1959. Anostraca, p. 558–571. *In* H. B. Ward and G. C. Whipple, Fresh-water biology. 2d ed., W. T. Edmondson (ed.). John Wiley & Sons, New York.

DOBBIN, C. N. 1941. Fresh-water Ostracoda from Washington and other western localities. Univ. Washington, Publ. Biol., **4**: 174–246.

DORCHESTER, J. N. 1959. Report of fisheries investigations. Basic survey and inventory of fish species in Murvaul Bayou Reservoir. Texas Game and Fish Comm., Austin, 29 p. (Processed.)

——. 1960. Report of fisheries investigations. Basic survey and inventory of fish species in Striker

Creek Reservoir. Texas Game and Fish Comm., Austin, 14 p. (Processed.)

DUNDEE, D. S., AND H. A. DUNDEE. 1958. Extensions of known ranges of four mollusks. Nautilus, **72**: 51–54.

EDMONDSON, W. T. 1935. Some Rotatoria from Arizona. Trans. Amer. Microscop. Soc., **54**: 301–306.

———. 1959. Rotifera, p. 420–494. *In* H. B. Ward and G. C. Whipple, Fresh-water biology. 2d ed., W. T. Edmondson (ed.). John Wiley & Sons, New York.

ELLIS, M. M. 1940. Water conditions affecting aquatic life in Elephant Butte Reservoir. Bull. U.S. Bur. Fish., **49**: 257–304.

EVANS, G. L. 1943. Diatomite in the High Plains region of Texas, p. 239–243. *In* Texas Mineral Resources, Univ. Texas Publ. No. 4301.

EVANS, G. L., AND G. E. MEADE. 1945. Quaternary of the Texas High Plains. Univ. Texas Publ. No. 4401: 485–507.

FASSETT, N. C., AND K. B. ARMITAGE. 1961. Aquatic plants of El Salvador. Unpublished manuscript, 16 p. + 54 fig., 6 tables.

FOLLETT, W. I. 1960. The fresh-water fishes—their origins and affinities, p. 212–232. *In* The biogeography of Baja California and adjacent seas. III. Terrestrial and fresh-water biotas. Systematic Zool., **9**.

FOREMAN, FRED. 1955. Palynology in southern North America. II. A study of two cores from lake sediments of the Mexico City basin. Bull. Geol. Soc. Amer., **66**: 475–510.

GERMOND, K. W. 1939. Lake basins of the Llano Estacado. The Compass of Sigma Gamma Epsilon, **20**: 162–165.

GERSBACHER, W. M. 1935. A survey of the waters of the Santa Fe and Carson National Forests, New Mexico. U.S. Bur. Fish., 38 p. (Mimeo.)

GRAHAM, ALAN, AND CHARLES HEIMSCH. 1960. Pollen studies of some Texas peat deposits. Ecology, **41**: 751–763.

GREEN, F. E. 1961. The Monahans Dunes area, p. 22–47. *In* Fred Wendorf (ed.), Paleoecology of the Llano Estacado. Museum New Mexico Press, Santa Fe.

GREENBANK, JOHN. 1937. A chemical and biological study of the waters of Elephant Butte Reservoir as related to fish culture. M.S. Thesis, Univ. New Mexico, 103 p.

HARRIS, B. B., AND J. K. G. SILVEY. 1940. Limnological investigation on Texas reservoir lakes. Ecol. Monogr., **10**: 111–143.

HARRIS, B. B., AND J. K. G. SILVEY. 1948. Algae control in fresh water or municipal reservoirs of the Southwest. Southwest Water Works J., April: 32–35.

HASKEL, W. L. 1959. Diet of the Mississippi threadfin shad, *Dorosoma petenense atchafalayae*, in Arizona. Copeia, 1959: 298–302.

HENSLEY, H. M. 1954. Ecological relations of the breeding bird population of the desert biome in Arizona. Ecol. Monogr., **24**: 185–207.

HERRICK, C. L. 1895. Copepoda of Minnesota. Geol.

Nat. Hist. Surv. Minnesota. Part I. 2nd Rept. State Zool.: 39–138.

HEVLY, R. H. 1961a. Notes on aquatic non-flowering plants of northern Arizona and adjoining regions. Plateau, **33**: 88–92.

———. 1961b. Notes on aquatic flowering plants with four additions to Arizona flora. Plateau, **33**: 115–119.

HEVLY, R. H., AND P. S. MARTIN. 1961. Geochronology of Pluvial Lake Cochise, southern Arizona. I. Pollen analysis of shore deposits. J. Arizona Acad. Sci., **2**: 24–31.

HILDEBRAND, S. F. 1925. Fishes of the Republic of El Salvador, Central America. Bull. U.S. Bur. Fish., **41**: 237–287.

HOLLOWAY, A. D. 1950. Recommendations for the development of the fishery resources of Guatemala, p. 99–140. *In* A fish and wildlife survey of Guatemala, U.S. Fish and Wildl. Serv., Spec. Sci. Rept. 5. (Processed.)

HUBBS, C. L., AND R. R. MILLER. 1948. Correlation between fish distribution and hydrographic history in the desert basins of western United States, p. 17–166 + figs. 10–29, 1 map. *In* The Great Basin with emphasis on glacial and postglacial times. Bull. Univ. Utah, **38**.

HUTCHINSON, G. E. 1957. A treatise on limnology. Vol. I. Geography, physics, and chemistry. John Wiley & Sons, New York. 1015 + xiv p.

HUTCHINSON, G. E., RUTH PATRICK, AND E. S. DEEVEY. 1956. Sediments of Lake Patzcuaro, Michoacan, Mexico. Bull. Geol. Soc. Amer., **67**: 1491–1504.

JESTER, D. B. 1960. Biological and chemical study of Conchas Reservoir. New Mexico Dept. Game and Fish, Santa Fe, 33 p. (Processed.)

JUDAY, CHANCEY. 1916. Limnological studies on some lakes in Central America. Trans. Wisconsin Acad. Sci. Arts Lett., **18**: 214–250.

JUDSON, SHELDON. 1950. Depressions of the northern portion of the southern High Plains of New Mexico. Bull. Geol. Soc. Amer., **61**: 253–274.

KINCAID, TREVOR. 1953. A contribution to the taxonomy and distribution of the American fresh-water calanoid Crustacea. Calliostoma Co., Seattle. 73 p.

KOSTER, W. J. 1957. Guide to the fishes of New Mexico. Univ. New Mexico Press, Albuquerque. 116 + vii p.

LAUNCHBAUGH, J. L. 1955. Vegetational changes in the San Antonio Prairie associated with grazing, retirement from grazing, and abandonment from cultivation. Ecol. Monogr., **25**: 39–57.

LEWIS, L. D., AND W. W. DALQUEST. 1957. A fisheries survey of the Big Wichita River System and its impoundments. Texas Game and Fish Comm., Austin: 1–64.

LINDEMAN, R. L. 1941. Seasonal food-cycle dynamics in a senescent lake. Amer. Midland Nat., **26**: 636–673.

LINDSEY, A. A. 1949. An optical effect in *Chlorella* bloom in nature. Ecology, **30**: 504–511.

———. 1951. Vegetation and habitats in a southwestern volcanic area. Ecol. Monogr., **21**: 227–253.

LITTLE, R. G. 1961. Biological and chemical study of Alamogordo Reservoir. New Mexico Dept. Game and Fish, Santa Fe, 34 p.

MADSEN, M. J. 1935a. A biological survey of streams and lakes of Coconino National Forest, Arizona. U.S. Bur. Fish., 23 p. (Mimeo.)

———. 1935b. A stream survey of parts of the Sitgreaves, Tusayan, and Coronado National Forests, Arizona. U.S. Bur. Fish., 6 p. (Mimeo.)

———. 1935c. A biological survey of streams and lakes of Tonto National Forest, Arizona. U.S. Bur. Fish., 19 p. (Mimeo.)

———. 1935d. A biological survey of streams and lakes of Apache and Crook National Forests, Arizona. U.S. Bur. Fish., 15 p. (Mimeo.)

MAGUIRE, BASSETT, JR. 1961. Regressive evolution in cave animals and its mechanism. Texas J. Sci., 13: 363–370.

MARSH, C. D. 1910. A revision of the North American species of *Cyclops*. Trans. Wisconsin Acad. Sci. Arts Lett., 16: 1067–1135.

———. 1929. Distribution and key of the North American copepods of the genus *Diaptomus*, with the description of a new species. Proc. U.S. Natl. Museum, 75: 1–27.

MARTIN, P. S. 1960. Effect of Pleistocene climatic change on biotic zones near the equator, p. 265–267. *In* Year Book of the American Philosophical Society, Philadelphia.

MARTIN, P. S., JAMES SCHOENWETTER, AND B. C. ARMS. 1961. Southwestern palynology and prehistory: The last 10,000 years. Univ. Arizona Press, Tucson. 119 p. + 14 pl.

MEEK, S. E. 1907. Synopsis of the fishes of the great lakes of Nicaragua. Field Columbian Museum, Publ. 121, Zoöl. Ser., 7: 97–132.

———. 1908. The zoölogy of lakes Amatitlan and Atitlan, Guatemala, with special reference to ichthyology. Field Columbian Museum, Publ. 127, Zoöl. Ser., 7: 159–206.

MEGARD, R. O. 1961. The diel cycle of stratification and productivity in two lakes of the Chuska Mountains, New Mexico. Amer. Midland Nat., 66: 110–127.

MEIGS, C. C., H. P. BASSETT, AND G. B. SLAUGHTER. 1922. Report on Texas alkali lakes. Univ. Texas Bull., No. 2234; 1–60 + maps.

MEINZER, O. E. 1922. Map of the Pleistocene lakes of the Basin and Range province and its significance. Bull. Geol. Soc. Amer., 33: 541–542.

MEINZER, O. E., AND F. C. KELTON. 1913. Geology and water resources of the Sulphur Spring Valley, Arizona. U.S. Geol. Surv., Water-Supply Paper 320: 9–213.

MERCADO SÁNCHEZ, PEDRO. 1961. Corrección y modernización del sistema de captura del camarón en aguas interiores del noroeste de México. Acta Zool. Mexicana, 4: 1–11.

MILLER, R. R. 1954. A drainage map of Arizona. Systematic Zool., 3: 80–81.

———. 1961. Man and the changing fish fauna of the American Southwest. Papers Michigan Acad. Sci. Arts Lett., 46: 365–404.

MITCHELL, R. W. 1956. Winter invertebrate metazoa of Goose lake, Muleshoe Wildlife Reserve, Texas. Southwestern Nat., 1: 6–15.

NAVARRE, R. J. 1958. Biological and chemical study of Willow Lake and Black River. New Mexico Dept. Game and Fish, Santa Fe, 54 p. (Processed.)

———. 1959. Basic survey of the Bottomless Lakes. New Mexico Dept. Game and Fish, Santa Fe, 43 p. (Processed.)

———. 1960. Clayton Lake rehabilitation. New Mexico Dept. Game and Fish, Santa Fe, 15 p. (Processed.)

NOEL, M. S. 1954. Animal ecology of a New Mexican springbrook. Acta Hydrobiol. Hydrogr. Limnol., 6: 120–135.

OLIVE, W. W. 1955. Subsidence troughs in the Castile anhydrite of the Gypsum Plain, New Mexico and Texas. Bull. Geol. Soc. Amer., 66 (Part 2): 1604. (Abstr.)

OSORIO TAFALL, B. F. 1942. Rotiferos planctonicos de Mexico. I, II y III. Rev. Soc. Mexicana Hist. Nat., 3 23–79.

———. 1943. Observaciones sobre la fauna acuatica de las cuevas de la region de Valles, San Luis Potosi (Mexico). Rev. Soc. Mexicana Hist. Nat., 4: 43–71.

———. 1944a. Las estudios hidrobiologicos en Mexico y la conveniencia de impulsarlos. Rev. Soc. Mexicana Hist. Nat., 5: 127–153.

———. 1944b. Biodinamica del Lago de Pátzcuaro. I. Ensayo de interpretacion de sus relaciones troficas. Rev. Soc. Mexicana Hist. Nat., 5: 197–227.

PARKER, J. M., AND C. J. WHITFIELD. 1941. Ecological relationships of playa lakes in the southern Great Plains. J. Amer. Soc. Agron., 33: 125–129.

PATTERSON, MARCILE. 1942. A study of the seasonal distribution of plankton in White Rock Lake. Proc. Trans. Texas Acad. Sci., 25: 72–75.

PEARSE, A. S. (ed.). 1936. The cenotes of Yucatan. A zoological and hydrographic survey. Carnegie Inst. Washington, Publ. 457.

———. (ed.). 1938. Fauna of the caves of Yucatan. Carnegie Inst. Washington, Publ. 491.

PECKHAM, R. S., AND C. F. DINEEN. 1953. Summer plankton of Lake Amatitlan, Guatemala. Amer. Midland Nat., 50: 377–381.

PENNAK, R. W. 1958. Some problems of freshwater invertebrate distribution in the western states, p. 223–230. *In* C. L. Hubbs (ed.), Zoogeography. Amer. Assoc. Advance. Sci.

PHALEN, W. C. 1919. Salt resources of the United States. U.S. Geol. Surv., Bull. 669: 1–284.

PLUMMER, F. B. 1941. Peat deposits in Texas. Univ. Texas, Mineral Resource Circ. 16: 1–10. (Mimeo.)

———. 1945. Progress report on peat deposits in Texas. Univ. Texas, Mineral Resource Circ. 36: 1–8.

PLUMMER, F. B., AND E. C. SARGENT. 1931. Underground waters and subsurface temperatures of the Woodbine Sand in northeast Texas. Univ. Texas Bull., No. 3138: 1–178.

POTTER, L. D. 1957. Phytosociological study of San

Augustin Plains, New Mexico. Ecol. Monogr., **27**: 113–136.

POTTER, L. D., AND JOANNE ROWLEY. 1960. Pollen rain and vegetation, San Augustin Plains, New Mexico. Botan. Gaz., **122**: 1–25.

POTZGER, J. E., AND B. C. THARP. 1943. Pollen record of Canadian spruce and fir from Texas bog. Science, **98**: 584–585.

POTZGER, J. E., AND B. C. THARP. 1947. Pollen profile from a Texas bog. Ecology, **28**: 274–280.

POTZGER, J. E., AND B. C. THARP. 1954. Pollen study of two bogs in Texas. Ecology, **35**: 462–466.

POWERS, W. E. 1939. Basin and shore features of the extinct Lake San Augustin, New Mexico. J. Geomorph., **2**: 345–356.

PRESCOTT, G. W. 1951. Ecology of Panama Canal algae. Trans. Amer. Microscop. Soc., **70**: 1–24.

RAMÍREZ GRANADOS, RODOLFO. 1952. Estudio ecologico preliminar de las lagunas costeras cercanas a Acapulco, Gro. Rev. Soc. Mexicana Hist. Nat., **13**: 199–218.

RASMUSSEN, D. I. 1941. Biotic communities of Kaibab Plateau, Arizona. Ecol. Monogr., **11**: 229–275.

RAUN, G. G. 1959. Terrestrial and aquatic vertebrates of a moist, relict area in central Texas. Texas J. Sci., **11**: 158–171.

RAWSON, D. S., AND J. E. MOORE. 1944. The saline lakes of Saskatchewan. Canadian J. Research, **22**: 141–201.

REARK, J. B. 1952. The forest ecology of the Reventazón Valley. M.S. Thesis, Instituto Interamericano, Turrialba, Costa Rica, 102 + xiv p.

REED, E. L., 1930. Vegetation of the playa lakes in the Staked Plains of western Texas. Ecology, **11**: 597–600.

RIOJA, ENRIQUE. 1953. Datos historicos acerca de las esponjas de agua dulce de Mexico. Rev. Soc. Mexicana Hist. Nat., **14**: 51–57.

ROACH, A. W., AND J. K. G. SILVEY. 1958. The morphology and life cycle of fresh-water Actinomycetes. Trans. Amer. Microscop. Soc., **77**: 36–47.

SCHWARZ, E. A. 1914. Aquatic beetles, especially *Hydroscapha*, in hot springs, in Arizona. Proc. Entomol. Soc. Wash., **16**: 163–168.

SEARS, P. B. 1952. Palynology in southern North America. I. Archeological horizons in the basins of Mexico. Bull. Geol. Soc. Amer., **63**: 241–254.

SEARS, P. B., AND K. H. CLISBY. 1955. Palynology in southern North America. IV. Pleistocene climate in Mexico. Bull. Geol. Soc. Amer., **66**: 521–530.

SHAFER, G. H. 1941. Peat deposits in Polk and San Jacinto counties, Texas. Univ. Texas, Mineral Resource Surv., Circ. 38, 6 p. (Mimeo.)

SILVEY, J. K. G., AND A. W. ROACH. 1959. Laboratory culture of taste- and odor-producing aquatic Actinomycetes. J. Amer. Water Works Assoc., **51**: 20–32.

SOULE, J. D. 1960. The distribution and affinities of the littoral marine Bryozoa (Ectoprocta), p. 100–104. *In* The biogeography of Baja California and adjacent seas. II. Marine biotas. Systematic Zool., **9**.

SPORT FISHING INSTITUTE. 1959. Bibliography of theses on fishery biology. R. M. Jenkins (ed.) Washington, D. C. 80 p.

STEARNS, C. E. 1956. San Augustin Plains—the geologic setting. Science, **124**: 539.

SWAIN, F. M., AND R. W. MEADER. 1958. Bottom sediments of southern part of Pyramid Lake, Nevada. J. Sediment. Petrol., **28**: 286–297.

TAYLOR, W. R., AND H. S. COLTON. 1928. The phytoplankton of some Arizona pools and lakes. Amer. J. Botany, **15**: 596–611.

TEXAS BOARD OF WATER ENGINEERS. 1961. A plan for meeting the 1980 water requirements of Texas. Austin, 198 p.

THOMAS, N. O., AND G. E. HARBECK, JR. 1956. Reservoirs in the United States. U.S. Geol. Surv. Water-Supply Paper 1360A, 99 p.

TILDEN, J. E. 1908. Notes on a collection of algae from Guatemala. Proc. Biol. Soc. Washington, **21**: 153–156.

TRESSLER, W. L. 1954. Fresh-water Ostracoda from Texas and Mexico. J. Washington Acad. Sci., **44**: 138–149.

UDDEN, J. A. 1925. Etched potholes. Univ. Texas Bull., No. 2509: 1–10 + 6 pl.

U.S. GEOLOGICAL SURVEY. 1957. Quality of surface waters of the United States, 1957. Parts 9–14. Colorado River Basin to Pacific Slope Basins in Oregon and Lower Columbia River Basin. U.S. Geol. Surv., Water-Supply Paper 1523, 497 + xiv p.

VAN SICLEN, D. C. 1957. Cenozoic strata on the southwestern Osage Plains of Texas. J. Geol., **65**: 47–60.

WENDORF, FRED (ed.). 1961. Paleoecology of the Llano Estacado. Museum New Mexico Press, Santa Fe. 144 p.

WIEBE, A. H. 1934. Suggestions for the improvement of Texas fishing lakes. Texas State Game, Fish and Oyster Comm., Bull. No. 7.

WIEN, J. D. 1958. The study of the algae of irrigation waters. Ann. Progr. Rept., Arizona State Coll. Tempe, 21 p. + 11 pl.

———. 1959. The study of the algae of irrigation waters. 2nd Ann. Progr. Rept., Arizona State Univ. Tempe, 26 p. + 21 pl.

WILLIAMS, HOWEL, AND HELMUT MEYER-ABICH. 1953. El origen del Lago de Ilopango. Comun. Inst. Trop. Invest. Cient., **2**: 1–8.

WILLIAMS, HOWEL, AND HELMUT MEYER-ABICH. 1954. Historía volcánica del Lago de Coatepeque (El Salvador) y sus alrededores. Comun. Inst. Trop. Invest. Cient., **3**: 107–120.

WILSON, M. S. 1955. A new Louisiana copepod related to *Diaptomus* (*Aglaodiaptomus*) *clavipes* Schacht (Copepoda, Calanoida). Tulane Studies Zool., **3**: 35–47.

WRIGHT, H. E. 1956. Origin of the Chuska sandstone, Arizona-New Mexico: A structural and petrographic study of a Tertiary eolian sediment. Bull. Geol. Soc. Amer., **67**: 413–434.

15 | *Gustavo A. Candelas*
Graciela C. Candelas

The West Indies

This is a report on the possibilities of limnological work in the West Indies, rather than of results obtained in this field. Only recently has biological research expanded from the previously limited areas of medical, systematic, and agricultural emphasis into broader fields of interest. In addition the uncertain political situation in the Caribbean has to some extent limited the communication among islands, so that part of what has been done remains buried in obscure local publications or has not been published at all.

However, there are many opportunities for major contributions to limnology in this region. A comparison of the ecology of tropical and temperate bodies of water would make it possible to check generalizations, which have often been derived from a study of only temperate areas. The rapid development of numerous artificial reservoirs permits convenient study of successional changes, and the equable climate facilitates year-round study. Within short distances it is possible to sample the whole climatic diversity of the Caribbean. Finally, the active economic development programs throughout the region are beginning to awaken governmental interests in limnology because of the development of fishing, irrigation systems, and reservoir control.

The Antilles or the West Indies form an archipelago extending from Florida in North America and Yucatan in Central America to Venezuela in South America. In the arch formed by the islands comprising the archipelago are enclosed the Gulf of Mexico and the Caribbean Sea. The islands are located between 10° and 27° N. latitude and 59° and 85° W. longitude.

The West Indies are divided into the Bahamas, the Greater Antilles (Cuba, Jamaica, Santo Domingo [Hispaniola], and Puerto Rico), and the Lesser Antilles, which includes all the other islands. All the small islands north of St. Lucia (such as Montserrat, Redonda, Antigua, Nevis, St. Kitts, Barbuda, Anguilla, and others) make up the subdivisions known as the Leeward Islands, while those south of St. Lucia (such as Barbados, Granada, Trinidad, and others) are known as the Windward Islands. (Fig. 15.1).

Limnologically the West Indies are characterized by a rarity of natural lakes, by a great abundance of small rivers and streams in the larger islands and a total lack of these in the smaller ones, and by the presence of the more rare freshwater habitats such as inland salt lakes, underground streams and river courses, and hot springs and freshwater springs coming up in the sea at some distance from shore.

Some environmental factors, such as temperature and rainfall, which are regulated by broad climatic and physical agencies, tend to bring uniformity to the whole area and to distinguish it from other parts of the world. Nevertheless, variation among the islands is brought about by local soil conditions, local topography, and differences in geological origin. (Fig. 15.2).

General climatological considerations

The climate for the whole area is generally tropical and oceanic or marine. These islands lie in the path of the trade winds, and their high temperatures are regulated by the steady trade winds, daily sea breezes, and cool nights.

Two main climatic seasons are recognizable in the area in general—a cooler dry period and a

Fig. 15.1.—Location map of the West Indies. Prepared by the University of Wisconsin Cartographic Laboratory.

warmer wet one. In some islands like Puerto Rico these two seasons are less marked, rainfall being more evenly distributed throughout the year, whereas in other islands like Trinidad these two periods are more distinct.

One of the most important features to consider about the climate of the West Indies is the reduced effectiveness of a given amount of rainfall as compared with its effect in the Temperate Zone. Most of the West Indies lie in the path of the trade winds, which blow almost continuously during the day, and this together with high temperatures causes high evaporation, thereby reducing the effectiveness of the rainfall. In Puerto Rico evaporation averages about 80 in./yr (Weather Bureau class A land-pan measurements). Roberts *et al.* (1942) calculated that in such an area a rainfall of 30 in. is equivalent to about 15 in. in the United States. The excessive evaporation taking place in the islands has a marked influence on their freshwater habitats, most of which are small and shallow. Studies on the biota of the freshwater ponds of the Carib-

bean have shown that life in these habitats seems not to be so rich as that observed in the Temperate Zone. They have also shown that in the wet regions of the area life in the permanent ponds is much richer and is persistent in continuity, and that the continuity of these permanent ponds has been sufficient to develop and preserve characteristic populations of organisms. In the drier areas of the Caribbean, however, the discontinuity produced by the drying of many of these ponds does not permit a diversification and richness of population comparable to that achieved in the humid areas of the region. Margaleff (1961) in his study of freshwater ponds in Nueva Esparta, Venezuela, in islands similar to those of the West Indies, found that while permanent ponds of humid areas had around 34 species of phytoplankters and 14 species of zooplankters, the temporary ponds of arid areas had only around 6 species of phytoplankters and 7 species of zooplankters.

Another important effect on the freshwater life is caused by the distribution of the rainfall

uring the year. The absence of runoff from rain-
all during the dry months causes reduction of
utrient salts in the lakes, swamps, and ponds of
he West Indies, in some cases almost to the
oint of exhaustion. There are many swamps in
he area in which not only a lack of oxygen but
lso a lack of nutrient salts may be limiting to
he biota. The influence of such a lack of nu-
rient salts in plankton production as indicated
y the abundance of plankton has been reported
y Bond (1935). According to him, in the sumner of 1932 Mr. J. C. Armstrong made a plank-
on haul at Laguna del Rincón at the Dominican
Republic during the rainy season, when the nu-
rients of the lake were probably being replen-
shed by runoff from the land. Dr. Bond found

that this haul was much richer than those he obtained during the dry season from two similar
freshwater lakes of the same area. Similar results
were obtained by Candelas (1956) in a plankton
study made on one of Puerto Rico's reservoirs,
Lake Caonillas. In this lake, studied during the
year 1952, the water level fluctuated about 40 ft
from its maximum level in the hot wet season
to its minimum level in the cold dry season. Figure 15.3 indicates that the plankton was more
abundant when the water level was highest during the hot wet season, and that there occurred
a decrease of the plankton with a decrease in the
water level of the lake. The conclusion that water level, through its influence on concentration

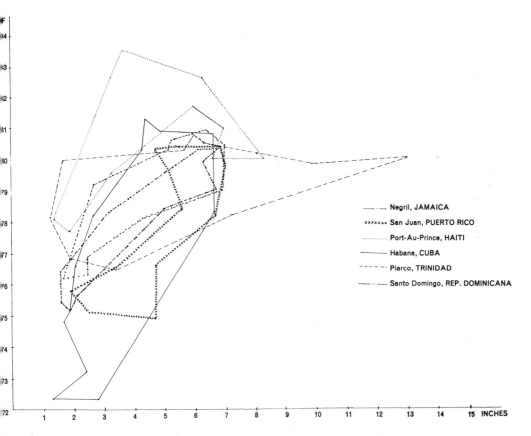

Fig. 15.2.—Temperature-moisture modified climograph
for one station of each of the major islands of the
West Indies. Based on mean monthly temperature and
rainfall data for 1941–50 from *World Weather Records*
(1941–59), U.S. Dept. of Commerce Weather Bureau,
Govt. Printing Office, Washington 25, D.C. Information for Santo Domingo supplied by the Weather Bureau Office of Puerto Rico.

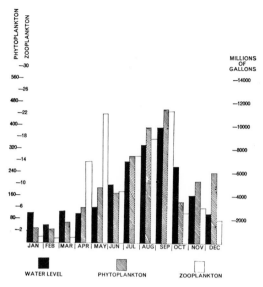

Fig. 15.3.—Seasonal fluctuations of the phytoplankton and zooplankton and of the water level of Lake Caonillas during 1952. The phytoplankton is shown as the average number of cells per liter, the zooplankton as the average number of organisms per liter, and the water level in millions of gallons.

of nutrient salts, may be a major factor affecting the increase or decrease of the plankton is supported by the data in Table 15.1: all the environmental factors studied, such as temperature, O_2 content, CO_2 content, alkalinity, pH, etc., showed negligible changes during the year.

Limnological resources of the Caribbean

The freshwater habitats in the West Indies consist of rivers and streams, salt lakes, lagoons and ponds, estuaries, swamps, and artificial reservoirs.

The major islands of the West Indies have numerous streams and rivers. For example, in Puerto Rico alone there are 1,200 separate streams, although only about 50 are large enough to be considered as rivers. Because of the influence of the mountainous topography of most of the islands, the streams and rivers of the West Indies have rapid currents. They are also short, and this is the result of the small distances through which they travel to reach the sea. The longest rivers in the area occur in Hispaniola, where their relatively great length and their sinuous course is due to the extensive and well-displaced mountain ranges. In many of the islands a number of streams have dry courses during the dry

season but can suddenly become full and turbulent during the wet cold season. A characteristic feature of the streams and rivers in limestone regions of this area is that many of them flow through subterranean courses for part of their length. A vivid description of this phenomenon is given by Schoerich (1918) for Dominican streams. He writes, "In the mountains there are brooks which gush out from the hillside, merrily ripple on for miles and vanish into the ground as mysteriously as they come. A number of coast streams sink into the sand of the beach, just before reaching the ocean. The Brujuelas River, which rises on the edge of the great plains northwest of Bayaguana flows south 25 miles through the plains and disappears in the ground a mile from the sea."

Lake Enriquillo, located in the Dominican Republic, is the only natural true lake in the West Indies. This is a salt-water lake (total salinity of 72‰) with a total area of 281 km² and a maximum depth of 30 m. The surface of the lake is 48 m below sea level. The biota is impoverished but interesting and includes some marine relict organisms.

TABLE 15.1

Average physical and chemical conditions of Lake Caonillas during the two main climatic seasons

		Hot wet season (May to Oct.)	Cold dry season (Nov. to April)
Temperature (°C)	Surface	29.6	26.4
	Bottom	27.4	23.5
Color (ppm)		26	28
pH	Surface	7.56	7.40
	Bottom	7.04	6.95
Visibility (ft)		3.66	3.83
Total alkalinity (ppm)	Surface	89.8	87.0
	Bottom	101.7	93.0
Carbonate (ppm)	Surface	13.3	14.33
	Bottom	0.0	0.0
Bicarbonate (ppm)	Surface	76.4	72.8
	Bottom	101.7	89.7
O_2 (ppm)	Surface	8.5	10.7
	Bottom	2.4	3.6
Free CO_2 (ppm)	Surface	0.0	0.0
	Bottom	5.0	5.6

The most characteristic bodies of standing wa·er in the West Indies are the lagoons. These are shallow, eutrophic bodies of water, which are ringed by vegetation and which have various amounts of open water. To this group belong the Laguna de Ariguanabo and Laguna del Tesoro in Cuba, Cartagena and Tortuguero lagoons in Puerto Rico, Laguna Rincón, Lago Limón, and Laguna Trujín in the Dominican Republic, and possibly the saline Etang Saumâtre of Haiti.

Because of the alternation of dry and wet seasons, these lagoons are constantly subjected to fluctuations of water level resulting from evaporation or sudden heavy rain. The organisms, especially those restricted to the shores, must adjust to such fluctuations. During the dry season many organisms with poor means of locomotion are left stranded on the shore if the recession of the water is too rapid, whereas if the recession is slower and only partial, the organisms follow the retreating water. However, in small lagoons that dry completely during the dry season, continual invasions or adaptational mechanisms for the dry conditions are necessary for those organisms living there.

Artificial reservoirs for various purposes are being constructed in the West Indies, and these will provide new habitats for aquatic organisms. Because of the economic aspects of their maintenance, reservoirs are already posing problems which require research in fundamental aspects of limnology. For example, problems created by such biological processes as water blooms need to be solved. In Puerto Rico these reservoirs are located in various regions of the island and vary considerably in size, ranging from small, shallow ones only a few acres in area to the larger and deeper ones such as Lake Guajataca, which covers an area of 1,000 acres during flood stages. Because these reservoirs are constructed in places where nearly vertical sides are necessary, they have no littoral zone and hence differ conspicuously from the lagoons in their lack of rooted marginal aquatic vegetation. Most of these reservoirs are subject to great fluctuation in water level, which results in limnological problems that lend themselves to future studies. In Puerto Rico the Water Resources Authority keeps regular records of water levels in the reservoirs, and it is likely that similar unpublished records are available for some of the other areas. These reservoirs could be used to compare sedimentation rates in the Tropics with those in the Temperate Zone. In the West Indies the combination of many factors such as steep land slopes, torrential rainfall, deeply weathered soil, and certain land use practices favors the introduction of large quantities of sediments into the rivers, and in turn the rivers introduce the sediments into the reservoirs. Arnow and Bogart (1960) presented evidence of the high rate of sedimentation taking place in two reservoirs in Puerto Rico. According to them, Guayabal Reservoir had a capacity of 10,000 acre-feet in 1913, but by 1948 this capacity had been reduced to about 41%; Comerio Reservoir had a capacity of 4,920 acre-feet in 1914, whereas in 1957 only about 400 acre-feet of storage capacity remained.

Ponds of different origins are found throughout the West Indies. They range from ponds formed in small volcanic craters to those of a temporary or permanent nature formed from the obstruction of rainfall drains in porous limestone or consolidated coral. Some of these ponds are fed by rainfall, and others by subterranean springs. Particularly interesting are ponds found on such islands as St. Kitts, Nevis, and Montserrat, in areas of volcanic activity where they are subjected to quite unusual physicochemical environmental conditions.

The transition from a lagoon to a swamp is a gradual one, and the change in the biota seems to be gradual also. There are several areas of swamps in the West Indies, the most extensive of which is the Cienaga Zapata of Cuba.

The estuaries of the West Indies are very interesting and lend themselves well to the study of the gradual change from a typically freshwater fauna and flora to a marine one in relatively short distances. Aguayo (1938) studied the effects of the gradual increase of NaCl on the distribution of Cuban gastropods in an estuary. According to Aguayo, freshwater forms of the genera *Physa, Lymnaea, Helisoma,* and *Tropicorbis* are the first to be eliminated by an increase in NaCl, followed by forms belonging to the genus *Neritina* and finally those of the genus *Cerithidea* in a regular order with increasing salinity. Within the last genus *C. iostoma* disappears first, *C. tenius* second, and *C. costata* last, after which more marine forms appear, until purely marine forms as *Smaragdia viridis* occur.

Limnological work on the area

A review of the literature has shown a conspicuous lack of research in relation to freshwater habitats in the Caribbean. Not only are there few limnological and ecological investigations, but all other biological aspects of freshwater organisms have been neglected as well. The reasons for this vary. One reason may be the lack of large and conspicuous bodies of inland waters. Even if rains in the Tropics may have attracted the attention of resident investigators and visitors to the area because of their force, suddenness, and general attractiveness as a natural phenomenon, this lack of major inland bodies of water may have diverted the interest of the investigators. Another factor resulting from the small size of the inland bodies of water is that they are of little importance in terms of fisheries, and, therefore, no governmental movement has oriented the research at experimental stations towards fresh water. Investigators, as well as tourists, seem to have been attracted more to the sea and to the luxuriant terrestrial vegetation than to inland bodies of water. Another reason may be that the presence of *Schistosoma mansoni* and the fear of acquiring schistosomiasis have stopped many investigators from making freshwater studies. However, the authors consider the most important reason to be the previous status of biological research in the area. Until now most investigations that have come from the area have been of an applied nature, and basic biological research in general has been very limited. Some important studies have been made by visiting investigators, but most of these studies were made in a relatively short time and by necessity they were of a preliminary nature. There have been few resident investigators to continue such preliminary work to completion. In many areas, basic biological research by resident investigators is now becoming more of a reality, but much remains to be done. Until there are more basic data available, fundamental work on limnology and general ecology will be limited.

A search through the literature has revealed several studies on the freshwater biota, most of which consist of descriptions of one or several new species or a list of species and their localities without any type of information on their function in the habitat or ecological relationships to their environment. The most extensive and

noteworthy of these studies in relation to the flora are those of Margalef (1948) on the algae of the Ariguanabo Lagoon of Cuba, Wille (1915) and Tiffany (1936, 1944) on the freshwater algae of Puerto Rico, Drouet (1942) on the filamentous Myxophyceae of Jamaica, Gardner (1932) on the Myxophyceae of Puerto Rico, Hagelstein (1939) on the Diatomaceae of Puerto Rico, and Sparrow (1950) on some Cuban Phycomycetes. In relation to the fauna the most important works are those of Brehm (1949) on the freshwater fauna of Cuba, van Oye (1937) on Protozoa of Hispaniola, Edmondson (1934) on the rotifers of Hispaniola, Rogick (1942) on the bryozoans, Osburn (1940) on the bryozoans of Puerto Rico, Stephensen (1933) on the Amphipoda of Bonaire, Curaçao, and Aruba, Shoemaker (1942) on the Amphipoda, Clench (Clench and Aguayo, 1937; Clench, 1940, 1952) on the freshwater mollusks of Hispaniola and the Bahama Islands, Jutting (1925) on non-marine Mollusca from Curaçao, Pilsbry (1930; Pilsbry and Aguayo, 1933) on the freshwater mollusks of Bahama and Cuba, Simpson (1895) on mollusks, Aguayo (1938) on the mollusks of Cuba, Rammer (1933) on the phyllopods of Bonaire, Curaçao, and Aruba, Wilbey (1935) on the harpacticoid copepods, Klie (1933) on the ostracods from Bonaire, Curaçao, and Aruba, Tressler (1941) on the Ostracoda from Puerto Rican bromeliads, Ortman (1902) on the freshwater decapods, van Name (1940, 1942) on the freshwater isopod crustaceans, Holthuis (1950) on palaemonid prawns, García-Díaz (1938) on the freshwater insects of Puerto Rico, and Eyerdam (1953) on the freshwater mollusks of Haiti.

Truly limnological works are meager for the Caribbean. The first of these was the work of Beattie (1932) demonstrating the effect of the concentration of such chemicals in natural waters as ammonium, nitrogen, and chloride on the breeding and larval survival of different species of mosquitoes in Trinidad. Breder (1934) published a paper on the ecology of an oceanic freshwater lake in Andros Island in the Bahamas. Andros Island is an uplifted coral reef formation with no connection with other formations or with the mainland. On this island there are numerous bodies of fresh water containing large amounts of dissolved calcium. These were found to be inhabited by various marine fishes that do not normally enter fresh water. Breder tried to demonstrate through laboratory studies employing a synthetically similar water, as well as other waters containing calcium, that the ability of such fishes to survive in fresh water was associated with calcium content. The only freshwater invertebrates were insect larvae and the snail *Physa*. Marine invertebrates had not invaded these waters to any significant degree. Breder traced the aquatic food chain back to a very abundant alga, *Batophora* sp.

Bond (1935) made a study of the hydrology and hydrography of some Hispaniolan lakes. His major contribution was the classification of inland salt lakes into two groups: the thalassohaline lakes with salts in approximately the same proportions as sea water and with osmotic pressure as the main limiting factor, and the athlalassohaline lakes with salts in proportions unlike sea water and with direct ion toxicity as the limiting factor. These terms have not become useful yet, because, as pointed out by Hutchinson (1957), very little is known of the ecological importance of the ionic ratios. Both authors, however, emphasize the fact that waters of saline lakes are not similar to sea water.

Candelas (1956) in his study of the freshwater plankton of Puerto Rico has shown that the zooplankton of this tropical area shows some conspicuous qualitative and quantitative differences from that of the cold lakes of the Temperate Zone. Rotifers are the most conspicuous and varied of the groups comprising the zooplankton. Thirteen genera and eighteen species were represented in the collections made, and all of the lakes studied had at least four different species of rotifers. Species of the genus *Brachionus* were the most common in the collections, and *Keratella cochlearis* was the most widespread species. Other widely distributed species were *Brachionus calyciflorus*, *Platyias patulus*, *Polyarthra trigla*, and *Brachionus angularis*. In a plankton analysis of some Hispaniolan lakes, Edmondson (1934) reported the occurrence of 37 species of rotifers and concluded that the "Rotatoria are clearly enough among the most prominent of the aquatic animals of the island." The cladocerans are much less conspicuous in numbers and in species, only eight genera having been recorded from the plankton of the lakes of Puerto Rico. The most commonly and widely distributed species seem to be *Ceriodaphnia cornuta* Sars, *Latonopsis serricauda* Sars, and *Moina rec-*

tirostris (Leydig). The copepods are more abundant than the cladocerans, but they are represented by only two genera and three species— *Diaptomus dorsalis* Marsh, *Mesocyclops leuckarti* (Claus), and *Mesocyclops tenuis* (Marsh). The number of ostracods (average of 1,940 per m^3) found in the plankton is surprising, since in most lakes in the United States they are primarily adventitious forms, properly belonging to the bottom fauna and only appearing accidentally in the plankton. Some of the species found in Candelas' study may be benthic forms and may be found occasionally or accidentally in the plankton, whereas others like *Physocypria xanabanica* are adjusted to a planktonic existence. A similar situation has been found to occur in other tropical lakes. Apstein (1910) in his studies on Lake Colombo in Ceylon found *Cypris purpurescens* adapted to pelagic life. Brehm (1932) found *Cypria pelagica* Brehm to be a common constituent of the plankton of Lake Peten in Guatemala. In general Candelas' study indicates that the plankton of Puerto Rico resembles quantitatively and qualitatively the plankton of warm, shallow temperate lakes such as those reported by Pennak (1937) rather than the plankton of the cold, deep lakes of the Temperate Zone.

There has always been interest in comparing the productivity of tropical regions with that of the Temperate Zone, and it has been shown that some tropical habitats, such as the coral reefs, are highly productive. No information is available as to the gross productivity of the freshwater habitats of the West Indies. However, some work has been done on plankton production. Candelas (1956), using the "standing crop" not as an index of gross productivity but as an indication of plankton production, was able to compare the plankton production of one of Puerto Rico's artificial reservoirs, Lake Caonillas, with seven Colorado reservoirs investigated by Pennak (1949). Lake Caonillas showed a low production of phytoplankton in comparison with the seven Colorado reservoirs (Table 15.2). With the exception of the protozoans, the zooplankton of Caonillas Lake compared quite favorably in plankton production with Lake Gaynor, the richest of the Colorado reservoirs.

There naturally have been many studies associated with the problem of schistosomiasis. Most of these have been of a clinical or statistical nature. A notable exception was the work of Pimen-

TABLE 15.2

Mean standing crop of plankton in Caonillas Lake and seven Colorado lakes

	Phytoplankton (Millions of cells per liter)			Zooplankton (Organisms per liter)			
	Diatoms	Blue-greens	Greens	Protozoa	Rotifera	Copepoda	Cladocera
Caonillas	0.01	0.001	0.001	406	606	164	136
Kosler	0.9	0.04	—	1,100	30	20	2
Baseline	0.1	0.7	0.02	15,700	479	45	58
Hayden's	0.1	0.5	0.01	46,200	158	43	73
Allens	0.3	0.3	0.03	88,400	169	94	16
Beasley	0.9	1.0	0.1	15,900	324	137	59
Boulder	0.8	6.5	1.5	61,700	163	74	67
Gaynor	3.6	20.2	3.6	767,400	774	602	60

tel (1957) on the geographic distribution of *Australorbis glabratus* in Puerto Rico. In this work Pimentel reported that the ecological distribution and diversity of the populations of *A. glabratus* depended generally on the type and geological formation of the bodies of water and on the rainfall distribution pattern. According to his studies, alluvial soils, uniform distribution of rainfall, and the presence of running waters, marshes, and small bodies of water favored higher population densities.

Laessle (1961) made an interesting study on the water accumulated in bromeliads as a micro-limnological system. In these small individual reservoirs with less than 20 cc of water, Laessle found a varied biota. Physicochemical factors such as pH, dissolved O_2 and CO_2, and temperature influenced the biota and the interrelationships existing among its members. An important contribution of this paper is the adaptation of techniques and methodology used in major habitats to the study of micro-environments.

Research institutions of the area

Most of the basic biological research done in this area is carried out by scientific personnel at the major universities in the islands. In Cuba there are the Universidad de la Habana, Universidad Católica de Santo Tomás de Villanueva, Universidad de Oriente (Santiago de Cuba), Universidad de Camaguey, and the Universidad de Santa Clara. In the Dominican Republic there is the University of Santo Domingo, and in Haiti the University of Haiti. In Puerto Rico there are several centers of research—the University of Puerto Rico, the Federal Experimental Station, the Puerto Rico Nuclear Center, and the Public

Health Research Laboratories. In Jamaica the University College of the West Indies carries on a very active research program in biological sciences.

Limnological possibilities of the West Indies

The West Indies represent an area of unique aquatic habitats and special limnological problems.

Such problems as the adaptations made by different organisms where fresh and salt water come in contact can be studied in many regions of the West Indies. In the Leeward Islands such islands as Antigua, St. Kitts, and Nevis have streams with fairly reliable flows which are freshwater for part of their course and saline for the rest. Other islands like Antigua have some streams which are completely saline, others completely fresh, and still others part saline and part fresh water. In Cuba there is a copious freshwater spring called "Catorce Arrobas," which comes up in the sea a short distance from the shoreline of Quinican. According to Massip and Massip (1942), this is probably the submarine opening of the Ariguanabo River, which submerges into a subterranean channel close to the city of San Antonio de los Baños. A similar situation has been reported to occur in Puerto Rico off the north coast in the region of Tortuguero Lagoon.

Such islands as St. Kitts, Nevis, and Montserrat, in which volcanic activity is still taking place, lend themselves well to investigations of successional changes in the aquatic biota as well as to studies of the adjustment of organisms to conditions of extremely high temperatures. In Montserrat, for example, there are some soufrieres, as the Galway's Soufrieres, in which

Martin-Kaye (1959) has reported an increase in temperature from 64° F in December 1936 to 00° F in December 1947. On the other hand, he Tar River reported on by Willmore (1952), n which the temperature decreased from 96° C n 1936 to 55° C in 1961, seems to be in the cooling phase.

The Major Islands

Cuba

Cuba, the largest island in the West Indies, is ocated between 19° 49′ and 23° 15′ N. latitude and 74° 08′ and 84° 57′ W. longitude. Including he Isla de Pinos and adjacent keys, it has an area of 44,218 mi² and extends approximately 745 mi from west to east. Its greatest width is about 22 mi with an average of 6 mi.

About three-fifths of Cuba is flat to gently rolling land; the rest of the country is mountainous or hilly. The principal topographic features are three main ranges of mountains located in the eastern, central, and western sections of the island. The most rugged are those within the Region of Oriente, where the now so well known Sierra Maestra parallels the south coast as far east as Guantanamo Valley. The Trinidad-Sancti-Spiritus Range is on the south coast between Cienfuegos and Sancti-Spiritus. The western highlands formed by the Cordillera de Guaniguanico are composed of the geologically interesting Alturas de Pizarras, the Cordillera de los Organos, and the Sierra del Rosario. Marshland is found in many places along the south coast and to a lesser extent along the north coast. The largest marshland area of Cuba is the Cienaga de Zapata, north of the Seboruco Peninsula. The coastal plains are mainly flat and frequently merge into swamps.

Although Cuba is just south of the Tropic of Cancer, its climate is more semitropical. It seems that the proximity of the island to the North American Continent allows the influence of the continental cold air masses to be felt, particularly in the western region. The temperature averages 75° F for the year, dropping to 70° F in winter and rising to 81° F in summer. Massip and Massip (1942) quote record temperatures of 107.6° F for July and of 36.5° F for January 1919. Because of the orientation and shape of the island, the temperature varies only slightly from one part to another. It also varies little between day and night except in the highlands. The total annual rainfall for all Cuba averages about 54 in. and except for Oriente shows little variation among the various provinces. In Oriente the rainfall averages about 15% less than that of the rest of the island. Only during periods of extreme drought is an occasional month devoid of rain; nevertheless, dry and wet seasons are recognizable. The dry season usually begins in early November and continues until late April. The wet season, which extends from May through October, accounts for about three-fourths of Cuba's rainfall. Two distinct peaks occur in the wet season, one in late May or June, the other in September and October.

Cuba (Fig. 15.4) does not possess true, natural freshwater lakes. There are several artificial reservoirs and lagoons. The largest lagoon, Ariguanabo, is a shallow eutrophic body of water approximately 72 km² in area, containing dense vegetation of vascular plants. In the Zapata Swamp is located another of the largest lagoons of the island, Tesoro Lagoon, with an area of 16 km². In addition to the artificial reservoirs and lagoons, there are many types of freshwater ponds of various origins.

Cuba possesses very many ponds, streams, and short turbulent rivers. Although there are nearly 200 streams entering the sea, none has any considerable length or volume owing to the shape of the island. The arrangement of the streams and rivers in Cuba is simple: except in the southwestern portion of Santiago Province, the stream courses are essentially direct to the coast. In Cuba the divide between northward and southward flowing streams follows the longitudinal axis of the island slightly towards the north. Because of the southward tilting of the plain, the northward-flowing streams occupy deeper channels than those flowing toward the south coast. However, the drainage of the southwestern portion of Santiago Province affords some exception to this general arrangement, since this is a lowland area, bordered on the north and south by mountains, and the tilting of the land is in a westerly direction. Thus, the Cauto River, originating at 810 m altitude in the Sierra Maestra, flowing westward through the center of Santiago Province in the Region of Oriente, and emerging into the Gulf of Guacanaybo close to Manzanillo.

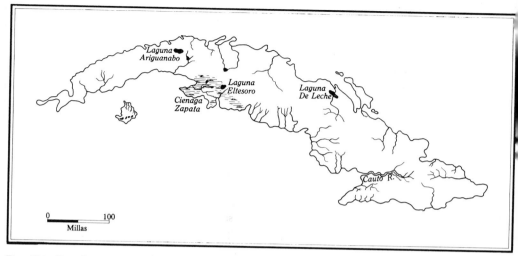

Fig. 15.4.—Location map of the freshwater habitats of Cuba. Prepared by the University of Wisconsin Cartographic Laboratory.

is Cuba's largest (241 km in length) river. Other important rivers are Sagua la Grande (150 km), the Agabama River (110 km), Yumurí River, and the Cuhaguateje (79 km).

Santo Domingo (Hispaniola)

The island of Santo Domingo (Hispaniola) is the second largest of the West Indies. It is situated between 17° 36′ and 19° 57′ N. latitude and 68° 20′ and 74° 29′ W. longitude. Its western portion is occupied by the Republic of Haiti and its eastern portion by the Dominican Republic.

Dominican Republic.—The Dominican Republic lies between 17° 36′ and 19° 57′ N. latitude and 68° 20′ and 72° 01′ W. longitude and has an area of 18,640 mi².

Four mountain ranges, running almost parallel to each other, cross the republic from east to west. These ranges are covered by thick, luxuriant vegetation. The Cordillera Central, the largest range, divides the country into almost equal parts. In the north there is the Cordillera Septentrional and in the south Sierra de Neiba and Sierra de Bahoruco. There are three main valley regions. The Valley of the Cibao or Vega Real between the Cordillera Central and the Cordillera Septentrional is the largest and most important valley and is considered by many as one of the most beautiful spots of the West Indies. The other major valleys are Valle San Juan, between the Cordillera Central and Sierra de Neiba, and the Enriquillo Valley extending from the frontier of Haiti and running between Sierra de Neiba that limits it in the north and Sierra de Bahoraco that limits it in the south.

The mean annual temperature varies from 64.4° F in the mountain region to 77° F in the southern regions. Temperatures as low as 32° F have been recorded in the mountains. These are obviously not the lowest temperatures, however, since some valleys situated in the center of the island are covered by frost during the cold season, and the highest peaks of the Cordillera are covered by permanent snow. Temperatures higher than 90° F have been recorded. During the period of 1947 to 1954, the rainfall fluctuated from 102.14 in. in Puerto Plata in the interior of the country to a minimum of 12.37 in. in El Seibo at the eastern end of the republic. A wet period extends from April to October with a higher concentration of rain occurring in May, June, and September. The dry season extends from November to March. These two periods, as in Puerto Rico, are more marked in the southwest and less noticeable in the northern part of the island. This, as in Puerto Rico, is the result of rain shadow effects created by the position of the mountain ranges in relation to the trade winds.

Possibly no other country the size of the Dominican Republic could be compared with it in relation to the number of rivers and streams,

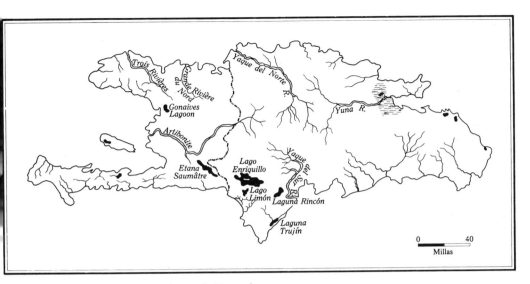

Fig. 15.5.—Location map of the freshwater habitats of Santo Domingo (Hispaniola). Prepared by the University of Wisconsin Cartographic Laboratory.

their volume, and their length. The largest river, Yaque del Norte (248 mi long), arises in the northern slope of the Cordillera Central, makes a circuitous course in the north where it receives numerous affluents from the mountains until it reaches the vicinity of the city of Santiago de los Caballeros, then turns northwesterly and flows through the Vega Real Valley where it is reinforced by many tributaries, and finally discharges into Manzanillo Bay. On the southern slope of the Yaque Peak arises the Yaque del Sur River (124 mi in length), which runs through San Juan Valley and, after receiving a number of tributaries, opens into the Caribbean Sea in Neiba Bay. In the same range of mountains, the Cordillera Central, but on the northeast slope of Banilejos Peak arises the Yuna River (189 mi in length), which runs easterly until it flows close to the town of Sanchez in the Samaná Bay. On the western slope of this cordillera arises the Artibonite, also called in the Dominican Republic Guayajayuco River (199 mi in length), which flows westerly into Haiti. These four rivers are the main rivers of the Dominican Republic (Fig. 15.5).

The only natural lake of considerable size and depth in the West Indies is Lake Enriquillo, a salt lake, lying wholly in the Dominican Republic. In addition to this lake, the Dominican Republic has several swampy, small lakes called lagoons, among which the largest are Laguna del Rincón, Lago Limón, and Laguna Trujín. Laguna del Rincón lies to the southwest of Lake Enriquillo. It is about 4.6 m above sea level and is more a swamp than a lake. Lago Limón lies directly south of Lake Enriquillo and is rather swampy but has a higher percentage of open water than the Laguna del Rincón. The other lagoon, Laguna de Trujín, lies in the southern peninsula of Barahona and is very close to the sea coast, but no information is available concerning the nature of its waters.

Based on data reported by Bond (1935), Lake Enriquillo is 29 km long and 10–11 km wide, with a surface area of 281 km². The shoreline measures 105 km, which gives a shoreline development of approximately 2. Maximum depth is 30 m, but the mean depth is only 6 m, yielding a total volume of 1.33 km³. The surface elevation is 48 m below sea level, and the total salinity is 72‰.

Haiti.—The Republic of Haiti occupies the western third of the island of Hispaniola. It is located between 17° 36′ and 19° 57′ N. latitude and 72° 01′ and 74° 29′ W. longitude and covers an area of 10,816 mi².

One mountain range, which includes the groups known as La Hotte and La Selle, extends from east to west along the lower peninsula. Two other ranges stretch from southeast to northeast across the mainland and the northern peninsula. Among these mountain ranges there are four important plains as follows: the North Plains that extend along the northern coast between the sea and the mountains, the Central Plains which border the Dominican Republic, and the Artibonite and the Cul-de-Sac plains which extend eastward from the Gulf of Gonâve.

In the warmest section of Haiti, the coast land, temperatures range from 90° F to 70° F. The temperatures in the mountainous region are much lower, and frost occurs in the higher peaks. Rainfall in most of the South Peninsula averages 60 in. yearly, but on the North Peninsula it varies from 60 to 20 in. In the semiarid coast between the two peninsulas rainfall fluctuates between 20 and 40 in., but in the Artibonite Valley it reaches a maximum value for all Haiti of 122 in. The rainy period occurs from April to June and from October to November.

In Haiti rivers and streams are very abundant, although most of them are short and of rapid current. The principal rivers are the Artibonite (321 km long), Trois Rivière (105 km), Grande Rivière du Nord (81 km), and the Estère and the Quinte (Fig. 15.5).

There are several lagoons or small lakes such as the one located on the Island of Gonâve and the Etang Saumâtre, the latter being Haiti's biggest lake. It is 23 km long, 9.5 km wide, and has a total area of 70.8 km². Its salinity is ⅓ to ¼ that of sea water.

Puerto Rico

Puerto Rico is the smallest of the islands composing the Greater Antilles. It lies between 18° 30′ and 17° 50′ N. latitude and 67° 15′ and 65° 30′ W. longitude.

The island is almost rectangular in shape, a little more than 100 mi long from east to west, and more than 35 mi wide. A surprising diversity in the topography of the island occurs in spite of its small size of only 3,421 mi². The central backbone of the island consists of a complex series of mountain ranges running east to west. These mountain ranges are flanked in the north and the south by foot-hills, which in turn are flanked by extensive costal plains. Individual valleys with alluvial plains are found along the east and west coasts. In addition two extensive alluvial valleys have developed in the eastern interior section.

TABLE 15.3

Data on principal rivers of Puerto Rico. From Arnow and Bogart, 1960.

River	Approximate drainage area (measured on 1/120,000 map) (mi²)	Straight-line distance, mouth to farthest watershed boundary (mi)	Total fall from highest point of watershed (ft)	Average fall (ft/mi)
Guajataca	71	17	1,740	102
Camuy	62	17	2,300	135
Arecibo	289	24	4,390	183
Manatí	224	25	4,150	166
Cibuco	100	18	2,100	117
La Plata	239	32	2,960	92
Bayamón	105	21	1,800	86
Loíza	308	26	3,520	135
Guayanés	50	12	2,130	178
Coamo	78	17	2,920	172
Jacaguas	94	17	4,300	253
Portugués-Bucaná	51	14	4,390	313
Tallaboa	35	10	3,410	341
Yauco	47	15	3,540	236
Guanajibo	129	20	2,950	148
Añasco	185	29	3,960	136
Culebrinas	114	21	1,740	83

The climate of the island is tropical oceanic, with marked variations caused largely by the diverse topography. The mean annual temperature ranges from about 68° F in the mountain areas to 78° F in the coastal areas. The effects of topography are more marked on rainfall than on the temperature, and the average annual rainfall varies from less than 30 in. to about 200 in. Nearly everywhere in Puerto Rico rainfall is considerably lower from November to April than from May to October. Nevertheless, seasonal differences are least marked along the northern and eastern coasts and most marked in the humid west-central and western parts of the island, where the summer rainfall is several times that of the winter.

Of the 1,200 streams that exist in Puerto Rico, only about 50 may be considered rivers. Table 15.3, reproduced from Arnow and Bogart (1960), gives some pertinent data for 17 of the most important rivers. The mean gradients are steep.

Contrary to the great abundance of rivers and streams, natural freshwater lakes are almost lacking in Puerto Rico. There is a small freshwater lagoon at the south coast (Cartagena Lagoon), and along the north coast is the Tortuguero Lagoon. Cartagena Lagoon, south of the town of

Lajas, is found in a depression in a small valley and receives its water from the surface drainage of the small surrounding hills. It has a mean depth of about 1.8 m and has a few acres of open water surrounded by a more extensive area of swamp conditions. Tortuguero Lagoon, with deeper waters, covers an area of about 4 by 1.5 km and represents the biggest natural body of fresh water in Puerto Rico. In addition to these lagoons, Puerto Rico possesses several artificial reservoirs, which are used mostly for hydroelectric, irrigation, and water supply purposes (Fig. 15.6).

Jamaica

Jamaica is located between 17° 43′ and 18° 32′ N. latitude and 76° 11′ and 78° 20′ 50″ W. longitude. Its greatest length, according to the latest measurements, is 146 mi, its greatest width is 51 mi, and its least width is 22¼ mi. Its total area is 4,411.21 mi².

The surface of the island is extremely mountainous, especially in the eastern part where altitudes of 7,402 ft are attained. A great central chain of mountains known as the Blue Mountains extends easterly and westerly and forms the axial part of the island. From this range subordinate ridges extend to the north and south. These ridges in turn divide into smaller ridges, which branch in every direction, so that the whole surface of the island is cut up into a series of ridges with gullies between them. Topographically Ja-

maica comprises three main physiographic regions: the interior range of mountains, the dissected hills and limestone plateaus, and the coastal plain and interior valleys.

Because of its topography, Jamaica has a great diversity of climate. Temperatures can fluctuate from 80° to 86° F at the sea coast to 40° to 50° F on the tops of the highest mountains. The mean annual rainfall for the whole island, based on observations over a 70-year period (1870–1959), is 77.12 in. Rainfall falls more heavily from May to November, and there is a drier period from December to April.

Jamaica possesses numerous rivers and springs. Because of the general east-west trend of the mountain ranges, most of the rivers are forced to flow to the south or to the north. Some exceptions to this rule are the Plantain Garden River, the Montego River, and some interior rivers such as the Cave and Hector's River, which sink into the limestone. Because of the great elevation from which most rivers flow, they have a very rapid descent and in rainy periods may develop very strong torrents. Some of Jamaica's most important rivers, in addition to the ones already mentioned, are the Black River, Río Minho (Dry River), Martha Brae River, Great River, and Cabarita River (Fig. 15.7).

Trinidad

Trinidad is the southernmost of the British West Indies. It is located between 9° 40′ and 10°

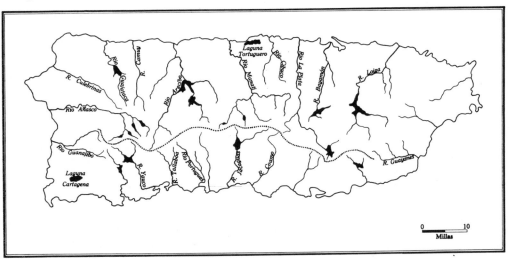

Fig. 15.6.—Location map of the freshwater habitats of Puerto Rico. Prepared by the University of Wisconsin Cartographic Laboratory.

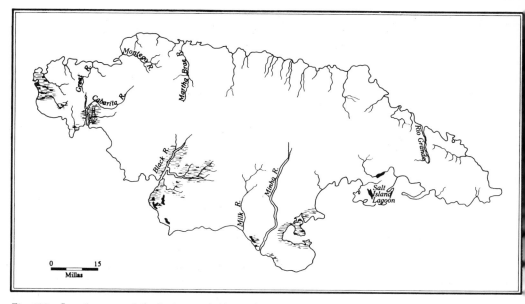

Fig. 15.7.—Location map of the freshwater habitats of Jamaica. Prepared by the University of Wisconsin Cartographic Laboratory.

50′ N. latitude and 60° 50′ and 61° 56′ W. longitude. The island has a more or less rectangular shape with some projections in the northwest and southwest. It has an area of 1,186 mi², with an average length of 50 mi and an average width of 37.5 mi.

The island is mostly flat, although there are three mountain systems crossing the island in different directions: the Northern and Southern ranges, which extend across almost the entire width of the island along the sea, and the Central Range which lies diagonally through the middle portion.

The climate is tropical. The mean annual temperature varies from 70° F to 88° F, and the mean annual rainfall varies from over 100 in. in the northeast to 50 in. in the west. There is a marked dry season from January to May and a wet season from June to December. In the wet season the rainfall is heavy but usually does not last long.

There are several rivers and streams in Trinidad. The most important rivers are the Caroni, which drains the northwestern portion, the Ortoire (Guatare), which drains the southeastern part, and the Oropouche, which drains the northeastern section of the island (Fig. 15.8).

References

Aguayo, C. J. 1938. Los moluscos fluviátiles cubanos. Mem. Soc. Cubana Hist. Nat., **12**(3) : 203–242.

Apstein, C. 1910. Das Plancton des Gregory-Sees auf Ceylon. Zool. Jahrb., Abt. Systemat., **29** : 661–679.

Arnow, T., and D. B. Bogart. 1960. Water problems of Puerto Rico and a program of water-resources investigations. Trans. Caribbean Geol. Conf., **2** : 120–129.

Beattie, M. V. F. 1932. The physico-chemical factors of water in relation to mosquito breeding in Trinidad. Bull. Entomol. Research London, **23**(4) : 477–500.

Bond, R. M. 1935. Investigations of some Hispaniolan lakes. II. Hydrology and hydrography. Arch. Hydrobiol., **28** : 137–161.

Breder, C. M. 1934. Ecology of an oceanic fresh-water lake, Andros Island, Bahamas, with special reference to its fishes. Zoologica (New York), **18**(3) : 57–88.

Brehm, V. 1932. Notizen zur Süsswasserfauna Guatemalas und Mexikos. Zool. Anz., **99** : 63–66.

———. 1949. Datos para la fauna de agua dulce de Cuba. Publ. Inst. Biol. Apl. (Barcelona), **5** : 95–112.

Candelas, G. A. 1956. Studies on the freshwater plankton of Puerto Rico. Ph.D. Thesis, Univ. Minnesota.

Clench, W. J. 1940. Land and freshwater mollusks of Long Islands, Bahama Islands. Mem. Soc. Cubana Hist. Nat., **14**(1) : 3–17.

———. 1952. Land and freshwater mollusks of Eleuthera Island, Bahama Islands. Rev. Soc. malacol. Carlos de la Torre, **8**(3) : 97–119.

Clench, W. J., and G. G. Aguayo. 1937. Notes and description of some new land and freshwater mol-

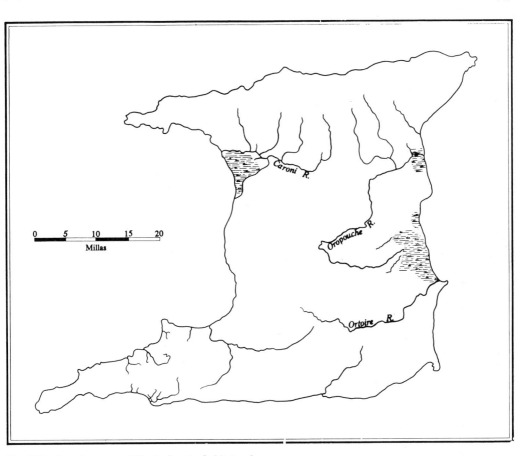

Fig. 15.8.—Location map of the freshwater habitats of Trinidad. Prepared by the University of Wisconsin Cartographic Laboratory.

lusks of Hispaniola. Mem. Soc. Cubana Hist. Nat., 11(1) : 31–42.

DROUET, E. 1942. The filamentous Myxophyceae of Jamaica. Field Museum Nat. Hist., Botan. Ser., **20** (5) : 107–122.

EDMONDSON, W. T. 1934. Investigations of some Hispaniolan lakes (Dr. R. M. Bond's Expedition). I. The Rotatoria. Arch. Hydrobiol., **26**(3) : 465–471.

EVERDAM, W. 1953. An excursion to Lake Moragoane, Haiti. Amer. Malacol. Union, Ann. Rept. No. 6 : 28–29.

GARCÍA-DÍAZ, JULIO. 1938. An ecological survey of the fresh water insects of Puerto Rico. I. Odonata with new life histories. J. Agr. Univ. Puerto Rico, **22**(1) : 43–96.

GARDNER, N. L. 1932. The Myxophyceae of Porto Rico and the Virgin Islands. Scientific survey of Porto Rico and the Virgin Islands. New York Acad. Sci., **8**(2) : 249–311.

HAGELSTEIN, R. 1939. The Diatomaceae of Puerto Rico and the Virgin Islands. Scientific survey of Porto Rico and the Virgin Islands. New York Acad. Sci., **8**(3) : 313–444.

HOLTHUIS, L. B. 1950. Preliminary description of

twelve new species of palaemonid prawns from American waters (Crustacea, Decapoda). Proc. Koninkl. Ned. Akad. Wetenschap. Amsterdam, **53** (1) : 93–99.

HUTCHINSON, G. E. 1957. A treatise on limnology. Vol. 1. Geography, physics, and chemistry. John Wiley & Sons, Inc., New York. 1015 p.

JUTTING, T. V. B. 1925. On a collection of non marine mollusca from Curaçao. Bijdr. Dierk. Lieden, **24** : 25–32.

KLIE, W. 1933. Süss- und Brackwasser-Ostracoden von Bonaire, Curaçao und Aruba. Zool. Jahrb., Abt. Systemat., **64** : 369–390.

LAESSLE, A. M. 1961. A micro-limnological study of Jamaican bromeliads. Ecology, **42**(3) : 499–517.

MARGALEF, R. 1948. Algas de agua dulce de la Laguna Ariguanabo (Isla de Cuba). Publ. Inst. Biol. Apl. (Barcelona), **4** : 79–89

————. 1961. La vida en los charcos de agua dulce de Nueva Esparta (Venezuela). Mem. Soc. Cienc. Nat. La Salle, **21**(59) : 75–111.

MARTIN-KAYE, P. H. A. 1959. Reports on the geology of the Leeward and British Virgin Islands. Voice Publishing Co., Bridge St. Castries, St. Lucia. 117 p.

MASSIP, S., AND S. E. MASSIP. 1942. Introducción a la Geografía de Cuba. La Habana. 250 p.

ORTMAN, A. P. 1902. The geographical distribution of freshwater decapods and its bearing upon ancient geography. Proc. Amer. Phil. Soc., 41(171): 267–400.

OSBURN, R. C. 1940. Bryozoa of Puerto Rico with resumé of the West Indian bryozoan fauna. Scientific survey of Puerto Rico and the Virgin Islands. New York Acad. Sci., 16(3): 321–486.

PENNAK, R. W. 1937. Species composition of limnetic zooplankton communities. Limnol. Oceanogr., 2: 222–232.

———. 1949. Annual limnological cycles in some Colorado reservoir lakes. Ecol. Monogr., 19: 233–267.

PILSBRY, H. A. 1930. List of land and freshwater mollusks collected on Andros, Bahamas. Proc. Acad. Nat. Sci. Philadelphia, 82: 297–302.

PILSBRY, H. A., AND C. J. AGUAYO. 1933. Marine and freshwater mollusks new to the fauna of Cuba. Nautilus, 46(4): 116–123.

PIMENTEL, D. 1957. Geographic distribution of Australorbis glabratus, the snail intermediate host of Schistosoma mansoni in Puerto Rico. Amer. J. Trop. Med. Hyg., 6: 1087–1096.

RAMMNER, W. 1933. Zoologische Ergebnisse einer Reise nach Bonaire, Curaçao und Aruba in Jahre 1930: Süss- und Brackwasser Phyllopoden von Bonaire. Zool. Jahrb., Abt. Systemat., 64: 357–363.

ROBERTS, R. C., et al. 1942. Soil survey of Puerto Rico. U.S. Dept. Agr., Soil Surv. Rept. Ser., 1936, No. 8.

ROGICK, M. 1942. Studies on fresh-water Bryozoa. XII. A collection from various sources. Ann. New York Acad. Sci., 43(3): 123–143.

SCHOERICH, OTTO. 1918. Santo Domingo—a country with a future. Macmillan Co., New York. 418 p.

SHOEMAKER, C. R. 1942. Notes on some American fresh-water amphipod crustaceans and descriptions of a new genus and two new species. Smithsonian Misc. Collect., 101(9): 1–31.

SIMPSON, C. T. 1895. Distribution of the land and the freshwater mollusks of the West Indian region and their evidence with regard to past changes of land and sea. Proc. U.S. Natl. Museum, 17: 413–450.

SPARROW, F. K. 1950. Some Cuban Phycomycetes. J. Washington Acad. Sci., 40(2): 50–55.

STEPHENSEN, K. 1933. Fresh and brackish water Amphipoda from Bonaire, Curaçao and Aruba. Zool. Jahrb., Abt. Systemat., 64: 415–436.

TIFFANY, L. H. 1936. Wille's collection of Puerto Rican freshwater algae. Brittonia, 2: 165–176.

———. 1944. Freshwater Chlorophyceae and Xanthophyceae from Puerto Rico. Ohio J. Sci., 44(1): 39–50.

TRESSLER, W. L. 1941. Ostracoda from Puerto Rico bromeliads. J. Washington Acad. Sci., 31(6): 263–269.

VAN NAME, W. G. 1940. A supplement to the American land and freshwater Isopod Crustacea. Bull. Amer. Museum Nat. Hist., 77: 109–142.

———. 1942. A second supplement to the American land and freshwater Isopod Crustacea. Bull. Amer. Museum Nat. Hist., 80: 299–329.

VAN OYE, P. 1937. An investigation of some Hispaniolan lakes (Dr. R. M. Bond's Expedition). Rhizopoden von Haiti. Arch. Hydrobiol., 32(2): 320–332.

WILBEY, A. 1935. Harpacticoid Copepoda from Bermuda. II. Ann. Mag. Nat. Hist., 10(15): 50–100.

WILLE, N. 1915. Report of an expedition to Porto Rico for collecting freshwater algae. J. New York Botan. Garden, 16(187): 132.

WILLMORE, P. 1952. The earthquake series in St. Kitts-Nevis 1950–51. St. Kitts. (Mimeo.)

16

T. G. Northcote
P. A. Larkin

Western Canada

Western Canada is divisible into two major physiographic regions—the Western Plains and Subarctic, which drain north and east to the Arctic, and the mountainous Cordillera on the western slope of the Continental Divide. There are many lakes in each area, largely as a result of relatively recent glaciation, but except for the opportunity which both regions provide the limnologist, they have little in common.

The provinces of Alberta, Manitoba, and Saskatchewan spread across the northern end of the Great Central Plains of the continent, enclose a transitional parkland bordering the boreal forest, and extend to the north through the sparse forest of the Canadian Shield to the edge of the tundra. The climate is continental, with warm summers, cold winters, and low precipitation. A low relief sloping gently to the north and east is indicative of the shallowness of the lake basins. The Western Plains essentially comprise a northwestward extension of the limnological regions of the midwestern United States.

On the other hand, the Cordilleran region, largely occupied by the province of British Columbia, is characterized by a diversity of biotic zones which reflect the coastal climate and its modification by a rugged and highly variegated physiography. At least 12 limnological regions can be distinguished, several of which cover a wide range of situations and would warrant subdivision. Climates range from maritime to arid semidesert and alpine-arctic. Lake basins range from long, deep, typical glaciated valleys to shallow potholes in glacial till and outwash.

In addition to their geographic dissimilarities, the plains and Cordilleran regions present different types of applied limnological problems. On the west coast the commercial importance of ana-

dromous Pacific salmon (*Oncorhynchus*) and the sport fishery for rainbow trout (*Salmo gairdneri*) have influenced the applied objectives of research on lakes and streams. In the plains area the fishery problems have centered on commercial production of lake whitefish (*Coregonus clupeaformis*), lake trout (*Salvelinus namaycush*), walleye (*Stizostedion vitreum*), and ciscoes (*Leucichthys* spp.) and on sport fisheries for lake trout, grayling (*Thymallus signifer*), and northern pike (*Esox lucius*).

The regions differ not only in their fish faunas but also in the composition of their zooplankton and bottom fauna communities. The relict Crustacea, for instance, do not occur over most of the Cordilleran region, reflecting the significance of the Continental Divide as a zoogeographic barrier.

Finally, the two western Canadian regions, for a variety of reasons, have not shared a common development in limnological literature. For the Western Plains, a review of limnological research is almost solely the scientific biography of the late D. S. Rawson. For over 30 years, from his base at the University of Saskatchewan, Rawson made studies of lakes over the whole of the plains. From 1944 to 1947 he conducted extensive investigations on Great Slave Lake in the Northwest Territories; because these studies were so closely related to his chief interest in lake productivity, they are included in this chapter. The late R. B. Miller, working from the University of Alberta, was responsible for the beginning of extensive limnological surveys in that province, and he joined with W. A. Kennedy in a reconnaissance of Great Bear Lake which is included in this chapter.

Rawson also contributed some of the earlier

limnological studies in British Columbia, and his former student (P. A. Larkin) initiated extensive lake surveys there. However, because of the importance of Pacific salmon, the region has had a substantial literature on lake studies, which is both distinctive and noteworthy. The Fisheries Research Board station at Nanaimo and the International Pacific Salmon Fisheries Commission have conducted extensive studies on many lakes which support Pacific salmon populations. Moreover, their intensive investigations of stream biology in connection with salmon production have few counterparts in the limnological literature of the plains region.

For all the above reasons, this chapter is divided into two parts, the first dealing with the lakes of the Western Plains plus the great lakes of the Northwest Territories and the second with the limnology of British Columbia (largely the Cordilleran region, from the Continental Divide to the Pacific).

The Western Plains

Limnological resources

The three plains provinces—Alberta, Saskatchewan, and Manitoba—extend between latitude 49° and 60° N. The main geological, climatic, and vegetation zones (Fig. 16.1) lie diagonally northwest to southeast across the whole region. Except for the Wood Mountain area in southern Saskatchewan, the entire area was overlain by the Laurentide ice sheet in the recent continental glaciation. As the ice retreated to the northeast, large glacial lakes drained to the south and east, creating wide valleys (e.g., Qu'Appelle Valley) which now contain a few small lake basins joined by small and sometimes temporary streams. Lakes Winnipeg, Winnipegosis, and Manitoba represent the substantial residues of the once immense glacial lake Agassiz (J. T. Wilson et al., 1958). In southern Saskatchewan, the old lake beds are now dry and so flat that there are virtually no substantial lakes. Farther to the north other complexes of lakes represent residues of once larger glacial lakes, the complete historical geology of which has not been described.

The present drainage is chiefly to the east into Hudson Bay via the Saskatchewan, Nelson, and Churchill rivers. Much of northern Alberta and the extreme northern part of Saskatchewan drain north by the Peace, Slave, and Mackenzie rivers to the Arctic. Only small areas in southwestern

Saskatchewan and southern Alberta drain southeast to the Missouri. Four interior drainages occupy almost one-half of the southern part of Saskatchewan and testify to the semiarid climate (Fig. 16.1D). Western Ontario and northern Minnesota drain north into Lake Winnipeg, while northeastern Manitoba drains directly into Hudson Bay.

In the Western Plains there are three distinct limnological groupings (Fig. 16.2) which are based on the total dissolved solids and which reflect the interaction of climate and edaphic factors: (1) saline lakes of the prairie and parkland, 500 to 118,000 ppm, (2) freshwater lakes of the parkland and northern coniferous forest, overlying sedimentary deposits, 200 to 550 ppm, and (3) lakes of the northern coniferous and transition forest on pre-Cambrian formations, less than 200 ppm. The lakes of the foothills region of Alberta are a mixed group transitional to the limnological regions of British Columbia. For the purpose of discussion they are considered as a part of the intermediate group of forest lakes.

Saline lakes.—There are few natural lakes on the prairie grassland of southern Alberta and southwestern Saskatchewan. Since the land is very flat, there are few large lake basins, although there are many small depressions. In recent decades lakes of both the prairie and the parkland areas have shown substantial fluctuations in salinity and size. Many of the shallow prairie basins have been reduced to temporary "sloughs" and others have become extensive, dry, alkaline flats (Clarke, 1924) from which deposits of Glauber's salts (Na_2SO_4) may be mined.

Most of the saline lakes occur in the parkland area and are of the sulfate rather than the chloride type. In a comprehensive study Rawson and Moore (1944) described the characteristics of the saline lakes of Saskatchewan, including a documentation of the decrease in size, increase in salinity, and associated changes in the Quill Lakes and other lakes over a period of 20 years (cf. Huntsman, 1922). The saline lakes show a seasonal salinity cycle and various long-term changes in salinity of 2% to 10% per year, with higher rates in lakes of lesser depth. Salinity also varies with depth within the lakes, its effects on stagnation being most severe in deeper lakes. All of the lakes have a winter ice cover, the duration of which is shortened by the high salinity. The effects of salinity on stagnation are of lesser magnitude in lakes

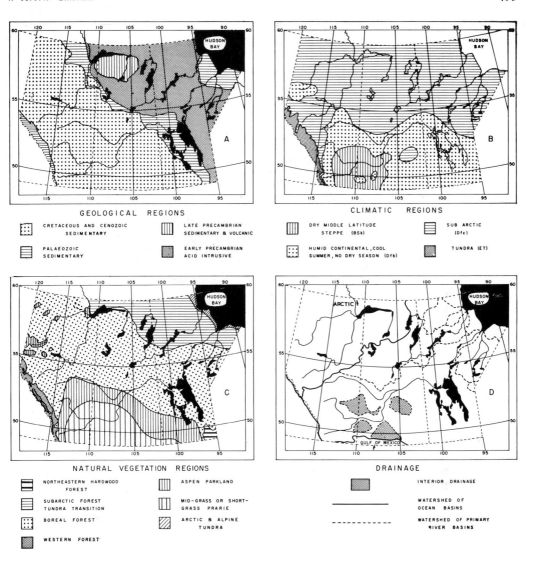

GEOLOGICAL REGIONS

| | CRETACEOUS AND CENOZOIC SEDIMENTARY | | LATE PRECAMBRIAN SEDIMENTARY & VOLCANIC |
| | PALAEOZOIC SEDIMENTARY | | EARLY PRECAMBRIAN ACID INTRUSIVE |

CLIMATIC REGIONS

| | DRY MIDDLE LATITUDE STEPPE (BSk) | | SUB ARCTIC (Dfc) |
| | HUMID CONTINENTAL, COOL SUMMER, NO DRY SEASON (Dfb) | | TUNDRA (ET) |

NATURAL VEGETATION REGIONS

	NORTHEASTERN HARDWOOD FOREST		ASPEN PARKLAND
	SUBARCTIC FOREST TUNDRA TRANSITION		MID-GRASS OR SHORT-GRASS PRARIE
	BOREAL FOREST		ARCTIC & ALPINE TUNDRA
	WESTERN FOREST		

DRAINAGE

	INTERIOR DRAINAGE
―――――――	WATERSHED OF OCEAN BASINS
-------------	WATERSHED OF PRIMARY RIVER BASINS

Fig. 16.1.—Geological, climatic, and natural vegetation zones and drainage in the Western Plains of Canada. Letters in parentheses in the map of climatic regions refer to the Köppen classification of climatic types. From *Atlas of Canada,* Dept. Mines Tech. Survey, 1957.

of moderate depth and are negligible in shallow lakes. Little Manitou Lake with a mean depth of 3.5 m is an exception because of its extremely high salinity of nearly 120,000 ppm. During the winter Glauber's salts precipitate as a bed of crystals on the lake floor. These crystals redissolve in midsummer, and though the lake is homothermous, there is no mixing because of the sharp salinity gradient.

With an increase in salinity the numbers of species of plankton, bottom organisms, and fish diminishes until in the most saline localities only a small group persists. Standing crops of bottom fauna and plankton are highest at intermediate salinities (Fig. 16.3). Recent surveys on lakes of the Qu'Appelle Valley and other saline lakes have been mimeographed and further document their limnology (Johnson and Koshinsky, 1961).

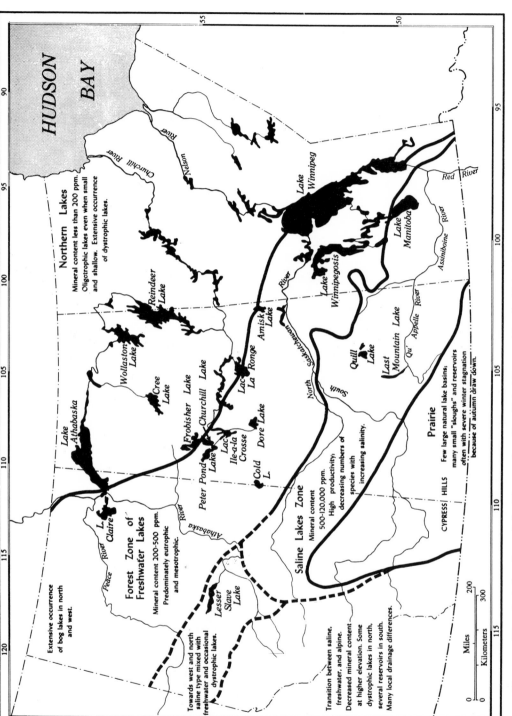

Fig. 16.2.—Limnological regions of the Western Canadian Plains. Prepared by the University of Wisconsin Cartographic Laboratory.

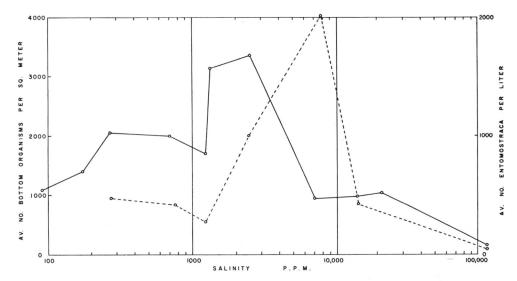

Fig. 16.3.—Standing crops of bottom fauna (solid line) and plankton (broken line) in lakes of vary-ing salinity in Saskatchewan. From Rawson and Moore, 1944.

Rawson and Moore (1944) concluded that the thermal and oxygen relations, transparency, lack of turbidity (cf. Hutchinson, 1937), the kinds and amounts of plankton and bottom fauna, the absence of large quantities of humic material, the salinity but not excessive alkalinity, and the pH range of 8.0 to 8.9, all warranted the description of this lake type in the parkland as saline eutrophic.

Miller and MacDonald (1950) and Miller and Paetz (1953) provided extensive lake survey observations which confirm the occurrence of saline lakes in the prairie and parkland of southeast and central Alberta (Saskatchewan River drainage) and which, for west-central Alberta in the Athabaska and Peace River drainages, suggest a slightly modified saline type of more northerly location. Many of these lakes are highly productive and have been the basis for a "pot-hole" lake fishery (Miller and Thomas, 1957).

The many thousands of small, often temporary "sloughs" of the southern prairie provinces warrant passing mention. Although many of them are scarcely larger than farm ponds, they play an important role as waterfowl producers and in the agriculture of the semiarid prairie. After the drought years of the 1930's, the Federal Government organized the P.F.R.A. (Prairie Farm Rehabilitation Act) under which many small reser-voirs were created. Neither the "sloughs" nor reservoirs have been the subject of detailed limnological study. Miller and Paetz (1953), on the basis of lake surveys and preliminary study, observed that in reservoirs wide fluctuation in level and particularly the drawdown to low levels just before winter were inimical to fish production. In the cold winter a complete ice cover for several months is typical; consequently, severe winter stagnation is a major limnological characteristic.

Forest lakes.—The transition of the parkland to the northern coniferous forest zone occupies a broad band across the Western Plains in which from southwest to northeast there is a decreasing proportion of deciduous forest, a change from Cretaceous through Mesozoic and Paleozoic to pre-Cambrian bedrock formations, and a gradually increasing severity of climate. The drainage is predominantly to Hudson Bay via the Saskatchewan, Nelson, and Churchill rivers, but in the widest part of this zone in northern Alberta, the drainage is by the Peace River to the Arctic. The lake types of this region are clearly distinguishable by their intermediate range of total dissolved solids—much less than that of the saline lakes (Rawson and Moore, 1944) but from two to four times the average of the northern lakes on the Canadian Shield. A small group of lakes in the unglaciated Cypress Hills (Wood Mountain) area of extreme southwestern Saskatchewan and others in the Riding Mountain area of southwest Manitoba also belong to this type.

In a review of 30 years' study Rawson (1960) compared 12 lakes which exemplify the lake types of the forest and northern regions. He observed that in northern Saskatchewan there were approximately 4,000 named lakes and "several thousand" additional smaller and as yet unnamed lakes, which spread across these two zones. At least as many occur in both Alberta and Manitoba, so that the whole area is a potential source of employment for several more generations of lake surveyors.

In general the characteristics of the large lakes of this central region favor their classification as eutrophic. The total dissolved solid content is relatively high (200 to 550 ppm) and includes a high proportion of carbonate and calcium. Mean depths in the classic eutrophic range of less than 18 m are typical, and both thermal stratification and oxygen stratification have been extensively observed. Plankton, bottom fauna, and fish production are high, and in consequence of the last the lakes have received intensive study as a basis for fisheries management.

In some instances the essentially eutrophic harmony is disrupted by unfavorable elements. Kingsmere Lake (Rawson, 1936), for instance, is oligotrophic because of great mean depth, though on the basis of other characteristics it might warrant eutrophic status. Lac Ile-à-la-Crosse has a diminished productivity because of a high flushing rate. By contrast, the eutrophic nature of Big Peter Pond Lake is substantially enhanced by the virtually continuous circulation resulting from the exposed location of the lake basin. Lakes which straddle the boundary of the two zones present some striking contrasts. The best known of these is at Lac la Ronge (Rawson and Atton, 1953) where Hunter Bay, a deep, cold, *Mysis*-inhabited, oligotrophic basin lying on pre-Cambrian rocks, is attached to a main body of water which borders on being eutrophic.

With the exception of Lake Winnipeg, the two largest lakes of the forest region are Lakes Winnipegosis and Manitoba, each with an area greater than 5,000 km². Like the larger Lake Winnipeg they have supported a commercial fishery (originally for whitefish) since before the turn of the century, Bajkov (1930a) made limnological ex-

plorations of both lakes. They are shallow (mean depths of 6.5 and 5 m, respectively), highly productive (Rawson, 1960), and would warrant classification as eutrophic despite their substantial area.

Studies of the non-saline lakes of central Alberta have been aimed primarily at their fisheries potential, but there have been extensive surveys as a basis for fisheries management (Miller and MacDonald, 1950; Miller and Paetz, 1953). In addition to large lakes such as Lesser Slave Lake, Lac la Biche, and Cold Lake which support commercial fisheries, the surveys in Alberta have included many small bodies of water for which generalization is difficult. Throughout the region there are some strongly saline lakes, but to the west and north there is a gradual intergradation through highly eutrophic freshwater types which eventually terminates in mesotrophic lakes and pockets of dystrophic "muskeg" lakes, similar (at least superficially) to those on the more acid pre-Cambrian.

On the western boundary of southern Alberta, a complex transition abruptly telescopes a variety of lake types. Rawson (1939a) observed "these lakes present such a variety of conditions that they are difficult to classify in any simple scheme." For convenience he arranged 49 lakes of Banff National Park into 8 groups, partly on the basis of size, altitude, and clarity of water and partly on the fisheries problems they posed. The larger lakes are deep, cold, and unproductive and may be heavily silted (Rawson, 1939a, 1942; Cuerrier and Schultz, 1957). At higher altitudes, lakes are generally smaller, and the presence of silt is again an important factor influencing trophic status. Even clear lakes of low mean depth may be oligotrophic in the high alpine areas where low mineral content and a severe climate limit productivity (Rawson, 1953a). One might anticipate the eventual subdivision of this foothill-to-alpine area into a number of limnological zones.

In the southern foothills many reservoirs have been constructed for irrigation and power developments (Miller and Paetz, 1959). Water level fluctuation adversely affects productivity in the high-altitude lake reservoirs; power project reservoirs on rivers and streams have high silt loads and fluctuating water levels. Irrigation dams at lower altitudes provide satisfactory environments, but autumn drawdown increases the likelihood of severe winter stagnation in stock-watering and small irrigation reservoirs.

The eastern slope of the Continental Divide is the source of the Saskatchewan, Athabaska, and Peace rivers, and a multitude of tributaries divide the foothills into many minor drainages. Extensive stream surveys have been conducted (Miller and MacDonald, 1950; Miller and Paetz, 1953) on the major drainage systems. To the south the streams are alkaline and clear, but to the north the drainages at lower altitudes are progressively more brown-stained.

Northern lakes.—The lakes of the Churchill and Peace drainages, which lie in the pre-Cambrian, comprise the third major limnological region of the Western Plains of Canada. In the low and irregular topography of the Canadian Shield, the multitude of highly dissected and shallow lakes is the dominant feature of the landscape. The drainages are meandering, in many places confusing, and in some instances indeterminate. Wollaston Lake, for example, has two outlets, one draining into the Arctic via Lake Athabaska and the other to Hudson Bay via Reindeer Lake. Rawson (1960) found that five large lakes of this region shared conditions uniformly conducive to oligotrophy—large area, great depth, low dissolved solids, and a northerly climate. Features redeeming of productivity are the tremendously irregular shorelines and great number of islands in the lakes. The latter prompted Rawson to suggest the inclusion of islands in measures of shoreline development. Despite the profusion of water in the northern areas, precipitation is not heavy, and high rates of flushing are not typical. However, at the focus of the substantial drainage areas in Manitoba, the many large rivers are frequently broadened into lakes which support considerable fisheries.

Rawson observed that to "complete the general picture, it will be necessary to investigate also a series of small and medium-sized lakes from the thousands which occur on the Precambrian Shield." A beginning in the study is provided by the work of Lawler and Watson (1958) of three lakes in northern Manitoba. On the headwaters of the Nelson River, Heming, Home, and Wapun lakes are small (about 2.4 km²), shallow (maximum depth less than 10 m), and low in total dissolved solids (60 ppm). With favorable climate and edaphic factors these lakes would be eutrophic. However, they neither stratify nor stagnate and

support only a moderate standing crop of plankton and bottom fauna. Presumably they are fairly typical of the many small lakes of the northern region. In southeastern Manitoba effects of the pre-Cambrian substrate are offset somewhat by considerable sedimentation and by the more southerly climate.

Great lakes of the Northwest.—Astride the margin of the pre-Cambrian Canadian Shield are the four "Great Lakes" of the Northwestern Plains (Fig. 16.4). All have areas in excess of 7,000 km² (Lake Winnipeg 22,867 km²; Athabaska 7,920 km²; Great Slave 27,195 km²; Great Bear 30,199 km²), and except for Great Bear they support commercial fisheries of substantial size. All of the lakes were much larger in the recent glacial period. The basins were largely sculptured by the advancing ice sheets, although some faulting is also involved. The limnology of Great Slave is the best known, being the subject of a group of papers by Rawson (1947a, 1947b, 1949a, 1950a, 1951a, 1953b, 1956a). As one of the great lakes of the world, this enormous and complex body of water has special limnological interest. The main basin, overlying Paleozoic formations, has an area of 19,425 km², a mean depth of 41 m, and deepens gradually toward the north and east. It receives on the south-central shore the Slave River, which drains an area of 606,000 km² and has an average flow of 3,340 m³/sec. This flow is approximately equal to that of the Fraser and one-half that of the St. Lawrence at the outlet of Lake Ontario. The Mackenzie River drains the lake to the northwest, in consequence of which the substantial influence of the Slave River is concentrated on the south side of the main lake basin. Each day in summer, the Slave River fertilizes Great Slave Lake with 54,000 metric tons of total dissolved minerals and 36,000 metric tons of suspended silt and, accordingly, has a great moderating effect on the oligotrophic conditions. The mineral content in the southern part of the main basin approximates 160 ppm.

The "islands" section, which comprises the eastern 7,800 km² of Great Slave Lake, and the northern shore of the main basin have total dissolved mineral content ranging from 22 to 82 ppm, reflecting their dilution by inflow from streams draining the pre-Cambrian Shield. In addition to the meager supply of minerals, some of the larger bays of the islands section are extreme'y deep (Christie Bay 614 m). Moreover, they lie

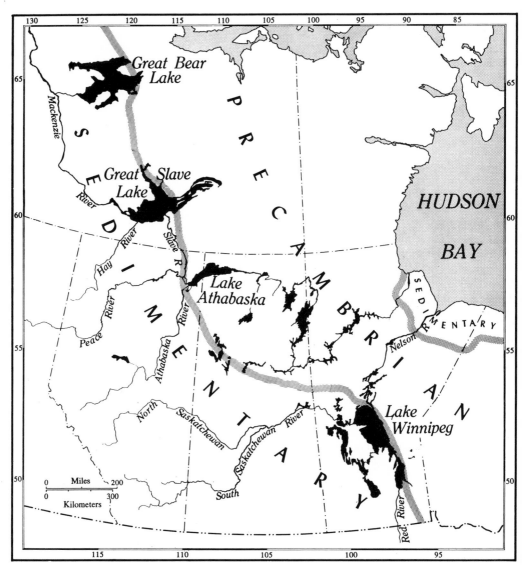

Fig. 16.4.—The four great lakes of the Canadian Northwest. Prepared by the University of Wisconsin Cartographic Laboratory.

farther within the subarctic zone of climate, most portions of the north shore exhibiting permafrost. The extremely oligotrophic setting is marked by low standing crops of plankton, a sparse profundal bottom fauna with only six species of organisms, and a relatively meager fish population.

The fish populations of Great Slave Lake have been under study since the beginning of the commercial fishery in 1945. Their biology and early exploitation have been documented by Kennedy

(1948, 1953, 1954, 1956). Work is continuing on the lake under the direction of the Fisheries Research Board station at London, Ontario (Keleher, 1959, 1961). As an indication of the shortness of the growing season in the subarctic environment, Kennedy (1953) observed that whitefish apparently put on one-half of their yearly growth increment in a two-week period in August.

Great Bear Lake, which lies on the Arctic Circle about 400 km northeast of Great Slave, has been less intensively studied but would appear to share many characteristics of the eastern islands section of Great Slave Lake. Much of the central basin of the lake is over 300 m deep, and productive areas are confined to the shallower bays (Miller, 1947). The lake has a relatively small drainage area lying to the north of the Mackenzie River, and its total dissolved solid content is only 98 ppm. The unfavorable morphometry and low mineral content are augmented by the northerly climate to result in extreme oligotrophy with low plankton, bottom fauna, and fish crops. Miller described the bottom deposit in the central parts of the lake as "a fine greyish material apparently devoid of organic matter." Kennedy (1949) reported on whitefish in Great Bear Lake.

Lake Athabaska is almost entirely within the pre-Cambrian, and only the extreme western end is involved in the major confluence of the Peace and Athabaska rivers to form the Slave. The mineral content in the central part of Lake Athabaska is only 58 ppm. However, the mean depth is 26 m, and the degree of oligotrophy is no more severe than in the main basin of Great Slave Lake (Rawson, 1947c).

Lake Winnipeg is the shallowest of the four great northern lakes and, despite its large area, has a mean depth of only 13 m. Its productivity is substantially higher than that of the other northwestern great lakes, and it has supported a commercial fishery of considerable magnitude since 1883 (Hewson, 1960). Except for the early survey of Bajkov (1930a), the lake has been little studied limnologically. His observations were probably unreliable in some instances, but it would appear from the main body of his data that the lake has a highly efficient circulation with strong winds ensuring warming and oxygen saturation to maximum depths (see also Hewson, 1959). The lake has a large drainage area predominantly from the sedimentary regions and, in consequence, has a relatively high dissolved solid content (about 220 ppm) particularly near the western shore. The production of fish would testify to a substantially higher level of productivity than Great Slave (Rawson, 1952a).

History of limnological endeavor

The earliest limnological studies in the Western Plains region were those of Huntsman (1922), who surveyed the fisheries possibilities of the Quill Lakes in Saskatchewan. Huntsman was a leading figure in aquatic biology in Canada at that time, ranging widely in his interest and travels. In the late 1920's, the Biological Board of Canada initiated a more systematic program of investigation. In the five-year period from 1925 to 1930, Alexander Bajkov and his associates (1) investigated lakes in Jasper Park, Alberta (Bajkov, 1927, 1929; Bere, 1929; Neave, 1929a, 1929b; Neave and Bajkov, 1929; Wallis, 1929), (2) surveyed the saline lake problem, assessing the introduction of fish into Quill lakes and reporting on "Manitou" Lake, (3) explored the limnology of Lakes Winnipeg, Winnipegosis, and Manitoba (Bajkov, 1930a; Neave, 1932), and (4) examined whitefish from a number of Manitoba lakes (Bajkov, 1930b). In all of these studies, interest was centered primarily on obtaining background information pertinent to fisheries problems. Fisheries potential of rivers tributary to Hudson Bay was investigated in the late 1920's and early 1930's. Porsild (1932) made observations of seiches under the ice of Great Bear Lake in the spring of 1928 when he was there making botanical studies.

Limnological research in the classic tradition began in the Western Plains with the arrival of D. S. Rawson in Saskatchewan. Rawson graduated from the University of Toronto in 1930 at which time the Ontario Fisheries Research Laboratory was the flourishing center of freshwater biology in Canada. His graduate work on the bottom fauna of Lake Simcoe, Ontario, is well known as a standard reference in limnology (Rawson, 1928, 1930). His work in Saskatchewan began with studies on Waskesiu and neighboring lakes in Prince Albert National Park (Rawson, 1932, 1936). Shortly after, he made studies of lakes in British Columbia (Rawson, 1934; Clemens et al., 1939), investigated reservoir sites and lakes in Alberta, and studied lakes of the mountain National Parks (Rawson, 1939a, 1940, 1941, 1942). At the same time his studies in Saskatchewan lakes were being expanded by the extensive saline lakes study (Rawson and Moore, 1944). All of these investigations resulted in recommendations for fisheries management, among which were a number of successful introductions of fish (Rawson, 1945, 1946). From 1944 to 1947 his prime interest was the investigation of Great Slave Lake and Lake Athabaska, reported at a length consistent with the complexity of the problem and the thoroughness of the study (Rawson, 1947a, 1947b, 1949a, 1950a, 1951a, 1953b, 1956a). Despite the work involved in the northern lakes study, he continued his interest in alpine lakes, reservoirs, and problems of successful introduction of fish (Rawson, 1947d, 1948, 1953a; Murray, 1950; Rawson and Elsey, 1950). At the same time he greatly encouraged the development of a Saskatchewan fisheries laboratory not only by his writing but by active cooperation with the provincial government. He participated with W. A. Clemens in a Royal Commission of fisheries for the province and wrote papers on its fish and fisheries (Rawson, 1949b, 1950b, 1957a). In the late 1950's his interest was again focused on Saskatchewan lakes, and with his students and the cooperation of the growing staff of the provincial laboratory, he engaged in comprehensive studies particularly of the lakes of the forest and northern areas (Rawson, 1952b, 1957b, 1958a, 1958b, 1959a, 1960, 1961; Rawson and Atton, 1951, 1953; Rawson and Wheaton, 1950).

Rawson was not only a productive scientist; he was the central figure in a changing group of graduate students and co-workers whose many contributions mirror his enthusiasm and sustaining interest in freshwater biology. Associated with Rawson's work are the studies of Rempel (1936) on *Chironomus*, Milne (1941) on Trichoptera, Kuehne (1941) on phytoplankton, Thompson (1941) on bottom fauna of saline lakes, and Moore (1952) on Entomostraca of saline lakes; on the great northwest lakes—Larkin (1948) on *Pontoporeia* and *Mysis*, Fuller (1955) on *Stenodus*, and Kennedy (1948, 1953, 1954, 1956) on fisheries statistics for whitefish and lake trout; on the reservoirs in Alberta, Nursall (1952); and on the Saskatchewan lakes—Mundie (1959) on diurnal movements of bottom fauna, Atton (1955) on thermal studies, Qadri (1955) on whitefish, Oliver (1960) on bottom fauna, and Novakowski (1955), Mendis (1956), Reed (1959), Ruggles (1959a, 1959b, 1959c), Kirch (1960), R. P. Johnson (1961a, 1961b), and Royer (1961) on productivity of various lakes.

Rawson also ventured into the topic of regional resource utilization, leading a study of the Big River area (Rawson et al., 1943) and contributing to a symposium on the potentialities of the Canadian Northwest (Rawson, 1959b).

With such a wide and varied experience of limnology in the whole of western Canada, it was not surprising that Rawson should produce a number of syntheses of his works that summarized his appreciation of lake biology. His first major review (Rawson, 1939b) appeared in the A.A.A.S. volume *Problems of Lake Biology*. Other syntheses were on mineral content (Rawson, 1951b), mean depth and fish production (Rawson, 1952a), plankton (Rawson, 1953c), arctic and subarctic limnology (Rawson, 1953d), morphometry (Rawson, 1955), algal indicators (Rawson, 1956b), and reservoirs (Rawson, 1958c).

Beginning in the early 1940's the limnological study of the plains was much enhanced by the presence of R. B. Miller at the University of Alberta in Edmonton. Miller, like Rawson, was a graduate of the University of Toronto and the Ontario Fisheries Research Laboratory. His graduate studies were on bottom organisms and chironomids, but his first work in the west was largely concerned with the biology of the parasite *Triaenophorus*, which occurs in the flesh of many species of freshwater fish. His many papers on this parasite are listed in his review of the subject (Miller, 1952). In 1947 Miller joined in the great northern lakes survey and with W. A. Kennedy was responsible for the survey of Great Bear Lake (Miller, 1946, 1947; Miller and Kennedy, 1948a, 1948b). In the late 1940's Miller was also engaged in preliminary surveys of Alberta watersheds, which were reported at length in Miller and MacDonald (1950) and Miller and Paetz (1953). Prior to his premature death in 1959, Miller had continued to encourage the growth of the Alberta provincial fisheries branch and was engaged in several significant studies of fishery biology (Miller, 1956, 1958; Miller and Thomas, 1957; Miller and Paetz, 1959).

Rawson and Miller have dominated the history of limnology in the Western Plains and have left a broad and significant literature. They were also responsible for the growth and development of provincial government agencies which have greatly enlarged the work of survey and management. The Saskatchewan Fisheries Laboratory at the University of Saskatchewan under Mr. F. M. Atton, the Alberta Provincial Fisheries group at Edmonton under Mr. M. J. Paetz, and the Manitoba Department of Fisheries under Mr. B. Kooyman are the current provincial centers of limnological and fisheries activity.

The Canadian Wildlife Service with headquarters in Ottawa has developed, under Dr. J. P. Cuerrier, a program of freshwater biology in the National Parks in the west. Much of the early

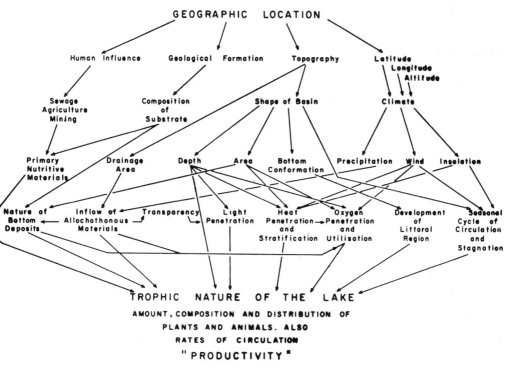

Fig. 16.5.—Rawson's (1939) chart suggesting the interrelations of factors affecting the metabolism of a lake.

urvey work had been done by Rawson (1939*a*, 940, 1941, 1942), and in recent years it has eveloped into a diversified program of fisheries iology (Cuerrier, 1954; Schultz, 1955; Cuerrier nd Schultz, 1957).

Major fields of limnological research

Aside from the important contribution to reional limnology which many years of lake studes and surveys have provided and the singular nterest of the saline lakes and Great Slave Lake bservations, there are some major fields of imnological research which have been augmented y the work that has been done on the Western Plains.

Rawson's outstanding achievement was the omplete and balanced view he brought to the nterpretation of factors influencing lake productivity. His first major review (Rawson, 939*b*) included the diagram shown here as Figre 16.5, which has been widely reproduced. In ll of his subsequent reviews he stressed this pproach, interpreting his observations first in elation to the climatic, edaphic, and morpho-

metric factors and second as they were modified by one or more of the complex of secondary factors and interactions. In a series of review papers (Rawson, 1952*a*, 1953*c*, 1955) he placed special emphasis on morphometric factors, preferring to consider them as "dominant" in determining trophic type and productivity in large lakes. His paper to the Twelfth Limnological Congress in Great Britain (Rawson, 1955) summarized his point of view. In a series of large lakes he demonstrated that mean depth was related to plankton and bottom fauna standing crops and to long-term fish production, in each instance the relation being an inverse curve of characteristic L shape, the more eutrophic lakes on the upper left limb, the more oligotrophic on the lower right (Fig. 16.6).

Rawson concluded his review by emphasizing that although morphometric conditions were dominant in large lakes, climatic and edaphic factors had important effects and that some type of combined evaluation appeared desirable. This conclusion anticipated the attempts of both Rawson (1960) and his junior colleagues in British

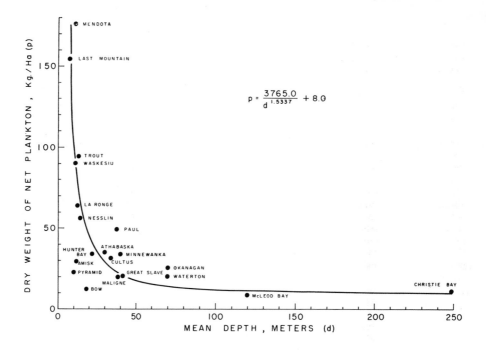

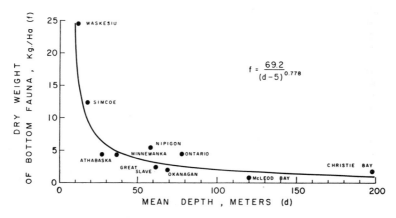

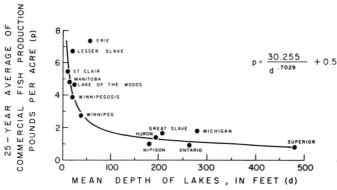

Fig. 16.6.—Relation between mean depth and plankton and bottom fauna standing crops and long-term
fish production in Canadian lakes. *Upper,* mean depth
and the average standing crop of plankton in 20
lakes; *middle,* mean depth and the average weight of
bottom fauna in 12 lakes; *lower,* mean depth and
the long-term average commercial fish production in
12 large lakes. From Rawson, 1955.

Columbia (Northcote and Larkin, 1956) to construct an index of physical and chemical conditions which could be associated with a combined measure of biological production. In essence, these were attempts to quantify Rawson's visualization of factors influencing productivity which he had summarized 20 years before in his diagram (Fig. 16.5).

Along the main stream of Rawson's work a number of side-channels were explored with notable results. For example, he stressed the need for planning introductions of fish so that balanced age distribution would result (Rawson, 1947*d*). He suggested that in using algal flora as an indicator of lake type, numbers of individuals of dominant species were more significant than numbers of species; "oligotrophic indicators" might respond to edaphic factors, not appearing in lakes where oligotrophy was of a morphometric or climatic origin (Rawson, 1956*b*). The usefulness of total mineral content as an indicator of productivity suggested its inclusion in lake surveys as a routine determination (Rawson, 1951*b*). His work on bottom fauna prompted the design of an "ooze sucker" (Rawson, 1930) and a special modification of the Ekman dredge for deepwater sampling (Rawson, 1947*b*).

Some significant limnological contributions are contained in the work of Rawson's students. Together with the saline lakes paper (Rawson and Moore, 1944), the work of Moore (1952) on the Entomostraca is an elegant description of the effect of salinity on distribution and abundance of organisms. From a study of 49 species distributed in 48 lakes Moore concluded that interspecific relations and means of dispersal were secondary to salinity in determining distribution. The glacial relict Crustacea problem, which occupies a prominent place in European literature, was studied by Larkin (1948) under Rawson's supervision. The question of North American distribution of relict Crustacea was reviewed by K. E. Ricker (1959). The mechanics of the Pleistocene glaciation are held responsible, and the absence of *Pallasea quadrispinosa* contradicts the notion of an arctic freshwater connection with Asia as a vehicle of circumpolar freshwater distribution. A further contribution on the relict question is contained in the work of McAllister (1961) on the cottid, *Myoxocephalus*.

Miller's work on the parasite *Triaenophorus* contains some observations of considerable value to limnological endeavor. The parasite has three hosts: (1) *Cyclops*, (2) plankton-feeding fish (whitefish, ciscoes, and others) in the flesh of which it encysts, and (3) piscivorous fish (pike) in which it is an intestinal parasite. The success of the parasite largely hinges on the coincidence, in the spring months, of pike spawning in shallow water where whitefish and ciscoes are feeding on *Cyclops*. If the shallow waters are warmed early, the whitefish and ciscoes retreat to deeper water, and the chain in the parasite life cycle is broken. Several other aspects of lake biology were shown to influence the distribution and abundance of the parasite. Attempts were also made to control the parasite. In one dramatic experiment (Miller and Watkins, 1946) 18 metric tons of concentrated sulfuric acid were spread along 13 km of shore area where pike spawned in Baptiste Lake. The objective was to reduce the pH to a level which would kill the *Triaenophorus* coracidia. The attempt was unsuccessful, perhaps because the lake water returned to its previous pH of 8.0 within half an hour and the bottom mud, within 12 hours, illustrating the chemical buffering capacity of the lake.

Biotal studies on lakes of the Western Plains have, in many instances, stemmed from investigations of Rawson and his students, his material being freely available for loan and study. Kuehne (1941) described the phytoplankton of 58 lakes of southern Saskatchewan from material collected by Rawson and Moore. Ide (1941) recorded the presence of two tropical genera of mayflies in Stoney Lake, Saskatchewan. Oliver (1958) listed the leeches of Saskatchewan from Rawson's collections, and M. S. Wilson (1958) studied 23 species of copepods from Saskatchewan, using Rawson's material. Fishes of Manitoba were given by Hinks (1943), supplemented by papers by Keleher (1952, 1956). Rawson (1949*b*) gave the fishes of Saskatchewan, and Atton and Johnson (1955) supplemented the list. Rempel (1953) monographed the mosquitoes of Saskatchewan. Bailey (1922) on diatoms and Mozley (1939) on mollusks described species of the saline Quill lakes. Herrington (1950) gave the Sphaeriidae of Athabaska and Great Slave lakes. Walker (1940) listed the Odonata of Saskatchewan. Reviews for the whole of Canada include Marshall (1929) on Hydracarina, Bousfield (1958) on Amphipoda, LaRocque (1953) on Mollusca, Walker (1953) on Odonata, and Scott (1958) on fishes.

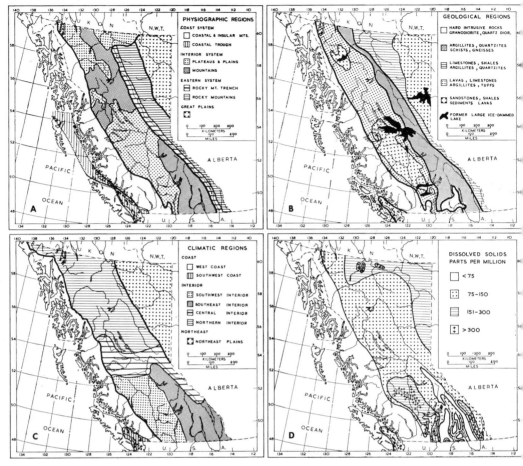

Fig. 16.7.—Physiographic, geological, and climatic regions and total dissolved solid content of lakes in British Columbia. Physiographic, geological, and cli-matic regions adapted from *British Columbia Atlas of Resources,* 1956.

British Columbia

Limnological resources

Although British Columbia has the largest land area (930,533 km²) of the four western Canadian provinces, it has the lowest percentage (1.9%) of fresh water. Manitoba, a province considerably smaller in land area than British Columbia, has over 15% of its surface covered with fresh water.

British Columbia is largely occupied by the Cordillera, a northwesterly trending system of mountains and plateaus varying from 550 to 650 km in width. The Cordillera itself has been subdivided into three major systems (Fig. 16.7A) —an Interior System of mountains, plateaus, and

plains flanked by the western Coast System and the Eastern System (Bostock, 1948).

In the Coast System a largely submerged coastal trough separates the mountains of Queen Charlotte and Vancouver Islands from the Coastal Mountains which are deeply indented with sinuous fiords and which rise sharply from sea level to heights of over 3,000 m. In the south, the Interior System is formed by (1) the large rolling plateau area deeply dissected by the Fraser River and other drainages and (2) the roughly triangular-shaped region of Columbia Mountains (Fig. 16.7A). The northern portion of the Interior System is a complex of plateaus, plains, and mountains generally exhibiting lower relief. A narrow

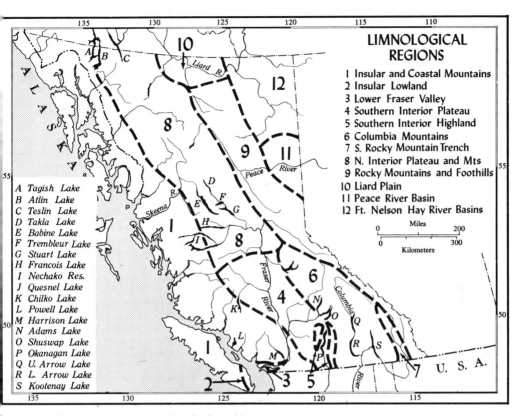

Fig. 16.8.—Limnological regions of British Columbia and lakes with surface area > 100 km². Prepared by the University of Wisconsin Cartographic Laboratory.

but well-defined trough, the Rocky Mountain Trench, separates the eastern flank of the Interior System from the Rocky Mountains of the Eastern System. Many peaks of the latter mountains exceed 3,000 m, especially in the section of the range along the Alberta border. Beyond the Cordillera a segment of the Great Plains of North America extends into the northeastern corner of the province. Here large mesas, cuestas, and valleys of the Liard and Peace River systems present the major relief in the broad plain.

There are at least 16,000 lakes in British Columbia, most of which are less than 1 km² in extent (Table 16.1). About one-half of the small lakes and over two-thirds of the largest lakes in the province are located in the Interior System. The large interior lakes (> 100 km²) are grouped in three widely separated regions (Fig. 16.8). Several are located in the Yukon Plateau in the extreme northwestern corner of the Interior System, e.g., Atlin Lake, with 562 km² of its surface area in British Columbia, and Teslin Lake. There are a number of lakes in the Nechako Plateau in the center of the Interior System, e.g., Babine Lake (475 km²), Takla Lake, and Stuart Lake. Six large lakes are situated in the Columbia Mountains region which occupies the southeast portion of the system, e.g., Kootenay Lake (the third largest lake in the province), Lower Arrow and Upper Arrow lakes, and Shuswap Lake.

All other large lakes are found in the Coastal System of British Columbia. Most of the larger of these—Tagish, Eutsuk, Whitesail (the latter two now part of an enormous reservoir), and Chilko—lie near or on the Coast and Interior System boundary. Harrison (226 km²) and Powell (117 km²) are the only large lakes entirely within the Coast System. The Eastern and Great Plains regions of the province have no large lakes and relatively fewer moderate-sized lakes than the Interior or Coast Systems (Table 16.1).

During the Pleistocene most of British Columbia was covered on at least two occasions by the Cordilleran ice sheet. The northeastern corner of the province, representing what is today the Great Plains region, likewise was buried under a portion of the immense Laurentide ice sheet. Although two sizeable gaps occurred between these sheets north of the 60th parallel, there were no unglaciated areas within British Columbia (J. T. Wilson et al., 1958).

Large ice-dammed lakes formed in at least four different areas of the province during retreat of the ice sheets (Fig. 16.7). One such basin is recognized in the Stikine Plateau in the northwestern portion of the Interior System, while another extends from the upper Peace River valley through the Great Plains into Alberta. The largest ice-dammed lake covered most of the Nechako Plateau in the central interior (Armstrong and Tipper, 1948). Mathews (1944) has described several glacial lakes in the Okanagan, Princeton, Nicola, and Thompson basins of the southern interior. Many of the existing lakes in all of these areas are remnants of former large ice-dammed lakes. Marked changes and reversal in drainage have been associated with the various stages in their shrinkage.

The combination of highly complex geology and soil cover with a marked diversity in climate makes it inevitable that British Columbia lakes exhibit a wide range in the quality and quantity of their total dissolved solids. Figures 16.1B and 16.1C further simplify regional differences in geology and climate given in the British Columbia Atlas of Resources Maps. The regional distribution of dissolved solids in the lake surface waters outlined in Figure 16.1D is based on analysis of samples from several hundred lakes, the majority concentrated in the lower third of the province. Complete sampling will undoubtedly reveal a more complex pattern especially in central and northern portions of the province.

Virtually the whole coast of mainland British Columbia, the Queen Charlotte Islands, and most of Vancouver Island are characterized by waters of very low dissolved solid content, many lakes having values below 25 ppm. Undoubtedly the resistant granitic substrate (Fig. 16.1B) and especially the high annual rainfall (over 150 cm) characteristic of the west coast climatic region (Fig. 16.1C) are largely responsible for low mineral solution. Only on the southeastern coast low-

TABLE 16.1

Number and size of lakes[a] in British Columbia

Physiographic region	Lake area in km²				
	<1	1–10	11–100	>100	Total
Coast System	4,519	461	59	7	5,046
Interior System	7,241	1,042	117	16	8,416
Eastern System	1,463	114	11	0	1,588
Great Plains	1,225	74	7	0	1,306
Total	14,448	1,691	194	23	16,356

[a] All lakes shown on British Columbia Department of Lands and Forests 10 miles to 1 inch map series ID, IE, IF, IG, and IK; 15.78 miles to 1 inch map used only for NW corner of province.

land of Vancouver Island, on the Gulf Islands, and on the Sechelt Peninsula of the mainland are coastal lakes found with total dissolved solid contents ranging from 75 to 150 ppm. It is precisely this region of coastal British Columbia that has a geology and climate conducive to development of higher dissolved solids in lake waters. The substrate is formed largely of sandstones and other sedimentary formations overlain in most regions with glacial till and interglacial sediments. The distinctive climate is characterized by a moderate precipitation (60–100 cm annually) and warm, dry summers.

Low dissolved solids are also typical of many lakes at higher elevations in the Columbia Mountains of the southeastern Interior System. Again the combination of extensive granitic intrusions and highly metamorphosed rocks with moderate to high precipitation (up to 250 cm annually) has favored low mineral solution in the lake waters.

An extensive area of British Columbia inland from the coast has lake waters with total dissolved solid content ranging between 75 and 150 ppm (Fig. 16.1D). In contrast with the granitic substrate of the coast, much of this region is underlain by lavas, limestones, and metamorphic formations with a variable cover of glacial till and lacustrine silt. Annual precipitation is low to moderate (40–100 cm) depending largely on elevation.

Lakes with moderate to high amounts of dissolved solids are found in three widely separated areas of the province (Fig. 16.8): (1) in the extreme north (Liard Plain) and northeast (Peace River portion of the Great Plains), (2) in the south-central Interior System (Fraser Plateau and Okanagan drainage), and (3) in the southern portion of the Rocky Mountain Trench. The predominant rocks in most of these areas are lavas or sedimentaries frequently covered with quaternary gravels, silts, clay, and saline soils. Annual precipitation is low (13–50 cm) in all regions and evaporation high. In a few lakes on the Liard Plain dissolved solid contents up to 350 ppm have been recorded, but much higher values are known from south-central regions of the Interior Plateau where several lakes have over 1,000 ppm, and some ponds exceed 300,000 ppm. There are a number of southern Rocky Mountain Trench lakes with total dissolved solid contents over 600 ppm, but values over 1,000 ppm are rare.

Giving recognition to geological and climatic areas of the province and their importance in determining dissolved solid content of the lakes, Northcote and Larkin (1956) distinguished ten different limnological regions in British Columbia. Little of the province above the 56th parallel was considered. Although relatively few lakes have been examined in the north, it is now possible roughly to delimit major limnological regions for the whole province (Fig. 16.8). Several of the regions, especially the Columbia Mountains and the Northern Interior Plateau and Mountains, show a diverse limnology which suggests subdivision following further study.

Insular and Coastal Mountains.—Insular and coastal lakes range morphologically from large, steep-sided, fiord-like bodies of water, often occupying cryptodepressions, to small, shallow basins formed by ice-scour on the hard granitic coast batholith. Owikeno Lake, described by Foskett (1958), is a typical fiord lake (Hutchinson, 1957) lying near the coast at an elevation of 15 m but with a maximum depth of at least 366 m. There is no evidence of any appreciable amount of salt in its bottom water. However, at Powell Lake, first noted as a fiord lake by Carter (1932), Williams *et al.* (1961) have found a bottom layer of water with a salinity over 16‰ which probably entered the basin some 10,000 years ago. Nitinat Lake on the west coast of Vancouver Island is a fiord lake at least 205 m deep and openly connected to the sea by a short river forming a sill less than 5 m deep. A thin layer of fresh water, usually less than 3 m in depth, rapidly changes to high salinity water (30‰) which fills the lake basin. Infrequent change of water at lower levels is indicated by the virtual absence of dissolved oxygen below 25 m. Conditions in a brackish coastal lagoon, now cut off

from the sea and artificially provided with fresh water, have been recorded by Carl (1937, 1940a). Pitt Lake, draining into the Fraser River about 30 km inland, nevertheless is subject to tidal influence.

An example of a small (9.9 km²) but deep (259 m) coastal lake is provided by Garibaldi Lake, situated in the upper part of a valley at an elevation over 1,900 m. The unusual origin of the lake, formed by a lava flow across a valley blocked by a remnant of the Cordilleran ice sheet, is given by Mathews (1952), who later described its physical limnology and sedimentation (Mathews, 1956).

Many coastal lakes at lower elevations and latitudes usually lack an ice cover and consequently undergo complete or partial circulation throughout winter. Such conditions are typical in Cultus Lake (W. E. Ricker, 1937a) and Cowichan Lake (Carl, 1953). Winter circulation may occur at temperatures above 4° C, placing them in the warm monomictic type (Hutchinson, 1957). Many other coastal lakes, for example Port John Lake (Robertson, 1954), would be classified as dimictic lakes of the second order.

Flushing rates in the order of days or weeks are common in smaller lakes near the coast which are fed by large drainage systems (Mottley, 1936; McMynn and Larkin, 1953). Other coastal lakes with small watersheds (Robertson, 1954) or larger lakes along the eastern margin of the coast range may require much longer periods for their water mass to be "exchanged."

Some coastal lakes are highly transparent, with Secchi disc readings of 20 m or more; others have very limited light penetration caused by suspended glacial flour, silt, or brown organic stains. The latter are common in northern coastal lakes, especially on Graham Island of the Queen Charlottes.

In most coastal and insular lakes the low degree of oxygen depletion in the hypolimnion, as well as low dissolved solids, suggests their predominantly oligotrophic nature. Northcote and Larkin (1956) recorded low standing crops of bottom fauna and fish in the 17 insular and coastal lakes studied. Plankton crops were variable but often low. Some lakes on the eastern margin of the Coastal Mountains, such as Lakelse (Brett, 1950), may be classified as eutrophic morphometrically but, nevertheless, may support lower amounts of plankton or fish than some oligotrophic coastal lakes.

Although three large rivers in British Columbia—the Fraser, Skeena, and Nass—pass through the coastal region, most of their drainage basin lies in the Interior System. Many other large rivers drain off the western slope of the Coast Range and off either side of the central spine of Vancouver Island mountains.

Along the coast maximum stream discharge generally occurs in late autumn and winter with lowest flow during summer months, following the climatic pattern of high winter rainfall and tendency for summer drought. Some rivers show a midsummer and midwinter low with high flows in late autumn and spring (Withler, 1961). This pattern results from heavy late-autumn and winter precipitation, midwinter freezing conditions in higher watersheds, and moderate spring precipitation combined with meltwater. A few rivers, for example the Cheakamus, which derive the major portion of their flow from glacial meltwater have maximum discharge in the summer. Sudden and extensive changes in discharge, resulting from heavy precipitation and rapid runoff, are characteristic of coastal and insular streams. The ratio of high to low daily recorded discharge may exceed 1,000 to 1. Effects of high and low discharge on the fauna, especially fish, have been discussed for British Columbia coastal streams by Neave (1953, 1958), Wickett (1958, 1959), and Hunter (1959).

Most coastal streams and rivers, cutting through deposits of glacial till, silts, or clay, become highly turbid in freshets but may be remarkably clear during periods of normal or low flow. Some streams, particularly those on the east coast of Graham Island (Queen Charlotte Islands), are heavily brown-stained.

Usually large streams and rivers reach maximum temperatures of 10° to 15° C during July and August; midwinter minimums between 1° and 4° C are typical. Small streams at low elevations along the coast may exhibit a wider temperature range seasonally. Larger streams or rivers draining low-lying lakes or reservoirs of the southern coast or Vancouver Island have higher winter minimum (5–6° C) and summer maximum (20–25° C) temperatures.

Few studies have been made on the invertebrate fauna of coastal and insular streams. Those of Idyll (1943) and Neave (1949) on the Cowichan River and Boyd (1939) on a tributary of

this system suggest a moderate or sparse bottom fauna.

Insular Lowland.—All lakes in this restricted but highly distinctive region are small bodies of water (<5 km^2) with low mean depth ($<$ 10 m). High surface temperatures, occasionally over 26° C, occur in midsummer, while bottom water temperatures may exceed 19° C. Dissolved solid contents are frequently above 100 ppm in the lakes and over 200 ppm in some Gulf Island ponds. Severe oxygen depletion of the deeper layers is typical for all lakes studied.

Northcote and Larkin (1956) recorded moderate standing crops of plankton and bottom fauna in four Insular Lowland lakes. A heavy fish mortality associated with summer plankton blooms and oxygen depletion in the lower layers of Quamichan Lake has been noted by Neave (1945).

Many of the streams tributary to or draining Insular Lowland lakes go dry in summer. Few large streams or rivers occur in the region except for the Cowichan River, which originates in the insular mountains and passes through the lowlands only near its mouth.

Lower Fraser Valley.—Like those on the Insular Lowlands, lakes of the Fraser Valley region are small and shallow, but in contrast all have much lower total dissolved solid contents. Temperature conditions are similar to the Insular Lowland lakes, and oxygen depletion occurs in lower layers of several lakes, in particular Hatzic (Northcote, 1952). Many lakes are slightly brown-stained, and some are distinctly acidic with a peat mat surrounding their margin. Wailes (1930) records a pH value of 5.5 near the sphagnum margin of Munday Lake. Low abundances of plankton, bottom fauna, and fish are typical (Northcote and Larkin, 1956).

Streams in this region, where watersheds are largely restricted to the valley floor, are small, slow, and meandering. Draining rich agricultural land and extensive peat deposits, many streams are highly colored with organic material. Heavy agricultural use of water intensifies the summer period of low flow, which may seriously affect production of salmonid fishes in these streams (McMynn and Vernon, 1954). Increased industrial use and suburban growth in the Lower Fraser Valley has resulted in pollution problems in many of the smaller streams. Lower reaches of some rivers entering into the ocean may have surges of saline water along their bottom (R. R. Wilson, 1951). *Neomysis mercedis* is a common crustacean in this environment, although it may occur as far as 100 km inland in Lakelse Lake (R. R. Wilson, 1951) or Hatzic Lake (Northcote, 1952).

Southern Interior Plateau.—In this region lakes range from the fourth largest in the province, Okanagan (370 km²), to the myriad of small saline ponds considerably less than 1 km² in area. Although the valley of the Okanagan system is of Tertiary origin (Schofield, 1943), glaciation has worked extensive change. Nearly all the larger lakes of the Southern Interior are remnants of former ice-dammed basins, many of which were interconnected (Mathews, 1944). Terraces evident today indicate that each of the large glacial lakes had several levels and different outlets. Smaller lakes throughout the Southern Interior provide examples of nearly every type of glacial formation on the mantle of drift; kettle lakes are common, and some small plunge pool basins in now abandoned meltwater channels are known.

The larger lakes lying in the valleys of the plateau, such as Okanagan and Kamloops Lake, are deep (maximum depths 232 m and 151 m, respectively) and steep-sided. Summer thermal stratifications are rarely sharp, and the extensive hypolimnion remains well oxygenated throughout the summer (Clemens *et al.*, 1939). Standing crops of plankton, bottom fauna, and fish are comparatively poorer than in smaller lakes of the plateau, indicative of the predominantly oligotrophic conditions. Spectacular temperature seiches recently have been recorded in Nicola Lake, where strong summer winds are channelled along the valley floor.

While some lakes on the plateau proper tend toward oligotrophy, for example Paul Lake (Rawson, 1934), the vast majority exhibit moderate to strong eutrophy. Sharp summer thermal stratifications with marked oxygen depletion in the hypolimnion are typical. Total dissolved solid contents of the lakes are usually well over 100 ppm and may range over 1,000 ppm in bodies of water supporting fish populations. Many lakes have dense summer blooms of blue-green algae, *Aphanizomenon* and *Anabaena* the predominant forms, occasionally associated with summer-kills of trout (Larkin, 1954). High populations of bottom organisms, especially amphipods, are usually sheltered in a littoral and sublittoral *Chara* zone.

The majority of these productive interior lakes originally contained no fish and have been stocked with rainbow trout within the last 50 years. Most, except the large ones in the valleys, have an ice cover from late November to May. Serious oxygen depletion again occurs in the lower layers and may cause winter-kill of trout (Larkin, 1954).

Highly saline lakes and ponds are found in the Okanagan and Kamloops areas and occur widely throughout the Fraser Plateau. Magnesium sulfate, sodium, and calcium are commonly dominant constituents, although much local variation is evident. The brine shrimp, *Artemia salina*, has been recorded in ponds near Kamloops where dissolved solids may exceed 300,000 ppm in autumn (Cameron, 1953). A number of ponds and shallow lakes throughout the interior which harbor waterfowl have been briefly described by Munro (1945).

The flow regime of many interior rivers reflects the more continental climate with maximum flow in spring and summer and minimum flow in winter, a pattern markedly different from that of coastal rivers. Moreover, many interior rivers and streams receive a large portion of their summer discharge from snow and glacial meltwater. Small streams often are subject to extreme freshets during a short, late spring or summer period, followed by long periods of low or no flow. Calcium carbonate hardness of many interior streams is above 100 ppm, in direct contrast to the values below 50 ppm typical of coastal streams.

Southern Interior Highland.—A number of small, shallow lakes lie on the west and east Okanagan Highland zone of Brink and Farstad (1949) at elevations over 1,000 m. A few similar lakes may occur at high elevation in other areas of the Southern Interior Plateau. Sharp thermal stratifications and severe hypolimnial oxygen depletions are characteristic of summer conditions. The lake waters are appreciably lower in dissolved solids (50–100 ppm) than other lakes of the Interior Plateau and all are slightly to moderately brown-stained. Lequime (Chute) Lake water is acidic (Clemens *et al.*, 1939) in contrast to the almost invariable alkaline reaction of Southern Interior Plateau lakes. Standing crops of plankton, bottom fauna, and fish are typically low (Northcote and Larkin, 1956).

Columbia Mountains.—In the Columbia Mountain region there are six large oligotrophic lakes each with a surface area well over 100 km². Listed in order of decreasing area, these are Kootenay (399 km²), Shuswap, Quesnel, Upper Arrow, Lower Arrow, and Adams (136 km²). All are deep lakes; the shallowest, Shuswap, has a maximum depth of 162 m, while Quesnel, which is probably the deepest, has a maximum known depth of 418 m but has not been adequately sounded. Kootenay Lake (Schofield, 1946), Shuswap (Mathews, 1944), and probably the other lakes have had a complex origin involving glacial modification of level and drainage.

The limnology of at least three of the lakes is markedly influenced by inflow of large rivers. Cold water from the Duncan River enters the north end of Kootenay Lake and dives below the surface. Its contribution to temperature structure and circulation in the lake can be detected up to 50 km away from the river mouth (Larkin, 1951a). The warmer, turbid Kootenay River, entering the south end of the lake, may discolor the lake surface almost as far as the West Arm, some 50 km to the north. Likewise, passage of the Columbia River, with an average flow of over 900 m³ per second, through Upper and Lower Arrow lakes has a far-reaching impact on their physical, chemical, and biological limnology.

The large lakes are thermally stratified in the summer, with surface temperatures only occasionally exceeding 25° C. Those in the south rarely are completely frozen over in the winter, while those farther north (Adams, Quesnel) may be so. At no time is any marked oxygen depletion observed in their massive hypolimnions. Standing crops of plankton and bottom fauna are usually low or only moderate in comparison with Southern Interior Plateau lakes (Clemens et al., 1938; Northcote and Larkin, 1956; Ward, 1957).

The smaller Columbia Mountain lakes are a heterogeneous group (over 1,000 in all) ranging from extreme oligotrophy (e.g., Trout Lake: Larkin, 1951a) to moderate eutrophy, with appreciable summer depletion of hypolimnetic oxygen. A few, such as Wilgress and Boundary, in the extreme south have total dissolved solid contents over 200 ppm, but most are below 150 ppm. Some features of shallow lakes in the Kootenay flats which have been subject to extensive agricultural use are given by Munro (1950).

Columbia Mountain rivers, similar to those of the Interior Plateau, typically have maximum discharge in summer and minimum discharge in winter. Only in the warm valleys below the 50th parallel do small streams become excessively low or dry in the autumn. Temperatures of many rivers, such as the Lardeau (Cartwright, 1961), are modified both by lakes which they drain and by cold, silt-laden glacial tributaries.

Southern Rocky Mountain trench.—The lakes in this small region, except Columbia and Windermere, are all less than 10 km² in area, and only six are in the 1–10 km² range. All are moderately shallow (mean depth <20 m). Their most distinctive feature is a high dissolved solid content: most are above 200 ppm, and some exceed 1,000 ppm. Sharp thermal stratification and oxygen-depleted hypolimnions are found in many but not all lakes. Some show extensive and rapid changes in water level associated with changes in groundwater supply, a feature which may lower littoral bottom fauna production. Moderate standing crops of plankton, bottom fauna, and fish were recorded in six lakes in this area (Northcote and Larkin, 1956).

Northern Interior Plateau and Mountains.—This region, like the Columbia Mountains, contains several large lakes, with at least seven over 100 km² in surface area. In addition, the "Tweedsmuir or Circle" lakes, two basins of which lie in the Coastal Mountain region, have now been made into a large reservoir (Nechako: Fig. 16.8) covering 1,334 km² at full height (Anon., 1953). Lake basins in this reservoir and the several other large lakes nearby (François, Babine, Stuart, Trembleur, and Takla) all are situated on the Nechako Plateau. The shallowest lakes, Trembleur and Stuart (maximum depths 103 and 97 m, respectively), lie along or within the area once covered by the large Nechako ice-dammed lake (Fig. 16.7B), while the others outside its former margin have maximum depths ranging from 207 m (Babine) to 287 m (Takla). Atlin and Teslin lakes, situated on the Yukon Plateau in the north, have maximum depths of 284 and 213 m, respectively.

Large Northern Interior lakes generally are not sharply stratified in midsummer. Surface temperatures there are often somewhat below 20° C, and only slight to moderate depletion of hypolimnial oxygen is evident (Clemens et al., 1945; Godfrey, 1955; Withler, 1956). Usually the lakes are frozen over in December and do not lose their ice cover until May. Low abundances of plankton and bottom fauna have been recorded in Babine, Teslin, and Atlin; these and the others are undoubtedly oligotrophic. W. E. Johnson (1956, 1958, 1961) has studied in detail the abundance, distribution, feeding, and growth of juvenile sockeye salmon in Babine Lake.

The small lakes of the Northern Interior region defy simple classification and range from what might be termed moderately oligotrophic to moderately eutrophic. Godfrey (1955) designates productive conditions in six small (7–28 km²) lakes of shallow to medium depth (13–132 m) in this region; four are considered oligotrophic and two eutrophic, although low bottom oxygen concentration occurs only in one lake. Moderate plankton and sparse bottom fauna abundances occur in the two Northern Interior lakes given by Northcote and Larkin (1956).

Nearly all studies on rivers of the Northern Interior have been concerned with possible or actual effects of hydroelectric structures on their limnology. The temperature, discharge, and clarity of Nechako River have been markedly altered by the Kenney Dam which formed an enormous reservoir out of several large lakes in Tweedsmuir Provincial Park. Probable effects of the hydroelectric scheme on sport fisheries of the Nechako drainage have been considered by Lyons and Larkin (1952), while those on sockeye salmon have been reviewed elsewhere (Anon., 1953). Detailed physical conditions of several tributaries of the Fraser, draining the Northern Interior, are given in the Fraser River Board Report (Patterson *et al.*, 1958). Lindsey (1957) has presented possible effects of hydroelectric diversions on fish distribution in headwaters of the Yukon, Taku, Liard, Stikine, Peace, and Fraser rivers, all of which have tributaries arising in the Northern Interior.

Rocky Mountains and Foothills.—Along the Alberta border this region merges with the transition zone shown in Figure 16.2. There are no large lakes, and only nine have surface areas exceeding 10 km². Moberly Lake, the largest, is 29 km² in area with a maximum depth of 42 m. Summer temperature series from the only two lakes examined, Grave in the south and Azouzetta in the middle of the region, showed fairly sharp thermal stratification with surface temperatures below 18° C. No appreciable depletion of oxygen was apparent in lower layers of the lakes. All lakes have ice cover from late autumn until spring. Highest dissolved solids are found in lakes in the southern (Grave, 190 ppm; Aid, 233 ppm) and northernmost (Muncho,

274 ppm) portions of the region. A few lakes fall below 100 ppm in total dissolved solids. Standing crops of plankton, bottom fauna, and fish are moderate to low in two lakes examined (Northcote and Larkin, 1956).

No studies have been made on the few high-elevation Rocky Mountain lakes in British Columbia. The work of Rawson and others on the more numerous alpine lakes in the Rocky Mountains of Alberta has been mentioned previously.

Liard Plain.—Little limnological work has been done in this region, where all the lakes are small (<10 km²) and tributary to the Liard River. They are, however, a distinctive group by virtue of their moderate to high dissolved solid content, ranging from 128 to over 400 ppm in nine lakes sampled. Good Hope Lake, one of the larger in the area, has 350 ppm dissolved solids. Several lakes have well-developed littoral *Chara* mats and give every appearance of being moderately productive.

Peace River Basin.—The portion of the Great Plains (Fig. 16.7A) drained by the Peace River and its major tributaries—the Alces, Kiskatinaw, Beatton, Pine, Moberly, and Halfway rivers—represents a northwestern extension of the saline lakes zone shown in Figure 16.2. There are few sizeable lakes in this region, Charlie Lake (28 km²) being the only one over 10 km² in surface area. All are shallow; Swan (20 m), One Island (11 m), and Charlie Lake (10 m) are probably some of the deepest. Charlie Lake has summer surface temperatures over 20° C, while the bottom water may exceed 15° C. Some oxygen depletion occurs in lower layers. Total dissolved solid content of most lakes is moderately high, ranging from 135 to 264 ppm in eight lakes examined. Cowan (1939) mentions two distinct types of ponds in this region—the marshy ponds and the dark-stained muskeg ponds. Tom's Lake, an example of the latter, has a total dissolved solid content of 98 ppm.

High abundance of plankton and fish and moderate abundance of bottom fauna were recorded by Northcote and Larkin (1956) for Charlie Lake, the only lake sampled in the Peace River Basin.

The Peace River and its tributaries are characterized by marked seasonal rise and fall (Cowan, 1939) and carry heavy silt loads during freshet. Distribution of fish, particularly in the streams, has been examined by Lindsey (1956).

Fort Nelson–Hay River Basin.—Most of this

region, encompassed by the drainages of the Fort Nelson, Hay, and Petitot rivers, lies at an elevation below 600 m and is characterized by organic soils formed on a shale and sandstone base. There are numerous small, stained bog lakes in the region but only one lake of considerable size, Kotcho Lake. It has a surface area of 78 km² but a maximum depth of only 3 m. Because of its exposure to wind and its shallow depth and ooze bottom, the water of Kotcho Lake is highly turbid (Secchi disc reading 0.2 m in June 1960). The only lakes sampled from this region, Kotcho and Clarke, have total dissolved solid contents of 151 and 167 ppm, respectively. A small, stained bog lake near Fort Nelson has 45 ppm dissolved solids. All lakes have an ice cover from the late autumn to spring.

Large rivers tributary to the Fort Nelson have a high summer maximum flow and carry a very large suspended sediment load at that time. During periods of low flow in autumn and winter they are considerably less turbid. The Hay River is distinctly brown-stained as are most of the smaller meandering streams draining the widespread bog country.

History of limnological endeavor

The first important limnological work in British Columbia was started in the summer of 1922 by R. E. Foerster, then a graduate student working under Professor C. McLean Fraser at the University of British Columbia. Foerster made a number of plankton collections and recorded physical information on Harrison Lake and several small lakes nearby. The following year he intensified his program, making regular observations on plankton abundance and distribution in Cultus Lake, combined with detailed study of its physical and chemical limnology. Analysis of the material was continued under the direction of Professor W. A. Clemens at the University of Toronto, from which Foerster shortly obtained his doctorate degree. Following publication of the study in 1925, Foerster, working with the Pacific Biological Station (Fisheries Research Board of Canada) under its new director, W. A. Clemens, continued to investigate the life history, propagation, and migration of sockeye salmon at Cultus Lake (Foerster, 1929a, 1929b, 1929c). In the meantime, interest was springing up in the distribution of larger freshwater invertebrates (Johansen, 1921a, 1921b; Thacher, 1923; Marshall, 1924), and G. H. Wailes had started records on algae and protozoans in lakes on Vancouver Island and the lower mainland (Wailes, 1925a, 1925b).

Some of the first notes on Paul Lake, near Kamloops, were made by Dymond (1930). Immediately thereafter, C. McC. Mottley, a biologist from the Pacific Biological Station at Nanaimo, began an intensive study on the production of rainbow trout at Paul Lake, which of necessity involved considerable limnological work (Mottley, 1931, 1932, 1933, 1938, 1940). In conjunction with Mottley's studies, Rawson conducted a limnological survey on Paul Lake and several other lakes in the Kamloops region in 1931, measuring standing crops of plankton and bottom fauna as well as recording physical and chemical conditions in the lakes (Rawson, 1934).

In 1934 W. A. Clemens, who had moved to British Columbia ten years previously as Director of the Pacific Biological Station at Nanaimo, reported on feeding habits of fish in a number of interior lakes (Clemens and Munro, 1934; Clemens, 1934). Another biologist from the Nanaimo station, W. E. Ricker, working since 1932 with Foerster at Cultus Lake, started an extensive program of limnological research on the lake. Ricker described the physical and chemical characteristics of Cultus Lake in detail (W. E. Ricker, 1937a), recorded the vertical distribution of its plankton (W. E. Ricker, 1937b), and produced the first comprehensive work on statistical treatment of plankton data (W. E. Ricker, 1937c). The following year he published on general problems in sampling plankton and described seasonal and annual variations in Cultus Lake plankton as well as growth of sockeye and squawfish (W. E. Ricker, 1938a, 1938b, 1938c). In conjunction with E. M. Walker of Toronto, he also noted Odonata from the Cultus Lake area (Walker and Ricker, 1938) and listed stoneflies of the region (W. E. Ricker, 1939).

Concomitant with this burst of limnological activity, other Nanaimo biologists were extending their interest from brackish water (Carl, 1937) to mountain lakes (Mottley, 1936), while Clemens et al. (1938) reported on earlier studies at the large inland lake, Shuswap. In 1935 Clemens, working with Rawson and McHugh on Okanagan Lake, conducted the first extensive limnological survey on a large British Columbian lake and also examined several smaller lakes in Okanagan Valley and high lands (Clemens *et al.*, 1939). Carl (1940*a*) continued work on the brackish water of Lost Lagoon and completed a comprehensive survey of the distribution of cladocerans and free-living copepods throughout the province (Carl, 1940*b*).

Idyll (1943) published the first strictly limnological study on a British Columbia river, the Cowichan, giving results of bottom fauna sampling carried out by the Fisheries Research Board. Later Neave (1949) reported more completely on physical features of the river and especially its game fish populations, summarizing information collected there since 1934.

In 1944 the Fisheries Research Board began a major investigation of the Skeena River salmon with part of the program centered at Lakelse Lake. Subsequently a number of workers, in particular J. R. Brett, described limnological features of this northern coastal lake (Pritchard and Brett, 1945; Brett and Pritchard, 1946*a*; Alderdice, 1946; Brett, 1950; McMahon, 1954). In addition the Nanaimo workers made limnological studies on a number of other lakes in the Skeena watershed (Brett, 1946; Brett and Pritchard, 1946*b*; McConnell and Brett, 1946; Foskett, 1947*a*, 1947*b*; McMahon, 1948*a*; Withler, 1948). Godfrey (1955) summarized limnological data for 20 Skeena lakes. Active investigation of Babine Lake, the largest natural body of fresh water entirely within British Columbia, began during this period (Withler *et al.*, 1949), although some observations had been made earlier on the lake (MacKay, 1931).

Up to the late 1940's, limnological endeavor in British Columbia had been almost solely carried out by biologists of the Pacific Biological Station or by limnologists, such as Rawson, brought in for specific investigations by the Fisheries Research Board. Two events now occurred which broadened the scope of freshwater research in the province. Dr. W. A. Clemens, who had left the directorship of the Pacific Biological Station at Nanaimo, became Head of the Department of Zoology, and in cooperation with the Provincial Game Commission in 1947, he began studies on fish cultural problems and production in several Southern Interior lakes (Clemens, 1947; Mac-Phee, 1948; Ferguson, 1949). He and the Game Commissioners were instrumental in arranging the appointment of a staff of permanent fishery biologists to begin active survey and research on lakes throughout the province. At about the same time biologists of the International Pacific Fisheries Commission, quartered at New Westminster, increased the scientific examination of rivers, streams, and large lakes within the Fraser River watershed

The first extensive lake surveys were begun in the summer of 1949 (Larkin, 1951*b*). Over several years, the surveys were conducted on a major scale in several regions of the province (Northcote, 1953) and now have been reported in some detail (Northcote and Larkin, 1956; Larkin and Northcote, 1958). Further surveys of a more specific nature have continued up to the present. Also in the late 1940's, interest was reactivated in the Paul Lake study (Clemens, 1948; Anderson, 1949; Larkin *et al.*, 1950).

In the early 1950's increased industrial demand on fresh waters of the province for hydroelectric and other uses introduced a new impetus to limnological study. Works of Larkin (1951*a*), Lyons and Larkin (1952), and McMynn and Larkin (1953) were largely concerned with possible or pending alterations to lakes and streams to be brought about by dams. Thomas (1953*a*, 1953*b*, 1954) gave results of chemical analyses of lakes and streams in several watersheds which are or may be used for industrial purposes. Also during this period, limnological interest continued among students at the university (R. R. Wilson, 1951; Northcote, 1952; Cameron, 1953).

In 1955 Larkin left the Game Commission to succeed Dr. Clemens as director of the recently formed Institute of Fisheries at the University of British Columbia. Subsequently students there reported on further aspects of Paul Lake limnology (Crossman, 1959; Crossman and Larkin, 1959; Johannes and Larkin, 1961), while others studied a variety of freshwater topics (Geen, 1955; Ward, 1957; Geen, 1958; MacLeod, 1960). Provincial, federal, and international government fisheries agencies likewise have continued limnological work in many fields (W. E. Johnson, 1956; Withler, 1956; Stringer and McMynn, 1958; Neave, 1958; Andrew and Geen, 1960; Cartwright, 1961; Geen and Andrew, 1961).

Throughout the development of limnological endeavor in British Columbia, the enthusiasm and interest of Dr. W. A. Clemens has been preeminent. He directed the first researches of Foerster at Cultus Lake as well as later phases of his program; he guided the widespread freshwater

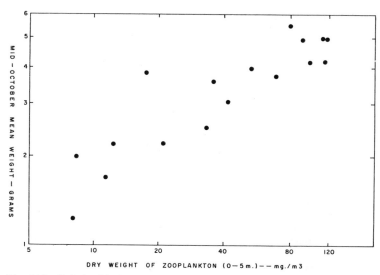

Fig. 16.9.—Relationship between mean weight in mid-October of age 0 sockeye salmon (*Oncorhynchus nerka*) and mean dry weight of zooplankton (0–5 m) during the period mid-June to mid-October. From W. E. Johnson, 1961.

investigations carried out by Nanaimo biologists in the 1930's and 1940's; he activated freshwater research at the University of British Columbia; he stimulated the Provincial Game Commission to form a division for scientific investigation of freshwater sport fishery problems; and he was personally involved in the initiation and growth of the International Pacific Salmon Fisheries Commission. All this was in addition to his important limnological research on lakes in many parts of the province. Today he continues to advise and inspire biologists in all fisheries agencies as well as to carry on further analysis in his own limnological research.

Major fields of limnological research

Emphasis in study of the inland waters of British Columbia logically has been directed by interest in the freshwater juvenile stages of the five species of Pacific salmon, by fish cultural and management activities in important freshwater sport fisheries dominated by rainbow trout, by man's alteration of the environment of these fishes, and finally by the unique geographical subdivisions of the province which present rare and challenging opportunities for the regional limnologist, zoogeographer, or systematist.

The freshwater environment in relation to Pacific salmon production.—Studies on lake ecology of juvenile sockeye salmon were the first limnological investigations in British Columbia

(Foerster, 1925), and they still contribute heavily to the recent literature (Geen and Andrew, 1961; W. E. Johnson, 1961). Throughout these four decades of study, an immense body of information has been built up on effects of lake temperature, light, chemistry, and other factors on distribution, abundance, feeding habits, and growth of these young salmon. Works of Foerster (1937), W. E. Ricker (1937*b*), Clemens *et al.,* (1938), Hamilton (1943), McMahon (1948*b*), Foskett (1951), Anon. (1957), Foskett (1958), and W. E. Johnson (1956, 1958) are only a few in this area. In addition, other research has been focused more specifically on plankton distribution and abundance and on the largely planktonic food habits of young sockeye in lakes (W. E. Ricker, 1938*b*; Foerster, 1934; Alderdice, 1946; McMahon, 1954; Ward, 1957). W. E. Johnson (1961) presented a direct relationship between plankton abundance and growth of young sockeye in Babine Lake (Fig. 16.9). Innumerable aspects of the lake residence of sockeye, such as competition and predation by other species, have not been noted here since they are less closely related to limnology.

Study of pink and chum salmon production has provided limnological information on a variety of coastal and insular rivers and streams ranging in size from the Fraser River (maximum discharge over 14,000 m³/sec) to small streams such as Hooknose Creek (maximum discharge

<17 m³/sec). For the most part data such as level, discharge, temperature, turbidity, and gravel permeability have been recorded and attempts made to relate these to estimates of young salmon output or adult return. Results of many studies on north coast and insular rivers and streams have been reviewed by Wickett (1958), while some data for the Fraser River and tributaries are considered by Vernon (1958). Stream temperature, discharge, and gravel permeability have been suggested as freshwater factors affecting pink and chum salmon production (Fig. 16.10).

The freshwater environment in relation to rainbow trout production.—Early fish culturists were able to exploit the food resources of productive "barren" lakes in the Southern Interior Plateau by introducing rainbow trout, the first species of fish in these lakes. Other faunal deficiencies occasioned by recent glaciation also have affected trout production in British Columbia lakes. *Pontoporeia* and *Mysis* have been introduced into Kootenay Lake in an attempt to improve its food resources for intermediate age classes of rainbow trout (Larkin, 1951b).

Paul Lake has been the site of the sole comprehensive study on rainbow trout production in British Columbia. The initial work of Mottley between 1931 and 1937 has been summarized (Mottley, 1940), as have the investigations of Clemens and others in the late 1940's (Larkin *et al.*, 1950). In general the studies emphasized the difficulty of relating trout production to the usual measurements of physical and chemical conditions in the lake or to standard estimates of plankton and bottom fauna standing crops. More recently the introduction of redside shiners into the lake has been shown to have a strong impact upon the feeding habits and growth of rainbow trout (Larkin and Smith, 1954; Crossman and Larkin, 1959). Plans are now being made to treat Paul Lake with toxaphene to eliminate both trout and shiners. Thus, it will be possible to follow the history of the formerly "barren" lake through a cycle involving rainbow trout, trout and redside shiners, no fish, and finally rainbow trout again.

Considerable success has been obtained in improving trout production in "coarse-fish lakes" by the use of fish toxicants, although results have not been well documented. MacPhee (1949) discussed effects of rotenone on invertebrate fauna of treated lakes, while Stringer and McMynn (1958, 1960) reviewed toxaphene treatment.

The effect of environmental alteration by man on lakes and streams.—Although Foerster (1930) described obstruction of sockeye salmon spawning runs by a power dam, scientific investigation of effects of alteration by man on lakes and streams in British Columbia started little more than a decade ago. Long-term effects consequently have not been well recorded. Nevertheless, the remarkable increase in number, degree, variety, and complexity of alterations has stimulated a most active interest by all fisheries agencies concerned with salmon and trout production in these waters.

Brett (1957) has considered problems created for salmon by multiple water use, while Larkin *et al.* (1959) have summarized effects on freshwater fisheries. Recent publications have dealt thoroughly with most limnological aspects of "fishpower" problems (Larkin, 1958) and have considered effects on salmon production of proposed dams in the Fraser River system (Andrew and Geen, 1960). Summaries of research conducted on the fish-power problem by fisheries agencies in British Columbia make available a considerable body of information not published elsewhere (Anon., 1960).

Few studies have been conducted on limnological effects of pollution; however, Crouter and Vernon (1959) report effects of DDT spray on bottom fauna as well as on fish in a number of Vancouver Island rivers.

Regional limnology and freshwater zoogeography.—Regional limnology is based on a study of biological production (Naumann, 1932). However, quantitative measurement of production has been and in many ways still is difficult and time consuming. Only in an area which presents sharp and wide diversity in physiography, geology, and climate could the regional limnologist expect to distinguish differences in production using the relatively crude techniques which were all that were available until recently. British Columbia is just such an area (Fig. 16.7A–D).

For 100 lakes throughout the province Northcote and Larkin (1956) demonstrated a significant positive regression between total dissolved solid content of the lake waters and standing crops of plankton or fish; a similar relationship was suggested for bottom fauna. The general form of the relationship between mean depth and standing crops of plankton, bottom fauna, or fish was hyperbolic as in Rawson's data (Fig. 16.6), with larger quantities in *some* lakes of low mean depth. However, the only generalization which

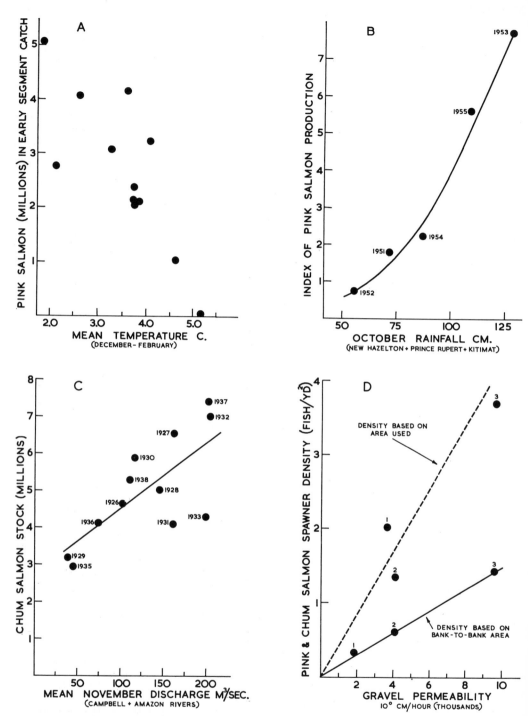

Fig. 16.10.—Some environmental factors in British Columbia rivers which may affect pink and chum salmon production. *A,* relationship of Fraser River water temperature during late winter and early segment of pink salmon catch two years later (Vernon, 1958); *B,* total October rainfall at three stations in Skeena River drainage area related to index of Skeena River pink salmon production (100 × stock/spawners) (Wickett, 1958); *C,* relation between combined November mean discharge (four years previously) of two Vancouver Island rivers and Vancouver Island chum salmon stocks (Wickett, 1958); *D,* relation between average gravel permeability of three coastal streams and densities of pink and chum spawners that gave maximum fry production: *1*—Nile Creek, *2*—Hooknose Creek, *3*—McClinton Creek (Wickett, 1958).

seemed justified was that quantities of fauna from lakes of great mean depth were never as high as those in *some* lakes of low mean depth. *Both* high and low standing crops were found in lakes of low mean depth. Thus, total dissolved solid content of the water appeared to be the most important single factor determining general level of productivity in lakes throughout the province. Differences in dissolved solids and summed indices of plankton, bottom fauna, and fish standing crops characterized some of the limnological regions distinguished previously for British Columbia (Fig. 16.11).

The unique geographical diversity of the province also has stimulated zoogeographical studies. Carl (1940b) first utilized its possibilities in a distributional study of some cladocerans and copepods. Later he extended his interests to freshwater fish (Carl and Clemens, 1948) and more recently has been joined by Lindsey and others (Lindsey, 1956; Carl et al., 1959; McAllister and Lindsey, 1961).

Biotal studies.—No attempt has been made to cover literature dealing with taxonomic, faunistic, or floristic studies on the freshwater biota of British Columbia. The following references, however, may serve as an introduction to some major works of particular interest to limnologists.

G. H. Wailes worked actively on freshwater algae and protozoans between 1925 and 1932; some of his studies during this period may be found in Wailes (1925a, 1925b, 1927, 1931, 1932). Taylor (1928) recorded algae from several alpine ponds in the Columbia Mountains, while Gee (1937) covered British Columbia freshwater sponges. Distribution of Cladocera and Copepoda was given by Carl (1940b). Bousfield (1958) listed the amphipod crustaceans.

Studies on freshwater insects include McDunnough (1939) for the Ephemeroptera, Whitehouse (1941, 1948) and Walker (1953, 1958) for the Odonata, W. E. Ricker (1943, 1959) for the Plecoptera, Lansbury (1960) for the Corixidae, Spencer (1942) for the Neuroptera, Hatch (1953) for the Coleoptera, Ross and Spencer (1952) and Schmid and Guppy (1952) for the Trichoptera, Hearle (1927) and Rempel (1950) for the mosquitoes. Hydracarina were covered by Crowell (1961). Carl et al. (1959) and Carl (1943, 1944) treated the freshwater fishes, amphibians, and reptiles at some length.

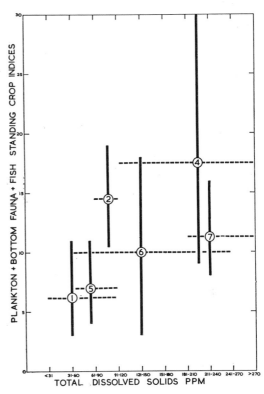

Fig. 16.11.—Means and ranges of total dissolved solids and combined indices of plankton, bottom fauna, and fish standing crop for lakes in seven limnological regions of British Columbia. *Region 1*, Insular and Coastal mountains; *2*, Insular Lowland; *3*, lower Fraser Valley (not shown, but overlapping *1*); *4*, Southern Interior Plateau; *5*, Southern Interior Highland; *6*, Columbia Mountains; *7*, southern Rocky Mountain trench. From Northcote and Larkin, 1956, where indices for standing crops are explained.

References

ALDERDICE, D. F. 1946. A study of the limnetic net plankton of Lakelse Lake, B.C. B.A. Thesis, Dept. Zool., Univ. British Columbia.

ANDERSON, G. C. 1949. A study of the production of Kamloops trout (*Salmo gairdnerii kamloops* Jordan) in Paul Lake, B.C. M.A. Thesis, Dept. Zool., Univ. British Columbia.

ANDREW, F. J., AND G. H. GEEN. 1960. Sockeye and pink salmon production in relation to proposed dams in the Fraser River system. Intern. Pac. Salmon Fish. Comm., Bull. 11, 259 p.

ANONYMOUS. 1953. A review of the sockeye salmon problems created by the Alcan project in the Nechako River watershed. Intern. Pac. Salmon Fish. Comm. Rept., 28 p.

———. 1957. Investigations of the distribution of sockeye fingerlings in Chilko Lake and of certain important factors affecting the productivity of

Chilko and Taseko lakes. Intern. Pac. Salmon Fish. Comm. Rept., 19 p.

———. 1960. Summaries of research on the fish-power problem and related work. Fish. Develop. Council, Research Sub-Committee Rept.

ARMSTRONG, J. E., AND H. W. TIPPER. 1948. Glaciation in north-central British Columbia. Amer. J. Sci., **246**: 283–310.

ATTON, F. M. 1955. Thermal studies of Lac la Ronge. M.Sc. Thesis, Dept. Biol., Univ. Saskatchewan, 95 p.

ATTON, F. M., AND R. P. JOHNSON. 1955. First records of eight species of fishes in Saskatchewan. Canadian Field-Nat., **68**: 82–84.

BAILEY, L. W. 1922. Diatoms from the Quill Lakes, Saskatchewan, and from Airdrie, Alberta. Contrib. Canadian Biol., **11**: 155–166.

BAJKOV, ALEXANDER. 1927. Reports of the Jasper Park lakes investigations, 1925–26. I. The fishes. Contrib. Canadian Biol. and Fish., N.S., **3**: 377–404.

———. 1929. Reports of the Jasper Park lakes investigations, 1925–26. VII. A study of the plankton. Contrib. Canadian Biol. and Fish., N.S., **4**: 343–396.

———. 1930a. Biological conditions of Manitoban lakes. Contrib. Canadian Biol. and Fish., N.S., **5**: 381–422.

———. 1930b. A study of the whitefish (*Coregonus clupeaformis*) in Manitoban lakes. Contrib. Canadian Biol. and Fish., N.S., **5**: 441–455.

BERE, RUBY. 1929. Reports of the Jasper Park lakes investigations, 1925–26. III. The leeches. Contrib. Canadian Biol. and Fish., N.S., **4**: 175–183.

BOSTOCK, H. S. 1948. Physiography of the Canadian Cordillera, with special reference to the area north of the fifty-fifth parallel. Geol. Surv. Canada, Dept. Mines and Resources, Ottawa, Memoir 247, 106 p.

BOUSFIELD, E. L. 1958. Fresh-water amphipod crustaceans of glaciated North America. Canadian Field-Nat., **72**: 55–113.

BOYD, O. G. 1939. A faunal survey of the lower reaches of Meade Creek, Cowichan Lake, Vancouver Island, B.C. B.A. Thesis, Dept. Zool., Univ. British Columbia, 36 p.

BRETT, J. R. 1946. Lakes of the Skeena River drainage. IV. Kitsumgallum Lake. Fish. Research Board Canada, Pac. Biol. Sta., Progr. Rept. 69: 70–73.

———. 1950. The physical limnology of Lakelse Lake, British Columbia. J. Fish. Research Board Canada, **8**: 82–102.

———. 1957. Salmon research and hydro-electric power development. Fish. Research Board Canada, Bull. No. 114, 26 p.

BRETT, J. R., AND A. L. PRITCHARD. 1946a. Lakes of the Skeena River drainage. I. Lakelse Lake. Fish. Research Board Canada, Pac. Biol. Sta., Progr. Rept. 66: 12–15.

BRETT, J. R., AND A. L. PRITCHARD. 1946b. Lakes of the Skeena River drainage. II. Morice Lake. Fish. Research Board Canada, Pac. Biol. Sta., Progr. Rept. 67: 23–26.

BRINK, V. C., AND LAWRENCE FARSTAD. 1949. The physiography of the agricultural areas of British Columbia. Sci. Agr., **29**: 273–301.

CAMERON, F. E. 1953. A study of the living organisms of some saline ponds in the Kamloops area of Brit-

ish Columbia. B.A. Thesis, Dept. Zool., Univ. British Columbia, 47 p.

CARL, G. C. 1937. Flora and fauna of brackish water. Ecology, **18**: 446–453.

———. 1940a. Some ecological conditions in a brackish lagoon. Ecology, **21**: 65–74.

———. 1940b. The distribution of some Cladocera and free-living Copepoda in British Columbia. Ecol. Monogr., **10**: 55–110.

———. 1943. The amphibians of British Columbia. British Columbia Prov. Museum Handbook, No. 2, 62 p.

———. 1944. The reptiles of British Columbia. British Columbia Prov. Museum Handbook, No. 3, 60 p.

———. 1953. Limnobiology of Cowichan Lake, British Columbia. J. Fish. Research Board Canada, **9**: 417–449.

CARL, G. C., AND W. A. CLEMENS. 1948. The fresh-water fishes of British Columbia. British Columbia Prov. Museum Handbook, No. 5, 1st ed., 132 p.

CARL, G. C., W. A. CLEMENS, AND C. C. LINDSEY. 1959. The fresh-water fishes of British Columbia. British Columbia Prov. Museum Handbook, No. 5, 3rd ed., 192 p.

CARTER, N. M. 1932. The oceanography of the fiords of southern British Columbia. Fish. Research Board Canada, Pac. Biol. Sta., Progr. Rept. 12: 7–11.

CARTWRIGHT, J. W. 1961. Investigation of the rainbow trout of Kootenay Lake, British Columbia, with special reference to the Lardeau River. British Columbia Fish and Game Branch, Mgmt. Publ. No. 7, 46 p.

CLARKE, F. W. 1924. The data of geochemistry. 5th ed. U.S. Geol. Surv., Bull. No. 770, 841 p.

CLEMENS, W. A. 1934. The predator and coarse fish problem in relation to fish culture. Trans. Amer. Fish. Soc., **64**: 318–322.

———. 1947. Game fish culture problems. British Columbia Game Dept., Proc. Game Conv., 1947: 45–49.

———. 1948. The story of Paul Lake. British Columbia Game Dept., Proc. 2nd Ann. Game Conv., 1948: 50–52.

CLEMENS, W. A., R. V. BOUGHTON, AND J. A. RATTENBURY. 1945. A preliminary report on a fishery survey of Teslin Lake, British Columbia. British Columbia Fish. Dept. Rept., 1944: 70–75.

CLEMENS, W. A., R. E. FOERSTER, N. M. CARTER, AND D. S. RAWSON. 1938. A contribution to the limnology of Shuswap Lake, British Columbia. British Columbia Fish. Dept. Rept., 1937: 91–97.

CLEMENS, W. A., AND J. A. MUNRO. 1934. The food of the squawfish. Fish. Research Board Canada, Pac. Biol. Sta., Progr. Rept. 19: 3–4.

CLEMENS, W. A., D. S. RAWSON, AND J. L. MCHUGH. 1939. A biological survey of Okanagan Lake, British Columbia. Fish. Research Board Canada, Bull. 56, 70 p.

COWAN, I. McT. 1939. The vertebrate fauna of the Peace River district of British Columbia. Occasional Papers British Columbia Prov. Museum, No. 1, 102 p.

CROSSMAN, E. J. 1959. Distribution and movements of a predator, the rainbow trout, and its prey, the redside shiner, in Paul Lake, British Columbia. J. Fish. Research Board Canada, 16: 247–267.

CROSSMAN, E. J., AND P. A. LARKIN. 1959. Yearling liberations and change of food as effecting rainbow trout yield in Paul Lake, British Columbia. Trans. Amer. Fish. Soc., 88: 36–44.

CROUTER, R. A., AND E. H. VERNON. 1959. Effects of black-headed budworm control on salmon and trout in British Columbia. Canadian Fish Cult., 24: 23–40.

CROWELL, R. M. 1961. Catalogue of the distribution and ecological relationships of North American Hydracarina. Canadian Entomol., 93: 321–359.

CUERRIER, JEAN-PAUL. 1954. The history of Lake Minnewanka with reference to the reaction of lake trout to artificial changes in environment. Canadian Fish Cult., 15: 1–9.

CUERRIER, JEAN-PAUL, AND F. H. SCHULTZ. 1957. Studies of lake trout and common whitefish in Waterton Lakes, Waterton Lakes National Park, Alberta. Canadian Wildl. Serv., Wildl. Mgmt. Bull., Ser. 3, No. 5, 41 p.

DYMOND, J. R. 1930. A possible critical factor affecting the production of trout in some British Columbia lakes. Trans. Amer. Fish. Soc., 60: 247–249.

FERGUSON, R. G. 1949. The interrelations among the fish populations of Skaha Lake, British Columbia, and their significance in the production of Kamloops trout (*Salmo gairdnerii kamloops* Jordan). B.A. Thesis, Dept. Zool., Univ. British Columbia, 84 p.

FOERSTER, R. E. 1925. Studies in the ecology of sockeye salmon (*Oncorhynchus nerka*). Contrib. Canadian Biol. and Fish., N.S., 2: 337–422.

———. 1929a. An investigation of the life history and propagation of the sockeye salmon (*Oncorhynchus nerka*) at Cultus Lake, British Columbia. I. Introduction and the run of 1925. Contrib. Canadian Biol. and Fish., N.S., 5: 1–35.

———. 1929b. An investigation of the life history and propagation of the sockeye salmon (*Oncorhynchus nerka*) at Cultus Lake, British Columbia. II. The run of 1926. Contrib. Canadian Biol. and Fish., N.S., 5: 39–53.

———. 1929c. An investigation of the life history and propagation of the sockeye salmon (*Oncorhynchus nerka*) at Cultus Lake, British Columbia. III. The down-stream migration of the young in 1926 and 1927. Contrib. Canadian Biol. and Fish., N.S., 5: 55–82.

———. 1930. The reaction of some sockeye salmon to a power dam. Trans. Amer. Fish. Soc., 60: 244–246.

———. 1934. The importance of Copepoda in the natural diet of sockeye salmon. Proc. 5th Pac. Sci. Congr., 3: 2009–2016.

———. 1937. The relation of temperature to the seaward migration of young sockeye salmon (*Oncorhynchus nerka*). J. Biol. Board Canada, 3: 421–438.

FOSKETT, D. R. 1947a. Lakes of the Skeena River drainage. V. Bear Lake. Fish. Research Board Canada, Pac. Biol. Sta., Progr. Rept. 70: 10–12.

———. 1947b. Lakes of the Skeena River drainage. VI. The lakes of the upper Sustut River. Fish Research Board Canada, Pac. Biol. Sta., Progr. Rept. 72: 28–32.

———. 1951. The relation of the ecological conditions in Bear Lake, Cassiar district, British Columbia, to the production of sockeye salmon. M. A. Thesis, Dept. Zool., Univ. British Columbia, 69 p.

———. 1958. The Rivers Inlet sockeye salmon. J. Fish. Research Board Canada, 15: 867–889.

FULLER, W. A. 1955. The inconnu (*Stenodus leucichthys mackenziei*) in Great Slave Lake and adjoining waters. J. Fish. Research Board Canada, 12: 768–780.

GEE, N. G. 1937. Canadian fresh-water sponges. Trans. Roy. Canadian Inst., 21: 285–296.

GEEN, G. H. 1955. Some features of the life history of the lake chub (*Couesius plumbeus greeni* Jordan) in British Columbia. B.A. Thesis, Dept. Zool., Univ. British Columbia, 33 p.

———. 1958. Reproduction of three species of suckers (Catostomidae) in British Columbia. M.A. Thesis, Dept. Zool., Univ. British Columbia, 117 p.

GEEN, G. H., AND F. J. ANDREW. 1961. Limnological changes in Seton Lake resulting from hydroelectric diversions. Intern. Pac. Salmon Fish. Comm., Progr. Rept. 8, 76 p.

GODFREY, HAROLD. 1955. On the ecology of Skeena River whitefishes, *Coregonus* and *Prosopium*. J. Fish. Research Board Canada, 12: 499–542.

HAMILTON, J. A. R. 1943. An investigation of the growth of the yearling migrant sockeye salmon (*Oncorhynchus nerka* Walbaum) of Cultus Lake in relation to scale circuli and certain environmental conditions in the lake. B.A. Thesis, Dept. Zool., Univ. British Columbia, 38 p.

HATCH, M. H. 1953. The beetles of the Pacific Northwest. I. Introduction and Adephaga. Univ. Washington Publ. Biol., No. 16, 340 p.

HEARLE, ERIC. 1927. List of mosquitoes of British Columbia. Proc. British Columbia Entomol. Soc., 24: 11–19.

HERRINGTON, H. B. 1950. Sphaeriidae of Athabaska and Great Slave lakes, northwest Canada. Canadian Field-Nat., 64: 25–32.

HEWSON, L. C. 1959. A study of six winter seasons of commercial fishing in Lake Winnipeg, 1950–55. J. Fish. Research Board Canada, 16: 131–145.

———. 1960. A history of the Lake Winnipeg fishery for whitefish, *Coregonus clupeaformis*, with some reference to its economics. J. Fish. Research Board Canada, 17: 625–639.

HINKS, DAVID. 1943. The fishes of Manitoba. Manitoba Dept. Mines and Nat. Resources, reprinted with suppl., 1957, 117 p.

HUNTER, J. G. 1959. Survival and production of pink and chum salmon in a coastal stream. J. Fish. Research Board Canada, 16: 835–886.

HUNTSMAN, A. G. 1922. The Quill Lakes of Saskatchewan and their fishery possibilities. Contrib. Canadian Biol. and Fish., N.S., 1: 125–141.

HUTCHINSON, G. E. 1937. A contribution to the

limnology of arid regions. Trans. Connecticut Acad. Arts Sci., 33: 47–132.

————. 1957. A treatise on limnology. Vol. I. Geography, physics, and chemistry. John Wiley & Sons, New York. 1015 p.

IDE, F. P. 1941. Mayflies of two tropical genera *Lachlania* and *Campsurus*, from Canada with descriptions. Canadian Entomol., 73: 153–156.

IDYLL, C. P. 1943. Bottom fauna of portions of Cowichan River, B.C. J. Fish. Research Board Canada, 6: 133–139.

JOHANNES, R. E., AND P. A. LARKIN. 1961. Competition for food between redside shiners (*Richardsonius balteatus*) and rainbow trout (*Salmo gairdneri*) in two British Columbia lakes. J. Fish. Research Board Canada, 18: 203–220.

JOHANSEN, FRITS. 1921a. Freshwater Crustacea from Canada. Canadian Field-Nat., 35: 99–100.

————. 1921b. A fairy-shrimp new to Canada and western North America. Canadian Field-Nat., 35: 132–133.

JOHNSON, R. P. 1961a. Report on Piprell Lake study, 1960. Fish. Branch, Saskatchewan Dept. Nat. Resources Rept., 23 p.

————. 1961b. Report on observations on Whalen Bay, Whiteswan Lakes, 1960. Fish. Branch, Saskatchewan Dept. Nat. Resources Rept., 16 p.

JOHNSON, R. P., AND G. D. KOSHINSKY. 1961. Biological survey of Buffalo Pound Lake, 1959. Fish. Branch, Saskatchewan Dept. Nat. Resources, Unpubl. Rept.

JOHNSON, W. E. 1956. On the distribution of young sockeye salmon (*Oncorhynchus nerka*) in Babine and Nilkitkwa lakes, B.C. J. Fish. Research Board Canada, 13: 695–708.

————. 1958. Density and distribution of young sockeye salmon (*Oncorhynchus nerka*) throughout a multibasin lake system. J. Fish. Research Board Canada, 15: 961–982.

————. 1961. Aspects of the ecology of a pelagic, zooplankton-eating fish. Verh. intern. Ver. Limnol., 14: 727–731.

KELEHER, J. J. 1952. Notes on fishes collected from Lake Winnipeg region. Canadian Field-Nat., 66: 170–173.

————. 1956. The northern limits of distribution in Manitoba for cyprinid fishes. Canadian J. Zool., 34: 263–266.

————. 1959. Fisheries research at Great Slave Lake. Fish. Research Board Canada, Biol. Sta. Technol. Unit London, Progr. Rept. 1: 41–44.

————. 1961. Comparison of largest Great Slave Lake fish with North American records. J. Fish. Research Board Canada, 18: 417–421.

KENNEDY, W. A. 1948. The relationship of fishing effort by gill nets to the interval between lifts. J. Fish. Research Board Canada, 8: 264–274.

————. 1949. Some observations on the coregonine fish of Great Bear Lake, N.W.T. Fish. Research Board Canada, Bull. No. 82, 10 p.

————. 1953. Growth, maturity, fecundity and mortality in the relatively unexploited whitefish, *Coregonus clupeaformis* of Great Slave Lake. J. Fish. Research Board Canada, 10: 413–441.

————. 1954. Growth, maturity and mortality in the relatively unexploited lake trout, *Cristivomer namaycush*, of Great Slave Lake. J. Fish. Research Board Canada, 11: 827–852.

————. 1956. The first ten years of commercial fishing on Great Slave Lake. Fish. Research Board Canada, Bull. No. 107, 58 p.

KIRCH, E. D. 1960. Biological survey of Madge Lake, 1959. Fish. Branch, Saskatchewan Dept. Nat. Resources Rept.: 1–59.

KUEHNE, P. E. 1941. The phytoplankton of southern and central Saskatchewan (Parts I and II). Canadian J. Research, C, 19: 292–322.

LANSBURY, I. 1960. The Corixidae (Hemiptera-Heteroptera) of British Columbia. Proc. British Columbia Entomol. Soc., 57: 34–43.

LARKIN, P. A. 1948. *Pontoporeia* and *Mysis* in Athabaska, Great Bear, and Great Slave lakes. Fish. Research Board Canada, Bull. No. 78, 33 p.

————. 1951a. The effects on fisheries of proposed West Kootenay water-storage project at Trout Lake. British Columbia Game Dept., Mgmt. Publ. No. 1, 25 p.

————. 1951b. Summary of investigation conducted by the Fisheries Research Group, attached to the British Columbia Game Department, in 1949. British Columbia Prov. Game Comm. Rept., 1949: 55–61.

————. 1954. Introductions of the Kamloops trout in British Columbia lakes. Canadian Fish Cult., 16: 15–24.

———— (ed.). 1958. The investigation of fish-power problems. H. R. MacMillan lectures in fisheries. Univ. British Columbia, 111 p.

LARKIN, P. A., G. C. ANDERSON, W. A. CLEMENS, AND D. C. G. MACKAY. 1950. The production of Kamloops trout (*Salmo gairdnerii kamloops*, Jordan) in Paul Lake, British Columbia. British Columbia Game Dept., Sci. Publ. No. 1, 37 p.

LARKIN, P. A., AND GRADUATE STUDENTS. 1959. The effects on fresh water fisheries of man-made activities in British Columbia. Canadian Fish Cult., 25: 27–59.

LARKIN, P. A., AND T. G. NORTHCOTE. 1958. Factors in lake typology in British Columbia, Canada. Verh. intern. Ver. Limnol., 13: 252–263.

LARKIN, P. A., AND S. B. SMITH. 1954. Some effects of introduction of the redside shiner on the Kamloops trout in Paul Lake, British Columbia. Trans. Amer. Fish. Soc., 83: 161–175.

LAROCQUE, AURELE. 1953. Catalogue of the recent Mollusca of Canada. Natl. Museum Canada, Bull. No. 129, 406 p.

LAWLER, G. H., AND N. H. F. WATSON. 1958. Limnological studies of Heming Lake, Manitoba, and two adjacent lakes. J. Fish. Research Board Canada, 15: 203–218.

LINDSEY, C. C. 1956. Distribution and taxonomy of fishes in the Mackenzie drainage of British Columbia. J. Fish. Research Board Canada, 13: 759–789.

————. 1957. Possible effects of water diversions on fish distribution in British Columbia. J. Fish. Research Board Canada, 14: 651–668.

LYONS, J. C., AND P. A. LARKIN. 1952. The effects on sport fisheries of the Aluminum Company of

Canada Limited development in the Nechako drainage. British Columbia Game Dept. Rept., 118 p.

McAllister, D. E. 1961. The origin and status of the deepwater sculpin, *Myoxocephalus thompsonii*, a nearctic glacial relict. Natl. Museum Canada, Bull. No. 172: 44–65.

McAllister, D. E., and C. C. Lindsey. 1961. Systematics of the freshwater sculpins (*Cottus*) of British Columbia. Natl. Museum Canada, Bull. No. 172: 66–89.

McConnell, J. A., and J. R. Brett. 1946. Lakes of the Skeena River drainage. III. Kitwanga Lake. Fish. Research Board Canada, Pac. Biol. Sta., Progr. Rept. 68: 55–59.

McDunnough, J. 1939. New British Columbia Ephemeroptera. Canadian Entomol., 71: 49–54.

MacKay, D. C. G. 1931. The Skeena River investigation. Fish. Research Board Canada, Pac. Biol. Sta., Progr. Rept. 8: 6–10.

MacLeod, J. C. 1960. The diurnal migration of peamouth chub *Mylocheilus caurinus* (Richardson) in Nicola Lake, British Columbia. M.Sc. Thesis, Dept. Zool., Univ. British Columbia, 54 p.

McMahon, V. H. 1948a. Lakes of the Skeena River drainage. VII. Morrison Lake. Fish. Research Board Canada, Pac. Biol. Sta., Progr. Rept. 74: 6–9.

———. 1948b. A comparative limnological study of Lakelse and Morrison lakes, B.C., with a view to assessing the suitability of Morrison Lake for the propagation of sockeye salmon. M.A. Thesis, Dept. Zool., Univ. British Columbia, 45 p.

———. 1954. The abundance and distribution of entomostracan plankton at Lakelse Lake, B.C., 1949–52. J. Fish. Research Board Canada, 11: 479–499.

McMynn, R. G., and P. A. Larkin. 1953. The effects on fisheries of present and future water utilization in the Campbell River drainage area. British Columbia Game Comm., Mgmt. Publ. No. 2, 61 p.

McMynn, R. G., and E. H. Vernon. 1954. Some physical and biological observations on the Salmon River, Fort Langley. British Columbia Game Comm. Rept., 22 p.

MacPhee, Craig. 1948. An ecological study of four interior lakes of British Columbia in relation to the coarse-fish problem. British Columbia Game Dept., Proc. 2nd Ann. Game Conv., 1948: 52–56.

———. 1949. A limnological study of a series of five lakes in the interior of British Columbia and the effects of rotenone on the fauna of two of these lakes. M.A. Thesis, Dept. Zool., Univ. British Columbia, 146 p.

Marshall, Ruth. 1924. Water mites of Alaska and the Canadian Northwest. Trans. Amer. Microscop. Soc., 43: 236–255.

———. 1929. Canadian Hydracarina. Univ. Toronto Studies, Biol. Ser. 33, Ontario Fish. Research Lab., Publ. 39: 55–93.

Mathews, W. H. 1944. Glacial lakes and ice retreat in south-central British Columbia. Trans. Roy. Soc. Canada, Ser. III, (IV), 38: 39–57.

———. 1952. Ice-dammed lavas from Clinker Mountain southwestern British Columbia. Amer. J. Sci., 250: 553–565.

———. 1956. Physical limnology and sedimentation in a glacial lake. Bull. Geol. Soc. Amer., 67: 537–552.

Mendis, A. S. 1956. A limnological comparison of four lakes in central Saskatchewan. Fish. Branch, Saskatchewan Dept. Nat. Resources, Rept. 2, 23 p.

Miller, R. B. 1946. Notes on the Arctic grayling, *Thymallus signifer* Richardson, from Great Bear Lake. Copeia, 1946: 227–236.

———. 1947. Great Bear Lake. Fish. Research Board Canada, Bull. No. 72: 31–44.

———. 1952. A review of the *Triaenophorus* problem in Canadian lakes. Fish. Research Board Canada, Bull. No. 95, 42 p.

———. 1956. The collapse and recovery of a small white-fishery. J. Fish. Research Board Canada, 13: 135–146.

———. 1958. The rôle of competition in the mortality of hatchery trout. J. Fish. Research Board Canada, 15: 27–45.

Miller, R. B., and W. A. Kennedy. 1948a. Observations on the lake trout of Great Bear Lake. J. Fish. Research Board Canada, 7: 176–189.

Miller, R. B., and W. A. Kennedy. 1948b. Pike (*Esox lucius*) from four northern Canadian lakes. J. Fish. Research Board Canada, 7: 190–199.

Miller, R. B., and W. H. MacDonald. 1950. Preliminary biological surveys of Alberta watersheds, 1947–49. Dept. Lands and Forests, Alberta, 139 p.

Miller, R. B., and M. J. Paetz. 1953. Preliminary biological surveys of Alberta watersheds, 1950–52. Dept. Lands and Forests, Alberta, 114 p.

Miller, R. B., and M. J. Paetz. 1959. The effects of power, irrigation, and stock water developments on the fisheries of the South Saskatchewan River. Canadian Fish Cult., 25: 13–26.

Miller, R. B., and R. C. Thomas. 1957. Alberta's "pothole" trout fisheries. Trans. Amer. Fish. Soc., 86: 261–268.

Miller, R. B., and H. B. Watkins. 1946. An experiment in the control of the cestode, *Triaenophorus crassus* Forel. Canadian J. Research, D, 24: 175–179.

Milne, D. J. 1941. The Trichoptera of Waskesiu Lake. M.Sc. Thesis, Dept. Biol., Univ. Saskatchewan.

Moore, J. E. 1952. The entomostraca of southern Saskatchewan. Canadian J. Zool., 30: 410–450.

Mottley, C. McC. 1931. Temperature and propagation of trout. Fish. Research Board Canada, Pac. Biol. Sta., Progr. Rept. 8: 11–14.

———. 1932. The propagation of trout in the Kamloops district, British Columbia. Trans. Amer. Fish. Soc., 62: 144–151.

———. 1933. The spawning migration of rainbow trout. Trans. Amer. Fish. Soc., 63: 80–84.

———. 1936. A biological survey of Jones Lake. British Columbia Game Comm. Rept. for 1935: 27–30.

———. 1938. Fluctuations in the intensity of the spawning runs of rainbow trout at Paul Lake. J. Fish. Research Board Canada, 4: 69–87.

———. 1940. The production of rainbow trout at

Paul Lake, British Columbia. Trans. Amer. Fish. Soc., **69**: 187–191.

MOZLEY, ALAN. 1939. The Quill Lakes Basin, Saskatchewan, Canada, and its molluscan fauna. Intern. Rev. Hydrobiol. Hydrogr., **38**: 243–249.

MUNDIE, J. H. 1959. The diurnal activity of the larger invertebrates at the surface of Lac la Ronge, Saskatchewan. Canadian J. Zool., **37**: 945–956.

MUNRO, J. A. 1945. The birds of the Cariboo Parklands, British Columbia. Canadian J. Research, D, **23**: 17–103.

——. 1950. The birds and mammals of the Creston region, British Columbia. Occasional Papers British Columbia Prov. Museum, No. 8, 90 p.

MURRAY, A. R. 1950. Limnological and fisheries investigations of Clear Lake in Riding Mountain National Park, May to September, 1950. Unpubl. Rept., Dept. Biol., Univ. Saskatchewan.

NAUMANN, EINAR. 1932. Grundzüge der regionalen Limnologie. Die Binnengewässer, **11**, 176 p.

NEAVE, FERRIS. 1929a. Reports of the Jasper Park lakes investigations, 1925–26. II. Plecoptera. Contrib. Canadian Biol. and Fish., N.S., **4**: 157–173.

——. 1929b. Reports of the Jasper Park lakes investigations, 1925–26. IV. Aquatic insects. Contrib. Canadian Biol. and Fish., N.S., **4**: 185–195.

——. 1932. A study of the May flies (*Hexagenia*) of Lake Winnipeg. Contrib. Canadian Biol. and Fish., N.S., **7**: 177–201.

——. 1945. A mortality in the fish life of Quamichan Lake, V.I. Fish. Research Board Canada, Pac. Biol. Sta., Progr. Rept. 65: 70–72.

——. 1949. Game fish populations of the Cowichan River. Fish. Research Board Canada, Bull. No. 84, 32 p.

——. 1953. Principles affecting the size of pink and chum salmon populations in British Columbia. J. Fish. Research Board Canada, **9**: 450–491.

——. 1958. Stream ecology and production of anadromous fish, p. 43–48. *In* P. A. Larkin (ed.), The investigation of fish-power problems. H. R. MacMillan lectures in fisheries. Univ. British Columbia.

NEAVE, FERRIS, AND ALEXANDER BAJKOV. 1929. Reports of the Jasper Park lakes investigations, 1925–26. V. Food and growth of Jasper Park fishes. Contrib. Canadian Biol. and Fish., N.S., **4**: 197–219.

NORTHCOTE, T. G. 1952. An analysis of variation in quantitative sampling of bottom fauna in lakes. M.A. Thesis, Dept. Zool., Univ. British Columbia, 95 p.

——. 1953. Four years of lake surveys. British Columbia Game Dept., Proc. 7th Ann. Game Conv., 1953: 112–115.

NORTHCOTE, T. G., AND P. A. LARKIN. 1956. Indices of productivity in British Columbia lakes. J. Fish. Research Board Canada, **13**: 515–540.

NOVAKOWSKI, N. 1955. The ecology of Reindeer Lake with special reference to fish. M.Sc. Thesis, Dept. Biol., Univ. Saskatchewan, 99 p.

NURSALL, J. R. 1952. The early development of a bottom fauna in a new power reservoir in the Rocky Mountains of Alberta. Canadian J. Zool., **30**: 387–409.

OLIVER, D. R. 1958. The leeches (Hirudinea) of Saskatchewan. Canadian Field-Nat., **72**: 161–165.

——. 1960. The macroscopic bottom fauna of Lac la Ronge, Saskatchewan. J. Fish Research Board Canada, **17**: 607–624.

PATTERSON, T. M., A. F. PAGET, A. J. WHITMORE, AND G. S. ANDREWS. 1958. Preliminary report on flood control and hydro-electric power in the Fraser River basin. British Columbia Fraser River Board, Victoria, 171 p.

PORSILD, A. E. 1932. Notes on seiches and currents in Great Bear Lake. Geograph. Rev., **22**: 474–477.

PRITCHARD, A. L., AND J. R. BRETT. 1945. A sockeye salmon tagging experiment in Lakelse Lake. Fish. Research Board Canada, Pac. Biol. Sta., Progr. Rept. 62: 4–6.

QADRI, S. V. 1955. The whitefish population of Lac la Ronge. M.Sc. Thesis, Dept. Biol., Univ. Saskatchewan, 112 p.

RAWSON, D. S. 1928. Preliminary studies of the bottom fauna of Lake Simcoe, Ontario. Univ. Toronto Studies, Biol. Ser. No. 31, Ontario Fish. Research Lab., Publ. 36: 75–102.

——. 1930. The bottom fauna of Lake Simcoe and its role in the ecology of the lake. Univ. Toronto Studies, Biol. Ser. No. 34, Ontario Fish. Research Lab., Publ. 40: 1–183.

——. 1932. The pike of Waskesiu Lake, Saskatchewan. Trans. Amer. Fish. Soc., **62**: 323–330.

——. 1934. Productivity studies in lakes of the Kamloops region, British Columbia. Biol. Board Canada, Bull. No. 42, 31 p.

——. 1936. Physical and chemical studies in lakes of the Prince Albert Park, Saskatchewan. J. Biol. Board Canada, **2**: 227–284.

——. 1939a. A biological survey and recommendations for fisheries management in waters of the Banff National Park. Dept. Mines and Resources (Canada), Unpubl. Rept. Natl. Parks Bur., 128 p.

——. 1939b. Some physical and chemical factors in the metabolism of lakes, p. 9–26. *In* F. R. Moulton (ed.), Problems of lake biology. Amer. Assoc. Advance. Sci., Publ. 10.

——. 1940. Sport fishing in Canada's National Parks. Canadian Geograph. J., **20**: 181–196.

——. 1941. The eastern brook trout in the Maligne River system, Jasper National Park. Trans. Amer. Fish. Soc., **70**: 221–235.

——. 1942. A comparison of some large alpine lakes in Western Canada. Ecology, **23**: 143–161.

——. 1945. The experimental introduction of smallmouth black bass into lakes of the Prince Albert National Park, Saskatchewan. Trans. Amer. Fish. Soc., **73**: 19–31.

——. 1946. Successful introduction of fish in a large saline lake. Canadian Fish. Cult., **1**: 5–8.

——. 1947a. Great Slave Lake. Fish. Research Board Canada, Bull. No. 72: 45–68.

——. 1947b. An automatic-closing Ekman dredge and other equipment for use in extremely deep water. Limnol. Soc. Amer., Spec. Publ. No. 18: 1–8.

——. 1947c. Lake Athabaska. Fish. Research Board Canada, Bull. No. 72: 69–85.

―――. 1947*d*. Deterioration of recently established trout populations in lakes of the Canadian Rockies. Canad'an Fish Cult., **2**: 14–21.

―――. 1948. The failure of rainbow trout and initial success with the introduction of lake trout in Clear Lake, Riding Mountain Park, Manitoba. Trans. Amer. Fish. Soc., **75**: 323–335.

―――. 1949*a*. Estimating the fish production of Great Slave Lake. Trans. Amer. Fish. Soc., **71**: 81–92.

―――. 1949*b*. A check list of the fishes of Saskatchewan. Saskatchewan Dept. Nat. Resources and Ind. Develop., 8 p.

―――. 1950*a*. The physical limnology of Great Slave Lake. J. Fish. Research Board Canada, **8**: 3–66.

―――. 1950*b*. The grayling (*Thymallus signifer*) in northern Saskatchewan. Canadian Fish Cult., **6**: 3–10.

―――. 1951*a*. Studies of the fish of Great Slave Lake. J. Fish. Research Board Canada, **8**: 207–240.

―――. 1951*b*. The total mineral content of lake waters. Ecology, **32**: 669–672.

―――. 1952*a*. Mean depth and the fish production of large lakes. Ecology, **33**: 513–521.

―――. 1952*b*. Biological and fisheries investigation, Amisk Lake, 1950–51. Unpubl. Rept. Fish. Branch, Saskatchewan Dept. Nat. Resources, 41 p.

―――. 1953*a*. The limnology of Amethyst Lake, a high alpine type near Jasper, Alberta. Canadian J. Zool., **31**: 193–210.

―――. 1953*b*. The bottom fauna of Great Slave Lake. J. Fish. Research Board Canada, **10**: 486–520.

―――. 1953*c*. The standing crop of net plankton in lakes. J. Fish. Research Board Canada, **10**: 224–237.

―――. 1953*d*. Limnology in the North American arctic and subarctic. Arctic, **6**: 198–204.

―――. 1955. Morphometry as a dominant factor in the productivity of large lakes. Verh. intern. Ver. Limnol., **12**: 164–175.

―――. 1956*a*. The net plankton of Great Slave Lake. J. Fish. Research Board Canada, **13**: 53–127.

―――. 1956*b*. Algal indicators of trophic lake types. Limnol. Oceanogr., **1**: 18–25.

―――. 1957*a*. The life history and ecology of the yellow walleye, *Stizostedion vitreum*, in Lac la Ronge, Saskatchewan. Trans. Amer. Fish. Soc., **86**: 15–37.

―――. 1957*b*. Limnology and fisheries of five lakes in the upper Churchill drainage, Saskatchewan. Fish. Branch, Saskatchewan Dept. Nat. Resources, Rept. 3, 61 p.

―――. 1958*a*. The limnology and fisheries of Cree Lake, Saskatchewan. Unpubl. Rept. Fish. Branch, Saskatchewan Dept. Nat. Resources, 68 p.

―――. 1958*b*. The limnology and fisheries of Wollaston Lake, Saskatchewan. Unpubl. Rept. Fish. Branch, Saskatchewan Dept. Nat. Resources, 68 p.

―――. 1958*c*. Indices to lake productivity and their significance in predicting conditions in reservoirs and lakes with disturbed water levels, p. 27–42. *In* P. A. Larkin (ed.), The investigation of fish-power problems. H. R. MacMillan lectures in fisheries. Univ. British Columbia.

―――. 1959*a*. Limnology and fisheries of Cree and Wollaston lakes in northern Saskatchewan. Fish. Branch, Saskatchewan Dept. Nat. Resources, Rept. 4, 73 p.

―――. 1959*b*. Biological potentialities, p. 61–75. *In* The Canadian Northwest: Its potentialities. Symp. Roy. Soc. Canada, 1958. Univ. Toronto Press, Toronto.

―――. 1960. A limnological comparison of twelve large lakes in northern Saskatchewan. Limnol. Oceanogr., **5**: 195–211.

―――. 1961. The lake trout of Lac la Ronge, Saskatchewan. J. Fish. Research Board Canada, **18**: 423–462.

RAWSON, D. S., AND F. M. ATTON. 1951. Fisheries investigation of Lac la Ronge, Saskatchewan, 1948, 1949. Unpubl. Rept. Fish. Branch, Saskatchewan Dept. Nat. Resources, 117 p.

RAWSON, D. S., AND F. M. ATTON. 1953. Biological investigation and fisheries management at Lac la Ronge, Saskatchewan. Fish. Branch, Saskatchewan Dept. Nat. Resources Rept., 39 p.

RAWSON, D. S., AND C. A. ELSEY. 1950. Reduction in the longnose sucker population of Pyramid Lake, Alberta, in an attempt to improve angling. Trans. Amer. Fish. Soc., **78**: 13–31.

RAWSON, D. S., E. C. HOPE, J. MITCHELL, AND E. W. TISDALE. 1943. The Big River survey. A comprehensive study of natural resources as an aid to improved utilization. Univ. Saskatchewan Publ., 37 p.

RAWSON, D. S., AND J. E. MOORE. 1944. The saline lakes of Saskatchewan. Canadian J. Research, D, **22**: 141–201.

RAWSON, D. S., AND R. R. WHEATON. 1950. Studies of *Triaenophorus crassus* in Nesslin Lake, Saskatchewan, 1950. Fish. Research Board Canada, Ann. Rept. Central Fish. Research Sta. for 1950, Appendix 4: 18–21.

REED, E. B. 1959. Report on the limnology and fisheries of Cumberland and Namew lakes, Saskatchewan. Fish. Branch, Saskatchewan Dept. Nat. Resources Rept., 74 p.

REMPEL, J. G. 1936. The life-history and morphology of *Chironomus hyperboreus*. J. Biol. Board Canada, **2**: 209–221.

―――. 1950. A guide to the mosquito larvae of western Canada. Canadian J. Research, D, **28**: 207–248.

―――. 1953. The mosquitoes of Saskatchewan. Canadian J. Zool., **31**: 433–509.

RICKER, K. E. 1959. The origin of two glacial relict crustaceans in North America, as related to Pleistocene glaciation. Canadian J. Zool., **37**: 871–893.

RICKER, W. E. 1937*a*. Physical and chemical characteristics of Cultus Lake, British Columbia. J. Biol. Board Canada, **3**: 363–402.

―――. 1937*b*. The food and the food supply of sockeye salmon (*Oncorhynchus nerka* Walbaum) in Cultus Lake, British Columbia. J. Biol. Board Canada, **3**: 450–468.

―――. 1937*c*. Statistical treatment of sampling processes useful in the enumeration of plankton organisms. Arch. Hydrobiol., **31**: 68–84.

———. 1938a. On adequate quantitative sampling of the pelagic net plankton of a lake. J. Fish. Research Board Canada, **4**: 19–32.

———. 1938b. Seasonal and annual variations in quantity of pelagic net plankton, Cultus Lake, British Columbia. J. Fish. Research Board Canada, **4**: 33–47.

———. 1938c. A comparison of the seasonal growth rates of young sockeye salmon and young squawfish in Cultus Lake. Fish. Research Board Canada, Pac. Biol. Sta., Progr. Rept. 36: 3–5.

———. 1939. A preliminary list of stoneflies (Plecoptera) from the vicinity of Cultus Lake, British Columbia. Proc. British Columbia Entomol. Soc., **35**: 19–23.

———. 1943. Stoneflies of southwestern British Columbia. Indiana Univ. Publ., Sci. Ser., No. 12, 145 p.

———. 1959. The species of *Isocapnia* Banks (Insecta, Plecoptera, Nemouridae). Canadian J. Zool., **37**: 639–653.

ROBERTSON, J. G. 1954. The trophic status of Port John Lake, British Columbia. J. Fish. Research Board Canada, **11**: 624–651.

ROSS, H. H., AND G. J. SPENCER. 1952. A preliminary list of the Trichoptera of British Columbia. Proc. British Columbia Entomol. Soc., **48**: 43–51.

ROYER, L. M. 1961. Biological survey of Thomson Lake, 1960. Fish. Branch, Saskatchewan Dept. Nat. Resources Rept., 43 p.

RUGGLES, C. P. 1959a. Biological and fisheries survey of Dore Lake, 1956. Fish. Branch, Saskatchewan Dept. Nat. Resources Rept., 4 p.

———. 1959b. Biological and fisheries survey of Lac la Plonge and Canoe Lake. Fish. Branch, Saskatchewan Dept. Nat. Resources Rept., 91 p.

———. 1959c. The nutritive ecology of Lac la Plonge and Canoe Lake. M.Sc. Thesis, Dept. Biol., Univ. Saskatchewan, 93 p.

SCHMID, F., AND RICHARD GUPPY. 1952. An annotated list of Trichoptera collected on southern Vancouver Island. Proc. British Columbia Entomol. Soc., **48**: 41–42.

SCHOFIELD, S. J. 1943. The origin of Okanagan Lake. Trans. Roy. Soc. Canada, Ser. III(IV): 89–92.

———. 1946. The origin of Kootenay Lake. Proc. Roy. Soc. Canada, Ser. III(IV): 93–98.

SCHULTZ, F. H. 1955. Investigation of the spawning of northern pike in Prince Albert National Park, Saskatchewan, 1953. Wildl. Mgmt. Bull., Ser. 3, 21 p.

SCOTT, W. B. 1958. A checklist of the freshwater fishes of Canada and Alaska. Roy. Ontario Museum, Div. Zool. Paleontol., 30 p.

SPENCER, G. J. 1942. A preliminary list of the Neuroptera of British Columbia. Proc. British Columbia Entomol. Soc., **38**: 23–28.

STRINGER, G. E., AND R. G. McMYNN. 1958. Experiments with toxaphene as fish poison. Canadian Fish Cult., **23**: 39–47.

STRINGER, G. E., AND R. G. McMYNN. 1960. Three years' use of toxaphene as a fish toxicant in British Columbia. Canadian Fish Cult., **28**: 37–44.

TAYLOR, W. R. 1928. Alpine algal flora of the mountains of British Columbia. Ecology, **9**: 343–348.

THACHER, T. L. 1923. Some freshwater crustacean from British Columbia. Canadian Field-Nat., **37**: 88–89.

THOMAS, J. F. J. 1953a. Industrial water resources of Canada. Water survey report 4. Columbia River drainage basin in Canada, 1949–50. Canada Dept. Mines, Tech. Surv., Mines Branch, No. 838, 80 p.

———. 1953b. Industrial water resources of Canada. Water survey report 5. Skeena River drainage basin, Vancouver Island, and coastal areas of British Columbia, 1949–51. Canada Dept. Mines, Tech. Surv., Mines Branch, No. 839, 53 p.

———. 1954. Industrial water resources of Canada. Water survey report 6. Fraser River drainage basin, 1950–51. Canada Dept. Mines, Tech. Surv. Mines Branch, No. 842, 91 p.

THOMPSON, J. S. 1941. The macroscopic bottom fauna of eight Saskatchewan lakes of varying salinity. M.Sc. Thesis, Dept. Biol., Univ. Saskatchewan.

VERNON, E. H. 1958. An examination of factors affecting the abundance of pink salmon in the Fraser River. Intern. Pac. Salmon Fish. Comm., Progr. Rept., 49 p.

WAILES, G. H. 1925a. Rhizopoda and Heliozoa from British Columbia. Contrib. Canadian Biol. and Fish., N.S., **2**: 507–518.

———. 1925b. Desmidieae from British Columbia. Contrib. Canadian Biol. and Fish., N.S., **2**: 519–530.

———. 1927. Rhizopoda and Heliozoa from British Columbia. Ann. Mag. Nat. Hist., Ser. 9, **20**: 153–156.

———. 1930. Munday Lake and its ecology. Vancouver Museum, Art Notes, **5**: 92–109.

———. 1931. Ecology of Sproat Lake, B.C. Vancouver Museum, Art Notes, **6**: 125–133.

———. 1932. Protozoa and algae from Lake Tenquille, B.C. Vancouver Museum, Art Notes, **7**: 19–23.

WALKER, E. M. 1940. A preliminary list of the Odonata of Saskatchewan. Canadian Entomol., **72**: 26–35.

———. 1953. The Odonata of Canada and Alaska. Vol. I, Part I: General; Part II: The Zygoptera—Damselflies. Univ. Toronto Press, Toronto. 292 p.

———. 1958. The Odonata of Canada and Alaska. Vol. II, Part III: The Anisoptera—four families. Univ. Toronto Press, Toronto. 318 p.

WALKER, E. M., AND W. E. RICKER. 1938. Notes on Odonata from the vicinity of Cultus Lake, B.C. Canadian Entomol., **70**: 144–151.

WALLIS, J. B. 1929. Reports of the Jasper Park lakes investigations, 1925–26. VI. The beetles. Contrib. Canadian Biol. and Fish., N.S., **4**: 221–225.

WARD, F. J. 1957. Seasonal and annual changes in availability of the adult crustacean plankters of Shuswap Lake. Intern. Pac. Salmon Fish. Comm., Progr. Rept., 56 p.

WHITEHOUSE, F. C. 1941. British Columbia dragonflies (Odonata), with notes on distribution and habits. Amer. Midland Nat., **26**: 488–557.

——. 1948. Catalogue of the Odonata of Canada, Newfoundland and Alaska. Trans. Roy. Canadian Inst., **27**: 3–56.

VICKETT, W. P. 1958. Review of certain environmental factors affecting the production of pink and chum salmon. J. Fish. Research Board Canada, **15**: 1103–1126.

——. 1959. Damage to the Qualicum River stream bed by a flood in January, 1958. Fish. Research Board Canada, Pac. Biol. Sta., Progr. Rept. 113: 16–17.

WILLIAMS, P. M., W. H. MATHEWS, AND G. L. PICKARD. 1961. A lake in British Columbia containing old sea-water. Nature, **191**: 830–832.

WILSON, J. T., G. FALCONER, W. H. MATHEWS, AND V. K. PREST. 1958. Glacial map of Canada. Geol. Assoc. Canada.

WILSON, M. S. 1958. New records and species of calanoid copepods from Saskatchewan and Louisiana. Canadian J. Zool., **36**: 489–497.

WILSON, R. R. 1951. Distribution, growth, feeding habits, abundance, thermal, and salinity relations of *Neomysis mercedis* (Holmes) from the Nicomekl and Serpentine Rivers, British Columbia. M.A. Thesis, Dept. Zool., Univ. British Columbia, 69 p.

WITHLER, F. C. 1948. Lakes of the Skeena River drainage. VIII. Lakes of the Lac-da-dah Basin. Fish. Research Board Canada, Pac. Biol. Sta., Progr. Rept. 74: 9–12.

WITHLER, F. C., J. A. McCONNELL, AND V. H. McMAHON. 1949. Lakes of the Skeena River drainage. IX. Babine Lake. Fish. Research Board Canada, Pac. Biol. Sta., Progr. Rept. 78: 6–10.

WITHLER, I. L. 1956. A limnological survey of Atlin and southern Tagish lakes. British Columbia Game Comm., Mgmt. Publ. No. 5, 36 p.

——. 1961. Variability in life-history characteristics of steelhead trout (*Salmo gairdneri*) along the Pacific Coast of North America. M.Sc. Thesis, Dept. Zool., Univ. British Columbia, 81 p.

17 F. E. J. Fry
Vianney Legendre

Ontario and Quebec

ONTARIO

Approximately one-fifth of the surface of the Province of Ontario is covered by water, the total area of water being some 80,000 mi² (Bensley, 1922). The Canadian waters of the Great Lakes, all of which are in Ontario, cover some 38,000 mi², and the remainder consists largely of the lakes in the innumerable basins of the Laurentian shield and their connecting waters. Except for the brief account of the Georgian Bay Biological Station given below, the Ontario waters of the Great Lakes are treated together with the American section in Chapter 19.

Ontario's waters present a range of variety commensurate with their extent. The province extends over approximately fifteen degrees of latitude, and its location is such that within its boundaries a range of climate is compressed which is greater than the range of latitude would suggest. The extreme mean annual isotherms that cut through the province are respectively 10° and −7° C. The southern tip of the province lies in the Carolinian life zone, while the northern tip is just touched by the subarctic tundra. The lakes, too, show all varieties of development, and their waters differ widely in their mineral content, depending on the geology of their basins and their location in the drainage chain. Some lakes still remain in their primitive state and have not even been explored from the limnological point of view, but more lakes, also usually uninvestigated, have been subjected to the influence of man. Dams have been built, water

levels influenced, drainage routes changed, and foreign substances introduced in major amounts. The clearing of southern Ontario for agriculture has greatly changed the character of the streams there, while the water table has been lowered drastically within comparatively recent memory. Finally, domestic and industrial eutrophication are taking place on an accelerating scale as the population of the province grows.

Bensley (1922, p. 10) subdivides the province as follows (see Fig. 17.1):

(a) The south western peninsula, or that portion lying to the west of a line connecting the south end of Georgian Bay with the north shore of Lake Ontario to the west of Toronto. This portion comprises the older agricultural part of the province, is noteworthy for the paucity of water areas, and is underlain by strata of Silurian and Devonian age covered by glacial soil deposits of considerable thickness. It is also that portion of the province having the principal frontage on the Great Lakes.

(b) A portion lying to the south of a line connecting the southern end of Georgian Bay with Lake Ontario in the region of Kingston. It forms the north shore of the larger part of Lake Ontario, contains some characteristic lakes including Simcoe (300 square miles), Rice (27 square miles) and Scugog (39 square miles), is underlain by Cambrian and Ordovician strata, and is transitional in many ways between the portion already described and the Precambrian area to the north.

(c) The northern Precambrian area of relatively great extent, including the Laurentian Highlands, and characterized by its exposed igneous and metamorphic rocks with innumerable lakes distributed over its surface. The larger lakes include Nipissing (330 square miles) and Nipigon (1,730 square miles).

(d) A north west portion containing the Lake of the Woods (1,851 square miles) and similar water areas lying beyond the height of land, and related both in aspect and origin (Lake Agassiz) to Lake Winnipeg and other lakes with the drainage system of which they are connected, though underlain by rock formations similar to the foregoing.

The section on Ontario was prepared by Fry; that on Quebec by Legendre.

Fig. 17.1.—Map of Ontario showing major lakes and streams. The heavy dashed lines demarcate Bensley's limnological regions described in the text. Prepared by the University of Wisconsin Cartographic Labora tory.

(e) The Hudson Bay drainage area, a region characterized by the broad coastal plain, and on the whole moderately inclined river basins of the Severn, Moose and Albany Rivers, and underlain in part with strata of Devonian age. . . .

The organized study of limnology in Ontario began in the closing years of the nineteenth century. The first need for such study was felt in connection with the commercial fisheries, particularly of the Great Lakes (e.g., Wright, 1892), and the major interest in limnology was hydrobiology until very recently. The first research sta-

tion was established on Georgian Bay in 190 (Bensley, 1911) through the initiative of the University of Toronto with the financial support of the Dominion Government. A history of the Georgian Bay Biological Station is available in Rigby and Huntsman (1958). When the station was first established, the grant for the work there was administered by an independent board consisting largely of members of the Madawaska Club on whose property at Go-Home Bay the station was located. The club was a university summer settlement founded by members of the

University of Toronto. In 1904, apparently because the original agreement had not worked well, the control of the station passed to the granting body, the Canadian Department of Marine and Freshwater Fisheries. Throughout its existence the station was largely staffed by the University of Toronto. The first director was R. R. Bensley, who soon went to the University of Chicago. He was succeeded by B. A. Bensley who continued in charge while the station existed. Work at the station ended in 1911 when it was proposed that it be moved to a more useful site from the point of view of fish culture. However, the site was never chosen, and the station was never opened again, although the facilities, which remained with the Madawaska Club, were used once more for fisheries research in 1928 (Tester, 1932). A large sample of the published work of the Georgian Bay Station is gathered in a single volume of *Contributions to Canadian Biology* (Canadian Dept. Marine and Freshwater Fish., 1915).

For various reasons the Federal Government has never supported a laboratory of its own for the investigation of the inland waters of Ontario, but otherwise it has made many contributions to the work.

The Fisheries Research Board of Canada has often supported individual researches in the universities and now is contributing significantly to the support of research in the Great Lakes Institute of the University of Toronto, which, despite its name, is concerned also with inland waters. The board has also cooperated with the province from time to time in individual projects on the inland waters. In Ontario, the Fisheries Research Board is responsible for research on Lake Superior. Work there has only recently gotten under way and at present is largely directed toward control of the lamprey (*Petromyzon marinus*) and rehabilitation of the lake trout (*Salvelinus namaycush*). The inland waters that are the concern of the board's Biological Station at London, Ontario, are in the western provinces. The National Research Council is a major source of support for research in the universities, which also from time to time receive aid in this respect from other federal agencies.

Hydrobiology at the National Museum in Ottawa has been largely concerned with the sea, but there is interest in the freshwater amphipods (Bousfield, 1958) and mollusks. The Canadian national collection of insects is housed in the Entomology Research Institute of Science Service, Department of Agriculture, Ottawa. It has a world-wide reputation among taxonomists owing to the selection and high standard of the material. It contains numerous type series, including many of those of J. H. McDunnough and C. H. Curran in Ephemeroptera and Diptera, respectively. Most of the taxonomic work from this institute has been published in the *Canadian Entomologist*. The Federal Department of Agriculture maintains a laboratory on the campus of the Ontario Agricultural College, Guelph, for the investigation of the biting Diptera.

Fundamental work on the uptake of dissolved substances by aquatic organisms and on sedimentation is carried on in the laboratory of the Atomic Energy Commission at Chalk River (e.g., Rigler, 1961).

Organized research in the inland waters of the province essentially began in 1921 when the recently formed Ontario Fisheries Research Laboratory, a branch of the Department of Biology of the University of Toronto, established a field party on Lake Nipigon (Clemens, 1923; Dymond, 1940). The laboratory had begun its operations on Lake Erie in 1920. An interesting item in the Lake Erie field work was the collection of the first sea lamprey (*P. marinus*) recorded for the upper Great Lakes (Dymond, 1922).

The field station of the Ontario Fisheries Research Laboratory remained at Lake Nipigon until 1926. During the same period parties also visited Lac Seul, Long Lac, and Lake Abitibi for various short periods. In 1927 the main field station was set up at Port Credit on Lake Ontario, with a subsidiary station at the eastern end of that lake, but work on the inland waters was continued (Ide, 1935; Rawson, 1930; Ricker, 1932). From 1929 to 1935 the laboratory was established at Lake Nipissing (Fry, 1937; Langford, 1938), following which its field work was moved to a permanent site at Lake Opeongo in Algonquin Park provided by the Ontario Department of Lands and Forests. During the Nipigon period the Royal Ontario Museum took a substantial part in the field work, and members of the museum were also frequent visitors to the Nipissing station. The researches of Fry (1939), Miller (1941), Kennedy (1943), Sprules (1947), and Langford and Martin (1941) are typical of the work carried on in Algonquin Park during the early years of the laboratory there.

In 1946 the Department of Lands and Forests

increased its activity in research and contributed staff of its own to the Opeongo Laboratory, largely taking over work which related immediately to fisheries but also contributing to the more fundamental limnological researches. Over the next five years an intensive effort was made to assess the limnological consequences of the addition of fertilizer to the relatively infertile waters of Algonquin Park (Langford, 1948). A contribution of the University of Toronto to this program was the development of a new plankton sampler (Langford, 1953), which, however, is again in the process of modification. The principle of this sampler is that a dropping tube engulfs a column of water at the same speed as that at which the tube is dropping.

In 1954 the university's rights in the buildings at the Opeongo Station were turned over to the province, and the facilities have been shared since then by the two agencies under the terms of an agreement entered into at that time. The Opeongo Laboratory is now known as the Harkness Laboratory for Fisheries Research (Anon., 1961b). The new name for the laboratory is particularly appropriate, since W. J. K. Harkness was associated with the Ontario Fisheries Research Laboratory from its very beginning and was its Director for many years. From 1949 until his death in 1960, he was Chief of the Fish and Wildlife Branch of the Ontario Department of Lands and Forests and in that office contributed much to the development of the administration of the province's renewable resources on a sound technical basis.

One of the major features of the work of the Opeongo Laboratory has been the intensive creel census of Lake Opeongo which has been continuous since 1936. In this census the fish are measured, their ages assessed, stomach contents examined, and the catch per unit effort recorded. A close estimate is also made of the total catch. There are two game species, the lake trout (*Salvelinus namaycush*) and the smallmouth bass (*Micropterus dolomieu*).

In 1946 the University of Toronto also widened the scope of its cooperation with the Department of Lands and Forests by entering into an agreement to operate a laboratory for experimental limnology to be built by the province at Maple, near Toronto (Anon., 1951, 1954, 1961a). Here work has been concentrated on the relations of fish to temperature, oxygen, and carbon diox-

ide. Much of the work on temperature is summarized in Brett (1956) and on respiration in Fry (1957). More recent publications from the laboratory are Basu (1959), Tait (1960), and Saunders (1961). Experimental work with plankton was not moved to Maple, however, and the almost unique work of Price (1958) on the cryptic speciation of copepods was carried out in Toronto, as was McCombie's (1960) work on the growth of algae in relation to temperature, light, and nutrient level.

The Ontario Fisheries Research Laboratory ceased to be recognized within the university in 1956, although the work it had done and the budget provided for it by the university continued. In 1960 the Great Lakes Institute was established in the University of Toronto to provide for cooperation in aquatic research among the various academic departments. The work of the university formerly carried on in the Ontario Fisheries Research Laboratory is now being largely pursued within the institute.

Much work, particularly on the physiology of behavior of fish has been carried out in the Department of Zoology of the University of Toronto, independent of the Ontario Fisheries Research Laboratory (e.g., Fisher, 1958; Sullivan, 1954). Such work is still being actively pursued. In addition, work on the cytogenetics of certain aquatic Diptera (Dunbar, 1958) and on the inorganic constituents of natural waters (Gorham, 1961) is proceeding in the Department of Botany, while the Department of Mathematics has contributed to the estimation of fish populations.

The taxonomy and distribution of fish has been a prime interest of the Royal Ontario Museum ever since the establishment of the Royal Ontario Museum of Zoology (Dymond, 1940; Scott, 1954). The museum has always been closely associated with the University of Toronto and is now an integral part of it. Outstanding among collections of aquatic insects in the museum is that of the Odonata made by E. M. Walker, forming the basis of his studies and of the culminating classical three-volume work on the Odonata of Canada and Alaska (Walker, 1953, 1958, in preparation). Collections of Plecoptera and Trichoptera, largely the material of W. E. Ricker and W. G. B. Wiggins, respectively, are also housed there (e.g., Wiggins, 1960).

Queen's University, Kingston, has a tradition in fisheries research extending roughly as far back as that of the University of Toronto. For example, Dr. A. P. Knight (1907) carried out early experiments on the effect of dynamite on fish in Kingston harbor, apparently soon learning by experience to lengthen the fuses somewhat. Dr. Knight also initiated one of the earliest attempts to measure the extent of survival of planted fish fry (White, 1924). Alfred Brooker Klugh (Dymond and Toner, 1936), one of Canada's pioneer ecologists, spent his working life at Queen's University (e.g., Klugh, 1926). However, Queen's interests in hydrobiology were largely concentrated on the Atlantic coast during this time, and it was not until the Queen's Biological Station was established at Lake Opinicon on the Rideau Canal in 1944 (Curran *et al.*, 1947) that the situation changed. One of the particular interests at Queen's has been the biochemistry of the chlorophyll derivatives in lake sediments (Vallentyne, 1955).

A great expansion in hydrobiological research in the universities came with the formation of the Ontario Research Commission in 1945. The Ontario Research Foundation now administers provincial funds to the universities and in its own right is interested in the parasitology of fish. Also in 1945 there was an increase in support for the universities through the National Research Council. Much of the increased activity at the University of Toronto was due to this increased support. Funds from these two sources have enabled McMaster University, Hamilton, to carry out studies of sedimentation (Kleerekoper, 1957) and of the sensory physiology of fish (Kleerekoper and Sibakin, 1957). Work on the Simuliidae is also carried on at McMaster (Davies, 1959). For some years the University of Western Ontario, London, maintained a small laboratory on Lake Erie supported largely by funds from the Ontario Research Council.

With the assistance of the Ontario Department of Lands and Forests, two members have been added to the faculty of the Ontario Agricultural College at Guelph to deal specifically with fisheries management, and the interest of other members there in the practical aspects of hydrobiology as related to fisheries has been encouraged. Particular attention is being given to farm fish ponds and the effects of planting hatchery fish (McCrimmon and Berst, 1961).

Limnology in the provincial civil service can be said to have started with C. W. Nash, who was first a lecturer in the Ontario Department of Agriculture and later became Provincial Biologist. Nash wrote an account of the fish of Ontario in his *Vertebrates of Ontario* (Nash, 1908). However, it is perhaps fairer to date the provincial contribution to the limnology of its inland waters from the appointment of H. H. MacKay as aquatic biologist in the Department of Game and Fisheries in 1926. A series of studies concerned with the inland waters of the province were carried out under MacKay's direction by specialists and students from the four universities existing in Ontario at that time. A second biologist was added to the staff of the department. Unfortunately, with the advent of the depression of the 1930's such work was greatly curtailed, and little was done again until after the war. Following the war the department was reorganized and incorporated into the Department of Lands and Forests. Two branches of the Department of Lands and Forests are concerned with limnology. The Research Branch operates the Harkness Laboratory, which was mentioned previously, as its main inland station. The Research Branch concerns itself with limnology as a whole but, as might be expected, is most concerned with fisheries investigations (e.g., Martin, 1960). It continues to carry on the creel census in Algonquin Park (Fry, 1939, 1949; Baldwin and Martin, 1953) instituted by the Ontario Fisheries Research Laboratory in 1936. The extensive work on the fertilization of oligotrophic lakes mentioned previously and some of the early work on the effects of DDT (Johnston *et al.*, 1949) on aquatic insects have been part of the branch's program in Algonquin Park.

The greater fraction of the Research Branch's budget is spent on the Great Lakes. The branch operates three research stations which are located respectively on South Bay, Lake Huron, at Wheatley on Lake Erie, and at Glenora on the Bay of Quinte, Lake Ontario. Workers at these stations are primarily concerned with fisheries investigations. One of their major concerns is the determination of the variations in year-class strength of various important species of fish and the search for the causes of these various fluctuations. The strengths of the year classes are being determined from the age composition of samples from the catches in various sport and commercial fisheries together with estimates of the total yields. The most extensive series of such data is that for the whitefish (*Coregonus clupeaformis*) fishery of eastern Lake Ontario. For these the scale collections go back to 1944, having been begun by the University of Toronto under a grant from the National Research Council and then continued in the last decade by the Research Branch. The first analysis of year-class variation in the Lake Ontario whitefish is now in a report soon to be submitted to the Journal of the Fisheries Research Board of Canada for publication. W. J. Christie (personal communication) has established a correlation of approximately 0.6 between an index that combines the deviations of the November and April temperatures from the long term mean and the deviations of the year-class productions from the historical trend in the fishery. A similar correlation between a temperature index and the year-class success for the smallmouth bass (*Micropterus dolomieu*), in which spawning success is related to a warm summer, has been established at the South Bay Laboratory (e. g., Watt, 1959). Both these correlations have been established with air temperatures, but McCombie (1959) showed that a close correlation exists between monthly mean air and surface water temperatures.

Since 1947 the South Bay Station has been keeping extensive records of the species composition of all the fish susceptible to capture in commercial gear that occur in South Bay, an almost totally enclosed arm of Lake Huron. While these observations have been in progress, the annihilation there of the lake trout (*Salvelinus namaycush*) by the lamprey (*P. marinus*) has been extensively documented (Budd and Fry, 1960, and earlier papers). Various other major changes in the species composition have also taken place in the same period. These include the re-establishment of the smelt (*Osmerus mordax*), the virtual disappearance of the lake herring (*Leucichthys artedii*), and the establishment of the alewife (*Pomolobus pseudoharengus*). In recent years the operations of the South Bay Laboratory have been extended to Lake Huron so that the commercial catch of fish in that lake is now being sampled routinely, and the waters of Georgian Bay are being sampled annually by experimental fishing. Routine observations of water temperature in South Bay have been carried on continuously since approximately 1950.

The Lake Erie Station has not yet been in operation for a sufficient time to provide a great backlog of year-class information, but from the data available, there appears to be a significant alternation in the year-class success in the smelt (*Osmerus mordax*), according to R. G. Ferguson (personal communication).

All three of the Great Lakes stations of the Research Branch are well-equipped for limnological investigation, and each has a research vessel sufficiently large to operate in the offshore waters of the Great Lakes. While the Fisheries Research Board of Canada does not have a permanent station on Lake Superior, it operates well-equipped field stations and has an offshore research vessel.

Recognizing the need for extensive limnological data, the Research Branch added a limnological section to its Great Lakes operations in 1953. D. V. Anderson was chosen for the post of limnologist. Through the efforts of Dr. Anderson, arrangements were made with the Royal Canadian Navy for the loan of a vessel large enough to be maintained offshore in winter in the Great Lakes. Further, a cooperative arrangement was made with various other government departments, in particular the Department of Transport of the Federal Government, for the cooperative operation of the vessel so that the fullest advantage might be taken of this major facility. The vessel, the *Port Dauphine,* began operations in Lake Ontario in 1958 and has to date spent most of its time in Lakes Ontario, Erie, and Huron. In 1960 the cooperative arrangement for the study of the meteorology and the physical limnology of the Great Lakes was reorganized so that it is now coordinated in the Great Lakes Institute of the University of Toronto. The Research Branch makes a grant to the Great Lakes Institute in lieu of operating its own limnological unit on the Great Lakes.

For the administration of its natural resources, Ontario is subdivided into some 22 districts, and within recent years the Fish and Wildlife Branch has generally provided a fisheries biologist in each district. It is the duty of this biologist to be familiar with the limnology of his district from the point of view of the needs of the fisheries and to conduct any further investigations as may be within his capabilities. In this way a substantial body of knowledge is accumulating concerning the waters of the province, particularly descriptions of their physical characters and lists of the fishes to be taken in them. Such material is largely unpublished, but it is on file in the various district offices. In all, Ontario now employs some 40 graduate biologists whose major concern is with its fisheries.

Two other provincial agencies are concerned with the limnology of the inland waters to a major degree. These are the Ontario Water Resources Commission and the Department of Commerce and Development. In addition, the Hydro Electric Power Commission has the responsibilities its name implies. The Ontario Water Resources Commission (Anon., 1961c) is responsible for water supply and sewage treatment. It investigates surface and ground water supplies and cases of water pollution. The commission's main laboratory, which can be considered the successor of one established by the Provincial Board of Health in 1907, is in Toronto. The chief concern of the Department of Commerce and Development with the waters of the province has been the recreational aspects and flood control. It has been systematically surveying the river systems of southern Ontario, which is the main agricultural and settled region. In characterizing the various reaches of the streams as to maximum temperatures reached and permanence of flow, much use has been made of the fundamental work of Ide and his students (e.g., Sprules, 1947) concerning the presence or absence of indicator organisms in the bottom fauna to supplement the physical data otherwise collected (e.g., Hallam, 1959). Reports on these river system surveys, together with plans for ameliorating the deficiencies found, become available as they are completed (e.g., Richardson, 1960).

Ontario's contribution to limnology thus far has been largely in the training of hydrobiologists for fisheries research, and incidental to this training, the aquatic resources of the province have been sampled. Most of these workers have carried on their more mature researches elsewhere in Canada. For example, Miller, Rawson, and Ricker are among the Canadian limnologists who were trained in Ontario. It was not until about 1945 that facilities for limnological research in the province advanced appreciably beyond the minimum required for the training of graduate students. However, growth up to that point had been healthy although restricted, and the expansion was based on a sound nucleus of achievement in the universities and the museum, so that there is promise for substantial advances in both pure and applied limnology in Ontario in the future.

References for Ontario

ANONYMOUS. 1951. Annual report of the Laboratory for Experimental Limnology. Toronto Dept. Lands and Forests, Research Rept. 23, 18 p.

———. 1954. Report of the Laboratory for Experimental Limnology for 1952 and 1953. Toronto Dept. Lands and Forests, Research Rept. 28, 12 p.

———. 1961a. The Laboratory for Experimental Limnology 1954–59. Toronto Dept. Lands and Forests, Research Rept. 44, 24 p.

———. 1961b. Harkness Fisheries Research Laboratory. Canada Dept. Fish., Ottawa, Trade News, 14(4): 6.

———. 1961c. Ontario Water Resources Commission. Toronto, O.W.R.C., 12 p.

BALDWIN, N. S., AND N. V. MARTIN. 1953. Effects of the alternate closure of Algonquin Park lakes. Canadian Fish Cult., 14: 26–38.

BASU, S. P. 1959. Active respiration of fish in relation to ambient concentrations of oxygen and carbon dioxide. J. Fish. Research Board Canada, 16: 175–212.

BENSLEY, B. A. 1911. The Georgian Bay Biological Station. Intern. Rev. Hydrobiol. Hydrogr., 4: 539–540.

———. 1922. A plan for the biological investigation of the water areas of Ontario. Univ. Toronto Studies, Biol. Ser. 20, Ontario Fish. Research Lab., Publ. 1, 23 p.

BOUSFIELD, E. L. 1958. Freshwater amphipod crustaceans of glaciated North America. Canadian Field Nat., 72(2): 55–113.

BRETT, J. R. 1956. Some principles in the thermal requirements of fishes. Quart. Rev. Biol., 31(2): 75–87.

BUDD, J. C., AND F. E. J. FRY. 1960. Further observations on the survival of yearling lake trout planted in South Bay, Lake Huron. Canadian Fish Cult., 26: 7–13.

CANADIAN DEPARTMENT OF MARINE AND FRESHWATER FISHERIES. 1915. Contributions to Canadian biology, being studies from the biological stations of Canada, 1911–14. II. Fresh water fish and lake biology. Suppl. to 47th Ann. Rept., Canadian Dept. Marine and Freshwater Fish., Fish. Branch, 222 p.

CLEMENS, W. A. 1923. The limnology of Lake Nipigon. Univ. Toronto Studies, Biol. Ser. 22, Ontario Fish. Research Lab., Publ. 11, 31 p.

CURRAN, H. W., JOHN BARDACH, R. I. BOWMAN, AND H. G. LAWLER. 1947. A biological survey of Lake Opinicon. Queen's University, Kingston, 48 p.

DAVIES, D. M. 1959. The parasitism of black flies (Diptera, Simuliidae) by larval water mites mainly of the genus *Sperchon*. Canadian J. Zool., 37: 353–369.

DUNBAR, R. W. 1958. The salivary gland chromosomes of two sibling species of black flies included in *Eusimulium aureum* Fries. Canadian J. Zool., 36: 23–44.

DYMOND, J. R. 1922. A provisional list of the fishes of Lake Erie. Univ. Toronto Studies, Biol. Ser. 20, Ontario Fish. Research Lab., Publ. 4, 17 p.

———. 1940. History of the Royal Ontario Museum

of Zoology. Contrib. Royal Ontario Museum Zool., No. 18, 52 p.

DYMOND, J. R., AND G. C. TONER. 1936. Alfred Brooker Klugh—A bibliography. Bull. Eastern Ontario Fish Game Protect. Assoc., Ganonoque, Suppl. 1, 12 p.

FISHER, K. C. 1958. An approach to the organ and cellular physiology of adaptation to temperature in fish and small mammals, p. 3–49. In C. L. Prosser (ed.), Physiological adaptation. Amer. Physiol. Soc., Washington.

FRY, F. E. J. 1937. The summer migration of the cisco, Leucichthys artedi (LeSueur), in Lake Nipissing, Ontario. Univ. Toronto Studies, Biol. Ser. 44, Ontario Fish. Research Lab., Publ. 55, 91 p.

———. 1939. A comparative study of lake trout fisheries in Algonquin Park, Ontario. Univ. Toronto Studies, Biol. Ser. 46, Ontario Fish. Research Lab., Publ. 58, 69 p.

———. 1949. Statistics of a lake trout fishery. Biometrics, 5: 27–67.

———. 1957. The aquatic respiration of fish, p. 1–63. In M. E. Brown (ed.), The physiology of fishes. Vol. I. Academic Press, New York.

GORHAM, E. 1961. Factors influencing supply of major ions to inland waters with special reference to the atmosphere. Bull. Geol. Soc. Amer., 72: 795–840.

HALLAM, J. C. 1959. Habitat and associated fauna of four species of fish in Ontario streams. J. Fish. Research Board Canada, 16: 147–173.

IDE, F. P. 1935. The effect of temperature on the distribution of the mayfly fauna of a stream. Univ. Toronto Studies, Biol. Ser. 39, Ontario Fish. Research Lab., Publ. 50, 76 p. + 10 pl.

JOHNSTON, R. N., et al. 1949. Forest spraying and some effects of DDT. Ontario Dept. Lands and Forests, Div. Research, Biol. Bull. No. 2, 174 p.

KENNEDY, W. A. 1943. The whitefish Coregonus clupeaformis (Mitchill) of Lake Opeongo, Algonquin Park, Ontario. Univ. Toronto Studies, Biol. Ser. 51, Ontario Fish. Research Lab., Publ. 62, 45 p.

KLEEREKOPER, H. 1957. Une étude limnologique de la chimie des sediments de fond des lacs de l'Ontario méridonial, Canada. Theses, Faculté Sci., Univ. Paris, 205 p.

KLEEREKOPER, H., AND K. SIBAKIN. 1957. An investigation of the electrical "spike" potentials produced by the sea lamprey (Petromyzon marinus) in the water surrounding the head region. II. J Fish. Research Board Canada, 14: 145–151.

KLUGH, A. B. 1926. The productivity of lakes. Quart. Rev. Biol., 1: 572–577.

KNIGHT, A. P. 1907. The effects of dynamite explosions on fish life. Contrib. Canadian Biol., 1902–1905: 21–30.

LANGFORD, R. R. 1938. Diurnal and seasonal changes in the distribution of the limnetic Crustacea of Lake Nipissing, Ontario. Univ. Toronto Studies, Biol. Ser. 45, Ontario Fish. Research Lab., Publ. 56: 1–142.

———. 1948. Fertilization of lakes in Algonquin Park, Ontario. Trans. Amer. Fish. Soc., 78: 133–144.

———. 1953. Methods of plankton collection and a description of a new sampler. J. Fish. Research Board Canada, 10: 238–252.

LANGFORD, R. R., AND W. R. MARTIN. 1941. Seasonal variations in stomach contents and rate of growth in a population of yellow perch. Trans. Amer. Fish. Soc., 70: 436–440.

McCOMBIE, A. M. 1959. Some relations between air temperatures and the surface water temperatures of lakes. Limnol. Oceanogr., 4: 252–258.

———. 1960. Actions and interactions of temperature, light intensity and nutrient concentration on the growth of the green alga, Chlamydomonas reinhardi Dangeard. J. Fish. Research Board Canada, 17: 871–894.

McCRIMMON, H. R., AND A. H. BERST. 1961. An analysis of sixty-five years of fishing in a trout pond unit. J. Wildl. Mgmt., 25: 168–178.

MARTIN, N. V. 1960. Homing behaviour in spawning lake trout. Canadian Fish Cult., 26: 3–6.

MILLER, R. B. 1941. A contribution to the ecology of the Chironomidae of Costello Lake, Algonquin Park, Ontario. Univ. Toronto Studies, Biol. Ser. 49, Ontario Fish. Research Lab., Publ. 60, 63 p.

NASH, C. W. 1908. Vertebrates of Ontario. Ontario Dept. Educ., Toronto, 104 p.

PRICE, J. L. 1958. Cryptic speciation in the vernalis group of Cyclopidae. Canadian J. Zool. 36: 285–303.

RAWSON, D. S. 1930. The bottom fauna of Lake Simcoe and its role in the ecology of the lake. Univ. Toronto Studies, Biol. Ser. 34, Ontario Fish. Research Lab., Publ. 40, 183 p.

RICHARDSON, A. H. (ed.). 1960. Twelve Mile Creek conservation report. Ontario Dept. Commerce and Develop., Conserv. Branch, 148 p.

RICKER, W. E. 1932. Studies of trout producing lakes and ponds. Univ. Toronto Studies, Biol. Ser. 36, Ontario Fish. Research Lab., Publ. 45: 111–167.

RIGBY, MARGARET S., AND A. G. HUNTSMAN. 1958. Materials relating to the history of the Fisheries Research Board of Canada (formerly the Biological Board of Canada) for the period 1898–1924. Canada, Fish. Research Board MS Rept. Biol. 660, 272 p.

RIGLER, F. H. 1961. The uptake and release of inorganic phosphorus by Daphnia magna Straus. Limnol. Oceanogr., 6: 165–174.

SAUNDERS, R. L. 1961. The irrigation of the gills in fishes. I. Studies of the mechanism of branchial irrigation. Canadian J. Zool., 39: 637–653.

SCOTT, W. B. 1954. Freshwater fishes of eastern Canada. Univ. Toronto Press, Toronto, 128 p.

SPRULES, W. M. 1947. An ecological investigation of stream insects in Algonquin Park, Ontario. Univ. Toronto Studies, Biol. Ser. 56, Ontario Fish. Research Lab., Publ. 69, 81 p.

SULLIVAN, C. M. 1954. Temperature reception and responses in fish. J. Fish. Research Board Canada, 11: 153–170.

TAIT, J. S. 1960. The first filling of the swimbladder in salmonoids. Canadian J. Zool., 38: 179–187.

TESTER, A. L. 1932. Food of the small-mouthed black bass (Micropterus dolomieu) in some Ontario waters. Univ. Toronto Studies, Biol. Ser. 36, Ontario Fish. Research Lab., Publ. 46, 33 p.

VALLENTYNE, J. R. 1955. Sedimentary chlorophyll determination as a paleobotanical method. Canadian J. Botan., 33: 304–313.

WALKER, E. M. 1953. The Odonata of Canada and Alaska. Vol. I. Univ. Toronto Press, Toronto. 292 p.

———. 1958. The Odonata of Canada and Alaska. Vol. II. Univ. Toronto Press, Toronto. 318 p.

———. In preparation. The Odonata of Canada and Alaska. Vol. III. Univ. Toronto Press, Toronto.

WATT, K. E. F. 1959. Studies on population productivity. II. Factors governing productivity in a population of smallmouth bass. Ecol. Monogr., 29: 367–392.

WHITE, H. C. 1924. A quantitative determination of the number of survivors from planting 5,000 trout fry in each of two streams. Contrib. Canadian Biol., 2(9): 135–150.

WIGGINS, W. G. B. 1960. A preliminary systematic study of the North American larvae of the caddis fly family Phryganeidae (Trichoptera). Canadian J. Zool., 38: 1153–1170.

WRIGHT, R. R. 1892. Preliminary report of the fish and fisheries of Ontario. Commissioners Rept., Ontario Game and Fish Comm., Toronto: 419–476.

QUEBEC

The early natural history writers on Canada were mostly botanists, doubtless because plants are easier to reach, to preserve, and to grow, and also because pharmacopeia of the time clamored for new panaceas, and more new spices were required for the gentlemen's tables. However, this did not deter botanists from studying aquatic as well as terrestrial plants.

Limnological studies did not come to be recognized as a basic need in Quebec until after the first quarter of the present century. Until then the bulk of the work was usually published as short notes dispersed throughout literature. On the other hand, some particiular groups, such as the aquatic insects, were more thoroughly examined, and these even since the second half of the last century when environmental observations began to be inserted into systematic studies or in reports from geological explorers, land surveyors, and ship expeditions around and into the territory.

However, publications dealing at one level or another with the freshwater environment in Quebec are surprising in number. But these papers are often extremely scarce, hard to locate and obtain, frequently left as unprinted theses, or, as rare books, usually expensive.

However, one huge set of works on early Canadian natural history is not examined in any detail here, and this is the Jesuit's *Relations*, constituting voluminous compendiums written by the priests of that Order, who had been evangelizing natives since the beginning of the 17th century. They include at least 54 volumes (Gagnon, 1895, pp. 414–415), edited and re-edited for different dates in different countries. In them are found dispersed many notes and texts on local natural history.

Reports of explorers and writings by naturalists

Works before the nineteenth century

From the beginning of the French colony in Canada, the majority of the explorers and some merchants, companies, and religious persons or congregations prepared manuscript reports, which usually were printed only much later. It was the same with the English and the Dutch who came here. Some of these earlier writings were crammed with fantasies, which were sometimes hard to discern later on. However, many of them mentioned natural products, mammals, birds, fishes, and plants, especially those taken for food.

Among the earliest reporters there are the following, regarding whom there is some doubt whether they really came to the country which was subsequently to be called the Province of Quebec: the Norse from Iceland and Greenland (10th century); Jean Cabot, a Genoan at the service of England (1497); Giovanni da Verrazano, a Florentine at the service of France (1524); Baron de Léry, France (1530; see Rumilly, 1955; pp. 7–13). The Basques do not appear to have written anything about their numerous travels, even though they seem to have been here for several centuries before the 16th century. When Jacques Cartier came into the Gulf of St. Lawrence for the first time in 1534 and again in 1535–36 (to which Gulf he gave the name of Saint-Laurent), he immediately identified in several places old stone kilns of Basque style, which had been used for rendering whale fat. At that period the Portuguese may also have been here, such as Gaspar Corte-Real (1500; see Giraud, 1950, p. 17).

Jacques Cartier from Saint-Malo, France, on his first voyage to Canada in 1534 when he arrived by the Gulf of St. Lawrence North Shore, reported the presence of several salmon ("*plu-*

sieurs saulmons," he wrote in the French of his day), as well as of sea fishes. In 1535 (see Pouliot, 1934) he made first mention of "many eels" that were brought to him by the Indians of the Ile aux Coudres, and regarding the same voyage, he said that the St. Lawrence holds "all sorts of fishes" and then, in spelling that now seems quaint, told of *"macquereaulx, mulletz, bars, sartres, grosses anguilles, épelan, lamproys, saulmon, brochetz, truyttes, carpes, branmes"* (mackerel, mullet, sea bass, large eels, smelts, lampreys, salmon, pike, trout, suckers, breams) (Pouliot, 1934, pp. 11–139).

Probably one of the least known revisional works on American natural history—because so seldom cited—is the masterly, panoramic work by Goode (1886). On page 36, the author cites Thomas Hariot, "the first English man of science who crossed the Atlantic" to New England in 1585. Among his other achievements, Hariot is mentioned (p. 41) as being the first to have brought to European knowledge the existence of the gar *Lepisosteus.*

Champlain, from Brouage, France, after his voyage to Mexico in 1599, came to Canada for the first time in 1603, but he referred only to sea fishes; later in 1608 he began to write about freshwater fishes. For instance, he was the first, in 1609, with a party of Indians to visit Lake Champlain, and he reported in it the presence of a fish called "Chaousarou" by the Indians (Laverdière, 1870, **3**, p. 190), of which he gave so exact a description that it is immediately identifiable as the *Lepisosteus* described by Lacépède in 1803 (Lacépède, 1833, **12**, p. 108). This *Lepisosteus* is our gar, which was known already to Hariot 25 years before Champlain.

Jacques Cartier, Champlain, and several other explorers made maps and descriptions of the various waterways they saw. Also, they often added more or less exact extensions to these, following fanciful hearsay from the Indians. In those brave times watery bodies were described and cited more often than landmarks.

Pierre Boucher (not mentioned in Goode's history) came to Canada in 1634 and was Governor of Trois-Rivières (Three Rivers, Quebec) in 1653–59 and 1663–67 (Le Jeune, 1931, 1, p. 212). In 1664 he published a natural history of New France (Boucher, 1664), which was reprinted in 1849 by the newspaper *Le Canadien* and in 1882 in Montreal by another printer. In this work the

author cited "for the benefit of the cousins left in France, the striking peculiarities of the fauna and of the flora of the country" (translated from Marie-Victorin, 1936). Among several items, he described the water courses, and for some aquatic plants, invertebrates, fish, amphibians, aquatic birds, and mammals, he gave the general habitat even as far up as the Great Lakes, which, he reported, were then called as a whole *Mer douce,* i.e., Fresh[water] Sea. He described also the lower Ottawa River and was the first author to give a differential distribution of the St. Lawrence River fishes, for example (I translate): ". . . quantities of salmon and trout, from the Gulf entrance up to Quebec; not found at Three Rivers nor at Mount Royal [Montreal]: but many in the Iroquois country [northwestern New England]" (Boucher, 1664, p. 80).

A further addition to Goode's otherwise very comprehensive list of North American early naturalists is the following. The first "biologist" —if the name may be used without anachronism for such an early date—to come to Canada and to live in the Province of Quebec (then called New France) was Michel Sarrazin, born in 1659 at Nuits-sous-Beaune, Côte d'Or, France. He was a medical doctor and arrived in Quebec in 1685, where, a year later, he was named surgeon-major to the troops. This nomination was confirmed in 1691 at Versailles by Louis XIV. Sarrazin returned to France, studied under the founder of modern botany, Joesph Pitton de Tournefort, and came back to New France in 1697 where, during 40 years, he practiced medicine and wrote several studies. Among these are a flora of 200 species from Quebec, researches on the anatomy, physiology, and behavior of the beaver and the muskrat, and chemical analyses of local mineral waters. He was also the one to discover the bog plant called pitcher-plant which was named after him by Tournefort, *Sarracenia purpurea* (Vallée, 1927).

Another important author is a Swede, Peter Kalm, who made a two-year trip in 1747–49 throughout Scandinavia, then went to England, afterwards to New England, and finally to New France. He published his observations at Göttingen in three big volumes (see Kalm, 1754, 1757, 1764). The author came up the Hudson River and traveled along Lake Champlain to enter Canada in 1749. He visited Montreal and Quebec City and also went further down the river. In his hird volume he devoted more than 300 pages (pp. 292–626) in describing at great length the St. Lawrence River, the lakes formed by it, and its branches around the Montreal Archipelago. He cited many aquatic plants and invertebrates with their habitats and their uses, and among many other things he described the local fishermen's methods.

A number of other travelers have written upon our aquatic animals and plants, among whom may be mentioned Sagard, Charlevoix, La Hontan, La Galissonnière, the two Forsters, Nicholas and Denys, etc. Again the writings of many of them were published by others, often only centuries later, and many were never printed but kept as manuscripts in large libraries. Extensive lists of references are found in the following authors, apart from that given by Goode (1886): Pennant (1784, especially footnotes on pp. cxxxiii–cxlii, cli, clvii, clxi–cc); Morgan (1867); Sabin (1876); Smith (1877); Gagnon (1895, 1913); Low (1896, pp. 7L–19L); Haight (1896); Low (1906, pp. 71–111); Marie-Victorin (1939, pp. 35–37); Dymond (1939, pp. 41–43); Pariseau (1939, pp. 58–68); Rousseau (1948); Watters (1960, pp. 674–709). An example of a large manuscript that was never printed is found under Anonymous (18th century) in the references. It deals with many freshwater matters and is found in the National Library in Ottawa where it was received in 1915 from the Bibliothèque nationale, Paris. A photostatic copy of it was made in 1952 by the National Library for the library of the Office of Biology, Quebec Department of Game and Fisheries.

Finally, a huge work which is a mine of information is Harris (1705). It lists and relates "voyages and travels" throughout the world. For example, in Vol. I, Book V, the chapters 17 to 19 (pp. 810–814) are on the voyages made to New France. Vol. II, Book IV is on America, and chapter 25 (pp. 925–926) "On the beasts, birds, fishes, insects, trees and fruits of the Northern America."

Works of the nineteenth and early twentieth centuries: Advent of institutions

With the invention of machines at an ever-increasing rate since the 17th century, with the advent in close succession of successful popular revolutions occurring toward the end of the 18th century and resulting in the liberation of the masses from feudal regimes in the United States (1783) and France (1789), and with the surge—and consequent urges—of the industrial revolution in the middle of the 19th century (Pearl, 1930, pp. 19–21), earth explorations multiplied and expanded greatly during the last century. More and more easily could specialists be found to go everywhere, and natural history researches developed and deepened. Thus, during this period, writings on Quebec natural history also became more numerous, important, and precise. Concerning freshwater biology, we will only indicate some of the leading works here.

We may start the century's natural history with a botanist, André Michaux, who in 1803 published the very first true American flora: *Flora boreali-americana* (in Latin; see Michaux, 1803). This was a precise work giving, for aquatic plants and others, many little notes as to their habitats (verbal communication, Dr. Ernest Rouleau, Professor, Department of Botany, University of Montreal). As early as 1792 Michaux had gone into the heart of the Province of Quebec, i.e., to Lake Mistassini, a large freshwater body 100 miles long and 10 miles wide. His plant collections are now in the Museum national d'Histoire naturelle, Paris, with notes in his own handwriting on the habitat of each specimen (Rousseau, 1948, p. 19).

At the opening of the 19th century the topography and hydrography of Canada were very little known. For the 23 years prior to 1815, Joseph Bouchette, lieutenant-colonel and surveyor-general of Lower Canada (Province of Quebec), had accumulated the necessary data for a description of the country. Thus, in 1815 a basic work defining all counties, townships, parishes, towns, seigneuries, and principal lakes and rivers was published in London, in French and in English simultaneously, as two separate books (see Bouchette, 1815a, 1815b). At several places the aquatic products are given. This work served as a basis for all ulterior surveys of the Canadian topography, for Lower Canada and for a part of Upper Canada (Province of Ontario). At the same time, geographical onomastics—names of places—were definitively fixed, as well as explained in many cases.

Soon thereafter a true scientific movement started in Lower Canada with the founding of societies. In 1824 the Literary and Historical Society of Quebec was formed, and it started publishing *Bulletins* and *Transactions* on natural history subjects in 1831. The society ended in 1924. In 1827 the Natural History Society of Montreal was founded and began publication of *Proceedings* in 1828 and stopped in 1883. But from 1830 to 1863 these *Proceedings* were published as *Annual Reports,* and from 1864 until 1883 they were incorporated within the *Canadian Naturalist and Geologist,* which had begun in 1857 and which became, under several later titles, the official organ of the Natural History Society of Montreal.

After the previously mentioned survey of Bouchette, which had dealt more particularly with the densely inhabited southern part of Quebec, it became necessary to prospect the upper Saguenay and Lake St. John region, where excellent agricultural lands were known to exist. Thus, in 1828, a party of engineers and surveyors was sent up there, and in 1829 Commissioners Andrew Stuart and David Stuart, in charge of the operation, presented their *Rapport des commissaires pour explorer le Saguenay* to the Lower Canada Legislative Assembly, accompanied by the detailed reports of the staff members (Stuart and Stuart, 1829). In the *Rapport* a wealth of details is found concerning many developmental possibilities of the region, which was then only sparsely inhabited by people of European descent. As regards the aquatic environment, many rivers and lakes are described, and their known or potential products are reported. Pages 67–81, by W. Nixon, deal mainly with natural history. For example, at the mouth of Ouiatchouan River on Lake St. John, dates of capture and size of ouananiche ("Awenahish") or freshwater salmon are given. On page 76 is the first list ever published of Lake St. John fishes. Pages 108–171 are a report by Joseph Bouchette, Jr., on the upper St. Maurice River in an expedition through forests and marshes to Lake St. John. The presence of leeches is cited for several lakes. On page 145 is mentioned "a little river strongly impregnated with iron carbonate and sulfur" (translated); on page 148, another list of the fishes of Lake St. John, including ouananiche ("wenanish"); on page 152, a very limpid lake; on page 154, a river with water of a red tint. All told, this is the earliest writing I can find where definite chemicals are reported in natural waters of Quebec, whatever is meant by "sulfur" hereabove.

At that time the obsession of the search for

the Northwest Passage from Europe to Asia reigned throughout the world. To that end many nations sent ships and even fleets to the north of America. Often with them were medical doctors—then usually called surgeons—and naturalists, who started more complete inventories of the wealth of the North. By the same token, because several of these expeditions landed first in Quebec City or in Montreal before proceeding westwards, occasions were provided for other natural history studies on eastern Canada.

From these travels, Sir William J. Hooker published two volumes from 1829 to 1840 of a *Flora boreali-americana*—the second work with this title, after Michaux (see preceding)—which included the plants gathered during travels in the Arctic (Hooker, 1829–40). This work may have included Quebec aquatic plants, but I have not seen it.

A noteworthy example of summation of results from several expeditions was published as *Fauna boreali-americana* by John Richardson, M.D., in four parts (Richardson *et al.,* 1829–37): Part 1, Quadrupeds, by Richardson, in 1829; Part 2, Birds, by Swainson and Richardson, in 1831; Part 3, Fish (with an appendix on Mollusca), by Richardson, in 1836; Part 4, Insects, by Kirby in 1837. Richardson was the first European ichthyologist or describer to come here and to make his descriptions and biological annotations from direct observation. His Canadian fauna of fishes was the first one ever published as such. Several others of his works on American northern life are shown in the large *Catalogue of the books . . . in the British Museum* (1913, **4**, pp. 1698–1699; 1940, supplement, **8**, p. 1074; see British Museum, 1903–1940, in references).

In 1840 appeared one of the very first—if not the first—natural history handbooks dealing with Lower Canada. It was written by P. H. Gosse (1840) and is based throughout on a set of questions and answers. Environment and life history of aquatic plants ("weeds"), insects, fishes, amphibians, "tortoise," birds, and mammals are treated here according to seasonal succession. In the case of several forms, the author gives the exact locations where observations were made and even dates.

In 1843 a very important event for the development of natural history in Canada occurred: this was the foundation of the Geological and Natural History Survey of Canada, later to become the Geological Survey, which grew more and more confined to the mineral, geological, and mining value and exploitation aspects. The earlier works emphasize coal measures, mineral waters, fossils, and soils. Then, in the *Report of Progress for the year 1857* appeared the first paper on Quebec freshwater biology, by Robert Bell, on the Lower St. Lawrence, Saguenay River, and Lake St. John (*Report* published in 1858). In the *Report* for 1858, published in 1859, Appendix IV was by W. S. M. D'Urban, on animals and plants of the Ottawa River region, whilst Appendix V by Robert Bell dealt with animals and plants of the St. Lawrence River south shore region. And thus, year in and year out, the Quebec life sciences—aquatic and terrestrial—were slowly established by geologists, who, in truth, were among the best of biologists, whilst trained biologists at that time were few or not at all extant. All these excellent works were collected by W. F. Ferrier and Dorothy J. Ferrier (1920) in a very important but almost unobtainable bibliographical catalogue, to which supplements by the Department of Mines of Canada were later added.

Another important occurrence in Canadian science was the foundation in Toronto in 1849 of the Canadian Institute, which became the Royal Canadian Institute on the 4th November 1851, by grant of a royal charter during Queen Victoria's reign. Its first serial, for the year 1852, published in 1853, was called *Canadian Journal*, but its title changed later to the *Transactions* and finally to the *Proceedings of the Royal Canadian Institute* (in reference list, see Royal Canadian Institute). At an early date the serial began dealing with natural history subjects concerning Quebec.

In 1849, 1850, and 1851 Moses H. Perley presented reports on the sea and river fisheries of New Brunswick before the legislature of that province, which had been incorporated in 1784 immediately after the separation of the United States from the British Provinces of North America. In 1852, Perley's reports were published as one book (Perley, 1852) in Fredericton, by the Queen's Printer, and this work was called the second edition. I have in hand a copy of the separate 1851 *Report upon fisheries of the Bay of Fundy* (Perley, 1851), and in it, the author gives a "Catalogue in part of the fishes of New Brunswick and Nova Scotia" (pp. 118–159), "according to the system of Baron Cuvier" (pp. iii–

iv). Here, the author also deals with the habitat and life history of freshwater fishes, together with those species inhabiting Quebec in the headwaters of St. John River, i.e., Lakes Temiscouata and Pohenegamook, and those found elsewhere in the two provinces concerned. For example, Perley cites the whitefish, *Coregonus albus* (*clupeaformis*), from Lake Temiscouata, which the French Canadians called *Poisson pointu* (pointed fish, i.e., point-nosed fish), which is still called *le Pointu*, and of which I saw specimens that had been sent to me in Montreal about ten years ago for identification. Perley was the first author to make an elaborate study of the Gulf of St. Lawrence sea and freshwater fisheries. Published in 1859, his work (Perley, 1859) described the habits and habitats of some of the freshwater as well as the marine fish species.

In 1849 Horatio Robinson Storer, son of one of the first leading United States ichthyologists, D. Humphreys Storer, went among other places to Labrador, the Gulf of St. Lawrence North Shore, and Anticosti and brought back to Boston a collection of sea and freshwater fishes. Among these he named and described a new species of char, *Salmo immaculatus* (Storer, 1857, pp. 264–265), the status of which remains highly uncertain to this day. The fish had been netted in a brook.

In 1855 essays on Canada were written for submission to the Paris Exhibition in a competitive examination after which three prizes were awarded by a Committee of Judges. This procedure was in high fashion at that time. The first- and second-prized essays, by J. Sheridan Hogan and Alexander Morris, respectively, printed in Montreal in 1855, had a second edition in London in 1856, under the joint title of *Canada and her resources* (see Hogan and Morris, 1856). Although concerned primarily with the financial values of natural resources, both essays were also extensively geographical, describing the Canadian Great Lakes and the St. Lawrence River and its tributaries. From the standpoint of water products, Morris' essay was more elaborate, citing, for example, the river fisheries of Anticosti Island (p. 23), abounding fish in the Ottawa River system (p. 27), the tomcod winter fishing in the St. Maurice (p. 47), a study on the climate of Lower Canada (pp. 112–114), and the use of peat from Longueuil as combustible material (p. 118).

In 1856 a new serial, the *Canadian Naturalist and Geologist,* was inaugurated by people from the Natural History Society of Montreal. Publishing started in 1857, and under a variety of titles, it lasted until 1916 (in references, see Natural History Society of Montreal). In its opening chapter, the geologist, E. Billings, defined its realm as to "be devoted to the Natural History and Geology of Canada and the neighbouring British Provinces." At that time, statutory Canada was only Quebec and Ontario. Right in this first volume, many aspects of freshwater life in Quebec were considered, for example, ducks (pp. 146–159), salmon (pp. 161–168), otter (pp. 228–232), raccoon (pp. 253–260), and classification of Canadian fishes (pp. 275–283; though very summary and done after Cuvier, this classification is the very first one on fishes of Canada, prepared by Frank Forelle).

In 1857 Richard Nettle published the first monograph on a fish in Quebec (Nettle, 1857). It was on the Atlantic salmon. Also, it was the first one on the salmon. It recalled the history of fish hatchery (pp. 94–97), mentioned the repellent action of sawdust (p. 104), cited freshwater salmon in Lake Ontario which the author took himself (pp. 106–107), and described the habitat for salmon in several rivers of the eastern provinces. By that time, since salmon and other fishes were vanishing quickly, usually because of industry, the author reproduced *An act for the protection of fisheries in Lower Canada,* 30th May 1855, which forbids to sell, and to catch with nets etc., salmon, maskinonge, and trout.

In 1857 the Department of Game and Fisheries was created in the Government of the Province of Quebec. Its serial publications started in the 20th century only.

At Université Laval in Quebec City, natural science teaching began in 1858 with botany courses by Abbé O. Brunet (Huard, 1926, p. 311). Later, various courses developed, and today a regular limnology course is given. Over the years, Université Laval has had several zoologists as professors and as graduates, who have studied aquatic conditions in Quebec, though the larger number of them have concentrated their work naturally on the Lower St. Lawrence River.

"In McGill University, natural history teaching was instituted in 1858 by Sir William Dawson" (Dymond, 1949, p. 111). This was the beginning of natural sciences courses at the university level in Quebec. Being a very broad-minded geologist, Professor Dawson could create a department where all aspects of natural history were taught. Since then, many leading scientists who graduated at McGill have studied freshwater biology and limnology in Quebec.

In 1858 the Provincial Museum of Ontario within the Department of Education was created in Toronto. Later it was merged with various other institutions, the body of which has now become the Royal Ontario Museums, with a strong emphasis on research in eastern Canadian natural history. One of the most noteworthy of the early publications, which dealt also with Quebec aquatic animals, was published in 1908 as *Vertebrates of Ontario* (Nash, 1908). It is largely taxonomical but gives also for each species one or two paragraphs on habitats, including those of some forms common to Quebec. The same may be said of several papers in serials started during the present century at the Royal Ontario Museum of Zoology, also merged recently into the Royal Ontario Museums.

In the *Canadian Naturalist and Geologist* A. F. Kemp (1858, **3,** pp. 331–345, 450–466) published the first papers to appear on the freshwater algae of Canada. The author described the habitat for each species, some of them from around Montreal.

In the same issue, on pages 192–193, George D. Gibb (1858) described a cave with water, located in Côte St. Michel in the center of the Island of Montreal. This was the first true cave ever mentioned in literature on Canada. I visited that cave myself several times and also found water in it; this water was exceedingly transparent and was lying in a bedrock fault many feet deep. Gibb (1861) followed this work by another in the 1861 issue, where he gave a list of the known caverns of Canada and described some of them.

Again in the *Canadian Naturalist and Geologist* of 1858, a new member of the Natural History Society of Montreal, W. S. M. D'Urban (1858), published the first elaborate fauna of gastropods, which he refers to as "inhabiting the lakes and rivers of Canada," but which originated solely from Montreal and from the Rideau River near Ottawa. Doubtless the author meant the statutory Canada of that time, i.e., Ontario and Quebec. But this was incorporated by J. F. Whiteaves (1863) in a much more extensive fauna, from

Ontario to Lake St. John, Lake Champlain, and Gaspesia, published as two parts in the same serial for 1863.

Another paper by Robert Bell (1859) was published in the *Canadian Naturalist and Geologist* after an expedition in 1858 in the Gulf of St. Lawrence. As in the majority of his other travels, Bell apparently collected everything he saw, thus reporting on life conditions of freshwater, marine, and terrestrial animals. In addition to the above paper, but under D'Urban's (1859a, 1859b) signature, catalogues of various groups collected by Bell are shown, with habitats, on pages 242–251. All of Bell's works give geographical distributions of species.

In the same periodical and year appeared the first elaborate study of the natural history of the Ottawa River territory and drainage, Quebec side, by W. S. M. D'Urban (1859–61). It continued in the issues of 1860 and 1861. He studied terrestrial and aquatic vertebrates and invertebrates and gave the habitats of the various forms. But in 1860, he was in Exeter, Devonshire, and at the end of his 1861 paper he announced that his other writings would be published elsewhere.

In 1859 the Province of Quebec Association for the Protection of Fish and Game was formed. Their publication, *Conservation,* started in 1930. In 1938 the association adopted a French serial, *La vie au grand air* (i.e., Outdoor life), as a version of the English serial. From the beginning the association had an *Annual Report.* This very advanced group brought together many noteworthy personalities of the province, several of them being social leaders. For that reason, they included people who could help obtain the necessary funds and sponsorships, and thus, they are the ones to whom we owe the majority of the works on limnology and hydrobiology here. It was in great part under their influence that the Office of Biology was created in 1942 as a regular budgeted service within the Quebec Department of Game and Fisheries. The association may have been the first conservation group to be founded in Canada.

In 1860 James Macpherson LeMoine started the publication of his two volume *Ornithologie du Canada.* The first volume was printed in April 1860, and the second in April 1861 (see LeMoine, 1860–61). (The author called them parts.) This was the first Canadian work on ornithology, and

along with descriptions, the food, habitat, and habits of each species are given, including those of aquatic birds. A second edition came out in May 1861, which testifies to the thirst of the Canadians of that time to improve their knowledge in local natural history. LeMoine also published several other works on Canadian or on Quebec natural history (Wood, 1931, p. 431). In addition to these, his book (LeMoine, 1863) on the fisheries of Canada (i.e., eastern Canada) was published. After Perley's works (see preceding), LeMoine was the second author to deal with fisheries and the first to write on it in French. On pages 40–46 he describes the salmon rivers. Elsewhere within the book he presents the habitat and geographical distribution of several freshwater fishes. Later LeMoine (1872) published in book form a selection of many of his sport and natural history writings; on pages 209–216 the distribution of some freshwater fishes is given. In 1887 he issued another one (LeMoine, 1887) on hunting and fishing in Canada. Here he describes the habitat of aquatic birds and fishes, and in this work G. H. Matthews gives the behavior, habitat, and distribution of several freshwater fishes from around Montreal (pp. 241–248). On pages 257–300, LeMoine gives an annotated bibliography of works on fishing and fisheries. Again, LeMoine (1889) wrote another book on fishes and their habitat and distribution around Quebec City, in the Lake St. John region (especially about the freshwater salmon called ouananiche or wananish), and the Eastern Townships.

One could say that with LeMoine and with Abbé Provancher (see following paragraph), a new era started in eastern Canada and especially in Quebec, an era that lasted until the 1920's. During this period many books on natural resources were composed by amateurs, such as anglers, hunters, and travelers, who often wrote romantically about nature, and frequently in verse. They were true nature lovers, and for that reason, they poked and nosed into all types of papers concerning natural history for the parts with which they had become enamored, even the most technical ones. At any rate, many of these authors eventually formed very important if not wealthy circles and had a strong influence in the right quarters for the promotion of many freshwater researches that developed during the 20th century. Several hundred books were published by such writers. I will mention only one of these by William Agar Adamson (1860): *Salmon-fishing in Canada by a Resident*, edited by Colonel Sir James Edward Alexander, in London. (The author's name is not on the title page but only on page 289 below the title of Appendix I. One has simply to know about such a state of affairs, and the authorship can be found from Staton and Tremaine [1934, p. 684].)

At this time there enters upon the scene the most renowned, the most tenacious and temperamental of teachers on natural history. He was Abbé Léon Provancher, who started out as a parish priest and botanist and ended as a parish priest and biologist. During his lifetime he studied the systematics of all multicellular groups—plant and animal—found within Quebec and proposed classifications for all. He started by writing a large flora of Quebec, founded in 1868 the periodical entitled *Le Naturaliste canadien,* and toward the end of his life laid the groundwork for a book on zoology, which was finally published by his pupil and successor in the editorship of the periodical, Abbé Victor-A. Huard. During a very somber phase of the life of *Le Naturaliste canadien,* Abbé Provancher continued writing his articles, claiming subscriptions from his readers who in large numbers received and kept the issues without paying their dues, openly fighting government authorities who refused him financial support, and paying out of his own extremely meager salary the printing and mailing of his *Naturaliste.* The politicians finally defeated him, and in 1891, after its 20th volume, the serial had to suspend publication. Abbé Provancher died the year after.

In 1858 he published an elementary text-book on botany (Provancher, 1858), in which the anatomy and habitat of various aquatic plants were briefly described. This was (according to Huard) the first book on botany published on and in Canada. (In 1862, he wrote another one on Canadian orchards.) But in 1863 (date printed on title page: 1862), he brought out an 842-page Canadian flora (Provancher, 1862), which covered Canada west to the Rocky Mountains, south to the Great Lakes, the states of New England to Massachusetts, north to the 50th parallel on the Gulf of St. Lawrence North Shore, and east to the end of the British Provinces (page v). The title showed that the work included aquatic plants, and for these as for the others, he described in brief their habitats and often gave exact geographical locations. That was the first Canadian flora. In 1878 the author wrote another book on Quebec trees, followed later by many other writings on plants of all groups, and on several other subjects not related to natural history.

From 1861 to 1865 Pierre Fortin was sent to the Gulf of St. Lawrence to regulate the work of the Federal Department of Fisheries there. As a partial result of these expeditions, four reports were published in 1863, 1864, 1865, and 1866, in separate French and English versions, the first report in Quebec City (Fortin, 1863), the three others in Ottawa (Fortin, 1864, 1865, 1866), on the marine and freshwater fishes in the Gulf of St. Lawrence. Their habitats, geographical distribution, and habits were described. These papers are exceedingly rare. Fortin also wrote several other expedition reports, sometimes in co-authorships.

In 1862 a botanical museum was founded at Université Laval under the direction of Abbé Ovide Brunet, Professor of Botany since 1858. All types of plants were assembled there, in large collections from all over the world. Quebec aquatic and terrestrial plants were studied over the years at the Musée de l'Université Laval. The museum never had serial publications: its research workers wrote a number of books and pamphlets and contributed to serials published by other institutions. This museum possesses the herbarium collected by Abbé Léon Provancher (Robitaille, 1930, pp. 250–254; see later, for the works by Provancher).

In 1866 H. Beaumont Small published a little book on some of the freshwater fishes of eastern Canada (Small, 1866), describing them summarily and giving their habits and habitats at some length (the title page bears 1865, but the author's preface is 1866). This book—being the second to present a Canadian fish fauna, after Richardson's 1836—was dedicated to the Montreal Fish and Game Protection Club, which had previously edited a similar book on mammals by the same author and later sponsored a third one on birds by M. LeMoine. I cannot find any other data as to the duration of that conservation group nor as to any other of its activities or publications if any. Concerning the destruction of searun fish populations by dams erected across rivers, especially of salmon, there is a footnote at the bottom of page 53 which reads thus: "Since the above was written, a law has been passed by the

Nova Scotia Legislature that a fish-ladder must be placed in every mill-dam in that Province prior to 30th Sept." Thus, I believe Nova Scotia has the priority record for Canada, if not for all North America, for erecting fish-ladders. In England such a law had been passed just a few years previously, in 1861; and was called *Salmon Fishery Act,* which was amended and amplified in 1923 in the *Salmon and Freshwater Fisheries Act* (Pryce-Tannatt, 1938, pp. 14, 17).

The Ottawa Natural History Society does not appear to have existed very long. From 1866 to 1868 it published *Transactions,* and that is all I know of it at this time, save that I note the following sentence in the annual report for 1880-81 of the Ottawa Field-Naturalists' Club published in its *Transactions,* 1881, No. 2, page 6, in a reference to a boat excursion to Kettle Island: "Among the guests present was Prof. Webster, founder of the old Ottawa Natural History Society."

In 1866 and 1867 the final movements establishing the Confederation of the Canadian Provinces were made whilst various administrative governmental departments or ministries were constituted. This was the case, amongst others, of the Department of Fisheries, which has published its *Annual Reports* as an unbroken series from 1867 to the present. These contain many excellent chapters on the aquatic biology of all the provinces. The department varied its name according to conditions of the times and for a while took the name, for example, of Department of Marine or of Naval Service. In time the department also edited various other serials or out-of-series issues and books on aquatic products, on the habitats and habits of marine and freshwater organisms. Moreover, on 9 May 1898 it laid the legal foundations for the institution called today the Fisheries Research Board of Canada, which is still under the jurisdiction of the Minister of Fisheries.

In December 1868 Abbé Léon Provancher started the edition of the serial *Le Naturaliste canadien.* In 1962 it has reached its 89th volume. *Le Naturaliste* has been the third longest-lasting periodical in Canada, after the journal of the Royal Canadian Institute in Toronto, started in 1853 (date printed on first issue: 1852), and *The Proceedings and Transactions of the Nova Scotian Institute of Science,* Halifax, Nova Scotia, started in 1863, this institute having been founded the previous year. Next to *Le Naturaliste*

comes the *Canadian Entomologist,* London, Ontario, published since 1869 (McMurrich, 1918, pp. 8–9). All aspects of Quebec terrestrial and aquatic life, in fact all aspects of natural history, are treated throughout its pages, even though in the beginning it was more taxonomical, which was to be expected. As the various related and intertwined branches of natural history of live beings, such as hydrobiology, limnology, ethology of aquatic beings, etc., became progressively differentiated from general natural history during the years, in the same way did the papers in *Le Naturaliste canadien* follow the current of events. It must be pointed out that this serial, *Le Naturaliste canadien,* is *not* a translation of the several other *Canadian Naturalists;* they are not at all related. A general index covering the recent decades of *Le Naturaliste* is sorely wanting, though one was published in June 1891 (Vol. 20, Nos. 11 and 12).

In many issues of *Le Naturaliste,* Abbé Provancher added supplements for some of the systematic groups about which he knew more or in which he was more personally interested. These resulted in books on the description and life of aquatic, as well as of terrestrial, groups of Quebec. The author, however, did the same work for other groups which had not been dealt with in the supplements. Thus, two books on Canadian birds (Provancher, 1874a, 1874b), including the aquatic ones, appeared as reprints. Abbé Provancher (1877, 1883, 1886) published his *Petite faune entomologique du Canada,* which, in fact, was a huge work of 1,670 pages, the first one of its kind in Canada. There were in addition several supplements made by the author, a single one of which, published in 1889, had 475 pages. These four volumes, with two supplements, made up a total of 2,530 pages (Huard, 1926, pp. 263–282). In 1891 the author edited a book on Quebec mollusks (Provancher, 1891). On the title page it is written that this is the first part, but the second part was never published, since Abbé Provancher died in 1892. In *Le Naturaliste canadien,* 1873, Vol. 5, he related the life and writings of a dozen of the earliest naturalists to deal with Canada. In *Le Naturaliste,* 1875, 7(4)–1876, 8(10), the author published his Canadian fauna of fishes, and this was the third of its kind—after Beaumont Small's 1866 work—but was never reprinted.

Abbé Provancher's heir in the editorship of *Le Naturaliste* was Abbé Victor-A. Huard, in 1894.

The latter followed the same method in his editorial work, publishing some works as reprints. Such is the case of an elementary treatise on zoology and hygiene (Huard, 1905), first published in 1905 and later reprinted several times. In this work the principal phyla of the animal kingdom are treated. For the purpose of the school lectures, phyla are described and illustrated with the help of species found in Quebec, whenever possible. Behavior, habits, habitats, and geographical distribution of many animals are given. Abbé Huard had also a little handbook of zoology (Huard, 1907b) first published in 1907, with later editions. There was also a manual of entomology in 1927 (Huard, 1927). Both the latter works, like the previous one, deal with the habitats of freshwater groups. In 1912 the author (Huard, 1912) studied the natural history terminology used by the French Canadians, including that of fresh waters. In 1897 he had also a travel book: *Labrador et Anticosti*. Named curator of the Musée de l'Instruction publique in 1904 (Huard, 1904, pp. 73–75) and Provincial Entomologist in 1913 (Huard, 1913, p. 97), Abbé Huard was director-proprietor of *Le Naturaliste canadien* until his death on 15 October 1929 (Maheux, 1930, p. 6). He was the first Quebec Government entomologist and was attached to the Department of Agriculture.

In 1869 *Le Naturaliste canadien* started the publication of papers by Dr. J. A. Crevier on Protista. This collaboration continued, with interruptions, until July 1888, when Dr. Crevier fell ill and died on 1 January 1889 in St. Césaire, Quebec. His work was essentially on the Canadian microscopic flora. He is reported to have described 856 new species of microorganisms, bringing the total known for Canada at the time to 1,645 different species (Huard, 1926, pp. 228–229, 240). Abbé Huard believed that Dr. Crevier was the first to write at some length on the Quebec freshwater microorganisms (Huard, 1926, p. 228). However, I tend to doubt this, since in Ontario the Toronto Microscopical Society had already been formed on 1 February 1859 (Canadian Nat. and Geol., 1859, **4**, pp. 155–158), and I should not be surprised if they had studied aquatic microorganisms from all sources, including Quebec, the more so because when the society was formed, the microscopists were already present. Furthermore, as seen from life histories and writings of microbiologists reviewed by Brunel (1944), at least a few books and various other

works had been published on Canadian aquatic microorganisms as early as 1841–42 (Brunel, 1944, p. 21). These works were undoubtedly the ones to which Dr. Crevier was said to have added new species (see also Kemp, 1858).

In 1870 the Société d'Histoire naturelle de Québec was founded. It did almost nothing. Reorganized on 15 March 1887 (Provancher, 1887, p. 160), its history finishes there. It was stillborn; reason: no money. But since then, several societies have been founded to take its place in the Quebec City region. Amongst them are the Société linnéenne de Québec, formed 13 December 1929 (Caron, 1930, pp. 13–14), and the Société zoologique de Québec, founded in 1931 (Potvin, 1941, p. 1), whose experts take part in the scientific and management aspects of the Quebec Zoological Garden founded the same year within the Quebec Department of Game and Fisheries (Brassard, 1933, pp. 188–189). The Linnean Society has no serial, but its scientists publish at large. In 1961 this society took a share in the administration of the Aquarium de Québec, founded recently by the Department of Game and Fisheries. The Société zoologique publishes several serials, with faunal and ecological, terrestrial and aquatic studies.

In 1870 Dr. J. William Dawson, originally from Nova Scotia, Professor of Geology and Paleontology and Principal of McGill University—then called McGill College—since 1855 (Adams, 1939, p. 18), published his *Handbook of Zoology* (Dawson, 1870), followed by at least three other editions. It is one of the earliest works in Canada in which protozoans are treated with metazoans. Within the pages of this book designed for teaching, many examples are found of aquatic and terrestrial animals from Canada, which are described and for which life cycles and environmental requirements are given.

The Université de Montréal (with the official English name of Montreal University—not to be confused with McGill University located also in Montreal) saw its birth in 1876, and courses started in 1878. It was then a branch of Laval University of Quebec City and was called Université Laval de Montréal until 1923 when its charter was granted by Rome as a Catholic University and it took the present name (Le Jeune, 1931, **2**, p. 311). But natural history has been taught at Montreal University only since 1920, when botany courses were begun by Brother Marie-Victorin (1941). The Laboratoire de Bilogie was formed in 1925 and in 1937, under the name of Institut de Biologie, started to publish *Contributions*. In these institutions publications were numerous on aquatic and terrestrial groups and environments. Several papers appeared on limnology and hydrobiology, and their serials will be treated in the next section which deals with writings on limnology and freshwater biology.

A tiny book written in 1876, measuring 3 × 4¼ inches, with a long, ambitious title (see Achintre and Crevier, 1876), by A. Achintre and Dr. J. A. Crevier (the same Crevier cited under *Le Naturaliste canadien* previously), was edited by a Montreal newspaper, about Ste. Helene Island in the St. Lawrence River opposite Montreal. For the island this work cites aquatic plants and insects, mollusks, crustaceans, amphibians, and aquatic birds and mammals. It says that the pools of stagnant water on the island "harbour more than 500 species" of infusorians.

It was in 1877 that the present-day Provincial Museum first took shape, when the Quebec Department of Agriculture purchased the collection of types of insect species from Abbé Léon Provancher (Provancher, 1889, p. 78). A Provincial Museum had been extant many years before in 1835, when the sum of $2,000 was voted for it and a large collection was purchased, but a few years later the building was destroyed by fire (Provancher, 1869, p. 141). The first curator was a botanist, D.-N. Saint-Cyr (Huard, 1907a, p. 141), named in 1882, former deputy from Sainte-Anne-de-la-Pérade, and in 1886 the Musée de l'Instruction publique was built (Mr. Robert Lagueux, Department of Game and Fisheries, Quebec, personal communication). After the death in 1904 of the second curator, Dr. L. Larue, the third curator, Abbé V.-A. Huard, was named (Huard, 1904, p. 73). Finally in 1931 the actual building was erected, and ever since its administration has been under the Provincial Secretary. Its scientific and especially biological personnel was never very numerous, but some papers on aquatic biology were published in periodicals at large. The museum never had any serial (Europa Publications, 1957, p. 139).

The Ottawa Field-Naturalists' Club, founded in 1879, started publishing its *Transactions* in 1880. In *Transactions* No. 2, 1881, page 27, there is a short paper touching Quebec, on the diatoms of the Ottawa River. After two name changes, the serial became the *Canadian Field-Naturalist*. In many issues it has published papers on the na-

tural history of Quebec waters, often dealing with environment and behavior of freshwater organisms.

In 1881 occurred another of the capital events which were to promote the study and research into the natural history of Canada. At Montreal on the 29th and 30th December of that year, the Royal Society of Canada was founded. In 1882 permission was granted by Queen Victoria for the name suggested for the society. The first volume of the *Proceedings and Transactions,* for 1882 and 1883, then printed in Montreal, was published in 1883. Immediately several papers appeared on the freshwater plants and animals of Quebec and other regions of Canada. To demonstrate the use and great interest of this serial, I shall cite one very interesting example of the material found within its covers. In volume 12 (1895) in the *Bibliography of the Members* of the society, on pages 8–12, are the titles and places of publication of the writings by Robert Bell, one of the geologists and biologists who made a great many explorations and observations on the Quebec aquatic flora and fauna. This particular bibliography shows 127 titles. On pages 75–78 a bibliography is given of the works of J. F. Whiteaves who, like the preceding author, wrote several papers on Quebec aquatic organisms: 67 titles of papers of his are listed, including those detailing his discovery of fossil Devonian fishes at Scaumenac Bay, Quebec, and also at Campbellton, New Brunswick.

When in 1896 E. T. D. Chambers brought out his famous book on the Quebec freshwater (landlocked) salmon (Chambers, 1896), he was not a newcomer on the scene of natural history writings. Previously, for example, he had had papers in the *Proceedings and Transactions of the Royal Society of Canada,* and furthermore, he later published several articles on Quebec fresh waters. His book describes, among other things, the aquatic environment, geographical distribution, food, and behavior not only of the ouananiche but also of several other freshwater fishes of Quebec. On pages 331–339 is found an extensive bibliography on these questions. In addition, in 1912, Chambers published a history of the Quebec fisheries, in English and French versions simultaneously (Chambers, 1912a, 1912b). In it he relates the advent of fish culture in North America and of the first hatchery in Canada (pp. 166–174), which "was situated in a house near the corner of St. Ursule and St. John Streets, in the city of Quebec," installed by Richard Nettle in 1857.

In 1896 the geologist A. P. Low issued a *Report on explorations in the Labrador Peninsula*, etc. (Low, 1896). On pages 329L–332L are given the distribution and behavior of freshwater Ungava (then called Labrador Peninsula) fishes. On page 330L freshwater salmon are cited from several places within that vast region covered by the expedition. On page 56L is reported one of the most curious facts of this province's natural history—the presence of a landlocked population of harbor seals (*Phoca vitulina*) as permanent residents of lakes (today called Upper and Lower Seal Lakes) on a tributary (Seal River) to Hudson Bay; therefore, landlocked seals are not exclusively in the large lakes of Siberia. Thus, the Seal Lakes must have an abundant population of readily available fishes to serve as food for the seals.

In Montreal in 1897 the fourth (after Provancher's) Canadian fish fauna was published by André-Napoléon Montpetit, the father of a renowned secretary general of the University of Montreal, Edouard Montpetit, a man of letters and a historian of Canada. That book (Montpetit, 1897) deals with freshwater fishes at great lengths, detailing many aspects of Quebec fish environment and behavior.

In 1898 one of the last important moves for the study and research on Canadian waters was made in the foundation of the Marine Biological Station (first located at Passamaquoddy Bay, New Brunswick), which was to give birth to the Biological Stations of Canada, then to the Biological Board of Canada, and finally to the Fisheries Research Board of Canada. During all these avatars, stations were erected for the study of the fresh waters also, and the serials multiplied and produced more and more papers on the limnology and hydrobiology of Quebec as well as of the other provinces and territories of Canada. The first paper concerning Quebec freshwater fauna, in the *Contributions to Canadian Biology, Being Studies from the Biological Stations of Canada*, new series, was on two copepod (crustacean) species of Lake St. John (Willey, 1923).

The *Check list of the fishes of the Dominion of Canada and Newfoundland* published by Andrew Halkett (1913) was the fifth (after Montpetit's) Canadian fish fauna, and for once was abundantly illustrated, though in halftone photographs. For each species a distribution is given and for the freshwater species, an indication whether each is fluviatile or lacustrine. Later Halkett (1929) issued a booklet which was a popular account of some Canadian fishes including some that are freshwater. For each species he gave the environment, behavior, and food.

In 1919 a pamphlet (Titcomb, 1919) was published at Boston, Massachusetts, which is a sample among a large number of others published on Quebec freshwater environment. It was written by John W. Titcomb, fish culturist for the State of New York, who was consulted by the St Bernard Fish and Game Club, Quebec. He came, analyzed, and inspected the waters of several of their lakes and made his recommendations with the aim of increasing the fish yield for the creel. At the same time, for several lakes, he reported his aquatic faunal observations.

Claude Mélançon is to present-day Quebec what Buffon was to old France: cultured to his finger tips, informed of the events and writings on natural history the world over, and himself author of many books on Quebec aquatic animal groups. Mélançon (1936) published his *Poissons de nos eaux* (i.e., *Fishes of our Waters*), which was the seventh and most recent Canadian fish fauna (the sixth was by the American authors, Evermann and Goldsborough, 1907). There were two other editions of Mélançon's *Fishes*, in 1946 and 1958, each increased by an abundance of scientific data on exigencies, environment, and habits of Quebec fishes. On Quebec animals, Mélançon (1950) wrote another book entitled *Inconnus et méconnus* (i.e., *Unknowns and Ignoreds*), which is on amphibians and reptiles. (The Quebec reptiles are turtles and snakes; there are no lizards.) Again, the life history of each species is related at some length.

The last but not the least among our naturalists, to end this part of the present work, was our former Quebec deputy minister, recently retired in December 1961 after 50 years of devotion to the Department of Game and Fisheries, Colonel L.-A. Richard, doctor at law. He was the promotor of the development of the great recreational parks in Quebec, the founder of the Quebec Zoological Garden, and a member of the Société zoologique de Québec and of several other conservation societies. He wrote nearly all our laws on hunting, fishing, and conservation and saw personally to their revisions as the body of scientific knowledge increased not only in Quebec but in the Northern Hemisphere. He was the promoter f the present system of fish warden education. Ie was the creator of several present fish hatcheries, of all the biological stations, and of the Quebec Office of Biology. He not only permitted .ut encouraged the printing of all the publications by departmental personnel on laws, conservation, .nd science. In addition to being a subscriber to a nass of educational and scientific periodicals, which he read and consulted often, he was himelf a writer. He published on several educational .ubjects among others and also on some aspects of Quebec natural history and scientific developmental prospects. In the references, I cite only wo of Colonel Richard's (1937, 1938) papers which, for the present purpose, I believe to be the best representatives of the thoughts and interests of his life.

Writings on limnology and freshwater biology

During the past three centuries, naturalists— often, though not always, self-made men, good amateurs, intelligent travelers, or observers—had written to their heart's content on nature and its life embodiment. During the first quarter of the present century, they, as artists, became nearly obsolete. During the last century the majority of Quebec and other Canadian institutions aiming at basic research in natural history were set up. The present century was to provide them with the tools to progress, that is, with the informed leaders and the high-aiming workers. The stage for modern science was set.

From then on, the terrain was prepared for research not only into the *how* but also into the *why*. Hard-headed and high-tempered students of nature—let us call them scientists or biologists— were to appear and attempt to delve into all questions, to question all previous interpretations or explanations, to seek interrelations between live being and environment, to establish life cycles, to build phylogenetic trees taking into account exigencies as well as homological transformations of groups, to devise hypotheses and test their theories both in broad nature and in the laboratory. With the advent of a multitude of adaptable instruments and techniques, of refined statistical methods and calculators, of microchemistry, ultraphysics, and radiobiology, of advanced meteorology and paleoclimatology, of functional cytology and modern genetics, combined with all the material and intellectual tools in hand, the systematist, the paleontologist, the embryologist,

and the ecologist were more readily capable of making their interpretations of nature as observed. And thus disappeared, overwhelmed by the material power of this new era—to the relief of the positive thinkers and readers—, the poets of nature, those who only wrote books for the fun of it, the writers with the sonorous sentences. They were displaced by the "egg-head," the man who *thinks* about the caprices of nature, the one who wants at any cost to know *why* nature works that way. Thus, limnologists and hydrobiologists were born. The latter are to former naturalists what 1960 atomicists are to 1890 physicists, or what a modern dye chemist is to a Tyrian purple dyer.

Up to this point in the chapter, books—individual books, reports, or other works—have had to be analyzed for the simple reason that almost nothing else had hitherto been written on hydrobiology. Now, in Canada as well as in the United States, with the advent of the last quarter of the 19th century and of the first quarter of the 20th century, writers have been more and more confined—except when as rich as Croesus—to write in serials and in periodicals if they wanted to be read at all. Hence, hereafter, there will be found a rather short set of works of Quebec or of Canadian origin concerning hydrobiology and limnology. On the other hand, serial writings, which outnumber all the others, will be treated in bulk and will not be analyzed individually, because they are too numerous. They will be associated with their institutions of origin or with their publishers, i.e., those who pay for their printing.

Books, pamphlets, reprints

This section consists of an annotated listing in chronological order of some of the more important works of the past three decades.

The flora by Louis-Marie (1931) is largely taxonomic, but it also discusses the distribution of aquatic vegetation. It has had several reprintings.

As a young man, Gustave Chagnon was already corresponding in 1890 with Abbé L. Provancher, editor of *Le Naturaliste canadien,* from whom he was requesting identification of aquatic organisms (*Nat. canadien,* 20(1), pp. 2–5) Chagnon (1933– 40) published a masterly work on Quebec Coleoptera, in six parts, including aquatic species and relating their environmental conditions.

The treatise by Marie-Victorin (1935) is the

monument to the Quebec vascular flora. It begins
with a sweeping synthesis on Quebec paleo- and
present climatology, goes on to divide the territory into phytogeographic regions, and next develops the elaborately described and illustrated
systematic part where, for each species, the
aquatic ones included, ecological factors are considered. It is a unique case among floras, because
for many of the species details are added concerning biological exigencies of the plants, their
ecological associations, their uses by people or in
pharmacopeia, and several historical facts. It has
been frequently reprinted.

We point out here a thorough systematical and
ecological study of the Quebec freshwater fish
fauna (the first one and still the latest), which
at the same time was a doctoral thesis. On 25
April 1935, Laurence R. Richardson, a New Zea-
lander, after four years of study and research under the sponsorship of McGill University and the
Department of Colonization, Game and Fisheries
of the Province of Quebec, presented his thesis at
McGill University (see L. R. Richardson, 1935).

Another great work, under the same sponsorship as above, representing 13 years (1930–42)
of really hustling research, but so far unpublished, was that of the pertinacious and exacting
Dr. V. C. Wynne-Edwards, who returned around
1945 to Scotland to take the direction of the Natural History Department, Marischal College, Ab-
erdeen University. In departing, Dr. Wynne-Edwards bestowed upon the present writer complete
copies of 75 Quebec maps showing the distribution
of a like number of freshwater fishes. These maps
record the examination, by means of seines or
otherwise, of almost all the rivers and streams of
the province south of the St. Lawrence, from the
Canada–United States border to the eastern ex-
tremity of Gaspé, as well as many lakes and
watercourses in the Plain of Montreal and the
Laurentian region, to latitude 48° N. from Temi-
scamingue to the Laurentides Park, as far as 49°
in the region of Lake St. John and the Saguenay,
and beyond 50° on the Gulf of St. Lawrence
North Shore. Dr. Wynne-Edwards authorized the
present writer to use these maps for the purpose
of publications on the distribution of Quebec
freshwater fishes. His collections of fish specimens are now kept in the collections of the Quebec Office of Biology.

A monastic work, in both the proper and fig-
urative senses, was done by Brother Irénée-Marie

(1938) on the algae of the desmid group, for the
Montreal region.

Rousseau *et al.* (1939) published a bibliography of all the writings on botany, including
bacteria, pigmented Protista, and aquatic plants,
which had appeared in the *Proceedings and Transactions of the Royal Society of Canada* from
their beginning until 1936. Papers are listed in
alphabetical order of authors' names, and there
are two alphabetical tables: the one, of the subjects treated in the papers; the other, of the taxonomic groups.

Dr. Jules Brunel was an early collaborator of
Brother Marie-Victorin, as well as Dr. Jacques
Rousseau and several others, and we must mention also the intensive and devoted works done
and published by several members belonging to
religious orders, Marie-Victorin's and others'. Dr.
Brunel, former director of the Department of
Botany, Montreal University, now Professor
there, published many papers on algae, diatoms,
and plankton, marine and freshwater groups, including ecological studies on them.

The first instance of a published paper, to my
knowledge, in which seried chemical analyses of
Quebec fresh waters were made, deals with lakes
of Gaspesia in 1935–37 by Honeyman (1939),
who is now Professor at George William College
in Montreal and was formerly director of the
Eastern Township Hatchery, Department of
Game and Fisheries.

The present writer, Legendre (1941), prepared
his M.Sc. Thesis on the physicochemical conditions in several lakes of the Laurentides Park. In
it, an attempt was made to correlate the disappearance of oxygen throughout summer with
the increase in carbon dioxide and the observed
pH conditions.

A typed report on observations of the ouananiche (freshwater salmon) of the Peribonka
River, Lake St. John northern region, dealing
also with the influence of a large electrical dam
on aquatic life, was prepared by Vladykov
(1942*a*; one copy in the Office of Biology library). His next report (Vladykov, 1942*b*) was
never published, either and being polycopied it
is distributed only on request, which ensures that
it will be used exclusively by scientists. It includes inspections, physical measurements, and
chemical analyses done in 1938–41 by the present
writer on 48 lakes of the Laurentides Park.

The volume by Préfontaine (1942) was never

published but was typed in 10 copies distributed in 1942 among certain Quebec Government agencies. It presented the results of the first two Quebec biological stations which worked for some time on the province's fresh waters and contained data obtained by Drs. George Préfontaine, Vadim D. Vladykov, Fred E. J. Fry, and by the present writer and several others. For each of the 39 papers contained therein, the authors are indicated.

The report by Güssow (1942), which is mimeographed and is represented by one copy in the Office of Biology library, deals in part with the physicochemical environment required by trout.

For anyone wishing to understand the development of aquatic research in Quebec, the three papers by Préfontaine (1944, 1945, 1946) are essential.

The first essay written in Quebec on the sociological correlations between fish and freshwater plants was by Dr. Pierre Dansereau (1945), former director of the Montreal Botanical Garden and of the Department of Botany, Montreal University, and assistant-director of the New York Botanical Garden since 1961.

The first elaborate study of Quebec freshwater plankton was done by a lady biologist (Lanouette, 1946) at the service of the Office of Biology. In this work physicochemical conditions of the environment were correlated with plankton.

The present assistant-director of the Management Service, Department of Game and Fisheries, prepared a M.Sc. Thesis (Lagueux, 1950) which was on an attempt to correlate the abundance of certain plankton groups with the use of mineral fertilizers.

The first physicochemical study made in Quebec on the nature of lake bottoms and the rate of sedimentation was by Kleerekoper and Grenier (1952).

Dr. Aurèle LaRocque (1953), a graduate from the Ottawa University, now Professor at Ohio State University, published a large catalogue of the Mollusca of Canada. Its bibliography includes the earliest sources, such as Parkhurst, 1578 (who came to Newfoundland), and Champlain, 1603 (who came to Quebec, then called Stadacona), with 30 pages showing 727 titles, a demonstration of the progress made in this field.

Among the many papers he wrote on hydrobiology and on the management of the renewable natural resources, Dr. Gustave Prévost,

former director of the Office of Biology until he left on 1 July 1961, prepared a most elaborate Ph.D. Thesis (Prévost, 1954) on the behavior of a fish in relation to many environmental conditions.

We are far from being well provided in our library at the Office of Biology with the works on freshwater biology produced at McGill University. However, we do have one of the most interesting works dealing with the phylogenetical passage of early vertebrates from marine to freshwater environment, and I should like to cite it here as being a masterpiece which was applauded the world over in the interested scientific circles (Berrill, 1955).

Among the numerous M.Sc. and Ph.D. theses submitted to the Department of Botany, Montreal University, I should like to cite only the one by Pageau (1959), which was prepared with the help of funds provided by the Quebec Department of Game and Fisheries to cover part of the cost of this study. The department contributed here because the work was on the ecology of freshwater plants in an enlargement of the St. Lawrence River at Montreal (Lake St. Louis). This work was done under the direction of Dr. Pierre Dansereau.

Dr. Jacques Rousseau, former director of the Montreal Botanical Garden, now Professor at La Sorbonne, Paris, France, crossed the Ungava several times in north-south and west-east directions. He brought back many specimens, among which the fishes were delivered to me. Dr. Rousseau had a large number of writings on Ungava and on other parts of Quebec, in many subjects, from Esquimaux to geology and to the history of science in Quebec, and from systematics to the ecology of terrestrial and freshwater organisms, but mostly on plants.

During several years, after expeditions through parts of Ungava, Abbé Ernest Lepage, School of Agriculture, Rimouski, Quebec, published studies on arctic terrestrial and freshwater groups, reporting at the same time on their environmental conditions. He published in *Le Naturaliste canadien.* In addition McGill University opened a biological station several years ago at Knob Lake in the heart of Ungava. Some of the papers written by scientists of the station have appeared in the periodical *Arctic,* journal of the Arctic Institute of North America.

As regards the Arctic freshwater fishes of

Quebec, Mr. Roger LeJeune (1959, 1961), Department of Game and Fisheries, studied the Arctic char of the George River, a tributary to Ungava Bay.

Under the powerful stimulation of Dr. T. W. M. Cameron, the director of the Institute of Parasitology at Macdonald College, Ste. Anne de Bellevue, near Montreal—a branch of McGill

University—many studies of parasites on aquatic organisms, and of the ecological conditions favoring their prosperity, were done in the last twenty years. Many papers, as well as M.Sc. and Ph.D. theses, have originated from these observations.

Raymond Desrochers, present director of the Lachine Fish Hatchery near Montreal, wrote his M.Sc. Thesis on the purple bacteria of lakes. He

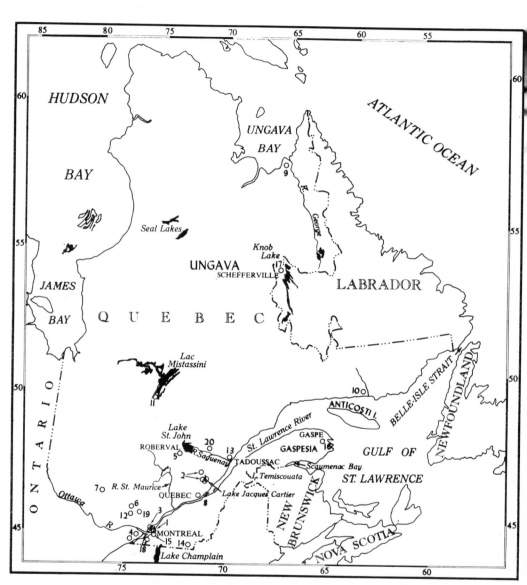

Fig. 17.2.—Quebec freshwater biological stations. Map prepared by the University of Wisconsin Cartographic Laboratory. In the description on the facing page, numbers 1 through 20 preceding the name of the sta-

tion key its location on the map. Following the name of the station is a description of its location and the date of its foundation or duration dates.

showed that bog lakes, compared to the other normal types of lakes, contain characteristically high counts of these purple bacteria. He has now concluded his Ph.D. thesis on sulfurous bacteria which have a role in the elimination of sulfite waste products from paper mills (Desrochers, 1962).

To end this enumeration with a curious case, the cosmopolitan freshwater coelenterate, *Craspedacusta sowerbyi*, makes appearances at irregular intervals of years in its medusa stage in the waters of Quebec. It was studied by biologists who published papers on aspects of its ecology (Fantham and Porter, 1938; Robert, 1956).

It is remarkable that in Quebec nothing much has been done on freshwater crustaceans (apart from those found in plankton), on vermiform groups living freely, on rotifers, bryozoans, and some other of the smaller phyla.

Serials

To summarize the works that have appeared on the hydrobiology and limnology of Quebec, I have grouped (Table 17.1) some of the principal institutions, with the accent on the Canadian ones, that have published studies on this province, along with the dates of foundation or of duration of these institutions and the date on

---

Quebec Ministry of Game and Fisheries Biological Stations

1	Biological Service	Montreal, McGill University	1930–60
2	Laurentides Park B.S. (moved to 4 locations)	Montmorency County, Laurentides Park, near Lake Jacques-Cartier	1938———
3	Office of Biology	Montreal	1942———
4	Montreal B.S. (moved to 2 locations)	Vaudreuil County	1942–43
5	Roberval B.S.	Lake St. John, Roberval	1944–45
6	Mont-Tremblant Park B.S.	Montcalm County, Mont-Tremblant Park, near Saint-Jovite	1949———
7	La Vérendrye Park B.S.	Pontiac County, La Vérendrye Park, near Lac des Loups	1958———
8	Quebec Biological Center	Quebec City	1959———
9	Kagnerloualoudjouark B.S.	Ungava Bay, George River	1959———
10	Nabesipi B.S.	Gulf of St. Lawrence North Shore, Nabesipi River	1960———
11	Lake Mistassini B.S.	Ungava, Lake Mistassini	1961———

Quebec Ministry of Game and Fisheries Fish Hatcheries and Biological Stations

12	Saint-Faustin F.H.	Terrebonne County, Saint-Faustin	1933———
13	Tadoussac F.H.	Tadoussac, Saguenay River	founded 19th century; studies 1943———
14	Eastern Townships F.H.	Stanstead County, near Lake Lester (Lyster)	founded early 20th century; studies 1949———
15	Lachine F.H.	Lachine, near Montreal	1949———
16	Gaspé F.H.	Gaspé, York River	founded 19th century; studies 1959———

McGill University Biological Station

17	Knob Lake B.S.	Ungava, Knob Lake	1955———

Montreal University Biological Stations

18	Montreal B.S. (2 locations simultaneously)	Perrot Island, and Châteauguay River, both on Lake Saint-Louis	1940–41
19	Montreal University B.S.	Terrebonne County, near Sainte-Marguerite-du-lac-Masson	1962———

Joliette College Biological Station (College in town of Joliette, Quebec)

20	Camp des Jeunes Explorateurs	Saguenay River, Cap Jaseur, Saint-Fulgence, near Chicoutimi	1958———

which they began their publishing on these subjects or the time during which these publications lasted. The majority of the dates, especially those of foundation, were extracted from the Quebec Statistical Year Books, published by the Ministry of Trade and Commerce. In practice, ministries are also called departments. In the table the names of the serials are *italicized*.

In the *Statistical Year Book* for 1948, published March 1949, pages 221–232, there is a bibliography by Jean-Charles Bonenfant: "French language books and reviews published in Canada during the past ten years." For completeness especially as regards serials published by the Federal Government of Canada, by governments and institutions of the other Canadian provinces, and by foreign organizations, see the polycopied work by Sansfaçon and Legendre (1957), which is distributed only on request by the Office of Biology. As its title indicates, the latter work is not

TABLE 17.1

Institutions	Dates of beginning or duration	Publications on Quebec fresh waters	Dates of beginning or duration
QUEBEC: Government			
Govt. of Canada (Quebec+Ontario)	1760–1791	?	
Govt. of Lower Canada (Quebec)[a]	1791–1840	?	
Govt. of Union (Quebec+Ontario)	1840–1867		
Ministry of Game & Fisheries[b]	1857——	*Annual Report*	1857——
Province of Quebec	1867——		
Ministry of Game & Fisheries[b]	1867——	*Annual Report*	1867——
Hatchery Service	1915——	*Annual Report*[c]	1915——
Biological Service	1930–1942	*Annual Report*[c]	1930–1942
Eastern Townships Hatchery[d]	1908——	*Propagation*	1961——
Lachine Fish Hatchery	1949——	*Contribution*	1961——
Office of Biology[e]	1942——	*Annual Report*	1944——
		Contribution	1934[f]——
		Notes biologiques[g]	1949
		Ephémérides de l'Office de Biologie[g]	1953–1954
		Ephemerides of the Quebec Office of Biology[g]	June 1954
		Journal de Bord de l'Office de Biologie[g]	1955–1961
		Activités de l'Office de Biologie[g]	1960
Mont Tremblant Biological Sta.	1949——		1952——
Dept. of Maritime Fisheries	1942——	*Annual Report*[h]	1943——
		Actualités marines	1957——
		Contribution	1912[f]——·
Biology Laboratory	1945——	(pub. in *Contribution* above)	
Laurentides Park Biological Sta.	1949——	(pub. in *Contribution* above)	
Centre biologique de Québec	1959——	?	
Provincial Parks Service[i]	1918——	*Annual Report*[c]	
LaVérendrye Park Biological Sta.	1959——		1959——
Quebec Salmon Commission	1937–1949		1938——?
Coordination Committee on the Atlantic Salmon	1949——		1951——
Ministry of Trade and Commerce[b]	1935——	*Statistical Year Book*[j]	1914——
Office de Recherches scientifiques	1937——	*Contribution*	1942——
Economic Geography Service	1953	(papers on natural history in geographical serials)	1953
Provincial Secretary's Dept.	1760?		
Biogeography Service	1943——	*Bulletin*	1944——
Quebec Streams Commission	1910——	(debits of rivers, soundings of lakes)	1910——

[a] Several exploratory expeditions.
[b] Name varied.
[c] Published in *Annual Report* of the Ministry. The Hatchery Service report of the Ministry of Game and Fisheries, Province of Quebec, contains natural history material.
[d] Formerly Baldwin's Mills Hatchery, and Lake Lester—corrupted into Lyster—Hatchery.
[e] Formerly Biological Bureau, and Bureau of Biology.
[f] Including previous papers.
[g] *Notes biologiques*, 3 issues only; *Ephémérides de*

l'Office de Biologie, 16 issues; *Ephemerides of the Quebec Office of Biology*, 1 issue only; *Journal de Bord de l'Office de Biologie*, 82 issues; *Activités de l'Office de Biologie*, 11 issues.
[h] Since 1941, *Annual Report* as Service of Maritime Fisheries.
[i] First created as forestry preserves or as national parks.
[j] Published at first by the Bureau of Statistics, Provincial Secretary's Dept.

TABLE 17.1 (*Continued*)

Institutions	Dates of beginning or duration	Publications on Quebec fresh waters	Dates of beginning or duration
QUEBEC: Universities			
McGill Univ. (started as McGill College, 1813)	1821——		
Dept. of Zoology	1858——	?	
Macdonald College	1905——		
Institute of Parasitology	1932——		
Knob Lake Research Laboratory[k]	1955——		1936——
Laval Univ., Quebec City	1852——		1955——
Collège de Sainte-Anne-de-la-Pocatière	1829——		
Ecole supérieure des Pêcheries[l]	1938——		1935[f]——
Institut de Géographie de l'Université Laval	?	*Cahiers de Géographie de Québec*	1953——
Laval Univ. Forest Research Foundation	?		1956
Montreal Univ.	1876——	*Revue canadienne de Biologie*	1942——
School of Higher Commercial Studies	1907——		1912——
Faculty of Sciences	1920——		
Biology Laboratory	1920——	*Contribution* (7 issues)	1925–1930
Institut de Zoologie	?	*Contribution*	1938——
		Travaux de l'Institut de Biologie générale et de Zoologie	1940——
Lake Jacques Cartier Biological Sta.	1938–1941		1939–1942
Montreal Biological Sta.	1941–1942		1942
Faculty of Letters	?		
Institut de Géographie de l'Université de Montréal	1947——	*Revue canadienne de Géographie*[m]	1947——
QUEBEC: Learned Societies			
Provancher Soc. of Natural History of Canada	1918——		1928——
Société de Biologie de Montréal	1922——		1942——
Canadian Soc. of Natural History	1923——		1933——
Association canadienne-française pour l'Avancement des Sciences (ACFAS)	1923——	*Annales de l'ACFAS*	1935——
Société linnéenne de Québec	1929——	(pub. in *Le Naturaliste canadien*)	1929——
Quebec Zoological Society	1931——		1941——
Société lévisienne d'Histoire naturelle	1931——	?	
Société historique du Saguenay, Chicoutimi, Québec	?	*Publication*	1934–1945
		Bulletin	1946–1958
		Saguenayensia	1959——
Société d'Histoire naturelle de la Pocatière	1936——		1948——
Société de Biologie de Québec	1946——		1948——
Canadian Society of Ecology	1952——		1952——
QUEBEC: Educational Societies			
4-H Clubs of Quebec	1942——		1945——
Cercles des Jeunes Naturalistes	1931——	*Tract*	1932——
Young Naturalists' Clubs		*Leaflets of Natural History*	1947——
Les Amis de la Nature	1949——		1949——
Séminaire de Joliette, Joliette, Québec		*La Viateur naturaliste*	1950–1951
		Le Jeune Naturaliste	1951——
Camp des Jeunes Explorateurs	1958——	*Rapport*	1958——
QUEBEC: Conservation Associations			
Montreal Anglers and Hunters	1936——		1936——
Quebec Federation of the Associations of Fish and Game	1946——		1946——

[k] Some of the papers published in *Arctic*, the journal of the Arctic Institute of North America.
[l] Government funds since 1941.

[m] Being also the journal of the Société de Géographie de Montréal.

TABLE 17.1 (*Continued*)

Institutions	Dates of beginning or duration	Publications on Quebec fresh waters	Dates of beginning or duration
QUEBEC: Periodicals and Companies' Serials			
Revue trimestrielle	1915——		1931——
Hudson's Bay Company		*The Beaver*	1920——
The Seignory Club, Lucerne-in-Quebec		*Le Seigneur*	1931——
Canadian Pacific Railway		*Sport and Recreation Bulletin*	1935?——
Drummondville Cotton Company		*Bluenose News*	1945——
Royal Bank of Canada		*Monthly Bulletin*	1946?——
Chasse et Pêche			1949–1955
L'Ami du Pêcheur			1951–1953
ONTARIO: Government			
Ontario Fisheries Research Laboratory	1921——		1927——
Dept. of Game and Fisheries			
Biological and Fish Culture Branch	1926——		1931——
ONTARIO: Universities			
University of Toronto			
Royal Ontario Museums			1939——
Ottawa University	?		?
ONTARIO: Learned Society			
Ontario Society of Biologists	1944——		1944——
ONTARIO: Company Periodical			
Carling Breweries		*Carling Conservation Digest*	1945——
CANADA: Government			
Dept. of Fisheries			
Fisheries Research Board of Canada	1898——		1909——
Dept. of the Interior			
Commission of Conservation	1909——		1911——
Service of Natural Resources	1921——		1923——
National Research Council	1917——		1924——
Canadian Broadcasting Corp.	1940——	*Radio-Collège*	1943——
CANADA: Conservation Associations			
Canadian Fisheries Association	1914——		1914——
Canadian Conservation Association			1941——
Atlantic Salmon Association	1948——		1948——
CANADA: Periodical			
Canadian Nature	1939——		1941——
INTERNATIONAL SOCIETY			
Arctic Institute of N. America	1945——	*Arctic*	1948——
		Technical Paper	1956——
		Special Publication	?
(In collaboration with Arctic Institute of N. Amer.)			
Catholic Univ. of Amer., Washington		*Contribution of the Arctic Institute*	1948——
U.S. Dept. of Defense		*Arctic Bibliography*	1953——

a list of individual papers which have appeared in serials, but only a gathering together into one book of as many of the serials as possible in which papers on these subjects have been published.

Manuscripts

During the twenty years of its existence, the Office of Biology, founded in 1942 by the deputy minister of that period, Colonel Louis-Arthur Richard, and organized and directed by Dr. Gustave Prévost, collected files on inspections of about 6,000 lakes and rivers of the Province of Quebec. In this province it has been calculated that there are about 1,000,000 lakes, so there is still some work left to be done. These inspection files are roughly classified in three types (see Legendre, 1953, Ninth Report of the Biological Bureau, 1950–52, pages 148–183), according to the touristic importance and the management interest of the waters concerned.

In addition, along the years, various types of studies or observations, originating from laboratory experiments and experiments in the field and in biological or fish hatchery stations, were concentrated into about 2,000 files in the library of the Office of Biology. These may vary from a single sheet of paper to the equivalent of a large book computing the observations from several seasons of work by one man or by a complete station. For scientific or management purposes, all of these files are placed as a matter of course at the disposal of anyone, whether from some other section of our own department, from other Canada departments or institutions, or from anywhere else in the world. These files constitute a mine into which workers may delve for the preparation of their own writings.

References for Quebec

ACHINTRE, A., AND J. A. CREVIER. 1876. L'ile Ste. Hélène. Passé, présent et avenir. Géologie, paléontologie, flore et faune. Ateliers du journal Le National, Montréal. 100 p.

ADAMS, F. D. 1939. The history of geology in Canada, p. 7–20. *In* H. M. Tory (ed.), A history of science in Canada. Ryerson Press, Toronto. 152 p.

ADAMSON, W. A. 1860. Salmon-fishing in Canada by a resident. Edited by James Edward Alexander. Longman, Green, Longman, and Roberts, London. 350 p.

ALEXANDER, J. E. See ADAMSON.

ANONYMOUS. 18th century. Traitté des animaux a quatre pieds, terrestres et amphibies, qui se trouvent dans les Indes occidentales, ou Amérique septentrionale. Suivi (fol. 65) d'un Traité des oyseaux et (fol. 78) d'un Traitté des poissons. Bibliothèque nationale [Paris], fonds français, 12223, 86 feuillets (supplément français 369). Photostat, 275 p.

BELL, ROBERT. 1859. On the natural history of the Gulf of St. Lawrence, and the distribution of the Mollusca of eastern Canada. Canadian Nat. and Geol., **4**(3): 197–220 and (4): 241–242. See also D'URBAN, 1859: 242–276.

BERRILL, N. J. 1955. The origin of vertebrates. Clarendon Press, Oxford. 257 p.

BOUCHER, PIERRE. 1664. Histoire veritable et natvrelle des moevrs et prodvctions du pays de la Novvelle-France. 3rd ed., 1882. Bastien, Montréal. 164 p.

BOUCHETTE, JOSEPH. 1815a. Description topographique de la province du Bas Canada, avec des remarques sur le Haut Canada, et sur les relations des deux provinces avec les Etats Unis de l'Amérique. Faden, London. 664 + lxxxvi p.

———. 1815b. A topographical description of the Province of Lower Canada, with remarks upon Upper Canada, and on the relative connexion of both Provinces with the United States of America. Faden, London. 640 + lxxxvi p.

BOUCHETTE, JOSEPH, LE JEUNE. See STUART AND STUART, 1829: 108–171.

BOYLE, GERTRUDE M., AND MARJORIE COLBECK. 1959. A bibliography of canadiana. 1st suppl. The Public Library, Toronto. 333 p. See also STATON AND TREMAINE, 1934.

BRASSARD, J.-A. 1933. Jardin zoologique de Québec— Quebec Zoological Garden. Prov. Quebec, Min. Colonization, Game and Fish., Gen. Rept., 1933: 188–205.

BRITISH MUSEUM. 1903–1940. Catalogue of the books, manuscripts, maps and drawings in the British Museum (Natural History). 8 v. British Museum, London. 3883 p.

BRUNEL, JULES. 1944. Les grandes étapes de l'algologie américaine. Contrib. Inst. botan. Univ. Montréal, **52**: 1–32.

CANADA. DEPARTMENT OF FISHERIES. Annual Report. 1867———.

CARON, OMER. 1930. La Société linnéenne de Québec. Naturaliste canadien, **57**(1): 13–14.

CARTIER, JACQUES. See POULIOT, 1934: 11–139.

CHAGNON, GUSTAVE. 1933–40. Contribution à l'étude des coléoptères de la province de Québec. Dépt. Biol., Univ. Montréal, 385 p.

CHAMBERS, E. T. D. 1896. The ouananiche and its Canadian environment. Harper & Brothers, New York. 357 p.

———. 1912a. The fisheries of the Province of Quebec. Prov. Québec, Min. Colonisation, Mines et Fish. 206 p.

———. 1912b. Les pêcheries de la province de Québec. Prov. Québec, Min. Colonisation, Mines et Pêch. 214 p.

CHAMPLAIN, SAMUEL. See LAVERDIERE.

DANSEREAU, PIERRE. 1945. Essai de corrélation sociologique entre les plantes supérieures et les poissons de la beine du lac Saint-Louis. (Contrib.

Inst. Biol., Univ. Montreal, No. 16.) Rev. canadienne Biol., 4(3): 369–417.

DAWSON, J. W. 1870. Handbook of Canadian Zoology. Dawson Brothers, Montreal. 264 p. (At least three other editions, the third in 1886, the fourth in 1889).

DESROCHERS, RAYMOND. 1962. Etude d'une population de bactéries réductrices du soufre dans la rivière Ottawa. Ph.D. Thesis, Faculté de Médecine, Univ. Montréal.

D'URBAN, W. S. M. 1858. Description of some of the fresh-water Gasteropoda, inhabiting the lakes and rivers of Canada. Canadian Nat. and Geol., 2(3): 195–215.

———. 1859a. Catalogue of Coleoptera collected by Mr. Robert Bell, 1858. Canadian Nat. and Geol., 4(4): 242–244.

———. 1859b. Catalogue of plants collected by Mr. Robert Bell, 1858. Canadian Nat. and Geol., 4(4): 246–251.

———. 1859–61. Observations on the natural history of the Valley of the River Rouge, and surrounding townships in the counties of Argenteuil and Ottawa. Canadian Nat. and Geol., 4(4): 252–276; 5(2): 81–99; 6(1): 36–42.

DYMOND, J. R. 1939. Zoology in Canada, p. 41–57. In H. M. Tory (ed.), A history of science in Canada. Ryerson Press, Toronto.

———. 1949. X. Zoology, p. 108–120. In W. Stewart Wallace (ed.), The Royal Canadian Institute centennial volume 1849–1949. Royal Canadian Institute, Toronto.

EUROPA PUBLICATIONS LTD. 1957. The world of learning. 8th ed. London, England. 1038 p.

EVERMANN, B. W., AND E. L. GOLDSBOROUGH. 1907. A check list of the freshwater fishes of Canada. Proc. Biol. Soc. Washington, 20: 89–119.

FANTHAM, H. B., AND ANNIE PORTER. 1938. Occurrence of the freshwater medusa, Craspedacusta sowerbii, in eastern Canada. Nature, 141: 515–516.

FERRIER, W. F., AND DOROTHY J. FERRIER. 1920. Annotated catalogue of and guide to the publications of the Geological Survey of Canada 1845–1917. Canada, Department of Mines, Geological Survey, No. 1723, King's Printer, Ottawa. 544 p.

FORTIN, PIERRE. 1863. List of cetacea, fishes, crustacea, and mollusca, which now inhabit and have inhabited the Canadian shores of the Gulf of St. Lawrence etc. Annual Reports . . . for the Protection of the Fisheries in the Gulf of St. Lawrence During the Seasons of 1861 and 1862, Quebec: 109–123.

———. 1863. Liste des cétacés, des poissons, des crustacés et des mollusques, qui fréquentent et habitent ou ont habité les côtes canadiennes du golfe St. Laurent etc. Rapports annuels . . . pour la protection des pêcheries dans le golfe St. Laurent pendant les saisons de 1861 et 1862, Québec: 113–129.

———. 1864. Continuation of the list of fish of the Gulf and River St. Lawrence. Annual report . . . 1863. Report of the Commissioner of Crown Lands

of Canada for the Year 1863. Sessional Papers (No. 5), A. 1864, 12 p.

———. 1864. Suite de la liste des poissons du golfe St. Laurent et des rivières qui s'y déchargent. Rapport annuel . . . 1863. Rapport du commissaire des Terres de la Couronne du Canada pour l'année 1863. Document de la Session (No. 5), A. 1864, 13 p.

———. 1865. Continuation of the list etc. Annual Report . . . 1864. Sessional Paper (No. 25), A. 1865: 61–69.

———. 1865. Continuation de la liste etc. Rapport annuel . . . 1864. Document de la Session (No. 25), A. 1865: 65–73.

———. 1866. Continuation of the list etc. Annual Report . . . 1865. Sessional Paper (No. 36), A. 1866: 69–79.

———. 1866. Continuation de la liste etc. Rapport annuel . . . 1865. Document de la Session (No. 36), A. 1866: 72–84.

GAGNON, PHILÉAS. 1895, 1913. Essai de bibliographie canadienne. 2 v. Tome I: Québec, 711 p.; Tome II: Montréal, Cité de Montréal, 462 p.

GIBB, G. D. 1858. On the existence of a cave in the Trenton limestone at the Côte St. Michel, on the Island of Montreal. Canadian Nat. and Geol., 3(3): 192–193.

———. 1861. On Canadian caverns. Canadian Nat. and Geol., 6(3): 184–190.

GIRAUD, MARCEL. 1950. Histoire du Canada. "Que sais-je?" Presses universitaires de France, Paris. 135 p.

GOODE, G. BROWN. 1886. The beginnings of natural history in America. Proc. Biol. Soc. Washington, 3: 35–105.

GOSSE, P. H. 1840. The Canadian naturalist. A series of conversations on the natural history of Lower Canada. Van Voorst, London. 372 p.

GÜSSOW, H. T. 1942. Artificial stocking versus natural reproduction with special reference to lakes controlled by the Byng Fish and Game Club, Farrellton, Quebec. Revised April 1943. Privately published. 68 p.

HAIGHT, W. R. 1896–98. Canadian catalogue of books. 2 parts. 3 suppls.: Annual Canadian catalogue of books. Haight, Toronto.

HALKETT, ANDREW. 1913. Check list of the fishes of the Dominion of Canada and Newfoundland. King's Printer, Ottawa. 138 p.

———. 1929. A popular account of the fishes of Canada from the lampreys and hagfishes to the viper fishes inclusive. King's Printer, Ottawa. 38 p.

HARRIS, JOHN. 1705. Navigantium atque itinerantium bibliotheca: or A compleat collection of voyages and travels: consisting of above four hundred of the most authentick writers; etc. 2 v. London. 862 + 928 + 56 p. (Folio.)

HOGAN, J. SHERIDAN, AND ALEXANDER MORRIS. 1856. Canada and her resources. 2nd ed. Low, London. 86 + 119 p.

HONEYMAN, A. J. M. 1939. Lacustrine investigations in the Gaspé Peninsula. Canadian J. Research, D, 17: 212–224.

HOOKER, W. J. 1829–40. Flora boreali-americana, etc. 2 v. London.

HUARD, V.-A. 1904. Au Musée de l'Instruction publique. Naturaliste canadien, 31(7) : 73–75.

——. 1905. Traité élémentaire de zoologie et d'hygiène. Québec. 260 p.

——. 1907a. Nos naturalistes d'il y a un demi-siècle. Naturaliste canadien, 34(9) : 141.

——. 1907b. Abrégé de zoologie. Marcotte, Québec. 130 p.

——. 1912. La terminologie franco-canadienne dans les sciences naturelles. Québec. 30 p.

——. 1913. Un entomologiste provincial. Naturaliste canadien, 39(7) : 97.

——. 1926. La vie et l'oeuvre de l'Abbé Provancher. Garneau, Québec. 511 p.

——. 1927. Manuel théorique et pratique d'entomologie. Québec. 164 p.

IRÉNÉE-MARIE, FRÈRE. 1938. Flore desmidiale de la région de Montréal. Laprairie. 547 p.

KALM, PETER. 1754, 1757, 1764. Beschreibung der Reise die er nach dem nördlichen Amerika auf den Befehl gedachter Akademie und öffentliche Kosten unternommen hat. 3 v. Bandenhoek, Göttingen. 568 + 592 + 648 p.

KEMP, A. F. 1858. The fresh water algae of Canada. Canadian Nat. and Geol., 3(5) : 331–345; (6) : 450–466.

KLEEREKOPER, HERMAN, AND F. GRENIER. 1952. The bottom sediments of Lake Lauzon, Montcalm County, Province of Quebec. I. Chemical and physical investigations. Canadian J. Zool., 3 : 219–242.

LACÉPÈDE, B. G. E. DELAVILLE, comte de. 1830–33. Histoire naturelle des poissons. 12 v. Pillot, Paris.

LAGUEUX, ROBERT. 1950. Etude sur les effets produits par l'introduction d'engrais dans le milieu lacustre. M.Sc. Thesis, Faculté des Sciences, Univ. Montréal.

LANOUETTE, CÉCILE. 1946. Le plancton du lac Horatio Walker, Parc des Laurentides; étude qualitative et quantitative. M.Sc. Thesis, Faculté des Sciences, Univ. Montréal, 113 p.

LAROCQUE, AURÈLE. 1953. Catalogue of the recent Mollusca of Canada. Canada, Dept. Resource and Develop., Natl. Museum Canada, Bull. No. 129, 406 p.

LAVERDIERE, C.-H. 1870. Oeuvres de Champlain [1599–1635]. 6 v. 2nd ed. Desbarats, Québec, under the patronage of the Université Laval. 1400 p.

LEGENDRE, VIANNEY. 1941. Contribution à l'hydrographie des lacs du Parc des Laurentides. M.Sc. Thesis, Faculté des Sciences, Univ. Montréal, 60 p.

——. 1953. 1. Inspection et étude des eaux de la province de Québec. 1. Inspection and study of the waters of the Province of Quebec. (French and English on facing pages.) Province of Quebec, Game and Fish. Dept., 9th Rept. Biol. Bur., 1950–52 : 148–183.

LEJEUNE, L. 1931. Dictionnaire général . . . du Canada. 2 v. Univ. d'Ottawa, Ottawa. 862 + 829 p.

LEJEUNE, ROGER. 1959. Aménagements, enquêtes et recherches. Rapport sur la pêcherie d'ombles chevaliers (*Salvelinus alpinus*) de Kagnerloualoud-jouark (rivière Georges) pour 1959 : 64–97. (Manuscript.)

——. 1961. Rapport sur la pêcherie d'ombles chevaliers de Kagnerloualoudjouark (Ungava, Québec), pour l'année 1960, 57 p. (Manuscript.)

LEMOINE, J. M. 1860–61. Ornithologie du Canada. Editio princeps. 2 parts. Fréchette, Québec. 398 p.

——. 1863. Les pêcheries du Canada. Atelier typographique du *Canadien*, Québec. 146 p.

——. 1872. L'album du touriste. Archéologie, histoire, littérature, sport, Québec. 2nd ed. Côté, Québec. 388 p.

——. 1887. Chasse et pêche au Canada. Hardy, Québec. 300 p.

——. 1889. Historical and sporting notes on Quebec and its environs. 2 parts. 4th ed. Demers, Québec. 133 p.

LITERARY AND HISTORICAL SOCIETY OF QUEBEC. Transactions. 1829–1924. Bulletin. 1900–1907?

LOUIS-MARIE, PÈRE. 1931. Flore-manuel de la province de Québec. Inst. agr. d'Oka, Contrib. No. 23, 320 p.

LOW, A. P. 1896. Report on explorations in the Labrador Peninsula along the East Main, Koksoak, Hamilton, Manicuagan and portions of other rivers in 1892–93–94–95. Geol. Surv. Canada, 1L–332L p.

——. 1906. Report on the Dominion Government expedition to Hudson Bay and the Arctic Islands on board the D.G.S. Neptune 1903–04. Govt. Printing Bur., Ottawa. 355 p.

McMURRICH, J. PLAYFAIR. 1918. President's address—Fifty years of Canadian zoology. Trans. Roy. Soc. Canada, Ser. 3, 11(4) : 1–14.

MAHEUX, GEORGES. 1930. Feu le chanoine V.-A. Huard, 1853–1929. Naturaliste canadien, 67(1) : 5–10.

MARIE-VICTORIN, FRÈRE. 1935. Flore laurentienne. Imprimerie de la Salle, Montréal. 917 p.

——. 1936. Un manuscrit botanique prélinnéen. Rev. trimestrielle canadienne, Sept. 1936.

——. 1939. Canada's contribution to the science of botany, p. 35–40. *In* H. M. Tory (ed.), A history of science in Canada. Ryerson Press, Toronto.

——. 1941. Histoire de l'Institut botanique de l'Université de Montréal 1920–40. Contrib. Inst. botan. Univ. Montréal, 40 : 1–70.

MATTHEWS, G. H. See LEMOINE, 1887 : 241–248.

MÉLANÇON, CLAUDE. 1936. Les poissons de nos eaux. Granger, Montréal. 248 p.

——. 1950. Inconnus et méconnus. Société zoologique de Québec, Québec. 150 p.

MICHAUX, ANDRÉ. 1803. Flora boreali-americana. 2 v. Paris. 330 + 340 p. Written by Louis-Claude Richard. Another edition in 1820.

MONTPETIT, A.-N. 1897. Les poissons d'eau douce du Canada. Beauchemin, Montréal. 552 p.

MORGAN, H. J. 1867. Bibliotheca canadensis: or A manual of Canadian literature. Desbarats, Ottawa. 411 p.

NASH, C. W. 1908. Vertebrates of Ontario. Toronto Dept. Educ., King's Printer, Toronto. 122 + 18 + 96 + 25 p.

NATURAL HISTORY SOCIETY OF MONTREAL. Proceedings, 1828–29.

Annual Report. 1830–63.

Canadian Naturalist and Geologist. 1857–68.

Canadian Naturalist and Quarterly Journal of Science. 1869–83.

Canadian Record of Natural History and Geology. 1884 (No. 1 only).

Canadian Record of Science. 1884–1916.

Canadian Naturalist [summary of original articles, 1857–83]. 1896.

Naturaliste canadien, (Le). 1868——.

NETTLE, RICHARD. 1857. The salmon fisheries of the St. Lawrence and its tributaries. Lovell, Montreal. 144 p.

NIXON, W. See STUART AND STUART, 1829: 67–81.

OTTAWA FIELD-NATURALISTS' CLUB.

Ottawa Field-Naturalists' Club, Transactions. 1880–87.

Ottawa Naturalist. 1888–March 1919.

Canadian Field-Naturalist. April 1919——.

OTTAWA NATURAL HISTORY SOCIETY. Transactions. 1866–68.

PAGEAU, GÉRARD. 1959. Etude descriptive structurale et fonctionnelle de la végétation aquatique supérieure du lac Saint-Louis dans la Grande Anse de l'île Perrot, province de Québec. M.Sc. Thesis, Faculté des Sciences, Univ. Montréal. 232 p.

PARISEAU, LÉO E. 1939. Canadian medicine and biology during the French regime, p. 58–68. In H. M. Tory (ed.), A history of science in Canada. Ryerson Press, Toronto.

PEARL, RAYMOND. 1930. The biology of population growth. Knopf, New York. 260 p.

PENNANT, THOMAS. 1784. Arctic zoology. Vol. I, Introduction. Hughs, London. CC p.

PERLEY, M. H. 1851. Report upon the fisheries of the Bay of Fundy. Queen's Printer, Fredericton. 176 p.

——. 1852. Reports on the sea and river fisheries of New Brunswick. 2nd ed. Queen's Printer, Fredericton. 294 p.

——. 1859. Report on the fisheries of the Gulf of Saint Lawrence. Canadian Nat. and Geol., 4(1): 40–56; (2): 84–100.

POTVIN, DAMASE. 1941. Les Carnets de la Société zoologique de Québec. Carnets Soc. zool. Québec, 1(1): 1.

POULIOT, J. CAMILLE. 1934. La grande aventure de Jacques Cartier [1534–36]. Québec. 328 p.

PRÉFONTAINE, GEORGES. 1942. Rapport de la Station biologique de Montréal et de la Station biologique du Parc des Laurentides pour l'année 1941. 4 fascicules. Inst. Biol., Univ. Montréal. 480 p.

——. 1944. L'aspect scientifique des pêcheries. Actualité économique, November 1944, 39 p. (Reprint.)

——. 1945. Etude biologique des eaux de la plaine de Montréal. Actualité économique, January 1945, 30 p. (Reprint.)

——. 1946. Le développement des connaissances scientifiques sur les pêcheries maritimes et intérieures de l'est du Canada. Actualité économique, January 1946, 68 p. (Reprint.)

PRÉVOST, GUSTAVE. 1954. Contribution à l'étude du comportement de la truite mouchetée (Salvelinus fontinalis fontinalis). D.Sc. Thesis, Faculté des Sciences, Univ. Montréal, 610 p.

PROULX, J. P. See STUART AND STUART, 1829: 171–182.

PROVANCHER, L. 1858. Traité élémentaire de botanique à l'usage des maisons d'éducation. Darveau, Québec. 118 p.

——. 1862. Flore canadienne ou description de toutes les plantes des forêts, champs, jardins et eaux du Canada etc. 2 v. Darveau, Québec. 842 p.

——. 1869. Nos musées. Naturaliste canadien, 1(6): 141.

——. 1874a. Les oiseaux du Canada etc. Québec. 26 p.

——. 1874b. Les oiseaux insectivores etc. Darveau, Québec. 30 p.

——. 1877, 1883, 1886. Petite faune entomologique du Canada. 3 v. Darveau, Québec. 786 + 830 + 354 p. With 4 suppl., 2530 p.

——. 1887. Société d'Histoire naturelle de Québec. Naturaliste canadien, 16(11): 160.

——. 1889. Le Surintendant de l'Education de la province de Québec et la science. Naturaliste canadien, 19(4): 77–80.

——. 1891. Faune canadienne. Les mollusques de la province de Québec. Première partie. Les céphalopodes, ptéropodes et gastropodes. Darveau, Québec. 154 p.

PROVINCE OF QUEBEC ASSOCIATION FOR THE PROTECTION OF FISH AND GAME.

Annual Report. 1860——.

Conservation; Fish and Game in Quebec. 1930——.

La vie au grand air. 1938——.

PRYCE-TANNATT, T. E. 1938. Fish passes in connection with obstructions in salmon rivers. Buckland Lectures for 1937. Arnold, London. 108 p.

RICHARD, L.-A. 1937. La faune de la province de Québec. Un aperçu de sa valeur économique. Dépt. Mines et Pêch, Québec. 16 p.

——. 1938. Les parcs nationaux. Cie de Publication de La Patrie, Montréal. 16 p.

RICHARDSON, JOHN, et al. 1829–37. Fauna boreali-americana. 4 v. Murray, London. 300 + 524 + 327 + 325 p.

RICHARDSON, L. R. 1935. The fresh-water fish of south-eastern Quebec. Ph.D. Thesis, Dept. Zool., McGill Univ., 196 p.

ROBERT, A. 1956. La méduse Craspedacusta sowerbii dans les lacs des Laurentides. Ann. de l'ACFAS, 1954–55, 22: 49.

ROBITAILLE, A. 1930. L'abbé Ovide Brunet et le Musée de Botanique de l'Université Laval. Naturaliste canadien, 57(12): 250–254.

ROUSSEAU, JACQUES. 1948. Le voyage d'André Michaux au lac Mistassini en 1792. Mém. Jardin botan. Montréal, No. 3, 34 p.

ROUSSEAU, JACQUES, MARCELLE GAUVREAU, AND CLAIRE MORIN. 1939. Bibliographie des travaux botaniques contenus dans les Mémoires et Comptes Rendus de la Société royale du Canada, de 1882 à 1936 inclusivement. Contrib. Inst. botan. Univ. Montréal, No. 33, 117 p.

ROYAL CANADIAN INSTITUTE.

Canadian Journal. 1853–55.

Canadian Journal of Industry, Science and Art. 1856–68.

Canadian Journal of Science, Literature and History. 1870–78.

Canadian Journal; Proceedings of the Canadian Institute. 1879–90.

Transactions of the Canadian Institute. 1890–1913.

Proceedings of the Canadian Institute. 1897–1904.

Transactions of the Royal Canadian Institute. 1914——.

Royal Canadian Institute, Year Book and Annual Report. 1912–14.

Proceedings of the Royal Canadian Institute. 1935——.

ROYAL SOCIETY OF CANADA. Proceedings and Transactions. 1883——.

RUMILLY, ROBERT. 1955. Histoire des Acadiens. 2 v. Editions Fides, Montréal.

SABIN, JOSEPH. 1876. Dictionary of books relating to America. 29 v. New York.

SANSFAÇON, JACQUES, AND VIANNEY LEGENDRE. 1957. Bibliography of the titles of serial documents having published on the fishes, fishing and fisheries of Canada. Preliminary edition. Office Biol., Min. de la Chasse et des Pêcheries, Montreal. 107 + xx p.

SMALL, H. B. 1866. The animals of North America. II. Fresh-water fish. Longmoore, Montreal. 72 p.

SMITH, D. M. 1877. Arctic expeditions from British and foreign shores from the earliest times to the expedition of 1875–76. Grange Publishing Works, Edinburgh. 824 p.

SOCIETE ZOOLOGIQUE DE QUEBEC.
Rapport annuel. 1932——.
Bulletin. 1933——.
Les Carnets. 1941–January 1960.
Tract. 1943——.
Les Carnets de Zoologie. April 1960——.

STATON, FRANCES M., AND MARIE TREMAINE (eds.). 1934. A bibliography of canadiana. The Public Library, Toronto. 828 p. (See also BOYLE AND COLBECK, 1959.)

STORER, H. R. 1857. Observations on the fishes of Nova Scotia and Labrador, with descriptions of new species. Boston J. Nat. Hist., 1850–57, **6**(14): 247–270.

STUART, ANDREW, AND DAVID STUART. 1829. Rapport des commissaires pour explorer le Saguenay. Bas-Canada, Chambre d'Assemblée. Neilson & Cowan, Québec. 197 p.

TITCOMB, J. W. 1919. The waters of the St. Bernard Fish and Game Club, St. Alexis des Monts, Quebec. Privately published, Boston. 24 p.

VALLEE, ARTHUR. 1927. Un biologiste canadien, Michel Sarrazin, 1659–1735, sa vie, ses travaux et son temps. Proulx, Québec. 291 p.

VLADYKOV, V. D. 1942a. Biological observations on the ouananiche of the Peribonka during September 1942. December 14, 1942, 22 + 5 + 3 p. (Manuscript.)

——. 1942b. Etude des lacs du Parc des Laurentides, 1938–41. 2 v. Dept. Game and Fish. 65 + 178 p.

WATTERS, R. E. 1960. A check list of Canadian literature and background materials 1628–1950. Univ. Toronto Press, Toronto. 789 p. (Reprint.)

WHITEAVES, J. F. 1863. On the land and fresh-water Mollusca of Lower Canada. Canadian Nat. and Geol., **8**(1): 50–65; (2): 98–113.

WILLEY, A. 1923. Notes on the distribution of free-living Copepoda in Canadian waters. Contrib. Canadian Biol. and Fish., N.S., **1**(16): 1–32.

WOOD, C. A. 1931. An introduction to the literature of vertebrate zoology etc. McGill Univ. Publ., Zool. Ser. XI, No. 24, Oxford Univ. Press, London. 643 p.

18 | *M. W. Smith*

The Atlantic Provinces of Canada

The area considered embraces the provinces of New Brunswick, Nova Scotia, Prince Edward Island, and Newfoundland (Fig. 18.1; Table 18.1). The first three are commonly designated the Maritime provinces of Canada. The province of Newfoundland comprises the island of Newfoundland and a large area of eastern Labrador. Subsequent references, however, will be to the two separate geographical areas. The Atlantic provinces extend over a wide range in latitude, from 43° N. in the south (Nova Scotia) to 61° N. in the north (Labrador).

Physical and climatic features of the area

Sources of information

Information on the physiography, geology, soils, and climate of the area is available in Government of Canada Year Books and annual issues

TABLE 18.1

Land and natural lake areas of Atlantic provinces of Canada (Canada Year Book, 1960)

Province	Area in mi²			Percentage of freshwater area in total
	Land	Lakes	Total	
Newfoundland	143,045	13,140	156,185	8.4
Newfoundland Island	41,164	2,195	43,359	5.1
Labrador	101,881	10,945	112,826	17.7
Prince Edward Island	2,184	<1	2,184	—
Nova Scotia	20,402	1,023	21,425	4.8
New Brunswick	27,835	519	28,354	1.8

of official Handbook Canada (Dominion Bureau of Statistics) as well as the Atlas of Canada (1957, Geographical Branch, Canada Department of Mines and Technical Services). Topographical maps to the scale 1:50,000 cover all of the Maritime provinces and the island of Newfoundland (Map Distribution Office, Canada Department of Mines and Technical Services). A few sections of Labrador have been mapped on this large scale. The Geological Survey of Canada (Department of Mines and Technical Services) has mapped in detail the surface geology of the Maritime provinces, as well as large areas of Newfoundland and Labrador. The Meteorological Branch of the Canada Department of Transport maintains 135 stations (1958) in the Atlantic provinces and issues monthly reports.

Physiography

Most of the area has been strongly glaciated. Two well-eroded geosynclines of the northernmost extension of the Appalachians cross the Atlantic provinces. The Long Range of northwest Newfoundland is the present-day evidence of one, the Laurentian. The other (Acadian) extends from southeast Newfoundland, through Nova Scotia and eastern New Brunswick, and persists as the uplands of these latter areas. In the Maritime provinces there are wide basins, underlain principally by sandstones, between the uplands. Much of Newfoundland consists of a plateau at 800 to 1,500 ft in elevation. Labrador lies in the eastern extreme of the Canadian Shield. Much of Labrador is a recently glaciated peneplain, tilted up-

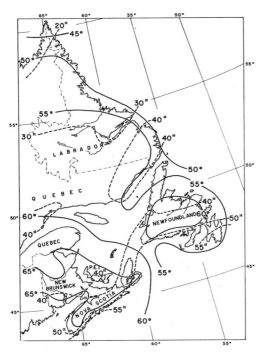

Fig. 18.1.—Map of the Atlantic provinces of Canada, showing mean annual total precipitation in inches and mean daily temperature for July in degrees F. Redrawn from *Atlas of Canada* (1957).

ward from about 800 ft in the southeast to somewhat over 5,000 ft in the Torngat Mountains in the northeast. The northern coastline of Labrador rises abruptly from the sea with prominent fiord development.

Surface geology

Paleozoic rocks, in generally disturbed beds, cover much of the Maritime provinces and Newfoundland. However, pre-Cambrian formations are encountered. These are limnologically of note since the lake districts of the region are found in the granites, gneisses, and quartzites of this era, as well as in similar rocks of the Ordovician, Silurian, and Lower Devonian in southwestern Nova Scotia, southeastern and central New Brunswick, and on the Newfoundland plateau. Carboniferous sedimentary rocks underlie eastern New Brunswick, northwestern Nova Scotia, and Prince Edward Island. Labrador is largely covered with pre-Cambrian schists and gneisses.

Climate

The climate of the Maritime provinces is essentially continental, lying as they do at the east-

ern edge of a large land mass over which the general movement of air is from west to east. However, most of the land areas in the Maritime provinces lie within 50 mi of the sea, and maritime influences are often strong. Lakes of the Maritime provinces are ice-covered usually from late November to early April. Newfoundland is also influenced by continental weather patterns, but there is an overriding influence on weather by the cold Labrador current, the waters of which practically encircle the island. Labrador has a rigorous climate with mean annual temperature below freezing, moderated somewhat, however, on the coast.

Isotherms and mean annual precipitation for the region are shown in Fig. 18.1.

Soils, forests, and farming

Podzol soils cover the Maritime provinces. In general they have low to moderate fertility and are usually acid. Soils of Newfoundland are also podzolic in character, but exposed rock, peat bogs, and swamps are more prominent features of the terrain. Labrador is covered with glacial, unconsolidated materials, rock outcrops cover large areas, and peat accrues in the poorly drained depressions. Northward beyond the tree line, tundra conditions obtain.

As a whole the Atlantic provinces are a forested area. The Acadian Forest Region takes in the Maritime provinces and Newfoundland (Anon., 1960). Conifers dominate generally, particularly northward, but mixed forest areas are common in southern New Brunswick and Nova Scotia where hardwood ridges are much in evidence. Most of Labrador is within the Boreal Forest Region, again with a dominance of conifers, which, as one goes northward, exist increasingly as a scrub growth, eventually to disappear.

Although small in comparison to the entire Atlantic region, notable agricultural areas, such as the St. John Valley, Annapolis Basin, and Prince Edward Island, are found in the Maritime provinces where underlying sedimentary rocks have given rise to good depths of friable soils. About 50% of the area of Prince Edward Island is under cultivation.

Limnological resources

Limnological resources of the Atlantic provinces are large. Mean annual total precipitation ranges from 20 to 55 in. Coastal fogs are a common occurrence. Much of the area is forested. Recent glaciation is manifest, particularly in Labrador, in disorganized drainage systems. These factors insure a well-watered area.

Lotic environments

New Brunswick, Nova Scotia, and Prince Edward Island are small and peninsular or insular in character. Accordingly the majority of streams are short but numerous, flowing independently into common estuaries or more directly into the sea along the more abrupt coastlines. However, there are a few drainage systems of substantial proportions such as the St. John, with headwaters in Maine, and the Miramichi which drains central New Brunswick (Table 18.2).

Maintenance of water flow in streams that drain thin soils overlying igneous rock formations is largely by surface runoff. Levels tend to become low and waters warm in such streams of the Maritimes in late summer, and the smaller ones dry up in the drier years. In contrast, greater stability of habitat is found in the small streams that drain deeper soils of sedimentary areas such as Prince Edward Island. Springs and spring seepage insure relatively good flow of cool water throughout the year.

The largest river systems of the Atlantic provinces are those that drain the plateaus of Newfoundland and Labrador (Table 18.2). Among the maze of streams and lakes at the headwaters, gradients are low. Where the rivers leave the plateaus, however, gradients are steep, and falls are common. Noteworthy is Grand Falls on the Hamilton River, Labrador, which is among the

world's greater cataracts (341 ft in one fall). This and lesser falls in Newfoundland and Labrador are physical limnological features that present serious problems in management of anadromous salmonids (Blair, 1943a).

Limnetic environments (natural)

Lakes of the Atlantic provinces originated almost entirely with Pleistocene glaciation (Table 18.2). The immature landscapes of Newfoundland and Labrador plateaus are dotted with thousands of ponds and lakes and share with the Canadian Shield as a whole in being the greatest lake region of the world. An estimated 8.4% of the area of Newfoundland and Labrador is covered by fresh waters, and this implies a much higher proportion at heads of river systems (Fig. 18.2).

Classification of the lakes with respect to origin from specific glacial processes largely awaits study. Scouring of peneplains, morainal damming, and kettle formation were doubtless all involved. Cirque lakes are found in such elevated areas as the Torngat Mountains of northern Labrador. Tanner (1947) refers to Melville Lake, Labrador, with a cryptodepression to 293 m, and adjacent Double Mer as transition forms between fiord and piedmont lakes.

In the more mature landscapes of the Maritime provinces, the lake districts are found in the igneous rock formations. Three of the larger districts are southwestern Nova Scotia, southwestern New Brunswick, and an area across the north-central part of the latter province. There are 600 lakes in New Brunswick and 2,580 in Nova Scotia that are 25 acres or more in area. Small fresh

TABLE 18.2

Larger rivers and lakes of Atlantic provinces of Canada (Canada Year Book, 1960)

	Rivers		Lakes	
	Name	Length (mi)	Name	Area (mi²)
Labrador	Hamilton	208	Melville	1,133
	Naskaupi	152	Michikamau	566
	Canairiktok	139		
	Eagle	138		
Newfoundland Island	Exploits	153	Grand	140
	Gander	102	Red Indian	65
			Gander	49
			Deer	24
			Victoria	15
New Brunswick	St. John	418	Grand	65
	Miramichi	135		

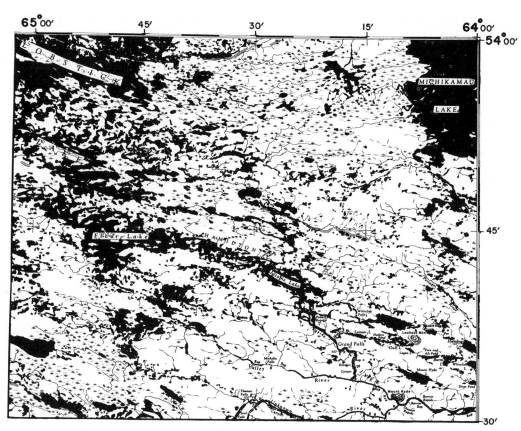

Fig. 18.2.—Map of an area of Labrador near headwaters of Hamilton River, illustrating the large number of fresh waters (in black) and disorganized drainage. Modified from National Topographic Map, Canada Department of Mines and Technical Surveys.

waters of less acreage number about 2,240 in the former and 6,800 in the latter province.

Few lakes occur in areas of sedimentary rocks, and they are for the most part senescent. However, Grand Lake (65 mi²), the largest freshwater area in New Brunswick, lies in such an area. This and Washademoak Lake, Belleisle and Kennebecasis bays (the last receiving much salt water), contiguous with the lower tidal portion of the St. John River, are drowned valleys of tributaries. Their levels are maintained by a marked narrowing and sill at the mouth of the St. John River, where there occurs a tide-controlled reversing falls.

Of additional limnological interest are (1) a few gypsum solution ponds in Margaree Valley, Nova Scotia, and (2) barrier or barachois ponds found along various stretches of the coastline of the Maritime provinces. The latter are small, shallow bodies of water usually, but not always, found at the mouths of streams and held by barriers of sand dunes and gravel bars (Smith, 1946). Many are subject to consistent, others to sporadic, incursions of salt water, while still others remain essentially freshwater habitats.

Impounded waters

Damming of rivers and lakes to provide reservoirs of fresh water for domestic and industrial uses is increasing with the economic advancement of the Atlantic provinces. Largely because of its geographic position, Labrador is as yet an exception. In New Brunswick there are 12 reservoirs for electric power on the Musquash and St. John river systems, holding approximately 17 mi² of impounded waters (New Brunswick Water Authority, personal communication). In addition nine municipalities take water from lakes, most of which have had their levels raised by damming. In Nova Scotia 57 reservoirs for hydroelectric purposes on 15 river systems have a total area of 175 mi^2 (Nova Scotia Power Commission, personal communication). In Newfoundland there are two major reservoirs on the Humber and Exploits rivers, estimated to have a total area of 250 mi^2, and in addition several scores of smaller hydroelectric developments for which statistics are scanty. In all of these areas reservoirs have been created both by flooding river valleys and by raising levels of existing lakes.

Lumbering is a major industry in the Atlantic provinces. Many headwater streams, particularly in Newfoundland, are dammed to insure ample water for floating logs downstream. The impoundments so formed usually lack permanency. Quality of water, flow patterns, and character of bottom are radically changed during their use, as well as after abandonment. Akin to these less permanent man-made impounds are beaver ponds. Beavers are common and with protection have increased in the Atlantic area.

Although there are as yet only 200 to 300 artificial trout ponds in the Maritime provinces plus a few on the Avalon peninsula of Newfoundland, public interest in them is increasing. One may anticipate that these artificial waters will assume greater significance as a limnological resource.

Estaurine waters

Estuarial development is extensive in the Atlantic provinces. Estuaries of the Maritime provinces are subject to extremes in tidal influence, from the large tidal amplitude in the Bay of Fundy to the relatively minor rise and fall on the open Atlantic coast and in the Gulf of St. Lawrence. Life histories of euryhaline forms are of obvious interest to limnologists generally, but estuaries of the Maritime provinces are of special interest to those limnologists whose concern is with the anadromous salmonid fish.

Control of water by "aboiteaux" for reclamation of lands in the Bay of Fundy area, whereby outflow of fresh water is allowed but incursions of salt water restricted, has altered stream and estuarial environments and presents difficulties to migrating fish.

Flora and fauna

The Atlantic provinces offer wide scope for the freshwater biogeographer. The wide range in latitude presents a gradient in amelioration of climate and habitat since glaciation. Colonization of fresh waters doubtless still proceeds naturally. Accepting the Eltonian contention that stability of biotic communities increases with diversity of the biota, we may expect instability in the freshwater communities, with "explosions" of species when they arrive in new and suitable habitats. Such has been observed with introductions of the exotic smallmouth black bass (*Micropterus dolomieu*) and with spread of the indigenous yellow perch (*Perca flavescens*) to new habitats in the Maritime provinces. Their colonization in lakes has often been at the expense of the brook trout, which persists without competition from such species in Maritime waters that are marginal for its well-being, particularly with respect to temperature.

The present freshwater flora and invertebrate fauna in the Maritime provinces would appear to be limited in distribution more by ecological factors than by geographical isolation. However, the latter remains of major importance in the distribution of less vagile forms, such as aquatic vertebrates. Only a few euryhaline species of fish are native to insular Prince Edward Island and Newfoundland. *Salvelinus fontinalis*, young *Salmo salar*, and in some habitats *Anguilla rostrata* are dominant residents in fresh waters above estuarine influence. Smith and Saunders (1955) found that the eel was scarce in the cool brooks of Prince Edward Island. Stenohaline species occur in the fresh waters of Nova Scotia, New Brunswick, and Labrador, but a restricted fauna is characteristic. Thus, the fresh waters of New Brunswick still contain only eleven cyprinids, two catostomids, two centrarchids, and one percid (no darters). Of biogeographical interest are relict populations of the Arctic char (*Salvelinus alpinus*) in at least two lakes of New Brunswick. Amphibians are not indigenous to Newfoundland.

Endemic development in the freshwater biota of the Atlantic provinces appears weak. Among invertebrates, the pelecypod, *Anodonta cataracta brooksiana*, and the sponges, *Spongilla johanseni* and *Corvospongilla novae-terrae*, may provisionally be considered endemics (E. L. Bousfield, National Museum of Canada, personal communication). However, taxonomic and distributional studies, considered either geographically or ecologically, fall far short of covering fresh waters of the Atlantic area. Reference to known occurrence may be had in the many monographs dealing with plants and animals of North American fresh waters. The following references are concerned more or less specifically with the aquatic biota of the Atlantic provinces: Backus, 1957; Bousfield, 1958; Hughes, 1949; LaRocque, 1953; Legendre, 1954; Livingstone, 1953; Logier, 1952; Scott and Crossman, 1959; Taylor, 1935; Walker, 1933. The author and others have published floral and faunal lists for various waters which were of concern in specific investigations (Bishop *et al.*, 1957).

Agencies and personnel in limnological research

Two agencies have been responsible for most limnological investigation in the Maritime provinces: (1) the Fisheries Research Board of Canada through its Biological Station, St. Andrews, New Brunswick, and, in less degree, its Biological Station, St. John's Newfoundland; (2) the Zoological Laboratory, Dalhousie University, Halifax, Nova Scotia.

The Department of Fisheries, Ottawa, through the Maritime Fish Culture Development Branch of the Conservation and Development Service, maintains 19 hatcheries and rearing establishments in the Maritime provinces. The branch is concerned with the propagation and distribution of fish, largely salmonids, and with physical and biological survey of streams and lakes to aid in effective use of the hatchery product, as well as maintenance of native stocks.

National Parks in the area are administered by the Department of Northern Affairs and National Resources, Ottawa, through the National Park Branch. Limnological reconnaissances of the fresh waters in the parks have been made by limnologists of the Canadian Wildlife Service of the above department.

The Canadian International Paper Company has from time to time supported limnological investigation in fresh waters, particularly with reference to sport species, on the extensive timberlands owned or held under lease in New Brunswick.

Individuals who have dealt with biogeography and taxonomy of the freshwater biota will not be detailed beyond the references in the bibliography of this paper. Additional information on distribution and taxonomy may be had, however, from the National Museum of Canada, Department of Northern Affairs and National Resources, Ottawa; from the Herbarium, Plant Research Institute, Department of Agriculture, Ottawa; and

from the Division of Applied Biology, National Research Council, Ottawa.

Persons now living who have made and are making contributions to limnological research in the Atlantic provinces through the above agencies or who remain active in this field elsewhere are listed in the appendix.

In 1949 the Federal-Provincial Co-ordinating Committee on Atlantic Salmon was set up "to develop a co-ordinated programme of research, regulation, compilation of statistics, and development of fish culture procedures, of Atlantic stocks in the five east coast provinces," with the Fisheries Research Board of Canada "responsible for the investigation and co-ordination of all Atlantic salmon investigations, and for carrying out the main research projects" (Kerswill, 1955a). In 1958 the scope of the committee was broadened to include other fisheries, and it is now designated the Federal-Provincial Atlantic Fisheries Committee. The Scientific Advisory Group of the Salmon and Trout Section of this committee meets annually to review, coordinate, and make recommendations to the parent committee on the research and management of these species. Since 1954 C. J. Kerswill has summarized annually the progress in research on the Atlantic salmon in issues of *Trade News*, published by the Canada Department of Fisheries, Ottawa.

Limnological research

For convenience in discussion, major limnological investigations in the Maritime provinces may be arbitrarily segregated into fields of theoretical and practical limnology. This is done with realization that much investigation, particularly that which may also be termed fishery biology, involves both fields.

Since about 1945 F. R. Hayes and his associates at Dalhousie University have enquired into the factors underlying the productivity of lakes, assessed productive levels, and contributed to the development of indices of productivity. (The recent establishment of the Institute of Oceanography at Dalhousie University, under the directorship of F. R. Hayes, implies a major expansion of interests in marine environments.)

The Biological Station, St. Andrews, New Brunswick, of the Fisheries Research Board of Canada, celebrated its fiftieth anniversary in 1958 (Hart, 1958). Over the years numbers of researchers on the staff of this station, or closely associated with it, have had a prime objective of improving the production and utilization of the Atlantic salmon and brook trout. During almost twenty years beginning about 1930, much attention was given to investigation of the Atlantic salmon under the leadership of A. G. Huntsman. Toward the goal of manipulating freshwater environments and fish populations for better utilization (principally) and production, as well as for prediction in these respects, basic information was sought in the response of the salmon as an organism as a whole to its environment (Hunstman, 1948a). During the last ten years research on Atlantic salmon has increased, coordinated under the Federal-Provincial Atlantic Fisheries Committee. Salmon research under the Fisheries Research Board is headed by C. J. Kerswill. Emphasis has been placed on monitoring population density and movements of young and adult salmon to provide necessary background information in assessment of contributions by the major Maritime rivers to the several commercial and sport fisheries, in determination of needed escapement of adults to spawning for full utilization of river carrying capacity for young salmon, and in predator control. In recent years particularly, the evaluation of effects on salmon populations in forest areas from spray with DDT to control the spruce budworm and the amelioration of these effects have been of major concern (Kerswill, 1955b).

The author has been largely responsible for development of trout research under the Fisheries Research Board in the Maritime provinces. He has held with others that increased production and yields of sport fish can only come from more control of both water and fish by altering natural freshwater environments in a positive fashion or by creating new ones. Determination of natural deficiencies limiting productive levels has led to experimentation in manipulation of environments and fish populations by a number of actions.

Theoretical limnology

Rapidity of loss from water and of uptake by solids of radioactive phosphorus, as illustrated when added to the small (4 ha) unstratified, primitive Bluff Lake, Nova Scotia, led Hayes *et al.* (1952) to postulate an active, yet simple, exchange system involving the phosphorus in water and participating phosphorus in lake solids. The authors derived an equation to express the dynamic equilibrium that obtained, viewing the

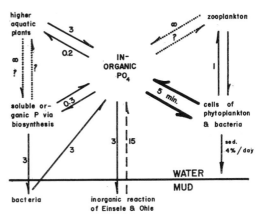

Fig. 18.3.—Transformations of phosphorus in a lake with turnover times for different equilibria. Very heavy lines indicate the first reaction with floating cells, time in minutes. Other times in days. Lighter solid lines are reactions at intermediate speeds—two or three orders of magnitude slower than the initial one. Dashed line is the return from mud by inorganic release, a still slower turnover. Dotted lines at top indicate reactions too slow to measure, called infinitely slow by comparison with the rest. After Hayes and Phillips, 1958 (Fig. 7, p. 473).

loss of phosphorus from water and return from solids to occur in an exponential manner. Calculation was then made for rate of exchange, expressed as turnover time, for phosphorus in the water and the solid phases. Thus, in Bluff Lake the turnover times for water and solids were calculated as 5.4 and 39 days, respectively.

The state of oxidation or reduction by conditioning, for instance, the equilibrium between ferrous and ferric iron has usually been considered to play the dominant role in phosphorus exchange in lakes. Hayes and Phillips (1958) demonstrated that bacteria and phytoplankters rapidly take up radioactive phosphorus, equilibrating in minutes, and that bacteria exhibit a surprisingly strong ability to hold phosphorus in water. Bacteria may accomplish this in good part by holding phosphate in organic form, thereby preventing it from participating in the chemical and absorptive processes operating in muds. The authors calculated turnover times for phosphorus in various water-solid equilibrium systems. Their schematic presentation of these is herein reproduced (Fig. 18.3). The relatively rapid order of absorption by bacteria and other organic growths would appear to leave little inorganic phosphate for inorganic exchange in sediments. The dominant position held by bacteria and phytoplankton, particularly the former in the laboratory but probably the latter in the lake, suggests that their action suppresses the underlying inorganic exchange mechanism, which thereby becomes subsidiary.

The above studies on phosphorus exchange emphasize increasing realization that measurements of water phosphorus do not provide a serviceable index of productivity. Hayes *et al.* (1958) examined the possible use of measurements of redox potential to provide a numerical index of productivity, prompted by Mortimer's observations for English lakes that the thickness of the oxidized mud layer during winter circulation appeared inversely related to summer hypolimnetic oxygen consumption. The attempt proved rather abortive, largely through difficulties in measurement and interpretation of results. Evidence was produced, however, "that the real oxidized layer was one mm or less thick, and that the reported break on the electrode curve at about one cm is caused by factors other than oxidation of iron salts. . . ."

In a balanced lake, elaboration and mineralization of organic matter attain equilibrium. Measurements of decomposition in which bacteria occupy a central position or measurements of changes in water chemistry attendant on this process might be expected to provide indices of production at higher trophic levels. In Maritime clear-water lakes, Hayes and Anthony (1959) found good correlation between bacterial count in sediments and other generally accepted indices of productivity, such as methyl orange alkalinity, conductivity, and oxygen consumption over mud. Such correlations were not found in brown-water lakes, so common in the Maritime provinces, where allochthonous organic matter creates imbalance. High bacterial counts were realized in such lakes, and a good correlation existed between counts and color measurements. It appeared possible, by allowing for the bog effect on bacterial count, to end up with a measurement of bacteria that is a meaningful index of productivity.

An objective in theoretical limnological research is to derive indices, based on the physical and biotic relationships in lake environments, that can be expressed numerically to permit prediction of fish production, the trophic level in which man has most interest. Adequate synoptic assessments are seldom available. Hayes (1957) attempted to derive a number that would express the inherent productive capacity of a lake. Data on standing crops and on angled and commercial

catches of fish from Maritime and many other North American lakes were employed. With due consideration to length of food chains among the fish, a productivity index, *PI*, was obtained by factoring to bring records for the several lakes to a comparative basis. *PI* was found to be inversely proportional to mean depth of water on a log-log plot. Hayes then proceeded to apply correction to the *PI*, deriving the relationship:

$$QI = PI \sqrt{\frac{m}{5}},$$

where *QI* is the quality index for a standard lake 5 m deep, and *m* is the mean depth in meters. The *QI*, the value of which varies about unity, is intended to screen the effect of depth out of the *PI* and give expression to the inherent productive capacity. Hayes and MacAulay (1959) presented the more generalized equation:

$$P = K \sqrt{\frac{5}{m}} \times QI \times b,$$

where *P* is productivity per unit area, *K* is a factor defining the nature of the crop (for fish it was arranged to have a value approximating unity), and *b* a bog factor which may be a function of color. Specifically relating oxygen consumed in water over sediment cores from nine Maritime lakes, for which there were measurements of fish biomass available, these authors found the following highly significant relation:

$$QI \text{ (for fish)} = 66.9 \times \text{oxygen consumed} -1.31,$$

where units of oxygen consumed are milligrams used per cm^2 mud surface per day.

Necessary brevity in this review does not permit presentation of background reasoning in experimentation and expression of results or reference to all studies. Hayes and associates have made valuable contributions to methodology.

Practical limnology

Practical limnology deals predominantly with alteration of freshwater environments and manipulation of populations of organisms for increased production and utilization, the product of prime interest usually being fish. Atlantic salmon, brook trout, and smelt have received most attention in the Atlantic provinces, with much less but increasing concern with the non-indigenous rainbow and brown trout and smallmouth black bass and the indigenous Arctic char.

Past and continuing life history studies on the Atlantic salmon and brook trout in the Atlantic area provide knowledge required for investigation in this field. Thus, Huntsman (1931) reported a periodic scarcity of salmon in the Atlantic area averaging 9.6 years over a 60-year period, basing his study on statistics of the commercial catches. He (Huntsman, 1941) related the periodicity to increased predation on young salmon, particularly the smolt, by fish-eating birds during periodic low river levels. White (1942) made a thorough study of environmental requirements for and construction of salmon spawning beds and of the deposition of the eggs in the redds. Artificial redds, constructed on the bases of these observations, were promptly used by salmon where natural physical conditions were otherwise poor or mediocre for spawning.

Many and varied studies have been made on the ecology of the Atlantic salmon and brook trout in Maritime waters, with emphasis on reactions of fish to conditions encountered in nature and under more controlled situations. Studies encompass response to water flow and change in water flow, reaction to and lethality of light, temperature, and parasitism, food and feeding, intra- and interspecific competition and predation, predation by birds and mammals, and behavior (ethology), as well as study of environments themselves.

References to these studies are found in indices and lists of publications of the Fisheries Research Board of Canada (Bishop *et al.*, 1957; MacIntyre, 1961). Reference to unpublished data may also be obtained from the Manuscript Report Series of the Fisheries Research Board, which can be consulted at the libraries of the board's stations. Not specifically pertinent, but of kindred interest to this review, are investigations and expressions of opinion on "homing" of salmon and brook trout and the possible role of heritable characteristics in movements between fresh and salt water.

The ecological studies indicated a number of promising approaches to manipulation of environment and fishes for increased production and utilization. Artificial freshets in rivers to attract salmon from salt water and to move them farther upstream for improved angling resulted in the anticipated response on the part of the fish to changing water levels, when other conditions were favorable (Huntsman, 1948b; Hayes, 1953). Once the salmon were in the river, subsequent low water and high temperature had a nullifying effect by reducing catchability.

White (1953, 1957) examined the role of mergansers and kingfishers as fish predators. Severe reduction of salmonids in Maritime trout and salmon streams was noted to result from predation by these birds, and their control markedly improved survival of fish. A long-term study has been made on the Pollett River, New Brunswick, to assess effectiveness of stocking and bird control in rehabilitation and establishment of this stream as a producer of young salmon (Elson, 1942, 1957a, 1957b, 1957c). A dam barred ascent of adult salmon to the lower sections and an impassable falls to the upper. With control of mergansers to a level of one bird per 10 mi of stream 30 ft wide, survival of planted underyearling salmon to the descending smolt stage was markedly improved. With this level of bird control, the mesotrophic Pollet is capable of producing five to six 2-year smolts per 100 yd^2 of stream bottom from a stocking of about 35 underyearlings on the same area basis. Stocking appreciably above this rate proved wasteful in that it overreached the carrying capacity of the stream for young salmon. Application of bird control to the Miramichi, a major salmon river of the Maritimes, resulted in an increase in density of native parr from 8 per 100 yd^2 in 1950 to 24 by 1953, when, however, spraying of forests in the area with DDT to control the spruce budworm caused fish mortalities and therefore made, evaluation of results of further bird control difficult (Kerswill, 1955b, 1961).

Stocking to improve and maintain trout production in natural Maritime waters has proved unrewarding without contemporaneous alteration of habitat to permit better growth and survival (White, 1930; Smith, 1952, 1955). Native stocks of young trout appear adequate in most waters to fill the trout-producing capacities. Reasonably good returns to anglers' catches obtain when fish of angling size are planted where the waters need to serve only as holding areas. However, Elson (1957b) found that stocking underyearling salmon was quite effective in the not-too-common situation where capacity to grow salmon was unfilled because adults were barred from the waters.

Mostly as a cooperative effort between the author and the Maritime Fish Culture Development Branch, Canada Department of Fisheries, a number of lakes were "reclaimed" by fish poisons and then stocked with trout (Smith, 1950). Although improvement in brook trout production usually followed treatments, it was di-

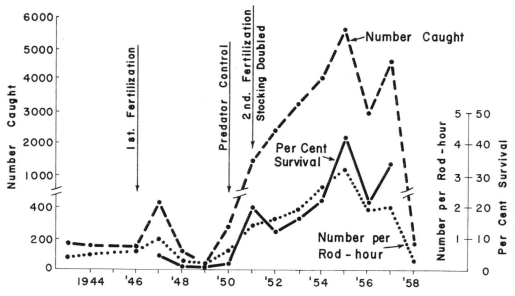

Fig. 18.4.—Anglers' catch, rate of capture, and survival of planted underyearling brook trout to anglers' creels at Crecy Lake, New Brunswick, affected by fertilization and predator control.

rectly commensurate with the trout-producing capacities of the lakes, which, even without competition and predation from unwanted species, are disappointingly low for this carnivore in the dominantly soft waters of the Maritime provinces. Hayes and Livingstone (1955) were able to control unwanted species, particularly yellow perch, by an annually repeated poisoning of the shallows of Copper Lake, Nova Scotia.

In general, lakes of New Brunswick and Nova Scotia are poorly mineralized, of poor to mediocre productivity, often with imbalance from dystrophy. Nutrients in the form of commercial fertilizers were added to clear-water, unstratified Crecy Lake (20 ha), New Brunswick (Smith, 1948, 1955). Eutrophication was manifest by a strong bloom of blue-green algae, normally minor constituents of the flora, and by an increased quantity of bottom organisms, but these manifestations were temporary. Growth of introduced trout improved, and survival of planted underyearlings to anglers' catches was modestly increased. The fertilization was repeated after a lapse of five years and stocking continued, but additionally control of fish-eating birds and mammals was imposed, as well as reduction of stock of older trout to curtail cannibalism (Smith, 1957). As illustrated in Figure 18.4, very favorable results were realized. Yield of trout to

anglers by number was increased many times, and catch per unit effort correspondingly improved over former levels. About 42% of planted underyearling trout survived to the anglers' creels, a situation that has been realized seldom, if at all, in stocking young salmonids in natural waters.

Currently Crecy Lake is stocked with rainbow trout, with replication of action previously taken with brook trout, to assess whether either of these species utilizes the productive capacity of the lake more effectively than the other. With this third fertilization of Crecy Lake at a five-year interval, strong blooms of blue-green algae developed not only during the year of fertilization but during the following summer as well, an event not observed after the two previous enrichments. Some cumulative effects from repeated fertilization were thereby suggested. However, nature is recalcitrant to changes of this sort. and eutrophication was only temporarily maintained when intermittently stimulated by actions of the scope attempted. Experience at Crecy Lake showed that, although one may seek a single action in alteration of natural environments or in manipulation of population for improved production, worthwhile results will probably be attained only when a number are taken concurrently, in this case stocking, fertilization, and predator control.

Pond formation creates new environments with more control of both water and fish than is possible under natural conditions. This is a step toward domestication and seemingly a necessary one if production of sport fish is to meet the future demands. Prince Edward Island streams and artificial ponds formed on the streams have been extensively studied by the author and his co-workers, with particular emphasis on trout production. The waters are strongly eutrophic, and standing crops of brook trout and their yields to anglers are high, being 125 kg/ha and 50 kg/ha, respectively. Brook trout move between fresh and salt water. Movements of brook trout out of and into Ellerslie Brook, Prince Edward Island, were observed over a period of years with the aid of tagging and year-round operation of counting fences, and these movements were associated with environmental conditions (Smith and Saunders, 1958). Movements in general were into preferred temperature and appeared to be conditioned by temperature and stimulated by changing water levels. A pond formed on the lower reaches of Ellerslie Brook held the trout, and few subsequently moved to salt water, although they were free to do so. The pond improved availability of trout to anglers to the point that the annual recruitment, largely yearlings, from the stream was thoroughly harvested—to 90% or more. The potential of the pond as a rearing area to produce older trout was poorly realized. Availability of suitable cover in Ellerslie Brook was a dominant factor in limiting the carrying capacity of yearling and older trout—recruits for the pond (Saunders and Smith, 1955). A recent program of stream improvement to provide greater depth of water and more cover resulted after one year in improved survival, so that the population of yearling trout was approximately doubled. An objective was to alter enough of the stream environment to avoid merely attracting fish to isolated improved areas.

For smelt (*Osmerus mordax*) McKenzie (1947) observed high egg mortality with heavy egg deposition. With more than 15,000 eggs per ft², both percentage hatch and actual number of larvae declined. Smelt occupied much greater stream area in spawning with removal of obstructions against their upstream movements. Greater larval production was associated with stream clearance.

Fisheries researchers in the Atlantic provinces have made substantial contributions to methods

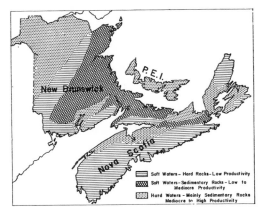

Fig. 18.5.—Zonation of Maritime provinces of Canada with respect to productivity of fresh waters.

and tools of investigation—construction and operation of counting fences, tagging, electrofishing, and SCUBA diving. References may be had from Bishop *et al.* (1957) and MacIntyre (1961).

Regional limnology

Newfoundland and Labrador fresh waters have received little study. Too little is known of these waters to attempt regional division on a productivity basis. Lindsay and Thompson (1932), Blair (1943*b*), and Frost (1940) studied life histories of salmon and trout in Newfoundland waters but with minor reference to the ecology of the species. Currently A. R. Murray (Fisheries Research Board) is investigating factors that may limit production of immature salmon in the Little Codroy River, Newfoundland. Two recent unpublished theses (McGill University Library) deal with Chironomidae and lake typology of Lake Astray (D. R. Oliver) and with the ecology of a meromictic lake near Nain (J. C. H. Carter) in Labrador.

Limnological investigation is much more extensive and intensive in the three Maritime provinces. Chemical composition of about 100 fresh waters has been reported (Leverin, 1947; Smith, 1946, 1952, 1961; Gorham, 1957; Hayes and Anthony, 1958). Standing crops of plankton, bottom fauna, and fish have been assessed with varying precision in a smaller number of waters by the author and others (Bishop *et al.*, 1957; MacIntyre, 1961). Available data permit zonation of the Maritime provinces into limnological regions with respect to productive levels as shown in Figure 18.5. Although delimitation of the regions is yet crude, it is sufficiently realistic to serve as a meaningful guide in limnological endeavor.

The zonation is primarily referable to character of soils and underlying geological formations. Low electrolyte content is expectedly encountered in waters of igneous rock areas, where most of the Maritime lakes are found. Dystrophy is persistently manifest in varying degree. Standing crops of bottom fauna have usually been found at less than 1 g/m^2 as dry weight without mollusk shells. Standing crops of fish, usually mixed populations, varied from 19 to 40 kg/ha in six lakes treated with fish poisons. Yields of brook trout to anglers have usually been below 5 kg/ha per annum.

A somewhat higher electrolyte content and moderate mesotrophy appear to characterize the waters, mainly streams, draining areas of Carboniferous (Pennsylvanian) sandstones and shales poor in lime. These areas occupy much of south-central and eastern New Brunswick and the Cumberland area of Nova Scotia.

In sharp contrast to the situation in the previously mentioned waters, comparatively strong mineralization and high productive capacity are encountered in drainages where the sedimentary rocks are a good source of lime. Waters of this sort have received most attention on Prince Edward Island with its Carboniferous sandstones, containing a calcareous matrix. Standing crops of brook trout of 50 to 125 kg/ha and yields to anglers up to 50 kg/ha have been recorded for ponds formed there. Cool waters and near absence of competing species are contributing factors. In this area and elsewhere in the Maritime provinces productive waters and agricultural development go hand in hand. Primitive fertility of waters is enhanced by drainage from enriched farm lands (Smith, 1959). Adverse factors, however, are increasing loads of silt and pollutants such as pesticides.

Limnology of polluted waters

Pollution is less a problem in Newfoundland and Labrador than in the Maritime provinces. Serious pollutants of fresh waters and estuaries are pesticides and effluents from pulp mills, oil refineries, mines, and food-packing plants. Domestic pollution increases in proportion to human population but is as yet much less acute in effects upon aquatic life. Deforestation of headwaters and stream banks may be expected to increase in the Maritime provinces with attendant harmful effects on water flow, levels, and temperature.

Since 1953 through 1961, with the exception of 1959, from 1.5 to 6.5 million acres of New Brunswick forest have been sprayed annually in June with DDT to control the spruce budworm. In years sprayed, the young salmon populations in such important salmon rivers as the Miramichi were drastically reduced, and this has resulted in predictably reduced numbers of adult salmon. Ecological relations in the rivers were materially altered. An exceptional observation made in the Northwest Miramichi in an off-spray year was that, with extra-favorable spawning and reduced intraspecific competition, progeny survived and grew well (Kerswill, 1960). Coincidentally, Ide (1957) observed a resurgence of chironomids and black fly larvae but a slow return of such large forms as caddis flies. Young salmon appeared to substitute snails for these latter important food items.

In 1958 a pollution investigational unit was set up by the Fisheries Research Board at St. Andrews, New Brunswick, with J. B. Sprague in charge. One objective is to provide investigation of cases of gross pollution. A long-term objective is to discover and document alteration of environments subject to small gradual changes over extended periods. To this end a baseline of present conditions is being sought for the St. John River, which will undoubtedly be subject to increasing use by industry and municipalities. Emphasis is on quantitative estimates of bottom organisms and shifting species composition.

Acknowledgment

The author is indebted to a number of researchers for assistance and advice in preparation of this review, particularly his co-workers at the Biological Station, St. Andrews, New Brunswick, and to Dr. F. R. Hayes, Dalhousie University, Halifax, Nova Scotia. Illustrations were prepared by Messrs. P. W. G. McMullon and F. B. Cunningham. This paper is published with permission of the Fisheries Research Board of Canada.

Appendix

Personnel in limnological investigation in the Atlantic provinces of Canada are listed below. Affiliations of those now working elsewhere in limnology or allied fields are given in parentheses.

FISHERIES RESEARCH BOARD OF CANADA

Biological Station, St. Andrews, New Brunswick

Andrews, C. W. (Memorial University, St. John's, Newfoundland)

Elson, P. F.

Hoar, W. S. (University of British Columbia, Vancouver, British Columbia)

Huntsman, A. G. (retired, 217 Indian Rd., Toronto, Ontario)

Ide, F. P. (University of Toronto, Toronto, Ontario)

Keenleyside, M. H. A. (University of Western Ontario, London, Ontario)

Kerswill, C. J.

Loftus, K. H. (Ontario Department of Lands and Forests, Maple, Ontario)

McKenzie, R. A.

Saunders, J. W.

Saunders, R. L.

Smith, M. W.

Sprague, J. B.

White, H. C. (retired, Petitcodiac, New Brunswick)

Biological Station, St. John's, Newfoundland

Blair, A. A.

Murray, A. R.

DALHOUSIE UNIVERSITY, HALIFAX, NOVA SCOTIA

Anthony, E. H.

Gorham, Eville (University of Minnesota, Minneapolis, Minnesota)

Hayes, F. R.

Livingstone, D. A. (Duke University, Durham, North Carolina)

CANADA DEPARTMENT OF FISHERIES, FISH CULTURE DEVELOPMENT BRANCH

Maritimes Area, Halifax, Nova Scotia

Logie, R. R.

Wilson, G. A. C.

Newfoundland Area, St. John's, Newfoundland

Taylor, V. R.

INTERNATIONAL PAPER COMPANY OF CANADA

Reppert, R. T. (Grenville, Quebec)

CANADA DEPARTMENT OF NORTHERN AFFAIRS AND NATIONAL RESOURCES

National Park Branch, Ottawa

Cuerrier, J-P.

Solman, V. E. F.

References

ANONYMOUS. 1960. Forestry, p. 505–536. *In* Canada Year Book, 1960. Canada Dominion Bureau of Statistics, Queen's Printer, Ottawa.

BACKUS, R. H. 1957. The fishes of Labrador. Bull. Amer. Museum Nat. Hist., 113(4): 273–338.

BISHOP, YVONNE, N. M. CARTER, DOROTHY GAILUS, W. E. RICKER, AND J. M. SPIRES. 1957. Index and list of titles, publications of the Fisheries Research Board of Canada, 1901–1954. Bull. Fish. Research Board Canada, No. 110, 209 p.

BLAIR, A. A. 1943a. Salmon investigations. I. Obstructions in Newfoundland and Labrador rivers. Newfoundland Dept. Nat. Resources, Fish. Research Bull., No. 12, 50 p.

———. 1943b. Salmon investigations. II. Atlantic salmon of the east coast of Newfoundland and Labrador, 1939. Newfoundland Dept. Nat. Resources, Fish. Research Bull., No. 13, 21 p.

BOUSFIELD, E. L. 1958. Fresh-water amphipod crustaceans of glaciated North America. Canadian Field-Nat., 72(2): 55–113.

ELSON, P. F. 1942. Behaviour and survival of planted Atlantic salmon fingerlings. Trans. 7th North Amer. Wildl. Conf.: 202–211.

———. 1957a. The importance of size in the change from parr to smolt in Atlantic salmon. Canadian Fish Cult., No. 21: 1–6.

———. 1957b. Using hatchery-reared Atlantic salmon to best advantage. Canadian Fish Cult., No. 21: 7–17.

———. 1957c. Number of salmon needed to maintain stocks. Canadian Fish Cult., No. 21: 19–23.

FROST, NANCY. 1940. A preliminary study of Newfoundland trout. Newfoundland Dept. Nat. Resources, Fish. Research Bull., No. 9, 30 p.

GORHAM, EVILLE. 1957. The chemical composition of lake waters in Halifax County, Nova Scotia. Limnol. Oceanogr., 2: 12–21.

HART, J. L. 1958. Fisheries Research Board of Canada Biological Station, St. Andrews, N. B., 1908–1958. Fifty years of research in aquatic biology. J. Fish. Research Board Canada, 15: 1127–1161.

HAYES, F. R. 1953. Artificial freshets and other factors controlling the ascent and population of Atlantic salmon in the LaHave River, Nova Scotia. Bull. Fish. Research Board Canada, No. 99, 47 p.

———. 1957. On the variation in bottom fauna and fish yield in relation to trophic level and lake dimensions. J. Fish. Research Board Canada, 14: 1–32.

HAYES, F. R., AND E. H. ANTHONY. 1958. Lake water and sediment. I. Characteristics and water chemistry of some Canadian east coast lakes. Limnol. Oceanogr., 3: 299–307.

HAYES, F. R., AND E. H. ANTHONY. 1959. Lake water and sediment. VI. The standing crop of bacteria in lake sediments and its place in the classification of lakes. Limnol. Oceanogr., 4: 299–315.

HAYES, F. R., AND D. A. LIVINGSTONE. 1955. The trout population of a Nova Scotia lake as affected by habitable water, poisoning of the shallows and stocking. J. Fish. Research Board Canada, 12: 618–635.

HAYES, F. R., AND M. A. MacAULAY. 1959. Lake water and sediment. V. Oxygen consumed in water over sediment cores. Limnol. Oceanogr., 4: 291–298.

HAYES, F. R., J. A. McCARTER, M. L. CAMERON, AND D. A. LIVINGSTONE. 1952. On the kinetics of phosphorus exchange in lakes. J. Ecol., 40(1): 202–216.

HAYES, F. R., AND J. E. PHILLIPS. 1958. Lake water

and sediment. IV. Radiophosphorus equilibrium with mud, plants and bacteria under oxidized and reduced conditions. Limnol. Oceanogr., **3**: 459–475.

HAYES, F. R., B. L. REID, AND M. L. CAMERON. 1958. Lake water and sediment. II. Oxidation-reduction relations at the mud-water interface. Limnol. Oceanogr., **3**: 308–317.

HUGHES, E. O. 1949. Fresh-water algae of the Maritime provinces. Proc. Nova Scotian Inst. Sci., **22** (2): 1–63.

HUNTSMAN, A. G. 1931. The Maritime salmon of Canada. Bull. Biol. Board Canada, No. 21, 99 p.

———. 1941. Cyclical abundance and birds versus salmon. J. Fish. Research Board Canada, **5**: 227–235.

———. 1948a. Method in ecology—biapocrisis. Ecology, **29**: 30–42.

———. 1948b. Freshets and fish. Trans. Amer. Fish. Soc., **75**: 257–266.

IDE, F. P. 1957. Effects of forest spraying with DDT on aquatic insects of salmon streams. Trans. Amer. Fish. Soc., **86**: 208–219.

KERSWILL, C. J. 1955a. Investigation and management of the Atlantic salmon. Canada Dept. Fish., Trade News, **7**(10): 3–11.

———. 1955b. Recent developments in Atlantic salmon research. Atlantic Salmon J., 1955(1): 26–30.

———. 1960. Investigation and management of Atlantic salmon in 1959–60. I. The research programme. Canada Dept. Fish., Trade News, **12**(12): 3–11.

———. 1961. The management of Atlantic salmon, p. 823–831. *In* Resources for tomorrow. Canada Dept. Northern Affairs and Natl. Resources, Ottawa, vol. 2.

LaROCQUE, AURELE. 1953. Catalogue of the recent Mollusca of Canada. Bull. Natl. Museum Canada, No. 129, 406 p.

LEGENDRE, VIANNEY. 1954. Key to game and commercial fishes of the Province of Quebec. Vol. I. The freshwater fishes. Société Canadienne d'écologie, Montreal, 180 p.

LEVERIN, H. A. 1947. Industrial waters of Canada. Canada Dept. Mines and Resources, Mines and Geol. Branch, Rept. 819, 109 p.

LINDSAY, S. T., AND HAROLD THOMPSON. 1932. Biology of the salmon (*Salmo salar* L.) taken in Newfoundland waters in 1931. Rept. Newfoundland Fish. Research Comm., **1**(2): 1–80.

LIVINGSTONE, D. A. 1953. The fresh-water fishes of Nova Scotia. Proc. Nova Scotian Inst. Sci., **23**(1): 1–90.

LOGIER, E. B. S. 1952. The frogs, toads and salamanders of eastern Canada. Clarke, Irwin & Company Ltd., Toronto, 127 p.

MacINTYRE, R. L. 1961. Lists of titles of publications of the Fisheries Research Board of Canada, 1955–60. Fish. Research Board Canada, Biol. Sta., Nanaimo, Circ. No. 58, 94 p.

McKENZIE, R. A. 1947. The effect of crowding of smelt eggs on the production of larvae. Fish. Research Board Canada, Atlantic Progr. Rept., No. 39: 11–13.

SAUNDERS, J. W., AND M. W. SMITH. 1955. Standing crops of trout in a small Prince Edward Island stream. Canadian Fish Cult., No. 17: 32–39.

SCOTT, W. B., AND E. J. CROSSMAN. 1959. The freshwater fishes of New Brunswick: A check list with distributional notes. Contrib. Roy. Ontario Museum, No. 51, 37 p.

SMITH, M. W. 1946. A biological reconnaissance of ponds in the Prince Edward Island National Park. Acadian Nat., **2**(6): 81–101.

———. 1948. Preliminary observations upon the fertilization of Crecy Lake, New Brunswick. Trans. Amer. Fish. Soc., **75**: 165–174.

———. 1950. The use of poisons to control undesirable fish in Canadian fresh waters. Canadian Fish Cult., No. 8: 17–29.

———. 1952. Limnology and trout angling in Charlotte County, New Brunswick. J. Fish. Research Board Canada, **8**: 383–452.

———. 1955. Fertilization and predator control to improve trout angling in natural lakes. J. Fish. Research Board Canada, **12**: 210–237.

———. 1957. Further improvement in trout angling at Crecy Lake, New Brunswick, with predator control extended to large trout. Canadian Fish Cult., No. 19: 13–16.

———. 1959. Phosphorus enrichment of drainage waters from farm lands. J. Fish. Research Board Canada, **16**: 887–895.

———. 1961. A limnological reconnaissance of a Nova Scotian brown-water lake. J. Fish. Research Board Canada, **18**: 463–478.

SMITH, M. W., AND J. W. SAUNDERS. 1955. The American eel in certain fresh waters of the Maritime provinces of Canada. J. Fish. Research Board Canada, **12**: 238–269.

SMITH, M. W., AND J. W. SAUNDERS. 1958. Movements of brook trout, *Salvelinus fontinalis* (Mitchill), between and within fresh and salt water. J. Fish. Research Board Canada, **15**: 1403–1449.

TANNER, V. 1947. Outlines of the geography, life and customs of Newfoundland-Labrador. Vol. II. University Press, Cambridge. 436 p.

TAYLOR, W. R. 1935. The fresh-water algae of Newfoundland. II. Papers Michigan Acad. Sci. Arts Lett., **20**: 185–230.

WALKER, E. M. 1933. The Odonata of the Maritime provinces. Proc. Nova Scotian Inst. Sci., **18**(3): 106–128.

WHITE, H. C. 1930. Trout fry planting experiments in Forbes Brook, P.E.I., in 1928. Contrib. Canadian Biol. and Fish., **5**: 203–211.

———. 1942. Atlantic salmon redds and artificial spawning beds. J. Fish. Research Board Canada, **6**: 37–44.

———. 1953. The eastern belted kingfisher in the Maritime provinces. Bull. Fish. Research Board Canada, No. 97, 44 p.

———. 1957. Food and natural history of mergansers on salmon waters in the Maritime provinces of Canada. Bull. Fish. Research Board Canada, No. 116, 63 p.

Alfred M. Beeton
David C. Chandler

19

The St. Lawrence Great Lakes

The Laurentian Great Lakes and their connecting waters constitute the largest body of fresh water on the surface of the earth (Table 19.1, Fig. 19.1). They represent a natural resource of ever-increasing importance. These lakes are vital in the national economics of both Canada and the United States. The fact that the lakes are connected to form a continuous waterway has been extremely important to the economy of east-central North America. Ocean vessels can now travel from the Atlantic Coast westward into Minnesota at the west end of Lake Superior, a distance of almost 2,000 mi. Shipping amounts to around 300 million tons per year. The Duluth-Superior harbor, in western Lake Superior, ranks second in the entire United States in the total tonnage handled. Traffic on the lakes has been increasing since the completion of the St. Lawrence Seaway.

The shoreline of the lakes, including both mainland and islands, totals about 9,600 mi. Along or near the extensive coast are vast coal fields, deposits of iron, copper, and other minerals, outcrops of high-quality limestone, and areas of productive agricultural land. The lakes also temper the climate and influence the nature and movement of storm systems over an extensive area. This combination of circumstances naturally favored the development of huge industries and large metropolitan areas along the Great Lakes. Approximately 40% of the United States population lives in Great Lakes states and 10% in counties bordering the lakes. Consequently, the lake waters are used for domestic and industrial purposes, including waste disposal. Extensive commercial and sport fisheries have existed for many years, and the lakes are used for boating, bathing, and other recreation.

Human activities have affected even these large bodies of water, and there is evidence of accelerated eutrophication. The fish populations, bottom fauna, and chemical content of the waters of Lake Erie have changed markedly during the past 50 years (Beeton, 1961), and the standing crop of plankton in southern Lake Michigan has increased significantly over the past 33 years

TABLE 19.1

Dimensions of the Great Lakes[a]

Lake	Length (mi)	Breadth (mi)	Area		Average surface elevation above mean sea level since 1860 (ft)	Mean discharge (cfs)	Maximum depth (ft)	Mean depth (ft)
			Water surface (mi²)	Drainage basin (mi²)				
Superior	350	160	31,820	80,000	602.20	73,300	1,333	487
Michigan	307	118	22,400	67,860	580.54	55,000	923	276
Huron	206	183	23,010	72,620	580.54	177,900	750	195
St. Clair	26	24	490	7,430	574.88	178,000	21	10
Erie	241	57	9,930	32,490	572.34	195,800	210	58
Ontario	193	53	7,520	34,800	246.03	233,900	802	283

[a] Data from U.S. Army, Corps of Engineers (1960) or personal communication.

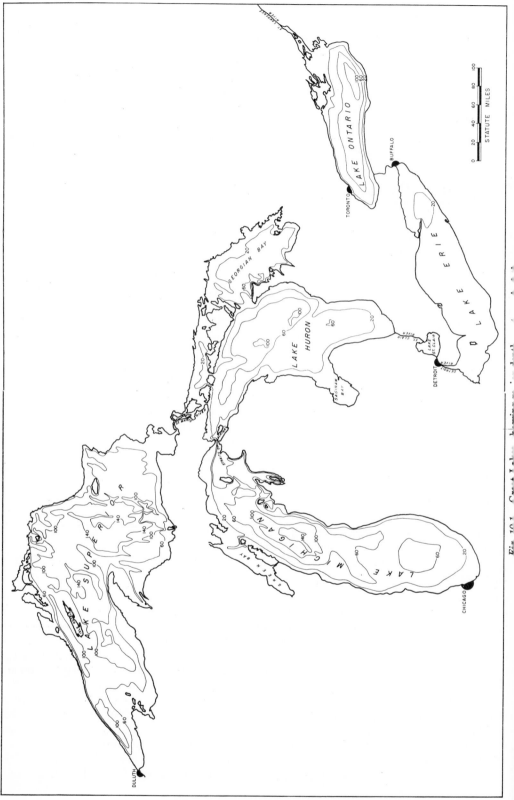

Fig. 10-1. Great Lakes bathymetry, in depth-contours of feet.

(Damann, 1960). Similar changes in the other lakes may be as yet too limited to detect or have gone undetected because we have insufficient information on past conditions.

Despite the widely recognized economic importance of these waters, fundamental knowledge about them is scanty. Investigations of the lakes before 1900 were few and sketchy. From 1900 to 1950 agencies concerned with commercial fisheries and water quality carried out much of the research. Since 1950 investigations have been extended to a great variety of practical and basic problems in addition to those of water quality and fisheries.

Characteristics of the Great Lakes

The large size of the lakes has limited the development of a knowledge of many aspects of their limnology. Considerable information has been amassed, however, on certain facets of Great Lakes limnology, especially those related to applied limnology such as water-level records. In other areas of interest very little is known. For example, even a list of the more common species comprising the plankton of Lake Huron would be an original contribution to the scientific literature. Much of the equipment and methods developed for study of smaller lakes are not applicable to the Great Lakes. Large vessels and sturdier equipment than those in use on small lakes are necessary. Vessels and suitable equipment have not been available, however, for extensive basic research until fairly recently. Consequently, the independent investigator has been hampered in undertaking any large-scale studies, and much of the literature deals with limited data collected in shallow areas near shore. Various ideas, as well as equipment, have been borrowed from the oceanographer. Bathythermographs have been in use on the lakes for many years, and Nansen bottles, reversing thermometers, Clarke-Bumpus plankton samplers, sonic fathometers, and coring devices are as commonplace on research vessels on the lakes as on oceanographic vessels. The methods used by the oceanographers are not entirely applicable to the lakes, however, and must be modified for the conditions peculiar to these bodies of water. As a consequence of the special problems involved in studying the lakes, they offer a common meeting ground between limnology and oceanography.

Investigators have been hampered by a lack of knowledge of past conditions, although various information compiled by water treatment plants, industries, etc. for other purposes is available. Much of this information has not been published, however, and is found only in mimeographed or typewritten reports or as raw data. A total of 1,177 sources of such data are known to exist (Powers *et al.*, 1959). A study was made in Lake Erie for the U.S. Bureau of Commercial Fisheries to determine the usefulness of these observations to limnologists and fishery biologists. Total alkalinity and turbidity measurements, made by D. C. Chandler and associates at the Stone Laboratory in western Lake Erie between September 1938 and December 1945 (Chandler and Weeks, 1945) and in the central and eastern basins by personnel aboard the *Shearwater* in 1929 (Fish, 1960), were compared with data collected at water plants during the same periods. Many of the data sources are not representative of open-lake conditions because of local runoff from tributary streams which reaches the water intakes. Nevertheless, it was demonstrated that certain onshore sources are representative of conditions in the open lake, and consequently, we have an additional means for studying past and present conditions (Powers *et al.*, 1960).

The lakes individually rank among the world's greatest. Lake Superior is the largest freshwater lake of the world. It is the deepest of the Great Lakes and is the uppermost lake in the system (Table 19.1). Lake Superior discharges into Lake Huron through the St. Marys River. Lakes Huron and Michigan rank fifth and sixth in size among the world's lakes. Lake Michigan drains into Lake Huron through the Straits of Mackinac, and their surfaces have the same elevation. For some purposes the two bodies are sometimes considered as a single lake, but they differ considerably in physicochemical characteristics. Lake Huron waters discharge through the St. Clair River, Lake St. Clair, and the Detroit River into western Lake Erie. Lakes Erie and Ontario are much smaller than the other Great Lakes. Nevertheless, they rank twelfth and fourteenth among the world's largest lakes. Lake Erie discharges into Lake Ontario through the Niagara River. The waters of the Niagara make a rapid descent from Lake Erie over Niagara Falls and through the rapids above and below the falls. The difference of mean surface level between Lakes Erie and Ontario is approximately 326 ft. The St. Lawrence

River carries the discharge from Lake Ontario to the Atlantic Ocean.

The bedrock of the Great Lakes region consists of undifferentiated pre-Cambrian and sedimentary Paleozoic rocks. The basins themselves have been formed by excavation of the outcrop belts of the less resistant rocks by glacial action. Most of the basin of Lake Superior and part of Georgian Bay of Lake Huron lie in the pre-Cambrian rock of the Canadian Shield. The rest of the bedrock formation of the Great Lakes is of various Paleozoic periods. Silurian rock forms the western and northern shore of Lake Michigan, the islands and peninsula separating Georgian Bay from Lake Huron, the Niagara escarpment, and the southern shore of Lake Ontario. The Devonian shales form part of the basins of Lakes Erie, Huron, and Michigan. Ordovician shales occur along the west shore of Green Bay and in the deeper areas of Georgian Bay. Most of the Lower Peninsula of the State of Michigan is undifferentiated Pennsylvanian and Mississippian rock. Extensive glacial deposits cover most of the bedrock formations in the Great Lakes region except for the Canadian Shield (Hough, 1958).

The levels of the lakes vary within the year from an average of slightly more than 1 ft for Lakes Huron, Michigan, and Superior to almost 2 ft on Lake Ontario. The highest level occurs in the summer and the low in late winter or early spring (Corps Engr., 1960).

Wind setups and seiches have been reported for all of the lakes, and these changes in water level are very apparent on the records from the gauges maintained by the U.S. Lake Survey (Harris, 1954). Most of the literature, however, is concerned with water-level fluctuation in Lake Erie. Differences in lake-level elevations between Buffalo and Toledo have been as great as 13.5 ft (Hunt, 1958). The results of a number of studies indicate that the uninodal longitudinal seiche has a period between 14 and 15 hours. Verber (1961) has presented evidence that the actual period of this seiche depends on the elevation of the lake and the direction of the wind blowing across the long axis of the lake. The nodal line may shift over a broad nodal zone approximately 60 mi wide and may pivot according to wind direction. The basins of the lake may have independent oscillations. Consequently, the water-level records show a number of fluctuations superimposed upon each other. Methods are being developed to forecast the lake level accurately, since the fluctuations are of considerable economic importance. People concerned with hydroelectric power generation in the Niagara River are especially interested in forecasting lake levels, since the hourly river flow can vary from 162,000 to 330,000 cfs in a week (Gillies, 1960).

Records of abrupt rises in water level are scattered in the literature. These waves, which have meterological origins, are referred to as surges. A recent surge in Lake Michigan on 26 June 1954 took a number of lives. This surge was produced by a fast-moving squall line that passed over the southern end of the lake and may have been due to resonant coupling between a moving pressure jump line and the lake (Harris, 1957). This theory did not provide an adequate explanation of another surge, and Donn and Ewing (1956) found that the theory of edge waves was more suitable. A numerical computation method has been successfully applied to the surge of 26 June 1954 in a study to develop a method for predicting these water-level fluctuations (Platzman, 1960).

Our knowledge of the currents of the lakes has increased considerably within the past few years. Nevertheless, current pattern determination remains in the early state of development. Most of the studies have been concerned with surface currents, and the nature of subsurface water movements and their relation to the surface remains a matter of conjecture. Furthermore, observations of surface currents have not extended over long enough periods to support conclusions regarding seasonal patterns (Johnson, 1958).

Several methods have been developed to study currents and water masses of the lakes. Drift missiles have been used for many years and remain a satisfactory method, especially in areas where the shores are highly populated. As many as 80% of the drift bottles from a single release may be returned in a short time. Synoptic surveys, i.e., the simultaneous observation of various limnological conditions at a number of points, have been employed by a number of agencies, usually on a cooperative basis. The contoured distribution of temperatures, transparency, various chemical constituents of the water such as calcium, sodium, chlorides, etc., as determined by these surveys, as well as direct current measurements with dye and large floats, have been useful in detecting water masses and currents. The oceanographers' dynamic-height method for determining currents has been modified for use on the lakes (Ayers, 1956). It has been demonstrated that methods for making estimates of flushing rates, seaward transport of river water, and exchange of sea and river water in marine estuaries can be used to evaluate the circulation of Saginaw Bay (Beeton and Hooper, 1961). A method for estimating the rate of littoral transport has been developed. An equation was derived relating transport rate to wave energy (Bajorunas, 1960).

Important direct factors in the production of nonperiodic horizontal currents in ... [the] Great Lakes appear to be the wind, rotation of the earth, the several effects of the lake basins which confine the lakes, and the flow-through of water supplied by runoff, ground-water seepage, and precipitation onto the lakes. As yet it is impossible to assess the relative value of all these factors, but at this time it appears logical to consider that the wind is the primary energy for the movement of water and the establishment of horizontal current patterns. The rotation of the earth modifies the direction in which wind energy is effective. The basins influence currents by modifying wind at the shores, by interposing physical barriers, as well as by bottom friction [Ayers et al., 1958].

Present evidence indicates that the currents in most of the lakes are variable and respond rather quickly to wind changes. Synoptic surveys of Lakes Huron and Michigan indicate that some large eddies develop in these lakes and that the flow-through in Lake Huron and the outflow of Lake Michigan lend some stability to the current patterns (Ayers et al., 1956, 1958). Johnson (1958) found no one characteristic current system in Lake Huron, although a general but highly variable west-to-east drift was usually present. Surface currents were highly variable in all areas of Lake Michigan, and a stable pattern was not detected during 1954 or 1955. A north-bound current was observed, however, along the eastern shore several times (Johnson, 1960).

An attempt has not been made to study the general circulation in all areas of Lake Superior. The published (Ruschmeyer et al., 1958; Beeton et al., 1959) and unpublished data show, however, that certain persistent currents occur. A well-defined littoral current flows from west to east along the south shore. This littoral current may be part of a general counterclockwise circulation of the entire lake.

All of the lakes exhibit some degree of thermal stratification during the warmer months. They probably mix deeply throughout most of the winter and spring, since solid ice sheets are mostly limited to such sheltered areas as embayments, channels, among islands, and along shore. Ice in the main lakes usually occurs as floes. The smaller lakes, Erie and Ontario, may have 80 to 95% of their surfaces ice-covered in severe winters. The ice cover also can extend large distances from shore in Lake Superior during an unusually cold winter. Lakes Huron and Michigan normally remain open, although shore ice may extend 8–10 mi out into the lakes. The effect of deep mixing is apparent in Lake Superior where homoiothermous water around 2°C occurs to depths of 600 ft (Beeton et al., 1959). The lakes differ chiefly in the rate at which they warm and in the stability of the thermal stratification. The deep waters of all the lakes probably remain close to 4° C throughout the year. Well-defined and persistent thermal stratification is usually established in Lake Erie by mid-June and in Lakes Huron, Michigan, and Ontario by the end of June. The epilimnion extends to about 45 ft in Lakes Huron, Michigan, and Ontario and to 65 ft in Lake Erie during the period of maximum stratification in August. Lake Superior, which is much colder than the other lakes, usually does not exhibit any well-defined stratification until mid-July. The lower limit of the epilimnion is around 45 ft. Thermal stratification is not uniform from area to area, and the metalimnion is usually poorly developed.

The Great Lakes consist of bicarbonate waters. Total alkalinity ranges from 46 ppm (as $CaCO_3$) in Lake Superior to 113 ppm in Lake Michigan (Table 19.2). The pH ranges from 8.0 to 8.5 for most of the waters, except Lake Superior. Sulfate concentrations are greater than chlorides in the upper lakes, and they are almost equal in Lakes Erie and Ontario. The proportions of calcium, magnesium, and sodium in the upper lakes are about 10:3:1. Potassium usually averages around 1 ppm in all the lakes. Silica usually fluctuates around 2–3 ppm, although only trace amounts of silica occur at times in the highly productive waters of Lake Erie. Concentrations of total phosphorus are low in the upper lakes and are usually less than 5 ppb in the open waters of Lake Superior. The phosphorus content of water from Lake Erie is about six times greater than that in the other lakes. The dissolved-oxygen content of most of the lake waters is near

TABLE 19.2

Average chemical characteristics of Great Lakes waters. U.S. Bureau of Commercial Fisheries data, unless designated otherwise. Data based on samples from various depths.

Lake	Calcium (ppm)	Magnesium (ppm)	Potassium (ppm)	Sodium (ppm)	Total alkalinity (ppm CaCO₃)	Chloride (ppm)	Sulfate (ppm)	Silica (ppm)	Total phosphorus (ppb)	pH	Specific conductance (micromhos at 18° C)
Superior	12.4	2.8	0.6	1.1	46	1.9	3.2	2.1	5	7.4	78.7
Huron	22.6	6.3[a]	1.0	2.3	82	7.0	9.7	2.3	10	8.1	168.3
Michigan	31.5	10.4	0.9	3.4	113	6.2	15.5	3.1	13	8.0	225.8
Erie	36.7	8.9	1.4	8.7	95	21.0	21.1	1.5	61	8.3	241.8
Ontario	39.3	9.1[b]	1.2	10.8	93[c]	23.5	32.4	0.3	—	8.5[c]	272.3

[a] Ayers et al., 1956.
[b] Leverin, 1947 (average from Toronto intake).
[c] New York State Dept. Health, 1958.

saturation, even at the greatest depths, and super-saturation is common. Dissolved-oxygen concentrations of less than 1 ppm have been found in Lake Erie. These low values have been detected in the bottom waters in an area of several hundred square miles of the central basin.

The Great Lakes plankton is characteristic of large and deep lakes. Diatoms are the most important constituents of the plankton, although zooplankton may occasionally equal the diatoms in biomass but not in numbers. Blue-green and green algae are especially abundant at times in Lake Erie and probably in Lake Ontario. Even in Lake Erie, however, diatoms usually comprise 75% of the phytoplankton. The more abundant diatom genera are *Asterionella*, *Cyclotella*, *Fragilaria*, *Melosira*, *Synedra*, and *Tabellaria*. Copepods make up the bulk of the zooplankton, although protozoans are more numerous. Cladocerans are very abundant in the summer, and rotifers, especially *Keratella*, are usually plentiful. *Cyclops bicuspidatus*, *Diaptomus minutus*, *D. sicilis*, *D. ashlandi*, and *D. oregonensis* are especially plentiful in Lake Erie and in the upper strata of the other lakes. The cold-water copepods *Limnocalanus macrurus* and *Senecella calanoides* are taken in the deep waters.

Little is known of the abundance of plankton in the lakes. Nothing has been published on Lake Huron plankton, and only a few studies have been made on the other lakes. Most of the work has been on Lake Erie. The studies that have been made indicate two periods of peak plankton abundance in spring and fall (Ahlstrom, 1936; Beeton et al., 1959; Chandler and Weeks, 1945; Davis, 1954; Fish, 1960; Wright, 1955).

The spring pulse consists almost entirely of diatoms. Populations of blue-green and green algae build up during August and September and contribute to the fall pulse, although diatoms are still dominant. These phytoplankton pulses are very important in the productivity of the lakes. Phytoplankton populations existing between pulses in Lake Erie in 1942 made up only 17% of the annual crop (Chandler and Weeks, 1945). Large zooplankters of Lake Erie are abundant in summer and the smaller ones in spring and fall (Davis, 1954). Most of the Crustacea in Lake Michigan reach only one population peak a year. Cladocerans and the copepods *Mesocyclops edax* and *Epischura lacustris* probably overwinter as eggs (Wells, 1960). *Cyclops bicuspidatus*, which is a winter and early spring form in Lake Erie (Andrews, 1953), is apparently plentiful throughout the entire year in the colder environment of Lake Michigan (Wells, 1960). Further generalization on plankton abundance would be meaningless, since special sampling problems have not been resolved, and most of the studies have been limited to observations during only part of the year. Sampling at a given station presents a problem, since different water masses are probably sampled on each visit (Davis, 1954). Year-round studies over four years in Lake Erie showed that each year the quality and quantity of the phytoplankton were different. Consequently, Chandler and Weeks (1945) concluded that "until a greater knowledge of the extent of the annual variations is acquired any attempt to generalize on the basis of observations limited to one season or even a complete year will have little meaning."

The results of the limnological surveys conducted in Lake Erie in 1928 and 1929 remain the best source for information on the horizontal distribution of plankton. Considerable variation existed in both the quality and quantity of plankton in different areas of the lake and at different times (Fish, 1960). The vertical distribution of eight species of cladocerans, nine species of copepods, and the two benthic malacostracans, *Pontoporeia affinis* and *Mysis relicta,* was studied in Lake Michigan (Wells, 1960). All species migrated toward and attained their greatest numbers at the surface late in the day, apparently in response to diurnal changes in light intensity. The number of individuals at the surface decreased toward midnight, and limited evidence indicated an increase for some species at the surface again slightly before dawn. A more detailed study of the migratory behavior of *M. relicta* indicated that light "triggers" and controls their migrations, while thermal conditions interact with and modify the influence of light (Beeton, 1960). As the length of day decreased following the summer solstice, the mysids ascended progressively earlier each evening and descended later each morning. Moonlight and fog influenced the time as well as the amplitude of the vertical migration. The mysids frequently migrated through the metalimnion when first ascending, but later in the night the majority occurred in or immediately below this layer.

Attempts to obtain estimates of the productivity of Great Lakes phytoplankton populations have met with certain problems not confronting limnologists working on most smaller lakes. The low plankton populations in Lake Superior made it necessary to use artificially concentrated samples for productivity measurements. Even a five-fold concentration was not sufficient, however, for measurement of photosynthesis by the light and dark bottle oxygen technique in Lake Superior (Putnam and Olson, 1961). Estimates of productivity made at a few stations are obviously not representative of conditions in an entire lake or even in the larger bays. Consequently, studies are being made to develop methods that would be applicable to large lakes (Bachmann *et al.,* 1961). Most of the work on productivity has been carried out in western Lake Erie. Methods for determining photosynthetic and respiratory rates by measuring pH differences have been developed for use in dark and light bottle experiments (Verduin, 1956) and under completely natural conditions (Verduin, 1960). Changes in pH are converted to CO_2 change by referring to a differential titration curve. Recent studies employing these methods indicate that when natural population densities are used, the photosynthetic yield (average 1.6 micromoles of CO_2 absorbed per microliter of plant volume per hour) is three times higher than previously reported yields from experiments using artificially concentrated populations. Furthermore, measurements of photosynthetic activity under completely natural conditions result in values significantly higher than those from photosynthesis in bottles (Verduin, 1960).

The deep-water bottom fauna of the Great Lakes is dominated by the amphipod *P. affinis* and the opossum shrimp (*M. relicta*). Oligochaetes, especially *Limnodrilus,* and the Sphaeriidae, *Pisidium* and *Sphaerium,* are also numerous. Midge larvae of the genus *Spaniotoma* are found at depths greater than 30 fathoms. The shallow-water fauna has many of the species common in the smaller inland lakes. Hirudinea and various tendipedids are plentiful at depths less than 40 fathoms. Various gastropods—*Lymnea, Valvata, Amnicola, Goniobasis*—are important in shallow areas. Trichoptera larvae and especially the ephemeropteran, *Hexagenia,* are abundant in some areas.

Hexagenia nymphs dominated the benthos of western Lake Erie prior to 1953. Data published by various investigators indicate that the population averaged around 400 nymphs per m². A severe reduction in dissolved oxygen in the bottom waters, associated with unusual thermal stratification of the western basin, killed a large percentage of the mayflies (Britt, 1955). Subsequent studies indicate that the mayfly population has remained at about 10% of its former abundance, and substantial increases have occurred in the population of oligochaetes and midge larvae (Beeton, 1961). These changes in the benthos certainly are not due to the one period of low dissolved-oxygen concentrations, and shifts in the fish populations and increases in the chemical content of the water indicate a changing environment.

An average of approximately 1,200 benthic animals per m² has been reported for Lake Huron (Teter, 1960) and Lake Michigan (Eggleton, 1937). The greatest concentration of organisms, 11,440 animals per m², was found in Lake Michigan, although a maximum of 10,556 occurred in Lake Huron. Seasonal changes in abundance of organisms and a zone of maximum abundance at about 140 ft, noted by Eggleton in Lake Michigan, were not found in Lake Huron (Teter, 1960) or during a more recent study of Lake Michigan (Merna, 1960).

The fish fauna of the Great Lakes and tributaries includes representatives of most families of North American fishes. Salmonid fishes dominated the early fisheries of all the lakes. In Lake Superior no other group has produced any substantial amounts. The lake trout (*Salvelinus namaycush*) and the coregonids (whitefish, lake herring, chubs) have been the most important commercial species in the upper lakes. Certain shallow-water areas, bays, and the lower lakes have yielded large quantities of Percidae, Catostomidae, and Ictaluridae. Yellow perch (*Perca flavescens*), the pike-perches (*Stizostedion* spp.), white bass (*Roccus chrysops*), and the freshwater drum (*Aplodinotus grunniens*) are abundant in Lake Erie. Native species include vast numbers of small fishes—various cyprinids, cottids, sticklebacks, trout-perch—that do not enter into the commercial catch, but some have value as bait fish. The fish fauna has been modified greatly by the introduction and immigration of exotic species. Carp were introduced the latter part of the 19th century, and substantial populations were well established by 1900. Smelt (*Osmerus mordax*) were stocked in a lake tributary to Lake Michigan in the 1920's. In a relatively short time they spread throughout the upper Great Lakes and into Lake Erie. They are native to Lake Ontario. The sea lamprey (*Petromyzon marinus*) and the alewife (*Alosa pseudoharengus*), now abundant in most of the lakes, were unknown except in Lake Ontario prior to the opening of the Welland Canal. Carp and smelt have contributed substantially to the commercial take. Alewife, despite its abundance, has proved difficult to market. The white perch (*Roccus americanus*) is a recent immigrant. A large population is established in Lake Ontario in the Bay of Quinte, and a number have recently been captured in eastern Lake Erie (Scott and Christie, 1961). Several pink salmon (*Oncorhynchus gorbuscha*) have been caught in Lake Superior in recent years. Apparently a number of these fish escaped from a hatchery, and a small population has been established that has spawned successfully (Schumacher and Eddy, 1960). The relationship of these exotics to other species is as yet unknown, except for the sea lamprey which has resulted in drastic decreases in the abundance of certain of our native fishes.

History of limnological research on the lakes

The development of an extensive scientific literature concerning the lakes within recent years has been phenomenal. Less than 100 years ago most of the lakes region was yet a wilderness, and only limited general information about the Great Lakes was available. The Great Lakes bibliography compiled by John Van Oosten in 1957, however, has almost 3,000 entries, and there are several thousand additional references, a good proportion from recent years.

The discussion of research on the lakes has been divided into 3 sections: pre-1900, *circa* 1900–1949, and *circa* 1950 to present. The apparent development of a different approach to research on the lakes around 1900 and the greatly increased tempo of research since about 1950 make these periods meaningful in the history of Great Lakes limnology.

Pre-1900

Professor Louis Agassiz and 15 fellow scientists and students embarked from Sault Ste. Marie on 30 June 1848 in one large Mackinaw boat and two canoes on what was probably the first purely scientific expedition on the Great Lakes (Agassiz, 1850). Their objective was to study the natural history of the north shore of Lake Superior. The observations made by this group stand as one of the best sources for information on this region while it was yet a wilderness. This expedition contributed little to our knowledge of the limnology of the lakes, although some observations were made of surface water temperatures, transparency, and water-level fluctuations. The discussions of the fishes of Lake Superior by Agassiz and of Coleoptera by Leconte, however, are especially valuable.

It is not to be implied that Agassiz's expedition is the start of scientific interest in the Great Lakes. Considerable knowledge had been accumulated on mineral deposits, and the Great Lakes were already important for shipping by 1848. The importance of shipping undoubtedly generated considerable interest in water-level fluctuations, since channels had not been dredged yet in important waterways such as the St. Clair River delta where depths of only 7 to 10 ft existed in the channel. Father Marquette in 1673, Father Louis Hennepin in 1679, Baron Honton in 1689, Charlevoix in 1721, as well as a number of military men in the early 1800's had observed short-term changes in the water level of Lake Michigan and had expressed the opinion that these fluctuations were produced chiefly by the winds (Dearborn, 1829). Considerable speculation arose that these fluctuations were tides, and Graham (1861) and Comstock (1872) presented evidence for a small tide in Lake Michigan of about 0.14 to 0.20 ft. Most of the changes in water level were shown to be seiches (Perkins, 1893; Henry, 1900), although there are a number of records of very abrupt and large changes in water level in the lakes which were called tidal waves by some investigators.

Interest in the physicochemical characteristics of the Great Lakes, other than water-level fluctuations, developed slowly. A few measurements of surface temperatures of Lake Ontario were made in 1838 (Dewey, 1838), but 50 more years passed before much was known of subsurface temperatures (Drummond, 1890). The U.S. Lake Survey had established water-level gauges at a number of harbors on the lakes prior to 1860 and conducted a number of surveys, so that by 1887 data on lake and watershed areas, mean and maximum depths, and elevation of lake surfaces above mean sea level had been compiled (Schermerhorn, 1887). Concern over sewage disposal and location of water intakes stimulated some early interest in lake currents (Clark, 1892). The major study of currents, however, was that made during 1892–94 by the U.S. Weather Bureau (Harrington, 1895). It is only recently that more detailed studies have been made, and Harrington's surface-current charts are still a reference source (Hough, 1958). Probably the best information on early chemical analyses of the lake waters is Lane's paper (1899), which includes data from as early as 1854.

Early work on plankton was usually related to water supply or fisheries. These studies were taxonomic or distributional, except for the quantitative sampling by Reighard (1893). Kellicott (1878), Mills (1882), and Vorce (1882) studied the microscopic life in the Lake Erie water supplies of Buffalo, N.Y., and Cleveland, Ohio. The earliest paper on Lake Michigan plankton is that of Briggs (1872), although Thomas and Chase (1887) had initiated their study of diatoms in the Chicago water supply in 1870. Birge's (1881) paper on Cladocera was based on samples from the Chicago water supply. Most of the studies made by Forbes (1891) were related to fishery problems.

Dredging for deep-water fauna in Lake Michigan was initiated by the Chicago Academy of Science in 1870. The collection of the crustaceans, *Mysis relicta* and *Pontoporeia affinis*, which have close marine affinities, off Racine, Wisconsin, in 1870 led to speculation that the bottom of Lake Michigan might be brackish (Hoy, 1872). The U.S. Army, Corps of Engineers, conducted extensive sounding and dredging in Lake Superior in 1871. The reports prepared by Sidney I. Smith (1874) remain as our only source of published data on the deep-water benthos of the open waters of Lake Superior. The first study of the Lake Ontario benthos was being conducted by Nicholson (1872) at this time.

The U.S. Commission of Fish and Fisheries survey of the fishery resources, initiated in 1871 (Milner, 1874), marked the beginning of the U.S. Government's interest in the Great Lakes fisheries. At that time the fishing industry on Lake Michigan alone employed about 2,000 men and operated about 600 fishing vessels. An estimated 32.2 million pounds of Great Lakes fish were handled by the major markets annually, but many additional pounds were undoubtedly consumed locally. Milner's tour of the shore and islands of Lake Michigan permitted him to compile considerable information on the life histories of the fishes. The revenue vessel *Johnson* was used for dredging and trawling on a two-week cruise in September 1871. Unfortunately Milner's collection of fish and invertebrates, stored at the Chicago Academy of Science, was destroyed in the great Chicago fire of 1871. Milner extended his survey to Lakes Superior, Huron, St. Clair, and Erie in 1872. His report mentions what was probably the first attempt to study fish migration in the lakes by tagging whitefish with a small metal tag.

Increasing public concern over the decline of the fisheries of the lakes, especially in the contiguous waters of Canada and the United States, led to the establishment of federal and state fishery agencies. The Michigan Board of Fish Commissioners, established in 1873, demonstrated great interest in the Great Lakes fisheries (Jerome, 1879). Recognition of the need for cooperation in preserving the lake fisheries led to a number of informal international conferences in the late 1870's. A Joint Commission was appointed by the United States and Great Britain in 1893 (Rathbun and Wakeham, 1897). Evidence of a decline in the fisheries had been offered as early as 1871 (Milner, 1874). Undoubtedly Milner's recommendations for artificial propagation of fish and protective legislation to reverse the decline in the abundance of fish guided future fishery work for many years on the lakes. By 1874 the Michigan Board of Fish Commissioners had established a hatchery on the Detroit River. The U.S. Government acquired the hatchery at Northville, Michigan, in 1880, primarily for the propagation of whitefish. A small station, to serve as a supplier to the Northville hatchery, was established at Alpena, Michigan, in 1882. By 1888 the U.S. Government was operating a hatchery owned by the state of Ohio at Sandusky, Ohio, and had started construction of a hatchery at Duluth, Minnesota. Additional hatcheries were established at Put-in-Bay, Ohio, and Cape Vincent, New York, in 1890 and 1896. Several of the lake states established hatcheries during this period, and the Canadians had operated a hatchery at Newcastle, Ontario, for about 20 years before establishment of the first U.S. Government station on the lakes.

The only additional fishery work of consequence during this period is the surveys, conducted by the U.S. Commission of Fish and Fisheries, of the history, apparatus, methods, and statistics of the fisheries in 1885 and 1892 (H. M. Smith, 1894).

1900–1949

Commercial fishing had become increasingly important during the latter part of the 1800's, but concern existed over declining fish populations, especially whitefish, and dissatisfaction developed over the methods being used to reverse this decline—restrictive legislation and the fish hatchery operations. Reighard's (1899) answer to this problem marked a new approach to study of the lakes: "Is it not better . . . to take up the study of the biology of the lakes from the point of view of pure science for the purpose of finding out as far as possible of the facts and making clear as many as possible of the principles? Then when, in the future, any fisheries problems arise, the facts and principles for their solution will have been already determined in large part." This concept was the basis for the biological investigations that Reighard undertook on Lake St. Clair in 1893 for the Michigan Fish Commission (Reighard, 1894) and on Lake Erie in 1898–1902 for the U.S. Commission of Fish (U.S. Comm. Fish, 1900). The studies made of Lake Michigan in 1894, under the direction of H. B. Ward for the Michigan Fish Commission (Ward, 1896), were a continuation of the research initiated on Lake St. Clair. Some of our country's foremost biologists were associated with these studies. The results of work conducted by E. A. Birge, C. A. Kofoid, Frank Smith, H. D. Thompson, Bryant Walker, R. H. Wolcott, and W. McM. Woodworth were published as appendices to papers by Reighard (1894) and Ward (1896). Papers by Jennings (1904) on the rotifers, Marsh (1895) on the copepods, Pieters (1894) and Snow (1904) on higher plants and algae, and Moore (1906) on Hirudinea and Oligochaeta were published separately.

The general concern generated by the collapse of the Lake Erie cisco fishery in 1925 resulted in two extensive limnological surveys. The production of this fishery had averaged about 20 million pounds annually, but it dropped to 5.5 million in 1925 and to 1.9 million in 1928 (Van Oosten, 1930). The state of Ohio undertook a survey in 1926, under the direction of Raymond Osburn, to determine the extent of pollution and its influence on the fish. The U.S. Bureau of Fisheries, also concerned over the loss of the cisco fishery, established the Great Lakes Fishery Investigations under the direction of John Van Oosten in 1927 (the U.S. Government had financed the researches of Walter Koelz [1929] on the taxonomy of the coregonids and of Van Oosten [1929] on the life histories of the lake herring and whitefish prior to this time), but the 1927 action was the beginning of a continuing federal fishery program on the lakes (Hile, 1957). The Bureau of Fisheries cooperated with the state of Ohio in the study of western Lake Erie in 1927. The program was expanded greatly in 1928 to cover the entire lake. The survey of the western basin continued under the auspices of the state of Ohio, although Stillman Wright, U.S. Bureau of Fisheries, directed the field work in limnology. Studies were made of the physical limnology, chemistry, plankton, and benthos (Wright, 1955). The Province of Ontario, Buffalo Museum of Science, New York Conservation Commission, Buffalo Health Department, and the U.S. Bureau of Fisheries cooperated in the survey of eastern and central Lake Erie during 1928–29. The Bureau of Fisheries assigned its 85-foot vessel, the *Shearwater* (previously assigned to the Put-in-Bay Hatchery), to this survey. This vessel was probably the first sizeable fishery research vessel on the lakes. The scope of the limnological survey of the eastern and central basins was similar to that of the survey in the west end, although the benthos was not included (Fish, 1960). Some additional information on this survey, especially on the fish, was included in an earlier report (New York Conserv. Dept., 1929).

The third major fishery-limnological survey was carried out from the 102-foot research vessel *Fulmar* by the Bureau of Fisheries in Lake Michigan in 1930–32. The states of Michigan and Wisconsin and four net manufacturers contributed financially to this investigation of the gill net mesh size that would allow the most efficient capture of chubs with the least destruction of small lake trout. Extensive limnological data were collected, and papers have been published on the plankton (Ahlstrom, 1936), benthos (Eggleton, 1937), surface currents (Deason, 1932; Van Oosten, 1962), and temperatures (Van Oosten, 1960). This survey marked the end of any extensive field work on the lakes by the U.S. Bureau of Fisheries for the next 15 years, 1933–47 (Hile, 1957).

Much of the work at the Franz Theodore Stone Laboratory, Ohio State University, has been related to fishery problems. David S. Kellicott, who promoted the establishment of the Lake Laboratory in the State Fish Hatchery at Sandusky, Ohio, in 1896, recognized the need for studies of biological problems related to fisheries. Two of the laboratory directors, Raymond Osburn and T. H. Langlois, were closely associated with the Ohio Division of Conservation. The laboratory was moved from Sandusky to Cedar Point in 1903, transferred to the State Fish Hatchery at Put-in-Bay in 1918, and relocated in its present site on Gibraltar Island in 1925.

Starting in 1938 the laboratory was operated full-time under the direction of Langlois and a research staff consisting of David C. Chandler, M. B. Trautman, and Charles F. Walker. Year-round studies, which led to the development of special equipment and methods for working through the ice, were conducted for ten years. The research program was concerned with the general ecology of western Lake Erie, including the terrestrial as well as the aquatic environment and the relationship of man to this environment. The philosophy back of this research program was that changes in the biota, especially in fish populations, were the result of environmental changes. Furthermore, these environmental changes were due to allochthonous as well as autochthonous processes which could be measured. A very broad program was undertaken to study conditions in the lake as well as on the watershed. Extensive meteorological data were collected for many years. Studies made by the staff, numerous graduate students, and visiting investigators added substantially to our knowledge of the life histories and ecology of fishes and numerous invertebrates. The circulation of western Lake Erie was naturally of interest to the various investigators, and several studies were made of currents. Individual water masses with their characteristic biota and physicochemical conditions were recognized. The plankton of Lake Erie is better known than in the other lakes primarily because of the work of L. H. Tiffany, C. E. Taft, and D. C. Chandler during this period. Detailed references to these studies are given in the summary by Langlois (1949).

The year-around program was discontinued in 1955; nevertheless, limnological research and teaching have been maintained during the summers by Jacob Verduin and N. Wilson Britt. Most of the present research has been directed towards problems related to the productivity of Lake Erie (Verduin, 1960).

Canadian fishery and limnological studies on the lakes were conducted by the Biological Board of Canada, the Ontario Fisheries Research Laboratory of the University of Toronto, and the Fisheries Research Laboratory of the University of Western Ontario. The Biological Board maintained the Georgian Bay Biological Station from 1901 to 1914. Results of most of the work at the station were published in a single volume and included, among others, papers by B. A. Bensley on fishes, G. O. Sars on Entomostraca, E. M. Walker on Odonata, and Wilbert A. Clemens on Ephemeridae (Prince, 1915). Several papers on Great Lakes fishes originated from the Ontario Fisheries Research Laboratory during the 1920's. The Fisheries Research Laboratory, at Erieau, Ontario, conducted limnological sampling in Lake Erie, primarily during the summers, in 1947–53. These data are included in a report by Powers et al. (1960).

An International Board of Inquiry for the Great Lakes Fisheries was established by Canada and the United States in 1940. A four-member board consisting of Hubert R. Gallagher (Council of State Governments), A. G. Huntsman (Fisheries Research Board of Canada), D. J. Taylor (Ontario Game and Fisheries Department), and John Van Oosten (U.S. Fish and Wildlife Service) was appointed to make a study of the fisheries and to make recommendations for preserving and developing the fisheries of the lakes (Intern. Board Inquiry, 1943). This inquiry included a historical review of the various international and interstate conferences on Great Lakes fisheries, detailed production statistics of the commercial fisheries, and recommendations for preserving the fisheries. A treaty was negotiated between the United States and Canada for international investigation and control of the lake fisheries. It was never ratified, however, and this attempt to obtain uniform regulation of the fisheries failed.

Concern over the decline in the quality of Great Lakes waters also resulted in several major surveys and a number of smaller investigations after 1900. The Lake Michigan Water Commission, established in 1907 by the states of Illinois, Indiana, Michigan, and Wisconsin, and several municipalities, made a number of studies of water chemistry, plankton, and currents between 1907 and 1911 (Lake Michigan Water Comm., 1911). During 1906–07 the U.S. Geological Survey carried out its investigation of the chemical content of Great Lakes water (Dole, 1909). The Boundary Waters Treaty of 1909 between Canada and the United States provided for the establishment of the International Joint Commission to investigate the pollution of boundary waters. The first of two major surveys made by this commission (in 1913) concerned coliform bacteria in the St. Marys River, the St. Clair-Detroit River and western end of Lake Erie, eastern Lake Erie and the Niagara River, and Lake Ontario and the St. Lawrence River. A larger study, including water chemistry, bacteria, and currents, was made in these same areas in 1946–48 (Intern. Joint Comm., 1951).

The U.S. Public Health Service made an investigation of pollution in southern Lake Michigan in 1924–25 (Crohurst and Veldee, 1927). The surveys of water quality in Saginaw Bay, Lake Huron, by the Michigan Stream Control Commission in 1935–36 resulted in the first published record of the use of the "synoptic survey" approach on the Great Lakes. The literature contains only scattered references to this study, although it is one of the most extensive surveys carried out on the lakes. This large bay was sampled about once a week, and the survey vessel traveled approximately 7,000 mi during the 15-month study (Adams, 1937). Surveys were made of pollution in southern Green Bay in 1938–39 (Williamson and Greenbank, 1939) and of the Ohio waters of Lake Erie in 1950–51 (Ohio Dept. Nat. Resources, 1953). The most recent survey is that of Lake Ontario in 1957 (New York State Dept. Health, 1958).

Numerous other smaller studies related to water quality and waste disposal have been made on the lakes, but many of these were conducted by municipalities, industry, and engineering firms and have not been published. Among those that have been published for Lake Erie are the studies of pollution and currents by Fell (1910), and of plankton by Davis (1955) and Gottschall and Jennings (1933). The important work on the hydrology of the Great Lakes by Horton and Grunsky (1927) was undertaken because of water-quality and pollution problems in southern Lake Michigan.

Several limnological investigations were made that were not especially related to fisheries or water quality. Among those concerned with physical limnology are Hayford's (1922) work on seiches, and the studies of lake temperatures by Millar (1952) and Hachey (1952). Church's (1942, 1945) investigation of the thermal cycle of Lake Michigan remains as our best source of information. The monumental work of Leverett and Taylor (1915) on the geology of the Great Lakes was completed during this period. Several publications appeared on plankton (Eddy, 1943) and benthos (Goodrich and van der Schalie, 1932).

1950 to present

The past twelve years have seen a substantial increase of interest in the Great Lakes and in the capability of a number of groups to conduct

Fig. 19.2.—Hammond Bay Laboratory, U.S. Bureau of Commercial Fisheries.

research on the lakes. These developments probably arose indirectly from man's greater concern over his environment and the possibility of controlling it, although serious changes in the lake fisheries, increased use of the lakes for water supply and waste disposal, shore-erosion problems, and the building of the St. Lawrence Seaway have generated heightened regional interest in the lakes.

Much of the recent work has been conducted by governmental and university agencies that have broad interests in the Great Lakes. Consequently, their research programs are discussed in some detail. Still other agencies have research programs concerned with particular aspects of the Great Lakes environment. Eighteen agencies presented reports at the Third Conference on Great Lakes Research in Ann Arbor in 1959. Much of their research is highly specialized, limited to certain facets of the environment, or associated with the broader programs of other agencies. These programs are described in less detail.

U.S. Bureau of Commercial Fisheries.—Fishery research on the lakes has laid special emphasis on control of the sea lamprey (*Petromyzon marinus*) since 1949. Sea lampreys were found above Niagara Falls in 1921, and they had migrated into Lake Huron by the early 1930's. Biologists had warned of the potential menace of the lamprey in the upper Great Lakes, but substantial funds for sea lamprey research were not allocated by the Congress of the United States until 1950. By that time the lake trout fishery had disappeared in the U.S. waters of Lake Huron, trout production had fallen by 95% in Lake Michigan, and lampreys had entered Lake

Superior (Applegate and Moffett, 1955). Fishes other than the lake trout have been affected by the lamprey. Whitefish and suckers have been the principal prey in shallower waters, although the walleye population of Saginaw Bay has been greatly reduced. In deeper waters populations of the larger chubs (*Coregonus* spp.) have suffered devastating inroads (Moffett, 1957).

The substantial allotment of funds in 1950 to the Great Lakes Fishery Investigations of the U.S. Fish and Wildlife Service (now the Ann Arbor Biological Laboratory, U.S. Bureau of Commercial Fisheries) made it possible for the first time for this agency to organize a comprehensive research program. In consideration of the burden involved in establishing and administering this greatly expanded program, Van Oosten was relieved of administrative duties to devote full time to the completion of his numerous researches in progress. James W. Moffett was appointed the new Chief of the Great Lakes Fishery Investigations. Ralph Hile has been Assistant Chief of the Investigations until a recent reorganization, whereby Leo Erkkila was appointed Assistant Director in charge of sea lamprey research and control, and Paul Eschmeyer was appointed Assistant Director of biological research. Ralph Hile has remained on the staff as a Senior Scientist.

Headquarters for the expanded program continued to be in Ann Arbor, Michigan. Field stations were established in 1950 at Hammond Bay (near Rogers City, Michigan, Fig. 19.2), Marquette, Michigan, and Sturgeon Bay, Wisconsin, and in 1956 at Ludington, Michigan. The Sturgeon Bay station was closed in 1953. A station was maintained at Oconto, Wisconsin, for a short time.

Fig. 19.3.—Type of electrical barrier used for control of sea lamprey.

The sea lamprey program was organized along two major lines: development of control procedures; testing of those procedures in a practical field program of experimental control.

Research was undertaken almost immediately to develop electrical barriers, since blocking weirs and other mechanical barriers to prevent the upstream spawning migration of the sea lamprey were found to be unsatisfactory. Although many improvements and refinements were made subsequently, effective electrical barriers, powered by 110-volt a–c current, were devised and turned over to the experimental control group in 1951. Several pilot models were tested in 1952, and ten barriers were in operation in Lake Superior tributaries in 1953 (Fig. 19.3). Barriers were installed in all of the important spawning streams along the U.S. shore of the lake, and considerable numbers were installed in the tributaries of northern Lake Michigan.

The staff of the Hammond Bay Laboratory was assigned next to a search for a selective toxicant that would kill sea lamprey ammocetes without damaging other fish and organisms. This highly speculative undertaking involved thousands of bioassays that covered more than 4,000 chemicals. Several effective compounds were discovered, one of which (3-trifluormethyl-4-nitrophenol) is being used in the present chemical control program. All Lake Superior tributaries containing larval lampreys have been treated by biologists of the bureau and the Fisheries Research Board of Canada, and a start has been made on streams of northern Lake Michigan and Georgian Bay of Lake Huron.

The sea lamprey program is a fine example first of federal-state and later of international cooperation. All of the states affected by sea lamprey depredations have supported the U.S. Government's program wholeheartedly. Michigan and Wisconsin assigned personnel to control operations and to a variety of special research projects.

The Bureau of Commercial Fisheries has developed a substantial fishery-limnological research program separate from the sea lamprey program. This research is intended to give the broad and continuing coverage that leads to basic understanding of fish stocks—the relations of species to each other, factors of fluctuations in growth and abundance, and the effects of the environment and of varying rates of exploitation. Major problems being studied at present are the rehabilitation of the lake trout populations, tremendous fluctuations in the abundance of certain fishes, and the effect on fish populations of a changing environment. Field stations have been established at Ashland, Wisconsin, and Sandusky, Ohio. The old fish hatchery at Northville, Michigan, is presently being used to rear coregonids for taxonomic studies including morphological differences and chromosomal and serological evidence on relations among species.

Three research vessels are assigned to fishery-limnological research. The 65-foot *Cisco* (launched in 1951) was the first vessel especially designed for investigations on the Great Lakes (Fig. 19.4). The *Siscowet,* a 55-foot gill net tug, remodeled for hydrographic work and for light trawling, is assigned to the Ashland station. These two vessels are equipped with most of the latest devices for sampling, measuring, recording, and analyzing limnological features of the lakes. The *Musky II* is a 45-foot trap net boat assigned to the Sandusky station. She is well equipped for limnological sampling in shallower waters of the lakes. A new 65-foot vessel, the *Kaho*, has been built for exploratory fishing and gear research.

Limnological research has consisted of general surveys, studies on particular unit problems, and long-term investigations. These divisions also reflect the development of the research program.

General fishery and limnological surveys were made in Lake Michigan in 1951, 1952, 1954, 1955, 1960, and 1961; Lake Huron in 1952 and 1956; Lake Superior in 1952, 1953, and 1959; and in Lake Erie in 1957 and 1958. Data from these surveys have been published as a complete unit (Beeton *et al.*, 1959) or used in special studies of currents (Johnson, 1960) and plankton (Wells, 1960). Considerable material has been used by graduate students in their studies for masters' or doctoral degrees.

The Bureau of Commercial Fisheries has participated in a number of special studies. The bureau cooperated with the Great Lakes Research Institute and Ontario Department of Lands and Forests in the synoptic surveys of Lake Huron in 1954. Three synoptic surveys were made in Saginaw Bay in 1956 in cooperation with the Michigan Department of Conservation. Three 3-day synoptics were completed in western Lake Erie in 1958 in cooperation with the Ohio Division of Wildlife. The bureau, Great Lakes Institute, Ohio Division of Wildlife, Ohio Division of Shore Erosion, Stone Laboratory of Ohio State University, Ontario Department of Lands and Forests, and Pennsylvania Fish Commission took part in one or more of the surveys made of Lake Erie in 1959, 1960, and 1961. The M/V *Siscowet* was used for preliminary survey of possible coring sites in the bottom-coring project conducted by the University of Minnesota and the Great Lakes Research Division in 1961.

A major weakness in Great Lakes research is the lack of long-term studies. Most of the past studies have the common fault of showing only the conditions existing during a short time in a particular area. To correct this situation, the bureau has undertaken limnological and fishery observations that will be made routinely for a long time. Areas of the lakes have been tentatively subdivided into ecological zones. A number of "index stations," which are assumed to be representative of these zones, have been established. Sampling of most aspects of the environ-

Fig. 19.4.—M/V *Cisco*, U.S. Bureau of Commercial Fisheries.

ment is conducted at these stations several times each year. Periodic review of materials and observations will indicate any need for changes in procedure or station locations. It is anticipated that various instruments and systems, such as the unmanned buoy system, being developed by oceanographers will be very useful in this program.

U.S. Lake Survey.—The U.S. Lake Survey, Army Corps of Engineers, is one of the oldest agencies working on the Great Lakes. It had its origin in 1841 when the Congress of the United States appropriated funds for a "Hydrographical Survey of the Northern and Northwestern Lakes." By 1882 all of the designated waters had been charted, and the agency was disbanded except for reproducing charts as stocks became exhausted. Funds were increased in 1889 to make additional surveys to correct the charts. These early surveys covered depths only to 18 ft. By the turn of the century, however, the rapid development of the manufacturing and shipping industries around the lakes made it obvious that the method of keeping the charts up to date was inadequate and that depths charted only to 18 ft were too shallow. Consequently, the U.S. Lake Survey was reorganized in 1901 and has been continuously active since.

The Lake Survey is authorized and directed to conduct all necessary activities to provide charts and related information for the safe navigation of all classes of vessels within the United States portion of the Great Lakes and their connecting and outflow waters. Hydrographic surveys have been conducted on all of the Great Lakes and connecting waters. A program of re-sounding the deep

Fig. 19.5.—M/V *Williams* used in sounding deep areas of the lakes by the U.S. Lake Survey.

areas of the lakes, which was initiated in 1945 and completed in 1960, covered approximately 58,600 mi² of open water with sounding lines approximately 1½ mi apart (Fig. 19.5). Water temperatures, meteorological data, and bottom sediments were collected. Inshore sounding from the shoreline to the five-fathom contour covered approximately 800 mi of coast line and about 300 mi of rivers with sounding lines spaced approximately 1,000 ft apart.

Hydraulic and hydrologic work includes continuous measurement of water levels of the lakes and their connecting rivers (the Lake Survey has approximately 50 recording gauges throughout the Great Lakes area) and periodic measurement of flows in the connecting rivers from which stage-discharge relationships have been developed for all ranges of lake stages. In addition many studies have been conducted to determine the effects of construction, water diversions, and dredging on Great Lakes water levels.

The first seasonal forecast of lake levels was issued in 1952. A consecutive six-month forecast replaced the seasonal forecast in 1958. Statistical analysis was made of the factors affecting lake levels, and investigations were made of factors affecting water supplies to the lakes. Currently an extensive study is being made of these individual factors.

Numerous investigations have been made on the effects of diversion into and out of the Great Lakes and on the effects of channel changes on lake levels. Several studies have been completed on evaporation from the lakes. Precipitation gauges were established in northeastern Lake Michigan in 1952 for a ten-year study of overland and overwater precipitation (Blust and DeCooke, 1960).

Great Lakes Research Division, University of Michigan.—The Board of Regents of the University of Michigan established a Great Lakes Research Institute on 16 May 1945 ". . . for the encouragement and integration of studies of the physical, chemical, biological, and other aspects of the Great Lakes and related areas." It has functioned as a research organization in the broadest sense with the objectives of stimulation, promotion, and coordination of research on the Great Lakes, as well as the implementation of the university's relevant teaching and research programs.

On 1 April 1960 the Great Lakes Research Institute was reorganized as the Great Lakes Research Division of the Institute of Science and Technology at the University of Michigan. This reorganization provided the division with a more satisfactory administrative position in the university, a broader base for establishing a research program, and greater facilities and financial assistance. Its objectives were not altered, however, by the reorganization.

Administration of this organization in 1945–59 was carried out by a twelve-man Council; the chairman served as the administrative officer. Chairmen of the Council were Paul S. Welch, Professor of Zoology, 1945–47; Frederick K. Sparrow, Jr., Professor of Botany, 1948–50; Earnest Boyce, Professor of Sanitary Engineering, 1951; James T. Wilson, Professor of Geology, 1952–55; David C. Chandler, Professor of Zoology, 1956–59. Administration of the Great Lakes Research Division is now carried out by a Director, David C. Chandler, assisted by a twelve-man Council and an Advisory Committee.

Since 1947 the university has supplied the institute and the division with a modest operating budget. Major support for the research program, however, is obtained from outside agencies in the form of grants, fellowships, and contracts.

Research prior to 1954 represented efforts of individuals encouraged but not financially supported by the institute. Corings of sediments in Lake Erie were made in 1948 and 1949 by James T. Wilson. Investigation of benthos of northeastern Lake Michigan in 1952 and plankton studies of Lake Superior in 1953 were made by David C. Chandler. These early studies and the conference on the Upper Great Lakes, sponsored by the institute at the University of Michigan Biological Station in the summer of 1953, served as a basis for the establishment of a larger integrated program continuous since 1954.

Five general areas of research were emphasized in the program from 1954 to 1961: currents and water masses, biology, geology, water quality, and meteorology. These studies, although diverse and of varying degrees of intensity, contributed to one or more of the following problems of water resources of the Great Lakes: water budget, water quality, translocation and circulation, air-water interface phenomena, effects of Great Lakes on regional meteorological conditions, ice cover, chronology of the Great Lakes, erosion and deposition, nature of lake basins, biological productivity, and biological resources. A list of the publications resulting from the various projects was published in the Proceedings of the Fourth Conference on Great Lakes Research (Ayers, 1961).

During the summer of 1954, the institute cooperated with the Ontario Department of Lands and Forests and the U.S. Fish and Wildlife Service in a mutiple-ship synoptic survey of temperature conditions, chemical characteristics, and currents in Lake Huron. The following summer a similar study was made of Lake Michigan. Both studies were aimed at determining the main current patterns and characteristics of the water circulation. These investigations, in addition to those made of the water transport in the Straits of Mackinac in 1956 and the physical limnology of Grand Traverse Bay in 1954, represent the major studies of currents by the Great Lakes Research Division.

The biological program has been continuous since 1955, concentrating on studies of benthos, primary productivity, and microorganisms. From 1955 to 1959 emphasis was placed on the relation of benthic organisms to sediments and currents in upper Lakes Michigan and Huron. In an area of 640 mi² more than 690 samples of sediment were collected for mechanical analysis and study of organisms (Lauff *et al.*, 1961). A similar study was conducted on Grand Traverse Bay during 1957 and 1958. Measurements of *in situ* integral photosynthesis by means of carbon-14 were made in Lake Huron in 1955 and in Grand Traverse Bay in 1959 and 1961. The latter studies compared *in situ* and calculated integral photosynthesis and developed a synoptic method for measuring primary productivity (Bachmann *et al.*, 1961). Preliminary studies have been made in Grand Traverse Bay on the distribution and abundance of bacteria in water and fungi in the sediments.

Geological studies consisting of sediment coring to determine the Lake Stanley low-water stage in Lake Huron and to construct the geological history of northern Lake Michigan were made in 1957 and 1958. In 1961 extensive coring was done in Lake Superior from an oil-well drilling ship to obtain combinations of punched and drilled cores through the sediment layers to bedrock. Studies of the chemistry and physical chemistry of trace elements in the overlying waters, interstitial waters, and sediments of several of the Great Lakes were initiated in 1961. Factors influencing the determination of recent rates of crustal uplift in the Great Lakes region were investigated in 1960.

Two major studies have been made of water quality and lake eutrophication. In 1957 and 1958 the location of sources and repositories of limnological and meteorological data pertaining to the Great Lakes was compiled to further the understanding of past events in the lakes and the detection of future trends (Powers *et al.*, 1960). These studies were intensified in 1961, when a four-year program was begun for the evaluation of the climatological, hydrological, limnological, and human factors affecting water quality. The ultimate aim was to analyze the causes of existing deterioration and to develop means for predicting future rates of deterioration.

Meteorological studies have been carried on by the division in various forms since 1954. The major studies concern the structure of atmospheric turbulence at the air-water interface in selected portions of Lake Michigan (Portman *et al.*, 1961) and atmospheric diffusion in transitional states (Brock and Hewson, 1961). These studies contribute to fundamental knowledge of evaporation over water—information greatly needed for accurate prediction of water levels—and contribute to the solution of air-pollution problems.

The division owns well-equipped 34-foot and 49-foot research vessels for inshore studies and a 114-foot motor vessel for open-lake investigations and large-scale operations (Fig. 19.6). Plans are under way to acquire other research vessels to meet the needs of the division's expanding program.

In May 1961 the university acquired the use of State Ferry Pier No. 3 at St. Ignace, Michigan. This property consists of two piers more than 200 ft long, four slips with depths of 20 ft or more, and about two acres of land suitable for construction of shops and shore laboratories. The division will use these facilities cooperatively with

Fig. 19.6.—M/V *Inland Seas,* Great Lakes Research
Division, University of Michigan.

other institutions as a base of operations for research in the lakes.

University of Minnesota.—The School of Public
Health, University of Minnesota, initiated limnological studies of Lake Superior in 1955. The work
of this group has been purposely varied to provide a broad basis for future research. The reports
for 1956 and 1957 dealt with physical limnology
(currents and temperatures); those for 1958 and
1959 concerned nutrients and the chemical characteristics of the lake waters. Recent studies
have dealt with the distribution, abundance, and
productivity of plankton (Putnam and Olson,
1961). The research has been supported by the
Minnesota Department of Health, the U.S. Public
Health Service, and the University of Minnesota.

Herbert M. Bosch has been responsible for the
project administration, and the technical work
has been under the direction of Theodore A.
Olson. Dr. A. C. Redfield, Woods Hole Oceanographic Institution, has served as consultant.

The limnological laboratory is presently situated
in the old Federal Fish Hatchery Building at Duluth, Minnesota. The interior of this building has
been remodeled, and it is now called the "Lake
Superior Research Station, University of Minnesota, at Duluth" (Fig. 19.7).

A greatly expanded program is anticipated,
since other disciplines within the university have
an increased interest in limnology. A new unit
was recently organized, which has been named
"The University of Minnesota Limnological Research Center." The fields of public health, geophysics, ecology, game and fish management,

parasitology, and geology are represented. Paul
Gast, the present director, is a geologist. The
center will be concerned with smaller lakes as
well as the large bodies of water. It is anticipated
that the Limnological Research Center ultimately
will become an active sponsor of scientific studies
in many fields and that it will provide the opportunity and encouragement necessary to stimulate
a variety of research in all phases of limnology.

Ontario Department of Lands and Forests.
—Most of the Canadian research on the Great
Lakes within recent years has been carried out by
the Ontario Department of Lands and Forests.
Four research stations are maintained on the
Great Lakes by the province at Glenora and
Maple on Lake Ontario, Wheatley on Lake Erie,
and South Bay Mouth on Lake Huron. Most
of the research of these stations has been directed by F. E. J. Fry, University of Toronto.
W. J. Christie is in charge of the Glenora
station, R. G. Ferguson the Wheatley station,
and John Budd the South Bay Mouth station.
Land has been acquired for a new laboratory
building at Wheatley, and a new research vessel,
the *Keenosay,* was commissioned for work on
Lake Erie in 1958. The vessel *Atigamayg* is assigned to the South Bay Station and the
Namaycush to the Glenora station. These stations are primarily concerned with fishery research, although a laboratory for experimental
limnology was established at the Southern Research Station at Maple in 1948. Investigations at this laboratory have been concerned
with the effects of environmental factors, especially temperature and low dissolved-oxygen
concentrations, on various species of trout and
other fish. Among the limnological studies conducted at the South Bay Station are the synoptic surveys of Georgian Bay in 1953 and 1954,
McCombie's (1959) work on the relationship

Fig. 19.7.—Lake Superior Research Station, University of Minnesota, Duluth, Minnesota.

between air and water temperatures, and an investigation of mixing caused by seiches in South Bay (Bryson and Stearns, 1959). Information on the fishery research programs conducted at these stations and elsewhere by the department has been presented by Loftus (1960).

For several years the Department of Lands and Forests sponsored a physics program, under the direction of D. V. Anderson, which was involved almost entirely with temperature, currents, winds, waves, bottom sediments, water levels, and their seasonal variations. The research capability of this unit was greatly expanded when the C.M.S. *Porte Dauphine,* a 125-foot, 400-ton, trawler-type vessel, was loaned to the department by the Royal Canadian Navy. She was operated in Lake Ontario in 1958 on a trial program conducted by the department on behalf of participating agencies of the Great Lakes Geophysical Research Group. This group was established in 1958 for formulation of recommendations, promotion, and liaison of research programs among various Canadian agencies. The *Porte Dauphine* made surveys in Lakes Erie, Huron, Ontario, and Superior in 1959. The study of the energy budget of Lake Ontario by Rodgers and Anderson (1961) is based on data from these surveys. The general program received support from the Ontario Hydro, Department of National Defense, Meteorological Branch of the Department of Transport, Hydrographic Service of the Department of Mines and Technical Surveys, and various Canadian oil companies.

Great Lakes Institute, University of Toronto.—The Great Lakes Institute, established by the University of Toronto in 1960, replaced the Great Lakes Geophysical Research Group. Most of the individuals concerned with the Geophysical Research Group are now connected with the institute. G. B. Langford, Head, Department of Geological Sciences, University of Toronto, is the Director of the institute. R. E. Deane is Director of Research, and F. E. J. Fry is Associate Director of Research. Limnological work is being carried out by investigators from the University of Western Ontario, Meteorological Branch of the Department of Transport, Ontario Water Resources Commission, and McMaster University, as well as the University of Toronto.

Extensive surveys of each of the lakes form the nucleus of the institute's research program.

A grid of stations has been established on a lake, and each station is occupied by the *Porte Dauphine* once a month. Data are gathered for each of the institute's programs in chemistry, meteorology, geology, physics, and zoology. Surveys are to be continued on a lake for two successive years to reduce the possibility of bias from abnormal conditions. Lake Ontario has been surveyed for two summers and one winter and Lake Erie for two summers. Several cruises have been made in Lakes Huron and Superior. Special cruises are arranged to study aspects of the geology, geochemistry, and geophysics of the lake basins (Langford, 1961).

The nature of the research program is apparent from the accomplishments of 1960. Meteorological studies included synoptic weather observations every three hours while the *Porte Dauphine* was underway. Gimbal-mounted rain gauges and an Eppley pyrheliometer, rubber-strip ozone samplers, a Hernion sampler, and a swing boom with instrumentation to measure wind velocity, temperature, and humidity at various heights above the water were installed aboard the *Porte Dauphine.* Sampling to detect pollution was conducted in cooperation with the Ontario Water Resources Commission. Quantitative sampling for plankton was carried out in Lakes Erie, Huron, and Ontario. Some of the samples are being analyzed for trace elements. A seismic study of the bed of Lake Erie was undertaken in cooperation with the Lamont Geological Observatory of Columbia University. Current studies, bottom sampling, and coring were conducted in Lakes Erie and Ontario.

U.S. Public Health Service.—The U.S. Public Health Service was authorized in 1960 to develop a comprehensive water-pollution-control program for the Great Lakes and the Illinois River basins. This authorization resulted from growing concern over the problem of maintaining the quality of our fresh waters despite a rapidly expanding population that makes greater and greater demands on this resource.

Laboratory facilities have been set up in Chicago, and a limnology section headed by James L. Verber has been established. Present plans call for intensive one-year limnological surveys of each of the lakes during the next five years. The initial study is being made in Lake Michigan, since information resulting from this study will be pertinent to the hearings on the diversion of water from Lake Michigan. Plans have been

Fig. 19.8.—Unmanned buoy being lowered into position in Lake Michigan for the U.S. Public Health Service study of currents.

made for the installation of 35 buoy stations equipped with devices for measuring low-velocity water currents, water and air temperatures, and wind direction and velocity (Fig. 19.8). A system of electronic interrogation is being considered for the telemetering of data to a shore-based communications center. Plans are being developed for a study of chemical and biological conditions. The U.S. Geological Survey will assist in stream gauging. The feasibility of constructing a model of Lake Michigan for water movement studies is being investigated by the U.S. Army Corps of Engineers (Poston, 1961).

Other organizations.—The various meteorological groups are concerned with the effects of the lakes on weather and climate of the region and the effects of various meteorological conditions on the lakes. The Canadian Meteorological Service and the U.S. Weather Bureau have equipped a number of lake ships with anemometers and water thermometers. Much of the Meteorological Service's work on automatic weather buoys or platforms, precipitation over land and water, water budgets, and the relation of gradient winds to water currents has been carried out in coopera-

tion with the Great Lakes Institute, University of Toronto. J. P. Bruce, as Head of the Hydrometeorological Section, has taken an active part in research on Great Lakes problems. The U.S. Weather Bureau has been concerned with both the short-period (Harris, 1954) and the long-term fluctuations (Brunk, 1960) in lake levels. Studies at the University of Chicago, Department of Meteorology, have centered around the transfer of heat and moisture from the lakes to the atmosphere, the Great Lakes' influence on the development of weather and motion systems (Petterssen, 1960), and numerical methods for study of wind tides and surge (Platzman, 1960).

Geology now forms an integral part of the several university organizations working on the lakes. This situation did not exist until recently, however, and Jack L. Hough, University of Illinois, had to rely upon assistance from the U.S. Geological Survey, U.S. Fish and Wildlife Service, U.S. Lake Survey, Woods Hole Oceanographic Institution, and the U.S. Coast Guard during the early phases of his work which led to the publication of the first comprehensive geological study of the lakes in over 40 years (Hough, 1958). Several of the states and the U.S. Geological Survey are concerned with problems of shore erosion. The Ohio Division of Shore Erosion, now part of the Ohio Geological Survey, has had an active research program on Lake Erie from 1949 to the present. During this period the entire shoreline and the bottom deposits of the Ohio portion of Lake Erie were mapped. Additional work has included studies of water levels, currents, wind and water temperatures, and sub-bottom surveys. Howard J. Pincus, Ohio State University, has directed the program. R. P. Hartley, geologist, and James L. Verber, hydrographer, have been in charge of field operations.

Two organizations—the Great Lakes Commission and the Great Lakes Fishery Commission—have been established within recent years with executive offices in Ann Arbor. These organizations are not actively engaged in limnological research; nevertheless, we would be remiss not to mention them, for they have stimulated interest in and directed attention to important areas of research. Furthermore, they have supported the compilation of two Great Lakes bibliographies. The Great Lakes Commission published the *Great Lakes Fauna, Flora, and their Environment* by John Van Oosten (1957). The Great Lakes Fishery Commission contracted with the University

TABLE 19.3

Libraries of organizations having the Great Lakes Fishery Commission Bibliography in working order

Bureau of Commercial Fisheries U. S. Fish and Wildlife Service Biological Laboratory Ann Arbor, Michigan	Minnesota Conservation Department Bureau of Research and Planning Division of Fish and Game 390 Centennial Office Building St. Paul, Minnesota
Department of Health, Education and Welfare Public Health Service 1819 W. Pershing Road Chicago 9, Illinois	Research Branch Ontario Department of Lands and Forests Maple, Ontario
Fisheries Research Board of Canada Biological Station London, Ontario	Ontario Fisheries Research Laboratory Library University of Toronto Toronto, Ontario
Great Lakes Fishery Commission 106 Natural Resources Building University of Michigan Ann Arbor, Michigan	University of Michigan Natural Science Library Ann Arbor, Michigan University of Minnesota School of Public Health Minneapolis, Minnesota
Institute for Fisheries Research Museums Annex University of Michigan Ann Arbor, Michigan	Western Reserve University Dr. C. C. Davis Department of Zoology Cleveland, Ohio

of Toronto for the compilation of a subject and author filing-card index to the scientific literature. About 20 copies of the file have been established in libraries in the Great Lakes region, including those shown in Table 19.3.

The Great Lakes Commission was established in 1955 by the Great Lakes Basin Compact as an official agency of six Great Lakes states. It receives support by equal legislative appropriations from the member states. The commission is concerned with all aspects of the development, use, and protection of the waters of the lakes including commerce, fisheries, lake levels and diversion, pollution and water supply, recreation, and transportation. Although it is concerned with research, its research function is principally that of dissemination of information on the aforementioned aspects of the lakes. The commission publishes the *Great Lakes News Letter* and cooperates with the Great Lakes Research Division, University of Michigan, in the publication of the *Great Lakes Research Checklist*. Marvin Fast is the Executive Director, and Albert Ballert is the Director of Research.

The Great Lakes Fishery Commission was established by treaty between the United States and Canada in 1955. This commission is charged with the implementation of a program for control of the sea lamprey and coordination of fishery research by various agencies. The operational phase of the program is contracted to the U.S. Bureau of Commercial Fisheries and the Fisheries Research Board of Canada. The commission has not found it necessary to undertake a research program, although it has the authority to do so, and it has functioned to formulate and coordinate research programs. In addition to the major problem of sea lamprey control, it has been especially concerned with the eventual rehabilitation of the lake trout. Norman Baldwin is the Executive Secretary, assisted by Robert Saalfeld.

It should be apparent that the research effort on the Great Lakes has been greatly intensified during the past decade. Many state and federal organizations of both the United States and Canada have active research programs under way, and although little of the information being accumulated has yet been published, we can confidently anticipate that our knowledge of the limnology and fisheries of the Great Lakes will rapidly expand.

References

ADAMS, M. P. 1937. Saginaw Valley report. Michigan Stream Control Comm., 156 p.

AGASSIZ, LOUIS. 1850. Lake Superior: Its physical character, vegetation, and animals. (Narrative of the tour by J. Elliot Cabot). Gould, Kendall, and Lincoln, Boston. 428 p.

AHLSTROM, E. H. 1936. The deep-water plankton of Lake Michigan, exclusive of the Crustacea. Trans. Amer. Microscop. Soc., 55: 286–299.

ANDREWS, T. F. 1953. Seasonal variations in relative abundance of *Cyclops vernalis* Fischer, *Cyclops bicuspidatus* Claus, and *Mesocyclops leuckarti* (Claus) in western Lake Erie, from July, 1946, to May, 1948. Ohio J. Sci., 53: 91–100.

APPLEGATE, V. C., AND J. W. MOFFETT. 1955. The sea lamprey. Sci. Amer., 192: 36–41.

AYERS, J. C. 1956. A dynamic height method for the determination of currents in deep lakes. Limnol. Oceanogr., 1: 150–161.

———. 1961. Great Lakes Research Division. Univ. Michigan, Great Lakes Research Div., Publ. No. 7: 205–213.

AYERS, J. C., D. V. ANDERSON, D. C. CHANDLER, AND G. H. LAUFF. 1956. Currents and water masses of Lake Huron. Univ. Michigan, Great Lakes Research Inst., Tech. Paper No. 1, 219 p.

AYERS, J. C., D. C. CHANDLER, G. H. LAUFF, C. F. POWERS, AND E. B. HENSON. 1958. Currents and water masses of Lake Michigan. Univ. Michigan, Great Lakes Research Inst., Publ. No. 3, 169 p.

BACHMANN, R. W., G. W. SAUNDERS, AND F. B. TRAMA. 1961. Investigations in lake metabolism—photosynthesis: A modified C[14] technique for estimations of photosynthesis in large lakes. Univ. Michigan, Great Lakes Research Div., Publ. No. 7: 163 (Abstract).

BAJORUNAS, L. 1960. Littoral transport in the Great Lakes. Proc. 7th Conf. Coastal Engr., Univ. California, Council Wave Research: 326–341.

BEETON, A. M. 1960. The vertical migration of *Mysis relicta* in Lakes Huron and Michigan. J. Fish. Research Board Canada, 17: 517–539.

———. 1961. Environmental changes in Lake Erie. Trans. Amer. Fish. Soc., 90: 153–159.

BEETON, A. M., AND F. W. HOOPER. 1961. The hydrography of Saginaw Bay. Univ. Michigan, Great Lakes Research Div., Publ. No. 7: 111 (Abstract).

BEETON, A. M., J. H. JOHNSON, AND S. H. SMITH. 1959. Lake Superior limnological data. U.S. Fish and Wildl. Serv., Spec. Sci. Rept., Fish. No. 297, 177 p.

BIRGE, E. A. 1881. Notes on Crustacea in the Chicago water supply, with a note on the formation of the carapace. Med. J. Examiner, 14: 584–590.

BLUST, F., AND B. G. DECOOKE. 1960. Comparison of precipitation on islands of Lake Michigan with precipitation on the perimeter of the lake. J. Geophys. Research, 65: 1565–1572.

BRIGGS, S. A. 1872. The Diatomaceae of Lake Michigan. The Lens, 1: 41–44.

BRITT, N. W. 1955. Stratification in western Lake Erie in summer of 1953: Effects on the *Hexagenia* (Ephemeroptera) population. Ecology, 36: 239–244.

BROCK, F. V., AND E. W. HEWSON. 1961. Analog computing techniques applied to atmospheric diffusion: Continuous point source. Univ. Michigan, Great Lakes Research Div., Spec. Rept. 12, 56 p.

BRUNK, I. W. 1960. Precipitation and the levels of Lakes Michigan and Huron. Univ. Michigan, Great Lakes Research Div., Publ. No. 7: 145–150.

BRYSON, R. A., AND C. R. STEARNS. 1959. A mechanism for the mixing of the waters of Lake Huron and South Bay, Manitoulin Island. Limnol. Oceanogr., 4: 246–251.

CHANDLER, D. C., AND O. B. WEEKS. 1945. Limnological studies of western Lake Erie. V. Relation of limnological and meteorological conditions to the production of phytoplankton in 1942. Ecol. Monogr., 15: 435–456.

CHURCH, P. E. 1942. The annual temperature cycle of Lake Michigan. I. Cooling from late autumn to the terminal point, 1941–42. Univ. Chicago Inst. Meteorol., Misc. Rept. 4, 48 p.

———. 1945. The annual temperature cycle of Lake Michigan. II. Spring warming and summer stationary periods, 1942. Univ. Chicago Inst. Meteorol., Misc. Rept. 18, 100 p.

CLARK, L. J. 1892. Currents in Lake Ontario. Trans. Canadian Inst., 2: 154–157.

COMSTOCK, C. B. 1872. Tides at Milwaukee, Wis. U.S. Engr., Ann. Rept., Appendix A: 1035–1040.

CORPS OF ENGINEERS, U.S. ARMY. 1960. Great Lakes pilot. U.S. Lake Surv., Detroit, 451 p.

CROHURST, H. R., AND M. V. VELDEE. 1927. Report of an investigation of the pollution of Lake Michigan in the vicinity of South Chicago and the Calumet and Indiana Harbors, 1924–25. U.S. Pub. Health Bull. 170, 134 p.

DAMANN, K. E. 1960. Plankton studies of Lake Michigan. II. Thirty-three years of continuous plankton and coliform bacteria data collected from Lake Michigan at Chicago, Illinois. Trans. Amer. Microscop. Soc., 79: 397–404.

DAVIS, C. C. 1954. A preliminary study of the plankton of the Cleveland Harbor area, Ohio. III. The zooplankton, and general ecological considerations of phytoplankton and zooplankton production. Ohio J. Sci., 54: 338–408.

———. 1955. A preliminary study of industrial pollution in the Cleveland Harbor area, Ohio. IV. Plankton and industrial pollution in Cleveland Harbor. Sewage and Ind. Wastes, 27: 835–850.

DEARBORN, H. A. S. 1829. On the variations of level in the great North American Lakes, with documents. Amer. J. Sci., Arts, 16: 78–94.

DEASON, H. J. 1932. A study of surface currents in Lake Michigan. The Fisherman, 1: 3–4, 12.

DEWEY, C. 1838. Temperature of Lake Ontario. Amer. J. Sci., 33: 403–405.

DOLE, R. B. 1909. The quality of surface waters in the United States. I. Analyses of waters east of the one hundredth meridian. U.S. Geol. Surv., Water Supply Paper 236, 123 p.

DONN, W. L., AND MAURICE EWING. 1956. Stokes' edge waves in Lake Michigan. Science, 124: 1238–1242.

DRUMMOND, A. T. 1890. Some temperatures in the Great Lakes and St. Lawrence. Canadian Record Sci., 4: 77–85.

EDDY, SAMUEL. 1943. Limnological notes on Lake Superior. Proc. Minnesota Acad. Sci., 11: 34–39.

EGGLETON, F. E. 1937. Productivity of the profundal benthic zone in Lake Michigan. Papers Michigan Acad. Sci Arts Lett., 22: 593–611.

FELL, G. E. 1910. The currents at the easterly end of Lake Erie and head of Niagara River: Their influence on the sanitation of the city of Buffalo, N.Y. J. Amer. Med. Assoc., 55: 828–834.

FISH, C. J. 1960. Limnological survey of eastern and central Lake Erie 1928–29. U.S. Fish and Wildl. Serv., Spec. Sci. Rept., Fish. No. 334, 198 p.

FORBES, S. A. 1891. On some Lake Superior Entomostraca. U.S. Comm. Fish. Rept. (1887): 701–718.

GILLIES, D. K. A. 1960. Winds and water levels on Lake Erie. Univ. Michigan, Great Lakes Research Div., Publ. No. 4: 35–42.

GOODRICH, CALVIN, AND HENRY VAN DER SCHALIE. 1932. The naiad species of the Great Lakes. Occasional Papers, Museum Zool., Univ. Michigan, No. 238, 14 p.

GOTTSCHALL, R. Y., AND O. E. JENNINGS. 1933. Limnological studies at Erie, Pennsylvania. Trans. Amer. Microscop. Soc., 52: 181–191.

GRAHAM, J. D. 1861. Investigation of the problem regarding the existence of a lunar tidal wave on the great freshwater lakes of North America. Proc. Amer. Assoc. Advance. Sci. (1860): 52–60.

HACHEY, H. B. 1952. Vertical temperature distribution in the Great Lakes. J. Fish. Research Board Canada, 9: 323–328.

HARRINGTON, M. W. 1895. Currents of the Great Lakes, as deduced from the movements of bottle papers during the seasons of 1892, 1893, and 1894. U.S. Dept. Agr., Weather Bur. Bull. B, 14 p.

HARRIS, D. L. 1954. Wind tide and seiches in the Great Lakes. Proc. 4th Conf. Coastal Engr., Univ. California, Council Wave Research: 25–51.

————. 1957. The effect of a moving pressure disturbance on the water level in a lake. Meteorol. Monogr., 2: 46–57.

HAYFORD, J. F. 1922. Effects of winds and of barometric pressures on the Great Lakes. Carnegie Inst. Wash., Publ. No. 217, 133 p.

HENRY, A. J. 1900. Lake levels and wind phenomenon. Monthly Weather Rev., 28: 203–205.

HILE, RALPH. 1957. U.S. federal fishery research on the Great Lakes through 1956. U.S. Fish and Wildl. Serv., Spec. Sci. Rept., Fish. No. 226, 46 p.

HORTON, R. E., AND C. E. GRUNSKY. 1927. Hydrology of the Great Lakes. Rept. Engr. Board Rev., Sanit. District Chicago, Part III, Appendix II, 432 p.

HOUGH, J. L. 1958. Geology of the Great Lakes. Univ. Illinois Press, Urbana. 313 p.

HOY, P. R. 1872. Deep water fauna of Lake Michigan. Trans. Wisconsin Acad. Sci. Arts Lett., 1: 98–101.

HUNT, I. A., JR. 1958. Winds, wind set-ups, and seiches on Lake Erie. U.S. Lake Surv., Corps of Engr. (Paper presented at 2nd Natl. Conf. on Appl. Meteorol., Ann Arbor), 37 p. (Mimeo.)

INTERNATIONAL BOARD OF INQUIRY. 1943. Report of the International Board of Inquiry for the Great Lakes fisheries. U.S. Govt. Printing Office, Washington. 213 p.

INTERNATIONAL JOINT COMMISSION. 1951. Report of the International Joint Commission United States and Canada on pollution of boundary waters. Washington and Ottawa, 312 p.

JENNINGS, H. S. 1904. Rotatoria of the United States. II. A monograph of the Rattulidae. Bull. U.S. Fish. Comm. (1902), Part 2, 22: 273–352.

JEROME, G. M. 1879. Third Biennial Report. Michigan State Board Fish. Comm. (1877–78), 96 p.

JOHNSON, J. H. 1958. Surface-current studies of Saginaw Bay and Lake Huron, 1956. U.S. Fish and Wildl. Serv., Spec. Sci. Rept., Fish. No. 267, 84 p.

————. 1960. Surface currents in Lake Michigan, 1954 and 1955. U.S. Fish and Wildl. Serv., Spec. Sci. Rept., Fish. No. 338, 120 p.

KELLICOTT, D. S. 1878. Notes on microscopic life in the Buffalo water supply. Amer. J. Microscop. Pop. Sci., 3: 250–252.

KOELZ, W. N. 1929. Coregonid fishes of the Great Lakes. Bull. U.S. Bur. Fish., 43: 297–643.

LAKE MICHIGAN WATER COMMISSION. 1911. Second Report. 204 p.

LANE, A. C. 1899. Lower Michigan waters: A study into the connection between their chemical composition and mode of occurrence. U.S. Geol. Surv., Water-supply Irrigation, Paper 31, 97 p.

LANGFORD, G. B. 1961. The Canadian Great Lakes research program. Univ. Michigan, Great Lakes Research Div., Publ. No. 7: 199–201.

LANGLOIS, T. H. 1949. The biological station of the Ohio State University. Franz Theodore Stone Lab., Contrib. No. 11, 64 p.

LAUFF, G. H., E. B. HENSON, J. C. AYERS, D. C. CHANDLER, AND C. F. POWERS. 1961. The bottom sediments of the Straits of Mackinac region. Univ. Michigan, Great Lakes Research Div., Publ. No. 6, 69 p.

LEVERIN, H. A. 1947. Industrial waters of Canada. Report on investigations, 1934 to 1943. Canadian Dept. Mines Research, Mines Geol. Branch, Rept. No. 819, 109 p.

LEVERETT, FRANK, AND F. B. TAYLOR. 1915. The Pleistocene of Indiana and Michigan, and the history of the Great Lakes. Monogr. U.S. Geol. Surv., 53: 1–529.

LOFTUS, K. H. 1960. Current status of fisheries research projects. Univ. Michigan, Great Lakes Research Div., Publ. No. 4: 115–119.

McCOMBIE, A. M. 1959. Some relations between air temperatures and the surface water temperatures of lakes. Limnol. Oceanogr., 4: 252–258.

MARSH, C. D. 1895. Cyclopidae and Calanidae of Lake St. Clair, Lake Michigan, and certain of the inland lakes of Michigan. Bull. Michigan Fish Comm., No. 5, 24 p.

MERNA, JAMES. 1960. A benthological investigation of Lake Michigan. Masters Thesis, Michigan State Univ., 74 p.

MILLAR, F. G. 1952. Surface temperatures of the Great Lakes. J. Fish. Research Board Canada, 9: 329–376.

MILLS, HENRY. 1882. Microscopic organisms in the Buffalo water-supply and in Niagara River. Proc. Amer. Soc. Microscop., 5th Ann. Meeting: 165–175.

MILNER, J. W. 1874. Report on the fisheries of the Great Lakes. U.S. Comm. Fish. Rept. (1872–73), Part 2: 1–78.

MOFFETT, J. W. 1957. Recent changes in the deep-water fish populations of Lake Michigan. Trans. Amer. Fish. Soc., 86: 393–408.

MOORE, J. P. 1906. Hirudinea and Oligochaeta collected in the Great Lakes region. Bull. U.S. Bur. Fish., 25: 153–171.

NEW YORK CONSERVATION DEPARTMENT. 1929. A biological survey of the Erie-Niagara system. 18th Ann. Rept. (1928), Suppl., 244 p.

NEW YORK STATE DEPARTMENT OF HEALTH. 1958. Lake Ontario surface water including specified tributaries. Lake Ontario Drainage Basin Surv. Ser., Rept. No. 4, 447 p.

NICHOLSON, H. A. 1872. Preliminary report on dredgings in Lake Ontario. Ann. Mag. Nat. Hist., Ser. 4, 10: 276–284.

OHIO DEPARTMENT OF NATURAL RESOURCES. 1953. Lake Erie Pollution Survey. Final Rept., 201 p.

PERKINS, E. A. 1893. The seiches in American lakes. Amer. Meteorol. J., 10: 251–263.

PETTERSSEN, SVERRE. 1960. Some weather influences due to warming of the air by the Great Lakes in winter. Univ. Michigan, Great Lakes Research Div., Publ. No. 4: 9–20.

PIETERS, A. J. 1894. The plants of Lake St. Clair. Bull. Michigan Fish Comm., No. 2, 10 p.

PLATZMAN, GEORGE. 1960. A numerical computation of the surge of 26 June 1954 on Lake Michigan. Univ. Michigan, Great Lakes Research Div., Publ. No. 4: 21–25.

PORTMAN, D. J., F. C. ELDER, AND EDWARD RYZNAR. 1961. Research on energy exchange processes. Univ. Michigan, Great Lakes Research Div., Publ. No. 7: 96–109.

POSTON, H. W. 1961. The Great Lakes-Illinois Waterway basins comprehensive water pollution control project. Univ. Michigan, Great Lakes Research Div., Publ. No. 7: 57–63.

POWERS, C. F., D. L. JONES, AND J. C. AYERS. 1959. Sources of hydrographic and meteorological data on the Great Lakes. U.S. Fish and Wildl. Serv., Spec. Sci. Rept., Fish. No. 314, 183 p.

POWERS, C. F., D. L. JONES, P. C. MUNDINGER, AND J. C. AYERS. 1960. Applications of data collected along shore to conditions in Lake Erie. Univ. Michigan, Great Lakes Research Div., Publ. No. 5, 78 p.

PRINCE, E. E. 1915. Preface. Contributions to Canadian biology. II. Fresh-water fish and lake biology. Dept. Marine Fish., Fish Branch, Sessional Paper No. 396, Suppl. 47th Ann. Rept.: i, ii.

PUTNAM, H. D., AND T. A. OLSON. 1961. Studies on the productivity and plankton of Lake Superior. School Pub. Health, Univ. Minnesota, 72 p. (Mimeo.)

RATHBUN, RICHARD, AND WILLIAM WAKEHAM. 1897. Report of the Joint Commission relative to the preservation of the fisheries in waters contiguous to Canada and the United States. House of Representatives, 54th Congr., 2nd Session, Document No. 315, 178 p.

REIGHARD, J. E. 1893. Some plankton estimates in the Great Lakes. Trans. Amer. Fish. Soc., 1893: 112–122.

———. 1894. A biological examination of Lake St. Clair. Bull. Michigan Fish Comm., No. 4, 60 p.

———. 1899. A plan for the investigation of the biology of the Great Lakes. Trans. Amer. Fish. Soc., 28: 65–71.

RODGERS, G. K., AND D. V. ANDERSON. 1961. A preliminary study of energy budget of Lake Ontario. J. Fish. Research Board Canada, 18: 617–636.

RUSCHMEYER, O. R., T. A. OLSON, AND H. M. BOSCH. 1958. Water movements and temperatures of western Lake Superior. School Pub. Health, Univ. Minnesota, 65 p. (Mimeo.)

SCHERMERHORN, L. Y. 1887. Physical characteristics of the northern and northwestern lakes. Amer. J. Sci., Ser. 3, 33: 278–284.

SCHUMACHER, R. E., AND SAMUEL EDDY. 1960. The appearance of pink salmon, Oncorhynchus gorbuscha (Walbaum), in Lake Superior. Trans. Amer. Fish. Soc., 89: 371–373.

SCOTT, W. B., AND W. J. CHRISTIE. 1961. A review of the invasion of the lower Great Lakes by the white perch (Roccus americanus). Univ. Michigan, Great Lakes Research Div., Publ. No. 7: 16 (Abstract).

SMITH, H. M. 1894. Report on the fisheries of the Great Lakes. U.S. Comm. Fish. Rept. (1892), Part 18: 361–462.

SMITH, S. I. 1874. Crustacea of the fresh waters of the United States. U.S. Comm. Fish. Rept. (1872-73), Part 2: 637–665.

SNOW, J. W. 1904. The plankton algae of Lake Erie with special reference to the Chlorophyceae. Bull. U.S. Fish. Comm., 22: 369–394.

TETER, H. E. 1960. The bottom fauna of Lake Huron. Trans. Amer. Fish. Soc., 89: 193–197.

THOMAS, B. W., AND H. H. CHASE. 1887. Diatomaceae of Lake Michigan as collected during the last sixteen years from the water supply of the city of Chicago. Notarisia, Commentarium Phycologium Anno 2, No. 6, 1887: 328–330.

U.S. COMMISSION OF FISH AND FISHERIES. 1900. Report for 1899: xxi, cxix.

VAN OOSTEN, JOHN. 1929. Life history of the lake herring (Leucichthys artedi Le Sueur) of Lake Huron as revealed by its scales, with a critique of the scale method. Bull. U.S. Bur. Fish., 44: 265–428.

———. 1930. The disappearance of the Lake Erie cisco—a preliminary report. Trans. Amer. Fish. Soc., 60: 1–11.

———. 1957. Great Lakes fauna, flora, and their environment. Great Lakes Comm., Ann Arbor, 86 p.

———. 1960. Temperatures of Lake Michigan, 1930-32. U.S. Fish and Wildl. Serv., Spec. Sci. Rept., Fish. No. 322, 34 p.

———. 1962. Surface currents of Lake Michigan, 1931-32. In press.

VERBER, J. L. 1961. Long and short period oscillations in Lake Erie. Ohio Div. Shore Erosion, 98 p. (Mimeo.)

VERDUIN, JACOB. 1956. Primary production in lakes. Limnol. Oceanogr., 1: 85–91.

———. 1960. Phytoplankton communities of western Lake Erie and the CO_2 and O_2 changes associated with them. Limnol. Oceanogr., 5: 372–380.

VORCE, C. M. 1882. Microscopical forms observed in water of Lake Erie. Proc. Amer. Soc. Microscop., 5th Ann. Meeting: 187–196.

WARD, H. B. 1896. A biological examination of Lake Michigan in the Traverse Bay Region. Bull. Michigan Fish Comm., No. 6, 99 p.

WELLS, LaRUE. 1960. Seasonal abundance and vertical movements of planktonic Crustacea in Lake Michigan. U.S. Fish and Wildl. Serv., Fish. Bull., 60: 343–369.

WILLIAMSON, B. L., AND JOHN GREENBANK. 1939. Investigation of the pollution of the Fox and East rivers and of Green Bay in the vicinity of the city of Green Bay, 1938-39. Wisconsin Comm. Water Pollution, Board Health, 242 p.

WRIGHT, STILLMAN. 1955. Limnological survey of western Lake Erie. U.S. Fish and Wildl. Serv., Spec. Sci. Rept., Fish. No. 139, 341 p.

20 | *Daniel A. Livingstone*

Alaska, Yukon, Northwest Territories, and Greenland

Introduction

Geographical

This enormous area (see Fig. 20.1), encompassing some 7,000,000 km² (2,700,000 mi²), includes some of the least-known lake districts on earth. There can be few places where so little is known about so many lakes.

Geologically the area is very complex, with surface rocks ranging in age from Pleistocene over much of Alaska to pre-Cambrian in the Canadian Shield. Locally, as in the southeastern parts of Alaska, there has been much vulcanism extending into the historic period, but sedimentary, metamorphic, and plutonic rocks are of much greater areal extent than volcanic ones. Evaporites are not of great importance, but ice is, for, excepting the Antarctic ice cap, this area contains the bulk of the existing glaciers. The old rocks of the Shield tend to be centrally located, and the peripheral areas of Alaska, Greenland, and the Queen Elizabeth Islands are composed largely of sedimentary rocks laid down since the beginning of the Paleozoic.

Topographically, most of Alaska and Yukon Territory to the west and Greenland and the large islands near it to the east is mountainous, with a broad expanse of relatively low-lying land in between. Along the sea a coastal plain is developed in some places, notably northern Alaska. Where mountains exist, they are partly glacierized and have been subjected to more extensive glaciation in the past, with an accordant production of pronounced alpine relief. The topographic

diversity is reflected, as we shall see, in the physical limnology.

In the west the climate is influenced by the Japan current, so that southeastern Alaska is temperate, despite its high latitude, and has an abundant precipitation. Away from the Pacific Ocean the winters are cold; the summers, short and in many places very cool. Precipitation is low, commonly less than 25 cm (10 in.), and so, although even the present climate is subarctic to high arctic, extensive areas of lowland appear to have escaped Pleistocene glaciation. The precipitation is comparable to that of arid or semiarid areas, but because it is combined with a very low rate of evaporation and extensive development of permafrost which inhibits subsurface drainage, most of the lakes are quite fresh, and it is only in certain parts of Greenland that one encounters moderately concentrated lake waters.

The northern limit of spruce trees is given in Figure 20.1. North and east of this line, tundra predominates. To the south and west of the tundra lies boreal forest, and in southeastern Alaska one finds a northward extension of the characteristic coniferous forest of the Pacific coast of North America.

Much of the area with which this chapter deals has been mapped only since World War II, and the available maps are not all of a satisfactory scale. Therefore, it is not possible to give a reliable estimate of the total number of lakes in this area. Rawson (1953), on the basis of maps available at that time, estimated that there were

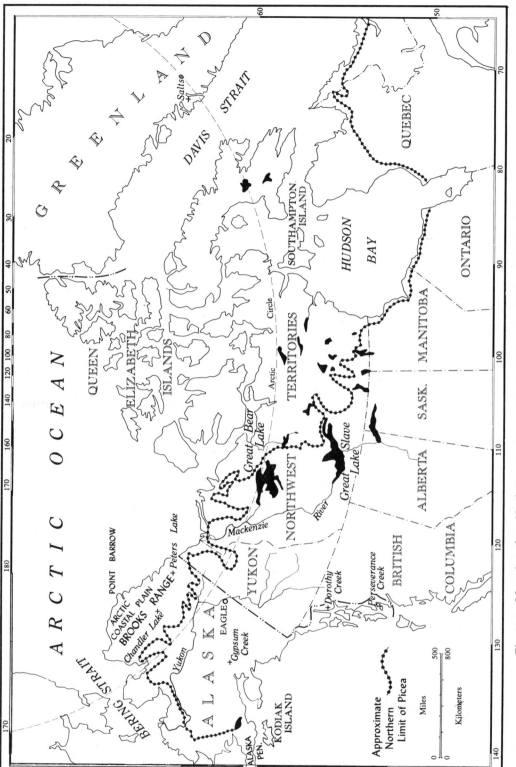

Fig. 20.1. — Map of northern North America. Prepared by the University of Wisconsin Cartographic Laboratory.

250 lakes of a size exceeding 65 km² (25 mi²) in area and hundreds of thousands of smaller ones within the tundra region of Canada alone. Black and Barkesdale (1949) estimated that the number of lakes on the arctic coastal plain of Alaska was "probably tens of thousands of lakes or lake basins," so it can be seen that the total number must be very great.

The two principal lake-forming agencies are glacier ice and permafrost. The former has been most effective in the Shield areas of gentle relief. The excavation of shallow rock basins and the disruption of the previous drainage system by glacial deposits has produced a large number of lakes, many of them quite small and shallow, although Great Slave Lake attains a depth of 614 m and an area of 30,000 km² (12,000 mi²). In the mountainous areas, valley glaciers have produced lakes of the usual valley glacier sorts, including some that are still dammed by ice, but these valley glacier lakes, although they have attractions of their own, are not so numerous as other types. A few of the ice-dammed lakes have attracted some popular interest because of the extreme regularity with which they melt glacier dams during the warm season of each year (Alseth, 1952; Stone, 1953).

Much of the area under consideration has been very heavily scoured by continental ice sheets with the result that kettles, which are associated with thick drift deposits laid down under stagnant ice conditions, are less abundant than they are farther south in America.

The other lake-forming agency, permafrost, is most effective in areas underlain by extensive deposits of unconsolidated fine-grained material. Thaw lakes are characteristic of coastal plains and river valleys through the area, and they occur in great profusion in many of these places. The total number of such lakes may be comparable with the total number of glacial ones, and the problems associated with their origin, development, and drainage, being characteristic of the region, have attracted the attention of limnologists and geologists who have gone to the permafrost zone.

Other lake forming agencies do not seem to be of great importance, although landslide lakes, tectonic lakes, volcanic lakes, meteoritic crater lakes, solution lakes, and, in the forested parts, biogenic lakes are to be expected.

Historical

The area we are considering has been the last of the North American continent to emerge from the status of "territory" to full political independence. It is a remote and inaccessible region, with a very low resident population and an accordant lack of facilities for research or even for travel. This remoteness is not the result of geographical isolation or historical accident, for the region has been partly known and has been subject to intermittent attempts at colonization by Europeans for at least a thousand years. The remoteness is due, rather, to lack of the natural resources necessary for the maintenance of a high population density in any way that has yet been discovered, but the effect on limnological investigation has been the same as that of geographical isolation.

Up to and including the first few decades of the twentieth century, the only limnological information was that which could be gleaned from the incidental notes made by travelers. Travel to the area was by ship and was often seriously hampered by sea ice. Travel within the area was by canoe or skin-boat in summer and by dog-sled in winter, except where, as on the Yukon River, local economic resources supported river steamers during the short summer season. Some of the early travelers who faced the inconvenience and expense of travel in the northern territories made observations of limnological interest, but most of them limited themselves to an account of when the ice left the rivers and lakes of the travel routes and when it was re-established in the fall, for the annual shift from sled to canoe was one of the high points of the travelers' lives.

The first serious work of interest to limnologists consisted of accounts of the fauna and flora. Activity of this sort has been greatest in Greenland, where a whole succession of competent workers has, over the years, built up a very extensive body of faunistic and floristic literature. Much of this work has been published in the *Meddelelser om Grønland*, and it is still being carried on. Studies of systematic aquatic biology in the rest of our area have been much scarcer, the most notable contributions being in the *Report of the Canadian Arctic Expedition* and the *Report of the Harriman Expedition* to Alaska. In addition, there exists a modest body of widely scattered literature of a similar sort for Alaska and northern Canada.

Comprehensive limnological studies, even of a descriptive sort, require more equipment and a longer period at the lake being studied than does the collection of a sample of zooplankton or vascular aquatic plants. Even in localities that can be reached by ship the maintenance of limnological parties in the field is not cheap, and it is not surprising that the first work of a limnological nature was carried out near the coast, at Karluk Lake on Kodiak Island in Alaska (Birge and Rich, 1927; Juday et al., 1932) where a very rich salmon fishery had begun to decline and thus called for biological investigation.

The logistic difficulties that hampered prospective arctic limnologists of a generation ago are still with us, but they have been mitigated by two things: the development of air travel and the great increase in the funds available for research. It is still not easy to study lakes in the remote north, but it is no longer impossible. The availability of aircraft and the presence of a few well-equipped permanent research facilities, such as the Arctic Research Laboratory at Point Barrow, have led to the beginning of serious limnological work in the Arctic and have resulted in a situation in which almost all of the important papers are ones that have appeared during the past ten years. Thus, a very large part of the relevant information on which a review of this sort ought to be based is still in the process of publication and is available only in the form of mimeographed reports or personal communications.

Chemical limnology

General composition

More information is available for the composition of lake and river waters in Alaska than in any other part of the territory in this review. Some of this material has been brought together in a number of reports (Dole and Chambers, 1917; Moore, 1949, 1950; Whetstone, 1951, 1954), but it is more conveniently available in several recent Water Supply Papers of the U.S. Geological Survey (Wells and Love, 1957, 1958a, 1958b). A few additional analyses of most of the major ions may be found in Livingstone et al. (1958) and in Hobbie (1960). Much less information is available for the Northwest Territories of Canada, the best sources being Leverin (1947)

and Thomas (1957), although a few data are presented by Rawson (1950) and Moore (1949). Only Böcher (1949) seems to have published general analyses of the water of Greenland.

As is generally true, the chemical composition (see Table 20.1) of lake and river water is influenced by two primary factors—the amount of precipitation and the nature of the country rock. In the humid parts of southeastern Alaska, for example, the concentration of dissolved material is generally rather low, about 25 ppm. In the Yukon basin, where the annual precipitation is much less, the concentration is higher, usually 100 to 200 ppm. This higher concentration is also found in at least some waters of the Arctic Ocean drainage in Alaska, although in the mountains, where the rainfall is higher, the concentration falls. Superimposed on this general pattern of precipitation-control are the effects of the country rock. Where the country rock is at least partly composed of easily dissolved sediments, as around Gypsum Creek, the concentration of dissolved solids rises. The relative abundance of the soluble substances contained in soluble rocks—in this case calcium and sulfate—is particularly high. Near the sea coast, as at Ikrowik Lake, the influence of sea spray may be quite marked and may lead to high percentages of chloride and sodium in the lake waters.

Where the rocks are resistant to chemical weathering and the precipitation is high, the waters of lakes and rivers are rather dilute. Hobbie (1960) found, for example, that the water flowing in Chamberlin Creek near Peters Lake was very little more concentrated than the precipitation falling on the glacier that fed it, although the lake into which the creek emptied had several times as much total dissolved material.

There do not seem to be any reports of Alaskan lakes with general water chemistry profoundly influenced by volcanic gases, but such lakes are not uncommon in volcanic regions elsewhere and would be expected in the volcanic parts of Alaska.

Such information as exists for the chemical composition of the surface waters of the Northwest Territories of Canada does not indicate that they are chemically unusual. The Mackenzie River which drains both temperate and arctic areas appears to be rather similar to large rivers of the temperate zone, such as the Mississippi, in its general chemistry. There do not seem to be

TABLE 20.1

Composition of some representative waters (mg/L)

Location, date, reference	HCO$_3^-$	SO$_4^{--}$	Cl$^-$	NO$_3^-$	F$^-$	Ca^{++}	Mg^{++}	Na$^+$	K$^+$	Fe^{+++}	Mn^{++}	SiO$_2$	Total
Perseverance Creek, Ketchikan 11 Oct. 1948 (Moore, 1950)	10	2	1.2	0.2	—	1.2	0.8	2.3	—	0.1	—	1.7	19.5
Dorothy Creek, Juneau, Alaska, 14 Apr. 1949 (*Ibid.*)	8	3.1	1.0	0.1	—	1.2	0.9	2.1	—	—	—	1.0	17.4
Gypsum Creek, Mile 112 Glenn Highway Alaska 10 Sept. 1949 (*Ibid.*)	—	2820	5.5	—	—	378	268	—	—	0.54	—	73	3545
Yukon R. at Eagle, Alaska[a], Apr.–Sept. 1951 (Whetstone, 1951)	121.8	27.6	1.6	0.72	0.02	35.9	8.7	4.0	—	0.08	—	7.4	207.8
Ikrowik, lake near Pt. Barrow, Alaska, 13 July 1951[b]	12	4.1	40	0.2	0.1	5.9	3.9	18	—	0.01	0.00	0.9	85.1
East Oumalik Lake, near edge of Arctic Coastal Plain, Alaska, 26 July 1951[b]	122	3.2	21	0.4	0.1	31	9.4	8.0	—	0.04	0.00	1.0	196.1
Precipitation at Chamberlin Glacier near Peters Lake, Alaska July & Aug. 1958 (Hobbie, 1960)	5.4	0.4	0.0	0.0	—	0.7	0.1	0.3	0.1	—	—	0.0	7.0
Chamberlin Creek (glacial), Alaska, 7–14 July 1958 (*Ibid.*)	8.6	1.4	0.2	0.0	—	1.5	0.1	0.1	0.0	—	—	0.3	12.2
Lake Peters, Alaska, 2 Sept. 1958 (*Ibid.*)	25	9.4	0.3	0.0	—	8.2	1.9	0.2	0.1	—	—	0.8	45.9
Great Slave Lake off Slave Delta, North-West Territory, 22 June 1946 (Rawson, 1950)	111.5	25	12	—	—	3.1	7.0	12.0	—	—	—	—	170.6
E. end McLeod Bay, Great Slave Lake North-West Territory 10 Aug. 1949 (*Ibid.*)	18.4	0.0	0.0	—	—	3.1	1.8	—	—	—	—	—	23.3
Mackenzie R. at Fort Simpson, North-West Territory, Aug. 1948 (*Ibid.*)	132	28.0	0.7	0.6	—	35.5	8.5	7.6[c]	—	trace	—	1.2	214.1
Small lake with *Sphagnum* West Greenland (Böcher, 1949)	29	0	4	—	—	3	2	6	—	—	—	9	53
Store Saltsø, West Greenland (*Ibid.*)	1286[d]	45	708	—	—	32	236	514	206	—	—	10	3037

[a] Mean of the analyses of 16 composite samples.
[b] U.S.G.S. analysis quoted in Livingstone *et al.* (1958). Two weeks earlier Ikrowik contained only 36.3 ppm of dissolved solids.
[c] Na+K by difference only.
[d] Includes 408 mg/L CO$_3$.

downstream analyses for any of the rivers which originate entirely within the Arctic.

The influence of country rock on the composition of lake water is demonstrated quite well by Great Slave Lake. McLeod Bay lies on bare pre-Cambrian rocks and has only 22 ppm of dissolved solids, while the main body of the lake, which receives its water from a large drainage area containing sedimentary rocks, contains 150 ppm.

Böcher's analyses for West Greenland waters, although they come from only a small number of lakes and cannot be taken as representative of the entire island, are of particular interest as the only example of arctic American lakes that lie in a climatic area sufficiently dry to result in noteworthy concentration of the lake water. Although these lakes are not concentrated enough in the summer to precipitate salts, the variation in their percentage composition with concentra-tion suggests precipitation, and it is possible that under winter conditions the concentration of dissolved material under the ice leads to the precipitation of salts.

This process of salting out has been studied by Boyd (1959), some of whose data are reproduced in Figure 20.2. Imikpuk near Point Barrow, the lake he investigated, received some sea water during the summer before his study (Brewer, 1958), and this accounts for the high percentage of the ions characteristic of sea water. Many arctic lakes are quite shallow, and the concentration of dissolved material by freezing out must be an important factor in the biology of overwintering organisms.

Chemical nutrients

Turning from general chemistry to nutrient elements, we find the suggestion (Livingstone *et al.*, 1958) that the processes of arctic weathering

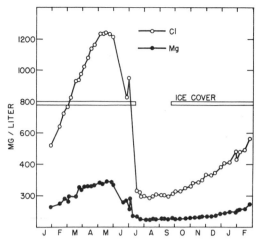

Fig. 20.2.—Seasonal changes in the chemical composition of Imikpuk, a small lake near Point Barrow in Alaska. Cl = total chlorides as NaCl; Mg = magnesium hardness as CaCO₃. After Boyd, 1959.

result in the mobilization of iron and aluminum from ferro-alumino-silicate rocks, leaving the silica behind in an insoluble form, so that the waters are deficient in this substance. Although there is certainly much residual silica over large areas in the Arctic and although at least some arctic waters contain low silica concentrations, it must be admitted that there is very little factual support for this idea.

In tundra environments the supply of plant nutrients appears to be low, and where there is a local source of phosphorus and nitrogen, as around human settlements or on snowy-owl lookout posts, the vegetation is noticeably more luxuriant. This general nutrient poverty is likely to characterize the lakes as well as the soils, and it has been suggested (Livingstone et al., 1958; Livingstone and Boykin, 1962) that the situation is aggravated by the characteristic nature of arctic lake soils, which are very silty rather than organic and may be expected to be a poor source of regenerated nutrients.

Matters of this sort call for experimental investigation, and this has been brought to bear on them only in the relatively temperate parts of southern Alaska. Dugdale and his co-workers (Dugdale and Dugdale, 1961; Dugdale et al., 1959) engaged in a detailed study of the nutrient economy of the lakes in a geochemically interesting environment near Kodiak Island, Alaska, where the lakes are influenced very much by recent volcanic-ash falls which provide a rich

source of phosphorus but not of nitrogen. The investigators have been particularly concerned with the effect of drainage area slope on the rate of phosphorus leaching and with the mechanisms whereby nitrogen is fixed under such circumstances, and they have found that Alnus viridis is of great importance in nitrogen fixation.

Nelson and Edmondson (1955) have carried out fertilization experiments in the Karluk Lake area of Kodiak Island, Alaska, where Birge and Juday began Alaskan limnology, and found that a large and rapid increase in productivity followed the addition of phosphorus and nitrogen to a small lake. Some of their results are presented in Figure 20.3.

Physical limnology

Heat

There is an acute shortage of basic data concerning the thermal regime of lakes in the area under consideration. Even the depth of maximum freezing during the winter and the highest temperature attained during summer have been measured for very few lakes.

Attempts to calculate a heat budget for arctic lakes north of the Brooks Range have been made by Livingstone et al. (1958) and, with more data, by Hobbie (1960, 1961). The size of the heat budget in these lakes is comparable with that of temperate lakes (27,000–31,000 cal/cm²), but the temperature range through which the warming takes place is very different. Most of the heat income goes to melt the ice formed during the winter, which is of a thickness approaching two meters. Even so, there are few lakes within our area that are known to be polar lakes in the sense of Forel. The amount of heat required to melt the ice is so great, and the extra amount needed to raise the temperature above 4° C is so small, that polar lakes are rather scarce. If a lake is very deep, then the amount of heat required to warm the entire water column is much greater, but although Crater Lake in Ungava does possess the qualifications of a polar lake, it lies south of our area.

There are, however, a few polar lakes, particularly in Greenland. These are lakes with an ice cover that does not melt completely during the summer, and it will be appreciated that they are likely to be rather unstable features. If the annual heat income is positive, the ice cover will gradually melt. If it is negative, the lakes will gradually freeze solid. At present the ice cover seems to be

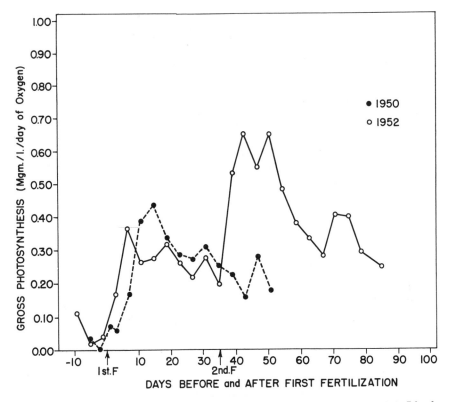

Fig. 20.3.—Effect of fertilization on gross photosynthesis of Bare Lake, Kodiak Island, Alaska. Points represent mean values during four-day exposure periods of the years 1950 and 1952. During 1951 and 1953 similar results with somewhat higher peak values for photosynthesis were obtained. After Nelson and Edmondson, 1955.

melting on at least some of these lakes (Barnes and Taylor, 1958).

The temperature attained during the ice-free season is a datum of some biogeographic importance which seems to have been considered for our area only by Iversen (1954). He concluded, on the basis of distributional data supplied by Porsild, that since the ranges of vascular aquatic plants paralleled the tree line in the northern parts of Canada, then presumably the water temperature must follow the air temperature, at least for shallow lakes.

By far the most important study of the temperature regime of a lake in our area is that of Brewer (1958) who studied Imikpuk near Point Barrow, Alaska, from 1951 to 1955 by means of multithermistor cables permanently installed in the lake and sunk in a borehole that extended 60 m (200 ft) into the mud beneath it. Some of his results are presented in Figures 20.4 and 20.5.

By extending his study over so many years Brewer was able to provide information about the seasonal changes from year to year. The maximum water temperature, for example, varied from 8° C in 1955, the coldest summer of the study, to 12° C in 1954, the warmest.

Imikpuk is only about three meters deep and is exposed to moderately strong winds; therefore, as might be expected, the water was isothermal for the most part. There was, however, some indication of stratification in the upper few decimeters of the water when the air temperature was much colder than the water temperature, thus setting up a weak unstable stratification near the surface of the lake. Under such conditions the temperature of the water changed as much as two degrees per day. The temperature of the mud in the bottom of the lake was also found to fluctuate, but the time and amplitude of these fluctuations were strongly damped with

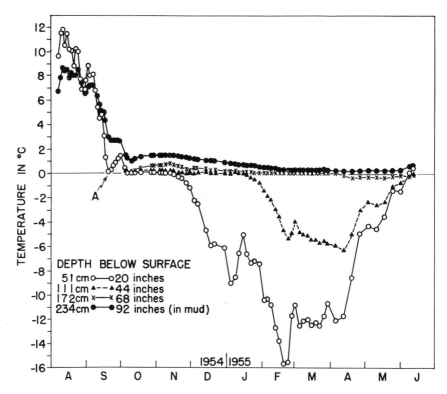

Fig. 20.4.—Time-temperature curves at several depths in Imikpuk, a small lake near Point Barrow, Alaska. The water was isothermal until late in September. After Brewer, 1958.

increasing depth in the mud. Similar temperatures and short-term fluctuations were found in other shallower lakes (maximum depth, 0.8 m or 2.6 ft) in the vicinity of Imikpuk.

Brewer was able to demonstrate a considerable complexity in the temperature changes that occurred in Imikpuk during the winter season. Although a thin skin of ice could be expected on the lake at any time after the first of September, permanent ice did not usually form until September 15–20, and was once as late as September 30. The temperature of the water when freezing took place was uniform through the bulk of the lake and was only a few tenths of a degree above the freezing point. Within two weeks the ice attained a thickness of 10–20 cm (4–6 in.). As soon as the lake was frozen completely, the temperature of the lake began to rise rapidly at all levels, except the freezing surface, to about 2° C during eleven days, while the temperature of the mud remained approximately constant. Although

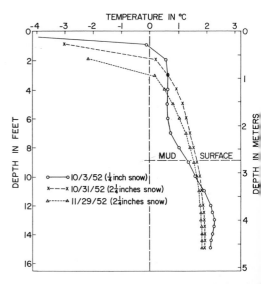

Fig. 20.5.—Thermal profiles through Imikpuk showing second heating and cooling of bottom water after formation of ice. After Brewer, 1958.

some of the heat may have been provided by conduction from the bottom mud or by bacterial activity, the amount was so great and the rise in temperature so rapid that most of it must have come through the ice as radiant energy. The heating ceased as soon as the lake was covered by a blanket of snow, and within five days the temperature of the lake, which was still isothermal, fell almost to zero again.

There followed a second period of much slower warming, through only about 1.5° C over a period of seven weeks. This warming was not uniform throughout the lake but was greatest near the bottom. During the winter the rate of loss of heat through the ice and snow cover gradually rose above the rate of gain from the sediment, and the lake began to cool slowly, until by May the maximum temperature had fallen to 0.6° C.

Temperature records from the deep cable inserted into the sediments of the lake showed that the freezing point is reached at 57 m (190 ft). There is some possibility that the ground water was not frozen even at this depth because of a lens of saline water in communication with the nearby Arctic Ocean.

Imikpuk is too shallow to furnish a heat budget comparable with the ones for Chandler and Peters lakes, but, for what it may be worth, the heat absorbed amounted to 18,000 cal/cm^2, of which 7% was used to raise the temperature of the ice to the melting point, 75% to melt the ice, and 18% to raise the temperature of the water.

Light

There have been a few Secchi-disc measurements on arctic lakes but no serious studies of lake optics. Shallow lakes, at least on the tundra, are often stirred by the wind until they become very turbid. Non-turbid waters range at least from dark brown to gray-green in color. Small pools on the tundra may have a brown color of as much as 250 units on the platinicobalt scale (personal observation).

Origin of thaw lakes

No problem has attracted so much of the attention of students of lakes in our area as the origin and subsequent development of thaw lakes. The interest is a continuing one, and it is clear that much remains to be learned about the dynamics of the processes involved. It appears likely that an understanding of thaw lake development will emerge as a major contribution of the regional limnology of the Arctic.

In regions of cold climate the ground temperatures at depth remain below the freezing point all year around. The upper part of the soil may thaw out during the summer, but sub-zero temperatures prevail below this, often to depths of many hundreds of meters. In bedrock these low temperatures do not have a great effect, but in areas where the bedrock is mantled by a thick cover of silt or other fine-grained material the results are important and often bizarre. The frozen soil water does not occur in uniform distribution throughout the soil, but as discrete lenses and wedges of ice. These large crystalline masses gradually grow by accretion until as much as 70% of the upper layers of the mantle may come to consist of solid ice. As long as the ice stays frozen, its principal effect is to throw the surface of the ground up into a polygonal network of mounds and trenches, but it frequently happens that it melts. If the melting is extensive enough, a lake will be formed.

Thaw lakes have been described for a variety of regions, particularly by Wallace (1948), Hopkins (1949), Black and Barksdale (1949), Mackay (1956), and Bostock (1948). In the area studied by Wallace, lakes were formed when the ground ice melted without disruption of the mantle of peat and vegetation over it, and it was possib'e, by examining the growth rings of scattered trees growing on the tundra mat, to determine the rate of expansion of some of the lakes. Under the prevailing climatic conditions the lakes were expanding at a rate of about one meter per year. Presumably a change to colder climatic conditions would slow down this rate of expansion or stop it completely.

Black and Barksdale (1949) presented a very complete account of the thaw lakes on the coastal plain of northern Alaska. There are many thousands of these lakes, perhaps as many as half a million, and they are of particular interest for their shape, which tends to be elliptical, and for their orientation, with the long axis of the ellipse aligned in a generally northwest-southeast direction. Most of the lakes are rather shallow, many being only a meter or two in depth, but they are quite extensive in area, many being as big as 14 × 5 km (9 × 3 mi) and one even 46 × 34 km (29 × 21 mi).

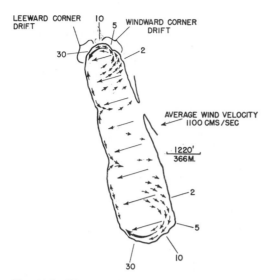

Fig. 20.6.—Diagram showing the circulation system in Loon Lake near Point Barrow, Alaska, during a wind of about 40 km (25 mi) per hour. The long straight arrows indicate leeward surface drift; the small curved arrows, the subsurface circulation pattern; and the large curved arrows, the leeward corner currents. Current velocities are in cm/sec and are shown in their approximate sites of measurement. After Carson and Hussey, 1960a.

The lakes (see Figs. 20.7–20.9) lie on an unglaciated coastal plain of unconsolidated sediment containing much ground ice. The relief is very slight, and the bedrock is so deeply covered by unconsolidated material that there does not seem to be any possibility of structural control.

Black and Barksdale (1949) suggested that the basins might owe their orientation to the direction of the prevailing wind. At present the wind blows across the lake, but because this seemed anomalous, they postulated a former wind direction at right angles to that now prevailing. Livingstone (1954), however, indicated that the lakes appeared to be in equilibrium with present wind conditions and suggested that a constant wind might set up a system of currents in a lake that would tend to erode it into an elliptical shape with the ellipse lying across the wind instead of along it. He presented an extremely crude theoretical model of circulation in a small shallow circular lake.

This suggestion met with some support from Mackay (1956), studying similarly oriented lakes in Canada, but objections were raised by Carson, Hussey, and their co-workers in a number of

papers (Carson and Hussey, 1959, 1960a, 1960b; Rosenfeld and Hussey, 1958; Rosenfeld et al., 1958). These investigators believed that a structural control might be operating, and they have been skeptical of the ability of wind-driven currents to change the shape of a lake basin, even in a permafrost terrain. More recently (Carson and Hussey, 1960a, 1960b) they have made observations on the actual currents found in a lake with a steady wind blowing across it (see Fig. 20.6). The data have been published only in summary form, but it appears that a system of currents such as would result from the Livingstone model is to be found only in very small ponds. In larger lakes a similar system, but flowing in the opposite direction and with more circulation cells, was observed.

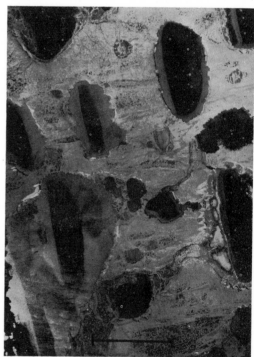

Fig. 20.7.—Elliptical thaw lakes on the Arctic Coastal Plain of Alaska. The scale line is approximately one kilometer (0.6 miles) long. North is toward the top of the photograph, and the lakes show the characteristic common alignment of long axes. Some of the lakes are actively expanding, with cuspate shorelines, while others have fallen below a former high-water level and occupy only part of their basins. Blowouts may be seen on the shores of several lakes, and the water in the lakes is sufficiently clear for the central deep, dark basin to be distinguishable from the shallow light shelf around it. U.S. Navy photograph.

Hussey and his co-workers measured currents up to 61 cm/sec in velocity, which seem adequate to erode a lake shore in permafrost. They also devised a new theoretical model for circulation in a shallow lake. This model is not complete, for it depends on an intuitive assessment of the current that would be produced by a hydrostatic gradient of 0.0022 cm/m, but the assumption that this current would be small is a reasonable one, and the predictions of the model seem to agree very well with their field observations. The Hussey model is preferable to the Livingstone one, which, although it fits the observed facts of basin shape, is in close agreement with the observed currents only in lakes so small that frictional forces and variations in wind stress over the surface may be safely ignored.

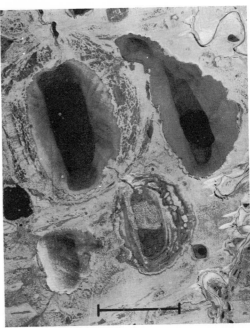

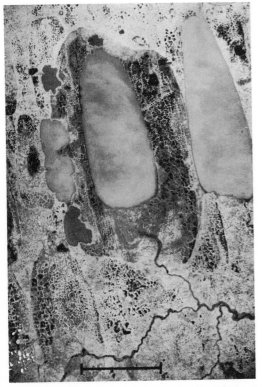

Fig. 20.8.—Elliptical thaw lakes in the vicinity of Point Barrow, Arctic Coastal Plain, Alaska. The scale line represents one kilometer (0.6 miles) and north is toward the top of the photograph. The lakes are so turbid that the bottom contours are not visible. The outlines of several generations of drained lake basins, now occupied by polygons and tundra pools, may be seen in the photograph, and the stream near the bottom is beaded with tundra ponds. U.S. Navy photograph.

Fig. 20.9.—Elliptical thaw lakes on the Arctic Coastal Plain of Alaska. The scale line represents one kilometer (0.6 miles) and north is toward the top of the photograph. The water in the two large lakes is very clear, and details of the bottom are clearly visible. A polygonal pattern has developed on part of the floor of the drained lake in the lower center. U.S. Navy photograph.

Rex (1961) has recently prepared a more thorough analysis of the hydrodynamics of small shallow lakes, using data from the oceanographic literature to predict lake waves, longshore currents, orbital velocities associated with shoaling waves, and the erosional effects of these phenomena. His treatment is by far the most complete of the three that have been attempted so far and is recommended to the attention of limnologists everywhere who are interested in the hydromechanics of shallow lakes.

The landscape and its associated lakes and organisms in areas of deep continuous permafrost, such as northern Alaska, provide a beautiful example of a complex ecosystem. Under the prevailing precipitation regimen, with about 25 cm (10 in.) or less of annual rainfall, all parts of northern Alaska above sea level would be a sandy desert if the permafrost were to melt. Instead of that, we have a landscape that is littered with lakes and ponds and with an almost complete vegetation cover on the swampy land between them.

Biological limnology

Fauna and flora

A great wealth of taxonomic information is to be found in *Meddelelser om Grønland,* the *Report of the Canadian Arctic Expedition,* 1913–18, and the *Report of the Alaska Harriman Expedition.* Most of the rest of the taxonomic literature is too scattered and too peripheral to the interests of limnologists to be summarized here, but a few recent papers of a comprehensive sort that provide an introduction to the older literature may be of interest. Hultén (1941–50) has provided a compendium with dot distribution maps of the vascular flora, including aquatic species, living in Alaska and Yukon Territory. Hilliard (1959), Prescott (1953), Taylor (1954), and Whelden (1947) may be consulted for aquatic algae. Wynne-Edwards (1952) has brought together the existing information about fish distribution, and Wilimovsky (1954) has summarized recent work on far northern fishes. Bardach (1954) and Wilson (1953) have made studies of zooplankters, while Bousfield (1958) and Townes (1945) have worked on important elements of the benthos. In this, as in other aspects of the limnology of our region, the *Arctic Bibliography* (Arctic Insitute of North America, 1953) is a useful guide to the literature.

Life history studies

The extreme arctic conditions that prevail over much of our area may be expected to exert a strong influence on the life histories of the organisms that inhabit its lakes, and enough information is now available to show that this is indeed the case. Comita (1956) and Edmondson (1955) have worked on a copepod and a cladoceran, respectively, in Imikpuk, a small lake near Point Barrow, Alaska. They found that the animals did not overwinter under the ice but spent at least part of the winter as resting eggs which hatched as soon as the ice began to melt around the shore of the lake in the spring. The number of generations was small, one for the copepod and two for the cladoceran, and of the cladoceran generations only one was of quantitive importance to the population. The bulk of the summer *Daphnia* population consisted of ex-ephippial females which produced ephippia before the coming of winter. Some of the ex-ephippial females produced a generation of non-ephippia-producing females, the offspring of which produced ephippia. There was

some possibility that a few of the fall ephippia hatched out during the same season. No males appeared at any time in the population. Attempts to produce males under suitable laboratory conditions, though not exhaustive, were not successful.

The failure of the zooplankton to overwinter in Imikpuk may not be a general feature of arctic lakes. Rodhe (1955, and personal communication) has found that in Lapland lakes at a comparable latitude and under a similar climatic regimen, small populations of zooplankton do survive the winter. The winter mortality in Imikpuk may be the result of chemical conditions, for the lake freezes so deeply that there is only about one meter of free water under the ice in the deepest part of the lake. As we saw previously, Boyd (1959) has shown that freezing concentrates salts in the free water during the winter time, and it is at least possible, in the light of the experience of Andersen (1946) in a lake of similar size in Greenland, that the oxygen is seriously depleted. Possibly in deeper lakes, where the winter changes in water chemistry would be less severe, zooplankton populations might overwinter as adults.

Several investigators (Cohen, 1953; Kennedy, 1957; Wohlschlag, 1953, 1954, 1957) have investigated the fish populations and have found that the rates of growth and mortality tend to be somewhat lower than in lakes at lower latitudes. There has been a tendency for these workers to consider their lakes as "unexploited," which they are only in a relative sense, for they are all exploited to some extent by native fishermen. In the case of Ikrowik, the lake studied by Wohlschlag and Cohen, this native exploitation can hardly be negligible, for the lake lies only a few miles away from an Eskimo village with a population of about one thousand people and is situated on one of the standard summer travel routes.

The standing crop of phytoplankton and benthos has been measured in a number of lakes, and the results are summarized in Table 20.2. In general the standing crop is rather low.

Although the primary productivity of no lake in our region has been studied in the detail that Rodhe (1958) has shown to be desirable in work of this sort, a number of investigators have made measurements over at least a short period of time by means of either the radiocarbon or the light and dark bottle methods. These have been brought together by Frey and Stahl (1958) (see Table 20.3) who reached the conclusion that the productivity of arctic and subarctic lakes was low, even during the season of active growth. Combined with the shortness of the growing period, this leads to an annual production rate that is very low indeed.

Their conclusion is probably a valid one, for it is in agreement with what is known about the general limnology of northern lakes. Hobbie (1960), for example, estimates photosynthesis in Schrader Lake at 8.4–12.8 mg C/m^2 per day, but further confirmatory observations would be welcome. Dugdale and Wallace (1960) found that the light and dark bottle method gave negative values for photosynthesis for a large part of the summer, and it is at least possible that some characteristic of the high-latitude environment makes this method give results that are spuriously low. Frey and Stahl (1958) used the carbon-14 method as well, and it gave results that were consistent with their light and dark bottle measurements, but all of their water samples were collected with an uncoated Kemmerer bottle, which might have introduced enough metal into the experimental bottles to lower the rate of photosynthesis.

Edmondson's (1956) investigations on Bare Lake have led him into a general consideration of illumination in the geography of photosynthesis.

Lake development

Livingstone et al. (1958) carried out microfossil analysis of a number of cores from the vicinity of Chandler Lake in Alaska and found that the number of microfossils of several kinds

TABLE 20.2

Standing crop of benthos and plankton in some Alaskan lakes. Benthos data from Livingstone et al. (1958); total phytoplankton from Prescott (1953).

	Benthos (kg/ha)	Total phytoplankton (cells/liter)
Chandler Lake	7.0	—
Little Chandler Lake	11.5	—
Lake A (near Chandler Lake)	9.5	—
East Oumalik Lake (near edge of Arctic Coastal Plain)	89	—
Ikrowik near Pt. Barrow	0.0	1,790
Imerksungk near Pt. Barrow	—	7,670
Imikpuk near Pt. Barrow	—	350,000
Skimo Lake near Pt. Barrow	—	20,500
Ridge Lake near Pt. Barrow	—	12,800
Radio Lake near Pt. Barrow	—	619,000

per unit volume of sediment remained essentially constant throughout the sedimentary column. They attributed this lack of any apparent change in productivity to the large amount of silt that was deposited in the lake by mass-wasting processes resulting from permafrost conditions. The silt apparently interfered with the regeneration of nutrients from the mud and prevented the sort of development that has been demonstrated for temperate zone lakes.

Outlook

With so large an unknown area it is safe to predict that at least part of the future research

TABLE 20.3

Rates of primary production in some arctic and subarctic lakes

Lake	Location	Area (ha)	Depth (m) Max.	Depth (m) Mean	mg C/ m^3/day[a]	mg C/ m^2/day[a]	Method	Authors
S-1, Southampton Island, NWT	64° 8′ N 83°10′ W	0.2	1	ca. 0.6	176	98	C^{14}	Frey & Stahl, 1958
Imikpuk, near Point Barrow, Alaska	71°17′ N 156°40′ W	61	2.1	2.1	58	120	O_2	Frey & Stahl, 1958 (after Comita & Edmondson, 1955)
Bare Lake, Kodiak Island, Alaska	57°11′ N 154°19′ W	49	7.5	7.5	25	100	O_2	Ibid.
S-7, Southampton Island, Alaska	63°36′ N 85° 4′ W	ca. 350	10	ca. 6	2.9	18	C^{14}	Frey & Stahl, 1958
Brooks Lake, Alaska (peninsular Alaska)	58°30′ N 156° 0′ W	—	—	45	0.84–4 23	—	—	Goldman, 1958 (as quoted in Hobbie, 1960), 1960

[a] The data for lakes S-1 and S-7 are not the same as originally reported by Frey and Stahl (1958). Verduin (1960; Limnol. Oceanogr., **5**: 372–380) pointed out that their original calculations based on Moore's method did not consider the fact that there are two atoms of C in each bicarbonate molecule. Accordingly, Frey has recalculated the values here. All figures reported in the publication by Frey and Stahl (1958) for carbon fixation based on the C^{14} method should be increased by the factor 1.955, which was the same for both lakes.

effort will be devoted to descriptive limnology. The Arctic is so different from the environments with which limnologists are most familiar that they are not likely to foresee the problems that it offers without first engaging in some descriptive work. The most interesting problem that has emerged so far, that of the formation of thaw lakes and the forces moulding their form, is one that could hardly have been foreseen. Others may be discovered by descriptive studies.

One large and important field, that of historical biogeography, has hardly been touched by limnologists. This is a promising area for such studies, since it was largely but not completely glaciated during the Pleistocene. The facts of distribution are just beginning to be made known, and the same is true of the history of deglaciation. A start has been made with fishes (Wynne-Edwards, 1952), but they are perhaps not the most suitable organisms, for fish fossils are scarce in Pleistocene deposits. Perhaps mollusks or chydorids would be more suitable material for working out patterns of repopulation after retreat of the continental ice sheets.

As is apparent from the foregoing account, experimental studies have been very few in the American Arctic, or even in the temperate parts of Alaska. This is only natural, because the difficulty and expense of carrying out experiments in remote places militates against them. Some experimental methods, however, such as those for measuring primary production, lend themselves to field work in remote localities, and one may reasonably expect that many more studies of primary production will be carried out in the next few years. With a light float airplane it would be possible for a limnologist to carry out measurements by the methods of Gran or Steemann Nielsen on many lakes in a relatively short time.

For potentially dangerous work involving the addition of radioactive substances to the water, the isolation of arctic lakes would be a great advantage, and high-activity work could be carried on better at a remote tundra pond on an uninhabited island than in any other place. Most tracer experiments involve no great risk of radiation damage, but any experiment to test the limnological consequences of high levels of radiation would do so.

The unusual heat budget of arctic lakes, with so much of the heat income being spent to melt the ice, and the limitation of the season of active growth, imposed by the lag in spring melting, present a challenge to anyone interested in manipulating the heat budget by experimental means. One thinks immediately of effecting some sort of seasonal control over the thermal emissivity of the lake, but it might be possible to control the evaporative heat loss by the use of monolayers as well. If even a moderate amount of success could be enjoyed by such means, it would have important economic consequences, not only because of the changes that might be effected in the annual productivity, but also because of the control it would give over the use of lakes as landing fields by aircraft.

In general, though, the outstanding characteristic of arctic lakes is probably their biological simplicity. The biological simplicity of the Arctic has been exploited by people concerned with small mammal populations for many years but hardly at all by limnologists. The single case in America appears to be Comita's (1953) work on Imikpuk, which was part of a comparative study of copepod biology involving several other lakes, all in accessible parts of the temperate zone. Because of the complexity of the life cycles of copepods in the other lakes, Comita was not able to draw firm conclusions without the expenditure of an inordinate amount of effort, but at Imikpuk, despite the difficulties of arctic field work, he was able to work out the copepod life history in a reasonable time and with considerable assurance.

The uses to which this biological simplicity may be put are not easy to predict, for it will be an advantage in the solution of limnological problems that cannot be foreseen. In terms of the problems that call for attention today, however, it is quite evident that arctic lakes represent an almost ideal material for the elucidation of the flow of energy through a food chain. One of the serious technical obstacles in this work has been the difficulty of measuring the energy flow through the herbivores. Lindeman (1941) estimated the standing crop of zooplankton and then applied to it a factor depending on guesses about the length of zooplankton generation time. Consider the advantages of using a lake like Imikpuk with only a single generation of zooplankton per year. In the Arctic, as in some other remote places, it would be possible to compare lakes with and without fish faunas or to introduce higher predators into the food chain of lakes without them and examine the results of such experimental introductions. It is only in the prosecution of such investigations, for which arctic lakes have a clear advantage over more accessible ones, that the logistic problems of working in remote areas are likely to be overcome.

Acknowledgements

This review was begun during tenure of a John Simon Guggenheim Memorial Foundation Fellowship, and the work was aided by grant G-8243 from the National Science Foundation to Duke University. I am much indebted to the many people who have sent me reprints, mimeographed reports, and personal letters describing their work on arctic and subarctic lakes. It has not been possible to refer to all of their work in this review, but knowledge of their activities was very valuable in building up a picture of the current state of limnology in the northern parts of the American continent.

References

ALSETH, I. B. 1952. Self-emptying lake. Nat. Hist., 61: 8–13.

ANDERSEN, F. S. 1946. East Greenland lakes as habitats for chironomid larvae: Studies on the systematics and biology of Chironomidae 11. Medd. Grønland, 100: 1–65.

ARCTIC INSTITUTE OF NORTH AMERICA. 1953. Arctic bibliography. U.S. Govt. Printing Office, Washington, 3 v. 4478 p.

BARDACH, J. E. 1954. Plankton Crustacea from the Thelon Watershed, N.W.T. Canadian Field Nat., 68(2): 47–52.

BARNES, D. F., AND L. D. TAYLOR. 1958. Preliminary results of study of a permanently frozen lake in Greenland. Bull. Geol. Soc. Amer., 69: 1751.

BIRGE, E. A., AND W. H. RICH. 1927. Observations on Karluk Lake, Alaska. Ecology, 8: 384.

BLACK, R. F., AND W. L. BARKSDALE. 1949. Oriented lakes of northern Alaska. J. Geol., 57: 105–118.

BÖCHER, TYGE. 1949. Climate, soil and lakes in continental West Greenland in relation to plant life. Medd. Grønland, 147(2): 63 p.

BOSTOCK, H. S. 1948. Physiography of the Canadian Cordillera with special reference to the area lying north of the fifty-fifth parallel. Canadian Geol. Surv., Mem. No. 247: 76–77.

BOUSFIELD, E. L. 1958. Fresh-water amphipod crustaceans of glaciated North America. Canadian Field Nat., 72(2): 55–113.

BOYD, W. L. 1959. Limnology of selected arctic lakes in relation to water-supply problems. Ecology, 40: 49–54.

BREWER, MAX C. 1958. The thermal regime of an arctic lake. Trans. Amer. Geophys. Union., 39: 278–284.

CARSON, C. E., AND K. M. HUSSEY. 1959. The method of multiple working hypotheses applied to Alaska's oriented lakes. Proc. Iowa Acad. Sci., 66: 334–349.

CARSON, C. E., AND K. M. HUSSEY. 1960a. Hydrodynamics in some arctic lakes. Proc. Iowa Acad. Sci., 67: 336–345.

CARSON, C. E., AND K. M. HUSSEY. 1960b. Hydrodynamics in three arctic lakes. J. Geol., 68: 585–600.

COHEN, D. M. 1953. Age and growth studies on two species of whitefish from Pt. Barrow, Alaska. M.A. Thesis, Stanford Univ., 70 p.

COMITA, G. W. 1953. A limnological study of planktonic copepod populations. Ph.D. Thesis, Univ. Washington, 196 p.

———. 1956. A study of a calanoid copepod population in an arctic lake. Ecology, 37: 576–591.

COMITA, G. W., AND W. T. EDMONDSON. 1953. Some aspects of the limnology of an arctic lake. Biological research in the Alaskan Arctic. Stanford Univ. Publ., Univ. Ser., Biol. Sci., 11: 7–13.

DOLE, R. B., AND A. A. CHAMBERS. 1917. Chemical character of some surface waters of Alaska. *In* G. A. Waring *et al.*, Mineral springs of Alaska. U.S. Geol. Surv., Water-Supply Paper 418: 99–109.

DUGDALE, R. C., AND V. A. DUGDALE. 1961. Sources of phosphorus and nitrogen for lakes on Afognak Island. Limnol. Oceanogr., 6: 13–23.

DUGDALE, R. C., V. A. DUGDALE, JOHN NEESS, AND JOHN GOERING. 1959. Nitrogen fixation in lakes. Science, 130: 859–860.

DUGDALE, R. C., AND J. T. WALLACE. 1960. Light and dark bottle experiments in Alaska. Limnol. Oceanogr., 5: 230–231.

EDMONDSON, W. T. 1955. The seasonal life history of *Daphnia* in an arctic lake. Ecology, 36: 439–455.

———. 1956. The relation of photosynthesis by phytoplankton to light in lakes. Ecology, 37: 161–174.

FREY, D. G., AND J. B. STAHL. 1958. Measurements of primary production on Southampton Island in the Canadian Arctic. Limnol. Oceanogr., 3: 215–221.

GOLDMAN, C. R. 1960. Primary productivity and limiting factors in three lakes of the Alaska Peninsula. Ecol. Monogr., 30: 207–230.

HILLIARD, D. K. 1959. Notes on the phytoplankton of Karluk Lake, Kodiak Island, Alaska. Canadian Field Nat., 73(3): 135–143.

HOBBIE, J. E. 1960. Limnological studies on Lakes Peters and Schrader, Alaska. Rept. 5 to Geophys. Research Div., Air Force Cambridge Research Center, Contr. AF 19(604)–2959: 1–47.

———. 1961. Summer temperatures in Lake Schrader, Alaska. Limnol. Oceanogr., 6: 326–329.

HOPKINS, D. M. 1949. Thaw lakes and thaw sinks in the Imuruk Lake area, Seward Peninsula, Alaska. J. Geol., 57: 119–131.

HULTÉN, ERIC. 1941–50. Flora of Alaska and Yukon. Lunds Univ. Årsskr. N.F., Avd. 2, Bd. 37–46, 1902 p.

IVERSEN, JOHS. 1954. The late-glacial flora of Denmark and its relation to climate and soil. Studies in Vegetational History in Honour of Knud Jessen. Danmarks Geol. Undersøgelse, II(80): 87–118.

JUDAY, C., W. H. RICH, G. I. KEMMERER, AND

ALBERT MANN. 1932. Limnological studies of Karluk Lake, Alaska: 1926–30. Bull. U.S. Bur. Fish., **47**: 407–436.

KENNEDY, W. A. 1957. Growth, maturity and mortality in the relatively unexploited lake trout, *Cristivomer namaycush*, of Great Slave Lake. J. Fish. Research Board Canada, **11**: 827–852.

LEVERIN, H. A. 1947. Industrial waters of Canada. Canada Dept. Mines and Resources, Rept. 819, 109 p.

LINDEMAN, R. L. 1941. The developmental history of Cedar Creek Bog, Minnesota. Amer. Midland Nat., **25**: 101–112.

LIVINGSTONE, D. A. 1954. On the orientation of lake basins. Amer. J. Sci., **252**: 547–554.

LIVINGSTONE, D. A., AND J. C. BOYKIN. 1962. Vertical distribution of phosphorus in Linsley Pond mud. Limnol. Oceanogr., **7**: 57–62.

LIVINGSTONE, D. A., KIRK BRYAN, JR., AND R. C. LEAHY. 1958. Effects of an arctic environment on the origin and development of freshwater lakes. Limnol. Oceanogr., **3**: 192–214.

MACKAY, J. R. 1956. Notes on oriented lakes of the Liverpool Bay area, Northwest Territories. Rev. Canadienne Biogeographie, **10**: 169–173.

MOORE, E. W. 1949. A summary of available data on quality of arctic waters. National Research Council, Div. of Med. Sci., Rept. to Subcomm. on Water Supply of its Comm. on Sanit. Engr. and Environment, 14 p.

———. 1950. Summary of additional data on Alaskan waters. National Research Council, Div. of Med. Sci., Rept. to Subcomm. on Water Supply of its Comm. on Sanit. Engr. and Environment, 25 p.

NELSON, P. R., AND W. T. EDMONDSON. 1955. Limnological effects of fertilizing Bare Lake, Alaska. U.S. Fish and Wildl. Serv., Fish Bull., **56**: 415–436.

PRESCOTT, G. W. 1953. Preliminary notes on the ecology of freshwater algae in the Arctic Slope, Alaska, with descriptions of some new species. Amer. Midland Nat., **50**: 463–473.

RAWSON, D. S. 1950. The physical limnology of Great Slave Lake. J. Fish. Research Board Canada, **8**: 1–66.

———. 1953. Limnology in the North American Arctic and Sub-arctic. Arctic, **6**: 198–204.

REX, R. W. 1961. Hydrodynamic analysis of circulation and orientation of lakes in northern Alaska, p. 1021–1043. *In* G. O. Raasch (ed.), Geology of the Arctic. Univ. Toronto Press, Toronto.

RODHE, WILHELM. 1955. Can plankton production proceed during winter darkness in subarctic lakes? Proc. Intern. Assoc. Limnol., **13**: 117–122.

———. 1958. The primary production in lakes: Some results and restrictions of the C^{14} method. Rappt. et Procès-Verbaux, Conseil Intern. Exploration de la Mer, **144**: 122–128.

ROSENFELD, G. A., AND K. M. HUSSEY. 1958. A consideration of the problem of oriented lakes. Proc. Iowa Acad. Sci., **65**: 279–287.

ROSENFELD, G. A., K. M. HUSSEY, AND J. B. O'SULLIVAN. 1958. Origin of oriented lakes, Arctic Coastal Plain, Alaska. Arctic Inst. of North Amer. Rept., 39 p.

STONE, K. H. 1953. Alaskan ice-dammed lake: Lake George. Ann. Assoc. Amer. Geograph., **43**: 192–193.

TAYLOR, W. R. 1954. Algae: Non planktonic, p. 363–399. *In* N. V. Polunin *et al.*, Cryptogamic flora of the Arctic. Botan. Rev., **20**.

THOMAS, J. G. J. 1957. Mackenzie River and Yukon River drainage basins in Canada, 1952–53. Canada Dept. Mines Tech. Surv., Mines Branch, Rept. No. 856: Industrial water resources of Canada, Water Surv. Rept. No. 8, 78 p.

TOWNES, H. K. 1945. The nearctic species of Tendipedini. Amer. Midland Nat., **34**: 1–206.

WALLACE, R. E. 1948. Cave-in lakes in the Nabesna, Chisana and Tanana River valleys, eastern Alaska. J. Geol., **56**: 171–181.

WELLS, J. V. B., AND S. K. LOVE. 1957. Compilation of records of quantity and quality of surface waters of Alaska through September, 1950. U.S. Geol. Surv., Water-Supply Paper 1372, 262 p.

WELLS, J. V. B., AND S. K. LOVE. 1958a. Quantity and quality of surface waters of Alaska, October 1950–September 1953. U.S. Geol. Surv., Water-Supply Paper 1466, 243 p.

WELLS, J. V. B., AND S. K. LOVE. 1958b. Quantity and quality of surface waters of Alaska, October 1953 to September 1956. U.S. Geol. Surv., Water-Supply Paper 1486, 229 p.

WHELDEN, R. M. 1947. Algae, p. 13–137. *In* N. Polunin, Botany of the Canadian Eastern Arctic. II. Thallophyta and Bryophyta. Bull. Natl. Museum Canada, **97**.

WHETSTONE, G. W. 1951. Chemical character of Alaska surface waters. U.S. Geol. Surv., Progr. Rept. No. 1, 23 p.

———. 1954. General chemical character of surface waters of Alaska. Proc. Alaskan Sci. Conf., 1952: 172–175.

WILIMOVSKY, N. J. 1954. Recent literature of far northern fishes. Copeia, 1954: 3.

WILSON, M. S. 1953. Some significant points in the distribution of Alaskan freshwater copepod crustaceans. Proc. 2nd Alaskan Sci. Cong., 1953: 315–318.

WOHLSCHLAG, D. E. 1953. Some characteristics of the fish populations in an arctic Alaskan lake. Stanford Univ. Publ., Univ. Ser., Biol. Sci., **11**: 19–29.

———. 1954. Mortality rates of whitefish in an arctic lake. Ecology, **35**: 388–396.

———. 1957. Differences in metabolic rates of migratory and resident freshwater forms of an arctic whitefish. Ecology, **38**: 502–510.

WYNNE-EDWARDS, V. C. 1952. Freshwater vertebrates of the Arctic and Subarctic. Bull. Fish. Research Board Canada, No. 94, 28 p.

21 | *Joe Kendall Neel*

Impact of Reservoirs

Damming streams is an ancient mammalian activity that reputedly began with beavers and was eventually adopted by prehistoric man. It is tempting to speculate that the first human structures were stick or bamboo weirs used to trap fish, and that familiarity with such practices led to impoundment and diversion of irrigation waters after the advent of agriculture. Regardless of developmental paths, man took to damming with a purpose that has grown stronger with passage of time and seems destined to affect all major and most minor watercourses on the face of the earth. The growing number of reservoirs is making them and their stream and watershed influences increasingly important fields for limnological endeavor.

In America dams have been built to furnish water power for mills and other small industries (Fig. 21.1), to hold public water supplies and irrigation reserves, and for hydroelectric power, flood control, navigation purposes, fish and wildlife protection and propagation, and, more recently, recreation. Some reservoirs are planned to trap large quantities of silt, and water releases for various ancillary purposes, such as dilution of sewage, improvement of water quality, etc., are often possible. As dam building techniques have improved, dam builders have advanced on our largest streams, and huge impoundments, each with a number of assigned functions, are attracting limnological attention in most regions of the continent.

Strictly speaking, a reservoir results when any watercourse, no matter how small, is dammed; however, distinctions are usually drawn between ponds and artificial lakes after rather indefinite surface areas are exceeded. There are a great number of artificial lakes of varied sizes that have purely local functions (Fig. 21.2). They extend many challenges to limnologists in their modifications of life, water chemistry, stream regimens, etc., and any extensive treatise on reservoirs would certainly be obligated to take note of them. Our concern with the impact of reservoirs naturally directs us first toward the large multiple-purpose impoundments. Because of the space limitations of this book, I have arbitrarily excluded most reservoirs with capacities less than 50,000 acre-feet.

Fig. 21.1.—Mill dams, now merging into the landscape, were among the first stream regulatory structures used by European immigrants on this continent. Photo by the author.

This chapter was written entirely on the author's own time, and hence does not represent a contribution in his official capacity as a governmental employee.

Fig. 21.2.—Small local reservoirs of this general nature, which often have marked effects upon stream limnology, have been largely ignored in impoundment studies. Photo by the author.

Reservoirs

Exemplary situations and practices

Two American rivers that have been brought under the control of a system of large multiple-purpose reservoirs are the Tennessee and the Missouri. The relative size of these two developments is strikingly illustrated by the fact that the total storage capacity of the Tennessee system—somewhat in excess of 11,000,000 acre-feet—is approximately one-half the volume of any one of the three largest Missouri River impoundments. Major characteristics of the six reservoirs situated along the main stem of the Missouri River (Fig. 21.3) appear in Table 21.1. (Big Bend Reservoir is yet to be completed.) Multiple-use capacities or pools are for power production, navigation, irrigation, and other legitimate water uses. The total storage possible, 76,040,000 acre-feet, almost equals three years' runoff at Sioux City, Iowa, about 55 mi downstream from the Gavins

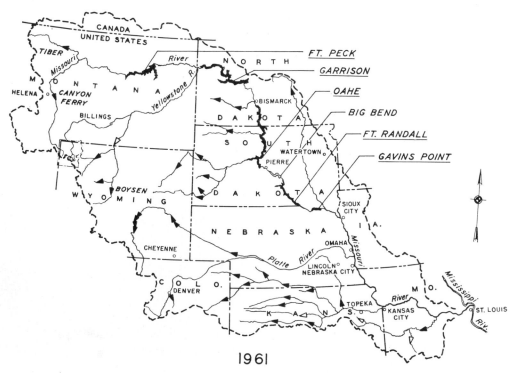

Fig. 21.3.—Main-stem and tributary reservoirs in the Missouri Basin. Figure courtesy of Missouri River Division, Corps of Engineers, U.S. Army.

Solid triangles indicate completed reservoirs; open triangles indicate those under construction.

TABLE 21.1
Missouri River main-stem reservoirs: storage allocations and hydrographic features. Data supplied by Missouri River Division, Corps of Engineers, U.S. Army.

	Fort Peck	Garrison	Oahe	Big Bend	Ft. Randall	Gavins Point	Totals
Exclusive flood-control reserve							
Elevation[a]	2,246–2,250	1,850–1,854	1,617–1,620	1,420–1,423	1,365–1,375	1,208–1,210	
Storage[b]	1,000,000	1,600,000	1,100,000	175,000	900,000	65,000	4,840,000
Annual flood-control and multiple-use capacity							
Elevation[a]	2,234–2,246	1,837.5–1,850	1,607.5–1,617	0	1,350–1,365	1,204.5–1,208	
Storage[b]	2,700,000	4,400,000	3,200,000	0	1,400,000	100,000	11,800,000
Carry-over multiple-use capacity							
Elevation[a]	2,160–2,234	1,775–1,837.5	1,540–1,607.5	1,415–1,420	1,310–1,350	1,195–1,204.5	
Storage[b]	11,200,000	13,600,000	13,800,000	260,000	2,400,000	220,000	41,480,000
Inactive capacity[c]							
Elevation[a]	2,030–2,160	1,673–1,775	1,415–1,540	1,345–1,415	1,230–1,310	1,160–1,195	
Storage[b]	4,500,000	4,900,000	5,500,000	1,465,000	1,400,000	155,000	17,920,000
Total capacity[b]	19,400,000	24,500,000	23,600,000	1,900,000	6,100,000	540,000	76,040,000
Average pool elevation[a]	2,230	1,829	1,603	1,410	1,348	1,207	
Depth at dam (ft)							
Maximum	220	185	205	65	145	50	
Average	200	164	188	65	118	47	
Length (river mi)							
Maximum	190	235	259	75	159	50	
Average	180	218	244	75	128	48	
Shoreline (mi)							
Maximum	1,600	1,600	2,350	120	—	100	
Average				120	550	—	
Area (acres)							
Maximum	245,000	390,000	376,000	19,800	118,400	33,000	
Average	217,000	326,000	311,000	19,800[d]	79,000	30,400	
Closure date	June 1937	Dec. 1953	Aug. 1958		Aug. 1952	Aug. 1955	

[a] Feet above mean sea level.
[b] Acre-feet.
[c] Minimum power pool.
[d] Not completed.

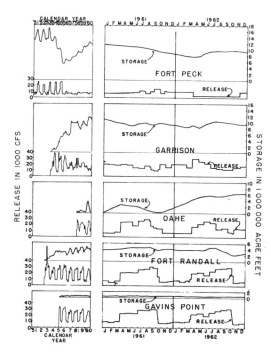

Fig. 21.4.—Operation of Missouri River main-stem reservoirs 1951–62. Courtesy Missouri River Division, Corps of Engineers, U.S. Army.

Point Dam. The control of river regimen possible with this capacity is readily apparent and needs no discussion here. Inactive capacity or minimum power pool amounts to 22.9% of the total volume. Annual flood control and multiple-use capacity indicate the volume that is expected to be devoted to these purposes each year, and carry-over capacities indicate reserves that may be built up for multiple use. Only 4.4% of total capacity is held exclusively in reserve for flood control.

When operation is integrated, a chain of reservoirs offers numerous economic advantages over a single impoundment. Sedimentation may be divided among the several lakes and the useful life of each greatly extended; open capacity behind a downstream dam often allows controlled release of carry-over storage to make room for anticipated local floods and so affords protection in the intervening reach with no significant loss of built-up reserves; power production is possible at a number of sites; upstream reservoirs allow firm commitments for demands on storage in their downstream counterparts; unusual emergency operations may often be carried out with

no permanent loss of reserves; impoundment of a new reservoir can be scheduled definitely through use of upstream storage; regulation of intermittent upstream releases is provided; etc.

Criticisms of a series of reservoirs usually refer to greater loss of farmlands and other real estate and augmented loss of runoff that stems from increased evaporative surface. Operation of a chain of reservoirs seldom meets with the approval of residents in all areas of the drainage system. Sentiment in upper reaches usually favors holding storage for power production, irrigation, and similar uses, whereas downstream opinion often attaches more merit to maintenance of sizable discharges for navigation, improvement of water quality, etc. Compromises arouse little enthusiasm in die-hards of either section.

Figure 21.3 also indicates the number of impoundments constructed on or now scheduled for various Missouri River tributaries. To date, only the main stems of the Yellowstone and Platte rivers lack reservoirs. Damming of these streams began early in this century, and an initial objective was the expansion of irrigation in a program of land reclamation. Later projects incorporated power production, flood control, and public water supplies.

Operation of the Missouri River main-stem reservoir system on a calendar year basis after 1951, on a monthly basis for 1961, and planned 1962 operation is shown in Figure 21.4. Fort Peck storage was used to fill Garrison beginning in 1955, and Gavins Point storage is kept constant by integration of its releases with those from Fort Randall. To date, no marked sacrifices of reserves have been made to filling of Oahe, and storage in the entire system is considerably below maximum capacity. This reservoir system must provide or help furnish 30,000 cfs at Kansas City over the duration of the navigation season from March until November. Discharges are gradually raised to these levels in the spring and are slowly brought down in the fall.

Operation of other reservoir systems or reservoirs often diverges widely from practices to date on the main stem of the Missouri River. Impoundments supplying irrigation water may be shut off completely for several months at the end of the agricultural season. Flow through hydroelectric generators may vary considerably with power demands upon individual units, and marked downstream fluctuations are possible unless regulation is provided by a lower dam. In some river systems power is produced mainly by irrigation releases from lower reservoirs while upper lakes are being recharged with snow water, and power production is largely shifted to upper impoundments in fall and winter as their releases are used to help rebuild reserves in the lower lakes. In many instances power production is the only demand, and operation is strictly on this basis. Operation for benefit of fish and waterfowl propagation may necessitate sudden drops in water level to discourage spawning of undesirable fishes, seasonal discharge restrictions to allow flooding of desirable waterfowl areas, etc. Mosquito control is often effected by varying releases to induce fluctuations in reservoir water level to combat growth of emergent vegetation.

Construction details

This section may appear superfluous, because it is common knowledge that a reservoir is formed by placing a dam across a stream, and materials used for this purpose appear to be of no particular limnological significance. However, functions assigned to a proposed reservoir dictate the type of dam it must have, and manners in which water is released through a dam can markedly affect characteristics of the reservoir and the stream below. The simplest type of dam allows use of stored water only, usually for public water supply, and excesses pass out over a spillway. Slightly more complicated structures have spillways through which volume of discharge may be regulated by a system of gates (Fig. 21.5) to correspond to downstream water

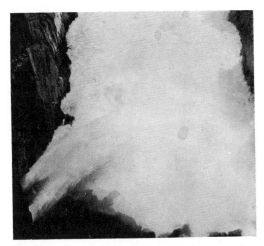

Fig. 21.6.—Discharge from fixed tunnels near a dam base. Photo by the author.

needs. Other dams allow flow only through tunnels near their bases (Fig. 21.6). Reservoirs with hydroelectric power units discharge through penstocks to the generators and also have spillways or tunnels for irrigation or flood-control releases and water level control. Large multiple-purpose reservoirs usually have penstocks, flood-control or irrigation release tunnels, and spillways as safety measures against long-term floods (Fig. 21.7). Maximum depth of such impoundments is normally measured at the level of the spillway crest.

Multiple-purpose dams have intake structures, either incorporated in the dam or shortly upstream, that regulate flow through penstocks and flood-control or irrigation release tunnels (Fig. 21.7). Large capacity flood-control tunnels have air ducts to expedite flow, and stilling basins are usually constructed in the downstream areas that receive reservoir discharges. These basins normally have variously shaped, widely spaced baffles that tend to break up streams and spread flow across the channel. The term "stilling" basin appears to be a misnomer when it is buffeted with surging releases from large flood-control tunnels that churn up a deafening maelstrom of bucking, straining water (Fig. 21.8).

Penstocks and flood-control tunnels usually withdraw water from just above the dead storage level, but selective level releases are often recommended for control of silting (Bell, 1942b). Water discharged from some depth often differs widely in character from that held at the reservoir surface.

Fig. 21.5.—A spillway with adjustable gates to regulate irrigation releases. Photo by the author.

Fig. 21.7.—A large multiple-purpose dam on the Missouri River. To the left of the spillway are flood control tunnels and power house. The intake structure is situated just above the dam. Smaller dams of this general type may have locks to allow passage of boats. Photo courtesy Omaha District, Corps of Engineers, U.S. Army.

Irrigation waters are usually led away from stream beds by diversion dams situated to service various water rights. They vary in size and withdrawal capacity with extent of land area served, and their operation, combined with fluctuating intermediate return flows, can produce weird river discharge patterns during irrigation seasons. A simple type of diversion structure is shown in Figure 21.9. Gates across the river control channel are operated to elevate the stage to the ditch overflow level, and diversion ceases with closure of the ditch gates.

Comparison with natural lakes

Reservoirs vary in a number of physical details from glaciated lakes that are interposed in river systems. Schematic longitudinal sections of each type of water body appear in Figure 21.10. Lakes formed when earthquakes block streams are very similar to reservoirs in a number of features.

Inlets and outlets of glaciated lakes are near the surface, but water may leave a reservoir at one of several depths or from two or three levels simultaneously. The lowest depression in a natural lake may occur anywhere in its basin, but maximum depth of a reservoir is always near the dam, unless a natural lake is included in the impoundment area. A reservoir bottom has a regular slope from head to tail that was established by the river before damming. A similar slope is

Fig. 21.8.—Stilling basin disturbance created by 30,000 cfs release through flood-control tunnel on right. Photo by the author.

Fig. 21.9.—A picket type diversion dam. Ditch gates are curved structures on left, and stream control channel is visible through handrail on the right. Photo by the author.

found in natural lakes that are formed by earthquakes, but basins of glaciated lakes were scooped out below river level, and non-uniformity of bottom slope is to be expected. Developments related to thermal stratification will be mentioned later.

General chemical relationships in the two types of lakes are largely determined by their origins. Glaciated lakes normally begin as oligotrophic bodies of water resting in clay, sand, gravel, and shingle basins. As a general rule, increases in productivity of their waters are gradually brought about by contributions of organic material originating in terrestrial life in their

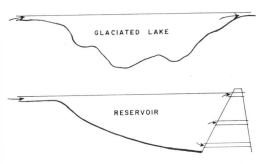

Fig. 21.10.—Schematic longitudinal sections of a glaciated lake and a reservoir. Arrows indicate possible paths of flow.

drainage basins, and development to the eutrophic condition usually requires a great number of years.

Reservoirs, on the other hand, inundate rich bottom lands and fertile topsoils on river slopes and normally begin their lives with high productivity potential since mineral nutrients and organic materials are leached from these soils. Reservoirs tend to suffer productivity declines with passage of time and never seem to regain their initial productivity level. More detailed discussion of these relationships is reserved for sections describing effects upon lotic conditions below dams. Phenomena leading to loss of productivity are becoming better known, but this area is still sorely in need of detailed limnological study. Stratification, density currents, rapidity of water replacement, most frequent withdrawal level, and prevalent operation practices all enter into productivity, as will be noted later, but precise knowledge of many relationships and numerous pertinent details still await data collection and interpretation.

Phenomena occurring in reservoirs

Filling and retention.—The life of a reservoir may be assumed to begin with closure, which usually refers to that phase of damming that moves discharge from the old river channel and

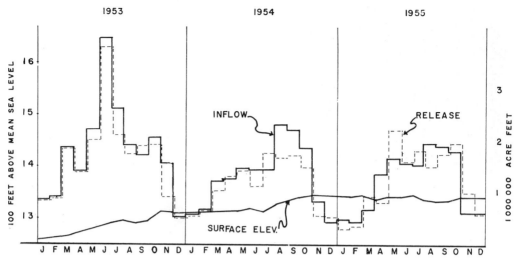

Fig. 21.11.—Operation of Ft. Randall Reservoir, 1953–55.

puts it through outlet structures in the dam. This shifting requires some elevation of water surface, and impoundment essentially begins, although "run of the river" discharges may be passed through tunnels for some months thereafter. After construction progress allows greater accumulation of storage, rise in reservoir level may be painfully slow, or it may proceed rapidly, depending upon discharge rates and downstream water commitments. Early operation of Fort Randall Reservoir on the Missouri River appears in Figure 21.11 (Anon., 1954, 1955, 1956). During much of 1953 upstream discharges were largely passed along to maintain navigation stages below, but inflow generally exceeded releases, and some storage was possible from retained segments of monthly discharges except September and December. In 1954 considerable build-up occurred in August, September, and October, and reservoir depth increased despite storage losses in April, July, and December. In 1955 storage was rebuilt to near its January 1 level after noticeable losses occurred in late summer.

This operation resulted in significant replacement in 1954 and 1955 of water accumulated each preceding year. Longer retention of early storage is possible when water may be held for power production, water supply, and other local uses. Heavy downstream demands, such as those levied against the main-stem Missouri River reservoirs, make storage accumulation a slow process during years of normal precipitation.

Erosion of basin.—Pick-up of rarer nutrient elements by impounded waters is frequently hard to demonstrate, because such materials are often used by the biota as soon as they become available. However, their effects upon plankton growth have often attested to their leaching by early storage. Solution of bed elements is commonly indicated with abundant compounds, such as calcium bicarbonate or sulfate. For example, in

Fig. 21.12.—The Temple in 1934. This limestone-capped butte was subsequently covered by Lake Mead. From Gould, 1954a. Photo by C. R. Longwell.

Fig. 21.13.—The Temple in 1948 showing fresh landslide scars. From Gould, 1954a. Photo by Bureau of Reclamation.

1955 as Garrison Reservoir was filling, bed-element solutes added 10 ppm to the annual average alkalinity concentration of the inflowing water and 14 ppm to the annual average hardness (Anon., 1956).

Erosion of readily soluble bed minerals, such as gypsum, often proceeds at an astonishing rate. It has been estimated that approximately 20 million tons of material were dissolved from the Lake Mead reservoir bed and banks over the period 1935–48. This total was made up of 12.2 million tons of sulfate, 5.1 million tons of calcium, and 2.7 million tons of sodium, potassium, and chloride (Gould, 1954b; Howard, 1954).

Lake Mead is also noted for its wave-cut terraces and reservoir-induced (lubrication, etc.) landslides that have markedly altered the physiog-

raphy of its basin. Figures 21.12 and 21.13 indicate the amount of destruction wrought upon The Temple in 13 years. Solids brought down by landslides and other erosive processes are being transported and mixed into layered bottom sediments (Gould, 1954a).

Erosion of reservoir bottoms by leaching of soluble materials, cutting away of banks, hills, etc. is much more characteristic of impoundments in arid areas than it is of those constructed on streams draining the well-washed soils of such regions as the Ohio Valley and eastern and southeastern coastal areas.

Operation during early stages of impoundment can markedly influence the lenitic effects of nutrients made available from the newly covered bed. The regimen of Fort Randall Reservoir in 1954 and 1955, which resulted in nearly complete replacement of volumes stored each preceding year, allowed the nutrients that these "storages" had dissolved to pass downstream with the discharges.

Sedimentation and mineral precipitation.— Some discussion of siltation is reserved for the section on stratification and density currents. In many instances siltation proceeds simply with suspended sediment dropping from inflowing water as current slows in the headwaters. Sometimes the junction of turbid and clear water is rather sharply delimited by a "convergence" line, but development of this condition usually indicates formation of a density current. Most sedimentation occurs in the upper ends of reservoirs where

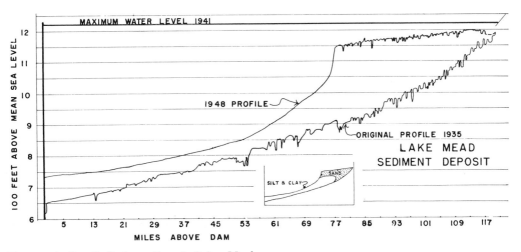

Fig. 21.14.—Longitudinal profile of Lake Mead through the Colorado River delta. After Gould, 1954a.

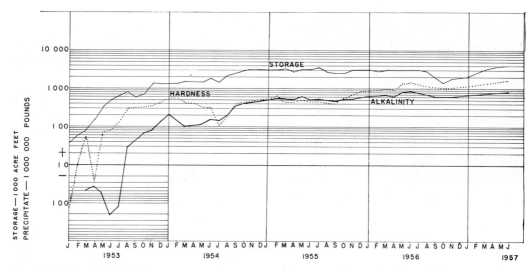

Fig. 21.15.—Progressive hardness and alkalinity precipitation with increasing and stabilized storage in Ft. Randall Reservoir. Minus values indicate quantities leached from the basin during early impoundment. After Anon., 1955, 1956.

it usually forms deltas (Fig. 21.14), but silt so deposited is subject to down-reservoir displacement by later currents or by bed and bank erosion of channels cut through the silt deposit following water level decline. The degree of silting is generally dependent upon amounts carried into the reservoir, but when quantities are carried in density currents, withdrawals of water at proper levels can significantly decrease settled loads (Bell, 1942b).

Mineral deposit in reservoirs is quite similar to that occurring in natural lakes; i.e., it results largely from marl precipitation by photosynthesis. Evaporation accompanying declining water levels is often responsible for conspicuous mineral coatings on rocks and sand just above the waterline. Calcium-sequestering organic particles that have been isolated from some surface runoff may also play some part in mineral removal, but no definite information supports or refutes this possibility.

Marl formation becomes noticeable in reservoirs after effects of early bed leaching have faded away, but in some reservoirs, e. g., Fort Randall on the Missouri River (Anon., 1954, 1955, 1956, and unpublished records), it was measurable almost at the beginning of impoundment. Marl laid down is often brought back into solution by stratification or other events that place it in contact with dissolved carbon dioxide. Figure 21.15 shows progressive accumulation of precipitated hardness and alkalinity on the floor of Fort Randall Reservoir. Bed leaching was evident during March-July 1953, but precipitation was then progressive until January 1954. Leaching and deposit alternated from March until August 1954, and precipitation then dominated until March 1955; thereafter, until June 1957, the trend definitely favored deposit, although floor accumulations suffered leaching each year. The largest bottom load of alkalinity (854,070,000 lbs) was present 30 June 1956, and the greatest amount of hardness (1,668,143,000 lbs) rested on the floor on 30 June 1957. Alkalinity and hardness build-up on the bottom showed a general similarity, which indicates that removal of each was due to precipitation of calcium carbonate (Anon., 1955).

Stratification and density currents.—Reservoirs often develop typical thermal stratification with formation of epilimnion, metalimnion, and hypolimnion. However, they are subject to periodic, intermittent, or even prolonged entrance of large quantities of water that differ markedly in density from any water stratum or region existing in them. These invading flows sink or rise to the proper density level and then move on down-reservoir as sharply defined layers that pass over

Fig. 21.16.—A turbid underflow moving down a model reservoir. From Bell, 1942*b*.

the surface or wedge their way between or under existing water strata. While in movement, they are referred to as density currents or flows. They continue until they break on the dam and then come to rest and form additional water strata. Density of these currents is often affected by suspended materials which normally make them heavier than reservoir surfaces and frequently increase their density above that of any reservoir layer. A density current that moves down along the bottom (Fig. 21.16) is termed an underflow, one that forces its way between two layers of water (Fig. 21.17) becomes an interflow, and one that moves over the surface (Fig. 21.18)

Fig. 21.17.—Density layer (dark strip) established by an interflow in a model reservoir. From Bell, 1942*b*.

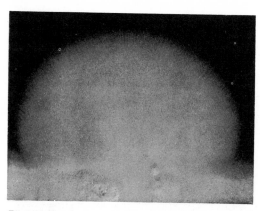

Fig. 21.18.—An overflow spreading over a model reservoir. The advance fringe of finger-like projections is also characteristic of convergence lines. From Bell, 1942b.

is called an overflow (Bell, 1942a, 1942b). The existence of turbid underflows and some muddy interflows can be determined readily by the presence of a convergence line where they drop below the reservoir surface and often by accumulation of debris in the same region when inflow is clear. Flotsam and jetsam are carried to this site by upstream surface currents (often caused by displacement from an under- or interflow) and are immobilized when they meet the downstream movement that forms the density current.

Since they often carry silt all the way to dams, density flows are responsible for the "bottomset" siltation that affects large areas of reservoir bottom. In Lake Mead (Fig. 21.14) density currents have apparently laid down all silt that occurs below the river deltas (Gould, 1954a). Precipitation of suspended particles from a density layer is a slow process, because fine silt particles are involved. Initial settling causes a contraction of thickness, and in only a few hours a turbid layer can become dense enough to divert subsequent flow above it to form an interflow (Bell, 1942b). Often the upper surface of an underflow has a slope toward the dam that facilitates movement of an interflow above it; if interflows must wedge their way between horizontal interfaces, their velocity is very slow indeed.

A water stratum in contact with the dam must be of considerable thickness to monopolize the water that traverses the exit. Layers beginning as density currents are seldom thick enough to avoid mixing with water above and below as they are pulled to an outlet; but muddy layers are

often built up by subsequent turbid interflows to a level that assures silty discharge for long periods of time. Prolonged discharge of muddy water is most common from reservoirs that are filled by drainage from clayey soils that have lost their vegetative cover through fire or improper agricultural practices. The Badlands drainage contributary to the Missouri River had not developed any muddy releases from the mainstem reservoirs through 1957 (Anon., 1954, 1955, 1956, and unpublished records).

Fate of seasonal river discharges.—It is often assumed for estimation of water quality effects and other purposes that reservoir releases will be chemically representative of the mixture of seasonal inflows stored. Occurrence of stratification or density currents militates against mixing, although two or more layers may be pulled through dam openings at the same time and so effect some "hybridization" if two adjacent water strata were laid down during different seasons. Some studies of sizable impoundments, however, indicated that significant homogenization of distinctive inflows may not be relied upon even when stratification is absent or ephemeral (Anon., 1954, 1955, 1956, and unpublished records). Records over five years indicated that the bulk of any seasonal river discharge tended to pass down a reservoir as prior inflows made way for it, although its waters mingled somewhat with those directly ahead and behind. The major reservoir effect was to increase time of passage of chemically distinct seasonal flows to any downstream site. Commingling of the edges of major discharge segments tended to produce more gradual approaches of extremes. As impounded vol-

TABLE 21.2

Variation in average monthly hardness concentration (ppm) below Ft. Randall Reservoir

Month	1953	1954	1955	1956	1957
Jan.	320	276	249	241	182
Feb.	304	309	259	252	192
Mar.	286	305	266	255	206
Apr.	270	250	275	265	207
May	256	232	267	211	227
June	263	216	268	254	224
July	155	223	231	263	
Aug.	176	169	228	250	
Sept.	230	188	106	210	
Oct.	234	231	197	198	
Nov.	239	244	203	189	
Dec.	248	252	210	188	

ame was augmented, the time required for the appearance of any seasonal segment was increased, and finally flows that were developed in summer runoff did not emerge until winter.

Table 21.2 shows how the natural river hardness regimen was altered below Fort Randall Reservoir. Until late 1953 "run of the river" discharge passed through this dam, and hardness variation occurring that year might be considered "normal" for the Missouri River. In 1954, following development of some storage, the maximum and minimum were each postponed one month; in 1955 storage was augmented, and annual extremes suffered additional delay; in 1956 hardness levels in the "normal" winter range occurred in July, and low summer concentrations were delayed until winter. As the age of the reservoirs increased, both upper and lower extremes were somewhat "leveled off" by longer contact with other inflow segments, and marl precipitation affected all stored waters. Longer retention time than was customary in main-stem Missouri River reservoirs might enhance mixing of snow melt with spring floods, and this *melange* might mix further with highly mineralized winter flows.

There are practically no other data evaluating reservoir releases. Salinity distribution studies of Lake Mead (Anderson and Pritchard, 1954) indicated that surface uniformity is attained in winter, but studies of releases were not reported. Lake Mead inflows come down two rivers, the courses of which join in an expanded part of the reservoir basin.

Studies of homogenization and rating of releases against inflows would provide better understanding of reservoir phenomena in many respects than has been possible with the number of stylized limnological investigations of impoundments that have been completed to date.

General.—By stilling flow and precipitating suspended silt, reservoirs often greatly increase the plankton productivity of their watercourses. Sheltered coves, shallow bays, and arms may also enhance development of lenitic rooted vegetation to replace any obliterated lotic beds. Dams usually make their impounded river reaches more attractive to waterfowl, and enrichment provided by fecal matter from large flocks of ducks and geese is sometimes responsible for troublesome algal growths in impoundments furnishing public water supplies. Reservoirs open to recreational pursuits have a great amount of surface

Fig. 21.19.—Silt beds (left) laid down by higher reservoir stages in Lake Mead being eroded by the Colorado River (right). From Gould, 1954a. Photo by Gould.

disturbance from congregations of boaters and water skiers, but possible limnological effects of such churnings have not been reported. Drawdowns of many reservoirs leave large areas of their bottoms high and dry for varying periods and subject silt deposits to bed and bank erosion in the narrow channels traversing them (Fig. 21.19). Drying effects upon total benthic productivity and richness of subsequent stored water would appear to be rewarding fields of investigation, as would be effects of great annual drawdowns and refills.

This account has attempted to list major features of reservoirs that have greatest limnological impact upon streams containing such impoundments. Many details have been omitted, and, in deference to authors reporting on limnological progress in different areas of the continent, references to individual reservoirs have been kept to a minimum.

Reservoir effects on streams

Discharge

Alteration of native discharge patterns depends upon the uses to which reservoirs are put and the stage of filling of individual impoundments or chains. Many reservoirs smooth out discharge in rivers by retaining peak flows and augmenting low stages. The latter process may stem from flood control, navigation, or power releases. The degree of control exercised by the main-stem Missouri River reservoir system is indicated by

TABLE 21.3

Average Missouri River discharges (cfs) at Omaha, Nebraska[a]

Month	1953	1954	1955	1956	1957
Jan.	13,050	9,123	9,667	9,219	8,521
Feb.	17,460	16,520	10,410	9,784	8,981
Mar.	40,890	26,990	21,470	24,930	10,170
Apr.	33,890	28,620	29,220	30,250	16,480
May	43,470	29,860	30,100	30,230	28,020
June	71,450	42,520	30,290	30,560	31,640
July	43,880	33,440	31,550	30,830	31,060
Aug.	34,690	32,310	28,660	33,400	30,620
Sept.	33,910	32,110	34,400	33,590	29,310
Oct.	32,430	32,340	32,140	27,930	
Nov.	20,500	14,510	13,950	13,460	
Dec.	13,950	12,710	9,047	8,831	
Year	33,350	25,960	23,430	23,620	

[a] U.S. Geological Survey Surface Water Supply Papers 1240, 1280, 1340, 1390, 1440, 1510, for Water Years 1953–57.

average monthly and yearly discharges at Omaha, Nebraska (Table 21.3). Fort Peck Reservoir was in operation in 1953, and its releases were used to maintain navigation stages (around 30,000 cfs at Omaha) over the period July–early November. The Missouri River originally had two high-stage periods each year—one in early spring occasioned by snow melt on the plains and another in June arising from mountain snow melt and rains over the plains. These two elevations characterized Omaha discharges in 1953 but were practically ironed out by reservoir control in 1954 and could not be recognized thereafter. Reduction of winter flows, possible with lowered water demands, increased reservoir storage. Average annual flows were almost identical in 1955 and 1956.

Reservoirs may, with power and other releases, maintain year-round flows in previously intermittent streams, the basins of which have been adversely affected by human activities that expedite runoff. Flow in irrigation rivers may be stopped abruptly by closing gates and may be increased from zero to several thousand cfs in a very short time by the reverse action. Effects of sudden flow stoppage on algal growth in the North Platte River are indicated by conditions shown in Figure 21.20. Daily fluctuations in reservoir releases, which are often occasioned by power peaking, discourage littoral stream life and cause many readaptations. Reduction of winter stages below normal unregulated levels (Table 21.3) is common and often reduces the stream's carrying capacity for many forms of life.

A system of artificial lakes or one reservoir exposes more water surface to evaporation and actually reduces annual runoff in any stream although flow regulation that produces longer periods of near-bank-full stages may give the opposite impression to a casual observer. Runoff losses are proportional to the total reservoir surface area and increase with size and number of impoundments. Irrigation canals and ditches also augment surface exposure, and rivers developed for this purpose suffer extreme evaporation loss.

Turbidity

Probably the most common reservoir effect on turbidity is complete or near-complete removal of carried-in silt and other suspended materials. Most silt contributes to deltas in headwaters, and water below this point becomes quite clear or soon develops plankton populations. Releases made at some distance below the surface are quite clear, and previously turbid or intermittently turbid receiving streams are clear the year around for varying distances. Muddy underflows and interflows are known to maintain turbid reservoir discharges for extended periods of time, and if their selective release is attempted to re-

Fig. 21.20.—Dried algal fronds stranded on the North Platte River bed following cutoff of irrigation releases. Photo by the author.

uce siltation (Bell, 1942*b*), they could conceivably maintain high river turbidity over most of the year. In areas with a high level of land erosion and frequent rainfall, density currents often build up great accumulations of suspended sediment in under- and interflows, and releases, if made from near the bottom, are usually if not always muddy.

Reservoir regulated discharges, which are held at or below the bank-full stage most of the time, reduce bank erosion and bed scour and decrease the amount of sediment picked up from the stream bed or brought in from flooding of bottom lands.

Reservoirs often disrupt patterns of bed erosion and deposit for a year or so following closure if releases are maintained in the "run of the river" range and for longer periods if discharge is sharply curtailed. Placement of outlet structures that induce erosion of what was formerly the alluvial side of the river can be followed by a bank-to-bank shifting of cutting and deposition that removes sand bars of long standing and fills in established channels. Formation or strength of eddies can also be altered. Bed materials are rearranged until the new pattern becomes stabilized, but the process may affect human use of the river by filling boat anchorages, eliminating ferry landings, etc. and may disrupt benthic development. On smaller streams dam releases often dig down to rocks that were previously covered by a few feet of sand, and a grading of bottom materials is often evident for some distance below.

Temperature

In general, reservoirs delay river temperature rise in the spring and decline in the autumn, since more time is required for their relatively great volumes of water to approach air temperatures. They also postpone ice formation and spring breakup. Annual temperature relationships of Fort Randall Reservoir to the river above and below it are shown in Table 21.4 (Anon., 1954, 1955, 1956). Gavins Point Dam, about three miles above Yankton, was closed in August 1955, but it did little to impair Fort Randall influences until December.

Thermal stratification and formation of density currents can markedly change stream temperatures if waters of lower reservoir strata take sufficient part in discharges. Low temperatures maintained over warmer seasons by hypolimnion

TABLE 21.4

Average monthly temperature of surface water (° C) 1955

Month	Above Ft. Randall	Ft. Randall Reservoir	Yankton, South Dakota[a]
Jan.	1.0	0.0	0.0
Feb.	1.0	1.0	4.5
Mar.	1.1	1.0	2.2
Apr.	12.2	6.2	9.7
May	18.0	12.3	16.9
June	21.5	18.2	20.5
July	26.0	24.0	25.0
Aug.	24.0	25.2	25.2
Sept.	13.0	20.0	19.0
Oct.	10.2	15.5	14.3
Nov.	4.2	5.5	6.0
Dec.	0.5	1.5	5.0

[a] 80 mi below Ft. Randall Dam.

releases have permitted development of trout fisheries for varying distances below dams in rivers previously too warm for these species. Density currents formed by inflows heavy with suspended sediment can markedly elevate river temperature if they replace or become incorporated in hypolimnion or thermocline releases.

As indicated above, river ice formation can be slowed by reservoir lags in temperature changes, and some stream distances may be kept ice-free by release of bottom water around 4° C. Daily fluctuations in discharge can keep ice broken up for varying distances below dams, usually over greater stretches than are kept open with releases of warmer bottom water. Experimental variation of Fort Randall releases in midwinter 1953 and 1954 removed ice from 35 mi of river below (personal communication from Corps of Engineers personnel).

Water chemistry

Reservoir modifications of water chemistry vary with age of impoundment, extent and duration of thermal stratification, frequency of density currents, depth of water release through or over dams, operational objectives, extent of drawdown and refill, type of release structures, etc. Listing of various detailed relationships that have been uncovered is beyond the scope of this chapter, but some indication of the role of major reservoir phenomena appears desirable.

The major effect of reservoir age upon quality of released water is rather obvious from the previous discussion of basin erosion. If soluble materials continue in contact with water, as in Lake Mead, dissolved mineral increases within the res-

TABLE 21.5

Average annual alkalinity and hardness concentration (ppm)

	1953	1954	1955	1956	1957[a]
		Alkalinity			
Above Ft. Randall Reservoir	157	154	158	154	159
Below Ft. Randall Reservoir	147	144	153	154	147
		Hardness			
Above Ft. Randall Reservoir	271	247	248	242	245
Below Ft. Randall Reservoir	250	240	236	234	205

[a] Semiannual.

ervoir area may be expected for a number of years, and pickup of such materials may amount to less during early impoundment than in subsequent years. However, if leaching of the bottom is restricted largely to the early impoundment period, mineral increase will soon cease, and reductions referable to photosynthetic precipitation of marl will then take place. The trend in Fort Randall Reservoir from 1953 on was mineral reduction, as is indicated by average hardness and alkalinity records in Table 21.5. In 1956 alkalinity was lowered in surface waters, but a buildup occurred near the bottom in January and February.

Stratification influences may well be imagined if releases are made from near the base of a dam. Marl that is precipitated from the photosynthetic zone will often be converted into bicarbonate in the hypolimnion and so increase mineral content of "deep" releases. Elevations in concentration of free CO_2, nitrogen, and phosphorus compounds, etc. may also be expected in the hypolimnion. Conversely, stratification teamed with surface releases will accentuate mineral and nutrient reduction. Density currents may increase or decrease dissolved mineral discharge: if they originate in cold rain or snow and drop their silt loads near the convergence line, they may have a relatively low mineral content; if they owe their being to fine suspended sediment, they may add to the discharged mineral load.

If decomposition in a hypolimnion exhausts oxygen supplies, the presence of stratification is often indicated by sulfide odors leaving releases. The writer will long remember such an odor given off by bottom releases from Kingsley Reservoir in August 1950 (Neel, 1953; Anon., 1951).

Hydrogen-ion concentration is affected by the depth of the discharge opening when stratification is present or absent. Surface waters often develop a high pH with photosynthesis, and waters below the zone of effective light penetration seldom attain similar levels. Significant increases in hydrogen-ion concentration develop from stratification, however.

Reservoirs often increase a stream's oxygen resources. They frequently promote photosynthesis to the level of oxygen supersaturation in upper layers, and the air draft to large release tunnels can often develop supersaturation in discharges from deeper waters (Anon., 1955). Photosynthetic opportunity leads to considerable improvement of streams that were quite muddy before impoundment. In the absence of an air draft, anaerobic hypolimnion releases acquire oxygen at a rate that is roughly proportional to the amount of surface disturbance they create. Atmospheric absorption often gets assistance from algae attached to various walls and structures in the stilling basin and below. By virtue of their high nutrient content, hypolimnion releases generally stimulate phytoplankton or other algal growth as physical conditions permit, and they may, in this manner, be responsible for high oxygen levels farther downstream.

Biological features

The development of lenitic conditions, which eventually follows impoundment where drawdown and other practices permit, brings about changes in benthos, nekton, plankton, etc. within the reservoir area, but usually only the plankton has much direct effect beyond the impoundment. Reservoir plankters suffer varied fates in rivers below dams. When surface or near-surface waters alone are released, and if no organic wastes or tributary flows enter within several miles, plankton will slowly or rapidly decline depending upon stream conditions and volume of reservoir releases. If surface releases join hypolimnion waters coming from power or other units (Fig. 21.21), plankton often displays an immediate proliferation and frequently reaches densities exceeding those developed in the reservoir (Neel, 1953). Similar increases often occur below entrances of municipal sewage or treated wastes. In the Big Horn River below Boysen Dam (Anon., 1954) lake plankters declined progressively for about 20 mi and then began rapid proliferation below city sewer outfalls. Water supplies taken from this previously very muddy river had not been troubled with phytoplankton growths before, and waste contributions had appeared of minor importance. Clarification by Boysen Dam threw a different light on such matters. Lake plankters that have developed in reservoirs usually predominate in the streams into which they are discharged if flow amounts to a few thousand second-feet and if they join no streams with greater discharge. In shallow situations they are often replaced by benthic algae (Neel, 1953; Anon., 1951).

Clarification, discharge of nutrients from deeper strata, stabilization of discharge, and decreased bank and bed erosion collectively or individually promote greater growths of algae than most streams develop prior to damming. Shallow streams have been noted (Anon., 1954) to develop exceedingly luxuriant crops of benthic algae below dams (Fig. 21.20). Detached fronds may spot the water surface for many miles downstream and have been known to clog screens and water intakes. "Haystacks" of dried algae that have been cleared from intakes are often useful indicators of past stream conditions. Benthic algae are often subject to sudden death in streams with abrupt water level changes.

Dams or high velocities of reservoir discharges often form effective barriers against the migration of fishes, and regions just below stilling basins are often crowded with frustrated piscine migrants, monotonously working their way, time after time, toward the overpowering jets of flood-control releases or jam-packed into quiet pools below dead spillways or swimming endlessly among the boils below power plants. Long-term effects of such interferences with the normal movements of fishes have not been estimated. A geneticist friend wonders if the various species will develop different gene frequencies in the isolated reaches and if the most successful species will be those that lose the migratory urge. No one can be sure at this time that there is no communication of fishes or transfer of their germ plasm through dams that appear to stop all fish movement. Some dams have structures designed to allow fish passage. Stoppage of flow in irrigation streams often imprisons fishes in isolated pools wherein they may be subject to above normal mortality as food and oxygen reserves decline and opportunity for predation increases. The biotic carrying capacity of these streams is largely determined by events occurring in such pools. Releases of cold water can effect readjustment of fish populations and encourage the introduction of exotic species. Fish growth is stimulated by stream modifications that increase benthic algae and bottom animals, but populations may differ from the originals.

Benthic fauna is adversely affected by flow variations that intermittently or periodically expose large areas of bottom, by long continued turbid releases that restrict or eliminate algal growth, and by diurnal discharge fluctuations that combat solidification of littoral areas. Although elimination of some benthic organisms has been verified over annual periods, no certainty exists that missing species have become extinct or cannot return if favored by operational change. Silt elimination from very turbid streams has often allowed benthos development in reaches where it previously appeared to be non-existent; it is also benefitted by regulation that promotes uniformity

Fig. 21.21.—Spillway release, left, merging with power plant discharge, right, below Guernsey Dam, North Platte River, Wyoming. Photo by the author.

of discharge. Effects vary with different groups of animals, but aquatic insects, especially those making long mating and egg-laying flights, seem best able to cope with controlled, fluctuating discharges. Sedentary forms of insects, clams, fixed oligochaetes, etc. find survival very difficult under such conditions. The most productive benthic sites—riffles and rapids—are frequently eliminated for the duration of regulated flows in the bank-full range, and these areas are the first to dry if flow is stopped.

Résumé and some future prospects

The damming program now under way on this continent has changed the nature of most of its largest streams, and lotic limnologists, who got off to a later start than their lake-delving brothers, are forever denied the opportunity of becoming acquainted with a really large temperate river that is not regulated in some manner. Unaffected rivers still flow in arctic and tropical regions, but their remoteness will probably keep them beyond the reach of concentrated limnological endeavor almost as long as it protects them from dam builders. However, numerous challenges are present on every regulated stream and in its reservoirs, and since increasing water use now seems to dictate eventual impoundment of all sizeable streams, except possibly those in national parks and wilderness areas, limnologists will suffer no loss of opportunity to dig into basic facts as proffered by various regulatory practices, increasing age of impoundments and regulated flow, new closures, etc. Truly fundamental ecological principles will eventually be brought to light in these situations.

Reservoirs have a fascination all their own. They frequently appear to violate every principle deemed proper and appropriate for bodies of standing water. They often have no behavior pattern that is even reasonably predictable, and they may occupy areas where it appears no lake has a right to exist. The awesome erosion of poorly washed soils and extreme rates of evaporation that occur in desert reservoirs are amazing to anyone experienced with our northern glaciated lakes. Density currents, grandiose fluctuations in water level, draining of hypolimnion, etc. are all items demanding attention in productivity studies.

Reservoir regulation provides greater quantities of water for human use, but it also provides more surface for evaporation, and its net effect is reduction of runoff. Losses to evaporation are now being felt in arid and semiarid regions, and methods for reducing this drain on water supplies are being sought. To date, some protection has been demonstrated with a monomolecular film of hexadecanol. Efforts to secure and maintain water supplies augur for continued reservoir construction until all permissible dam sites are utilized or some other natural brake is applied.

The present trend toward multiple-purpose reservoirs appears in the best interest of stream productivity. Extreme and abrupt flow variations are becoming less common on irrigation streams following installation of power units at or below older dams and construction of new multiple-purpose dams between older reservoirs. There is a growing suspicion that hydroelectric units are not particularly economical sources of power for all regions, and they may suffer a declining rate of construction as atomic plants are developed. New reservoirs are shortening lotic reaches, and the productivity of stratified and density-layered impoundments may be rather low. Efforts to conserve captured runoff and protect it against evaporation and seepage are expected to change environmental conditions and possibly to lead to altered operation in a number of cases. It is anticipated that reservoir storage will become more and more ear-marked for specific purposes.

Eventual consequences of present damming programs will concern future generations, and predictions at this time may range far wide of the mark, since water use and availability may be drastically changed by a number of technological developments. In the now-predictable course of events reservoir utility will decline with capacity losses occasioned by silting and aquatic vegetation. However, it is possible that filling processes will be brought under control and a status quo of some future date indefinitely sustained. Interference with normal sedimentation will probably involve sediment removal in discharges, and stream productivity and water quality may suffer unless off-channel disposal is feasible. If river regulation as now practiced is replaced by a system offering greater conservation of water or if it declines in economic importance, reservoirs will in all likelihood be retained for some purposes, possibly flood control, recreation, etc. Operation for these categories may de-emphasize storage, and maintenance of capacity may decline in pace with anticipated economic return. Reservoirs will be here for some time in any event, and their aging and changing effects upon streams should hold limnological attention for the next few generations.

Author's note

The role of reservoirs in development of water resources and their limnological consequences called for the preceding type of presentation. Many phenomena were handled with a single sentence or less, although details have considerable limnological fascination. Space limitations also precluded reference to the Tennessee Valley Authority, the Pacific Northwest area, and other regions. It is hoped that these gaps will be filled in by authors reporting on regional developments and histories in preceding chapters. References cited here were used for illustrative materials or to document a particular occurrence or situation. The author drew upon personal experience with a number of reservoirs, reservoir systems, and regulated rivers for most material.

References

ANDERSON, E. R., AND D. W. PRITCHARD. 1954. Physical limnology. Lake Mead comprehensive survey 1948–49. U.S. Dept. Interior, Geol. Surv.: 186–210.

ANONYMOUS. 1951. North Platte River Basin water pollution investigation. Fed. Security Agency, U.S. Pub. Health Serv., Missouri Drainage Basin, Kansas City, Missouri, 156 p.

ANONYMOUS. 1954. Central Missouri River water quality investigation, August 1952–December 1953. U.S. Dept. Health, Educ., and Welfare, Pub. Health Serv., Missouri Drainage Basin, 72 + xxv p.

ANONYMOUS. 1955. Central Missouri River water quality investigation—1954. U.S. Dept. Health, Educ., and Welfare, Pub. Health Serv., Missouri Drainage Basin, 42 + xxxiv p.

ANONYMOUS. 1956. Central Missouri River water quality investigation—1955. U.S. Dept. Health, Educ., and Welfare, Pub. Health Serv., Missouri Drainage Basin, 50 + xxxvii p.

BELL, H. S. 1942a. Density currents as agents for transporting sediment. J. Geol., 50: 512–547.

———. 1942b. Stratified flow in reservoirs and its use in the prevention of silting. U.S. Dept. Agr., Misc. Publ. 491, 46 p.

GOULD, H. R. 1954a. Sedimentology. Lake Mead comprehensive survey, 1948–49. U.S. Dept. Interior, Geol. Surv.: 211–265.

———. 1954b. Amount of sediment. Lake Mead comprehensive survey, 1948–49. U.S. Dept. Interior, Geol. Surv.: 281–329.

HOWARD, C. S. 1954. Chemical limnology. Lake Mead comprehensive survey, 1948–49. U.S. Dept. Interior, Geol. Surv.: 173–186.

NEEL, J. K. 1953. Certain limnological features of a polluted irrigation stream. Trans. Amer. Microscop. Soc., 72: 119–135.

22 | *J. S. Dendy*

Farm Ponds

Farm ponds, as discussed in this chapter, include (1) ponds made by constructing dams or dikes to impound water from springs, streams, wells, direct precipitation, and surface runoff, (2) ponds made by digging depressions or pits to hold water, and (3) ponds resulting from combinations of these two methods. Manageability is a typical feature of farm ponds. Although most farm ponds are small, their sizes are highly variable: the surface areas range from less than one acre to more than 100 acres. Most ponds that are to be used for production of fish are constructed so that the water can be drained at will, and in this respect they are unlike natural ponds. Removal of water from pits usually requires pumps.

History

A general account of the early history of pond culture was presented by Edminster (1947). In China the use of ponds to produce fish for food was well established some 500 years B.C. The Romans had fish ponds in the first century A.D. Neess (1949) described the development of fish ponds in 1358 at Wittingau (Czechoslovakia), subsequently a center of fish cultural activities for several hundred years. The chief fish raised in these early ponds was the common carp. Later extensive culture of this fish developed in Germany, Yugoslavia, Poland, France, and Italy. Pond culture spread to England, where carp were introduced in 1514 and pike (*Esox*) in 1537 (Edminster, 1947).

Fish ponds in North America were a later development. Early settlers built mill ponds on streams to obtain power for grinding grain. Edminster (1947) recorded one fish pond in Maryland in 1792. Townsend (1907, 1914), Dyche

(1914), and Embody (1915) gave evidence that the decrease in abundance of fish in natural waters and the convenience of having one's own pond created much interest in the culture of American species of fish in what we now term as farm ponds.

The culture of fish in these early ponds was something of a trial-and-error attempt to make conditions in the artificial body of water conform to those observed in natural waters that were known to produce the kinds of fish desired. In addition some artificial feeding was practiced. Actually little was added to the fish cultural practices of the ancient orientals. Fish culture was an art based on empirical information gained from observations of the naturalist and fisherman. Elaborate instructions were presented regarding the selecting and planting of rooted aquatic vegetation, now generally considered to be undesirable in pond culture. The effectiveness of aquatic vegetation in aerating water and in protecting young fish from predation was recognized, and so was the tendency for stunting caused by overcrowding, but the relation between weeds and stunted populations was to be recognized later. The need for an abundance of good water was evident, but control of excess water was related chiefly to prevention of turbidity, siltation, and loss of fish. Each pond was somewhat of an experiment, and although certain records were kept regarding cultural practices, no use was made of modern scientific experimental procedures to develop principles and methods of pond management.

H. S. Swingle and E. V. Smith, two agricultural scientists, the former an entomologist and the other a botanist, neither trained in the bias of fisheries biologists, began work on farm fish ponds in 1934 at the Agricultural Experiment Station of the Alabama Polytechnic Institute (now Auburn University), Auburn, Alabama. Ponds were subjected to the same principles of testing that had been used for many years to make scientific improvements in farming. Small ponds were built close together and as nearly alike as practicable, so that experiments could be replicated and results compared with those from control ponds. The weight of fish produced per unit area was the means of measuring productivity. Weights alone were not enough. The distribution of the weights among desirable kinds and sizes of fish determined the success of the productivity. The first report, to be followed by many others, on the work of this team was by Swingle and Smith (1938). Larger ponds were constructed in which to try out the findings gained from experiments with smaller ones. Experiments had to be repeated for verification. Always the aim was at least twofold: (1) to produce better yields of fish and (2) to learn why certain practices were successful and others less desirable, or even failures.

The effectiveness of this approach to the study of farm ponds became evident quickly. As information was gained, more questions arose that needed to be answered. The answers required more experiments and more ponds. Fortunately, the late Dean M. J. Funchess, an agronomist and an ardent fisherman, recognized the significance of the work on farm ponds and encouraged it. Aside from the actual information obtained, which stimulated the development of the farm fish pond program throughout North America and other parts of the world, Swingle and Smith made a major contribution to aquatic biology by demonstrating the importance of the experimental approach to the management of waters through the use of methods widely used in agricultural experiment stations. It appears safe to state that by the extensive use of their approach to the study of farm fish ponds, more useful information and more basic understanding has been acquired in less than thirty years than was obtained in all pond work prior to 1934.

Purposes

The major purposes of ponds on farms, which are as diverse as the needs for water, are the following:

Livestock water	Household and barn
Irrigation	water
Fire protection	Attraction of wild fow
Spray water for orchards	Swimming, boating, skating
Fish production for sport, food, bait	Aesthetic values
Production of ice	Erosion control

Compton (1952) lists the first four of the preceding purposes as being of greater importanc than the production of fish. However, a pon constructed for one of these major purpose might serve several others also, including the pro duction of fish. The main purpose of a pond wil determine largely the construction details and th management practices employed.

Because most of the biological, physical, an chemical data regarding farm ponds have re sulted from investigations related to the cultur of fish, the major emphasis in the discussion i this chapter will be on ponds constructed an managed, at least in part, for this purpose.

If a pond is used for fish, benefits may resul in several ways, such as fishing for food an recreation by owner, family, and friends, leasin fishing privileges to a group, sale of fishing per mits by owner, sale of fish for bait, sale of fis and other products for food.

Each use of a pond influences the life in tha pond. Because of the wide variety of uses an the many shapes, sizes, depths, kinds of water amounts of rainfall, ratios between rainfall an runoff, ratios between area of watershed and are of pond, types of soils, differences in insolation annual fluctuations in temperature, kinds an sizes of fish and other organisms present in ponds and rates of harvest, the ponds present such complexity of differences that no two can b said to be truly alike.

Numbers and distribution

Information from the U.S. Fish and Wildlif Service (Table 22.1) shows that for ponds no exceeding 10 acres in area artificial ponds fa exceed natural ponds both in number and in tota area. Many farm ponds having greater areas are not included in these figures.

Estimates of the numbers of ponds in various regions were obtained by direct inquiry to appropriate agencies in the separate states. Information is lacking from a few states. In New England the estimated numbers of farm ponds were 1,400 in Maine, 1,500 in New Hampshire and 2,000 in Massachusetts. Southward along the Atlantic the estimates were 4,000 in Maryland

TABLE 22.1

Numbers and total acreage of ponds not exceeding 10 acres in area producing fish of interest to the angler, and non-productive ponds. Information for 1960 was provided by the State Fish and Game Departments of the 48 contiguous states. Published by permission of the U.S. Department of the Interior, Fish and Wildlife Service, Branch of Fishery Management Services.

	Number	Acres	Subtotal Number	Subtotal Acres	Total Number	Total Acres
Productive natural ponds						
Private, cold water	250	900				
Private, warm water	2,800	10,000	3,050	10,900		
Public, cold water	23,000	122,000				
Public, warm water	10,700	45,000	33,700	167,000	36,750	177,900
Productive impoundments						
Private, cold water	8,100	9,400				
Private, warm water	1,423,000	1,535,000	1,431,100	1,544,400		
Public, cold water	1,200	6,000				
Public, warm water	5,900	13,000	7,100	19,000	1,438,200	1,563,400
			GRAND TOTAL Productive Ponds		1,474,950	1,741,300
			Rounded to		1,500,000	1,750,000
Non-productive ponds						
Natural ponds	7,100	31,250				
Impoundments	60,200	143,000				

41,000 in North Carolina, 32,000 in Georgia, and approximately 4,000 in Florida, a state well supplied with natural lakes and ponds. Among the "Great Lakes States" New York had approximately 16,000 ponds, Michigan reported 2,500, and Minnesota 3,500. Along the Mississippi River the estimates were 22,000 in Iowa, 16,000 in Illinois, 79,000 in Kentucky, 80,000 in Mississippi, and 19,000 in Louisiana. The figures for Arkansas could hardly be compared with those of surrounding states because of the extensive use of fallowed rice lands as reservoirs for production of fish. By far the greatest numbers of ponds per state were reported for Texas and Oklahoma, 341,000 and approximately 250,000, respectively. Estimates for Kansas, Nebraska, and South Dakota were 11,000, 15,000, and 63,000, respectively. Montana reported approximately 24,000 ponds. Idaho's figure was over 91,000. Oregon reported only approximately 3,500. Sparsely settled Nevada had 386 ponds, Utah approximately 5,000, and Colorado an estimated 22,500. The numbers of ponds in the southern provinces of Canada appear to be somewhat comparable to the numbers in states across the boundary. Ontario reported 10,500 "useable farm ponds," which apparently referred to use for production of fish.

Differences in the uses of ponds in various areas were conspicuous. In the Southeast most ponds are used for production of fish. In Texas and Oklahoma most ponds are used for watering cattle, and relatively few are stocked for fishing. In more arid sections irrigation is an important use of the water in ponds. In regions of heavier rainfall ponds may furnish water for irrigation only during unusually dry periods.

Almost all reports indicated that a vigorous pond-building program was in progress. States that had 15,000 to 20,000 reported that ponds were being constructed at a rate of approximately 1,000 per year. Farm ponds are now sufficiently numerous to contribute significantly to the agricultural economy, to the food supply, and to the recreation of most areas of North America. With the continued increase in numbers of ponds and improvements in their uses and management, it appears that farm ponds will be far more numerous and important in the future.

Construction

Many principles in the construction of small impoundments were well known to engineers before the farm fish pond program began rapid expansion in the 1930's. But each land owner faces problems that may be new to him when a pond is to be constructed. With the development of the farm fish pond program, need arose for simple and practical instructions to the farmer for construction of ponds. Swingle (1938) prepared a mimeographed paper to supply the immediate needs. Personnel of the Soil Conservation Service of the U.S. Department of Agriculture, under the leadership of Mr. Verne E. Davison, developed an extensive program of pond construction. This program began in the Southeast and spread rapidly into other parts of the country. Assistance was given to a very large number of persons who wished to build ponds. The Soil Conservation Service, and especially Mr. Davison, must be credited with having a major influence in the popularity and success of the farm pond program in the United States.

J. M. Lawrence (1949) presented detailed information on the construction of farm fish ponds, based on experiences in building numerous ponds on the Agricultural Experiment Station of the Alabama Polytechnic Institute and elsewhere in Alabama. He emphasized that the nature of the soils, especially the subsoils, was extremely important in determining whether a site would support a pond. In an area that has an average rainfall of 54 in. per year and an average runoff of 18 in., the amounts of runoff water from areas of different soils indicated that where heavy clay soils were present, drainages from 4 to 8 acres of pasture land or from 6 to 16 acres of woodland would furnish enough water for a pond one acre in area. In deep sand regions there is normally not enough clay in the soil to hold water.

Other details of construction were presented. The width of the spillway to carry off flood waters was related to drainage area. A 100-acre drainage area should have 82 ft of spillway, 200 acres required 146 ft, and 300 acres 172 ft to maintain less than 1 ft of head over the spillway. The importance of a diversion ditch to prevent undesired water from entering the pond was discussed.

The numerous other publications from various regions that followed presented the same general principles with changed details for definite areas and purposes. The Soil Conservation Service of the U.S. Department of Agriculture (1958) prepared a handbook on farm ponds for work unit staffs, which has been revised through 1958. Some of the representative papers that dealt with construction of ponds are Atkinson (1949), Holton (1950), Davison (1953), Tiemeier et al. (1954), L. N. Brown (1958), C. J. D. Brown and Tho-

reson (1958), Winkelblech (1958), and Eipper (1960). These references represent pond construction information for farmers in a wide geographical distribution. The cost per acre for the construction of 20 ponds in West Virginia was given by Dugan (1951), with the average being $531.37.

Laws regarding water rights vary from one state to another. The U.S. Soil Conservation Service (1957) presented some of the problems that a person should consider regarding water rights *before* constructing a pond.

The construction of ponds for irrigation in Alabama was discussed by Swingle (1951a). The amounts of runoff water and the importance of the minerals dissolved in these waters as potential fertilizer were presented in tabular form. The loss per acre per year from Alabama soil was estimated at $3.00. "The impoundment of these run-off waters and their use for supplemental irrigation would in large measure return these nutrients to the land for crop production."

The depths of ponds in colder climates must be greater than those farther south in order to prevent winter-kill during periods of ice cover.

Management for sport fishing: Cold-water ponds

Trout are usually the only fish stocked in cold-water ponds. The maximum temperature of the water during summer is the factor that determines whether a pond should be used for trout or for warm-water fish. Eipper (1960) stated that trout can withstand water temperatures as high as 80° F for periods of one or two days without undue mortality, but prolonged periods of water temperature above 74° F will cause trout to die. Borell and Scheffer (1961) reported that trout grow best at temperatures between 55° and 68° F but will survive a slightly wider temperature range. If the water in a pond does not get warmer than 70° F 6 in. below the surface of the deep water, it will probably be cool enough for trout. On the other hand in mountain ponds where temperatures seldom go above 50° F, the trout grow slowly.

McCrimmon (1961) defined cold-water ponds as those having a maximum summer water temperature less than 72° F at a depth three feet below the surface. For trout ponds Brown and Thoreson (1958) set the maximum summer temperature two feet below the surface over deep

Fig. 22.1.—Trout are likely to succeed in darkened areas. Water temperature, not location, determines whether trout can be grown successfully. From Borell and Scheffer, 1961.

water at 74° F. Marginal ponds (those that during occasional summers are too warm for survival of trout) often gave high production of trout (McCrimmon, 1961). Rawson and Rutton (1952) considered that in northern regions it is essential to have much of the pond deeper than 15 ft to avoid winter-kill.

The geographical distribution of cold-water ponds is related to latitude and altitude, both of which influence the temperature of the water. Borell and Scheffer (1961) presented a map of the United States (Fig. 22.1) designating the areas in which trout are likely to succeed in ponds. The border line between the cold-water and warm-water ponds is the region that presents fisheries biologists with most troubles. Philip F. Allan, Northeastern Biologist of the Soil Conservation Service (personal communication), stated that ponds marginal for trout and for a bass-bluegill combination constitute a major problem in New York.

Brook, rainbow, and brown trout can be raised in ponds. Rainbow trout are preferred west of the Mississippi and in parts of the Southeast, whereas brook trout are favored in parts of the East. The brown trout will stand a wide range of water conditions, but it is more cannibalistic and harder to catch than the others (Borell and Scheffer, 1961). Saila (1952) considered brook trout better than rainbow in New York, because the brook trout is short-lived and easy to harvest. However, since the rainbows are spring spawners,

they are in poor condition for spring fishing. Brown and Thoreson (1952) preferred brook trout to rainbow for Montana ponds.

The stocking of trout in ponds is usually based on the general principle that the trout will not reproduce, although where a small cold-water stream flows directly into the pond, especially in Canada (McCrimmon, 1961), trout do reproduce and restocking is occasionally unnecessary. The vital statistics of farm pond trout must be understood in order to stock and manage ponds intelligently. Eipper (1960) reported that in a pond during the first summer following stocking with spring fingerlings approximately two inches long, the survival of farm pond trout was highly variable and averaged about 30%. In the two succeeding summers the average survival was about 50%. The overwinter survival of trout in each year of pond life was commonly between 60% and 80%. His results, presented in Figure 22.2, show the average number of brook or rainbow trout remaining in an unfished farm pond at a given time during the three years following stocking at a rate of 600 fall fingerlings per acre. If lower rates were used, similar results were obtained, the number of trout simply being lower throughout. The solid line shows the total pounds of trout that would be present in an average New York farm pond at any time during the first three years following stocking at this rate, if none were removed by fishing. Total poundage reached a maximum of about 110 lbs per acre (230 fish)

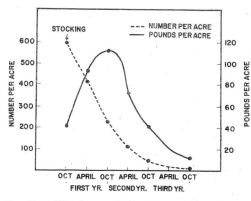

Fig. 22.2.—Numbers and pounds of trout remaining in an unfished farm pond after stocking with 600 fall fingerlings per acre. From Eipper, 1960.

in the fall of the first year after stocking. Next fall there were only 41 lbs per acre (45 fish). Thus, most of the trout in an unfished farm pond will have died from natural causes by October of the second year.

Eipper emphasized that fall fingerlings should be used in repeat stocking, because by being larger they are less vulnerable to predation by holdover trout. Ponds should be restocked every other year to provide adequate fishing. Similar stocking practices have been advocated by most other workers.

McCrimmon (1961) advocated stocking of trout according to expected utilization. Modest angling requirements were met by stocking 200 5- to 7-inch yearling trout per acre in June on alternate years. Higher demands required 500 to 1,000 autumn fingerlings or spring yearlings. Borell and Scheffer (1961) recommended 500 to 1,000 advanced fry 1 to 2 inches long or 300 to 600 fingerlings per acre of fertile water. For eating-sized trout 100 to 300 per acre was the suggested rate. Saila (1952) recommended 150 to 600 fingerlings per acre and suggested 300 as a reasonable number for New York ponds. Brown and Thoreson (1958) recommended that 1½- to 3-inch fingerlings be stocked at rates from 250 to 1,000 per acre, depending upon food conditions.

The production of trout from farm ponds that rely on natural reproduction may be highly variable and is dependent on both biological and human factors. Regarding such ponds, McCrimmon (1961) recorded the highest continuous harvest level on record for Ontario ponds from one of three ponds in a 5.1-acre fishing unit from

which an average of 71.4 lbs of trout was harvested annually over the 1956–59 period. During this time 3,007 man-hours of angling caught 12,802 trout, of which only 4,709 fish were actually kept. Various degrees of put-and-take fishing are employed to meet greater demands of higher fishing pressures.

Eipper (1960) suggested that the establishment of a natural food supply could be hastened by fertilizing newly-dug ponds at the rate of 300 lbs of inorganic fertilizer per acre as the pond is starting to fill. Usually trout growth can be increased somewhat by applications up to about 300 lbs per acre of fertilizer per year.

From the preceding it can be seen that the various workers on cold-water ponds agree fairly well on rates of stocking and methods. The culture of a single species that does not reproduce, except in unusual ponds, frees the owner of the pond from many problems that beset those individuals who have marginal ponds or even clearcut warm-water ponds.

Management for sport fishing: Warm-water ponds

The manageability of a typical farm fish pond is a major characteristic by which it differs from a natural pond. If a given fish population ceases to yield enough to the fishermen, the pond can be drained, refilled, and restocked. This is management in a simple form, but this is a drastic measure that takes the pond out of production for a year or more. Clinical cure is preferable to the surgeon's knife. It is in the clinical matters regarding management that most differences of opinion have developed. Here, pond fish culture has advanced from an art to a young science. Some of the important management measures that have stimulated great interest are (1) the kinds, numbers, and sizes of fish or other animals to be used in stocking different waters, (2) the need or lack of need for various formulations of fertilizers and the details of the application of these, (3) methods of reducing turbidity resulting from suspensions of clay in the water, (4) the control of aquatic weeds long considered to be essential to fish culture but now recognized as being objectionable, (5) the establishment and maintenance of a balance between populations of predatory and forage fishes so that the pond will yield to the angler suitable numbers and sizes of desired species, (6) the control of parasites and diseases so that there will be adequate survival, growth, and reproduction of the fish stocked, (7) the constant efforts to increase the yields, whether they be of sport fish, bait minnows, or commercial fish for food, and (8) the uses of supplemental feeding to increase the efficiency of the pond.

Stocking

Thompson and Bennett (1939) found that carp, buffalo, suckers, catfish, and the usual fish put in ponds for forage stirred up mud. Bass, bluegill, and crappie did not. These workers recommended largemouth bass, bluegill, white crappie, and black bullhead for small artificial ponds in Illinois. Rough fish with short food chains produced higher total weights than bass and "fine fish." However, the largemouth bass-bluegill combination for ponds was recognized as being particularly good.

Scientific approach to the stocking of farm fish ponds began in 1934 with the work of Swingle and Smith (1939b). They found that the production of bluegill in unfertilized ponds was approximately 100 lbs per acre year after year regardless of differences in stocking.

Swingle and Smith (1941a) reported that up to this time there was no experimental information available concerning the most suitable combination of species, the sizes, and the numbers of each which should be used in stocking ponds or lakes. Ponds were stocked in any fashion appealing to the owner, often with extremely poor results from the standpoint of fishing. Great variations in results were found to be due almost entirely to the initial method of stocking the pond.

To provide good fishing a body of water should be capable of supporting at least 100 lbs of fish per acre, consisting mainly of legal-sized game and pan fish. Stocking ponds with only bluegills produced unsatisfactory populations, in which even after 5 to 10 years there were few legal-sized fish. Carnivorous fish must be present as well. Swingle and Smith (1941a) stocked a 1.3-acre pond in February 1937 with bluegills and largemouth bass at the rate of 1,500 and 100 per acre, respectively. Top minnows were added for mosquito control, and the pond was treated with inorganic fertilizer. In the following December when the pond was drained, more than 89% of the total weight of the bluegills consisted of legal-sized fish. The bass had effectively balanced the

pond. In addition they had reduced the numbers of small bass to approximately the correct number for the size of the pond, so that if all the legal-sized bass had been removed, the number remaining would have balanced the pond the next year.

At this time little information was available concerning what constitutes proper balance between forage and carnivorous species in ponds. Stocking with adults of bluegills, white crappies, yellow bullheads, and largemouth bass was extremely unsatisfactory, resulting in overcrowding of some and lack of reproduction in others.

In another experiment Swingle and Smith (1941b) stocked 2½ lbs of bluegill fry per acre in one pond and 180 lbs of bluegill fingerlings per acre in another similar pond having the same plankton content. At the end of the year the ponds contained 105 and 92 lbs per acre, respectively, indicating that these ponds produced only enough food to support about 100 lbs per acre and that excessive stocking resulted merely in higher mortality.

Swingle and Smith also demonstrated that the weight of fish that can be produced by a given body of water varies with the type of fish and their food habits. Thus, those species feeding to a large extent on phytoplankton (goldfish and golden shiner) yielded 750 to 1,100 lbs per acre in fertilized ponds, species feeding largely on insects (bluegills and bullheads) yielded 500 to 600 lbs per acre, and species feeding mainly on other fish (largemouth bass and white crappie) yielded only 150 to 200 lbs per acre in well-fertilized ponds.

By the use of the "mark and recapture" technique Ricker (1945) showed that in a population of bluegills subjected to fishing, natural mortality accounted for 41% out of a total mortality rate of 60%, and 47% out of a total mortality rate of 77%. The causes of natural mortality were predation, parasites and disease, and senility, the last being the most important cause of death among bluegills 125 mm and larger.

Even when great care was used in handling the fish and no fishing was permitted, Swingle (1951b) observed significant natural mortality among bass and bluegills. Where there is no fishing, approximately 25% of the bass stocked may be expected to die within the first 6 months and an additional 20% during the following year. Where no bluegills are removed by fishing, approximately 15% of the fish stocked may be expected to die during the first year and an additional 19% the following year. Bass fry survived better in the spring than did the fingerlings stocked in the fall. This was .thought to be due to a better supply of food for the fry planted in the spring than for the fingerlings in the fall.

Stocking fingerling bluegills is satisfactory in the South, because if they are stocked before November, they will spawn the following spring. This is not so in the North where growth is much slower.

Improvement in pond fish management is demonstrated by the harvest of fish from a 12.5-acre pond (Swingle and Smith, 1943b). Using the best techniques available at the time, they obtained an annual harvest during the period 1932 to 1938 of 28, 19, 34, 20, and 22 lbs per acre. During the period 1938 to 1942 new techniques of management were employed, including fertilization. The harvest for the last 5 months of 1938 amounted to 33.5 lbs per acre, and the annual harvest for each of the three following years was 110, 172, and 274 lbs per acre. The total cost of fertilizer for the second period amounted to 11.3 cents per pound of fish.

Swingle (1945) recommended the combination of bluegills and largemouth bass in all ponds regardless of size, although other writers had recommended that no bass be stocked in any ponds smaller than 2 to 3 acres.

Variations of the bluegill-bass combination included substituting redear sunfish for up to one-third of the bluegill. Warmouth was always a minor element when mixed with bluegill and bass. White crappie added to the total catch in some ponds, but additional experimentation was needed to determine accurately the value of this species for use with bass and bluegill.

In a summary publication prepared as instructions for pond owners, Swingle and Smith (1947) reviewed the principles of pond management and outlined management practices. Recommendations for rates of stocking per acre were given for fertilized and for unfertilized ponds. Because the relative fertility of unfertilized ponds varies from watershed to watershed, the proper stocking rate would depend upon the carrying capacity of the water.

The recommendations for the rates of stocking bluegills and bass in fertilized ponds may vary from state to state. The range of most generally accepted variations is from 750 to 1,500 bluegills per acre and from 100 to 125 bass per acre. The U.S. Fish and Wildlife Service generally recommends 1,000 bluegills and 100 bass per acre.

In ponds fertilized to an average carrying capacity of 400 lbs of fish per acre, bluegill fingerlings were stocked in triplicated experiments at rates of 8, 100, 248, 500, 748, and 1,000 per acre in December, and 100 one-inch bass fingerlings per acre were added the following May. In two other ponds 1,500 bluegills and 100 bass were stocked. The stocking of 500 bluegills or less gave unsatisfactory results, with one exception. The stocking of 748 to 1,500 bluegills resulted in balanced populations, with one exception (Swingle, 1951b).

Various combinations of largemouth bass, bluegills, golden shiners, gizzard shad, and mosquitofish in 0.25-acre ponds were reported by Swingle (1949). Golden shiners gave higher bass production for a 1- to 2-year period but could not maintain high production over a longer period. Goldfish could not be used with bluegills because the latter ate goldfish eggs and prevented reproduction. Goldfish were not satisfactory when used with bass only, because many young grew too large for bass to eat and ate their own eggs, thus preventing further reproduction. Gizzard shad produced a high poundage of bass, but the young rapidly grew too large for the bass to eat and overcrowded the ponds. Mosquitofish were unsatisfactory as forage fish because bass eliminated them almost entirely from ponds in a few months.

By 1950 the stocking of ponds to obtain a desired balance in the resulting fish population was based on experimental data that had been assimilated into well-founded theories. Swingle's (1950) paper on the relationships and dynamics of balanced and unbalanced fish populations (to be discussed in the section on balance) was published, and a set of ratios and symbols for them were available. Swingle (1951b) showed that with careful stocking various survival rates could be expected, and that by use of these survival rates one could predict with a reasonable degree of accuracy the results regarding balance or unbalance of the population. In comparing various rates of stocking bluegills with 100 bass per acre, he found that the average production of harvestable fish per acre increased and the cost per pound decreased with increase in the rates of stocking bluegills up to 1,500 per acre. The conclusion was reached that the principal cause of differences in ponds receiving the same treatment was variation in the survival rates of the fish stocked. An experiment in which bluegills in a fertilized pond were fed poultry laying mash during spring and summer gave highest bass survival (92%).

Stocking with adult bass and bluegill often fails to give a balanced population because of the lack of food for adult bass. Failure of the bass to spawn results in a population overcrowded with forage fish. Stocking with 6- to 8-ounce bass produces a balance, but the bass are too small for legal harvest in most states. Even if proper ratios could be worked out for successful stocking, a difficulty in using this method would be the inability of hatcheries to produce large numbers of this size of bass for stocking purposes.

A wide variety of species of native fishes is available for possible use in pond culture. Bennett (1943) listed the following species, with pertinent comments on each, which might be of interest in small artificial impoundments:

Largemouth bass	Black bullhead
Smallmouth bass	Yellow bullhead
White crappie	Speckled (brown)
Black crappie	bullhead
Bluegill	Carp
Warmouth	Bigmouth buffalo
Green sunfish	Black buffalo
Orangespotted sunfish	Smallmouth buffalo
Yellow perch	Gizzard shad
Pumpkinseed	Golden shiner
Yellow bass	

The species well suited to artificial lakes were listed as largemouth bass, crappies, bluegill, and bullheads.

Swingle (1952) listed the various species that have been or are being tested for suitability in pond culture at Auburn as follows:

Redeye bass	Mosquitofish
Largemouth bass	Yellow bullhead
Smallmouth bass	Speckled variety of
Chain pickerel	brown bullhead
White crappie	Channel catfish
Black crappie	Blue catfish
Warmouth	Flathead catfish
Bluegill	Bigmouth buffalo
Redear sunfish	Smallmouth buffalo
Green sunfish	Carp
Redbreast	Goldfish

Hybrid bluegill ×	Gizzard shad
green sunfish	Threadfin shad
Hybrid bluegill ×	Chubsucker
redear	Fathead
Flier	Golden shiner

In testing these species for use in ponds, a more or less routine procedure has been followed. First each was isolated to determine whether it would reproduce without special manipulations and to prevent introduction of diseases and parasites. Those species that failed to reproduce were considered for possible use as commercial species and were tested for production in ponds with fertilization and by use of supplemental feeding. If they reproduced under ordinary pond conditions, they were considered of possible value for use both as commercial fish and in combination with other species. Next they were tested in 1- to 2-year experiments to determine the production that might be obtained both alone and in combination with other species. They were then placed in 3- to 7-year experiments to learn what they contributed to the fishermen's catch and to see if they could maintain themselves adequately in the population. It thus requires at least 3 to 5 years merely to determine whether a species is of any value and 5 years or more to determine how promising species may best be used.

McCarraher (1959) stocked farm ponds in north-central Nebraska with a combination of northern pike and bluegills. Both species reproduced. The ponds produced good pike fishing, and the growth of pike was better than growth of bass and catfish in similar ponds.

Two species of *Tilapia*, because of their great popularity in other parts of the world, were imported to Auburn. Kelly (1957) found that *Tilapia mossambica* Peters gave 2.97 times greater growth than bluegill in feeding experiments, 1.67 times in fertilization experiments, and 1.97 times in manuring experiments. *Tilapia* ceased feeding at approximately 60° F, and deaths began at 52° to 58° F. Swingle (1960) reported results on the Java tilapia (*Tilapia mossambica*) and the Nile tilapia (*T. nilotica*). The total production of Java tilapia at various rates of feeding ranged from 1,477.1 lbs per acre in 168 days to 4,383.9 lbs per acre in 191 days when stocked as brood fish. When 20,000 fingerlings were stocked per acre, the pond produced 2,945.7 lbs in 111 days. Limited tests with feeding the Nile tilapia produced a maximum of 4,003.7 lbs per acre in 208 days when stocked as adults, and 2,380 lbs per acre in 113 days when 16,000 fingerlings per acre were stocked. When Java tilapia were stocked with largemouth bass, the highest production of harvestable fish was produced by delaying the addition of bass until August, when many tilapias were too large for the bass to eat. The maximum catches in two years were 593.6 lbs per acre in 1957 and 590.6 in 1958. The Nile tilapia grew larger than the Java tilapia but were caught less readily by fishermen. The catch was only 128 lbs per acre in a pond that contained 1,621 lbs of harvestable tilapia.

The stocking procedures for farm ponds in other parts of the country have varied considerably. Bennett (1954) reported management of fish populations in "Ridge Lake," a pond with an area of 18.1 acres, in Illinois, by draining and restocking at intervals of two years. Only a part of the population obtained upon draining was restocked into the pond. Thus, the population was not crowded and was able to expand. Much of the success of this management proved to be the control of the numerical size of the population of fishes other than bass. Bennett and Durham (1951) reported the costs of bass fishing on the same lake. A catch of 49.1 lbs per acre per year cost fishermen $8.66 per pound of bass. Each pound of bass required 7.1 hours of fishing.

Clark (1952) recommended for Kentucky ponds the stocking of 30 adult bluegills and 100 bass fry per acre, with the stocking of bluegills from October to June and the bass fry in May of the same year. He stated that harvest was important in maintaining balance. Tiemeier *et al.* (1954) recommended the following stocking per acre for Kansas ponds: 100 bass and 300 bluegill for clear water; 100 bass, 100 crappie, and 300 bluegill for slightly cloudy water; 100 bass, 100 channel catfish, 100 crappie also for slightly cloudy water; 200 channel catfish alone; and 100 bass, 300 bluegill, 100 to 200 bullheads if desired. Cooper (1955) stated that in midwestern states 100 fingerling bass and 10 adult bluegill per acre appeared to be the most accepted stocking rates for new ponds. It was seldom necessary to restock ponds with these two species so long as bluegill reproduction was kept under control by predation from bass and by other control measures. Pond owners who preferred largemouth bass were recommended to try this species alone

or in combination with golden shiners as a forage species. Good production of the basses (largemouth and smallmouth) as the sole harvestable species was obtained in weedy ponds, with golden shiners or crayfish as their principal source of food. Moorman (1957) discussed factors related to success of fish populations in Iowa farm ponds and stated that in stocking bluegill with bass the rates of stocking bluegill from 300 to 1,000 per acre had little influence on the success or failure of the pond. Also in this experiment aquatic vegetation was not considered important in determining success. Hall (1959) reported that the most successful rates of stocking for all types of ponds in Kentucky were 100 fry bass and 50 adult bluegill per acre and 80 fry bass and 500 fingerlings per acre. Brynildson and Truog (1959) recommended the stocking of largemouth bass alone in Wisconsin ponds that are too warm for trout. If bluegills are desired, they should not be introduced until one or two years after the bass. Stockdale (1960) recommended for farm ponds in Ohio the stocking rate of 200 largemouth bass fingerlings and 1,000 bluegill fingerlings per acre. Brumsted (1960) recommended for ponds in New York the stocking of 100 bass fingerlings 1 to 2 in. long in the summer and 500 to 1,000 bluegill fingerlings in the summer of the same year or preferably one year after the bass.

It is evident that there still remain numerous unsolved problems regarding the general subject of stocking bass and bluegill in farm ponds located in different sections of the country. Until replicated experiments are carried out with adequate controls in different regions, an understanding of the reasons for regional differences in success with various rates of stocking will not become clear.

Fertilization

Fertilizers are applied to farm ponds in order to increase yield, control aquatic weeds, and decrease turbidity caused by suspended particles of clay.

Organic fertilizers include various types of animal manures, plants, and plant products. Nutrients are released as these materials decay. Some organic fertilizers serve as direct food for certain herbivorous species of fish. Unconsumed portions of supplemental feeds serve as organic fertilizers.

Inorganic fertilizers are commercially prepared agricultural fertilizers with known contents of nitrogen, phosphorus, and potassium. The N-P-K values refer to the percentages by weight of available nitrogen, phosphoric acid, and potash in the mixture. The nutrients are soluble in water and do not depend upon decay for their release. Two important papers have presented reviews of literature on fertilization of pond water. Neess (1949) noted that the application of fertilizers in fish culture is a practice of long standing in many parts of the world. He discussed the importance of bottom soils and the various elements commonly used in fertilizers. Maciolek (1954) attempted to show how and where fertilization applies to the present culture, management, and investigation of freshwater fisheries in this country.

The use of inorganic fertilizers in planned experiments to increase yields in farm fish ponds began with the work of Swingle and Smith (1939a). They determined the growth response of a uniform inoculum of cultured algae to varying nutrient conditions established in 4-liter jars in a greenhouse by the addition of commercial fertilizers. The fertilizer materials used were ammonium sulfate, superphosphate (16%), and muriate of potash. The N-P-K ratio 4-1-1 was the most effective. High concentrations of ammonium sulfate increased the acidity so much that in other experiments calcium carbonate (basic slag) was added to give N-P-K-CaCO$_3$ ratio 4-1-1-8.

To determine the value of fertilizers in ponds Swingle and Smith conducted a series of experiments in dirt ponds, fertilized at different rates. Data from one set of experiments are presented in Table 22.2. In another series of experiments, using the ratio 8-4-2-16 of N-P-K-CaCO$_3$ in a pond 0.1 acre and averaging 3 ft deep stocked with bluegill, redeye bass, white crappie, and yellow bullhead, a production rate of 578 lbs per acre was obtained between April 2 and November 8, 1937. An unfertilized control pond produced the same species at the rate 134 lbs per acre.

Smith and Swingle (1939) studied the relationship between plankton production and fish production in 15 small ponds, 12 of which were treated with various combinations of inorganic fertilizers, the other 3 serving as controls.

Experimental work on fertilization produced recommendations that applied directly to farm fish ponds. Swingle and Smith (1938) recommended that the following amounts of fertilizer

TABLE 22.2

Fertilizer tests and plankton and fish production in small ponds, 9 September 1935 to 1 May 1936. From Swingle and Smith, 1939a.

Pond No.	Treatment	Average plankton production (mg/L)	Fish production (lbs/acre)
1	None	4.8	90
2	Superphosphate	3.5	134
3	Superphosphate-NaNO$_3$	6.5	156
4[a]	Superphosphate-(NH$_4$)$_2$SO$_4$	11.7	174
5	Superphosphate-NaNO$_3$-KCl	8.0	251
6	Superphosphate-NaNO$_3$-KCl-CaCO$_3$	24.4	330
7	NaNO$_3$	4.5	79

[a] Pond 4 developed excessive acidity.

be added to an acre of water at each application: 40 lbs of sulfate of ammonia, 60 lbs of superphosphate (16%), 5 lbs of muriate of potash, 30 lbs basic slag or 15 lbs ground limestone. Approximately similar results can be secured by using 100 lbs of 6-8-4 plus 10 lbs nitrate of soda per acre at each application. Swingle and Smith (1939b) reported that 10 to 14 applications per year were required for maximum production of fish.

The production of bottom organisms in relation to the abundance of plankton and to production of fish in fertilized and unfertilized ponds was reported by Howell (1942). Dry weight of plankton averaged 5.81 mg/L in fertilized ponds and 2.54 mg/L in unfertilized control. Bottom organisms averaged 68.27 mg/ft^2 and 19.62 mg/ft^2, respectively. Fish production was 382.9 and 147.1 lbs per acre, respectively. Chironomid larvae, a major item of food for fish, averaged 26.96 mg/ft^2 and 3.26 mg/ft^2, respectively.

Control of *Najas guadalupensis* in ponds by use of fertilizers was reported by Smith and Swingle (1941a). Details will be discussed in the weed control section. Their recommendation was that no fertilization be used during cold months, except following original stocking in fall or winter. Swingle and Smith (1942) advised the use of fertilizer to increase food supply as one step in the management of a pond with a stunted fish population.

In a study of a 12-acre "lake" Swingle and Smith (1943) related the many mistakes that were made and described the use of fertilizer for improving fishing in this club-owned water.

In reports on natural waters there are numerous references to fertility and lime content of the waters. J. M. Lawrence (1943) studied the need of limestone in fertilizers. Applications of 1,000 and 2,000 lbs of ground dolomitic limestone per acre did not increase fish production or plankton production. Zeller and Montgomery (1958) found that many ponds in Georgia needed lime in their fertilization.

Smith and Swingle (1944) noted that waters from fertilized ponds improved stream fishing. Swingle (1945) found that fertilizing old ponds increased the catch of fish. Swingle and Smith (1947) summarized the use of fertilizer in farm fish ponds, along with other management practices.

Smith and Swingle (1943) reported that organic fertilizers increased food for fish but decreased fishability of the pond by encouraging growth of filamentous algae. Materials used were cottonseed meal, cottonseed meal plus superphosphate (16%), poultry laying mash, soybean meal, and soybean meal plus superphosphate. The highest yield, 615 lbs per acre, was with the last-named combination. Although organic fertilizers produced heavy growth of filamentous algae, inorganic fertilizers did not cause such growths but increased cloudiness of the water, thereby increasing the frequency of biting.

Swingle (1947) studied plankton production in a series of 27 adjacent quarter-acre ponds at Auburn. These ponds had a common water supply and were practically identical in length, width, and depth. Yet, when given identical fertilizer treatments, no two had the same appearance either to the naked eye or under the microscope.

On any one day these pond waters appeared to be of various shades of green, brown, black, yellow, or red due to the different types of plankton dominant at the particular time. When these ponds were observed carefully, their appearance was found to change daily and even at various times during the same day. The algae produced by inorganic fertilization were largely genera of the Chlorophyceae—*Scenedesmus, Ankistrodesmus, Chlorella, Staurastrum, Pandorina, Cosmarium, Chlamydomonas, Nannochloris, Pediastrum, Coelastrum,* and others. The Euglenophyceae—*Trachelomonas, Cryptoglena, Euglena,* and *Phacus*—were also abundant and occasionally dominant. The Dinophyceae—*Glenodinium, Hemidinium,* and *Peridinium*—were often present but never in large numbers. Of the Chroococcaceae, or blue-greens, *Coelosphaerium* and *Microcystis* occasionally became abundant for limited periods. Diatoms, which are so abundant in the marine plankton, were relatively unimportant in these fertilized freshwater ponds.

This same work reported the production of fish by using the following organic fertilizers in combination with inorganic fertilizers: flour, manure, dry grasses, hardwood leaves, dry pine needles, fresh pine sawdust, and $NaHCO_3$. Twelve applications of 120 lbs of 6.6-8-2 per acre plus a total of 4,000 lbs of manure gave the highest production of fish, 410.4 lbs per acre.

Recommendations for fertilization of farm ponds have been used widely in the Southeast and in some other areas, but acceptance has been far from universal. Where waters are already rich, fertilization is not recommended for farm fish ponds. The reason is partly that with the existing production in unfertilized waters, the fish in most ponds are not being adequately harvested. Also in many areas where ponds freeze over for extended periods, there is a danger of losing the fish because of winter-kill.

Bennett (1948) approved the use of fertilizer for control of weeds, but not in ponds where the fishing pressure was low. Krumholz (1950a, 1950b, 1952) stated that fertilization was not needed in farm ponds in Indiana. Brown and Thoreson (1952) pointed out the danger of fish-kills when fertilizer was used in ponds in Montana. In experiments in Michigan a fertilized pond produced, without exception, greater total weight of organisms than did the unfertilized pond (Ball, 1949). Ball and Tanner (1951) found that fertilization of a natural lake resulted in a winter-kill. Ball (1952) stated that in comparable ponds in Michigan fertilized water produced an average of 365 lbs of fish per acre, while unfertilized water produced an average of 260 lbs, but other considerations made the use of added nutrients questionable. Carlander (1952) found that many ponds in the fertile soil of Iowa needed no fertilizer. Barnickol and Campbell (1952) showed that in Missouri ponds fertilization made more difference in the growth of bass than it did in the growth of bluegill. Saila (1952) found that in New York fish grew better in fertilized than in unfertilized waters, but results were unpredictable because of great variation in soil and water conditions. In Kansas (Tiemeier *et al.*, 1954) the soils are rich, the waters fertile, large weights of fish are produced, and the fish are not well harvested. For these reasons fertilization is not justified. Eipper and Brumsted (1959) recommended fertilization for weed control. Brady and Hulsey (1959) recommended the use of fertilizer in the propagation of buffalo fish.

Hansen *et al.* (1960) reported that in Illinois fertilization was detrimental to rooted aquatic vegetation. Fertilization did not seem to improve fishing quality. Yet the fertilized ponds yielded an average of 48 lbs of fish per acre, while unfertilized control ponds yielded only 25 lbs per acre. Fertilization was thought to improve bluegill fishing but was of questionable value to bass fishing.

A highly specialized type of pond culture was described by Johnson and Fielding (1956) in which sea water was pumped into ponds for the culture of mullet and of shrimp. The fertilizer used was 7-9-0.

The effectiveness of fertilization in increasing the productivity of ponds has been well demonstrated. If maximal yields are to be obtained at minimal costs, a considerable amount of research will be needed to adjust the fertilizer applications to the needs of the particular waters involved. Where extremely high productivity is achieved, the fish populations and other organisms are faced with the possibility of environmental changes that produce drastic kills in either winter or summer. Unless the crop is to be harvested by public fishing or for commercial purposes (to be discussed in another section), there is a strong tendency in many areas for ponds to be inadequately fished. Thus, although research effort should continue to be directed toward the production of maximum yields of fish per unit area, much work needs to be done to learn the most practical and economical use of fertilizers for ponds in various areas and for various degrees of cropping of fish.

Control of aquatic weeds

Any plant is a weed if it is objectionable, either by the nature of the plant itself or because it occupies space and uses nutrients that could serve a more desirable purpose. Major objections to weeds in farm ponds are given often in the literature. They include (1) protection of small fish from predation, thus favoring overcrowding of the forage species, (2) use of plant nutrients that are needed by more beneficial phytoplankton, (3) interference with harvest of fish, (4) interference with swimming and boating, and (5) production of a mosquito hazard.

The types of plants that are considered weeds in ponds are (1) certain planktonic algae, (2) filamentous algae, including mono-filamentous forms that are favored by cold weather, branched filamentous forms that are favored by warm weather, and attached algae that are highly developed, (3) submerged vegetation, (4) emergent vegetation, (5) marginal vegetation, and (6) floating plants.

The first control measure that should be taken is to construct the pond in such a way that shallow areas are minimal. A depth of 2 feet around the margins of the pond should be obtained by constructing the pond with steep slopes to that depth (Swingle, 1938, 1946; Lawrence, 1949; and others).

Control of weeds in a pond is not permanent. The job must be repeated at intervals. The objective in weed control research is to reduce the cost of control measures and to increase the intervals between the treatments. As soon as a pond starts to fill with water, habitats for aquatic weeds are provided. Probably the easiest and most economical way to avoid future troubles is to remove weeds by hand while they are still small in size and few in number. This is especially true for marginal weeds like cattails. Frequent visits to the pond during the growing seasons may be required to keep up with the newly developing weeds.

Fertilization is used to prevent weeds from establishing themselves in ponds and to control weeds that are already growing in ponds. This use of fertilizer, which was introduced by Smith and Swingle (1941*a*, 1941*b*), has been accepted and is recommended in most parts of the country. In some of the more northerly areas, however, especially where soil fertility is high, other methods of weed control are preferred. Fertilization helps control weeds by producing dense algal growths that smother or shade the rooted vegetation until it dies. Details were described by Smith and Swingle (1941*a*) and Swingle (1947). The fertilizer should be applied early in the season while the water is still cold and again at intervals of approximately three weeks until the plankton is so abundant that visibility is 18 in. or less. When the water becomes clearer and the visibility increases, another application of fertilizer should be made. Recommendations as to the amounts and formulations of fertilizer vary from place to place. Fertilization must be done correctly or it may serve to increase weeds rather than to control them. J. M. Lawrence (1954*b*) recommended the application of fertilizer from platforms a few inches below the surface of the water. Walker (1959) applied fertilizer as water soluble 16-20-0 formulation of ammonium phosphate using floating dispensers that allowed the chemicals to go into the water slowly. He stated that this method was preferred because it produced a continuous bloom of unicellular algae and dense populations of zooplankton.

Frequently additional control measures are needed. Whenever possible it is desirable to use biological controls and convert the plant nutrients into some other form that is usable. Swingle (1957d) listed some of the important herbivorous fishes of different parts of the world and reported that in experiments at Auburn the Israeli strain of carp fed on the troublesome alga *Pithophora* and reduced it severely. *Tilapia mossambica* controlled *Pithophora* and a midget sedge. It appears that none of the native North American species of fish will control weeds in ponds.

Surber (1949), summarizing earlier work on chemical control of aquatic weeds, recommended 1 ppm copper sulfate for control of *Chara* and pond scum and sodium arsenite at a concentration of 4 ppm As_2O_3 for controlling submerged rooted aquatics.

The use of chemicals for control of weeds is a last resort treatment that is quite popular. The three chemicals that appear to be most widely used are copper sulfate, 2,4-dichlorophenoxyacetic acid (2,4-D), and sodium arsenite. The effectiveness of copper sulfate decreases with increase in hardness of the water. Applications of 4 ppm copper sulfate are recommended for control of algae in ponds in many hard-water areas. Where the water is very soft, the concentration should be reduced by one half (Eipper and Brumsted, 1959) or in some cases to 1 ppm or less. The effectiveness of 2,4-D in control of emergent aquatic vegetation was demonstrated by Snow (1948, 1958). Since it is toxic to terrestrial plants also, care should be exercised to avoid drifting of this chemical onto desirable plants. Various forms of this chemical have been used and tested extensively. Also it is used in combination with 2,4,5-T (2,4,5-trichlorophenoxyacetic acid).

J. M. Lawrence (1954a) reported that the most satisfactory and economical control of *Pithophora* "at present" was to treat the entire pond with dehydroabiethylamine acetate. Concentrations of 0.5 ppm controlled the alga, but concentrations of 0.7 ppm were toxic to bluegills, goldfish, and young bass. Applications had to be repeated, and great care had to be taken to avoid killing fish.

Sodium arsenite is dangerously toxic to man, livestock, fish, fish-food organisms, and to most aquatic weeds. When other treatments fail to give control of weeds, sodium arsenite is used as a dangerous but usually effective chemical. J. M. Lawrence (1958b) reported a relatively safe method of applying sodium arsenite to a pond by use of gravity flow from a drum of the chemical on a boat through a tube into the water behind the propeller of an outboard motor. One or more applications of 4 ppm As_2O_3 as sodium arsenite produced fairly good control of *Pithophora* in a majority of ponds if applied while the alga was still in an active growing stage. A number of ponds that had been recently treated with sodium arsenite experienced delayed reproduction of bluegill and poor growth of bluegill and largemouth bass. The As_2O_3 tends to accumulate in pond bottoms and is not easy to remove. Sodium arsenite has been used successfully for weed control in many ponds. Rarely are the other effects of the treatments seen, evaluated, or reported. However, extreme precautions should be exercised when using this chemical.

Numerous other toxic chemicals have been tested for control of aquatic weeds. J. M. Lawrence (1958a) summarized information on control of more objectionable aquatic weeds in ponds, giving data in tabular form. For one reason or another most of the newer chemicals are not entirely desirable. A vigorous program of research is in progress to screen new chemicals and evaluate them with respect to their control of aquatic plants. Those chemicals that appear to be effective are being tested to determine their toxicity to various species of fish.

Clearance of muddy waters

Turbidity caused by suspended particles of clay or mud in ponds is undesirable. Muddy waters constitute a major problem in many areas, especially where ponds are subject to strong winds or the trampling of cattle. Hall (1959) stated that many potentially good ponds in Kentucky have been ruined by cattle. Carlander and Moorman (1956) recorded poor standing crops in Iowa ponds with high turbidities. Irwin (1945) observed that newly impounded waters that had inundated vegetation tended to clear rapidly after being muddied by runoff water. Impoundments that did not cover vegetation remained muddy. If aquatic vegetation developed, the water remained clear. After vegetation decayed, the waters gradually lost their capacity to precipitate colloidal clay. The colloidal clay particles were negatively charged and could be precipitated by acids that would release enough positively charged ions to neutralize the negative charges. The addition of various organic materials resulted in clearing of water in ponds through the release of CO_2 during decay. Irwin suggested that probably the vegetation from an area equal and comparable to that of the pond would produce desired results. In order to maintain clear waters, suitable buffer agents should be put into the waters. He suggested superphosphate as a fertilizer that would furnish the desired buffer effects. Swingle (1947) and Irwin and Stevenson (1951) found that use of organic materials as fertilizers tended to clear muddy ponds. Swingle's (1947) recommendation was a three-to-one mixture of cottonseed meal and superphosphate at the rate of 100 lbs per acre or manure at the rate of 1 ton per acre. The application should be repeated at intervals of two to three weeks until the water is clear. Keeton (1959) accomplished long term decrease in turbidity in ponds by applying oil field brine, which contains ions of Na, Ca, K, and Cl. He recommended the use of brine for clearing turbid ponds and advised intermittent applications rather than single application. He stated that the brine was not harmful to the biota as a whole but was harmful to cladocerans, copepods, and tendipedids. Increase of light penetration into the water was credited as being the factor that increased productivity.

Turbidity caused by clay should not be confused with the turbidity that is caused by plankton in fertilized water.

Balance

The interrelationships in fish populations are satisfactory if the populations yield, year after year, crops of harvestable fish that are satisfactory in amount when the basic fertilities of the bodies of water containing these populations are considered. Such populations are considered to be "balanced populations" and the species within such a population are "in balance."

In order to produce annual crops of harvestable fish, it is evident that the species within a balanced population must be able to reproduce periodically, usually at least annually, in order to replace the harvested individuals. Ability to reproduce within the environment, therefore, must be one criterion of a balanced population.

Thus defined is the concept of balance discussed in Swingle's (1950) much quoted paper on population dynamics. Before some of the content in that paper is summarized, it seems desirable to present some of the background information regarding largemouth bass, bluegill, and a few other species in pond culture.

Swingle and Smith (1943a) reported that in Alabama ponds bluegill were found to spawn at an age of 4 months and at a size of 1 to 2 ounces. Bluegill spawning occurred from April to October where there was ample food. When other food was scarce, bluegill ate their own eggs and eggs of bass. The spawning activities of bluegill reflected conditions in the pond. Thus, reproduction was considered to be highly important, and is was recommended that ponds should be checked to determine whether or not the bluegills had reproduced. Bass spawned in April, May, and June. Bass spawned at the age of 10 to 12 months. The smallest bass that were found to spawn were 5 to 6 ounces. The bass fingerlings grew satisfactorily and could spawn on a diet of aquatic insects, tadpoles, etc., but adult bass required a diet of fish in order to spawn. In colder climates bluegill spawned at the age of one year, but bass required at least two years (Bennett, 1948).

Swingle (1945, 1949) experimented with various combinations of species as forage fish in populations with largemouth bass. Bluegill proved to be the most satisfactory species, but redear sunfish could be substituted for up to 50% of the bluegill. Bullhead catfish could be used with bluegill and bass. White crappie gave some good results and some that were unsatisfactory. Golden shiners served as forage fish both with and without bluegill. The shiners were unable to maintain their numbers in ponds without cover. Both gizzard shad and goldfish grew so rapidly that they were soon too large for bass to eat. Goldfish did not reproduce in ponds with bass and bluegill. Krumholz (1950b) preferred redear, instead of bluegill, in combination with bass in Indiana ponds, because the redear's reproductive capacity was less, and hence the ponds did not tend to become overcrowded with forage fish.

A satisfactory forage species must continue to supply the carnivorous species with food and yet maintain its numbers for future reproduction. In turn the carnivorous species must eat enough of the young forage fish so that the population will not become overcrowded and stunted. An analysis of the interrelations of species in 89 separate well-established fish populations from 2 to 30 years old furnished the basis for Swingle's (1950) paper, which will now be discussed briefly.

The F/C ratio is the ratio of the total weight of all forage fishes (F) to the total weight of all carnivorous (piscivorous) fishes (C) in a population. The C species of fishes are those that feed principally upon other smaller fishes and that cannot grow to normal average adult size without such food. All other fishes in a population are included in the F species. The F species feed largely upon plants, plankton, Crustacea, and insects, but may occasionally eat small fish. The largemouth bass is the principal C species used in pond-fish culture.

F/C ratios from 3.0 to 6.0 appear to be the most desirable in the balanced range, and 77 per cent of the best producing populations fell within this group. However, 66 per cent of the poorest of the balanced ponds also was in the same range. It is, therefore, apparent that other relationships within a population, in addition to the F/C ratio, must be known in order to adequately describe the capacity of a population to produce yearly crops of harvestable fish.

. . . .

The Y/C ratio equals the Y value, or the total weight in pounds of all those individuals in the "F" group that are small enough to be eaten by the average-sized adult in the "C" group, divided by the C value, or the total weight in pounds of the "C" group. In other words, it is the pounds of small fish of the "F" species available as food for each pound of "C" species in a population . . . .

The most desirable range for the Y/C ratio appeared to be 1.0 to 3.0. All populations with Y/C ratios in excess of 4.8 were unbalanced and were incapable of producing yearly crops of harvestable fish. These populations were composed largely of overcrowded forage fishes . . . .

The Y/C ratio is a dynamic value—changing with changes in predation pressure and varying rates of harvest, yet remaining within a rather narrow range in balanced populations.

The A_T value (total availability value) is the percentage of the total weight of a fish population composed of fish of harvestable size . . . . Within the range of balanced populations, the most desirable portion of the range appeared to be between 60 and 85. Populations with A_T values above 85 had too few intermediates for replacement and too few small fishes to furnish adequate food for the "C" species; in other words, this was the range containing populations having overcrowded "C" fishes . . . . This value is the most useful indicator of balance and is a measure of the efficiency of a population in production of harvestable fish.

"The E value of a species or group is the per-

centage by weight of the entire population composed of that species or group." This value is the survival efficiency of a species. Consistently low E values for a species in various combinations of species indicate that the species is of relatively little importance from the standpoint of sport fishing or commercial fishing.

Other relationships and their importance in population dynamics were discussed. In conclusion emphasis was placed on the effects of harvest of C and F species and the need for adequate harvest of both, which is not always realized in many regions.

With a comprehension of some of the dynamics involved in populations of pondfish, methods of determining balance become meaningful. Swingle (1956a) presented factors that influence reproduction of bass and bluegill and then furnished a key to pond analysis by seining. Briefly summarized, without explanatory details, his findings are presented here.

1. Size of brood fish—Bluegills spawn at a size of 0.3 ounces (3-inch group). Bass must reach a size of 6 ounces (9-inch group) to spawn. A 1-ounce bluegill female may produce 70 young, while a 4-ounce female can produce 2,560 young. Thus, other conditions being equal, heavy reproduction indicates large brood fish.

2. Food available during period of egg formation—Heavy reproduction by bluegills results from rapid growth, light reproduction reflects slow growth, and no reproduction means no growth or a loss of weight by brood fish. Bluegills form eggs in approximately one month at temperatures between 65° and 75° F. Reproduction is related to conditions 1 to 3 months prior to spawning.

3. Crowding—Lack of reproduction by bluegills may be due to crowding either by bluegills or by some other competitive species.

4. Egg-eating habit—Crowded bluegills may eat their own eggs or eggs of other species. Lack of reproduction by bass may result from crowding of bass or from crowding of bluegills.

5. Repressive factor (first observed for goldfish, carp, and buffalo populations: Swingle, 1954, 1956a, 1956b)—A hormone-like factor which is secreted or excreted into the water prevents reproduction in ponds that have large weights of fish present for several months prior to spawning time. When other conditions such as temperatures, etc. are suitable, the fish will spawn

if much of the old water is removed and new water is added to the pond, or if the fish are transferred to a pond in which fish had not been present.

6. Water temperature—Bass lay eggs when the temperature rises to between 68° and 75° F and occasionally in the fall when these temperatures are reached. Bluegills reproduce when the temperature is 80° F or above. Some ponds may get warm enough for bass to reproduce, but not warm enough for reproduction of bluegills.

7. Silt-laden waters—These waters often are unsuitable for reproduction of bass and bluegills.

8. Water fluctuation—Drawdown may affect the ability of bass and bluegills to reproduce. Rapidly rising water may result in heavy spawning of bass because of release from the repressive factor by dilution.

9. Salinity—Bass can reproduce at higher salinities than can bluegills. Neither can reproduce at a salinity of 5 to 5.5 ‰.

10. pH of water—At acidities of pH 5 to 5.5, bluegill and bass spawn sparingly. Alkalinities in excess of pH 10.0 to 11.0 appear to be toxic to young of both species.

11. Light—Bass spawning in muddy ponds has been delayed as much as 30 days later than in clear ponds.

Pond analysis for balance.—Pond analysis is done chiefly in the summer months and involves the use of a minnow seine 15 ft long, 3 ft deep, with 6 or 8 meshes per inch, and a large seine 50 ft long, 6 ft deep, with 2 meshes per inch. One end of the seine is anchored at the bank and the other is taken straight out full length into the pond. The sample is taken by sweeping the deep end of the seine in an arc back to the bank. Each sample is from a quadrant area. Several samples are taken with the minnow seine first. The large seine is then used to corroborate findings of the minnow seine and to get other species or larger fish not in the minnow seine.

"Recently hatched bluegills" refers to those less than one inch in size that have apparently hatched within the last month. "Intermediate bluegills" refers to the 3-, 4-, and 5-inch groups. "Young bass" refers to young-of-the-year fry or fingerlings. Numbers in various inch-groups for each species and other pertinent information should be recorded for each seine haul.

Swingle (1956a) prepared a key to aid biologists in determining balance in their ponds from the results obtained with these standardized sampling techniques.

In unbalanced ponds, the catch is principally composed of small bluegills of the 3-, 4-, and 5-inch groups . . . . The bass caught are few, but usually larger than 2 pounds.

In normally balanced ponds, most bluegills caught are above the 6-inch group in size. The average bass caught is from 1 to 2 pounds, but smaller ones and possibly larger ones are also taken. Bluegills are found on beds several times during the spring and summer.

In ponds crowded with bass, almost all bluegills caught are large fish, averaging in excess of 0.3 pound. They are found on beds several times in the spring and summer. The bass caught average less than 1 pound and are in poor condition.

Remedial treatments for stunted populations

Ponds with stunted fish populations are apparently common throughout the United States. Stunted populations may be defined as occurring when only a few of the fish present in a pond have been able to reach legal size. The principal causes for such a condition are overstocking, absence of sufficient carnivorous fish, and heavy weed growth in ponds (Swingle and Smith, 1942). The simplest corrective treatment is either to drain the pond or to poison the entire fish population, and then restock with the correct numbers and species of fish. One of these methods may be dictated by the presence of obnoxious species in the pond. However, removal and destruction of the stunted population is not always possible or desirable.

Four management practices recommended for correcting conditions that produce stunted populations in ponds are control of dense weed growth, stocking with largemouth bass if they are not already present, fertilization of the pond to increase the food supply for forage fish and carnivorous fish, and heavy fishing to reduce farther the number of small fish.

Other methods have been tried. The removal of excess small fish by seining was considered too time consuming by Swingle *et al.* (1953). Trapping of bluegills by means of wire baskets removed fish, but not rapidly enough to restore balance in an overcrowded pond (Cobb, 1952). The use of traps made of one-inch mesh chicken wire was advocated by the Department of Conservation, Cornell University (1959), for improving ponds with stunted populations of bluegills.

Partial poisoning with formulations of rotenone was described by Swingle *et al.* (1953). Poisoning the margins of ponds was recommended when most of the overcrowded fish were from 3 to 5 in. long. One pound of material containing 5% rotenone was used per 200 to 300 linear ft. The poison was applied in a continuous line 15 to 30 ft from the bank. All of the fish between the line of poison and the bank were killed, while most of those outside the line moved away and were not killed. Thus, it was possible to kill most of the small fish in shallow water without injury to many of the larger fish. Several retreatments may be necessary at weekly intervals if the bluegills have been extremely small and crowded. At temperatures above 80° F the water treated with rotenone loses its toxicity to fish in 24 hours.

Partial poisoning has produced desirable results in many trials. Hooper and Crance (1960) reported partial poisoning as an effective method of restoring balance to overcrowded populations in state-owned lakes in Alabama.

An additional technique in the use of rotenone became available when J. M. Lawrence (1956) found that 1 ppm emulsifiable 5% rotenone could be counteracted by 2 ppm potassium permanganate.

Hester (1959) tested the tolerance of carp, largemouth bass, fathead minnows, green sunfish, goldfish, bluegills, golden shiners, and brown bullheads to three rotenone formulations. In aquaria, with water temperatures of approximately 70° F, the bullheads 6 to 8 in. long were the most tolerant, and bass and carp were least tolerant. Bluegills tolerated approximately twice as much rotenone as did bass. These facts need to be considered in planning a partial poisoning to correct overcrowding.

Yield

The catch of fish measured in pounds per acre gives a satisfactory measure of the yield of a body of water. Unit effort required to harvest the crop adds more information. As already pointed out, many regions have ponds that are not adequately fished. Byrd (1959) reported data on the yield from some rather heavily fished waters that were managed and fertilized. These ponds, or "lakes" as the report calls them, fall into the classification of farm ponds even though they are not on farms and are a bit large for comparison with most typical farm ponds.

The 12 lakes contained a total of 841 acres; three of these lakes totalling 155 acres, have been open to continuous fishing for 8 years, 3 containing 163 acres for 7 years, 1 with 40 acres for 6 years, 4 containing 233 acres for 5 years and 1 with 250 acres for 2 years. . . . These lakes furnished a total of 4,286 acre-years of fishing during the period of 1950 to 1958. During this time, a total of 695,282 fishermen caught 2,530,182 fish weighing 746,598 pounds.

A summary of the figures presented as averages per acre is given in Table 22.3.

The charge per fisherman above the age of 16 was $0.50 per day. Boat rentals were $1.00 per day. Gross income averaged $143.00 per acre, and net annual income was $12.00 per acre.

Ricker (1958) showed that the mathematical relationships between yield, recruitments into harvestable size groups, and mortalities are such that either the individual size of the fish caught or the catch per unit effort can be favored by suitable regulation of the population without significant loss of yield. He presented a mathematical model for better understanding of the events regarding mortalities, recruitments, and yields in a population of fish.

Commercial production of fish in ponds

The use of fish ponds for production of food antedates the culture of sport fish by thousands of years. On a world-wide basis, even today, far more ponds produce fish for food than for sport. In this country scientific culture of commercial fish is a quite recent development.

A species for commercial production, aside from having good sale value, must possess certain characteristics in order to be a success in pond culture. It must be able to reproduce in captivity, so that adequate young fish for stocking can be available easily. However, it must not reproduce in growing ponds, because this would result in a population with too many small fish. It must be

TABLE 22.3

Summary of records from 4,286 acre-years of fishing on 12 public fishing lakes in Alabama. From Byrd, 1959.

	Range per acre	Average per acre
Pounds of fish caught		
Bluegill and redear sunfish	74.8–220.7	137.1
Bass	11.3– 50.9	29.5
Bullhead	0.0– 67.0	7.0
Crappie	0.0– 6.1	0.6
Pounds of all fish caught	129.2–248.2	174.2
Number of fisherman-trips	89 –242	162.2

able to grow rapidly and efficiently on the food in the pond and on supplemental feeds that are inexpensive.

In order to determine which species might have potential value as commercial fish, Swingle (1954) began a series of tests with several species. The bluegill has no carbohydrate splitting enzyme (F. B. Lawrence, 1950) and cannot make use of some of the more economical feeds. It was found to be of no value as a commercial fish. The carp is used in many parts of the world, but it muddies pond water, reducing the photosynthetic activity in the pond, and produces only moderately high weights of fish per acre without supplemental feeding. The bigmouth buffalo and the smallmouth buffalo do not muddy the water and produce greater weights of fish per acre with fertilization than does the carp. Hendricks (1956) found that smallmouth buffalo in carp ponds were able to gain weight while carp lost weight. Brady and Hulsey (1959) experimented with 3 species of buffalo, preferred the bigmouth buffalo, and gave instructions for its propagation. Swingle (1954) preferred the same species because it reproduced better than the smallmouth. He outlined a procedure for raising it as a commercial fish (Swingle, 1957c).

In culture of buffalo fish, or of carp, reproduction in growing ponds is not a problem, because a repressive factor that apparently is produced by the fish controls reproduction (Swingle, 1956b). The manipulation of this repression of reproduction becomes one of the keys to successful management of buffalo, as well as the management of many other species both in this country and abroad. The fish can be made to reproduce in season by the elimination or dilution of the repressive factor when reproduction is desired, or it can be kept from reproducing, according to the management. Johnson (1959) described extensive culture of the bigmouth buffalo in Arkansas as an alternate use of rice fields during years of fallowing. A well-organized fish-farmers' cooperative handled much of the harvesting, freezing, and marketing of the fish. This insured a product of high quality. Frequently largemouth bass were stocked in the buffalo ponds to control wild fish that would compete with the buffalo. The presence of bass furnished additional income either through sale of fishing permits or through its desirability for market.

When culturing the speckled variety of brown bullhead as a commercial fish, the lack of adequate repression of reproduction was one of the chief problems. Swingle (1957a) outlined a procedure for production of this species and included special plans to prevent unwanted reproduction. Obtaining young for stocking was not a problem.

Channel catfish was not considered as a species with capacities for producing high poundages per acre in early experiments (Swingle, 1954). However, in later tests with higher rates of stocking and with feeding, Swingle (1957b, 1959) found it to be one of the most desirable species for commercial culture and as a fish for anglers to harvest. This fish does not normally reproduce in ponds and thus meets one of the requirements for a good species for commercial production. Nelson (1957), describing the propagation of channel catfish, stated that in his 1953 experiment he was able to produce young fish at a cost of $0.0035 per fish. Swingle (1959) studied the efficiency of channel catfish in converting pounds of feed into pounds of fish. He clarified terminology regarding conversion factors, and proposed a new conversion factor,

$$S = \frac{\text{Pounds of feed added}}{\substack{\text{Total pounds of fish produced} \\ \text{by natural plus added feeds}}}.$$

In this formula the pounds of fish produced equals the pounds of fish recovered at the end of the experiment minus the pounds of fish originally stocked. The S value is a measure of the efficiency under the conditions of the experiment.

Pelleted feed was compared with dry mix flour. The pelleted form yielded an S value of 1.6 and the other form an S value of 3.3. In this study the pelleted feed, known as Auburn No. 2 Fish Feed, had the following composition:

Soybean oil meal (44% protein) 35%
Peanut cake (53% protein) 35%
Fish meal (60% protein) 15%
Distillers dried solubles (24% protein) 15%

The pellets were ⅜ in. in diameter and 1 in. long. The conversion was better with spring stocking ($S = 1.87$) than with fall stocking ($S = 3.0$). The cost of feed and fertilizer per pound of catfish produced was $0.117 with spring stocking and $0.188 with fall stocking. The most effective utilization of feed was when it was supplied at rates between 2% and 4% of the body weight of fish per day. The maximum weight of feed that could be applied with safety was 25 lbs per acre per day using dry mix and 30 lbs per acre per day using the pelleted form.

Phillips *et al.* (1959), and numerous other papers by the same senior author and various associates, presented basic information on the dietary requirements of trout. Although the requirements of other fish differ to some extent from those of trout, the principles discussed by Phillips should be understood before attempting to formulate feeds for other species.

The channel catfish is popular among anglers. For this reason, a pond stocked with channel catfish can serve two commercial purposes. The owner can sell fishing rights to anglers, and he can then harvest the remaining fish when the pond is drained. A 12.4-acre pond operated in this manner (Prather, 1959b) was stocked with 2,000 channel catfish fingerlings (3 in.) per acre on February 27, 1958, and 1,000 adult fathead minnows per acre on April 28. Also 66 largemouth bass fingerlings per acre were added June 7 to 26 to control green sunfish. The pond was fertilized, and the fish were fed 5,423.9 lbs per acre between 1 April 1958 and 3 October 1959. The food was Auburn No. 2 Fish Feed in pelleted form. The pond was open to fishing from 24 September to 8 December 1958 and from 14 March to 6 October 1959. Per acre, 579 fishermen caught 1,241 channel catfish weighing 1,292.5 lbs, in addition to 36.9 lbs of bass and 27.0 lbs of miscellaneous fish. The harvest removed 62% of the catfish stocked. Upon draining the pond an additional 180 catfish per acre (9% of those stocked) were recovered. Thus, 71% of the catfish stocked were accounted for. The income from fishing was $593.37 per acre and from the harvest upon draining, $140.83 per acre. The cost of fingerlings, fertilizer, and feed was $481.46 per acre. A balance of $252.74 per acre was left for labor and capital.

A scientific approach to commercial culture of fish places it on a basis that is comparable to the production of other farm animals such as cattle, swine, and poultry. Commercial culture of these other animals would be unthinkable if the farmer were to use wild, unimproved breeds. Yet, in our ponds almost all of our fish are from wild, unimproved stock. As was recognized by

Riggs and Sneed (1959), one of the greatest needs that faces pond-culturists is a well-planned program of fish-breeding that will produce some highly efficient strains of desirable species for commercial culture.

Research on the culture of commercial fish in ponds is being conducted by the Fish and Wildlife Service of the U.S. Department of the Interior. The newly established station for commercial pond-fish culture, located in Arkansas, gives evidence of the interest that has developed in this phase of pond culture.

Culture of bait minnows

Good fishing in a million or more farm fish ponds in America has created a huge demand for baits. Streams no longer supply enough minnows, and most fishermen find it undesirable to dig worms or to catch crickets and similar baits when they are available on the market or can be raised easily for one's own use. The sale of baits has become a thriving business wherever fishing is good. In general the baits on the market may be classified as minnows for bass or other piscivorous fish, and worms and insects for bluegill and species with similar feeding habits. Only the culture of bait minnows will be discussed here.

To most fishermen a "minnow" is a small fish, whether it belongs to the Cyprinidae, the Catostomidae, or some other family. Some of the more recent papers that give instructions for culturing bait fish are Dobie *et al.* (1948), Wascko and Clark (1948), Hedges and Ball (1953), Prather *et al.* (1953), Dobie *et al.* (1956), and Forney (1955, 1957, 1958). Most of these works describe construction of spawning ponds, rearing ponds, holding ponds and tanks, and other facilities and the general phases of management including selection of species and brood stock, rates of stocking, techniques of obtaining spawning, fertilization of ponds, feeding, precautions and treatments for control of parasites and diseases, harvest, and transportation. The fish considered included one or more of the following: goldfish, golden shiner, silvery minnow, bluntnose minnow, fathead minnow, creek chub, white sucker, and lake chubsucker.

Special phases of this culture were treated in detail in other reports, some of which will be mentioned briefly. Ball and Bacon (1954) described the use of pituitary materials of carp to induce spawning of creek chub. By use of their techniques the creek chub could be stripped of viable eggs six weeks prior to normal spawning time. Prather (1957) reported results of experiments on the use of supplemental feed in the culture of golden shiners. Prather (1958, 1959a) described work with fathead minnows and presented his formulation called Auburn No. 1 Fish Feed, which contained 35% soybean oil meal, 35% peanut oil meal, 15% fish meal, and 15% distillers dried solubles. Auburn No. 2 Fish Feed, which involved slight changes and pelleting to avoid waste, was mentioned in the section on commercial fish.

By means of stocking certain numbers of fish of a given size per acre and feeding given percentages of body weight of fish per day, one can predict with fair accuracy the sizes that the fish will obtain by the date of harvest. Thus, if bait fish are to be used for bass, the management can be planned for fewer but larger minnows, whereas if they are to be used for crappie, the ponds can support larger numbers of smaller minnows and the price per minnow can be less.

Some of the earlier papers described the culture of goldfish in detail and indicated that the demand for this species was good. However, goldfish do not attract fishermen as well as they did in former years. Whether bass have changed their preference remains an unsettled question. In the Southeast, at least, most of the minnow raisers produce fewer goldfish and more golden shiners and fathead minnows.

Parasites and diseases

Parasites and diseases of fish in natural bodies of water usually go unnoticed. The populations of such waters frequently include numerous species of fish and their respective pathogens, none of which is present in great concentrations. Such conditions are not conducive to outbreaks of disease and heavy infestations of parasites. In pond culture for sport fishing on the other hand, the number of species of fish is usually reduced to one or two or at most a few, and the concentration of individuals per unit area is greatly increased. Also the exchange of water in these ponds is minimal. Such conditions provide a much better environment for development of parasites and disease organisms. The culture of minnows for bait or of commercial fish for food usually involves very high concentrations of only one

species per pond. This condition is even more ideal for the spread of parasites and diseases, and epidemics become so common that definite control measures must be practiced to prevent disaster. The more important parasites and diseases of game fish and the methods for their control are described by Davis (1956). Dobie *et al.* (1956) describe treatments for use in minnow culture.

Fish lice (*Argulus* sp.) can be controlled by application of hydrated or chlorinated lime to the ponds (Prather *et al.*, 1953) or by adding benzene hexachloride (Hindle, 1949; Thiemmedh, 1955). Control of these and other ectoparasites on individual fishes can be accomplished by acriflavine, 10 ppm $KMnO_4$, or 15 ppm formalin (Swingle, 1957a).

Control of gill flukes, *Gyrodactylus*, on the speckled variety of brown bullheads was obtained by treating an entire pond with 5.5 ppm formalin (Allison, 1957a). Potassium permanganate at a concentration of 3 ppm in a pond gave 89.4% control of the protozoan, *Trichodina* sp., on the same species of fish within 72 hours, and 4 weeks after treatment all of the fish examined were free of these parasites.

In laboratory tests Allison (1957b) found that channel catfish infested with tapeworms (*Corollobothrium fimbriatum* Essex) and flukes (*Alloglossisium corti* Lamont) were completely freed of these parasites by administering, in commercial feed, 250 mg of di-*n*-butyl tin oxide per kg of body weight of fish. Presumably this treatment could be given directly in ponds.

For control of columnaris disease, Shell (1954) determined the toxicity levels of some chemicals to the causal organism, *Chondrococcus columnaris* (Davis). From laboratory tests he selected acriflavine, malachite green, potassium permanganate, pyridylmercuric acetate, Roccal, and sulfamerazine as chemicals that were worthy of further research and possible trials in ponds. At present there seems to be no sure and safe method of controlling this disease.

Treatment of relatively small quantities of fish, such as brood stock, by dipping them for short periods in chemicals that are toxic to pathogens or by exposing fish to treatments in raceways, although ever so useful in hatcheries, are not techniques that are applicable to fish in ponds. Fish in ponds must be treated in ponds if control measures are to be effective. The treatment must be with chemicals that are readily available and are inexpensive. Since most ponds cannot be flushed out after treatment, the chemicals at concentrations used for treatments should not be deleterious to the fish or to organisms that might constitute the food chain or in other ways be of importance to the fish being treated.

Schistosome dermatitis, or swimmers' itch, in a farm pond in New York was reported by Swanson *et al.* (1960). Although this parasite causes no reduction in the fish population, it limits the usefulness of the pond by causing discomfort to swimmers. The snail involved in this instance was *Lymnaea palustris* as intermediate host for the parasite *Schistosoma douthitti*. Several other species of cercariae are known to produce swimmers' itch in America. Snails of the genera *Lymnaea, Stagnicola, Physa, Gyraulus,* and *Helisoma* may be their intermediate hosts.

Names of fishes

The following list of common names of fishes used in this chapter employs the nomenclature of species presented by Bailey *et al.* (1960). A common name for one subspecies requires its inclusion in the list.

Gizzard shad	*Dorosoma cepedianum* (LeSueur)
Threadfin shad	*Dorosoma petenense* (Günther)
Rainbow trout	*Salmo gairdneri* Richardson
Brown trout	*Salmo trutta* Linnaeus
Brook trout	*Salvelinus fontinalis* (Mitchill)
Chain pickerel	*Esox niger* LeSueur
Northern pike	*Esox lucius* Linnaeus
Goldfish	*Carassius auratus* (Linnaeus)
Carp	*Cyprinus carpio* Linnaeus
Silvery minnow	*Hybognathus nuchalis* Agassiz
Golden shiner	*Notemigonus crysoleucas* (Mitchill)
Bluntnose minnow	*Pimephales notatus* (Rafinesque)
Fathead minnow	*Pimephales promelas* Rafinesque
Creek chub	*Semotilus atromaculatus* (Mitchill)
White sucker	*Catostomus commersoni* (Lacépède)
Lake chubsucker	*Erimyzon sucetta* (Lacépède)
Smallmouth buffalo	*Ictiobus bubalus* (Rafinesque)

Bigmouth buffalo	*Ictiobus cyprinellus* (Valenciennes)
Black buffalo	*Ictiobus niger* (Rafinesque)
Black bullhead	*Ictalurus melas* (Rafinesque)
Yellow bullhead	*Ictalurus natalis* (LeSueur)
Brown bullhead	*Ictalurus nebulosus* (LeSueur)
Speckled variety of brown bullhead	*Ictalurus nebulosus marmoratus* (LeSueur)
Blue catfish	*Ictalurus furcatus* (LeSueur)
Channel catfish	*Ictalurus punctatus* (Rafinesque)
Flathead catfish	*Pylodictis olivaris* (Rafinesque)
Mosquitofish	*Gambusia affinis* (Baird and Girard)
Yellow bass	*Roccus mississippiensis* (Jordan and Evermann)
Flier	*Centrarchus macropterus* (Lacépède)
Warmouth	*Chaenobryttus gulosus* (Cuvier)
Redbreast sunfish	*Lepomis auritus* (Linnaeus)
Green sunfish	*Lepomis cyanellus* Rafinesque
Pumpkinseed	*Lepomis gibbosus* (Linnaeus)
Orangespotted sunfish	*Lepomis humilis* (Girard)
Bluegill	*Lepomis macrochirus* Rafinesque
Redear sunfish	*Lepomis microlophus* (Günther)
Redeye bass	*Micropterus coosae* Hubbs and Bailey
Smallmouth bass	*Micropterus dolomieu* Lacépède
Largemouth bass	*Micropterus salmoides* (Lacépède)
White crappie	*Pomoxis annularis* Rafinesque
Black crappie	*Pomoxis nigromaculatus* (LeSueur)
Yellow perch	*Perca flavescens* (Mitchill)
Striped mullet	*Mugil cephalus* Linnaeus

Species of the cichlid genus, *Tilapia*, had no common name in this country prior to the recent introductions. The names applied are descriptive of the source of the stock imported or of the source as indicated by specific name.

Java tilapia	*Tilapia mossambica* Peters
Nile tilapia	*Tilapia nilotica* Linnaeus

References

ALLISON, RAY. 1957a. Some new results in the treatment of ponds to control some external parasites of fish. Progr. Fish-Cult., 19: 58–63.

———. 1957b. A preliminary note on the use of di-n-butyl tin oxide to remove tapeworms from fish. Progr. Fish-Cult., 19: 128–130. Literature cited, Progr. Fish-Cult., 19: 192.

ATKINSON, W. S. 1949. How to build a farm pond. U.S. Dept. Agr. Leaflet 259. U.S. Govt. Printing Office, Washington, 8 p.

BAILEY, R. M., ERNEST LACHNER, C. C. LINDSEY, C. R. ROBINS, P. M. ROEDEL, W. B. SCOTT, AND L. P. WOODS. 1960. A list of common and scientific names of fishes from the United States and Canada. 2nd ed. Amer. Fish. Soc., Spec. Publ. No. 2, Ann Arbor, Michigan, 102 p.

BALL, R. C. 1949. Experimental use of fertilizer in the production of fish-food organisms and fish. Michigan State Coll. Agr. Expt. Sta., Sect. of Zool., Tech. Bull. 210, 28 p.

———. 1952. Farm pond management in Michigan, p. 266–269. *In* Symposium on farm fish ponds and management, J. Wildl. Mgmt., 16: 233–288.

BALL, R. C., AND E. H. BACON. 1954. Use of pituitary material in the propagation of minnows. Progr. Fish-Cult., 16: 108–113.

BALL, R. C., AND H. A. TANNER. 1951. The biological effects of fertilizer on a warm-water lake. Michigan State Coll. Agr. Expt. Sta., Sect. of Zool., Tech. Bull. 223, 32 p.

BARNICKOL, P. G., AND R. S. CAMPBELL. 1952. Summary of selected pond studies in Missouri, p. 270–274. *In* Symposium on farm fish ponds and management, J. Wildl. Mgmt., 16: 233–288.

BENNETT, G. W. 1943. Management of small artificial lakes, a summary of fisheries investigations 1938–42. Illinois Nat. Hist. Surv. Bull., 22 (Article 3): 357–376.

———. 1948. Review of *Fish Ponds for the Farm* by Frank C. Edminster. J. Wildl. Mgmt., 12: 215–217.

———. 1954. Largemouth bass in Ridge Lake, Coles County, Illinois. Illinois Nat. Hist. Surv. Bull., 26 (Article 2): 217–276.

BENNETT, G. W., AND LEONARD DURHAM. 1951. Cost of bass fishing at Ridge Lake, Coles County, Illinois. Illinois Nat. Hist. Surv., Biol. Notes No. 23: 1–16.

BORELL, A. E., AND P. M. SCHEFFER. 1961. Trout in farm and ranch ponds. U.S. Dept. Agr. Soil Conserv. Serv., Farmers' Bull. 2154. U.S. Govt. Printing Office, Washington, 18 p.

BRADY, LEE, AND ANDREW HULSEY. 1959. Propagation of buffalo fishes. Southeastern Assoc. Game and Fish Comm., Proc. 13th Ann. Conf.: 80–90.

BROWN, C. J. D., AND N. A. THORESON. 1952. Ranch fish ponds in Montana, p. 275–278. *In* Symposium on farm fish ponds and management, J. Wildl. Mgmt., 16: 233–288.

BROWN, C. J. D., AND NELS THORESON. 1958. Ranch fish ponds in Montana, their construction and management. Montana Agr. Expt. Sta., Bull. 544, Montana State Coll., Bozeman, 26 p.

BROWN, L. N. 1958. Small earth dams. California Agr. Expt. Sta. Extension Service, Circ. 467, Berkeley, 21 p.

BRUMSTED, H. B. 1960. Stocking farm fish ponds. New York State Coll. Agr., Cornell Extension Bull. 1046, Ithaca, 4 p.

BRYNILDSON, C. L., AND J. R. TRUOG. 1959. Fish management of Wisconsin farm ponds. Wisconsin Conserv. Bull., 24(11): 1–4.

BYRD, I. B. 1959. Angling success and seasonal distribution of catch in Alabama State-owned public fishing lakes. Trans. 24th N. Amer. Wildl. Conf.: 225–237.

CARLANDER, K. D. 1952. Farm fish pond research in Iowa, p. 258–261. *In* Symposium on farm fish ponds and management, J. Wildl. Mgmt., 16: 233–288.

CARLANDER, K. D., AND R. B. MOORMAN. 1956. Standing crop of fish in Iowa ponds. Proc. Iowa Acad. Sci., 63: 659–668.

CLARK, MINOR. 1952. Kentucky's farm fish pond program, p. 262–266. *In* Symposium on farm fish ponds and management, J. Wildl. Mgmt., 16: 233–288.

COBB, E. S. 1952. The use of fish traps in the management of farm ponds. M.S. Thesis, Alabama Polytech. Inst., 56 p.

COMPTON, L. V. 1952. Farm and ranch ponds, p. 238–242. *In* Symposium on farm fish ponds and management, J. Wildl. Mgmt., 16: 233–288.

COOPER, E. L. 1955. Small ponds for fishing. Wisconsin Conserv. Bull., 20(1): 26–29.

CORNELL UNIVERSITY, DEPARTMENT OF CONSERVATION. 1959. A trap for harvesting bluegills in New York farm ponds. Wildlife Mimeo. 16, 2 p.

DAVIS, H. S. 1956. Culture and diseases of game fishes. Univ. California Press, Berkeley. 332 p.

DAVISON, V. E. 1953. Homemade fishing. Bass and trout waters you can build yourself. Stackpole Co., Harrisburg, Pennsylvania. 205 p.

DOBIE, JOHN, O. L. MEEHEAN, S. F. SNIESZKO, AND G. N. WASHBURN. 1956. Raising bait fishes. U.S. Dept. Interior, Fish and Wildl. Serv., Circ. 35, 123 p.

DOBIE, J. R., O. L. MEEHEAN, AND G. N. WASHBURN. 1948. Propagation of minnows and other bait species. U.S. Dept. Interior, Fish and Wildl. Serv., Circ. 12, 113 p.

DUGAN, R. F. 1951. Fish production records on some West Virginia farm ponds. Trans. 16th N. Amer. Wildl. Conf.: 403–421.

DYCHE, L. L. 1914. Ponds, pond fish, and pondfish culture. State Dept. Fish and Game, Kansas State Printing Office, Topeka. 208 p.

EDMINSTER, F. C. 1947. Fish ponds for the farm. Charles Scribner's Sons, New York. 114 p.

EIPPER, A. W. 1960. Managing farm ponds for trout production. New York State Coll. Agr., Cornell Extension Bull. 1036, Ithaca, 29 p.

EIPPER, A. W., AND H. B. BRUMSTED. 1959. How to control weeds and algae in farm ponds. New

York State Coll. Agr., Cornell Extension Bull. 1014, Ithaca, 31 p.

EMBODY, G. C. 1915. The farm fish pond. Cornell Reading Courses, Country Life Ser. 3, 4(94): 213–252.

FORNEY, J. L. 1955. The bait fish business. New York Conserv., Dec.-Jan. 1954–55: 25–27.

———. 1957. Bait fish production in New York ponds. New York Fish and Game J., 4: 150–194.

———. 1958. Raising bait fish and crayfish in New York ponds. New York State Coll. Agr., Cornell Extension Bull. 986, Ithaca, 30 p.

HALL, J. F. 1959. Final report on the success of largemouth bass-bluegill and largemouth bass-shellcracker rates and ratios in Kentucky farm ponds. Southeastern Assoc. Game and Fish Comm., Proc. 12th Ann. Conf. (1958), Contrib. 116: 91–116.

HANSEN, D. F., G. W. BENNETT, R. J. WEBB, AND J. M. LEWIS. 1960. Hook-and-line catch in fertilized and unfertilized ponds. Illinois Nat. Hist. Surv. Bull., 27 (Article 5): 345–390.

HEDGES, S. B., AND R. C. BALL. 1953. Production and harvest of bait fishes in ponds. Michigan Dept. Conserv., Inst. Fish. Research, Misc. Publ. 6, 30 p.

HENDRICKS, L. J. 1956. Growth of smallmouth buffalo in carp ponds. Progr. Fish-Cult., 18: 45–46.

HESTER, F. E. 1959. The tolerance of eight species of warm-water fishes to certain rotenone formulations. Southeastern Assoc. Game and Fish Comm., Proc. 13th Ann. Conf.: 121–133.

HINDLE, E. 1949. Notes on the treatment of fish infected with *Argulus*. Proc. Zool. Soc. (London), 119: 79–81.

HOLTON, H. N. 1950. Holding water in farm ponds. U.S. Dept. Agr., Soil Conserv. Serv., in cooperation with Virginia Agr. Expt. Sta., SCS-TP-93, 10 p.

HOOPER, A. D., AND J. H. CRANCE. 1960. Use of rotenone in restoring balance to overcrowded fish populations in Alabama lakes. Trans. Amer. Fish. Soc., 89: 351–357.

HOWELL, H. H. 1942. Bottom organisms in fertilized and unfertilized fish ponds in Alabama. Trans. Amer. Fish. Soc., 71: 165–179.

IRWIN, W. H. 1945. Methods of precipitating colloidal soil particles from impounded waters of central Oklahoma. Oklahoma Agr. Mech. Coll. Bull., 42(11): 1–16.

IRWIN, W. H., AND J. H. STEVENSON. 1951. Physico-chemical nature of clay turbidity with special reference to clarification and productivity of impounded waters. Oklahoma Agr. Mech. Coll. Bull., Arts and Sci. Studies, Biol. Series, 48(4): 1–54.

JOHNSON, M. C. 1959. Food-fish farming in the Mississippi Delta. Progr. Fish-Cult., 21: 154–160.

JOHNSON, M. C., AND J. R. FIELDING. 1956. Propagation of the white shrimp, *Penaeus setiferus* (Linn.), in captivity. Tulane Studies Zool., 4: 175–190.

KEETON, DEE. 1959. Limnological effects of introducing oil field brine into farm ponds to reduce

turbidity. Oklahoma Fish. Research Lab., Norman, Rept. 72, 47 p.

KELLY, H. D. 1957. Preliminary studies on *Tilapia mossambica* Peters relative to experimental pond culture. Southeastern Assoc. Game and Fish Comm., Proc. 10th Ann. Conf. 139–149.

KRUMHOLZ, L. A. 1950a. Indiana ponds, their construction and management for fishing. Indiana Dept. Conserv., Lake and Stream Surv., Div. Fish and Game, and Indiana Univ., 35 p.

———. 1950b. New fish stocking policies for Indiana ponds. Trans. 15th N. Amer. Wildl. Conf.: 251–270.

———. 1952. Management of Indiana ponds for fishing, p. 254–257. In Symposium on farm fish ponds and management, J. Wildl. Mgmt., 16: 233–288.

LAWRENCE, F. B. 1950. The digestive enzymes of the bluegill bream, *Lepomis macrochirus* Raf. M.S. Thesis, Alabama Polytech. Inst., 46 p.

LAWRENCE, J. M. 1943. The effects of ground dolomitic limestone on fish production and plankton production in ponds. M.S. Thesis, Alabama Polytech. Inst., 40 p.

———. 1949. Construction of farm fish ponds. Alabama Polytech. Inst., Agr. Expt. Sta., Circ. 95, 55 p.

———. 1954a. Control of a branched alga, *Pithophora*, in farm ponds. Progr. Fish-Cult., 16: 83–86.

———. 1954b. A new method of applying inorganic fertilizer to farm fishponds. Progr. Fish-Cult., 16: 176–178.

———. 1956. Preliminary results on the use of potassium permanganate to counteract the effects of rotenone on fish. Southeastern Assoc. Game and Fish Comm., Proc. 9th Ann. Conf.: 87–92.

———. 1958a. Methods for controlling aquatic weeds in fish ponds with emphasis on use of chemicals. Alabama Polytech. Inst., Agr. Expt. Sta., Progr. Rept. Ser. 69, 8 p.

———. 1958b. Recent investigations on the use of sodium arsenite as an algicide and its effects on fish production in ponds. Southeastern Assoc. Game and Fish Comm., Proc. 11th Ann. Conf.: 281–287.

McCARRAHER, D. B. 1959. The northern pike-bluegill combination in north-central Nebraska farm ponds. Progr. Fish-Cult., 21: 188–189.

McCRIMMON, H. R. 1961. A review of farm trout ponds in southern Ontario. Canadian Comm. on Freshwater Fish. Research, Ottawa. Mimeo. January 1961 meeting, 7 p.

MACIOLEK, J. A. 1954. Artificial fertilization of lakes and ponds. A review of the literature. U.S. Dept. Interior, Fish and Wildl. Serv., Spec. Sci. Rept., Fish. 113, 41 p.

MOORMAN, R. B. 1957. Some factors related to success of fish populations in Iowa farm ponds. Trans. Amer. Fish. Soc., 86: 361–370.

NEESS, J. C. 1949. Development and status of pond fertilization in central Europe. Trans. Amer. Fish. Soc., 76: 335–358.

NELSON, BEN. 1957. Propagation of channel catfish

in Arkansas. Southeastern Assoc. Game and Fish Comm., Proc. 10th Ann. Conf.: 165–166.

PHILLIPS, A. M., JR., AND D. R. BROCKWAY. 1959. Dietary calories and the production of trout in hatcheries. Progr. Fish-Cult., **21**: 3–16.

PRATHER, E. E. 1957. Experiments on the commercial production of golden shiners. Southeastern Assoc. Game and Fish Comm., Proc. 10th Ann. Conf.: 150–155.

———. 1958. Preliminary experiments on winter feeding small fathead minnows. Southeastern Assoc. Game and Fish Comm., Proc. 11th Ann. Conf.: 249–253.

———. 1959a. Further experiments on feeds for fathead minnows. Southeastern Assoc. Game and Fish Comm., Proc. 12th Ann. Conf.: 176–178.

———. 1959b. The use of channel catfish as sport fish. Southeastern Assoc. Game and Fish Comm., Proc. 13th Ann. Conf.: 331–335.

PRATHER, E. E., J. R. FIELDING, M. C. JOHNSON, AND H. S. SWINGLE. 1953. Production of bait minnows in the Southeast. Alabama Polytech. Inst., Agr. Expt. Sta., Circ. 112, 71 p.

RAWSON, D. S., AND R. A. RUTTON. 1952. Pond fish studies in Saskatchewan, p. 283–288. *In* Symposium on farm fish ponds and management, J. Wildl. Mgmt., **16**: 233–288.

RICKER, W. E. 1945. Natural mortalities among Indiana bluegill sunfish. Ecology, **26**: 111–121.

———. 1958. Handbook of computations for biological statistics of fish populations. Fish. Research Board Canada, Nanaimo, B.C. 300 p.

RIGGS, C. D., AND K. E. SNEED. 1959. The effects of controlled spawning and genetic selection on the fish culture of the future. Trans. Amer. Fish. Soc., **88**: 53–57.

SAILA, S. B. 1952. Some results of farm pond management studies in New York, p. 279–282. *In* Symposium on farm fish ponds and management, J. Wildl. Mgmt., **16**: 233–288.

SHELL, E. W. 1954. Columnaris disease in warmwater fish and lethal toxicity levels of some chemicals to the causal organism, *Chondrococcus columnaris* (Davis). M.S. Thesis, Alabama Polytech. Inst., 63 p.

SMITH, E. V., AND H. S. SWINGLE. 1939. The relationships between plankton production and fish production in ponds. Trans. Amer. Fish. Soc., **68**: 309–315.

SMITH, E. V., AND H. S. SWINGLE. 1941a. The use of fertilizer for controlling the pond-weed *Najas guadalupensis*. Trans. 6th N. Amer. Wildl. Conf.: 245–251.

SMITH, E. V., AND H. S. SWINGLE. 1941b. Control of spatterdock (*Nuphar advena* Ait.) in ponds. Trans. Amer. Fish. Soc., **70**: 363–368.

SMITH, E. V., AND H. S. SWINGLE. 1943. Organic materials as fertilizers for fish ponds. Trans. Amer. Fish. Soc., **72**: 97–102.

SMITH, E. V., AND H. S. SWINGLE. 1944. Ponds for improving stream fishing. Alabama Polytech. Inst., Agr. Expt. Sta., Leaflet 20, 7 p.

SNOW, J. R. 1948. A preliminary study of the tox-icity of 2,4-D to pond fishes and its effectiveness in the control of emergent species of pond weeds. M.S. Thesis, Alabama Polytech. Inst., 87 p.

———. 1958. A preliminary report on the comparative testing of some of the newer herbicides. Southeastern Assoc. Game and Fish Comm., Proc. 11th Ann. Conf.: 125–132.

STOCKDALE, T. M. 1960. Farm pond management. Ohio State Univ., Agr. Extension Serv., Bull. 374 (Revised 1960), 21 p.

SURBER, E. W. 1949. Control of aquatic plants in ponds and lakes. U.S. Dept. Interior, Fish and Wildl. Serv., Fish. Leaflet 344, 20 p.

SWANSON, GUSTAV, H. R. ERICKSON, AND J. S. MACKIEWICZ. 1960. Swimmers' itch in farm ponds in New York State. New York Fish and Game J., **7**: 77–79.

SWINGLE, H. S. 1938. Construction of farm ponds. Alabama Polytech. Inst., Agr. Expt. Sta. Mimeo., 5 p.

———. 1945. Improvement of fishing in old ponds. Trans. 10th N. Amer. Wildl. Conf.: 299–308.

———. 1946. Construction of farm ponds. Alabama Polytech. Inst., Agr. Expt. Sta., Progr. Rept. Ser. 8, 4 p.

———. 1947. Experiments on pond fertilization. Alabama Polytech. Inst., Agr. Expt. Sta., Bull. 264, 34 p.

———. 1949. Experiments with combinations of largemouth black bass, bluegills, and minnows in ponds. Trans. Amer. Fish. Soc., **76**: 46–62.

———. 1950. Relationships and dynamics of balanced and unbalanced fish populations. Alabama Polytech. Inst., Agr. Expt. Sta., Bull. 274, 73 p.

———. 1951a. Impounding water for irrigation. Alabama Polytech. Inst., Agr. Expt. Sta., Proc. Ann. Staff Conf.: 105–115.

———. 1951b. Experiments with various rates of stocking bluegills, *Lepomis macrochirus* Rafinesque, and largemouth bass, *Micropterus salmoides* (Lacépède), in ponds. Trans. Amer. Fish. Soc., **80**: 218–230.

———. 1952. Farm pond investigations in Alabama, p. 243–249. *In* Symposium on farm fish ponds and management, J. Wildl. Mgmt., **16**: 233–288.

———. 1954. Experiments on commercial fish production in ponds. Southeastern Assoc. Game and Fish Comm., Proc. 7th Ann. Conf.: 69–74.

———. 1956a. Appraisal of methods of fish population study. IV. Determination of balance in farm fish ponds. Trans. 21st N. Amer. Wildl. Conf.: 298–322.

———. 1956b. A repressive factor controlling reproduction in fishes. Proc. 8th Pac. Sci. Congr., 8(1953). Vol. IIIA: 865–871: Oceanogr. and Zool. Natl. Research Council of the Philippines, Univ. Philippines, Diliman, Quezon City.

———. 1957a. Commercial production of red cats (speckled bullheads) in ponds. Southeastern Assoc. Game and Fish Comm., Proc. 10th Ann. Conf.: 156–160.

———. 1957b. Preliminary results on the commercial production of channel catfish in ponds. Southeastern Assoc. Game and Fish Comm., Proc. 10th Ann. Conf.: 160–162.

———. 1957c. Revised procedures for commercial production of bigmouth buffalo fish in ponds in the Southeast. Southeastern Assoc. Game and Fish Comm., Proc. 10th Ann. Conf.: 162–165.

———. 1957d. Control of pond weeds by the use of herbivorous fishes. Southern Weed Conf., 10: 11–17.

———. 1959. Experiments on growing fingerling channel catfish to marketable size in ponds. Southeastern Assoc. Game and Fish Comm., Proc. 12th Ann. Conf.: 63–72.

———. 1960. Comparative evaluation of two tilapias as pond fishes in Alabama. Trans. Amer. Fish. Soc., 89: 142–148.

SWINGLE, H. S., E. E. PRATHER, AND J. M. LAWRENCE. 1953. Partial poisoning of overcrowded fish populations. Alabama Polytech. Inst., Agr. Expt. Sta., Circ. 113, 15 p.

SWINGLE, H. S., AND E. V. SMITH. 1938. Management of farm fish ponds. Alabama Polytech. Inst., Agr. Expt. Sta. Mimeo., 6 p.

SWINGLE, H. S., AND E. V. SMITH. 1939a. Fertilizers for increasing the natural food for fish in ponds. Trans. Amer. Fish. Soc., 68: 126–135.

SWINGLE, H. S., AND E. V. SMITH. 1939b. Increasing fish production in ponds. Trans. 4th N. Amer. Wildl. Conf.: 332–338.

SWINGLE, H. S., AND E. V. SMITH. 1941a. Experiments on stocking of fish ponds. Trans. 5th N. Amer. Wildl. Conf.: 267–276.

SWINGLE, H. S., AND E. V. SMITH. 1941b. The management of ponds for the production of game and pan fish, p. 218–226. In Symposium on hydrobiology. Univ. Wisconsin Press, Madison. 405 p.

SWINGLE, H. S., AND E. V. SMITH. 1942. The management of ponds with stunted fish populations. Trans. Amer. Fish. Soc., 71: 102–105.

SWINGLE, H. S., AND E. V. SMITH. 1943a. Factors affecting the reproduction of bluegill bream and largemouth black bass in ponds. Alabama Polytech. Inst., Agr. Expt. Sta., Circ. 87, 8 p.

SWINGLE, H. S., AND E. V. SMITH. 1943b. Effect of management practices on the catch in a 12-acre pond during a 10-year period. Trans. 8th N. Amer. Wildl. Conf.: 141–155.

SWINGLE, H. S., AND E. V. SMITH. 1947. Management of farm fish ponds. Alabama Polytech. Inst., Agr. Expt. Sta., Bull. 254, 30 p.

THIEMMEDH, JINDA. 1955. The effect of BHC (Lexone 10-GW, gamma isomer of benzene hexachloride) on fish food organisms and fish production in ponds. M.S. Thesis, Alabama Polytech. Inst., 42 p.

THOMPSON, D. H., AND G. W. BENNETT. 1939. Fish management in small artificial lakes. Trans. 4th N. Amer. Wildl. Conf.: 311–317.

TIEMEIER, O. W., SETH WAY, AND ROY SCHOONOVER. 1954. Construction and management of Kansas ponds. Forestry, Fish and Game Comm., Pratt, Kansas, Bull. 9, 35 p.

TOWNSEND, C. H. 1907. The cultivation of fishes in small ponds. Trans. Amer. Fish. Soc., 36: 128–139.

———. 1914. The private fish pond—a neglected resource. Trans. Amer. Fish. Soc., 43: 87–92.

U.S. DEPARTMENT OF AGRICULTURE, SOIL CONSERVATION SERVICE. 1957. Water rights and soil and water conservation. U.S. Dept. Agr., Soil Conserv. Serv., PA-306, 8 p.

———. 1958. Engineering handbook for work unit staffs. 9. Farm ponds. 60 p.

WALKER, C. R. 1959. Control of certain aquatic weeds in Missouri farm ponds. Weeds, 7: 310–316.

WASCKO, HAROLD, AND C. F. CLARK. 1948. Pond propagation of bluntnose and blackhead minnows. Ohio Div. Conserv. Nat. Resources, Wildl. Conserv. Bull. 4, 16 p.

WINKELBLECH, C. S. 1958. Farm ponds in New York. New York State Coll. Agr., Cornell Extension Bull. 949, 32 p.

ZELLER, H. D., AND A. B. MONTGOMERY. 1958. Preliminary investigations of chemical soil and water relationships and lime treatment of soft water in Georgia farm ponds. Southeastern Assoc. Game and Fish Comm., Proc. 11th Ann. Conf.: 71–76.

23 | *W. H. Bradley*

Paleolimnology

A prime objective of paleolimnology is to illuminate the evolutionary stages through which a lake has passed. The sequence must be established by inference from the stratigraphic record and fleshed out by further inference from the chemical and mineralogical composition of the sediments and from the remains of organisms found in them. Lacustrine sediments and all that they contain, as Deevey (1955, p. 11) aptly says, "document ontogeny" of the lake. This recognizes that as long as a lake persists, it undergoes change. Perhaps the simplest manifestation of this is the fact that the morphometry of a lake changes progressively as its sediments accumulate and as the earth's crust deforms. But always in the evolution of a lake or of any geomorphic feature, there is a tendency to come to equilibrium with the controlling factors of climate and deformation of the earth's crust. And these two dynamic factors are themselves influenced by the antecedent geologic history, that is, by the structure and composition of the terrain. Our objective, however, is really broader than just being able to reconstruct the history of a lake in terms of its stages and typology. We should also try to reconstruct the paleoclimate and the hydrography and physical geography of the surrounding terrain. These are desirable objectives partly because it is commonly possible to deduce them from the evidence available and partly because they improve our understanding of any extinct lake. But perhaps our most important objective should be to quantify dimensions and the rates at which events took place, the amounts

of substances grown, moved, or fixed, the concentrations of dissolved substances, and, if at all possible, the magnitude of the forces involved.

As a matter of historical interest, perhaps the earliest paleolimnological work in the United States was done by G. K. Gilbert (1891). This was an elaborate study and reconstruction of Pleistocene Lake Bonneville, the ancestor of the present Great Salt Lake of Utah. The fact that this classical investigation was prompted by a desire to understand the geologic history and the fact that it turned out to be also a classic in paleolimnology illustrate how smoothly geology grades into limnology along the path of paleolimnology. The reaction is, of course, completely reversible.

Lake Bonneville, at its maximum stage, was a large freshwater lake with an area of 19,750 mi^2 and a maximum depth of 1,050 ft. Gilbert considered its morphometry, hydrography, the organisms that lived in it, and the sediments it laid down. Long sections of his monograph have more the flavor of limnology than of geology, though the terminology is simpler than it would be today.

Closely parallel in time and scope was I. C. Russell's study (1885) of Lake Lahontan, another large Pleistocene lake in western Nevada. Russell's work actually followed that of Gilbert but was published six years earlier. After these two comprehensive studies comparatively little that could be thought of as paleolimnology was done for several decades.

In trying to reconstruct the history of an extinct lake, one must adjust to the hard fact that virtually all the evidence is fragmentary. All interpretations draw heavily on inference and

Publication authorized by the Director, U.S. Geological Survey.

analogy. The facts that we have come from observing and measuring stratigraphic sections of the layered rocks that were laid down as muds in the ancient lake. Such sections depend on accidents of erosion, though, if we are fortunate, there may also be cores taken from holes drilled usually, but not always, for another purpose.

We have, in sum, four means by which we can interpret the more or less lithified representatives of muds deposited in an ancient lake: (1) analogy with known geologic processes, (2) inference that the fossil organisms lived in the same kinds of environment as their living counterparts do now, (3) analogy with the limnology and sediments of existing lakes, and (4) inferences drawn from the chemical composition and mineralogy of the sediments, particularly the authigenic minerals. These means are used singly or in any combination that seems most likely to be useful. Controlled speculation is as necessary as it is for a detective.

Paleolimnological interpretations of a number of extinct lakes are summarized from published accounts or from information furnished by the authors prior to publication of fuller reports. They are arranged according to their geologic ages, the oldest coming first. Included are results only of investigations in which the author made an appreciable effort to interpret a lake's history.

Permian—Wellington Formation

Attempts to reconstruct the limnology of any freshwater deposits in Paleozoic rocks in the United States, as far as I know, are restricted to one very brief account given by Tasch and Zimmerman (1961). They found a considerable number of localities in the outcrop belt of the Wellington Formation that contain identifiable remains of pemphicycliid, estheriid, and leaiid conchostracans. Having found these, which are of Permian age (*ca.* 260 million years: Kulp, 1961), they set about an elucidation of the paleolimnology by making a comparative study of the living Conchostraca in the same area (Central Kansas and the adjacent part of Oklahoma) and the limnological environments in which they lived. About 12% of the 550 ponds examined contained conchostracans. *Cyzicus mexicanus* (Claus) was the only species common to all.

They concluded on the basis of a comparative study of the sediments and phyllopods in the ancient and present-day environments that the Permian ponds were temporary, free from currents, that the bottoms of the ponds consisted of limy clay, and that the water was probably very shallow. They inferred, further, that the water in these ancient ponds was probably turbid a good part of the time because the mineral particles enclosing the fossils are so very fine grained. As in the modern ponds, there was little evidence of submerged or emergent plants, though the authors found charophytes and spores [*sic*] associated with some of the fossil Conchostraca. In other parts of the formation there are abundant plant remains. The shallowness of some of the Permian ponds is indicated by the fact that the valves of these minute animals are numerous in some of the mud-cracked beds. Not all the Permian ponds, however, were small, because conchostracan shells were found continuously for many hundred feet along some strata.

Although Tasch and Zimmerman found no Conchostraca in brackish waters of modern ponds, they did find gypsum and casts of salt crystals in the conchostracan beds of Permian age. Associated with the fossil phyllopods were remains of aquatic insects—Odonata (both damselflies and dragonflies), Ephemeroptera, and Neuroptera. They also found, as fossils, several leaf hoppers.

Jurassic—Todilto Limestone

Geology and geography

The paleolimnology and history of a very large lake of Late Jurassic age (*ca.* 135 million years ago: Kulp, 1961) that once existed in northwestern New Mexico, southwestern Colorado, and northeastern Arizona has lately been published by Anderson and Kirkland (1960).

The sediments laid down in this ancient lake are known as the Todilto Limestone, which consists of a thin, very extensive limestone member 7 to 8 ft thick (though locally around the margins it is about twice as thick) and an overlying massive gypsum member that is generally 70–100 ft thick. This formation rests on clean sand of the Entrada Sandstone, largely of eolian origin, and is overlain by the fluviatile sediments of the Morrison Formation. The limestone of the lower member is dark, fetid, and characterized by its paper-thin laminations, which are annual and therefore varves. This varved limestone grades upward into the overlying gypsum member. Although the gypsum member appears to be massive, actually it contains, through its entire thickness, thin limestone laminae that are broken and twisted almost beyond recognition.

On the basis of the varves the authors estimate that the limestone was deposited in about 14,000 years and the gypsum member in about 6,000 years, making the total life of the lake only 20,000 years.

Nothing is said about how this lake basin came into existence, but considering its great area (approximately 34,600 mi²), it can hardly be ascribed to anything but a broad crustal downwarp.

Anderson and Kirkland made a critical study of the varves in the sediments deposited in the ancient lake and based their reconstruction of the lake, its limnology, and hydrography very largely on the characteristics and composition of the varved sediments. But they also used the fossil fish fauna to good advantage and discussed the one species of ostracod found. Analogy with existing lakes is used only a little.

Hydrography and climate

Their map (Fig. 23.1) shows the outline of the lake at its maximum extent and during the restricted second stage (about 12,000 mi²) when the gypsum member was deposited. Also shown are highlands and mountains, areas of low relief, and inferred streams. I have connected the headwaters of those hypothetical streams with a dashed line and find that the area so enclosed is about 150,000 mi². This is probably an unwarranted extrapolation from the authors' already speculative stream pattern, but it is interesting to see that, if this were the area of the hydrographic basin, the lake at its maximum occupied about 23%. Anderson and Kirkland's map shows the lake as closed even at the maximum stage. Since there is no evidence of salts other than CaCO₃ during the limestone-depositing stage, one wonders if the lake might not have overflowed intermittently even though it lost most of its income through evaporation.

The following line of reasoning leads them to some reasonable inferences about the climate of the area during the maximum stage of the lake: from the varves they know that on the average 0.127 mm of CaCO₃ was deposited each year and that the area of limestone deposition (equivalent to the area of the lake) was *ca.* 34,600 mi²,

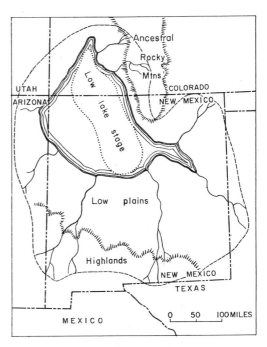

Fig. 23.1.—Dashed line shows the inferred outline of the hydrographic basin; full line, the maximum extent of the Todilto lake and the inferred streams; dotted line shows the low lake extent when gypsum deposited. Modified and redrawn from Anderson and Kirkland, *Bull. Amer. Assoc. Petrol. Geol.*, 1960.

and assuming the streams had on the average the same CaCO₃ content as the present-day streams crossing Permian and Triassic formations in that area and assuming a closed lake, they calculate the volume of stream water of that composition needed to yield that much CaCO₃ annually. The water lost by evaporation comes out to 86 in. a year. Then, because the arid regions today where the evaporation losses from free water surfaces are 80–90 in. have average summer temperatures of about 85° F and average winter temperatures of about 57° F, they assume that these are reasonable temperatures for Todilto time. "The climate was probably arid-subtropical, somewhat like the climate in the interior of southern California today. The basin itself was arid around its margin and was fed by rivers with their headwaters in distant moist uplands." From analyses of cyclic variations in the thickness of the varves they conclude that, "Intervals of warm dry climate alternated with intervals of cooler temperature and probably increased moisture about every 180 years. At other times the

TABLE 23.1

Composition of stream water (ppm) in southern New Mexico. After Anderson and Kirkland, 1960.

Ionic concentration		Molecular concentration	
Ca	363	$CaCO_3$	158
HCO_3	192	$CaSO_4$	1,260
SO_4	1,296		

warm and cool alternations occurred at 60-year intervals."

The lake and its varved deposits

Each varve in the limestone member consists of a lamina of $CaCO_3$, a lamina of organic matter, and a lamina of clastic mineral particles. Anderson and Kirkland believe, with sound reasons, that the carbonate particles were precipitated from the lake water by summer warming of the water and by photosynthesis of the phytoplankton. Nipkow (1920, p. 116), to my knowledge, was the first to recognize that the photosynthesis of the spring plankton algae in Zürichsee caused precipitation of calcite particles from the surface waters and that these formed a distinct carbonate lamina each year in the bottom sediments. He also recognized that the organic particles, derived from the plankton during the spring, summer, and autumn, sank more slowly all through the rest of the year and made up an organic-rich lamina, which overlay the carbonate lamina. Nipkow demonstrated most convincingly that such pairs of laminae are annual and can be used for dating events in the history of a lake. Minder (1923) confirmed these findings. In a very detailed study of the sediments of Faulenseemoos near Spiez, Welten (1944) showed that the calcareous member of each varve is produced in the spring and early summer by the vernal bloom of plankton, and Frey (1961) found this to be so likewise in Schleinsee.

The organic laminae (average thickness 8 μ) were derived very largely from the partial decay of plankton organisms, though each organic lamina examined microscopically contained carbonized fragments of tracheids and fibers of vascular plants. Anderson and Kirkland believe the sapropelic sediment was preserved in a relatively cool hypolimnion of a lake stratified both thermally and chemically where the water was charged with hydrogen sulfide and much $CaCO_3$ was held in solution, in other words, in a meromictic lake.

They remark, "The toxic environment probably accounts for the almost complete absence of fossils in the limestone. The same conditions, on the other hand, resulted in the excellent preservation of fossil fishes found at several localities around the edge of the basin." I can reinforce this with evidence from the Eocene Green River Formation and its world-famous fossil fish: the well-preserved fish are found only in varved sediments; others that settled to the bottom above the chemocline, and therefore are in non-varved sediments, were torn to pieces and scattered by scavengers.

The very thin, discontinuous laminae of clastic particles represent material brought in as wind-blown dust and stream-borne particles. Since these overlie the organic laminae, they must have come in during the spring of each year. This assumes that it took all winter for the particles of organic matter to settle to the bottom and that the clastic particles arrived just before the spring plankton bloom began to precipitate particles of calcite. The clastic and calcite laminae are reciprocally related: if one is thick, the other is thin.

After about 14,000 years of this kind of deposition, calcium sulfate began to deposit. Then for about 3,000 years each annual deposit consisted of a calcite lamina followed by a gypsum lamina. Both organic matter and clastic particles are also present, but their sequential relationship to the better defined calcite and gypsum laminae is obscure.

Anderson and Kirkland believe the lake received most of its salts from streams that crossed the sulfate-rich Permian and Triassic formations exposed south, southeast, and southwest of the lake. The ancient streams probably carried the same salts and at a concentration comparable with modern streams, as shown in Table 23.1.

They do not interpret the transitional sequence of beds between the varved limestone member and the gypsum member in terms of lake stage, but it seems to me to indicate that the lake had already become permanently closed before the end of the varved limestone stage and had become so concentrated that during part of each year, presumably in the winter, calcium sulfate precipitated. Also, because the organic matter became progressively less during this stage and because it is not always clearly segregated into laminae, the lake probably was becoming shallower by thinning of the mixolimnion. Surely by the time calcium sulfate became the dominant sediment, the mixolimnion must have been reduced to a seasonal flooding with a sheet of fresher water that evaporated or mixed into the chemocline before the year was over.

During the gypsum stage the lake deposited each year a lamina of calcite (*ca.* 0.25 mm thick) that contained so much organic matter it was dark brown and a much thicker lamina of gypsum (average, *ca.* 5.8 mm thick). Mixed with the gypsum and limestone were the clastic particles in about the same absolute amount as in the varved limestone. During this gypsum-depositing stage, sediments accumulated about 50 times as rapidly as the varved limestone. At this stage the area of the lake was only about one-third that of its maximum extent.

At the top of the gypsum member of the Todilto Limestone are about 40 ft of beds that are transitional into the overlying fluviatile Morrison Formation. These beds consist of an alternation of gypsum layers that average about 10 cm thick, and red, reddish-brown, and green shale layers that range in thickness· from a few millimeters to more than 40 cm. Anderson and Kirkland interpret this sequence as an indication that an increased amount of water was brought into the basin, carrying the mud and silt·to make the shale layers. It seems to me rather more probable that the lake had become nearly filled, and as a consequence stream-laid sediments simply built farther and farther out into the basin during low stages of the lake, and then these were covered by gypsum at the somewhat higher stages. A significantly greater influx of water, it seems, would have enlarged the lake and re-established the mixolimnion from which both calcite and organic matter would again have been deposited.

Following an argument I advanced some years ago (Bradley, 1929*b*, p. 104) that there are theoretical reasons for believing the effect of the sunspot cycle would be recorded in variations in thickness of lacustrine varves, particularly in lakes losing much or all of their inflow by evaporation, Anderson and Kirkland measured the thicknesses of a continuous series of 1,592 of the carbonate laminae in the varved limestone. The graphs showing the variations in thickness were analyzed at the Dendrochronology Laboratory at the University of Arizona. Bryant Bannister of that laboratory found "a strong disposition to

10-unit and 13-unit cycle lengths. Significantly, these cycles are related to each other (one changing into the other and vice versa) in exactly the same manner as many tree-ring series in western America. Dr. Douglass feels that the 10–13 complex is directly related to the sunspot cycle and can appear in this fashion only in annual layers which are to some degree a function of climatic forces." Bannister also found a 180-year cycle that tends to break down into 60-year units and "a less obvious 170± cycle which is made up of two 85's."

The fossil fish belong to two species, *Pholidophorus americanus* Eastman and *Leptolepis schowei* Dunkle. They were found in "death assemblages" near the margin of the lake. Previous authors have referred to the marine affinities of these fish, but Anderson and Kirkland cast doubt on that interpretation and present environmental evidence that suggests they were non-marine.

Only one species of ostracod, *Metacypris todiltensis* Swain, has been found and that at one locality not far from the margin of the basin. Swain (1946) reported that this is closely related to a species, *M. whitei* Jones, found in the fluviatile sediments of the overlying Morrison Formation.

Lower Cretaceous—Newark Canyon Formation

Lake beds are known to make up part of the Newark Canyon Formation in the area south and east of Eureka, Eureka County, Nevada. Because these beds are poorly exposed and the geologic structure is complex, neither their lateral extent nor thickness is known. The formation contains unionids, fossil fish, and fossil plants, all of which indicate an Early Cretaceous age. According to Kulp (1961, p. 1111) the Lower Cretaceous ranges from 110 to 135 million years old. This formation is currently being studied in the field by T. B. Nolan of the U.S. Geological Survey. His field work shows that at two different times, only a few years apart, landslides came down into this ancient lake and disturbed the thinly laminated sediments that were accumulating there.

I have examined some of the specimens of these lake beds, which Mr. Nolan and Mr. C. W. Merriam, also of the Geological Survey, have collected. I find that many have varves similar to those forming today in a number of existing

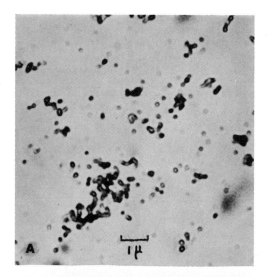

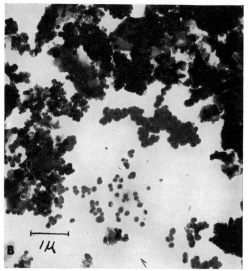

Fig. 23.2.—Fossil bacteria from a black, lacustrine marlstone of the Lower Cretaceous Newark Canyon Formation. A: Photomicrograph showing *Actinomyces* and micrococci; B: Electronmicrograph showing isolated and bunched micrococci and micrococci attached to shreds of organic matter.

lakes, that is, paired laminae, one of which is made up predominantly of microgranular carbonates (calcite in these rocks) and the other more or less rich in organic matter but containing little or no microgranular carbonate.

The varves range from 0.002 to more than 0.3 mm and average about 0.2 mm. This indicates an average rate of accumulation for this particular kind of lake sediment of about 1,500 years per foot of compacted rock. Inasmuch as these sedi-

ments apparently contain no dolomite and as there is no other evidence of salinity, it may be inferred that the lake was essentially fresh.

The fossil fish, which are small (40–58 mm long), are well preserved and are apparently restricted to varved sediments, as they are in the beds of other extinct lakes. Lore David (1941) has described these fish and assigned the new species, *nevadensis*, to the genus *Leptolepis* Agassiz.

The organic remains in these varved lake beds are really astonishing. They consist largely of bacterial cells, a few of which are silicified and transparent, but most of them consist of black, apparently carbonized, remains of the bacteria themselves. That they are not pyrite spherules was shown by the fact that x-ray fluorescence showed no iron and by the fact that they are decomposed by Clorox. By far the greater number of these bacteria are coccoid forms that are either dispersed individual cells or, much more rarely, ordered in small regular plates. These apparently are *Micrococcus* sp. They are most abundant on and close to scraps of organic matter, most of which are dark yellowish-brown and appear to be less carbonized than the bacteria. These micrococci are less than 1μ in diameter. In addition to *Micrococcus* sp. there are a few *Streptococcus* sp., whose individual cells are approximately the same diameter as the micrococci, but they are arranged in chains of 2 to 15 cells. Irregular, forked, stubby cells are also fairly common. These are apparently *Actinomyces* sp. Short rods, less than 1μ in diameter and about 2μ long, are also found, but they are very rare. These might be *Actinomyces* spores (Fig. 23.2).

Bacteria are so numerous in some varved marlstone beds that they make the rock almost black. If such rocks are dissolved in hydrochloric acid, only a black sludge remains. This consists almost wholly of black organic and clear silicified bacterial cells. Mixed in with these, however, are irregular shreds and bits of plant tissue, leaf cuticle, and spores. All such organic constituents are generally coated with bacterial cells, some so thickly that only the bacteria are visible. Scattered through these diverse organic remains are fine particles of quartz and feldspar.

Two kinds of organisms, or plant parts, in these ancient lake sediments may ultimately be identifiable. One is spherical, about 20μ in diameter, and has its surface ornamented with more or less sinuous, narrow ridges. Between these ridges the surface has sharply defined circular to elliptical pits. These objects resemble chrysomonad cysts, but, thus far, I have found only one that has a suggestion of a collar. This one, however, has a smooth surface ornamented with sinuous, thin ridges and suggests *Celloniella* sp. But as most of the others have no discernible plugs or collars, they may be zygospores or some other kind of resting spore. The other objects that may be identifiable are also spherical but are only 3 to 6µ in diameter. These also have rough coats, but they are so commonly covered with coccoid bacteria that the configuration is uncertain. Although these smaller spheres generally occur as isolated individuals, they also occur as aggregates of 3 to 10 individuals.

Paleocene and Eocene—Flagstaff Limestone

Geology and geography

La Rocque (1960) has recently given us a satisfying reconstruction of the limnology of a large lake that existed for two or three million years in central Utah and in which the Flagstaff Limestone was deposited. This formation bridges two geologic ages, the latter part of the Paleocene and the early part of the Eocene—some 55 to 59 million years ago (Kulp, 1961). At that time the land in the general vicinity of the lake had a moderate to low relief, though the region was undergoing some intermittent crustal warping and block faulting. Subsequent block faulting on a grand scale gave the region its present high relief and scenic splendor. In developing the paleolimnology of this long-extinct lake, La Rocque has drawn heavily on the ecology of the large molluscan faunas. And, as one must, he also drew heavily on the geologic interpretation of the sediments themselves.

He divided the sediments into three units, each of which represents a different phase of the lake's history (Table 23.2).

If one assumes that these limy rocks accumulated at an average rate of about 2,000 years per foot (Bradley, 1929*b*, p. 99) and adds together the maximum thickness of each unit, the Flagstaff lake must have existed for about 2.75 million years.

Genesis of lake basin and climate

La Rocque believes that the Flagstaff lake formed in a depression caused by movement of fault blocks. Such movement occurred in a long succession of pulses measured in a few feet, and each pulse caused a deepening of the lake and renewed downcutting of the outlet and gradual lowering of lake level. Such alternate changes in depth help explain the alternation of limestone and shale and changes in the molluscan fauna.

In the land snails, which occur sparingly in the lake basin sediments, La Rocque finds some evidence for a warm, semiarid climate. All the snails "are capable of living in a semiarid environment, and some, the bulimulids particularly, now live far south of Utah" (La Rocque, 1960, p. 62).

The Flagstaff lake stages

During most of the first phase, Flagstaff lake had an area of about 2,800 mi² (Fig. 23.3). During the second and third stages, the lake expanded so that its area was about 4,000 mi². At times it may possibly have had an area as great as 7,000 mi², but at that maximum extent there may have been two or more lakes. In the first two stages the lake had an island of upturned Cretaceous rocks. Sediments of the third stage buried this island.

During the first and third stages, La Rocque believes, for the following good reasons, that the lake was shallow over much of its great expanse: (1) common occurrence of ripple marks on many bedding surfaces, (2) the abundance and wide distribution of Mollusca, which are confined by their food requirements to shallow water, (3) the evidence of wave action, revealed by the high proportion of shell fragments in many beds, and (4) abrupt lateral and vertical variation of the beds, a feature unlikely in a deep-water environment. The sediments also indicate that there were,

TABLE 23.2

Gross stratigraphic units of the Flagstaff Limestone. From La Rocque, 1960.

Unit	Lithologic character	Thickness (in ft)
3	Gray to tan shales and limestones with much chert	140–510
2	White limestone with minor amounts of light-colored shale; channel sandstone, much gypsum, some chert	30–110
1	Dark blue-gray calcareous shale and limestone alternating in thin beds, 3 in. to 4 ft thick; some thicker shale beds	30–755

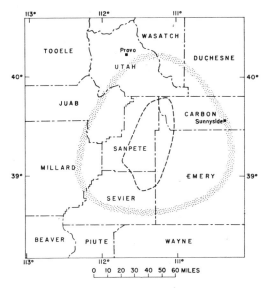

Fig. 23.3.—Dashed line shows the extent of the Flag-staff lake at an early stage; the stippled boundary, the inferred extent during a late stage. After La Rocque, *Bull. Geol. Soc. Amer.*, 1960.

from time to time, deeper areas where Mollusca did not thrive. In these areas almost pure lime muds accumulated.

Judging by the abundance of calcium carbonate in the sediments, including the shale beds, this was a hard-water lake. La Rocque attributes most of the calcium carbonate precipitation to summer evaporation and warming of the water. He does not mention the possible, or probable, role of phytoplankton as an additional effective agent for precipitating calcium carbonate (Nipkow, 1920; Welten, 1944) in hard-water lakes. The chemistry of the water during the second phase was radically different; it became rich in calcium sulfate—so rich, in fact, that a very considerable amount of gypsum was precipitated in beds and as a constituent of the other sediments. Apparently this came about largely because some of the feeding streams began to erode Jurassic rocks containing an abundance of gypsum and because the lake ceased to overflow for considerable intervals of time. In fact, La Rocque postulates that the lake level fluctuated considerably in response to climatic controls, alternating between a closed lake and one that overflowed, thereby accounting for the alternating beds of limestone and gypsum.

Biology of the lake

Each phase of the Flagstaff lake provided an environment suitable for a specific assemblage of organisms.

During the first phase an extensive growth of submerged and emergent rooted plants flourished here and there around the margin of the lake, on shoals, and around the islands. A microflora must have flourished too, for La Rocque points out that the majority of the Mollusca fed on microscopic algae, and because the population of mollusks was very large, one must suppose that their food was correspondingly abundant. Such a line of reasoning depends on the plausible inference that since the nearest living relatives of these animals feed on microscopic algae, it is highly probable that their closely similar Paleocene and Eocene forebears did likewise. The abundant plant life during this stage left its mark on the sediments in the form of carbonaceous particles, which make both the limestone and the shale rather dark gray. But the only recognizable plant remains in these beds are the oogonia of charophytes, which have been described by Peck and Reker (1948).

The pelecypods of this stage belong to two groups, the Naiades and Sphaeriidae; the Naiades are represented by a single species *Elliptio mendax* (White), which, however, was so abundant it made up as much as 16% of the total number of individuals found. La Rocque speculates that the small number of species may be accounted for by a limited fish fauna. But he is careful to point out the assumption that these early Naiades depended, like their living counterparts, on a certain kind of fish to complete their life cycle.

Two genera of sphaeriids, *Sphaerium* and *Pisidium*, are represented by one species each and these not in large numbers. This La Rocque finds difficult to account for unless the wave action was too strong for such animals, although there are species of *Sphaerium* that live in streams and on the sandy littoral benches of lakes.

Gastropods are represented by gill breathers and lung breathers. The gill breathers belong to the genera *Viviparus, Lioplacodes, Hydrobia, Micropyrgus,* and *Goniobasis.* Judging by their living relatives, these throve in turbid, wave-agitated waters on soft, muddy bottoms. Species of *Gyraulus, Carinulorbis, Ferrissia,* and *Physa* and probably *Pleurolimnaea tenuicosta* (Meek and Hayden) were lung breathers. One of the most striking aspects of this assemblage is the great abundance of *Hydrobia utahensis* (White). It makes up 32–91% of the individuals in the significant collections.

Land snails form a small proportion of the shells found and presumably were washed in from the adjacent land.

The fish and turtle remains are too fragmentary for identification. No remains of mammals were found.

In the second or middle phase, the Flagstaff lake, though about double the size of the first phase, was a barren environment, apparently because of its high sulfate concentration. The lack of carbonaceous particles in the sediments indicates an absence of aquatic plants, both rooted and planktonic. No molluscan shells, other than a few land snails, were found.

La Rocque assumes from the absence of ripple marks and mudcracks, except near the top of this sequence of beds, that the lake was relatively deep and quiet. One might speculate that the lake was stratified during a considerable part of this stage and that the energy of the wind was absorbed in the epilimnion.

During the third or final phase, the lake retained its large size but returned to very much the same sort of habitat it was during the first phase. In other words, it apparently became again an open, hard-water, shallow lake.

The molluscan fauna, however, was different. *Lioplacodes* and *Micropyrgus* are not represented, perhaps because water weeds appear to have been very sparse. Naiades are represented by two genera *Elliptio* and *Lampsilis,* and the species of *Elliptio* are different. The Sphaeriidae are represented by only the single species, *Sphaerium* (cf. *formosum* Meek and Hayden). The gill-breathing gastropods are represented by *Viviparus paludinaeformis* Hall, *Goniobasis tenera* Hall, and *Hydrobia ephraimensis* La Rocque. Land snails are about as scarce as in the earliest unit of the Flagstaff Limestone.

At the end, the Flagstaff lake diminished in size and migrated northward where it merged with the expanding, young, and much larger Green River lake, which was to continue for some millions of years longer. The paleolimnology of the Green River lakes is considered next. Why the Flagstaff lake migrated is not certainly known, perhaps because much of it filled with fluviatile sediments or perhaps because of crustal warping down into the basin of the newly formed Green River lake to the northeast.

Eocene—Green River Formation

Geology and geography

The Green River Formation of southwestern Wyoming, northwestern Colorado, and northeastern Utah was deposited in two large lakes and one somewhat smaller lake that were essentially contemporaneous. They are of early and middle Eocene age, about 50 million years old (Kulp, 1961). The largest lake, Lake Uinta, in Utah and Colorado, was in existence between 5 and 8 million years. Gosiute Lake, in Wyoming, lasted some 4 million years, and the smallest, as yet unnamed, lake that occupied the Fossil Syncline in extreme southwest Wyoming probably had a considerably shorter life. All three lakes lie in intermontane basins that were formed soon after the Upper Cretaceous seas withdrew. The mountains and hills bounding these large basins are made up of a great variety of igneous, metamorphic, and sedimentary rocks that range in age from pre-Cambrian to Pleistocene. The sedimentary rocks include thick formations of limestone and dolomite. Before the lakes formed, several thousand feet of generally fine-grained fluviatile sediments were deposited in each of the basins, thereby leveling up the floors into extensive alluvial plains.

Because I have studied more fully the geology and paleolimnology of the sediments laid down in the ancient Gosiute Lake in Wyoming, the greater part of the following discussion will be restricted to that lake. Moreover, the geology, the present topography, and the fact that many boreholes have been drilled into these lake beds make them the most suitable of the three for paleolimnological study.

In trying to develop the paleolimnology of Gosiute Lake, I have drawn heavily on analogy with the limnology of existing lakes and their sediments. I have also, of necessity, drawn heavily on the geology and geochemistry of the lake beds themselves. The rich and varied fossil flora and fauna of the lake beds and the contemporaneous land around the lake have also been used for whatever light they might shed on the paleolimnology and paleoecology of the lake and its environs.

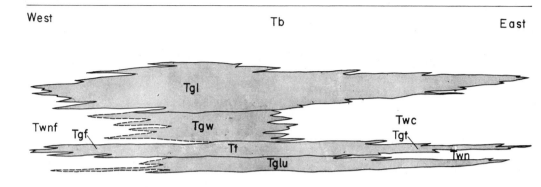

Fig. 23.4.—Schematic cross section of the Green River Formation showing the relative size and extent of each lithologic member. Each member represents a well-defined stage of the ancient Gosiute Lake. *Tw* = Wasatch Formation; *Twnf* = New Fork Tongue, *Twn* = Niland Tongue, and *Twc* = Cathe-dral Bluffs Tongue of the Wasatch Formation. *Tglu* = Luman Tongue, *Tt* = Tipton Shale Member, *Tgt* = Tipton Tongue, *Tgf* = Fontenelle Tongue, *Tgw* = Wilkins Peak Member, and *Tgl* = Laney Shale Member, all of the Green River Formation. *Tb* = Bridger Formation.

Lake sediments and duration of Gosiute Lake

The Green River Formation that accumulated in Gosiute Lake constitutes a great lens of lacustrine sediments in a matrix of generally fine-grained fluviatile sediments, the Wasatch Formation below and the Bridger Formation above. Laterally the Green River beds intertongue with contemporaneous fluviatile sediments belonging, roughly, in the lower half to the Wasatch Formation and in the upper part to the Bridger Formation. The Green River Formation is divided into six members or tongues, several of which represent distinctive stages in Gosiute Lake's history (see Fig. 23.4).

At the base of the Green River Formation is the Tipton Shale Member and a basal tongue, the Luman Tongue, running far out to the east. It also has a higher tongue running far out to the east, the Tipton Tongue. Extending far to the west is the Fontenelle Tongue. Both the Fontenelle and Tipton tongues represent much of the time span of the Tipton Shale Member, whereas the Luman Tongue represents only the early part of Tipton time.

The Luman Tongue and its equivalent part of the Tipton Shale Member consists of rather soft,

limy shale that ranges from black to light grayish-brown. Nearly all of it contains organic matter, the black shale, of course, containing the most. Interbedded with the shale are a few thin beds of sandstone and ostracod marl. In one large area spanning the Wyoming-Colorado line, the Luman contains a prodigious quantity of *Oxytrema, Viviparus,* and *"Unio"* shells, carbonaceous shale, and thin coal beds. This was a shallow, weedy bay for several hundred thousand years. The Luman Tongue gradually changes in thickness over its large areal extent and ranges from 180 to 500 ft, being thickest where sedimentation was more rapid in the weedy bays.

The Tipton Shale Member consists largely of soft, grayish-brown, flaky shale but has a considerable thickness of low grade oil shale in its upper part and at its base a transgressive sandy limestone that contains *Oxytrema, "Unio,"* and *Viviparus* shells and locally oolite. It is about 150 ft thick but thickens where it approaches the ancient shoreline and becomes sandy and conglomeratic.

A little more than the lower half of the Tipton Tongue consists of soft, flaky, brown and grayish-buff shale, but the upper part consists of hard, flaky marlstone that weathers bluish-white to white. Both the shale and the marlstone on fresh fracture are brown owing to the contained organic matter. The marlstone unit contains layers of algal limestone that extend over thousands of square miles. At its base is a sandy fossiliferous limestone like that at the base of the Tipton Shale Member. Over much of its area the Tipton Tongue ranges from 200 to 300 ft but thickens to 500 ft near the mountains, where it is sandy and conglomeratic, and thins to a feather edge far to the east and southeast.

The Fontenelle Tongue, essentially the western equivalent of the Tipton Tongue, contains much less lime. It is made up largely of buff to gray shale, mudstone, more or less limy sandstone, and a minor amount of hard marlstone. It has a maximum thickness of about 250 ft and thins both northward and southward to feather edges.

The Tipton Shale Member and its eastern and western equivalents (Tipton and Fontenelle tongues) represent the first great expansion of Gosiute Lake, an area exceeded only by the final or Laney stage. The lake had an outlet during both Luman and Tipton stages.

Following the Tipton stage Gosiute Lake became a closed lake, shrank to about one-fourth to one-tenth of its former size, and deposited great quantities of sodium salts, trona, shortite, and others. During this low stage the Wilkins Peak Member of the Green River Formation was deposited. This consists largely of hard, greenish-gray to brownish-gray dolomitic mudstone, dolomitic marlstone, and volcanic ash. Interbedded with these are beds of fairly rich oil shale and 17 to 20 fairly thick beds of trona ($Na_2CO_3 \cdot NaHCO_3 \cdot 2H_2O$) and a great many thin ones. Scattered through the major part of this member are myriads of isolated or grouped crystals of shortite ($Na_2CO_3 \cdot 2CaCO_3$) and lesser amounts of northupite ($Na_2CO_3 \cdot MgCO_3 \cdot NaCl$). At repeated levels in this member there are groups of alternating beds: beds with and without mudcracks, beds with and without salt molds. These represent rising and falling stages of the closed lake. The Wilkins Peak Member is 900 to 1,000 ft thick and in places grades out laterally into marsh deposits or fluviatile sediments.

After this low Wilkins Peak stage, Gosiute Lake again expanded, this time to its maximum extent, and again overflowed. In this much enlarged and deepened lake were deposited the beds of the Laney Shale Member.

The Laney Shale Member has at its base a unit of varved marlstone that grades up into buff, tuffaceous marlstone, which includes great lenses and channel deposits of granular volcanic ash. Most of the Laney, however, consists of rather massive to chippy buff marlstone containing more or less volcanic ash and a few beds of fairly rich oil shale. In its upper part it becomes progressively more sandy and tuffaceous and grades into the overlying tuffaceous fluviatile beds of the Bridger Formation. The Laney Shale Member ranges in thickness from about 600 to nearly 1,900 ft over most of its extent, but to the north and east it thins out rather abruptly.

The varves in various parts of the Green River Formation give us one measure of the rate at which the sediments accumulated. Carbon-14 age determinations in the sediments of both fresh and saline lakes in existence today give us another measure, by analogy, of the rates at which comparable kinds of lacustrine sediment probably accumulated in Gosiute Lake. In addition, we have some direct observations on rates of accumulation of sediment, both mud and marl, in modern lakes. Using all these measures and making allowance for the fact that the sedimentary rocks of the Green River Formation are considerably thinner than the original sediment layers at time of deposition by reason of compaction beneath great loads of overlying sediment, I arrive at the following estimated rates of accumulation for the commonest kinds of rocks in this formation (Table 23.3).

The estimated rates are most reliable for the varved sediments, next most reliable for the brown shale, and least reliable for the sandstone, which, fortunately, makes up relatively little of the Green River Formation. No time values are assigned to the volcanic ash layers because the time intervals are insignificantly brief.

Multiplying these rates by the aggregate thicknesses of each kind of rock and rounding off to the nearest half million years give the following duration for the major stages in the history of Gosiute Lake:

Tipton and Luman stages	1.0 million years
Wilkins Peak stage	1.0
Laney stage	2.0
Total	4.0

TABLE 23.3

Estimated rates of accumulation of the commonest
kinds of rock in the Green River Formation

Kind of sedimentary rock	Rates of accumulation	
	Years per ft	Years per cm
Shale, with more or less organic matter and limy	2,000	65
Shale, carbonaceous and sandy	900	30
Marlstone, varved and organic	1,800	60
Marlstone, massive or crudely bedded	900	30
Mudstone, limy and dolomitic	3,000	100
Oil shale, moderately rich, varved	4,700	154
Sandstone, limy	1,800	60
Bedded sodium salt, trona	145	4.8

Genesis of the lake basin

There is good geologic evidence for believing
that the basin of Gosiute Lake formed by intermittent or, at times, nearly continuous downwarp
of the earth's crust after the original intermontane basin had been partially filled with fine-
grained fluviatile sediment. When the nearly level
floor began to warp downward, the terrain became poorly drained, and first carbonaceous sediment and then peat (which subsequently became
a few inches of coal) accumulated. Immediately
thereafter, the lake formed and gradually expanded until it had an area of several thousand
square miles.

From a unit of essentially uniform brown shale
60 ft thick in the Tipton Shale Member, we can
estimate the minimum average rate of downwarp
during an interval of about 120,000 years. The
following assumptions are necessary: that this
sediment, which contains a few uniformly distributed shells of *Valvata* sp. and *Sphaerium* sp.,
accumulated in an essentially constant depth of
water (deeper than that required for rooted
aquatic plants—perhaps 30 to 50 ft); that the
original sediment, as deposited, had a porosity of
about 85%; that the porosity decreased paraboli-
cally downward to about 55% at its base (rate of
decrease based on observed rates of decrease in
modern sediments); and that the 60-ft unit of
shale was represented by 250 ft of mud at the
time the last layer of this unit was laid down.
If the water depth remained constant, the downwarp must have been 250 ft in 120,000 years or
at an average rate of 480 yrs · ft^{-1}—about 0.2 ft

per century. If the water deepened, the rate must
have been greater. The water could not have
shoaled enough to permit the growth of rooted
aquatic plants, for these would have left plainly
evident remains in such a shale.

This average rate of downwarp is only about
one-tenth that at which southern Denmark appears to be sinking today.

Hydrography

The boundary of the hydrographic basin of
the ancient Gosiute Lake (Fig. 23.5) can be
drawn with assurance along the crests of some
of the bounding mountain ranges, e.g., the Uinta
and Wind River mountains. But in other places
it is inferred from the geologic structure, with
various degrees of assurance, for the drainage pattern has obviously changed much since the Eocene. The boundary, as drawn, includes roughly
48,500 mi^2.

We know where all the large rivers, and some
of the smaller ones, entered the basin or the lake
itself. The former sites of these streams are indicated by conglomerates and channel sandstones
in the Wasatch, Green River, and Bridger formations. We know from the volume and coarseness
of the conglomerates that there were high mountains where the Uinta, Wind River, and Wyoming ranges now stand. Moreover, most of these
conglomerates are not muddy and ill-sorted so the

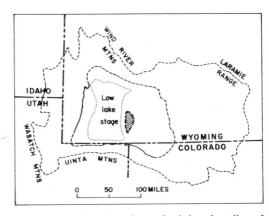

Fig. 23.5.—Dashed line shows the inferred outline of
Gosiute Lake's hydrographic basin; the full and
dashed line within represents the maximum extent
of Gosiute Lake during the Laney Stage; the dotted
line within represents the maximum extent of the
low, or Wilkins Peak, stage; the diagonally ruled
area in the center of the lake was a large island
during the Tipton and Laney stages.

streams were not torrential desert streams. They were fairly well regulated mountain rivers such as come from high mountains. Furthermore, from the stratigraphic range of the conglomerates we know that most of the rivers maintained their loci, at least where they came out of the mountains, for intervals measured in hundreds of thousands or even millions of years.

Reasoning by analogy we can gain some idea of the probable altitude of the highest parts of these high mountain ranges. The oil shale of the Green River Formation contains a great abundance of pine pollen but only a little spruce and fir pollen (Wodehouse, 1933, p. 487). As will be seen in the next section of this chapter, we have reasons for believing that the climate during much of the Green River epoch was rather similar to that of our Gulf Coast States today. How high then would mountains have to be in a Gulf Coast climate to support spruce and fir along their crests? Fortunately, the altitudinal and latitudinal range of spruce and fir trees along the crest of the Appalachians has been studied by Oosting and Billings (1951, pp. 84–103). They found that the southernmost spruce and fir forests on the Appalachians grow at altitudes of about 6,700 ft. It seems reasonable to infer that the spruce and fir of the Green River epoch, which probably also grew in relatively small patches, grew at comparable altitudes above the surrounding terrain. I have assumed, from the gradient of the stream needed to take the lake's overflow to the nearest ocean, that the surface of Gosiute Lake, at high level, must have been about 1,000 ft above sea level. So the crests of the mountains near this lake may well have stood 6,000 to 8,000 ft above sea level, and perhaps even higher, because it appears that the rainfall was lower and more strongly seasonal around Gosiute Lake than it is today in the Great Smokies at the southern end of the Appalachian Range.

Gosiute Lake certainly had an outlet all during the Luman and Tipton stages and again later during all the Laney stage. I infer that this outlet was at the eastern end of the Uinta Mountains, because the Green River Formation only a few miles south of that gap has a large and thick deltaic facies laid down by a stream that came from the proper direction.

Climate

One of the elements of the middle Eocene climate that can be estimated with some reasonableness is the average annual temperature. In an earlier treatment of the climate of the Green River epoch (Bradley, 1929b, pp. 92–93), I deduced that the average annual temperature was about 66.5° F. This was based on an elaborate statistical study by Brooks (1926, pp. 42, 45, 233) of the effects upon climate produced by the relative distribution of land and sea, the altitude of the land, the direction and strength of ocean currents, and the relative amount of volcanic activity. The large and varied flora of the Green River Formation, according to paleobotanists, indicates a climate comparable to that now found in the Gulf Coast States. It is interesting, therefore, to note that the present mean annual temperature along the Gulf Coast is about 70° F. As mentioned before, Gosiute Lake is estimated to have been about 1,000 ft above sea level. If one applies the general lapse rate of temperature with altitude (3.3° F per 1,000 ft) to the Gulf Coast's 70° F, an average annual temperature of 66.7° F results. This very close correspondence (66.7° vs. 66.5° F) should not blind us to the fact that both are estimates, and both estimates harbor significantly large potential errors. The principal value of these two figures, however coincidental their near identity is, lies in the fact that they come from independent lines of deduction.

At or close to the end of the Tipton stage, Gosiute Lake went through a critical stage, perhaps many times, on its way toward becoming a closed and saline lake when the loss of water by evaporation from the lake surface equaled the amount it received as direct rainfall and runoff from the land. Recently Walter B. Langbein of the U.S. Geological Survey completed an analysis (Langbein, 1961) of the various relationships among temperature, rainfall, runoff, evaporation from free water surfaces, evapotranspiration, and lake levels and salt accumulation in closed lakes. Using his formulas and data based on many existing closed lakes in various parts of the world, it is possible, with the knowledge we now have about Gosiute Lake, to quantify a number of other climatic and hydrologic factors of Gosiute Lake and its hydrography.

Langbein's formula (1) states the balance between income and loss by evaporation. Given here also are the area of Gosiute Lake at maximum extent and the area of its watershed.

$$A_L E_L = P_L A_L + r A_W \qquad (1)$$

where

A_L = area of lake; 15,500 mi²
E_L = evaporation from lake, per unit area
P_L = precipitation on the lake
r = runoff into lake, per unit area
A_W = watershed; 33,000 mi²;

$$r = P_W - E_T \qquad (2)$$

where

P_W = precipitation on watershed
E_T = evapotranspiration from watershed;

$$E_L = \text{a function of } T_L \quad \text{and} \quad P_L \qquad (3)$$

where

T_L = mean annual temperature at lake; 66.5° F;

$$E_L = \text{a function of } T_T \quad \text{and} \quad P_W \qquad (4)$$

where

T_T = mean annual temperature in watershed area;

$$T_T = T_L - c\Delta H \qquad (5)$$

where

c = lapse rate of temperature with altitude and
ΔH = difference in altitude (in 1,000's ft) between average altitude of watershed and lake surface;

$$P_W = P_L + k\Delta H \qquad (6)$$

where

k = incremental rate of precipitation per 1,000 ft of altitude;

We can now write

$$P_L = \frac{E_L + (E_T - k\Delta H)\dfrac{A_W}{A_L}}{1 + \dfrac{A_W}{A_L}}. \qquad (7)$$

The following values are used in making the calculations:
$T = 66.5°$ F
$H = 1$, that is 1,000 ft average altitude of watershed above lake surface. The way this value was obtained is discussed below.
$c = 3.3°$ F per 1,000 ft altitude
$k = 4$ in. per 1,000 ft altitude

$$\frac{A_W}{A_L} = \frac{33,000 \text{ mi}^2}{15,500 \text{ mi}^2} = 2.13 \quad \text{or} \quad 2.$$

Now because E_T and E_L are both functions of P_L, equation (7) must be solved by converging approximations. Assume

$$P_L = 30 \text{ in.}$$

Then from the graph Fig. 23.6,

$$E_L = 57.5 \text{ in.}$$

From

$$T_T = T_L - c\Delta H \qquad (5)$$
$$T_T = 63.2° \text{ F}$$

and from the graph Fig. 23.6,

$$E_T = 27 \text{ in.}$$

Substituting in Eq. (7)

$$P_L = \frac{57.5 + (27 - 4 \times 1)2}{3} = 34.5 \text{ in.}$$

Assuming

$$P_L = 34.5 \text{ in.}$$
$$P_L = \frac{52 + (29 - 4)2}{3} = 34 \text{ in.}$$

Several other values for P_L ranging from 25 to 40 were tried but the assumption that $P_L = 35$ gave the best agreement, 34.1 vs. 34.3 in., so that solution was accepted.

The calculated values are

$$P_L = 34 \text{ in.}$$
$$E_L = 52 \text{ in.}$$
$$E_T = 29 \text{ in.}$$
$$P_W = 38 \text{ in., from Eq. (6)}$$
$$r = 8.5 \text{ in., from Eq. (1).}$$

It should be borne in mind that these values are for the climate when the lake was just full but did not overflow. The rainfall surely was somewhat greater (but an unknown amount) during the times when the lake overflowed and, of course, less when it was a closed, saline lake. This latter value is estimated below.

From the lapse rates for changes of rainfall and temperature with altitude, we can calculate the mean annual rainfall and temperature for various altitudes in Gosiute Lake's hydrographic basin (Table 23.4).

Because all the mountain ranges in, or partially in, the hydrographic basin of Gosiute Lake are still mountain ranges today (though some are lower and others higher than in the Eocene), it is possible to make a crude estimate of the distribution of altitudes in the ancient watershed area. Such an analysis gives the following values:

TABLE 23.4

Calculated mean annual rainfall and mean annual temperature for a range of altitudes in the hydrographic basin of Gosiute Lake

ΔH (ft above lake surface)	P_W (in. per unit area)	T (° F)
500	36	65
1,000	38	63
2,000	42	60
3,000	46	57
4,000	52	53
5,000	56	50
6,000	60	47
7,000	64	43

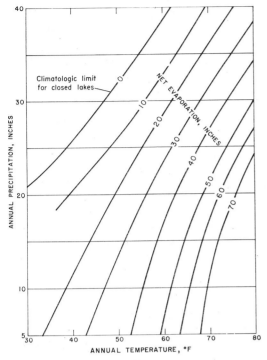

ANNUAL PRECIPITATION, INCHES

Climatologic limit for closed lakes

NET EVAPORATION, INCHES

ANNUAL TEMPERATURE, °F

Fig. 23.6.—Graph showing the relationship between annual precipitation, temperature, and net evaporation. Taken from W. B. Langbein, U.S. Geol. Surv., Profess. Paper 412, 1961, p. 3.

mountain crest areas (5,000 to 7,000 ft above lake level) aggregate about 1,000 mi², lower slopes and foothills (averaging about 2,500 ft above lake level) make up about 6,000 mi², and the remaining area (averaging about 500 ft above lake level) makes up 16,000 mi². The weighted average of these estimates is approximately 1,000 ft above lake level.

A very rough measure of the decrease in rainfall needed to balance evaporation with decreasing size of the lake, after it became closed and so strongly saline that trona began to precipitate, in other words after it reached its salting level, can be obtained from data available. Now the salting level is peculiar to each individual lake, but it depends more heavily on the ratio of the area of the lake to the area of its drainage basin than it does on the kind of climate and composition of the brine in the lake. Langbein has found that if two lakes are at salting level and occupy about the same percentage of their respective drainage basins, they have in common a factor of aridity, which he calls "net evaporation." Net

evaporation he defines as the evaporation from the lake surface minus the amount of rain that falls directly onto the lake. It happens that Great Salt Lake in Utah is close to its salting level and that it also occupies just about the same percentage of its drainage basin as Gosiute Lake did at its salting stage. Great Salt Lake has a net evaporation of about 40 in. If we make the bold, but not implausible, assumption that Gosiute Lake at salting level also had a net evaporation of 40 in. and that the average annual temperature stayed at 66.5° F, we can read from Langbein's graph (Fig. 23.6) that the mean annual rainfall must have been about 24 in. Actually, in any shift of climate toward aridity it is likely that the temperature would rise appreciably, so the corresponding rainfall would have to be somewhat higher to keep the net evaporation constant. For example, if the temperature rose to 70° F, the graph shows a rainfall between 26 and 27 in. We have no way of estimating temperature changes, however, so the estimate of 24 in. for the mean annual rainfall at the time of maximum aridity will have to suffice. If this is of the right order, it indicates a very marked change of climate during the Eocene, a change that lasted about one million years. After that, the climate again became more humid, and the lake enlarged to its maximum size (Laney stage) and overflowed for something like two million years before it filled with sediment and became extinct.

Morphometry of the lake

A cardinal difficulty confronts the paleolimnologist when he tries to determine the form ratio of an ancient lake that was in existence several million years, for it is certain that the depth kept changing by accumulation of sediments and by downwarping of the lake bottom. Moreover, the actual shoreline is preserved only in a few places, and both the shores and the lake beds have been gently deformed by crustal movements since the lake became extinct. The surface area of Gosiute Lake can be estimated reasonably well because most of the sediments are still there, including the near-shore facies, if not the actual shores.

At its maximum extent (Tipton and Laney stages) Gosiute Lake had a simple, subrectangular shape, but some of this simplicity derives from our ignorance of the exact location of shorelines. The development of shoreline D_L is 1.58. For comparison, this ratio for Lake Tahoe is 1.58 and for Lake Erie 2.1 (Hutchinson, 1957, pp. 168, 169).

The lake contained one large elliptical island of Upper Cretaceous rocks near its center, the ancestral Rock Springs uplift, and several small islands of steeply upturned Jurassic rocks along its western margin. The area of the large island is quite uncertain. As inferred, the insulosity was about 2%.

Inasmuch as the lake formed by the downwarp of nearly level alluvial plains, its bottom must have been virtually featureless, except for the islands and deltas of gravel and sand off the mouths of rivers. As Figure 23.5 shows, the lake had two large basins, one on either side of the central island. The connecting channels north and south of the island were always shallow as shown by the sediments laid down in them. During the arid Wilkins Peak stage, all the water drained out of the eastern basin and the channels, resulting in the lake's being restricted to a part of the western basin.

During parts of the Laney and Tipton stages, the lake was deep enough in both basins to be permanently stratified, for at those times varved beds of marlstone and oil shale were laid down. For a lake of that area this must have meant a depth of more than one hundred, and probably several hundred, feet. During much of the time, however, Gosiute Lake was evidently so shallow that its sediments were not varved, though many beds do occur that are rather thin, regular, and of great lateral extent.

The varves in the Green River Formation consist of one lamina of microgranular carbonates (calcite and dolomite) and one lamina of virtually structureless organic matter in which are particles of carbonates. Particles of clastic minerals, presumably windblown dust, are scattered in differing small amounts through the whole varve. The varves range in thickness from 0.014 to 9.8 mm, the weighted average being 0.18 mm. They were established as varves (Bradley, 1929b) almost wholly by analogy with the varves now forming in the Lake of Zürich, which were so beautifully and compellingly elucidated by Nipkow (1920) more than 40 years ago. The sunspot cycle is apparently reflected in these varved Eocene beds.

During the Wilkins Peak stage, the lake became very shallow and at the lowest stages may

have been subdivided into smaller lakes and ponds. But at the higher-water stages of its history as a closed lake it was meromictic, and the fresher part of the mixolimnion produced an abundant plankton. As a result of the large plankton crops, beds of low- to high-grade oil shale formed. Most of these oil shale beds are varved.

During most of the Laney stage when little else but marl was deposited (except for numerous beds of volcanic ash), Gosiute Lake must have been rather shallow for so large a lake— probably less than 100 ft deep and perhaps appreciably less.

We know from the character of the sediments in extensive shore facies that the water was shallow far out into the lake. Locally, however, as in the shallow channels north and south of the big island, the shores were steeper, and in such places extensive algal reefs and beds formed (Bradley, 1929a). Associated with the algal deposits are oolites and ostracod marls. Only along the north flank of the Uinta Mountains and around the small rocky islands at the western margin were the shores of the lake steep and the beaches rocky, gravelly, or sandy.

Chemistry of the lake water

Because the sediments laid down in Gosiute Lake are characteristically high in $CaCO_3$ and $MgCO_3$, it is reasonable to assume that the streams feeding the lake were relatively high in Ca, Mg, and HCO_3. The average amount of Ca in 9 limy shales and marlstones from the Tipton and Laney shale members (without weighting them according to the relative abundance of the kinds of rocks represented in these two members) is 9.6%. Making allowance for the density of the rock and its estimated rate of accumulation (65 yrs per cm), we find that, on the average, 0.004 g Ca came down per cm² per yr. If 52 in. of water evaporated from the lake surface each year to balance the income of 34 in. of rain and 18 in. of stream water containing this Ca in solution, and the rain water is assumed to have contained only 1 ppm Ca, then the stream water must have contained about 85 ppm Ca. This is very high and is comparable to the upper range of Ca content found in the streams draining into Lake Michigan, which range from 21 to 91 ppm Ca and from 20 to more than 38 ppm Mg (Clarke, 1924, pp. 13–14). Gosiute

TABLE 23.5

Chemical composition of Summer Lake, Oregon, Soap Lake, Washington, and the inferred composition of Gosiute Lake brine at trona salting level

	Summer Lake, Oregon[a] (ppm)	Recalculated analysis	Soap Lake, Washington[a] (ppm)	Recalculated analysis	Mean of recalculated analyses— inferred Gosiute Lake brine
SiO_2	110	4,169	61	816	2,492
Ca	2.5	947	2.2	29	488
Mg	0.3	113	15	201	157
Na	2,830	107,350	8,030	107,350	107,350
K	115	4,358	733	9,822	7,090
HCO_3	1,880	71,252	3,410	45,694	58,473
CO_3	1,230	36,617	4,130	55,342	45,978
SO_4	348	13,189	3,930	52,662	32,925
Cl	1,600	60,640	3,730	49,982	55,311
F	5.4	205	n.d.	—	205
Br	7.2	273	n.d.	—	273
I	0.9	34	n.d.	—	34
PO_4	18.0	682	n.d.	—	682
Total	7,200	299,829	22,300	321,898	311,458

[a] Unpublished recent analyses by the U.S. Geological Survey.

Lake, even while it overflowed, was certainly a hard-water lake.

When the lake concentrated down to the trona salting level, which it did repeatedly under the arid climate of the Wilkins Peak stage, we can infer something about its possible composition, though the approximation is very rough. From the large number of sodium carbonate and sodium-calcium carbonate minerals in the sediments, it is evident that the brine must have been a Na_2CO_3-$NaHCO_3$ brine. It may be instructive, therefore, to draw an analogy with the compositions of the brines in existing sodium carbonate lakes. Good modern analyses are rare, but we have them for Summer Lake in Oregon and Soap Lake in Washington. Using these as a base, we can approximate the brine from which the trona beds in the Green River Formation came. Eugster, who is joint author with me of a report in preparation on the paleolimnology and geochemistry of the saline member of the Green River Formation, finds (Milton and Eugster, 1959) that trona cannot precipitate until the Na concentration has reached at least 8.8% in equilibrium with the CO_2 in the air. At a density of 1.220 this corresponds to 107,350 ppm Na. From the analyses of Summer and Soap lakes, we calculated the composition of a brine whose Na content was raised to 107,350 ppm and each other constituent raised proportionately. These are given in Table 23.5, together with the mean

of these two calculated analyses, as the hypothetical composition and concentration of Gosiute Lake at trona salting level.

Raising each constituent by the same large factor ignores expectable differential changes between constituents with concentration. Old analyses of Summer Lake show that in 1912, when it contained 16,633 ppm dissolved solids, it contained only a trace of Ca and 0.4 ppm Mg. In 1901, when it was still more concentrated (36,530 ppm), it contained no Ca or Mg. On the other hand, Barghoorn and Nichols (1961) report a small saline pond in Antarctica which has 132,620 ppm of total dissolved solids, containing respectively 1,130 and 4,890 ppm of Ca and Mg. Summer Lake at its 1901 stage contained only 268 ppm SiO_2, and Alkali Lake, Oregon, with 95,100 ppm dissolved solids contained only 162 ppm PO_4. But even if the amounts of all these constituents were much lowered, or eliminated, the total concentration would still be over 300,000 ppm. This compares with Great Salt Lake at its recent (1932) lowest stage when its brine contained 276,000 ppm total dissolved solids.

How close this hypothetical composition of the Gosiute Lake brine may be to the actual brine is only conjecture, but it may be seriously low in Cl. Eugster has found in his current study of the system $NaHCO_3$-Na_2CO_3-$NaCl$-H_2O that high concentrations of NaCl favor the precipitation of trona and at temperatures as low as

TABLE 23.6

Composite of 12 analyses of water from the Green River at Jensen, Utah, taken at regular intervals between June 1 and Sept. 30 (weighted for river discharge), and the recalculated analysis inferred to represent the average composition of runoff that fed Gosiute Lake during the Wilkins Peak saline stage

	Green River at Jensen, Utah[a] (in ppm)	Recalculated (in ppm)
SiO_2	10.53	14.1
Fe	0.07	0.1
Ca	41.14	55.1
Mg	13.83	18.5
Na	29.76	39.9
K	2.20	3.0
HCO_3	152.20	204.0
SO_4	80.60	108.0
Cl	12.04	16.1
F	0.30	0.4
NO_3	0.97	1.3
BO_3	0.15	0.2
Total	266.4	461

[a] Quality of surface waters of the United States, 1947. U.S. Geol. Survey, Water Supply Paper 1102, p. 613.

30° C in equilibrium with CO_2 in the air. We shall know more about these relationships as Eugster's work progresses.

We do know, however, from the geology and mineralogy of the .trona deposits that at more than 20 different times the brine of Gosiute Lake became concentrated enough to precipitate trona beds, which range in thickness from ½ in. to about 38 ft. Locally, at least, a number of these beds in the deepest part of the basin contain halite (NaCl) either as scattered crystals or in layers. In a few trona beds halite makes up as much as 50% of the bed.

We know also from the mineralogy that the lake never dried up completely, because no potassium minerals and only traces of one sulfate-bearing mineral have been found. Therefore, a considerable body of brine rich in Na, K, SO_4, and Cl must always have been present. Moreover, at the end of the 800,000-year saline stage, this residual brine must have been diluted by the expanding Laney stage lake and ultimately washed out of the basin. Presumably if there was bromine or iodine in the brine, it also was lost, for neither of these has been found in the minerals or rocks of the Green River Formation. Fluoride, borate, and phosphate minerals, however, have been found along with considerable amounts of SiO_2 as authigenic quartz.

From the estimated percentages of the minerals and from a considerable number of chemical analyses, it is possible to infer something about the chemical composition of the runoff that fed Gosiute Lake during the saline Wilkins Peak stage. Of all the elements in solution brought into a closed basin, Ca is most likely to be trapped permanently. Theoretically, one would expect a 1-to-1 relationship. Because of this, we calculated from the runoff, the ratio of lake area to watershed, and the total amount of Ca cm^{-2} in the whole column of rocks in the saline zone that, on the average, the runoff water must have contained 55.1 ppm Ca. Using this as a base, we increased the concentration of the water of the Green River at Jensen, Utah, by a factor of 1.34 for each constituent, the factor being determined by the rise of Ca content in the water as analyzed (41.1 ppm) to 55.1 ppm. The Green River was chosen because it drains, under an arid climate, a large part of the same hydrographic basin that Gosiute Lake occupied during the Wilkins Peak stage. The analysis of water from the Green River and the recalculated analysis are given in Table 23.6.

The plausibility of this inferred composition for the runoff was then tested by striking geochemical balances between the amounts of Mg, Na, Cl, and S found in the sediments and the amounts of these constituents brought into the lake during the saline stage (Table 23.7). In these calculations, the amounts brought in by evaporating the lake down to one-third its original size, the amounts brought in by rain, and the amounts brought in from mineral springs were omitted because they were found to be negligible in comparison with the amounts brought in by runoff during the 800,000-year saline stage. In

TABLE 23.7

Calculated balances between constituents found in the sediments of the saline zone, Wilkins Peak Member of the Green River Formation, and the amounts estimated to have been brought in by streams

	Found in sediments ($g \cdot cm^{-2}$)	Supplied by streams ($g \cdot cm^{-2}$)
Mg	1,888	1,380
Na	2,201	3,059 (including 89 g from volcanic ash)
Cl	330	1,190
S	309	2,600

the Na calculation, however, the amount estimated to have been leached from volcanic ash that fell into the lake was included. The amounts of the constituents brought in were calculated from the formula

$$\frac{rCD_S}{kA_L} = \text{grams cm}^{-2} \text{ of lake bottom} \qquad (8)$$

where

r = runoff in liters yr^{-1} from watershed (44,000 mi²)
C = concentration of constituents in runoff (mg liter⁻¹)
D_S = estimated duration of saline stage of Wilkins Peak member (8.0×10^5 yrs)
k = 1,000, to convert mg to g
A_L = area of lake at high level of Wilkins Peak stage (4,500 mi² or 1.165×10^{14} cm²).

The excess of Na supplied by an arid-climate river of not unusual concentration indicates that no extraordinary sources, such as ancient bedded salts, need be called on to account for the many billions of tons of trona and other sodium salts found in the Green River Formation. The S was trapped with ferrous Fe as pyrite and pyrrhotite and a minute amount as organic S in the oil shale. Only negligible traces of one sulfate mineral have been found, so the great excess of S brought in as SO_4 is expectable. The excesses of S, Cl, and Na presumably went into the residual brine mentioned previously. The excess of Mg in the rocks suggests a deficiency of Mg in the hypothetical runoff.

Waves

On a lake as large as Gosiute Lake was during overflow stages, it is reasonable to expect that big storms produced waves of the order of 1.1 to 1.5 m high with wave lengths of about 20 to 30 m. This assumes an average fetch of 120 km and an extreme possible fetch of 195 km. The wave heights, h_w, were calculated from the Stevenson empirical formula (Hutchinson, 1957, p. 356),

$$h_w = 0.105\sqrt{x}$$

where x is the fetch. Such waves would have an effective wave base about 8 m below the surface. Judging by the maximum heights of waves observed on modern lakes (Hutchinson, 1957, p. 359), however, Gosiute Lake may have had waves 3 or 4 m high.

Seiches

We know nothing of seiches in Gosiute Lake, but from the fact that it was meromictic in certain stages when it was also deep and large, we can speculate that it very probably had internal seiches. Because the two basins on either side of the central island were more or less elliptical, it is not improbable that each subbasin had at times a rotating internal seiche.

Biology of Gosiute Lake and its environs

Marginal land flora.—The large and varied flora that lived near the lake, on the alluvial plains surrounding the lake, on the foothills, and in the mountains has been known for some years from the published reports of R. W. Brown (1929, 1934), E. W. Berry (1925, 1930), R. P. Wodehouse (1933), and H. O. Kruse (1954). Unpublished identifications made by R. W. Brown and E. B. Leopold (pollens), both of the U.S. Geological Survey, add an appreciable number of genera and species.

From these sources we can reconstruct the following picture of the land flora in the hydrographic basin. Near the lake were cypress swamps, and on the broad alluvial plains grew trees whose nearest relatives—japonica, mimosa, cinnamon, figs, and a variety of aromatic shrubs and trees—now live in the warm-temperate parts of the earth. Where the soil was sandy, palms grew. Vines like our modern grape, gourds, climbing ferns, and cat brier grew here and up into the foothills. Such trees and vines gave way upward to forests of oaks, maple, hickory, and gum. Above, and on drier hills and ridges, were extensive forests of pine—forests that must have extended high up the mountain flanks. Spruce and fir apparently grew only along the crests of the highest ranges.

One rather interesting constituent of the flora is *Ephedra*, which is represented only by its highly distinctive pollen grains. If its Eocene forebears lived in the same parched environment as the *Ephedra* of the Rocky Mountain region of today, it is odd that it should show up in the sediments of the earliest stage (Luman) of Gosiute Lake. It also occurs, as would be expected, in the deposits of the later saline stage.

The presence of *Ephedra* pollen agrees with an observation by R. W. Brown (1929, pp. 280–281) that certain thick, coriaceous leaves in the Green River flora indicate hot, dry sum-

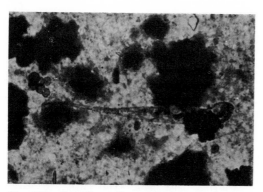

Fig. 23.7.—Germling cell of *Spirogyra* sp. with its spiral chloroplast preserved intact. This single cell, which is 0.2 mm long, is embedded in very rich oil shale from the Eocene Green River Formation. The black areas are pyrite crystals and near the tapered end of the *Spirogyra* cell is a group of small, unidentified algal cells.

mers like those of southern California. Moreover, MacGinitie (1953, p. 46) wisely pointed out that any fossil flora is likely to contain a disproportionately high percentage of riparian elements and so indicate a more mesic environment than actually prevailed over the whole terrain. Plants that grow on the drier interfluves and uplands have a much poorer chance of being represented in a lacustrine fossil flora.

Near the end of the Green River epoch, the plants growing around the margin of the lake took on a somewhat more tropical aspect, to judge from the fossil wood studied by Kruse (1954). Most of his genera are those established for fossil wood, but the inferred relationships to living genera are apparent, for example, in *Talauma, Forschammerioxylon, Ameridoxylon, Fagara, Suriana, Heveoxylon, Schinoxylon, Edenoxylon,* and *Aspidospermoxylon.*

Littoral and subaquatic flora.—In the carbonaceous shale beds, which were deposited in weedy bays and along gently sloping shores, species of the following genera have been identified: *Potamogeton, Nymphaea, Typha, Pontederia, Sparganium, Myriophyllum, Lemna, Salvinia, Equisetum, Pediastrum, Chara,* and a chrysophyte. Curiously, *Chara* is represented in the Green River and Bridger formations only by very rare stem fragments. No oogonia have been found, though in other formations the fruiting bodies only are found.

Plankton and other microorganisms.—Most of the microorganisms are preserved in the struc-

tureless organic matter of the beds of rich oil shale. These include a large number and variety of fungus spores, at least one lichen spore, many pollen grains, spores of mosses and ferns, a rather considerable algal flora, and such things as plant hairs, insect parts such as wing scales, hairs, and fragments of wings and carapace. A number of these found in oil shale in Colorado and Utah were described and figured in an earlier paper (Bradley, 1931).

A new algal flora of about 20 genera is being studied and will be reported in subsequent papers. These algae came from a very thin, very rich oil shale from the saline facies of the formation and, because they are predominantly if not wholly freshwater forms, they represent the flora of the epilimnion during one of the relatively high stages when Gosiute Lake was meromictic. These algae, as tentatively determined, belong to about 5 genera of blue-greens, 6 genera of chrysophytes, and 9 genera of greens. One of the most remarkable of these is a single germling cell of *Spirogyra* in which the spiral chloroplast has been preserved (Fig. 23.7).

No diatoms have been found even in the earliest swamp and lake beds, and no freshwater diatoms as old as the Eocene are known (K. E. Lohman, personal communication).

Fauna of the lake margins.—The commonest fossils in the fluviatile sediments immediately adjacent to the margin of the lake are the fragmentary remains of turtles and crocodiles. Judging by the abundance of these in parts of the partly contemporaneous and overlying Bridger Formation, these animals must have been very numerous. Fish and bird bones, all fragmentary, are also found in these lake margin beds, along with at least one virtually perfect snake. Farther back from the lake, remains of marsupials, insectivores, tillodonts, primates, rodents, carnivores, condylarths, perissodactyls, and artiodactyls have been found.

Littoral and off-shore fauna.—In the beds of the Green River Formation that formed in shoal water, the commonest fossils are the snails *Oxytrema, Viviparus,* the clam *Unio* (?), and ostracods. Two genera of ostracods have been identified, *Cypridea* and *Candona.* In the carbonaceous shale beds estheriid shells are locally extremely numerous, and in at least one nearshore locality caddis fly cases were found (Bradley, 1924). Locally in the less carbonaceous shale beds mycetophyllid and tabanid fly larvae are found in great abundance. Adult insects, however, are exceedingly rare, but they are locally common in the Green River Formation of Colorado and Utah, from which area more than 300 species have been described (Scudder, 1878; Cockerell, 1916). Fragmentary and well-preserved fossil fish, all small, are found locally in Gosiute Lake beds. The famous, beautifully preserved fossil fish represented in museums here and abroad come from the Fossil Syncline—the small Green River lake that lay west of Gosiute Lake. Shells of *Sphaerium, Valvata,* and a small freshwater mussel occur sparingly in beds that formed in somewhat deeper water, along with ostracods.

Plankton fauna.—Very little is known about the microfauna of Gosiute Lake. Partly broken, clathrate loricae with rather coarse, rounded openings have been found. I infer that these are tintinnids, perhaps *Dictyocysta* sp. Associated with the tintinnids are rather thin-walled, saccate forms with a small terminal opening that are thought to be arcellids. They resemble *Corycia* sp. Dujardin.

Under study by a specialist are a large number of more or less fragmentary remains of probably several microscopic animals thought to include midge fly larvae and Cladocera.

Productivity of Gosiute Lake

Because some of the sediments in the Green River Formation that contain considerable amounts of organic matter are varved, we can make very crude estimates of the lake's plankton productivity at certain times. This organic matter, which contains pollen grains, spores, algae, and fragments of insects, is the hardened, and presumably polymerized, derivative of sapropel or gyttja that accumulated in the hypolimnion of the lake. It always contains ferrous sulfide (pyrite or pyrrhotite). Almost certainly this organic matter, except for the pollen and wind-blown spores, is derived from plankton organisms that lived in the epilimnion plus the bacterial plate when there was one. The organic matter, then, represents the more resistant constituents such as the so-called lignin complexes (not true lignin), resins, waxes, porphyrins, and hydrocarbons.

For the purpose of the following calculations, we need to know how much organic matter per year is found in a particular bed of oil shale.

The oil shale chosen is from the saline facies of the Wilkins Peak Member (sec. 2, T. 18N., R. 110W., Sweetwater County, Wyoming, depth 1,663 ft below the surface). It contains 25.32% organic matter and has a rock density of 1.978. The varves have not been measured, but by inspection they are essentially the same as in a similar oil shale at approximately this stratigraphic level. The varves are assumed to have the same average thickness as that oil shale, namely, 0.0065 cm. Then the amount of permanent organic matter accumulated each year equals

$$d\overline{V}O_P$$

where

d = rock density* of the oil shale (1.978 g·cm^{-3})
$\overline{V}$ = average thickness of the varves (0.0065 cm)
O_P = percent of organic matter in the oil shale (25.32)

This comes out to 0.0033 g·cm^{-2} yr^{-1} of lake bottom in the hypolimnion.

The capital difficulty in estimating how much original living organic matter this represents lies in the fact that we have very inadequate means of knowing how much organic substance was lost in reducing the plankton biochemically to the resistant organic constituents that finally became the organic matter in the oil shale. We have several ways of getting around this difficulty, but only two of the least objectionable will be given here.

The organic matter in oil shale is obviously rich in hydrocarbons. On destructive distillation it yields gas and crude shale oil, which is a complex mixture of saturated hydrocarbons, high molecular weight paraffins, and unsaturated hydrocarbons of the naphthalene and ethylene series. It also contains a group of amines, phenols, and tar acids (Guthrie, 1938, pp. 138–150). This suggests that the original organic matter may have reached so advanced a stage of decomposition that only constituents most resistant to microbial action remained. P. V. Smith, Jr. (1954, p. 401), analyzed a sample of marine plankton and found that it contained more than 0.2% of paraffin-naphthene and aromatic hydrocarbons.

The original organic matter that grew in Gosiute Lake surely was not degraded this much, for if it had been, the Green River Formation would have contained petroleum instead of oil shale. It is much more probable that such con-

* Rock density takes into consideration the rock's porosity as well as the specific gravity of the constituent minerals.

stituents as pigments, resins, waxes, and the so-called lignin complexes persisted, too. Indeed, W. E. Hanson of the Mellon Institute suggested (oral communication) that perhaps the hydrocarbons and related compounds (such as P. V. Smith, Jr., found) attached themselves by some sort of bonding to the lignin complex of the lacustrine sapropel. By this means the several kinds of resistant components are eventually integrated into the extremely refractory organic matter found in oil shale. This is an attractive suggestion, and I hope someone will be sufficiently challenged to try to find out what the lignin complexes really are, and if and how they might bond the hydrocarbons, resins, porphyrins, etc.

For the first calculation, assume that the plankton was reduced to lignin complexes and that there was no loss of the lignin complexes, and ignore the porphyrins, waxes, resins, paraffins, and the amazing list of other organic compounds identified in lake sediments (Vallentyne, 1957a). These latter may amount to about 0.5%, judging by the amounts Kleerekoper (1957, pp. 80, 85–88) extracted with benzol from the surface muds of 15 Canadian lakes. Swain (1961, p. 544) reports up to 0.4% amino acid content in the sediment of a eutrophic lake. Birge and Juday (1922, p. 196) give the average amount of lignin in Lake Mendota net plankton as 11.37% of the dry weight of the plankton and in the nannoplankton as 5.40%. The average nannoplankton is 4.75 times the net plankton, so that the weighted average lignin content in the total plankton is 6.4%. Using this value, the 0.0033 g·cm^{-2} average annual increment of organic matter in the oil shale is equivalent to 6.4% of the original plankton (dry weight). Restoring this to 100% gives 0.05 g·cm^{-2} of plankton (dry weight) produced annually in Gosiute Lake at that particular stage. This is equivalent to 5,000 kg per ha (4,450 tons per acre). If this plankton is assumed to have the same gross composition as the average of seven analyses of freshwater algae given by Milner (1953), it contained approximately 54% carbon. On this assumption, Gosiute Lake produced about 2,700 kg of carbon per ha per year. Inasmuch as this estimate is based on total plankton, it cannot be regarded as a measure of primary production.

The second way of estimating the productivity is based on the amounts of porphyrins found in the oil shale and in living algae. Moore and Dunning (1955, pp. 1440–1443) found that a rich oil shale from the Green River Formation of Colorado contained 0.0065% by weight of porphyrins. Since this oil shale contains 21.5% organic matter, the organic matter itself contains 0.03% porphyrins. Algae contain from 0.5 to 1.5% (dry weight) of chlorophylls (Rabinowitch, 1945, p. 408). We can reasonably assume that the chlorophylls from algae were the principal source of the porphyrins in the oil shale (Seward R. Brown, Yale University, oral communication, Aug. 22, 1958). Then, taking 1% as the average content of chlorophylls given by Rabinowitch for algae, the Lake Gosiute algae must have contained $\dfrac{1.0}{0.03}$ or 33 times as much "porphyrin" as the oil shale. Hence, if the Wyoming oil shale used here as a basis for the productivity calculations contains the same percentage of porphyrins as Moore and Dunning found in Colorado oil shale (a reasonable assumption), the annual crop of plankton algae in Gosiute Lake at that stage was 0.0033 g·cm^{-2} × 33 = 0.109 g·cm^{-2}, or 10,900 kg per ha (9,700 tons per acre). Assuming the plankton contained 54% carbon, this is equivalent to 5,886 kg of carbon per ha per year.

Neither estimate takes into consideration the production of higher plants around the margin of the lake. We have no means of making such an estimate, and if we did, it surely would constitute an unwarranted refinement of two crude estimates that differ by a factor of 2. About all that can be said of these estimates of the productivity is that they are of plausible magnitude.

The productivity of existing lakes is notoriously difficult to measure. Consequently, very few figures are available to compare with these crude estimates of productivity in Gosiute Lake. Nygaard (1955, Fig. 4) measured the gross production of Furesø in Denmark and expressed the results in terms of glucose: 22.57 g·cm^{-2} yr^{-1} or 9.03 g·m^{-2} yr^{-1} carbon. This is equivalent to 90.3 kg carbon per ha—a value far below the smaller of the two estimates for Gosiute Lake. Steemann Nielsen (1952, p. 138) estimated 1.5 × 10^{10} tons carbon as the net production of all the oceans. Dividing by the area of the oceans (3.61 × 10^{8} km^{2}), this comes out to 416 kg carbon per ha per year. Verduin (1956, p. 85) gives production figures for 9 lakes, most of which "show yields between 150 and 200 millimoles (1.8 and 2.4 g) C per square meter per day." These amounts are equivalent, respectively, to 6,570 and 8,760 kg carbon per ha per year. Only this last estimate is comparable in magnitude with the estimated productivity of Gosiute Lake given above.

Because the oil shale chosen occurs in the saline facies of the Wilkins Peak Member, these estimates give a measure of the productivity of the mixolimnion of Gosiute Lake when it was meromictic and at one of the relatively high stages between salting stages.

Undoubtedly in a lake that had as long and complex a history as this one, the productivity differed with time over a considerable range. This is revealed, in part, by the large differences in content of organic matter in successive beds up through the whole thickness of the Green River Formation. For example, the several tens of feet of moderately rich oil shale in the upper part of the shale of the Tipton represent a long interval when the lake was eutrophic and probably permanently stratified. On the other hand, during much of the late part of thé lake's history (latter part of the Laney stage), the sediments are very poor in organic matter. This, of course, may have been owing more to the inferred shallowness of the lake than to lack of productivity.

Energy relations

The organic matter in oil shale has a high calorific value, which results in large part from degradation of plankton (mostly phytoplankton), but some (estimated to be a few per cent) of this high fuel value is derived from the wind-blown pollens and waxy spores found in the oil shale. This organic matter in the oil shale represents a marked concentration of energy into small compass, and it is of some speculative interest to compare the number of calories it contains with the number of calories estimated to have been available to the autotrophic organisms in Gosiute Lake during a year when this much organic matter was trapped in the sediments.

For these calculations, the oil shale mentioned previously is used. In this oil shale the average varve contains 0.0033 $g \cdot cm^{-2}$ of organic matter. Although the calorific value of this organic matter has not been determined, the calorific value has been determined on the organic matter isolated from ten different beds of oil shale from the Green River Formation in northwestern

Colorado. This work was done by John Ward Smith of the U.S. Bureau of Mines, Laramie, Wyoming, who has kindly given me his yet unpublished calorific values (letter of June 29, 1961). They are remarkably uniform, which makes it plausible to use his average value, 9,530 $cal \cdot g^{-1}$, for this Wyoming oil shale. J. W. Smith (1961, pp. 7–13) also found that the gross chemical composition of the organic matter in his oil shales was nearly uniform from bed to bed. The average composition is the following: C, 80.5; H, 10.30; N, 2.39; S, 1.04; O, 5.75. The carbon content of the average varve in the Wyoming oil shale is therefore taken as 80.5% of 0.0033 $g \cdot cm^{-2}$ yr^{-1} or 0.0028 $g \cdot cm^{-2}$ yr^{-1}.

Verduin (1956, p. 88) shows that there is a close correspondence between the solar radiation and amounts of carbon synthesized in western Lake Erie throughout the year and that the solar radiation was about 112,500 $cal \cdot cm^{-2}$ yr^{-1} (from his Fig. 2). For western Lake Erie he found the production of carbon to be 0.067 $g \cdot cm^{-2}$ yr^{-1}, and that for eight other eutrophic lakes it ranged from 0.0657 to 0.0876 $g \cdot cm^{-2}$ yr^{-1}. If we assume that Gosiute Lake, at that stage, produced comparable amounts of carbon, then something like 23 to 31 times as much was produced as was permanently trapped. If this ratio is of the right order of magnitude, it means not only that Gosiute Lake was meromictic at that stage, but also that its monimolimnion was a pretty efficient trap for organic matter.

The organic matter in the average varve in this Wyoming oil shale is capable of yielding 9,530 $cal \cdot g^{-1}$ × 0.0033 $g \cdot cm^{-2}$ = 31.5 $cal \cdot cm^{-2}$, whereas 112,500 $cal \cdot cm^{-2}$ of solar energy fell on western Lake Erie in one year to produce 0.067 $g \cdot cm^{-2}$ of carbon or 0.122 $g \cdot cm^{-2}$ of ash-free, dry weight phytoplankton having the gross composition of *Scenedesmus obliquus*. (Steemann Nielsen, 1952, p. 126). Assuming Gosiute Lake produced exactly the same amount of phytoplankton as western Lake Erie in the year Verduin measured it, and that the necessary fraction of this was permanently trapped in the sediments to make 0.0033 $g \cdot cm^{-2}$ of oil shale organic matter, the organic matter so trapped could yield 9,530 $cal \cdot g^{-1}$ at an original cost of 112,500 $cal \cdot cm^{-2}$ yr^{-1} of solar energy available to the microorganisms. Since the available input is only about 12 times the energy stored, this

TABLE 23.8

Typical section of the lacustrine sediments in the old Princeton locality, 3.3 mi south of Florissant, Colorado. From MacGinitie, 1953.

	ft	in.
17. Sandy tuff-shales.................		4
16. Rusty paper shales.................		7
15. Hydraulic tuff; weathers in thin slabby layers; contains fossil leaves........	1	2
Hiatus		
14. Massive gray, fine-grained tuff........	2	0
13. Paper shales with thin tuff interbeds...		10
12. Brown, gravelly tuff; weathers a conspicuous yellow..................		6
11. Fine-grained gray-brown tuff.........		2
10. Paper shales with thin tuff and pumiceous interbeds, fossiliferous........	2	0
9. Brown, gravelly tuff.................		3
8. Paper shales with tuff interbeds, fossiliferous........................	2	0
Hiatus		
7. Ironstone shales, hard and slabby.....		3
6. Gypsum layer.....................		$\frac{1}{2}$-1
5. Paper shales with tuff interbeds; cemented with gypsum at top, rusty at base........................	1	0
Hiatus		
4. Massive gray-brown, fine-grained tuff..	6	6

seems like a remarkably efficient biogeochemical process.

Oligocene—Florissant lake beds

Despite a voluminous literature on the remarkable fossil plants and insects found in these beds, very little has been done with the paleolimnology. MacGinitie, in his admirably critical study (1953) of the Florissant flora, uses resourcefully the evidence from the plants, the insects, and the geology to reconstruct a satisfying picture of the surrounding terrain and the climate but only a sketchy picture of the lakes themselves. The age, in years, of the Oligocene is given by Kulp (1961, p. 1111) as 36 million.

MacGinitie gives (p. 8) the following section of the "lake beds" (Table 23.8):

Overlying and underlying this sequence are volcanic rocks. MacGinitie emphasizes that the characteristics of the lake beds differ from place to place and that it is difficult to correlate beds from one locality to another "because of stream channeling and changes in the ponded areas, which rapidly filled and changed in depth and area. There is evidence that any particular lake would form, fill up, and dry out, possibly later to be replaced by another" (p. 9). MacGinitie

thinks these lakes and ponds formed because volcanic ash falls and mud flows disrupted the streams and clogged them to cause ponding. The lacustrine shales contain considerable amounts of fine volcanic ash particles. This fact, taken together with the numerous beds of volcanic ash that separate the thin units of lacustrine shale, shows that explosive volcanoes were intermittently active in the region. Nevertheless, these episodes were plainly separated by intervals long enough to permit a diverse flora and fauna to become fully established and to flourish.

The lake beds also contain diatoms, sponge spicules, and pollen grains. "In addition to the common fossil plants and insects, there are thin layers covered with enormous numbers of ostracod shells and also ephippia or egg cases of water fleas (Cladocera). In places, flattened shells of fresh water gastropods are abundant, as are fish coprolites with masses of insect fragments. In a few places fish skeletons are common and well preserved, especially in the lower, punky shales" (p. 9). These "punky shales" he interprets as having been deposited in the deepest lakes, none of which is likely to have been more than 50 ft deep.

MacGinitie visualizes the terrain as being not more than 3,000 ft above sea level and having a low relief but rising gradually to rather high mountains (8,000 ft or more) some miles back from the river bottoms where the ponds and lakes were.

He reconstructs the climate as "warm temperate with an annual rainfall not exceeding 25 inches, and probably not more than 20 inches. There are indications of a pronounced dry season, since (1) the leaves of the Florissant plants are predominantly coriaceous and of small size, and, in many cases, are more serrate or divided than the leaves of the related living species; (2) the annual rings of *Sequoia* show a narrow zone of summer wood, and the transition from spring to summer wood is usually abrupt; (3) there are several species related to subxeric living species of western Texas and northeastern Mexico. These facts suggest a season of reduced precipitation and an abundance of intense sunlight" (p. 57).

Miocene—Barstow Formation

In a remarkable paleontologic paper Palmer (1957) gives us a very brief account of an extinct, shallow closed lake in the Mojave Desert of southern California. The beds deposited in this lake are of middle or late Miocene age (roughly 20 million years, according to Palmer). This lake formed in a terrain made up of pyroclastic and sedimentary rocks of middle Tertiary age. The Barstow Formation consists of about 2,000 ft of lacustrine and fluviatile sediments, but Palmer considers only about 78 ft of this section. In this limited part are alternating beds of brown to greenish shale and either limestone or gypsum. Significant for the interpretation of the lake is the fact that several of the units herein are made up of thin laminae, the alternate laminae of brown shale and limestone being each only a few millimeters thick. Other units are similarly thinly laminated, but in them the alternating laminae are of brown shale and gypsum. A few thicker gypsum beds are also present. Two laminated brown shale or brown shale and limestone units contain numerous concretions in which the remarkable aquatic and terrestrial arthropods have been preserved. In reconstructing his picture of the extinct lake, Palmer uses the sedimentary record and analogy with one existing closed lake but draws most heavily on the ecology of the aquatic fauna.

Composition and ecology of the fauna

The aquatic fauna "is dominated by three species: dytiscid beetle larvae belonging to *Schistomerus californense* Palmer, n. sp., larvae and pupae of *Dasyhelea australis antiqua* Palmer, n. subsp., and an indeterminate fairy shrimp. These constitute 98 percent or more of the assemblage, and totals of 560, 530, and 2,860 individuals or parts of individuals respectively were counted in residues of nodules from the measured section. Next most abundant are larval water mites belonging to *Protoarrenurus convergens* Cook, n. sp., which constitute less than 2 percent of the assemblage" (p. 242). Other aquatic forms include pupae only of *Culicoides megacanthus* Palmer, n. sp., and *Dasyhelea stenoceras* Palmer, n. sp. Represented only by larvae are dragonflies belonging to *Orthemis* (?) sp. and a tendipedid, probably *Calopsectra* sp.

In a later paper Palmer (1960, pp. 447–452) described fossil copepods from the Barstow Formation. These are the first fossil copepods to be described from beds older than the Pleistocene. They include a harpacticoid species of the living genus *Cletocamptus* and an undetermined cyclopoid species. These copepods have a remarkably modern aspect.

The nonaquatic fauna contains more species but fewer individuals, the most numerous being thrips. Included also are beetles, a leaf hopper, several bugs, and one spider, *Argenna fossilis* Petrunkevitch, n. sp. Many of these arthropods are astonishingly well preserved, some showing a considerable amount of the internal anatomy.

Palmer points out the striking fact that the strictly aquatic species, except perhaps for the fairy shrimp, are represented only by immature forms. Adult midges, however, were found as well as the immature stages. Palmer argues from this and from "the presence of fairy shrimp, many of which normally hatch between late January and May in temperate latitudes," that this is "evidence for considering the fossil fauna at each horizon as a late winter or spring-time fauna" (p. 243).

The fact that the aquatic species are immature at each of thirteen levels in the sedimentary column where they are found leads him to believe that "the conditions favorable for the preservation of the fauna and the growth of the nodules can most probably be correlated with seasonal physicochemical conditions of the water and the bottom muds" (p. 243).

Paleolimnology

The remarkably regular alternation of thin layers of brown shale and calcite or brown shale and gypsum strongly suggests seasonal deposits, the calcite or the gypsum being the summer deposit and the brown shale the winter deposit. If these beds were as much compacted as the varved beds of the Green River Formation, the assumption that each pair of beds represented one year would mean that deposition in this Barstow lake occurred at 100 to 300 times the rate at which sediments accumulated in the Eocene Green River lakes. Actually, this may not be an unrealistic comparison, because deposition in a small desert lake would be expected to be much faster than in a very large lake. Indeed, such a rapid rate of deposition might have been the critical condition that favored the remarkable preservation of the arthropods. If this high rate of sedimentation obtained (and these are my speculations, not Palmer's), it must have meant a marked change in both the volume and concentration of dissolved solids each year—a condition that would favor the growth of a large population of aquatic and semi-aquatic animals each winter and early spring. Moreover, it seems to me a little difficult to account for so many thin, regular laminae of gypsum any other way. The few thicker beds of gypsum and of limestone evidently represent long intervals of dry years when no appreciable amount of mud or silt was brought in by winter rains.

Palmer draws an analogy between the Miocene Barstow lake and Soap Lake in central Washington, where he found, in July, "larval dytiscid beetles similar to the Miocene fossils and floating pupal skins of aquatic diptera were abundant" (p. 243).

Miocene? Unnamed formation

Just recently Palmer has studied the fauna of some similar lake beds, thought to be of Miocene age, from an unnamed formation from the Monterey Group on the north side of Lockwood Valley in northern Ventura County, California. These lake beds are much like those just described from the Barstow Formation. Beds of gray and dark-brown to greenish-brown shale alternate with thin beds, lenses, and nodules of buff to black limestone and thin-bedded mudstone, siltstone, and tuff. Many of the shale and limestone beds are finely laminated. The limestone concretions contain larval and adult Diptera, predominantly tendipedid midges. In addition to the midges, Palmer found one termite wing, daphniid ephippia, harpacticoid copepods, bones and scales of small fish, and coprolites that contain abundant fish bones and rare pine pollen grains. The plants include ferns, but these are being studied and no report is yet available. The fish bones, some of which are well preserved, have been studied by Gerald Smith of the University of Michigan, who reports that they are centrarchids (sunfish).

The fauna has a distinctly freshwater aspect, so the lake either had freshwater stages or, if it were meromictic, a freshwater epilimnion. But the presence of borate minerals (colemanite) in some of the concretions indicate plainly that the lake was, intermittently at least, closed and saline. Neither the thickness of the lake beds nor the areal extent of the lake is presently known. Nothing has yet been published about this extinct lake or its fauna.

Pleistocene lakes

General statement

A consideration of Pleistocene lakes is very likely to lead into the limnology of existing lakes, because most of our natural lakes are of Pleistocene age. To be sure, most of them were born as the last glaciers melted away, but some came into being early in the Pleistocene epoch. Meinzer (1922), many years ago, focused attention on at least 68 extinct Pleistocene lakes in the Basin and Range Province of the western and southwestern part of the United States. These included the two very large, and to geologists well-known, extinct lakes Bonneville and Lahontan. Several of these extinct lakes, which existed only because of a marked climatic change, are now known to have come into being early in the Pleistocene—perhaps a million years ago—and it is reasonable to infer that most of them are that old. The histories of very few, however, are known. Only a few of these older Pleistocene lakes will be mentioned in this chapter.

Lake Bonneville, Utah

Most of the recent work on Lake Bonneville and its descendant, Great Salt Lake, Utah, has been done by, or under the direction of, Eardley (1938; Eardley et al., 1957; Eardley and Gvosdetsky, 1960). At its maximum stage Lake Bonneville occupied a large part of the western half of Utah and extended a little way into Nevada and Idaho. It probably was in existence for the whole Pleistocene epoch—something on the order of a million years. Sharing the wide-swinging changes of the Pleistocene climate, its history has been comparably variable. During the glacial stages it was large and fresh, but during the interglacial and postglacial stages it was smaller and saline, as witnessed by the strongly saline remnant of today, Great Salt Lake.

Eardley's studies began with a comprehensive investigation of the sediments now forming in Great Salt Lake. This was essentially a geological study, though the results have limnological value, especially since he considered the biota and the extensive tufa deposits formed by algae.

Next Eardley and his colleagues (1957) studied the hydrology of Lake Bonneville, the naturally exposed sediments and beaches of the lake, and the soils that formed in the hydrographic basin during the Pleistocene. The approach was essentially limnological, and considerable attention was given to the chemistry of the lake waters, the salt budget, the lake stages, and the climatic controls of lake fluctuation.

The last, and fully paleolimnological phase, of Eardley and Gvosdetsky's (1960) work was on a 650-ft core of the lake sediments, which represented a large part of the total history and, consequently, a large part of the Pleistocene epoch.

Sediments and duration of Lake Bonneville.— They suggest that the 650-ft core penetrated sediments deposited during the Wisconsin (glacial), Sangamon (interglacial), Illinoian (glacial), Yarmouth (interglacial), Kansan (glacial), and part of the Aftonian (interglacial) stages. This leaves the remainder of the Aftonian and the oldest glacial stage, Nebraskan, unexplored. Presumably the lake came into existence early in the Nebraskan Glacial Stage. Since their 1960 report was written, additional cores in deeper parts of the lake basin have been taken and are being studied. Eardley and Gvosdetsky estimated that the oldest sediments penetrated by their Saltair core hole were a little. more than 600,000 years old and that the whole Pleistocene epoch lasted about 800,000 years. These estimates were based on rates of sediment accumulation determined by several radiocarbon dates in the upper part of this and other cores of Great Salt Lake sediments. The last freshwater lake existed from about 23,000 to 13,500 years ago. Prior to that, there were seven comparable freshwater stages when the lake was large and overflowed. Some lasted only a few thousand years, whereas the two (or possibly only one) high stages during the Kansan Glacial Stage lasted roughly 150,000 years. From the characteristics of the sediments in the core, the authors estimate that the lake was fresh but shallow for long intervals of time during interglacial stages, but that, within these intervals, the lake level dropped repeatedly to rather brief saline stages. The saline stages are manifested by several features, but an important index is the presence of brine shrimp fecal pellets. Eleven times during the 600,000-year interval the lake level fell so low at the site of the core that the bottom was exposed long enough for very immature to rather mature soil profiles to develop. At the site of the core, a soil profile having typical A, B, and C horizons has developed in Postglacial time to a depth of about 6 ft. This soil profile, however, represents a rather complex

history and, according to their interpretation, includes an interval when the lake level was considerably lower than it is today. That extreme low level, they believe, occurred during the altithermal interval, which seems entirely reasonable.

In studying the sediments in this long core, they found no single feature that was plainly diagnostic of either fresh water or salt water and none that, alone, was surely indicative of either deep water or shallow water. Their conclusions about the successive stages of the ancient lake are, therefore, based on appraisals of several factors in combination. As indicators or potential indicators of lake stages they measured the kinds and amounts of clay minerals, the amounts of Ca and Mg carbonates, the presence or absence of oolites, brine shrimp fecal pellets, mollusk and ostracod shells, and the ecological significance of the organisms as interpreted by specialists for each group of organisms. The pollens found in the core are being studied by Robert C. Bright at the University of Minnesota.

An important stratigraphic marker found in the lower part of the core (548 ft) is the Pearlette Ash Member of the Sappa Formation and its equivalent, a layer of distinctive volcanic ash known from Kansas through the Rocky Mountain region into the Northwest. This ash has been dated as of the Kansan Glacial Stage.

Eardley and Gvosdetsky were unable to relate the stages of Lake Bonneville, as they interpreted them from this core, with the lake stages they, and others before them, had deduced from quite extensive studies of the shorelines and near-shore sediments of Lake Bonneville. This lack of correlation reflects the difficulty of interpreting the sediments in a core and, I think, especially the difficulty of interpreting the shore features. Possibly study of the later cores will help to resolve some of these uncertainties.

Table 23.9 gives the areas and corresponding volumes of Lake Bonneville (Eardley *et al.*, 1957), the basin of which is of tectonic origin— predominantly by block faulting.

Climate.—The average annual rainfall over the Great Salt Lake drainage basin today is 15.6 in., and the average annual temperature is 46° F (Eardley *et al.*, 1957). The authors speculate on, but leave unanswered, how much these values may have changed during the glacial and interglacial stages of the Pleistocene.

Morphometry of Lake Bonneville.—As one

TABLE 23.9

Areas and volumes of Lake Bonneville at various stages (converted to metric units) as given by Eardley *et al.*, 1957

Altitude above sea level (ft)	Surface area (km²)	Volume (km³)	Salinity[a] (%)
5,135±	13,300	8,900	
4,820±	12,480	4,702	Last outlet
4,500	11,660	1,724	0.2
4,400	11,400	947	0.4
4,300	11,140	338	1.2
4,245	11,000	138	2.6
4,230	10,960	87	4.8
4,220	10,930	47	7.7
4,200[b]	10,878	16	23.0

[a] Assuming present-day salt inventory of Bonneville Basin.

[b] Approximate level of Great Salt Lake.

might expect of a large lake in a complexly block-faulted basin, Lake Bonneville had a very long and complex shoreline (Gilbert, 1891). Its development of shoreline (D_L) is 4.8. Lake Bonneville also contained numerous islands, some of which were large.

Chemistry of the lake water.—From the average amounts of Na, K, Cl, and SO_4 in solution in the major tributary streams and springs, all weighted for discharge, it is estimated that about 1.1×10^6 tons of salt are presently being delivered to Great Salt Lake each year. The total salt in the Bonneville Basin in the form of salt crusts, salt water in clays, and salt in the Great Salt Lake brine aggregates approximately 6×10^9 tons. If the rate of influx of salts remained constant, then the apparent interval since the last overflow stage was only about 6,000 years, whereas C^{14} dates indicate that the last overflow stage ended about 12,000 years ago. Eardley *et al.* (1957) attribute the difference to loss of salts carried out of the drainage basin by wind. There are apparently no measures of such deflation losses from closed basins, but their estimate seems, intuitively, to be high. Langbein's important paper (1962) on the hydrology and salt economy of closed lakes, which, of course, was not available to Eardley and his colleagues, makes a strong case for a significantly large storage of soluble salts in the marginal mudflats of closed lakes each time their surface levels fall. It is possible that Eardley's excellent inventory of the salts in the Bonneville Basin would come closer to a balance with income if the salts in a larger

expanse of the marginal mudflats were re-evaluated with this in mind.

It is beyond the scope of this chapter to consider the waters of Great Salt Lake. Nevertheless, Eardley's 1938 paper, in addition to considering the relationship between river water and the brines and the related problem of $CaCO_3$ solubility in the brines, calls attention to the regimen of Mg in those brines. The role of Mg in the brines and the form in which it is presently being deposited is of decided importance to anyone concerned with the paleolimnology of ancient saline lakes.

In general the Great Salt Lake brine contains 25 to 30 times as much Mg as Ca. The sediments contain not only $CaCO_3$ (mostly as aragonite) but also dolomite, which may be precipitating out of the brine or may be forming in the sediment as a product of very early diagenetic processes (Miller, 1961). Alderman and Skinner (1957) showed convincing evidence that dolomite and calcite precipitate out of natural brines in which the salinity may be only half that of sea water in environments where active photosynthesis is going on. As a result, the pH of the brine is raised to 9.2 or even higher. Such disequilibrium systems may be much more important in natural bodies of water than the equilibrium-dominated physical chemistry of late years has led us to believe.

Eardley (1938, pp. 1344–1345) found some evidence that a hydrated magnesium silicate, possibly parasepiolite ($2MgO \cdot 3SiO_2 \cdot 4H_2O$), is precipitating out of the magnesium-rich brines or is forming soon after deposition as an early diagenetic product. Parasepiolite and sepiolite have been found in a number of deposits that formed in saline lakes.

Algae and their deposits.—Up to the time Eardley's 1938 report was written, various investigators had reported a fauna in Great Salt Lake consisting of 1 crustacean (*Artemia salina*), 3 flies, and 5 or 6 protozoans. Of the plants 13 species are algae, 12 bacteria, and 62 are diatoms. Eardley points out that it is almost certain some of these are freshwater forms that have been washed into the lake. (Papers dealing with all these organisms have either been published or are available in theses on deposit at the University of Utah.) But Eardley made a number of collections of algae growing on calcareous deposits, which had formed in response to the photosynthesis of the algae. Francis Drouet of the University of Missouri identified in these collections *Aphanothece packardii* and a species of *Pleurocapsa* close to *entophysaloides* Setchel.

The calcareous deposits, bioherms, are restricted to shallow water and make extensive, irregular sheet-like deposits that have an aggregate extent of about 100 mi². They form in water that ranges from a few inches to 10 or 12 ft in depth. Characteristically these deposits are made up of flat-topped mounds that are almost, or quite, confluent. The individual mounds range from 6 to 36 in. high and average about 18 in. More than 50% of the surface of these mounds is covered with the "brown to pink, blue-green, unicellular, colonial alga *Aphanothece packardii*." The calcareous deposits themselves are nodose, lamellar, or arborescent, and most of them are very porous. Although these extensive algal bioherms formed in salt water, others form in entirely freshwater lakes, for example, Green Lake, New York (Bradley, 1929a).

Lake San Augustin, New Mexico

This extinct lake occupied an elongate basin in west-central New Mexico. During late Pleistocene time it had a maximum area of 225 mi², a maximum depth of 165 ft, and occupied about 13% of its hydrographic basin. During this late Pleistocene stage it cut many shore terraces and built bars and beach cusps (Powers, 1939).

Deep water wells indicate that the lake had a much longer history. Several years ago a hole 645 ft deep was drilled and cored specifically to explore the ancient history of this lake and particularly to obtain information about past climates. The pollens found in the upper 300 ft of this core have been reported in a preliminary paper by Clisby and Sears (1956). Carbon-14 dates at 19- and 28-ft depths indicate ages of 19,000 and 27,000 years, respectively. If the rates of sedimentation indicated by these age determinations hold for the rest of the core, a history of some 650,000 years is represented.

A well-defined spruce pollen maximum in the upper 60 ft of the core appears to reflect one or more late Pleistocene glacial stages. But below that, only one rather feeble spruce maximum was found, between 110 and 160 ft. On the other hand the curve representing non-tree pollen (chiefly chenopods, composites, and grasses) continues strong from a depth of about 50 ft to 300

ft, with the exception of a short stretch near the bottom where no data are available.

Searles Lake, California

The stratigraphy and the later part of the history of Searles Lake in southeastern California has been presented, along with 33 radiocarbon dates, by R. F. Flint and W. A. Gale (1958). In this study their objectives were to relate lake history to glacial history and to shed as much light as possible on the kind and magnitude of climatic changes revealed by the sedimentary record and by the lake's history. The approach, therefore, was primarily geologic and climatologic. Nevertheless, as in a number of similar studies, paleolimnological interpretations emerge.

The ancestral Searles Lake occupied three adjacent, typical Great Basin block-faulted valleys. It was a product of both tectonic and climatic changes. At its maximum extent it had an area of about 385 mi² and a maximum depth of at least 750 ft. Because the present-day Searles Lake contains an enormous volume of valuable salts and brine, many exploratory boreholes have been drilled in its sediments and cores taken. A number of these cored holes are about 300 ft deep, and at least one is 875 ft deep. Flint and Gale's studies were based on information revealed by cores of the salts and sediment.

Sediments and duration.—Cores from the part of the basin which is still flooded intermittently and where salt is normally exposed to the air (an area of about 12 mi²) show that the surface bed of complex salts, called the "upper salt," is about 60 to 90 ft thick and has relatively few, thin mud partings. Below this is a sharply defined bed of greenish-gray to nearly black mud, the "parting mud." This is 10 to 13 ft thick, and much of it is finely laminated with pairs of alternating light and dark laminae. Below this "parting mud" is another nearly solid salt sequence, the "lower salt," which is 25 to 35 ft thick. This lower salt also consists of a complex mixture of salts but has more thin partings of mud than does the upper salt. Below the "lower salt" is the "bottom mud," which is about 100 ft thick. Like the "parting mud," this also has a sharply defined top, overlain by a trona bed, but downward it differs by the presence of an increasing number of thin evaporite layers. The "bottom mud" grades downward into a unit known locally as the "mixed layer," which consists of an alternation of mud layers and beds of nahcolite, trona, and gaylussite, but no halite.

Most of the C^{14} dates are on samples taken from the "parting mud" and from a zone near the base of the lower salt and the upper part of the "bottom mud." But these permitted Flint and Gale to fix the duration of each stratigraphic unit, except the "bottom mud," most of which is too old for C^{14} dating.

The time intervals represented are

Upper salt   *ca.* 10,000 years
Parting mud *ca.* 13,000 years
Lower salt   *ca.* 9,000 years
Bottom mud *ca.* 14,000 years for the top 10 ft

Hydrography.—The ancient Searles Lake received most of its water from the overflow of Owens Lake, which, in turn, received its water from the high Sierras. At its highest stages Searles Lake overflowed into a lake in Panamint Valley that had a maximum surface area of 272 mi^2 and a maximum depth of more than 900 ft.

Flint and Gale interpret the "parting mud" as sediment laid down during the last pluvial (glacial) stage of the Wisconsin and at least the upper part of the "bottom mud" as representing the next older pluvial stage of the Wisconsin. The upper and lower salt zones, of course, represent, respectively, the arid postglacial stage and a similarly arid interglacial stage. The sharply defined boundaries at the top and bottom of the "parting mud" and the sharp boundary at the top of the "bottom mud" are ingeniously, and plausibly, accounted for by the fact that Searles Lake received most of its water from the overflow of Owens Lake. When that lake began or ceased to overflow, the regimen of Searles Lake changed abruptly, either becoming deeper and fresher or abruptly shrinking to such a low level that salts began to precipitate.

The "parting mud," when fresh and moist, is a dark greenish-gray, but it dries to a pale, fulvous green. Some is massive and some is more or less silty, but much of it is laminated. Flint and Gale report alternating light layers "mostly less than 2 mm thick, and thicker dark layers—up to 1 cm thick." They also observed that the darker laminae are themselves subdivided into still finer laminae. I have examined some of the "parting mud" that has the best-developed lamination and find that the conspicuous white laminae, 0.1 to about 1.0 mm thick, consist of minute crystals

of aragonite. These are separated by layers of clay that range in thickness from about 0.5 mm to 3 or 4 mm. These clay layers contain only moderate amounts of organic matter. I regard these pairs of laminae, one layer of organic clay and one layer of microgranular carbonate, as lacustrine varves, though they are atypical in that the carbonates consist of the orthorhombic form of $CaCO_3$, aragonite, in place of the usual calcite, which is rhombohedral. So far as I know aragonite is very rare in lacustrine deposits and probably reflects an unusual composition of the lake water during that stage.

But shorelines and beaches well above the present lake seem to necessitate the postulate that during considerable intervals while the "parting mud" formed, the lake was large and probably overflowed. Even so, it is not improbable that, since the lake had just deposited 25 to 35 ft of salts, it was meromictic through this 13,000-year interval.

The "parting mud" contains fossil fish (a cyprinid, probably *Siphateles*) and pollen grains, which have been studied by Roosma (1958). The pollen study shows "through the stratigraphic distribution and relative abundance of juniper compared with *Artemisia* and chenopods, that the local climate was cooler and wetter during deposition of the Parting Mud than during precipitation of the overlying Upper Salt" (Flint and Gale, 1958, p. 698).

Flint and Gale report that organic matter dissolved from the nearly black mud is orange and possesses a marked fungicidal property. They say (p. 698), "Because of its color and its molybdenum content it is believed to have originated, in part at least, in some of the various forms of chromogenic organisms such as the red and green bacteria now living on the surface of Searles Lake. These red bacteria have been found to contain comparable amounts of molybdenum."

Vallentyne (1957*b*) studied the organic matter from samples of the "parting mud" and found "a number of carotene compounds, xanthophylls and possibly echinenone, together with several other unidentified substances. The Parting Mud was also found to contain green chlorophyll-like pigments, extractable with methanol but not with acetone" (Flint and Gale, 1958, p. 698).

A series of more comprehensive reports on the sediments and history of Searles Lake, it is hoped, will be available in the next few years from George I. Smith of the U.S. Geological Survey. He has been studying the cores, salts, and brines of Searles Lake since 1955 and in the past few years has mapped the lake basin and its environs in the hope of being able to relate the lacustrine sediments above, and peripheral to, the salt beds with the subsurface stratigraphy.

References

ALDERMAN, A. R., AND H. C. W. SKINNER. 1957. Dolomite sedimentation in the south-east of Australia. Amer. J. Sci., **255**: 561–567.

ANDERSON, R. Y., AND D. W. KIRKLAND. 1960. Origin, varves, and cycles of Jurassic Todilto Formation, New Mexico. Bull. Amer. Assoc. Petrol. Geol., **44**: 37–52.

BARGHOORN, E. S., AND R. L. NICHOLS. 1961. Sulfate-reducing bacteria and pyritic sediments in Antarctica. Science, **134**: 190.

BERRY, E. W. 1925. Flora and ecology of so-called Bridger beds of Wind River Basin. Pan-Amer. Geol., **44**: 357–368.

———. 1930. A flora of Green River age in the Wind River Basin of Wyoming. U.S. Geol. Surv., Profess. Paper No. 165: 55–79.

BIRGE, E. A., AND CHANCEY JUDAY. 1922. The inland lakes of Wisconsin: The plankton. I. Its quantity and chemical composition. Bull. Wisconsin Geol. Nat. Hist. Surv., **64**, 222 p.

BRADLEY, W. H. 1924. Fossil caddice fly cases from the Green River Formation of Wyoming. Amer. J. Sci., **7**: 310–312.

———. 1929*a*. Algae reefs and oolites of the Green River Formation. U.S. Geol. Surv., Profess. Paper No. 154: 203–223.

———. 1929*b*. The varves and climate of the Green River epoch. U.S. Geol. Surv., Profess. Paper No. 158: 86–110.

———. 1931. The origin of the oil shale and its microfossils of the Green River Formation in Colorado and Utah. U.S. Geol. Surv., Profess. Paper No. 168: 37–56.

BROOKS, C. E. P. 1926. Climate through the ages. R. V. Coleman, New York. 439 p.

BROWN, R. W. 1929. Additions to the flora of the Green River Formation. U.S. Geol. Surv., Profess. Paper No. 154: 279–293.

———. 1934. The recognizable species of the Green River flora. U.S. Geol. Surv., Profess. Paper No. 185–C: 45–68.

CLARKE, F. W. 1924. The data of geochemistry. U.S. Geol. Surv., Bull. No. 770: 13–14.

CLISBY, K. H., AND P. B. SEARS. 1956. San Augustin Plains—Pleistocene climatic changes. Science, **124**: 537–539.

COCKERELL, T. D. A. 1916. Some American fossil insects. Proc. U.S. Natl. Museum, **51**: 91–92.

DAVID, LORE. 1941. *Leptolepis nevadensis*, a new Cretaceous fish. J. Paleontol., **15**: 318–321.

DEEVEY, E. S. 1955. The obliteration of the hypolimnion. Mem. Ist. Ital. Idrobiol., suppl., **8**: 11–36.

EARDLEY, A. J. 1938. Sediments of Great Salt Lake,

Utah. Bull. Amer. Assoc. Petrol. Geol., **22**: 1305–1411.

EARDLEY, A. J., AND VASYL GVOSDETSKY. 1960. Analysis of Pleistocene core from Great Salt Lake, Utah. Bull. Geol. Soc. Amer., **77**: 1323–1344.

EARDLEY, A. J., VASYL GVOSDETSKY, AND R. E. MARSELL. 1957. Hydrology of Lake Bonneville and sediments and soils of its basin. Bull. Geol. Soc. Amer., **68**: 1141–1201.

FLINT, R. F., AND W. A. GALE. 1958. Stratigraphy and radiocarbon dates at Searles Lake, California. Amer. J. Sci., **256**: 689–714.

FREY, D. G. 1961. Developmental history of Schleinsee. Verh. intern. Ver. Limnol., **14**: 271–278.

GILBERT, G. K. 1891. Lake Bonneville. U.S. Geol. Surv. Monogr. I, 438 p.

GUTHRIE, BOYD. 1938. Studies of certain properties of oil shale and shale oil. U.S. Bur. Mines, Bull. 415, 150 p.

HUTCHINSON, G. E. 1957. A treatise on limnology. John Wiley & Sons, New York.

KLEEREKOPER, HERMAN. 1957. Une étude limnologique de la chemie des sediments de fond des lacs de l'Ontario meridional Canada. Uitgevery Excelsior, 's-Gravenhage: 1–205.

KRUSE, H. O. 1954. Some Eocene dicotyledonous woods from Eden Valley, Wyoming. Ohio J. Sci., **54**: 243–267.

KULP, J. L. 1961. Geologic time scale. Science, **133**: 1105–1113.

LANGBEIN, W. B. 1961. The salinity and hydrology of closed lakes. U.S. Geol. Surv., Profess. Paper No. 412: 1–20.

LA ROCQUE, AURELE. 1960. Molluscan faunas of the Flagstaff Formation of Central Utah. Mem. Geol. Soc. Amer., **78**: 1–100.

MACGINITIE, H. D. 1953. Fossil plants of the Florissant beds, Colorado. Carnegie Inst. Washington, Publ. 599: 1–188.

MEINZER, O. E. 1922. Map of the Pleistocene Lakes of the Basin and Range Province and its significance. Bull. Geol. Soc. Amer., **33**: 541–552.

MILLER, D. N., JR. 1961. Early diagenetic dolomite associated with salt extraction process, Inagua, Bahamas. J. Sediment. Petrol., **31**: 473–476.

MILNER, H. W. 1953. The chemical composition of algae, p. 285–302. *In* J. S. Burlew (ed.), Algal culture from laboratory to pilot plant. Carnegie Inst. Washington, Publ. 600.

MILTON, C. M., AND HANS EUGSTER. 1959. Mineral assemblages of the Green River Formation, p. 113–150. *In* P. H. Abelson (ed.), Researches in geochemistry. John Wiley & Sons, New York.

MINDER, LEO. 1923. Über biogene Entkalkung im Zürichsee. Verh. intern. Ver. Limnol., **1**: 20–32.

MOORE, J. W., AND H. N. DUNNING. 1955. Interfacial activities and porphyrin contents of oil shale extracts. Ind. Engr. Chem., **47**: 1440–1444.

NIPKOW, FRITZ. 1920. Vorläufige Mitteilungen über Untersuchungen des Schlammabsatzes im Zürichsee. Rev. Hydrol., **1**: 100–122.

NYGAARD, GUNNAR. 1955. On the productivity of five Danish waters. Verh. intern. Ver. Limnol., **12**: 123–133.

OOSTING, H. S., AND W. D. BILLINGS. 1951. A comparison of virgin spruce-fir forest in the northern and southern Appalachian system. Ecology, 32: 84–103.

PALMER, A. R. 1957. Miocene arthropods from the Mojave Desert, California. U.S. Geol. Surv., Profess. Paper No. 294–G: 237–277.

———. 1960. Miocene copepods from the Mojave Desert, California. J. Paleontol., 34: 447–452.

PECK, R. E., AND C. C. REKER. 1948. Eocene Charophyta from North America. J. Paleontol.; 22: 85–90, Pl. 21.

POWERS, W. E. 1939. Basin and shore features of the extinct Lake San Augustin, New Mexico. J. Geomorphol., 2: 345–356.

RABINOWITCH, E. I. 1945. Photosynthesis and related processes. Vol. I. Interscience Publ., New York.

ROOSMA, AINO. 1958. A climatic record from Searles Lake, California (abstr.). Science, 128: 716.

RUSSELL, I. C. 1885. Lake Lahontan. U.S. Geol. Surv. Monogr. 11, 288 p.

SCUDDER, S. H. 1878. The fossil insects of the Green River shales. U.S. Geol. Geograph. Surv., Terr. Bull. No. 4: 747–776.

SMITH, J. W. 1961. Ultimate composition of organic material in Green River oil shale. U.S. Bur. Mines R.I. 5725: 1–16.

SMITH, P. V., JR. 1954. Studies on origin of petroleum: Occurrence of hydrocarbons in recent sediments. Bull. Amer. Assoc. Petrol. Geol., 38: 377–404.

STEEMANN NIELSEN, E. 1952. The use of radio-active carbon (C^{14}) for measuring organic production in the sea. J. Conseil Permanent Intern. Exploration Mer, 18: 117–140.

SWAIN, F. M. 1946. Middle Mesozoic nonmarine ostracoda from Brazil and New Mexico. J. Paleontol., 20: 543–545.

———. 1961. Limnology and amino-acid content of some lake deposits in Minnesota, Montana, Nevada, and Louisiana. Bull. Geol. Soc. Amer., 72: 519–545.

TASCH, PAUL, AND J. R. ZIMMERMAN. 1961. Fossil and living conchostracan distribution in Kansas-Oklahoma across a 200-million year time gap. Science, 133: 584–586.

VALLENTYNE, J. R. 1957a. The molecular nature of organic matter in lakes and oceans, with lesser reference to sewage and terrestrial soils. J. Fish. Research Board Canada, 14: 33–82.

———. 1957b. Carotenoids in a 20,000-year-old sediment from Searles Lake, California. Archiv. Biochem. Biophys., 70: 29–34.

VERDUIN, JACOB. 1956. Primary production in lakes. Limnol. Oceanogr., 1: 85–91.

WELTEN, MAX. 1944. Pollenanalytische, stratigraphische und geochronologische Untersuchungen aus dem Faulenseemoos bei Spiez. Veröffentl. Geobotan. Inst. Rübel, 21: 1–201.

WODEHOUSE, R. P. 1933. The oil shales of the Green River Formation. Tertiary Pollen II. Bull. Torrey Botan. Club, 60: 479–524.

24 | *Clarence M. Tarzwell*

Sanitational Limnology

Man has waged a continuous battle to improve his living conditions. Through the development and use of tools, he has established dominance over the larger organisms—sometimes eliminating them and other times using them as food, fiber, or fuel or for the provision of shelter or as beasts of burden. Through continual improvements in housing, heating, and the production of clothing, man to a large degree has become independent of adverse elements of weather by creating his own environment. The development of modern civilization has been an evolutionary process in which each new development is based upon those that came before. These developments have made possible the growth of large cities and our ever-expanding industries, which have in turn created many new environmental problems. In the headlong rush for progress and the better things of life, man is modifying his environment and adding to the air and water materials never invented by nature. What the long-term effects of these modifications will be is unknown. However, many feel that man may become his own worst enemy unless the basic requirements for life—air, water, soil, and sunlight—are better conserved to maintain a favorable environment.

Biology, the science of life, is becoming increasingly important in the effort to maintain a favorable environment for man in our modern complex civilization. While nature can be bent to the will of man, at a cost, it is much better and less expensive to recognize the laws of nature and to work in accordance with them. Environmental health and sanitation are particularly important in areas of dense population, because most of the wastes are water-borne and are discharged into watercourses. Within the past few years the public has become much more aware of the significance and value of our water resources. Our supplies of fresh water are dependent on rainfall and thus are definitely limited, since no economically practicable methods for increasing rainfall have yet been developed. Although sea water can be converted to fresh water for use in coastal areas, the present high costs of production and transportation dictate that the existing supplies of fresh water be used to the fullest extent and re-used where necessary. Consequently, public support has been generated for water conservation and management and for research programs directed toward the more effective use of water and the development of means for its re-use.

It is now widely recognized that many of our supplies of fresh water will have to be used over and over if they are to meet our future needs. Effective and efficient re-use of water requires that each user return his waste or process water to the watercourse in a condition suitable for the next use of the water. The ability to do this depends on definite knowledge of the quality of water required for each kind of use. The principal uses of water may be grouped under the following eight headings: (1) domestic and municipal, (2) agricultural, (3) industrial, (4) aquicultural (sport and commercial fishing and the rearing of fishes), (5) recreational (boating, swimming, water skiing, etc.), (6) aesthetic, (7) power production, (8) navigation.

All of these uses, except the aesthetic, result in the addition of materials to the water or in changes in its character or quality that may make the water less satisfactory or even unsatisfactory for other uses. Since the production and disposal of wastes are an integral part of each water use, the treatment of wastes and the return of water to its source in a condition suitable for other desired purposes should be the responsibility of the users. We cannot afford much longer the luxury of using our waters only once, nor can we continue to discharge untreated or poorly treated human wastes into the same stream from which we take our drinking water. Over the years strange attitudes have developed in regard to sewage disposal. Before the development of sewers and the water transport of wastes, the disposal of human wastes was essentially a personal problem. Now, however, when our wastes are quickly washed into common underground sewers and discharged below town, out of sight, they are quickly out of mind, and the general public feels little personal responsibility for them. We would not think of dumping our garbage onto our neighbor's front lawn, but there is no social stigma attached to dumping our fecal wastes into his drinking water.

Growth in population and industry not only increases the demands on our water supplies but also results in more materials being added to them, which greatly change the quality or character of the water. These changes seriously limit the value of the water for other uses and thus constitute pollution. We continually need more and more suitable water for our various uses, while at the same time wastes resulting from these uses are rendering unsuitable more and more of our water supplies. Pollution presents the greatest threat to our future water supplies, and it must be controlled or eliminated.

In our present system of intensive water use, the objective of pollution abatement is to provide water of a suitable quality and in sufficient quantity for the following purposes: (1) domestic and municipal uses; (2) agricultural uses, such as irrigation and stock watering; (3) food processing and manufacture and all other industrial uses; (4) the maintenance of sport fishing and the production of crops of aquatic organisms of commercial or recreational importance; (5) aesthetic enjoyment and recreational uses, such as swimming, boating, and water skiing; and (6) navigation and power production.

An examination of the objectives of pollution abatement leads to the conclusion that many of the problems involved in the detection, evaluation, and abatement of pollution are biological, since they are concerned with the protection, control, or production of living things. One of these is the toxicity of waste materials to plants and animals. With the great expansion of the petrochemical and synthetic organic chemicals industries, the detection and control of toxic materials in waste discharges is assuming an ever-increasing importance (Middleton and Rosen, 1956; Middleton and Lichtenberg, 1960). During 1960 some 637 million pounds of synthetic organic pesticides were manufactured in the United States. A certain amount of these materials reaches our waters either directly or indirectly, with consequent harm to the biota (Tarzwell and Henderson, 1957; Tarzwell, 1959; Henderson et al., 1960). Other important problems result from the acute or chronic toxicity of industrial wastes to aquatic life, changes in the aquatic environment caused by the addition of various wastes, and the effects of sublethal concentrations of various wastes (Tarzwell, 1958a; Ingram and Doudoroff, 1953; Ingram and Tarzwell, 1954). Large amounts of organic wastes and materials added to our waters act as fertilizers which encourage the growth of algae and other microorganisms (Tarzwell and Palmer, 1951). These may cause nuisance problems such as tastes and odors in water supplies, the clogging of filters in water treatment plants, growths on the surface and walls of storage reservoirs or in water distribution systems, and changes in color, pH, or other characteristics of the water (Palmer, 1959). Still another biological aspect of water quality control is that the treatment of sewage and other organic materials depends upon the activity of those organisms that break down or metabolize these waste materials. The so-called natural purification process in streams, lakes, and reservoirs also is largely brought about by living organisms.

The science of limnology, which includes much of aquatic biology but is broader in concept and coverage, is of great importance in the detection, evaluation, abatement, and control of water pollution. Limnology originally was concerned mainly with the life processes going on in lakes, but now it encompasses the physical, chemical, and biological factors governing productivity in all inland waters as well as the ecology of aquatic organisms. As stated by Welch (1935), "Limnology depends upon the proper application and integration of certain facts, principles, and methods of chemistry, physics, geology, hydrography, meterology, and other sciences to the solution of problems which are in the end biological in nature." The same author defined limnology as that branch of science concerned with biological productivity of inland waters and with all the causal influences that determine it. Limnologists are, therefore, vitally interested in water pollution and its effects on the aquatic biota, including their environment and overall productivity, the manner in which different pollutants in different waters affect water supply, waste treatment, natural purification, and the value of waters and their biota for various uses.

Limnology of water supplies

Some of the earliest applications of limnological methods to the solution of problems in environmental sanitation were in the field of water supply. About the middle of the last century, Dr. Hassall (1850, 1856) of London pointed out the value of microscopic examination of water for the understanding of water problems. In this country Sedgwick (1888) was a leader in the application of biological methods to water supply problems. The Massachusetts State Board of Health was the first agency in the United States to set up a systematic biological examination of water supplies. Two years later, in 1889, the state of Connecticut undertook similar work, which was followed by the establishment of a laboratory at Chestnut Hill Reservoir by the Water Board of the City of Boston. In the same year Prof. William T. Sedgwick and George W. Rafter developed the method of counting plankton that, with later modifications, came to be known as the Sedgwick-Rafter method. Certain improvements in the method were made by George C. Whipple, who designed the ocular micrometer for making field counts and who in 1899 published the first edition of *The Microscopy of Drinking Water*. This book summarized the work of the leaders in this field and greatly stimulated the study of microscopic organisms in drinking water and their effects on water quality. The methods described for the collection, concentration, and enumeration of plankton were endorsed by the Committee on Standard Methods of Water Analysis.

These methods were used in forecasting water-blooms, and methods for controlling blooms were subsequently developed. Moore and Kellerman (1905) first used copper sulfate to eradicate growths of phytoplankton, and since that time it has been used extensively and intensively for the prevention or destruction of algal blooms in water supplies. Treatment is generally initiated when build-ups in the populations of undesirable forms are indicated by microscopic examination. The concentration of plankton by means of a centrifuge, which was used by Kofoid (1897) in his studies on the Illinois River in the 1890's, became much more popular during the third and fourth decades of the present century in the microscopic examination of water.

Men closely associated with problems of water treatment have emphasized the importance of plankton in causing tastes and odors, filter clogging, and interference with effective chlorination and coagulation. They have experimented with various procedures for the chemical control of algae and have considered some biological control methods. They have developed practical laboratory procedures for the detection and evaluation of odors and have devised methods for their removal. Some of the men who have done outstanding work in this field in North America during the twentieth century are John R. Baylis of Chicago, F. E. Hale and B. C. Nesin of New York City, D. H. Matheson of Ontario, R. L. Derby and C. Wilson of California, G. C. Turre of Denver, L. C. Billings of Texas, S. O. Swartz and E. A. Swartz, Jr., of Massachusetts, W. D. Monie of Maine, James B. Lackey, formerly of the U.S. Public Health Service and now of Florida, and C. K. Calvert of Indianapolis. Most of these men are engineers who have been responsible for the operation of particular water treatment plants. Only a few biologists have worked in the field of water supply; outstanding among them are W. T. Sedgwick, W. C. Purdy, J. B. Lackey, C. T. Butterfield, and C. M. Palmer. While few limnologists have worked directly in the field of water supply, the basic work of such men as Birge, Juday, Kofoid, Needham, Reighard, Welch, and Ward has served as a background for the investigations that have been carried out.

In actual practice there has been no clear-cut division of labor between sanitary limnology and microbiology, although admittedly microbiologists are concerned more with the pathogenic and parasitic problems of water supply, while limnologists are concerned more with the detection, identification, and control of nuisance organisms. This latter problem has been increasing in importance, and it can be expected to become even more critical in the future. During the nineteenth century the main source of domestic water supplies was ground water, which is largely free of nuisance growths. However, with the great increases in population and the massive conflux into cities and towns, it became imperative to turn more and more to surface water supplies. Many of the larger cities have found it necessary to build large reservoirs to store water, some of which are considerable distances from the city. When water is stored for extended periods and is exposed to sunlight and the open air, growths of microorganisms usually develop and under certain conditions may become quite abundant. Some of these organisms can create serious problems in the provision of a potable water supply. Two forces are at work to intensify these problems: on the one hand our rapidly growing cities require progressively larger quantities of good, pure water, while on the other hand these same cities are discharging into our watercourses an ever-increasing volume of rich organic wastes which stimulate the growth of nuisance organisms and reduce the number of suitable water supplies. Nuisance growths of algae are increasing in severity and extent and are becoming problems throughout the country. Present methods of waste treatment break down materials or change their form, but they do not remove the nutrients that stimulate the development of dense growths of algae and other plankters. Instead these are released in the form of nitrates, phosphates, carbon dioxide, and trace elements, which are readily utilized by the algae. New approaches are needed for the solution of these problems.

Tastes and odors are the most troublesome problem to water plant operators. Because observations have indicated that one or more kinds of certain algae are always present when trouble develops, these algae are suspected to be the cause of the trouble. Results of treatments for the control of algae have lent credence to these suspicions and have incriminated certain genera of algae as being responsible for the tastes and odors. While these conclusions are based on circumstantial evidence, they may be correct and should be verified by pure-culture investigations in the laboratory to determine whether or not the principal species of algae in question do in fact produce taste and odor materials. Studies of this nature were initiated by the Aquatic Biology Section of the Robert A. Taft Sanitary Engineering Center of the U.S.P.H.S. in 1950 (Tarzwell, 1950; Palmer and Maloney, 1953). Although unialgal cultures can be grown in the laboratory quite readily, and some 30 species were grown in pure culture, great difficulty was encountered in growing in pure culture those algae that are believed to be the source of the odoriferous materials. It was concluded that certain materials produced by bacteria or other organisms were essential for the growth of these algae. Limited success, attained through the addition of vitamins, soil extracts, peat extracts, and other materials, indicated that the odoriferous materials are fatty acids or substances related to them. However, no definite identifications of these substances were made, and the work was discontinued for lack of funds needed for the large-scale project which would carry the investigations to completion. It was hoped that if the taste and odor materials could be isolated and identified, some substance could be added to the coagulation chambers in water treatment plants that would break down or unite with these odoriferous substances to render them innocuous. Chlorine is now applied for this purpose and is useful to a certain extent. It is not universally effective, however, and hence the need continues to discover other substances that will more specifically remove or inactivate these undesirable compounds.

Actinomycetes also have been implicated in the production of odoriferous materials in water supplies. Studies at the Robert A. Taft Sanitary Engineering Center have shown that the genus *Streptomyces* is the most obnoxious in this respect. The *Streptomyces* are much more abundant in muds along the shoreline and in soils subject to flooding than they are in the open water. It has been demonstrated that the odoriferous materials produced in soils·can be leached from the soil, and hence some of the odors occurring in surface water supplies may result from such soil leaching. Materials have been isolated from cultures of *Streptomyces* that will produce detectable odors at a dilution of one part in six billion parts of water. Laboratory studies, however, have indicated that, unlike the materials produced by algae, those produced by the streptomycetes studied to date can be removed by chlorination and activated carbon (Romano, 1958; Romano and Safferman, 1963).

Copper sulfate is the material used most widely for the prevention or control of algal blooms in water supplies. Several other algicides are now on the market, but some are more expensive, and all present, to some degree, the drawbacks of broad-spectrum chemical toxicants. Chemical control is a repetitive process and in time becomes very costly. Also, the continued use of chemical algicides may so greatly reduce the effectiveness of such biological controls as predators, competitors, and parasites that eventually control may depend entirely on the use of chemicals. In time, species resistant to the chemical used may build up and cause serious trouble, because as dosages must be increased to achieve control, concentrations may become lethal to fishes or other desirable organisms. In soft water at a *p*H below 7, copper sulfate can be toxic to fish at concentrations as low as 0.04 ppm. Its effects on the invertebrates important as fish food are not well known.

There is a definite need for better and more specific controls for nuisance algae. If materials can be found that are toxic to the nuisance algae and relatively non-toxic to the others, a combination of chemical and biological control could be achieved. With the broad-spectrum algicides now in use, nearly all the species of algae are drastically reduced. This is injurious to overall productivity and usually results in the dominance of weed species when algal growths are re-established. By the use of specific algicides only the undesirable species would be reduced, and the desirable species, which are valuable in the food chains, would increase in numbers to fill the space formerly occupied by the nuisance forms. This would make it more difficult for the nuisance forms to come back in as large numbers, and a form of biological control would thereby be achieved. In the early 1950's studies were undertaken at the Taft Center to discover more specific algicides. Several materials were found to be much more toxic to certain groups or genera than they were to others (Maloney and Palmer, 1956), but because of a lack of adequate testing facilities, the program was temporarily discontinued. Work toward the discovery of natural algicides has now been resumed.

Studies made in oxidation ponds or sewage lagoons have indicated that some organisms produce materials that are toxic to and inhibit the growth of other organisms. More than 600 species of actinomycetes, bacteria, and fungi have been screened to determine if they produce anti-algal materials. A considerable number were found to have some anti-algal activity, and two were found that produce substances quite effective and specific against blue-green algae. These offer hope for biological or specific controls. Difficulty has been experienced, however, in the isolation and recovery of these materials which are soluble in both water and organic solvents.

An extensive research program is needed to develop biological controls for algae. Biological controls that work continuously are much more desirable than the now widely used chemical controls which are repetitive, costly, and may have adverse side effects. It is known, for example, that certain bacterial phages occur in nature; intensive investigation should be able to discover comparable biological controls for nuisance organisms in water supplies. The problems exist, and there is a long-felt need for limnologists to take a greater interest in water-supply problems. This applies not only to problems created by algae but also to those caused by sulfur and iron bacteria, fungi, Protozoa, worms mollusks, crustaceans, and insects. Many of these organisms have occurred in such numbers in water distribution systems that they have clogged pipes and water meters and produced corrosion.

Environmental manipulation can be quite effective in helping alleviate conditions caused by nuisance organisms. The amount of nutrients reaching streams and reservoirs can be limited or reduced through soil erosion control and modification of agricultural practices. Sewage treatment methods can be changed or modified so that the nutrient elements are removed and utilized rather than added to the watercourses. Carriers for detergents may be modified so they do not act as fertilizers.

Limnologists can be of service in the selection of sites for water storage reservoirs so that the reservoirs are less productive. There is also a very promising field in the management of reservoirs. Water levels can be managed so as to limit the production of aquatic, semi-aquatic, and marsh plants. Plants in the fluctuation zone can be removed by burning. Marsh or shallow-water areas that cause problems can be dredged, filled, or dyked and dewatered. Predators and competitors of undesirable organisms can be encouraged, and the production of harvestable crops can be promoted as a means for removing nutrients from the system.

Limnology of waste treatment

The increasing amounts of waste organic materials being added to our waters as a result of population and industrial growth are causing many problems. The existing, so-called "complete treatment" methods for sewage and other organic wastes break down 90% or less of the organic materials. Since 10% or more of the wastes are not broken down, the "completely treated" wastes from a city of 1,000,000 would represent about the same load as the untreated wastes from a city of 100,000 people. It is easy to see, therefore, why streams can be overwhelmed by population growth in spite of so-called complete treatment of wastes. However, this is only a portion of the picture. Modern methods of waste treatment change only the form or composition of the waste materials and do not remove the breakdown products—ammonia, nitrates, phosphates, silicates, sulfates, carbonates, chlorides, and trace elements—that are discharged from sewage plants and serve as nutrients for algae and other organisms. Thus, modern methods of sewage treatment do very little to reduce pollution as far as nuisance aquatic growths are concerned. We are now adding to our streams each year 1.5 to 2 billion pounds of detergent carriers. These algal nutrients go through our treatment plants virtually undiminished. Additional problems are created by the lack of effective treatment methods for certain organic materials. The breakdown of many is slow or difficult, and treatment of these does not even approach 90% removal. Wastes, such as those from paper mills which add immense amounts of wood sugars, are discharged into streams often after little or no treatment.

These ever-increasing loads of wastes are producing in streams nuisance growths of organisms that are unsightly, harmful to bottom organisms essential as fish food, detrimental to the spawning of fishes and the development of their eggs and fry, and damaging to fishermen through the clogging of their nets. Massive growths of *Sphaerotilus*, fungi, and Protozoa occur in many areas, and excessive growths of algae are present in many lakes, reservoirs, and streams. Effluents from sewage treatment plants support dense growths of attached algae in some streams. During the day the algae produce great quantities of oxygen through photosynthesis. In lakes and reservoirs this excess or supersaturation of oxygen is usually sufficient to provide the oxygen needed for respiration of the plants, animals, and bacteria during the hours of darkness. In streams having numerous riffle areas, however, much of the oxygen produced by photosynthesis is released to the air, so that during the hours of darkness the respiration of the dense algal growths stimulated by the sewage nutrients may reduce the oxygen content to levels that are lethal to fishes.

The treatment of putrescible wastes through the application of biological principles offers a fertile field for limnological research. Present waste treatment processes have been developed largely by empirical methods with little regard for or appreciation of biological principles. In evaluating a treatment installation or the efficiency of a treatment plant for handling a particular waste, the practice has been to test only the final effluent, and little or no attention has been paid to the biota doing the work. Thus, in some runs of a treatment plant or under some conditions results are good, yet in others they are poor, while the reasons for this variability remain obscure. Investigations should therefore be made to identify the organisms involved in breaking down or utilizing the wastes, and research should be carried out to determine the environmental requirements of these organisms so that they can be provided with a suitable environment in which to carry on their purification activities at the highest rate. Such an approach is essential. Without a knowledge of the organisms doing the work and of their environmental requirements, how can a process be effectively designed or improved? Such an approach would pay dividends in the operation of trickling filters, activated sludge plants, and oxidation ponds and is essential for the development of new or special waste treatment processes.

Present waste treatment methods are designed to incinerate, degrade, or otherwise change the form of organic waste materials. Not only are these procedures wasteful, but also they will not be adequate for meeting our future needs. As already pointed out, effluent from treatment plants may overwhelm receiving streams with that portion of the waste that is not treated. Moreover, basic plant nutrients are not removed but are discharged into the stream where they can cause a host of problems. It is apparent that most organic and inorganic nutrient materials must be removed from waste waters before they are discharged into streams if these latter are to serve other useful purposes. Research should be carried out to develop methods by which microorganisms can convert waste organic materials into useful products. The use of such processes would reduce the wastage of valuable materials, assist in pollution abatement, and be an incentive to industry and municipalities to carry out more effective treatment of all wastes. The development of such processes presents problems in applied ecology, physiology, biochemistry, engineering, and economics.

Limnologists can and should play a prominent role in devising, testing, and evaluating methods for the treatment of organic wastes. As yet they have paid little attention to these problems, but the basic principles that have been discovered can best be applied by limnologists. If they do not enter into applied research and into the application of their principles and findings, others not so well fitted by training and experience will do so. Environmental health and sanitation require the knowledge and efforts of many disciplines in order to progress and meet the problems of the present and future.

Limnology of pollution abatement

Definitions

The term "pollution" has been loosely used and has come to mean different things to different people. To some, pollution is the addition of any waste or chemical material to a stream. To others it means any change in water quality brought about by the activities of man. Some maintain that pollution is any interference with the balance of nature or any change in the quantitative relationship of the biota. None of these definitions is entirely correct. If the simple addition of chemicals constitutes pollution, then those materials used in water treatment for the provision of a potable water would be pollutants. If the mere addition of a waste material to a stream is called pollution regardless of its effect, fertilizing materials added to increase productivity would be pollutants. A waste that constitutes pollution from the standpoint of one use of the

water might not be pollution from the standpoint of a second, and it might actually be beneficial for a third use. For example, even a small amount of domestic sewage discharged into a municipal water supply would lessen the value of that water for municipal use and would therefore be considered pollution; a small amount of organic matter discharged into water used for navigation or the generation of power would not be considered pollution, since it would not affect the use of the water for these purposes; and small amounts of sewage discharged into a barren stream would act as fertlizer, stimulating the production of aquatic life and providing attendant benefits. In the latter case addition of sewage would constitute pollution if the discharge of organic material were increased to the extent that its bacterial decomposition resulted in sufficient depletion of the dissolved oxygen to kill or otherwise adversely affect fish or other desired organisms. If pollution is regarded merely as a change in water quality, the addition of distilled water would constitute pollution, as would the addition of pure stream water from another stream having different water quality.

A change in the composition of the biota of a water might have a harmful effect, no effect, or a beneficial effect on the production of a desired crop or species. When the effects of the elimination of a species or a number of species of microorganisms, whose space is taken over by other microorganisms, are unknown or do not adversely affect the production of a desired crop, such changes cannot be called pollution. A relationship must be established between a change in the biota and an undesirable effect if the causal agent is to be classed as pollution.

Water pollution may therefore be defined as the addition of any material or any change in the quality or character of a water that interferes with, lessens, or prevents its use for a desired purpose. Under this definition pollution is tied to usage, and water is not polluted unless its desired use is adversely affected. Pollution and toxicity are relative terms and do not exist unless the concentration or level of certain materials or conditions exceeds desirable or safe limits. This applies to silt, organic materials, temperature, and substances that can be toxic. For example nitrates, phosphates, carbon dioxide, calcium, magnesium, sodium, potassium, copper, zinc, molybdenum, iron, sulfur, and selenium are all needed in certain quantities for survival, growth, and reproduction of the biota, but at high concentrations they become toxic.

Pollutants are customarily classified by origin, such as sewage or industrial wastes. Perhaps pollution problems would become more clear-cut if the pollutants were grouped according to their effects on the receiving waters. Pollutants fall into one or more of the following six categories: (1) inert inorganic and organic materials or wastes, (2) putrescible wastes, (3) toxic wastes, (4) wastes with a significant heat content, (5) radioactive wastes, (6) contaminants or tainting materials. Until fairly recently the first group—chiefly silt from land erosion—was our most widespread pollutant. Now, however, putrescible wastes, including sewage and all organic materials that can be broken down by microorganisms, constitute the most widely treated type of waste. Toxic wastes are increasing with the development of the petrochemical and synthetic organic chemical industries and the extensive and intensive use of pesticides. Steam-generated electric power plants are creating local temperature problems, which are expected to become more widespread in the future. Radioactive wastes are similar to silt and pesticides in that they do not always originate at a point source but may come from entire watersheds. The tainting of fish flesh and other aquatic organisms by waste materials is increasing.

The problem of pollution is not static but is ever changing. Frequent surveys and studies are essential to keep abreast of old problems and to discover and evaluate new ones. Because survey methods, equipment, and objectives have changed over the years, a review of past surveys is helpful in understanding past and present problems.

Surveys and investigations

The survey of the Illinois River by the Illinois Natural History Survey under the direction of Dr. S. A. Forbes was one of the first in this country that clearly demonstrated the biological effects of pollution. Changes in the river as a result of the ever-increasing load of organic wastes from Chicago were documented by the continuing biological studies of the river (Forbes and Richardson, 1913, 1919; Forbes, 1928). Kofoid's work on the plankton, which was the most detailed up to that time, demonstrated changes in plankton populations associated with pollution (Kofoid, 1903, 1908). Work on the bottom fauna

was also emphasized, and since studies continued over a number of years, changes caused by increasing organic enrichment were described in some detail and correlated with changes in the fish fauna as pollution extended downstream and became more severe. Richardson (1921, 1925, 1928) clearly described the changes in the bottom and shore fauna of the Illinois River that resulted from the downstream movement of pollutional conditions. Fish production and changes in the composition and volume of the catch, and in the composition of the entire population, as recorded by the survey, demonstrated dramatically some of the effects of organic enrichment and pollution (Forbes, 1907, 1914).

Another notable early survey was the investigation of the pollution and sanitary conditions of the Potomac River in 1913 and 1914 by the U.S. Public Health Service. In this survey Purdy (1916) found that the shallow flats of the Potomac River were of great importance in the natural purification of organic wastes. He observed that sunlight and turbidity were prominent factors in determining oxygen levels; that the content of dissolved oxygen was higher over the flats than in the river channel; that at high tide waste waters having lower dissolved oxygen contents moved from the river channel out over the flats, whereas at low tide clearer water having higher dissolved oxygen contents returned from the flats to the river channel; and that flats having large growths of submerged aquatic vegetation acted as purifiers and clarifiers of the water. He also observed that there were diurnal variations in dissolved oxygen and variations between sunny and cloudy days; that certain organisms among the plankton and bottom-dwelling groups were more prevalent in those portions of the river into which sewage was discharged; and that these organisms gradually disappeared with increase in distance downstream.

The U.S. Public Health Service Stream Investigations Laboratory, which was established in Cincinnati, Ohio, in 1914 and which has continued under the successive names of Environmental Health Center and Robert A. Taft Sanitary Engineering Center, has carried out a number of classical stream pollution surveys. The surveys of the Ohio River in 1914 to 1918 and 1939 to 1941, the Illinois River in 1921 and 1922, the Scioto River from 1937 to 1939, and the Upper Mississippi River in 1926 and 1927 resulted in much valuable information on the natural purification process, the effects of pollutants (especially organic wastes) on aquatic populations, and the development of pollutional zones with the life characteristic of each (Purdy, 1923, 1926, 1930, 1937; Butterfield and Purdy, 1931; Kehr *et al.,* 1941; Butterfield, 1935, 1940).

In support of stream surveys and investigations, Butterfield, Purdy, and their co-workers at the U.S. Public Health Service Laboratory in Cincinnati, carried on a series of basic studies of the natural purification process (Purdy and Butterfield, 1918; Butterfield, 1929, 1933, 1940). Their studies of the effect of plankton animals upon bacterial death rates disclosed, first, that in a medium of a given concentration the presence of a definite number of bacterial cells, living or dead, prevents further multiplication and, second, that certain of the Protozoa are responsible for ingesting large numbers of bacteria, thereby eliminating enough to maintain the bacterial population below its limiting value. This control of bacteria by Protozoa assures continual regeneration of a vital population of bacteria, which is most effective in the breakdown of organic wastes.

During the past several years the U.S. Public Health Service Laboratory at Cincinnati has investigated the biological aspects of many local or area problems and has assisted in many of the river basin studies in which pollutional conditions were evaluated and enforcement actions recommended.

The U.S. Fish and Wildlife Service, formerly the U.S. Bureau of Fisheries, has conducted many field investigations and surveys throughout the country to determine the effects of pollution on aquatic life. The work of Ellis (1937) on the detection and measurement of pollution, the effects of various wastes on stream environments, and the toxicity of various materials to fishes is a classic. Ellis used bioassay techniques to determine toxicity and physiological methods to detect and evaluate sublethal effects. His methods (Ellis *et al.,* 1946) are widely used as are his recommendations regarding safe levels of environmental conditions and concentrations of toxicants. Results of many of his studies were described in a series of research reports (Ellis, 1940*a*, 1940*b*, 1940*c*, 1943*a*, 1943*b*, 1943*c*).

A number of significant surveys and investigations have been conducted by state organizations variously designated as water resource committees, agencies, or boards; water pollution control boards; state health departments; and state conservation or fish and game departments. From 1926 to 1936, New York State surveyed all the streams and lakes of the state, region by region. The results of these investigations were published in a series of reports that appeared annually, each one dealing with a specific area. In these surveys pollutional conditions and the effects of pollution on the aquatic biota were studied, and several of the reports contain articles on the biological effects of pollutants (e.g., Claassen, 1927; Farrell, 1931).

Louisiana, which for many years has studied biological effects of pollution, was one of the first states to conduct bioassay investigations for the evaluation of toxicity problems. A number of states now have biologists on the staff of their agency dealing with water pollution, and several are conducting surveys and making bioassays to determine the toxicity of industrial and other wastes.

Biological indicators of organic enrichment

Ever since the classical papers of Kolkwitz and Marsson (1908, 1909) outlined the saprobic system, those working on the biology of organic enrichment or pollution in North America have noted some relationships among the extent of enrichment, chemical and physical conditions, and the presence or absence of different species of organisms in specific areas. Kolkwitz and Marsson made their studies in areas in which domestic sewage was the dominant waste, and they formulated a system based upon both plants and animals to indicate the degree of "pollution." Scientists in America have followed their work in part but have broadened the concept to include other organic wastes and pollutants and have used different names for the so-called pollutional zones. Various workers have used the groups of organisms in which they are most interested as possible indicators of pollution. Purdy (1916) demonstrated the value of certain organisms for indicating areas of the Potomac River receiving sewage discharges. Later he used plankton populations as indicators of the presence of organic wastes and the degree of their purification. Richardson (1921, 1925, 1928) made extensive studies of bottom organisms, the composition of populations, their value to the fishery, and their value for indicating the severity and extent of stream pollution.

A study by Weston and Turner (1917) of the effects of a sewage-filter effluent on a small clean stream clearly demonstrated the effects of organic enrichment, the sudden change in the biota after the introduction of the waste, and the progressive recovery of the biota downstream as the wastes were utilized until the original upstream condition was almost regained. The study also indicated typical associations of plants and animals, which have since come to be correlated with the different pollutional zones.

While with the U.S. Public Health Service at the Cincinnati Laboratory, Brinley and Lackey investigated the value of aquatic organisms as indicators of organic enrichment or "pollution." Brinley's (1944) findings, made in connection with the Ohio River Survey, recognized five stream zones and three classes of organisms. His class-one organisms were those found in water of good sanitary quality and able to survive scarcity of organic food, sudden changes of temperature, low temperature, and relatively high acidity. The class-two organisms were those that prefer a rich nutritive medium or feed on bacteria and solid particles, while the intermediate group contained all other organisms.

The role of microorganisms in stream purification and their indicator value has been the special interest of Dr. J. B. Lackey, who has published many papers on this subject (Lackey, 1939, 1941, 1942, 1944). He reported that relatively few plankton organisms show clear-cut responses to pollution or its absence. This lack of response appears to be particularly true of the Euglenidae when considered as a group and applies also to the Volvocales. Certain individual species of these groups appear to favor sewage-laden water, while others favor clean water, and still others appear to be widely tolerant. Two classes of algae—the olive-green flagellates or Cryptophyceae and the yellow-green flagellates or Chrysophyceae—have been found as a group to react adversely to pollution, and thus they seem to be indicators of clean water if they are present in moderate or great numbers. Even different species of the same genus of Protozoa may react differently, one preferring clean water and another enriched water. Lackey concluded that no group of organisms as a whole can be used to indicate the sanitary condition of the water, but

that individual species must be considered for this purpose.

Dr. Ruth Patrick and her co-workers at the Philadelphia Academy of Natural Sciences have developed and used extensively a method based on the community structure of diatoms rather than the presence or absence of particular species. Dr. Patrick has defined a "healthy" stream as one able to support greatly diverse populations of diatoms. The Catherwood diatometer, developed at the academy, is an apparatus for holding microscope slides near the surface of the water in any aquatic habitat (see Fig. 6.10). After about fourteen days' exposure in the aquatic habitat, the community of diatoms established on the slides is assumed to have attained an ecological equilibrium and hence to be representative of the diatom population as a whole. From 8,000 to 40,000 diatoms per sample are identified and counted, and the results are plotted as the number of species containing stated numbers of individuals arranged in intervals as 1–2, 2–4, 4–8, etc. A truncated normal curve results, from which an interpretation is made, based on the shape, height, and position of the curve. With increased enrichment the height of the mode increases, and the tail of the curve becomes longer (Patrick, 1950; Patrick et al., 1954).

Studies of the pollution and natural purification of Lytle Creek in southwest Ohio confirmed many of the findings of former stream studies and led to some new concepts. In these studies five zones representing stages in stream degradation and recovery were recognized. These were designated as degradation, septic, upper recovery, lower recovery, and clean water zones. While each of these zones graded gradually into the next, a portion of each zone had a biota characteristic of that zone (Gaufin and Tarzwell, 1956). It is suggested that these zones be called life zones rather than pollutional zones, because they are usually recognized and delimited by their biotas. These zones changed with the seasons, becoming longer and almost indistinct chemically in the winter and shorter and more intense in the summer. Diurnal changes were also greater in the warm months (Gaufin and Tarzwell, 1956). The number of species of macro-invertebrates and vertebrates decreased rapidly in the degradation zone, which was very short in this instance, reached a low in the septic zone, then gradually increased in the recovery zones, and reached or exceeded their former number in the clean water zone (Tarzwell and Gaufin, 1953; Katz and Gaufin, 1953; Katz and Howard, 1955). Conversely, the number of individuals per species of macro-invertebrates increased to a peak in the septic zone and then declined to a low in the clean water (Gaufin and Tarzwell, 1952, 1955). The number of species found regularly in the septic zone was usually about ten, consisting of those organisms, such as *Tubifex,* that can live at very low levels of dissolved oxygen; those that can live for a time without free oxygen such as some of the chironomids (Paine and Gaufin, 1956); and those that use atmospheric oxygen such as pulmonate snails, rat-tail maggots, and mosquito larvae.

In evaluating aquatic organisms as indicators of organic enrichment, one should exercise great caution, since several organisms that may occur in large numbers in polluted situations may also be found in limited numbers in cleaner situations. Furthermore, environmental factors other than pollution can greatly influence the number of species and individuals and their distribution. Thus, both the qualitative and the quantitative compositions of the biota must be considered in determining the presence of organic enrichment or pollution. Clean waters are generally marked by a great variety of habitats; therefore, they have large numbers of species but many fewer individuals of each species than do enriched areas. Clean waters are characterized by the larger gill-breathing aquatic insects—mayflies, stoneflies, and caddisflies. Species of these groups found in the recovery zone usually have more than one method of respiration. The presence of large numbers of such organisms as rat-tail maggots, sludge worms, and blood worms usually indicates marked organic enrichment, especially if the number of different species in the biota is 15 or less. The absence of clean water forms is also a good indicator of environmental conditions.

The complex or association of organisms that develops in a given area is indicative both of the prevailing environmental conditions and of the extreme conditions that have occurred during the lives of the component members. By looking at the bottom fauna, experienced limnologists can tell a great deal about the severity and extent of organic enrichment and the degree of stream recovery. Through experience and by associating stream populations with chemical, physical, and bacterial conditions, they have learned that certain communities of organisms are characteristic of different conditions of pollution. While this relationship is based on circumstantial evidence, it nevertheless has a good foundation: the extremes of the environmental conditions determine what organisms will constitute the population. Organisms able to withstand existing conditions prosper and increase in numbers, while the other forms decrease or even disappear. If it is desired to ascertain definitely the levels of environmental factors through the use of the populations of organisms considered to be "biological indicators," the environmental requirements of the organisms in question must be determined experimentally by multi-environmental factor studies. Supplied with such data, the limnologist can go down a stream, determine the limiting extremes of dissolved oxygen, pH, and temperature that had occurred, and thus be able to assess the severity and extent of stream pollution and the degree of recovery. Such data would be very useful in solving pollution control problems.

Water quality criteria for aquatic life

Many materials that adversely affect aquatic organisms are being added to our streams. To protect our aquatic life resources adequately, we must have water quality criteria that define the environmental conditions essential for the survival, growth, reproduction, and general well-being of the aquatic biota (Tarzwell, 1957). Such criteria must be based upon a sound and detailed knowledge of the environmental requirements of the organisms we wish to protect. The acquisition of such biological data will necessitate much detailed, careful, long-term research by competent men in many different areas (Tarzwell, 1962). Preliminary work has been done on the dissolved oxygen requirements of fishes, but much more information is needed on the requirements of different species and groups of organisms as well as the influence of different levels of carbon dioxide, temperature, pH, and other environmental factors on their minimum oxygen requirements (Katz *et al.*, 1959; Davison *et al.*, 1959; Tarzwell, 1958*b*; Whitmore *et al.*, 1960). Temperature and oxygen requirements are so intimately related that they must be considered together. To determine minimum levels that are safe under conditions of long-term exposure, it is necessary to use the multivariant approach in order to evaluate the effects of variations in factors other than oxygen.

Methods have been developed for short-term bioassays of toxicity using fish (Tarzwell and Henderson, 1956; Tarzwell, 1958c). These are described in the 11th edition of *Standard Methods for the Examination of Water and Waste Water* (Anon., 1960). Short-term studies serve to indicate relative toxicities and allow comparisons of toxicities to different organisms, but they do not indicate what concentrations are safe under conditions of continuous exposure. Long-term studies are helpful in determining direct toxic effects, but since there is need to determine the effects of sublethal concentrations of toxicants, additional studies are essential. Physiological and histological studies may be used to indicate the effects of sublethal concentrations and those which are not harmful under conditions of continuous exposure. Because of the immense backlog of materials to be studied and the many new ones appearing each year, a large-scale, continuous research program is needed. Because the problem is so broad and involves so many different organisms, it is necessary that studies be carried out by a large number of different workers. Such studies are essential and should be given the first priority for research directed toward the abatement of pollution affecting aquatic life. Without knowledge of the environmental requirements of aquatic life, we do not know the degree of pollution abatement needed, because we do not know the environmental conditions that must be maintained in the stream. Lacking this knowledge, we cannot effectively detect and evaluate pollution nor determine the level of waste treatment needed. Such knowledge is a prerequisite for the establishment of effective water quality criteria. Adequate criteria would serve to inform the general public of the needs for pollution abatement, thus making the public a more effective force in securing pollution control; water users would be informed of the objectives of waste treatment; and the processing of pollution enforcement actions would be made easier.

References

ANONYMOUS. 1960. Standard methods for the examination of water and waste water. Prepared and published jointly by Amer. Pub. Health Assoc., Amer. Water Works Assoc., and Water Pollution Control Fed., 11th ed. 626 p.

BRINLEY, F. J. 1944. Ohio River pollution control. Supplement F—Biological studies. II. Rept. U.S. Pub. Health Serv., House Document No. 266, 78th Congr., 1st Session: 1275–1364.

BUTTERFIELD, C. T. 1929. Experimental studies of natural purification in polluted waters. III. A note on the relation between food concentration in liquid media and bacterial growth. Pub. Health Repts., **44**: 2865–2872.

———. 1933. A note on the food habits of *Colpidium*. Pub. Health Repts., **48**: 814–818.

———. 1935. Biological and bacteriological relationships in water purification and sewage treatment. Kansas Water and Sewage Works, Bien. Rept., 1934–35: 106–109.

———. 1940. Some functions of bacteria in the purification of polluted water. J. Bacteriol., **39**: 527–533.

BUTTERFIELD, C. T., AND W. C. PURDY. 1931. Some interrelationships of plankton and bacteria in natural purification of polluted water. Ind. Engr. Chem., **23**(2): 213–218.

CLAASSEN, P. W. 1927. A biological survey of the Genesee River System. III. Biological studies of polluted areas in the Genesee River system. State of New York Conserv. Dept., Suppl. 16th Ann. Rept., 1926: 38–46.

DAVISON, R. C., W. P. BREESE, C. WARREN, AND P. DOUDOROFF. 1959. Experiments on the dissolved oxygen requirements of cold-water fishes. Sewage and Ind. Wastes, 31(8): 950–966.

ELLIS, M. M. 1937. Detection and measurement of stream pollution. U.S. Dept. Commerce, Bur. Fish., Bull. No. 22. *Also in* Bull. No. 48: 365–437.

———. 1940a. Pollution of the Coeur d'Alene River and adjacent waters by mine wastes. U.S. Dept. Interior, Bur. Fish., Spec. Sci. Rept. No. 1, 60 p.

———. 1940b. Pollution studies of effluents from the Dickinson salt works, Malden, West Virginia. U.S. Dept. Interior, Bur. Fish., Spec. Sci. Rept. No. 9, 14 p.

———. 1940c. Water conditions affecting aquatic life in Elephant Butte Reservoir. U.S. Dept. Interior, Bur. Fish., Bull. No. 34: 258–304.

———. 1943a. Mine-waste pollution of Bear Butte Creek, Black Hills, South Dakota. U.S. Dept. Interior, Fish and Wildl. Serv., Spec. Sci. Rept. No. 12, 9 p.

———. 1943b. A study of the Mississippi River from Chain of Rocks, St. Louis, Missouri, to Cairo, Illinois, with special reference to the proposed introduction of ground garbage into the river by the city of St. Louis. U.S. Dept. Interior, Fish and Wildl. Serv., Spec. Sci. Rept. No. 8, 21 p.

———. 1943c. Stream pollution studies in the state of Mississippi. U.S. Dept. Interior, Fish and Wildl. Serv., Spec. Sci. Rept. No. 3, 13 p.

ELLIS, M. M., B. A. WESTFALL, AND M. D. ELLIS. 1946. Determination of water quality. U.S. Fish and Wildl. Serv., Research Rept. No. 9, 122 p.

FARRELL, M. A. 1931. New York State Survey. A biological survey of the St. Lawrence watershed. IX. Studies of the bottom fauna in polluted areas.

New York Conserv. Dept., Biol. Surv. No. 5, Suppl. 20th Ann. Rept.: 192–196.

FORBES, S. A. 1907. On the local distribution of certain Illinois fishes: An essay in statistical ecology. Bull. Illinois State Lab. Nat. Hist., **7**: 273–303.

——. 1914. Fresh water fishes and their ecology. Illinois State Lab. Nat. Hist., 19 p.

——. 1928. The biological survey of a river system—its objects, methods, and results. State of Illinois Dept. Registration Educ., Div. Nat. Hist. Surv., **17**(7): 277–284.

FORBES, S. A., AND R. E. RICHARDSON. 1913. Studies on the biology of the upper Illinois River. Bull. Illinois Nat. Hist. Surv., **9**(10): 481–574.

FORBES, S. A., AND R. E. RICHARDSON. 1919. Some recent changes in Illinois River biology. Bull. Illinois Nat. Hist. Surv., **13**(6): 139–156.

GAUFIN, A. R., AND C. M. TARZWELL. 1952. Aquatic invertebrates as indicators of stream pollution. Pub. Health Repts., **67**(1): 57–64.

GAUFIN, A. R., AND C. M. TARZWELL. 1955. Environmental changes in a polluted stream during winter. Amer. Midland Nat., **54**(1): 78–88.

GAUFIN, A. R., AND C. M. TARZWELL. 1956. Aquatic macro-invertebrate communities as indicators of organic pollution in Lytle Creek. Sewage and Ind. Wastes, **28**(7): 906–924.

HASSALL, A. H. 1850. A microscopic examination of the water supplied to the inhabitants of London and the suburban districts. London.

——. 1856. The diatomaceae in the water supplied to the inhabitants of London. Microscopic examination of the water. London.

HENDERSON, C., Q. H. PICKERING, AND C. M. TARZWELL. 1960. The toxicity of organic phosphorus and chlorinated hydrocarbon insecticides to fish. Trans. 1959 Seminar, Biological Problems in Water Pollution, Robert A. Taft Sanit. Engr. Center, Tech. Rept. W60-3: 76–88.

INGRAM, W. M., AND P. DOUDOROFF. 1953. Selected bibliography of publications on industrial wastes relating to fish and oysters. U.S. Pub. Health Publ. 270, Bibliography Ser. 10: 1–28.

INGRAM, W. M., AND C. M. TARZWELL. 1954. Selected bibliography of publications relating to undesirable effects upon aquatic life by algicides, insecticides, weedicides. U.S. Pub. Health Publ. 400, Bibliography Ser. 13: 1–28.

KATZ, MAX, AND A. R. GAUFIN. 1953. The effects of sewage pollution on the fish population of a midwestern stream. Trans. Amer. Fish. Soc., **82**: 156–165.

KATZ, MAX, AND W. C. HOWARD. 1955. The length and growth of the 0-year class creek chubs in relation to domestic pollution. Trans. Amer. Fish. Soc., **84**: 228–238.

KATZ, MAX, A. PRITCHARD, AND C. WARREN. 1959. The ability of some salmonids and a centrarchid to swim in water of reduced oxygen content. Trans. Amer. Fish. Soc., **88**(2): 88–95.

KEHR, R. W., W. C. PURDY, J. B. LACKEY, O. R. PLACAK, AND W. E. BURNS. 1941. A study of pollution and natural purification of the Scioto

River. U.S. Pub. Health Serv., Pub. Health Bull. 276, 153 p.

KOFOID, C. A. 1897. Plankton studies. Methods and apparatus. Bull. Illinois State Lab. Nat. Hist., **5**: 1–25.

——. 1903. The plankton of the Illinois River, 1894–99, with introductory notes upon the hydrography of the Illinois River and its basin. I. Quantitative investigations and general results. Bull. Illinois State Lab. Nat. Hist., **6**(2): 95–629.

——. 1908. The plankton of the Illinois River, 1894–99, with introductory notes upon the hydrography of the Illinois River and its basin. II. Constituent organisms and their seasonal distribution. Bull. Illinois State Lab. Nat. Hist., **8**(1): 1–361.

KOLKWITZ, R., AND M. MARSSON. 1908. Oekologie der pflanzlichen Saprobien. Ber. deut. botan. Ges., **26a**: 505–519.

KOLKWITZ, R., AND M. MARSSON. 1909. Oekologie der tierischen Saprobien. Intern. Rev. ges. Hydrobiol. Hydrol., **2**: 126–152.

LACKEY, J. B. 1939. Aquatic life in waters polluted by acid mine wastes. Pub. Health Repts., **54**(18): 740–746.

——. 1941. Two groups of flagellated algae serving as indicators of clean water. J. Amer. Water Works. Assoc., **33**: 1099–1110.

——. 1942. The effects of distillery wastes and waters on the microscopic flora and fauna of a small creek. Pub. Health Repts., **57**: 253–260.

——. 1944. Stream microbiology, p. 227–265. *In* E. B. Phelps, Stream sanitation. John Wiley & Sons, New York.

MALONEY, T. E., AND C. M. PALMER. 1956. Toxicity of six chemicals to thirty cultures of algae. Water and Sewage Works, **103**: 509–513.

MIDDLETON, F. M., AND J. J. LICHTENBERG. 1960. Measurements of organic contaminants in the nation's rivers. Ind. Engr. Chem., **52**: 99*A*–102*A*.

MIDDLETON, F. M., AND A. A. ROSEN. 1956. Organic contaminants affecting the quality of water. Pub. Health Repts., **71**(11): 1125–1133.

MOORE, G. T., AND K. F. KELLERMAN. 1905. Copper as an algicide and disinfectant in water supplies. Bur. Plant Ind., U.S. Dept. Agr., Bull. 76.

PAINE, G. H., JR., AND A. R. GAUFIN. 1956. Aquatic diptera as indicators of pollution in a midwestern stream. Ohio J. Sci., **56**(5): 291–304.

PALMER, C. M. 1959. Algae in water supplies. Supt. Documents, U.S. Govt. Printing Office, Pub. Health Serv. Publ. 657, 88 p.

PALMER, C. M., AND T. E. MALONEY. 1953. The use of algal cultures in experiments concerned with water supply problems. Butler Univ. Botan. Studies, **11**: 87–90.

PATRICK, RUTH. 1950. Biological measure of stream conditions. Sewage and Ind. Wastes, **22**: 926–938.

PATRICK, RUTH, M. H. HOHN, AND J. H. WALLACE. 1954. A new method for determining the pattern of the diatom flora. Notulae Naturae, Acad. Nat. Sci. Philadelphia, No. 259, 12 p.

PURDY, W. C. 1916. Investigations of the pollution

and sanitary conditions of the Potomac watershed. Potomac plankton and environmental factors. U.S. Pub. Health Serv. Hyg. Lab., Bull. No. 104: 130–191.

——. 1923. A study of the pollution and natural purification of the Ohio River. I. The plankton and related organisms. Pub. Health Bull. No. 131, 78 p.

——. 1926. The biology of polluted water. J. Amer. Water Works Assoc., 16(1): 45–54.

——. 1930. A study of the pollution and natural purification of the Illinois River. II. The plankton and related organisms. Pub. Health Bull. No. 198, 212 p.

——. 1937. Experimental studies of natural purification in polluted waters. X. Reoxygenation of polluted waters by microscopic algae. Pub. Health Repts., 52(29): 945–978.

PURDY, W. C., AND C. T. BUTTERFIELD. 1918. Effect of plankton animals upon bacterial death rates. Amer. J. Pub. Health, 8(7): 499–505.

RICHARDSON, R. E. 1921. Changes in the bottom and shore fauna of the Middle Illinois River and its connecting lakes since 1913–15 as a result of the increase, southward, of sewage pollution. Bull. Illinois Nat. Hist. Surv., 14(4): 33–75.

——. 1925. Illinois River bottom fauna in 1923. Bull. Illinois Nat. Hist. Surv., 15(6): 391–422.

——. 1928. The bottom fauna of the Middle Illinois River 1913–25, its distribution, abundance, valuation, and index value in the study of stream pollution. Bull. Illinois Nat. Hist. Surv., 17(12): 387–475.

ROMANO, A. H. 1958. Identification of odors produced by actinomycetes. Pub. Works, 89(12): 100–101.

ROMANO, A. H., AND R. S. SAFFERMAN. 1963. Studies on actinomycetes and their odors. J. Amer. Water Works Assoc., 55(2): 169–176.

SEDGWICK, W. T. 1888. Recent progress in biological water analysis. J. Northeastern Water Works Assoc., 4(Sept.).

TARZWELL, C. M. 1950. The role of biological investigations in the pollution abatement program. Proc. Southern Branch Am. Pub. Health Assoc.

——. 1957. Water quality criteria for aquatic life.

Trans. 1956 Seminar, Biological Problems in Water Pollution, Robert A. Taft Sanit. Engr. Center, Tech. Rept. W57–36: 246–272.

——. 1958a. The use of bioassays in the safe disposal of electroplating wastes. Amer. Electroplaters Soc., 44th Ann. Tech. Proc.: 60–62.

——. 1958b. Dissolved oxygen requirements for fishes. Robert A. Taft Sanit. Engr. Center, Tech. Rept. W58-2: 15–24.

——. 1958c. Disposal of toxic wastes. Ind. Wastes, 3(2): 48–52.

——. 1959. Pollutional effects of organic insecticides. Trans. 24th North Amer. Wildl. Conf.: 132–142.

——. 1962. Development of water quality criteria for aquatic life. J. Water Pollution Control Fed., 34(11): 1178–1185.

TARZWELL, C. M., AND A. R. GAUFIN. 1953. Some important biological effects of pollution often disregarded in stream surveys. Purdue Univ. Engr. Bull., Proc. 8th Ind. Wastes Conf.: 295–316.

TARZWELL, C. M., AND C. HENDERSON. 1956. The toxicity of some of the less common metals to fishes. Proc. of Seminar sponsored by AEC and PHS, Dec. 6–9, 1955. Ind. Wastes, 5(1): 12 (1960).

TARZWELL, C. M., AND C. HENDERSON. 1957. The toxicity of dieldrin to fish. Trans. Amer. Fish Soc., 86: 245–257.

TARZWELL, C. M., AND C. M. PALMER. 1951. Ecology of significant organisms in surface water supplies. J. Amer. Water Works Assoc., 43(7): 568–578.

WELCH, P. S. 1935. Limnology. McGraw Hill Book Co., Inc., New York and London. 471 p.

WESTON, R. S., AND C. E. TURNER. 1917. Studies on the digestion of a sewage filter effluent by a small and otherwise unpolluted stream. Massachusetts Inst. Tech., Sanit. Research Lab. and Sewage Expt. Sta., 10: 1–43.

WHIPPLE, G. C. 1899. The microscopy of drinking water. John Wiley & Sons, New York and London. 300 p.

WHITMORE, C. M., C. E. WARREN, AND P. DOUDOROFF. 1960. Avoidance reactions of salmonoid and centrarchid fishes to low oxygen concentrations. Trans. Amer. Fish. Soc., 89(1): 17–26.

25 | *George H. Lauff*

A History of the American Society of Limnology and Oceanography

The American Society of Limnology and Oceanography and its predecessor, the Limnological Society of America, have functioned for promotion of the interests of aquatic sciences in America for over twenty-five years. Though the Limnological Society of America was not established until 1936, the events leading to its organization can be traced back a decade or more and were intimately tied to the activities of the Committee on Aquiculture of the Division of Biology and Agriculture, National Research Council. In reviewing the activities of the Committee and the series of special programs it organized and conducted in connection with the holiday meetings of the American Association for the Advancement of Science (AAAS), the struggles in the evolution of aquatic research and the necessity of promoting it are apparent. The mechanism for effecting a better organization to further interest and research in limnological science was delineated at the Committee's regular meeting in Pittsburgh in December 1934 when a subcommittee for the organization of an American limnological society was appointed. The Society was formally established on 2 January 1936 at St. Louis, and since then it has grown rapidly in scope in terms of both membership and services rendered to the aquatic sciences. In 1948 the expansion of the Society's marine interests resulted in its present name. The Pacific Section was also established in that year and was materially strengthened by amalgamation with the Oceanographic Society of the Pacific.

The historical account that follows will consider the chronology of pertinent events in the evolution, growth, and development of the Society, beginning with activities of the Committee on Aquiculture. Since the Committee was of considerable importance in the formulation of the concept of aquatic research during the period, and since its records are not generally available, its progress has been documented in some detail. The limitations of space prevent presentation of the Society's more routine activities after 1936 and make it impractical to give specific recognition to the many members who have provided guidance over the years and rendered services in the many facets of the Society's operation. It is hoped that the appended tabulations will suffice, and that the inadequacies of the information or inabilities of the writer to unravel the record will cause no injustice.

To assist in providing as complete a transcript as possible, the Appendices 25.1–25.5 present reference information pertinent to the development of the Society: Appendix 25.1 and Appendix 25.2 list the formal progression of Society officers and those of the Pacific Section, as well as their terms of office; Appendix 25.3 indicates the meeting places of the Society, the principal affiliate organizations and societies that have assisted in the conduct of meetings and sponsorship of programs, and the relative growth in membership; Appendix 25.4 lists the publications of the Society; and Appendix 25.5 presents a compilation of the Society's committee membership and its representatives, based on existing records.

There are few published materials that document the early period prior to the formal organization of the Society; the majority of the information on which the account is based has been derived from correspondence on file at the Department of Zoology, The University of Michigan, and from correspondence and reports that have been contributed to the records of the Society. The periods after 1936 are quite well documented by the annual *Proceedings* printed and distributed by the Society and by data obtained from reports, correspondence, and other Society records available in the office of the Secretary-Treasurer.

Committee on Aquiculture

The Committee on Aquiculture was formed in a preliminary fashion at a meeting in Washington, D.C., on 26 May 1925 when Dr. Maynard M. Metcalf, Chairman of the Division of Biology and Agriculture, invited Dr. Robert E. Coker, University of North Carolina, and Dr. R. A. Harper, Columbia University, to a conference to consider establishing a committee to study the problems of aquatic production of food and the effects of pollution. It was anticipated that the proposed committee might, in part, continue the activities of the Division's Committee on Stream Pollution, which was inactive owing to the subject's being before Congress. The formal announcement of the Committee on Aquiculture was made on 1 July 1925. Dr. Metcalf was appointed Chairman, and Dr. Coker Vice-Chairman; other members were Drs. Harper, Chancey Juday, E. N. Transeau, S. W. Beyer, and S. A. Forbes.

In corresponding with Dr. Paul S. Welch in 1942 concerning his early impressions of the Committee, Dr. Coker wrote:

We did not think too much about the name...at the beginning, but it was clear to most of us, I think, and I am sure it was to me, that the function of the Committee was to stimulate scientific research on problems underlying aquiculture conceived in the broadest sense. The name was not very appropriate from the start, and it might have been better had we changed or supplemented it then; but no one thought it worthwhile at the moment to make a point of terminology. We commonly referred to [it] ... as the Committee on Aquiculture and Hydrobiology but, once ... [it] was set up under a particular name, it seemed difficult to make a formal change.

A statement touching upon some of the problems confronting the Committee was published in *Science* for 13 November 1925, in which it was announced that initial efforts were to be directed toward securing information on the status of personnel, facilities, and research in aquiculture, with the recognition that recommendations should be forthcoming regarding

the research work that should be pursued to establish the foundation of scientific data requisite for the development of practical methods of preserving and increasing the productivity of waters.... Undoubtedly it is desirable that there should be experimental work of a relatively direct nature, but strictly scientific in method, in reference to such matters as the nutrition of fishes and selective breeding. It is also probable that no less important in the long run will be physiological, physico-chemical and other studies not utilitarian in viewpoint but still having to do with problems underlying the *biological productivity* of bodies of water.

The Committee was temporary and reappointed annually. Membership varied from year to year and at times became quite large (20), but the major effort was carried by a few individuals. A special program and conference were held during the AAAS meeting in Philadelphia in December 1926 with the objective of promoting the development of research and training in hydrobiology, which seemed essential to the advancement of aquiculture; an invitational program on oceanography had been arranged by the Ecological Society of America (ESA) at the meeting.

The early efforts of the Committee were directed toward a series of proposals: a survey of European and Oriental aquiculture to determine the nature, status, and conditions of related research and the kind and extent of training in aquiculture; a bibliography on hydrobiology and aquiculture; university training in hydrobiology and aquiculture; the establishment of an independent or affiliated limnological institute; a journal of hydrobiology or limnology; and the possibility and desirability of a conference of hydrobiologists with participation by foreign workers. The last proposal included the possibility of inviting the International Association of Limnology to meet in America in 1930.

In late November of 1927 the Committee was informed that their request for funds to support a survey of European aquiculture and a conference of hydrobiologists was not granted. Whether this announcement was effective in reducing the attendance at the Nashville meeting in December is not known, but only four members (Forbes, Juday, Transeau, and Coker) attended the Committee's business meeting. Despite the disheartening results of their first attempts to obtain funds for the support of the Committee's program, it was decided that the Committee should be continued until other possibilities of financial support could be tested and that the several practical matters previously suggested should be implemented.

Prior to the Committee meeting held in New York in December 1928, Dr. Coker requested that a new chairman be appointed, in part because of his other obligations and in part because there was much to be said for the principle of rotation in office, since perhaps new ideas and new lines of approach would be more successful. There was no program at the New York meeting, and only five members were present at the Committee's business session. It was voted that the Committee be continued, and Dr. J. G. Needham was later appointed Chairman, beginning 1 July 1929. The group in attendance was anxious that the 1929 meeting at Des Moines be larger so that items of business might be more thoroughly discussed.

The two topics that received major consideration at the Des Moines meeting were the preparation of a concise summary regarding the opportunities to be found at the various laboratories for research in hydrobiology and the feasibility of establishing an aquiculture experiment station. The task of assembling information on the research opportunities in hydrobiology was given to Dr. P. S. Welch, a newly appointed Committee member. Dr. Needham was authorized to request financial support for a proposed flood-plain experiment station. The Division of Biology and Agriculture voted an expression of interest in the proposed aquicultural experiment station, but the plan prepared by Dr. Needham was dropped, primarily owing to the large measure of financial support required and the duplication of effort by state and federal agencies.

In December of 1930 a special program on Hydrobiology and Aquiculture was held under the auspices of the AAAS at its Cleveland meeting. Nineteen papers were presented by title; there is no record available of the business meeting, though later correspondence suggests that attendance was again very limited.

In the late fall of 1931 Dr. Needham requested that the National Research Council provide funds to enable the entire Committee on Aquiculture to hold a special meeting in Washington. He pointed out that the Committee had never had a satisfactory meeting owing to limited attendance, and that the conditions during the holiday sessions of AAAS made a meeting difficult because of the many interests involved. It was agreed that travel expenses for six members east of the Mississippi would be covered, and that the group would meet in Washington, together with the local members and the Division Chairman, Dr. D. S. Johnson. Further, the group would function as an "executive subcommittee" designated by the National Research Council and would report to the larger Committee.

The meeting was held in Washington on 23 February 1932 with the following members present: Drs. Needham, Coker, Juday, Welch, H. S. Davis, F. G. Hall, Will Scott, and Mr. Lewis Radcliffe. In addition to the regular members, the following were present by invitation: Dr. D. S. Johnson, Dr. A. H. Wiebe, and Dr. Elmer Higgins. Dr. Needham presided, and after a brief review of the history of the Committee on Aquiculture, he raised the question whether its past activities justified its continuance, and if continuance was found desirable, what steps should be taken to obtain funds for development of the field. There followed a round-table discussion in which all participants expressed their views on the research activities in hydrobiology and aquiculture and the needs for support of research efforts in this area. An extended informal discussion of plans for the future resulted in the appointment of two subcommittees: Dr. Juday (Chairman), Dr. Welch, and Dr. Coker were appointed to a Subcommittee on Hydrobiology to draft a new proposal for research in hydrobiology and to solicit funds for its support; Dr. Scott (Chairman), Dr. Hall, and Mr. Radcliffe were appointed to a Subcommittee on Aquiculture to develop a connection between investigators in the field of aquiculture and the state agencies that must apply the results of aquicultural research.

During the remainder of 1932 the Subcommittee on Hydrobiology was active in preparing a draft of a general program for fundamental research in freshwater hydrobiology. A request was distributed to workers active in aquatic work to gather information on their ideas relating to fundamental and applied problems in the physics, chemistry, and biology of fresh water. A 48-page report entitled *Research Problems in Freshwater Hydrobiology* was prepared, which discussed the interdisciplinary nature of hydrobiology, including the geological, physical, chemical, and biological aspects. A chapter was also devoted to the relation of physiology to hydrobiology.

The report of Dr. Juday's Subcommittee on Hydrobiology and that of Dr. Scott's Subcommittee were the two items on the agenda for the second Washington meeting of the "executive subcommittee" on 26 and 27 April 1933. It was the group's opinion that the report of the Subcommittee on Hydrobiology was an excellent presentation of the field and its problems, and that a definite plan of action should be presented to be used as a basis for requesting funds. In the discussion of the report of Dr. Scott's Subcommittee on Aquiculture, the suggestion was made by Mr. Radcliffe that an American society of hydrobiologists be organized and that it meet at the same time and place as the American Fisheries Society. He stated that there was in existence a Committee on Hydrobiology of the American Fisheries Society, but that the organization was not active because of lack of interest by the men representing the field. It was pointed out that an independent organization such as Mr. Radcliffe had in mind would have a much better chance to grow than one that must fit into the scheme of a mother organization.

Dr. Scott was appointed Chairman of a committee to invite hydrobiologists to attend the next meeting of the American Fisheries Society, at which time a formal meeting would be held to determine more definitely if it was desirable to form a society of hydrobiologists.

In accordance with the action taken at the Washington meeting in April, another meeting was held in Columbus, Ohio, on 18 September in connection with the annual meeting of the American Fisheries Society. The desirability of organizing an American society of hydrobiology was freely discussed with members of the Committee and with others present as guests. The need for such a society was generally expressed, along with the conviction that the time (considering the national economy) was not a good one for its launching. It was then agreed that further consideration of the matter should be postponed to a meeting to be held in connection with the AAAS meeting at Pittsburgh in December 1934.

In the fall of 1934 Chairman Needham distributed a call for papers for a special program on Hydrobiology and Aquiculture to be held in connection with the AAAS meeting in Pittsburgh on Thursday, 27 December 1934. Seventeen papers were offered in response. Though time limitations made the program a relatively short one, it was the first separate listing on the overall AAAS program and marked the beginning of activities to establish a society dealing with the basic and applied aspects of hydrobiology.

At its business meeting the Committee on Aquiculture considered the question of effecting better organization for the purpose of presenting a more permanent united front in its efforts to promote research and training in limnological science. A Founding Committee for the establishment of an American limnological society was appointed, consisting of Dr. Welch, Chairman, and Drs. Juday, Needham, Scott, Coker, and L. H. Tiffany. Three officers for the proposed society were suggested: president, vice-president, and combined secretary-treasurer; Drs. Juday, Coker, and Welch were named as first holders of these respective positions.

A circular was distributed by Dr. Welch in January 1935 announcing the organization of an American limnological society. A brief review of its development was presented, and it was indicated that the initial meeting of the society would be held in connection with the St. Louis meeting of AAAS. All who were interested in freshwater biology in any of its phases were invited to join, and those who sent dues ($1.00) before the close of the St. Louis meeting would be entered upon the rolls of the society as charter members.

One of the most perplexing problems facing the Founding Committee was the discovery that a group on the West Coast had also formulated preliminary plans for the inauguration of a society and a journal. After preliminary correspondence Dr. Welch wrote them at length urging the desirability of uniting forces in the new Limnological Society of America and of giving it a chance to fulfill the needs of all. The West Coast group was particularly vigorous in their interest in having a journal founded immediately. It was the feeling of members of the Founding Committee that the issue of a journal be kept distinctly in the background, at least until the Society was a going concern. Efforts at uniting were only partially successful, however, and the Oceanographic

Society of the Pacific was established on 28 June 1935.

The Founding Committee met in St. Louis on 1 January 1936, and Secretary-Treasurer Welch presented the proposed Constitution and By-Laws for the Limnological Society of America, which were to be offered for final adoption at the first annual meeting to be held on the following day.

On 25 March 1936 Dr. Needham reported to the National Research Council that the past activities of the Committee on Aquiculture had led to the organization of the Limnological Society of America with a charter membership of over two hundred (221). Since, in the opinion of the Committee, there was nothing that it had been doing in the past that could not be done as well by the new Society, it was recommended that the National Research Council's Committee on Aquiculture be discontinued.

In commenting on the development of the Limnological Society of America and the role of the Committee on Aquiculture therein, Dr. Coker wrote Dr. Welch in 1942:

The Committee obviously has a history which led to no results measurable in terms of money obtained and spent. It has been thought of by some as an unproductive committee. Certainly we did not win the good ears of those who distribute funds, but I believe, nevertheless, that the Committee served a definitely useful purpose and had real effect in promoting hydrobiological research. It is a mistake to measure always the value of the activities of a group of scientific people by their success in getting into the strong boxes of Foundations. I think possibly we were overly diffident, but we had definite obstacles and we could never hold for long the ear of any of the Foundations at any time in the life of the Committee, which, after 11 years, metamorphosed in 1935 into the Limnological Society of America. It is, of course, hard to appraise less tangible results; nevertheless, I feel, and I believe you do, that the Committee actually accomplished much in tying limnologists together, in initiating special limnological programs, in increasing the confidence of young limnologists in the significance and scientific standing of their work, and, more tangibly, in bringing about the development of the Limnological Society of America. I know my personal psychology changed from a condition bordering on discouragement with respect to an early general development of limnological research to one of optimism and confidence. The state and standing of such research is certainly different now from what it was in 1925. There would have been some improvement anyway, but the Committee and its offspring, the Society, have most certainly played some part.... Most of the members of the Committee, at all times, were deeply interested and willing and effective workers. We should not, however, lose sight of the fact that a great debt is due to the initiative, endorsement and active cooperation of certain leaders who were not then actually engaged in studies ordinarily classified as hydrobiological.

Limnological Society of America

The formal organization of the Society was established with 221 charter members at the first annual meeting held in St. Louis, Missouri, on 2 January 1936. The Constitution and By-Laws presented by the Founding Committee were adopted, and the Society was recognized by AAAS as an *affiliate society*, entitled to one representative on its Council. One of the first functions of the Society was the appointment of an Identification Service Committee instructed to compile a list of biologists competent to make authoritative taxonomic identifications of aquatic organisms. During 1936 the first edition of *Sources of Limnological Apparatus and Supplies* was published as Special Publication No. 1, which represented the beginning of a series that was to continue as a source of information on methods, apparatus, and techniques until 1956 (Appendix 25.4).

The Society activities in 1936 and 1937 were mostly concerned with the more routine matters of a growing organization. Program planning and places of meeting were discussed, as well as the future services to be rendered to the Society. The activities of the Identification Service Committee culminated in Special Publication No. 2, the first edition of which was published in 1937.

The question of the desirability of establishing a new journal was presented to the membership in 1938, and though the majority expressed a favorable opinion, the magnitude and vigor of the opposition vote discouraged any attempt at that time. The Special Publication series was well received, and by 1939 the demand from non-members necessitated that the publications be sold. An increasing number of requests was being made for additional Society services, and organizations were more actively seeking the support of the Society in their endeavors. However, the limited resources available made it necessary to deny any financial assistance. The membership in the newly formed Society had increased by 50% within the first five years of its existence, totaling 327 in December 1940.

Though the United States had entered World War II by the time of the annual meeting, plans for a symposium to be held at the New York meeting of AAAS in 1942 continued. There was general favor of continuance of joint sessions with ESA. In the fall of 1942 the membership received the usual call for papers to be presented at the meeting scheduled to occur at New York in December in affiliation with AAAS. It was later announced that because of inadequate program material and for other important reasons arising from the national emergency, the Society's proposed meeting was cancelled. The Executive Committee decided to omit the annual election and allow the term of the officers then holding office to be extended another year or until such time as their successors could be appointed. (No election was held until April 1946.) In the interim its affairs were to be continued by mail. On 27 November 1942 a communication was received from AAAS stating that "in compliance with the request of the Office of Defense Transportation, the Executive Committee of the American Association for the Advancement of Science had voted to postpone the New York meeting."

The 1942–46 period was a critical one for the Society and its officers, who had the increased burden of continuing the organization's affairs without the benefit of regular meetings. There were several matters of concern, but chief among them was the effort to maintain membership with the losses caused by deaths and resignations related to military service. With the passage of time since the 1941 meetings, the question of how long a society could defer its meetings without deterioration became increasingly important. The several papers that appeared in the Special Publication series during the war period did much to keep the Society active in the absence of formal meetings.

Though there was no meeting in 1943, there was a continued effort on the part of the Executive Committee of AAAS to assist affiliate societies in maintaining their activities. In 1944 an AAAS meeting was held in Cleveland, but the Society's Executive Committee was opposed to holding a Society program or meeting with the limited response from the membership and the travel restrictions imposed by the Office of Defense Transportation. It was possible, however, for those members who were in attendance at Cleveland to meet informally.

In May 1945 the Executive Committee made provision to conduct an election of officers via mail if a regular meeting was not soon arranged. However, AAAS announced a meeting to be held in late March 1946, and the election of officers was deferred until that time.

The eighth annual meeting of the Society was held in affiliation with AAAS in St. Louis on 29 March 1946. Since it was the first in five years, an informal report of the general activities of the Executive Committee was presented, and committee appointments were announced. Two committees of particular note were the Special Projects Committee, established to propose, finance, and administer projects that could be suitably carried out under the auspices of the Society, and the New Publications Committee, which was to explore the desirability and feasibility of organizing a journal of aquatic biology. The report of the Special Projects Committee recommended that the Society promote or participate in the promotion of a *Fauna of the Inland Waters of North America*. Appreciation was expressed to the officers who had assisted in maintaining the organization during the war years and particularly to the retiring Secretary-Treasurer whose services covered the first ten years of the Society's existence.

At the meeting in Boston in December 1946 the New Publications Committee was authorized to negotiate with limnologists overseas to obtain support for the revival of the *Internationale Revue der gesamten Hydrobiologie und Hydrographie*. The Special Projects Committee was also authorized to seek support for sixteen proposed monographs for *Fresh Water Fauna of North America*. A Committee on Expansion of Marine Interests was appointed to determine the desirability of expanding the marine interests of the Society to the same extent as the freshwater interests. At this meeting it was voted to accept the membership invitation of the National Resources Council of America and to encourage the establishment of a National Science Foundation (NSF). The Society also instructed its representatives to the AAAS Council to move for a time of meeting other than the Christmas holidays.

The report of the Committee on Expansion of Marine Interests, presented at the tenth annual meeting in Chicago in December 1947, resulted in a proposal to expand the Society's interests to include oceanography. Certain advantages of this proposed expansion were pointed out, including the possibility of supporting a journal for limnology and oceanography, a suggestion made earlier by the New Publications Committee. The Society also approved in principle the formation of the proposed American Institute of Biological Sciences (AIBS) and recommended affiliation, provided satisfactory financial arrangements were made.

American Society of Limnology and Oceanography

The results of a mail ballot after the tenth annual meeting indicated that the membership was in favor of changing the Society's name to the American Society of Limnology and Oceanography, and appropriate amendments to the Constitution and By-Laws were later approved via mail (1 July 1948).

The September 1948 meeting at College Park, Maryland, was the first independent meeting of the Society. At this meeting word was received that the International Association of Limnology had presented the Society with one of the Naumann medals for remarkable contributions to the limnological sciences. Following the proposal of the Special Projects Committee that the Society encourage the publication of a revised and enlarged edition of Ward and Whipple's *Fresh-water Biology,* the Society approved in principle the proposal of the New Publications Committee for the sponsorship of a revival of the *Internationale Revue der gesamten Hydrobiologie und Hydrographie* and empowered the Executive Committee to continue negotiations toward definite publication. The membership was later polled regarding their support, but a favorable reply was not obtained. On the recommendation of the Executive Committee, the Pacific Section of the Society was established. The Oceanographic Society of the Pacific officially amalgamated with the Society on 6 November 1948.

In November 1948 the Society became a member of the International Association of Limnology, and at the twelfth annual meeting held in New York in December 1949 the question of membership or affiliation with AIBS was discussed. Certain proposed amendments to the Constitution and By-Laws relating to the Nominating Committee and elections were also discussed and adopted; the Society voted that the Executive Committee consider meeting with societies in fields in addition to biology, such as physics, chemistry, and geology.

The September 1950 meeting at Columbus, Ohio, was the first held in conjunction with the newly formed AIBS, and at the annual business meeting it was voted that the Society affiliate with AIBS. It was pointed out that affiliation in no way implied that the non-biological aspects of limnology and oceanography would fail to receive proper emphasis in the activities of the Society nor obligated it to meet with AIBS. The problem of a publication dealing with various projects in limnology and oceanography was reviewed, but no definite action was taken until September 1951, when the Publications Committee was dissolved and the Editorial Board substituted and authorized to investigate the format, cost, and related questions pertinent to publication of an annual Society journal.

The membership in the Society had grown to 1103 by 1951, the highest yet achieved. In discussing the proposed journal at the 1952 annual meeting, the Editorial Board estimated that a minimum of 600 membership subscriptions would be required to insure its financial success. The membership was circularized to determine the desirability and the extent of support of the proposed journal, and though the majority favored the journal, the overall response was quite limited, indicating questionable support for initiating publication. At the 1953 meeting a Special Journal Committee was appointed to investigate other means of publication, perhaps through cooperation with an existing periodical, as well as sources of financial support for the proposed new journal. The new committee reported in 1954 that the need and desire for a Society journal had apparently increased, and the Committee planned for a quarterly publication of 400–500 pages per year, open to all phases of research in limnology and oceanography. It was proposed that journal publication would result in an increase in annual dues, though it was hoped financial support could be obtained for the first few years.

In April 1955 a proposal for a grant to defray publication deficits of the proposed journal, LIMNOLOGY AND OCEANOGRAPHY, was forwarded to selected foundations; support was obtained from the National Science Foundation for a three-year period. At the annual meeting appropriate amendments to the By-Laws were adopted, including an increase in the annual dues to a level expected to support the new journal. The Executive Committee was empowered to select and appoint an interim managing editor and editorial board to conclude a contract with a printer and issue the first volume. A later amendment to the By-Laws provided for necessary election or appointment of future editorial staffs. In a discussion of places of meeting, the desirability of holding independent meetings at oceanographic and limnological stations was reviewed.

The first volume of LIMNOLOGY AND OCEANOGRAPHY was published in 1956. At the annual meeting it was announced that, under authorization extended to the Executive Committee in 1955, the Society had become incorporated in the state of Wisconsin, Articles of Incorporation had been formulated, and the By-Laws appropriately revised. After a report on the Helsinki, Finland, meeting of the International Association of Limnology, the Board of Directors (Executive Committee) was authorized to investigate the feasibility of inviting the Association to hold its 1962 Congress in North America. At the time of the 1957 annual meeting, it was reported that a special committee had been appointed to proceed with the organization for a proposed 1962 Congress to be held at the University of Wisconsin and to extend the invitation to the Association.

The overall finances of journal operation arose as a problem in 1957 and 1958, since the journal was operating at a deficit owing to increased costs, despite the encouraging growth of the Society.

During 1959, 24 applicants accepted awards of travel expenses to the XIVth International Congress of Limnology in Austria from money furnished by NSF. The Society's invitation to the International Association to hold its 1962 Congress in North America was accepted.

At the 1959 annual meeting a standing Committee on Education and Recruitment was appointed to take active part in furthering the aims of the Committee on Oceanography of the National Academy of Sciences-National Research Council for the assistance and encouragement of organizations concerned with increased oceanographic research, training, recruitment, and facilities. It was also decided that two special meetings would be held at centers of aquatic research to emphasize oceanography. The Articles of Incorporation were amended to permit the Society to acquire a "tax exempt" status as an organization operated exclusively for educational and scientific purposes. To assist in resolving an increasingly difficult financial condition with regard to the journal operation, the Board of Directors approved a change in printers for LIMNOLOGY AND OCEANOGRAPHY with Volume 5.

In 1960 the role of special meetings to emphasize the problems of physical oceanography and to increase the Society membership was discussed. The need of independent meetings was noted, and it was the opinion of the Board of Directors that the meetings with AIBS and its affiliates should continue, but a series of special meetings to promote oceanography should be held at strategically located laboratories, since continued regular meetings with AIBS were perhaps unfair to the overall membership and functioned in hindering the growth and development of a strong broad program. The financial status of the Society was again favorable owing to a reduction in publication costs through the change in printers and also because of a rapid growth in membership and journal subscriptions. Under a grant from the National Science Foundation, the report of the Committee on Education and Recruitment, entitled *Education and Recruitment of Oceanographers in the United States,* was published in recognition of the Society's responsibilities in connection with the education of additional personnel required by the expansion of all fields of oceanography envisaged by the Committee on Oceanography of the National Academy of Sciences. Planning continued for the organization of the XVth International Congress of Limnology to be held in Madison, Wisconsin, in 1962.

In 1961 the Society received a grant from the U.S. Atomic Energy Commission to defray costs of publication of the report *Effects of Nuclear Explosions on Marine Biology.* The Society's overall financial status continued to improve with the increase in membership and subscriptions. The report of the Joint ESA-ASLO Committee on Aquatic Sciences, appointed in 1959 to function as a liaison between the two societies during the formation of the Aquatic Ecology Section of ESA, offered a series of recommendations on the organization and activities of the Society that were instrumental in the initiation of certain amendments of the By-Laws.

In the few months since the 24th annual meeting in 1961, some of the proposals of the Joint Committee have been initiated and should result in the Society's assuming a more important role in promoting the welfare and progress of aquatic science. It is hoped that the organization will continue to grow both in terms of membership and with respect to the services rendered to its members and scientists in related fields, and that future meetings, together with the journal, will function in the dissemination of information on aquatic research and provide a common meeting-ground for the exchange of comments and ideas for a larger sphere of disciplines.

The rapid rise in interest in aquatic science during the past decade and the increased financial support for research have placed new responsibilities on the Society; it can be anticipated that there will be no lessening of pressure in the years to come. The expansion of the nation's

marine interests and the continuing need for trained scientists in all fields of aquatic work will undoubtedly bring into sharper focus the Society's role in providing advice and counsel in the recruitment and training of scientific personnel, as well as in acquainting federal agencies with the needs and requirements of the profession. Parallel with the growth of aquatic science, the Society must assist in establishing effective mechanisms for the collection and distribution of pertinent information of interest to its membership and must provide the direction and stimulus which will permit aquatic research to reach its full potential.

APPENDIX 25.1

Past officers of the Limnological Society of America and the American Society of Limnology and Oceanography

Date	President	Vice-President	Sec.-Treas.	Exec. Comm. Member (Member-at-Large)
1935–36[a]	Chancey Juday[a]	R. E. Coker[a]	P. S. Welch[a]	
1936–37	Chancey Juday	R. E. Coker	P. S. Welch	L. H. Tiffany (1 yr)
				L. P. Schultz (2 yrs)
				W. J. K. Harkness (3 yrs)
1937–38	J. G. Needham	L. H. Tiffany	P. S. Welch	F. F. Fish
1938–39	R. E. Coker	R. C. Osburn	P. S. Welch	E. B. Powers
1939–40	L. H. Tiffany	G. E. Hutchinson	P. S. Welch	E. P. Cheatum
1940–41	W. J. K. Harkness	J. B. Lackey	P. S. Welch	G. W. Prescott
1941–42	R. C. Osburn	W. L. Tressler	P. S. Welch	H. B. Hungerford
1942–4/46	G. L. Clarke	A. H. Wiebe	P. S. Welch	G. E. Hutchinson
4/46–46	P. S. Welch	A. D. Hasler	G. L. Clarke	D. S. Rawson
1946–47	D. S. Rawson	C. E. Taft	G. L. Clarke	A. D. Hasler
				W. E. Ricker (to complete D. S. Rawson's term)
1947–9/48	G. E. Hutchinson	I. T. Wilson	G. L. Clarke	C. L. Hubbs
9/48–49	C. E. ZoBell	D. C. Chandler	G. L. Clarke	F. E. J. Fry
1949–9/50	A. D. Hasler	E. S. Deevey	T. S. Austin	R. W. Pennak
9/50–9/51	C. L. Hubbs	J. W. Leonard	T. S. Austin	P. R. Needham
9/51–9/52	R. H. Fleming	F. E. J. Fry	T. S. Austin	D. G. Frey
9/52–9/53	F. E. J. Fry	J. W. Moffett	B. H. Ketchum	G. A. Riley
9/53–54	T. C. Nelson	W. E. Ricker	B. H. Ketchum	H. T. Odum
1954–9/55	D. G. Frey	D. W. Pritchard	B. H. Ketchum	A. C. Redfield
9/55–9/56	A. C. Redfield	R. C. Ball	B. H. Ketchum	J. L. Hart
9/56–9/57	D. C. Chandler	D. F. Leipper	B. H. Ketchum	J. R. Vallentyne
9/57–9/58	D. F. Leipper	R. W. Pennak	B. H. Ketchum	F. F. Hooper
9/58–9/59	W. E. Ricker	B. H. Ketchum	G. H. Lauff	J. H. Ryther
9/59–9/60	B. H. Ketchum	G. W. Prescott	G. H. Lauff	C. M. Tarzwell
9/60–9/61	W. T. Edmondson	G. A. Riley	G. H. Lauff	F. R. Hayes
9/61–9/62	G. A. Riley	J. C. Ayers	G. H. Lauff	J. W. Hedgpeth

[a] Officers named by the Founding Committee, January, 1935.

(Appendices continued on following pages)

APPENDIX 25.2

Past officers of the Pacific Section, American Society of Limnology and Oceanography

Date	President	Vice-President	Sec.-Treas.	Exec. Comm. Member (Member-at-Large)
9/48–6/49	—	C. L. Hubbs[a]	R. P. Dempster[a]	—
6/49–6/50	G. F. McEwen	W. T. Edmondson	J. P. Tully	—
6/50–6/51	W. T. Edmondson	M. W. Johnson	J. P. Tully	C. A. Barnes (1 yr)
6/51–6/52	M. W. Johnson	J. L. Hart	J. P. Tully	P. R. Needham (2 yrs)
6/52–6/53	C. A. Barnes	W. M. Cameron	G. L. Pickard	N. W. Rakestraw
6/53–6/54	W. M. Cameron	M. B. Schaefer	G. L. Pickard	E. C. LaFond
6/54–6/55	M. B. Schaefer	E. C. LaFond	G. L. Pickard	K. O. Emery
6/55–6/56	J. C. Marr	K. O. Emery	Maurice Rattray, Jr.	R. W. Kiser
6/56–6/57	G. L. Pickard	M. C. Sargent	Maurice Rattray, Jr.	G. H. Tucker
6/57–6/58	M. C. Sargent	W. V. Burt	Maurice Rattray, Jr.	A. H. Seymour
				Michael Waldichuk (1 yr)
				J. R. Brett (2 yrs)
6/58–6/59	W. V. Burt	Maurice Rattray, Jr.	E. H. Ahlstrom	J. W. Hedgpeth
6/59–6/60	Maurice Rattray, Jr.	J. F. T. Saur	E. H. Ahlstrom	R. H. Parker
6/60–6/61	J. F. T. Saur	W. S. Wooster	E. H. Ahlstrom	M. K. Robinson
6/61–9/62	E. H. Ahlstrom	F. R. Richards	Maurice Blackburn	O. E. Sette

[a] Appointed by ASLO President G. E. Hutchinson.

APPENDIX 25.3

Chronology of meetings, program affiliations, and growth in membership: Limnological Society of America and American Society of Limnology and Oceanography

Date	Place of meeting	Program affiliations	Membership Active	Membership Total	Non-member subscriptions
1/2/1936	1st Annual Meeting St. Louis, Missouri	AAAS	221		
12/30/1936	2nd Annual Meeting Atlantic City, New Jersey	AAAS	266		
12/28–30/1937	3rd Annual Meeting Indianapolis, Indiana	AAAS; 1, 2	274		
12/28–29/1938	4th Annual Meeting Richmond, Virginia	AAAS	299		
12/28–29/1939	5th Annual Meeting Columbus, Ohio	AAAS; 1	322		
12/28–29/1940	6th Annual Meeting Philadelphia, Pennsylvania	AAAS; 1	327		
12/29–31/1941	7th Annual Meeting Dallas, Texas	AAAS; 1	380		
1942–1945	No meetings; World War II				
3/28–29/1946	8th Annual Meeting St. Louis, Missouri	AAAS	359		
12/28–30/1946	9th Annual Meeting Boston, Massachusetts	AAAS; 1	485		
12/29–31/1947	10th Annual Meeting Chicago, Illinois	AAAS; 1	531		
9/10–12/1948	11th Annual Meeting College Park, Maryland	—; 1, 3	627		
12/28–30/1949	12th Annual Meeting New York, New York	AAAS; 1	865		
9/11–13/1950	13th Annual Meeting Columbus, Ohio	AIBS	947		
9/12–14/1951	14th Annual Meeting Rochester, New York	—; 4	1,053		
9/8–10/1952	15th Annual Meeting Ithaca, New York	AIBS; 1, 2	1,103		
9/5–10/1953	16th Annual Meeting Madison, Wisconsin	AIBS; 1, 3	1,056		

APPENDIX 25.3 *(Continued)*

Date	Place of meeting	Program affiliations	Membership Active	Membership Total	Non-member subscriptions
9/5–8/1954	Special Meeting Gainesville, Florida	AIBS; 1	—		
12/28–30/1954	17th Annual Meeting Berkeley, California	AAAS; 1, 5, 6	1,033		
9/6–9/1955	18th Annual Meeting E. Lansing, Michigan	AIBS; 1	944		
8/25–29/1956	19th Annual Meeting Storrs, Connecticut	AIBS; 1	671[a]	707[b]	79[a]
8/25–29/1957	20th Annual Meeting Palo Alto, California	AIBS; 7	715	751	147
9/3–6/1957	Special Meeting Woods Hole, Massachusetts	—	—	—	—
8/24–27/1958	21st Annual Meeting Bloomington, Indiana	AIBS	783	819	217
8/30–9/3/1959	22nd Annual Meeting University Park, Pennsylvania	AIBS; 1, 2	833	865	298
8/28–31/1960	23rd Annual Meeting Stillwater, Oklahoma	AIBS; 1	948	984	401
8/27–31/1961	Special Meeting Lafayette, Indiana	AIBS; 1, 2, 4	—	—	—
9/11–15/1961	24th Annual Meeting Woods Hole, Massachusetts	—; 8	1,047	1,085	515

[a] Subscriptions to LIMNOLOGY AND OCEANOGRAPHY.
[b] Includes emeritus and associate members.

Program affiliations:
  Primary affiliation:
    American Association for the Advancement of Science (AAAS)
    American Institute of Biological Sciences (AIBS)
  Program co-sponsorship:
    1. Ecological Society of America
    2. American Society of Zoologists
    3. Biometrics Society
    4. American Fisheries Society
    5. Arctic Institute of North America
    6. Western Society of Naturalists
    7. American Society of Ichthyologists and Herpetologists
    8. Instrument Society of America, Marine Science Division

APPENDIX 25.4

Publications, 1939–61: Limnological Society of America and American Society of Limnology and Oceanography

SPECIAL PUBLICATIONS:

No. 1 Sources of Limnological and Oceanographic Apparatus and Supplies. (Revised and enlarged edition, April 1959.)

No. 2 Identification Service. (Third edition, September 1950.)

No. 3 A Rowboat Crane for Hauling Limnological Sampling Apparatus, by C. J. D. Brown and R. C. Ball. March 1940.

No. 4 A New Square-foot Aquatic Sampler, by James L. Wilding. June 1940.

No. 5 The Plankton Sampler—an Instrument for Quantitative Plankton Investigations, by G. L. Clarke and D. F. Bumpus. (Revised 1950.)

No. 6 New Limnological Sampling Equipment, by A. D. Hess. April 1941.

No. 7 A Meter for Measuring Rope Used to Lower Limnological Instruments into Water, by W. H. Irwin. November 1941.

No. 8 A Modification of the Juday Plankton Trap, by E. Berner Clarke. June 1942.

No. 9 Rod Casting for Bog Samples, by Paul S. Conger. June 1942.

No. 10 A Gear Pump Sampler for Chemical Limnology, by Charles E. Renn. June 1942.

No. 11 A Portable Field Chemistry Kit, by C. J. D. Brown and C. M. Flaten. March 1943.

No. 12 Coloring Lake Maps, by C. J. D. Brown. March 1943.

No. 13 Frame for Operating Two Reversing Thermometers Simultaneously, by P. S. Welch. March 1943.

No. 14 The Hatchet Planimeter as a Limnological Instrument, by Paul S. Welch. May 1944.

No. 15 The Calculation of Oxygen Saturation Values and Their Correction for Altitude, by D. S. Rawson. May 1944.

No. 16 Chancey Juday, by L. E. Noland; and Publications by Chancey Juday, by A. D. Hasler. April 1945.

No. 17 A Visual Comparator for the Estimation of Turbidities of Lake Water of Less Than 25 ppm, by O. B. Weeks and D. C. Chandler. May 1945.

APPENDIX 25.4 (*Continued*)

No. 18 An Automatic-Closing Ekman Dredge and Other Equipment for Use in Extremely Deep Water, by Donald S. Rawson. April 1947.

No. 19 Collecting Shipworms, by Ruth D. Turner. June 1947.

No. 20 Prairie Ice Jigger, by M. W. Sprules. November 1949.

No. 21 A New Counting Slide for Nannoplankton, by C. Mervin Palmer and T. E. Maloney. March 1954.

No. 22 A New Bottom Sampler, by W. R. Kellen. March 1954.

No. 23 A Method for Recording and Sorting Oceanographic and Limnological Data, by Steacy D. Hicks. February 1955.

The Special Publications series was discontinued on the publication of the quarterly journal LIMNOLOGY AND OCEANOGRAPHY in 1956.

LIMNOLOGY AND OCEANOGRAPHY:

Volume 1: 1956, 316 pp.
Volume 2: 1957, 380 pp.
Volume 3: 1958, 488 pp.
Volume 4: 1959, 507 pp.
Volume 5: 1960, 440 pp., with supplement, "Education and Recruitment of Oceanographers in the United States," 18 pp.
Volume 6: 1961, 496 pp.

APPENDIX 25.5

Committees, representatives, and editorial staff: Limnological Society of America and the American Society of Limnology and Oceanography

I. COMMITTEES (asterisk denotes chairmen)

A. Standing Committees and Special Annual Committees

Identification Service Committee (1936——)

L. E. Noland 1936–39	E. H. Ahlstrom 1936–39	W. E. Ricker 1950–52
H. T. Spieth 1936–50	F. E. Eggleton 1936–47*	J. W. Hedgpeth 1954–60*
W. J. K. Harkness 1936–47	P. R. Needham 1946–49	J. L. Brooks 1955–62
	R. R. Langford 1948–51	A. H. Banner 1955–58
C. L. Hubbs 1936–50	W. T. Edmondson 1948–51*	N. J. Wilimovsky 1959–61
	C. O. Berg 1950–52	

Apparatus and Supplies Committee (1949——)

D. M. Pratt 1949–54*	M. W. Ewing 1950–52	C. O. Berg 1955
N. T. Allen 1949–51	G. A. Cole 1952–54	R. F. McAllister 1956–58
J. D. Isaacs 1949–50	F. F. Hooper 1952–54	G. H. Lauff 1957–59
P. S. Welch 1949–50	D. F. Bumpus 1952–54	C. S. Yentsch 1958–60
L. O. Whitney 1950–52	J. H. Ryther 1955–62*	V. Tonolli 1960–63
	F. R. Hayes 1955–56	

Committee on Education and Recruitment (1960——)

A. C. Redfield 1960*	A. D. Hasler 1960	B. H. Ketchum (ex officio) 1960
R. Arthur 1960	D. W. Hood 1960–61	G. L. Pickard 1961
J. C. Ayers 1960–61*	F. Koczy 1960–61	Consultants: G. A. Riley 1960
C. A. Barnes 1960	D. W. Pritchard 1960–61	M. B. Schaefer 1960

Nominating Committee (1935——)

L. H. Tiffany 1935, 1946	W. L. Tressler 1941*	C. J. Fish 1952
Will Scott, 1935*	W. J. K. Harkness 1946	T. H. Langlois 1952
W. R. Taylor 1936	John Van Oosten 1946	A. D. Hasler 1952*
A. S. Hazzard 1936	I. T. Wilson 1946	D. S. Rawson 1953, 1955*, 1956
C. L. Hubbs 1936*, 1939, 1958	J. B. Lackey 1946	P. S. Welch 1953
	F. E. Eggleton 1946*	C. E. ZoBell 1954, 1957*
H. S. Davis 1937	R. W. Pennak 1947, 1960	G. L. Clarke 1954, 1956
E. P. Cheatum 1937	W. T. Edmondson 1947, 1962*	J. S. Gottschalk 1955
T. C. Nelson 1937*, 1959	K. F. Lagler 1948	J. C. Ayers 1955
F. C. Baker 1938	A. C. Redfield 1948	D. G. Frey 1956, 1958
J. G. Needham 1938	R. W. Fleming 1949	R. C. Ball 1957
Chancey Juday 1938*, 1940*, 1941	J. P. Tully 1949	D. F. Leipper 1959
	J. G. Mackin 1949	W. E. Ricker 1960*
R. E. Coker 1939, 1946*, 1948*, 1953*	A. D. Hess 1949*	G. L. Pickard 1960
	K. D. Carlander 1950*	M. C. Sargent 1960
E. L. Wickliff 1939*	D. F. Bumpus 1950, 1957	B. H. Ketchum 1961*
D. C. Chandler 1940, 1947*, 1954, 1958*	J. L. Hart 1950, 1959*	J. F. T. Saur 1961
	E. H. Ahlstrom 1951	E. W. Fager 1961
F. P. Ide 1940	R. B. Tibby 1951	D. W. Pritchard 1961
E. S. Deevey 1941	M. W. Johnson 1951*	

APPENDIX 25.5 (*Continued*)

Auditing Committee (1935——)

F. E. Eggleton 1935*, 1936*, 1939, 1941*
M. R. Raymond 1935
John Van Oosten 1936, 1945
A. S. Hazzard 1937, 1943*
C. L. Hubbs 1937*
C. J. D. Brown 1938, 1941
M. B. Trautman 1938*
W. R. Taylor 1939*, 1944*
Calvin Goodrich 1940

Ralph Hile 1940*
F. W. Jobes 1942
K. F. Lagler 1942*
H. van der Schalie 1943
W. F. Carbine 1944
G. P. Cooper 1945
W. T. Edmondson 1946
W. H. Weston 1946*
D. M. Pratt 1947*
W. J. Clench 1947
R. L. Edwards 1948
T. R. Rice 1948
H. A. Goodwin 1949
E. S. Barghoorn 1949
W. L. Tressler 1950, 1951

L. A. Walford 1950
F. E. Elliott 1951
F. R. Richards 1952
A. C. Redfield 1952
H. W. Graham 1954–58
Mary Sears 1954–56
A. R. Miller 1957, 1958
F. F. Hooper 1959
J. W. Moffett 1959
J. C. Ayers 1960
D. C. Chandler 1960, 1962
A. M. Beeton 1961
C. F. Powers 1961
John Bardach 1962

Tellers (1949——)

D. S. Rawson 1949
D. F. Bumpus 1949
C. M. Weiss 1950
R. V. Truitt 1950
R. A. Littlewood 1951
H. H. Haskins 1951, 1955
D. J. Zinn 1951
Maurice Rattray, Jr. 1952
D. F. Leipper 1952

Nelson Marshall 1953
F. C. W. Olsen 1953
J. W. Hedgpeth 1954
Demorest Davenport 1954
H. P. Clemens 1955
J. B. Lackey 1956
D. E. Carritt 1956
B. H. Ketchum 1957
T. S. Austin 1957
C. S. Yentsch 1958

S. W. Watson 1958
A. M. Beeton 1959
J. H. Johnson 1959
K. W. Cummins 1960
M. Parker 1960
J. C. Ayers 1960
G. R. Marzolf 1961
D. J. Hall 1961
R. M. Bailey 1962
F. F. Hooper, 1962

B. Committees for Special Purposes

Biological Abstracts Committee (1939–47)

G. W. Prescott*   R. E. Coker   G. E. Hutchinson

Editorial Board for Special Publications (1940–49)

P. S. Welch 1941–46*
Chancey Juday 1941–44

L. H. Tiffany 1941–47
A. D. Hasler 1945–48*

E. S. Deevey 1948–50
A. D. Hess 1948–49

(Activities assumed by Publications Committee in 1949)

New Publications Committee (1946–49)
(*Publications Committee*, 1949–51)

R. W. Pennak 1946–50
Daniel Merriman 1946–50

W. J. K. Harkness 1946–48
D. G. Frey 1950–52*
A. D. Hasler 1946–48

E. S. Deevey 1946–49*, 1950–51
L. W. Hutchins 1949–51
R. H. Fleming 1950–52

(Dissolved on formation of Editorial Board in 1951)

Editorial Board (1952–55)

D. J. Zinn 1952–55*
G. A. Riley 1952–55
D. M. Pratt 1952–55

R. W. Pennak 1952–54
J. K. Neel 1952–54
D. F. Leipper 1952–54

H. H. Haskins 1952–56
D. G. Frey 1952–56
W. T. Edmondson 1952–56

(In 1955, Editorial staff appointed for LIMNOLOGY AND OCEANOGRAPHY)

Special Projects Committee (1946–51)

W. L. Tressler 1946–51
W. H. Bradley 1946–51
Ruth Patrick 1946–47, 1948–49*

W. E. Ricker 1946–49
G. E. Hutchinson 1946–47*, 1948–50
C. E. Renn 1949–50

T. C. Nelson 1949–51
D. S. Rawson 1950–52*
P. I. Tack 1950–52

(Dissolved in 1952; Tack retained as Chm., Selective Service Comm.)

Membership Committee (1946–47)

C. L. Hubbs
R. W. Pennak

E. S. Deevey
D. C. Chandler

J. B. Lackey*

Evaluation Committee (1946)

C. E. Renn
A. S. Hazzard

A. H. Wiebe
P. B. Sears

R. E. Coker*

APPENDIX 25.5 (*Continued*)

Committee on Expansion of Marine Interests (1947–48)

A. D. Hasler*	D. S. Rawson	A. G. Huntsman
F. E. Eggleton	G. L. Clarke	

National Advisory Committee (1949–55)

Ruth Patrick 1949–56*	W. B. Hart 1951–54	C. M. Tarzwell 1949–51
G. L. Clarke 1949–54	N. W. Rakestraw 1951–54	G. A. Riley 1949–51
D. C. Chandler 1949–54	C. E. ZoBell 1955–56	John Lyman 1955–57
	R. J. Robinson 1949–52	

  (Dissolved 1955)

Committee of Ecological Effects of Waste Disposal (1955–56)

Ruth Patrick 1955–56*	John Lyman 1955–56	C. E. ZoBell 1955–56

  (Dissolved 1956)

Selective Service Committee (1949–50, 1951–52)

  P. I. Tack

Special Journal Committee (1954–55)

C. A. Barnes	H. H. Haskins	D. S. Rawson
D. C. Chandler	B. H. Ketchum, ex officio	A. C. Redfield
	R. W. Pennak*	

Interim Advertising Committee (1957)

F. F. Hooper*	J. H. Ryther

Interim Library Subscription Committee (1957–58)

F. C. W. Olsen 1957	W. E. Ricker 1958

Committees on XV Congress of the International Association of Limnology (1957–62)

  Executive Committee

A. D. Hasler*	G. H. Lauff	J. C. Wright, Exec. Sec.
D. G. Frey	D. S. Rawson (W. E. Ricker)	K. D. Carlander

  Advisory Committee

W. E. Ricker	F. E. J. Fry	B. H. Ketchum, ex officio
R. W. Pennak	T. T. Macan	George Sprugel, Jr.
D. S. Rawson	G. H. Lauff	S. R. Galler
D. G. Frey	E. S. Deevey	A. D. Hasler*
	R. W. Hiatt	

  Program Committee

D. G. Frey*	R. C. Ball	J. R. Vallentyne
W. T. Edmondson	F. R. Hayes	C. M. Tarzwell

  Committee on Excursions
    K. D. Carlander*

  Committee on Funding of Excursions and Fellowships
    J. R. Olive

  Finance Committee
    G. H. Lauff

  Committee on Transportation
    S. R. Galler

  Canadian Representative on SIL Grants Committee

F. R. Hayes*	W. E. Ricker

  U.S. Representative on SIL Grants Committee
    W. T. Edmondson

Committee on NSF Travel Grants for Attendance at the 1959 Congress of Limnology in Austria (1959)

D. C. Chandler*	H. T. Odum	D. S. Rawson
W. T. Edmondson	Ruth Patrick	

APPENDIX 25.5 (*Continued*)

Committee on Cost of Publication (1959)

F. F. Hooper*	G. H. Lauff	K. M. Rae
	H. T. Odum	

Joint Committee on Aquatic Sciences (ESA-ASLO) (1959–61)

B. H. Ketchum* 1959–60	D. G. Frey	J. R. Vallentyne
M. R. Carriker	A. D. Hasler	J. H. Ryther
G. L. Clarke	H. T. Odum	K. M. Rae
E. W. Fager	George Sprugel, Jr.* 1961	C. L. Hubbs
	F. Koczy	F. R. Hayes
	D. W. Pritchard	

Cooperative Ship Committee (1960–61)

H. T. Odum*	Sidney Fox	D. F. Leipper
F. G. Walton Smith	Gordon Gunter	

Russian Translations Committee (1961———)

W. E. Ricker*

II. Representatives and Consultants

AAAS Council

P. S. Welch 1936	A. H. Wiebe 1947	G. L. Clarke 1953
J. G. Needham 1937–46	C. E. Renn 1948–52	W. L. Schmitt 1954–61

AAAS Inter-Society Committee on Science Foundation Legislation

C. McC. Mottley 1947	Stillman Wright 1950
(G. L. Clarke, Alt.)	(T. S. Austin, Alt.)

NAS-NRC (NRC)

Division of Biology and Agriculture	
Will Scott 1937	Chancey Juday 1939–44
P. S. Welch 1938, 1945–47	(P. S. Welch, Alt.)
(G. E. Hutchinson, Alt.)	L. A. Walford 1948-59
	(G. E. Hutchinson, Alt.)
	Fenner Chace 1960———

Division of Earth Sciences
D. W. Pritchard 1961———

AIBS

C. McC. Mottley 1948–52	D. C. Chandler 1956–57	T. C. Dorris 1960
John Lyman 1953–55	B. G. Anderson 1959	C. J. Goodnight 1961

Natural Resources Council of America

T. H. Langlois 1947–49, 1953–61	R. P. Hunter 1950–52

Council of Union of American Biological Sciences

P. S. Welch 1945–47	T. H. Langlois 1945–47

Foundation for the Study of Cycles
G. E. Hutchinson 1943–50

7th Pacific Science Congress
C. L. Hubbs 1949

American Society of Professional Biologists
A. D. Hess 1950–52

Consultant to AIBS

"Specialties List"—G. L. Clarke 1959–61	Publication Services—G. L. Clarke 1951–61

Congress of International Association of Quaternary Research (INQUA)

D. G. Frey 1960———	F. Koczy 1960———

III. Editorial Staff of Limnology and Oceanography

Editor

D. G. Frey 1956–59	K. M. Rae 1959———

APPENDIX 25.5 (*Continued*)

Editorial Board

1956	1956–57	1956–59
G. E. Hutchinson	W. T. Edmondson	A. D. Hasler
F. R. Richards	K. O. Emery	D. W. Pritchard
R. H. Fleming	H. H. Haskins	D. S. Rawson
J. H. Ryther		

1957–60	1958–61	1959–62
H. T. Odum	J. C. Ayers	C. H. Mortimer
W. E. Ricker	D. E. Carritt	Trygve Braarud
J. H. Ryther	J. W. Hedgpeth	L. A. Walford
	C. E. ZoBell	

1960–63	1961–64
R. O. Reid	J. H. Connell
G. A. Rounsefell	Maurice Rattray, Jr.
Jacob Verduin	H. L. Sanders

26 | *G. E. Hutchinson*

The Prospect before Us

To consider the future of any science is a difficult and invidious task. All that the enthusiastic practitioner can do is to express certain hopes, and these will necessarily be subjective and somewhat one-sided.

In this conclusion to *Limnology in North America*, emphasis will be placed on the fact that limnology exists as a science by virtue of its synthesis of methods from various more analytical disciplines to elucidate what is happening in a more or less discrete part of the hydrosphere. The great difficulty of limnology is that many quite disparate things must be done at once.

The present essay explores primarily some of the directions in which research may be profitably pursued in the immediate future, particularly bearing in mind the synthetic nature of our discipline. In dealing with any aspect of limnology, as perhaps of any other branch of science, it is impossible to avoid the thought that no work is perfect and that the greater proportion of published investigations are very imperfect indeed. Every one of us is at fault in some way or another; every one of us must attempt to achieve progressively higher standards in accuracy, scope, and imagination. In any part of the field we need many more facts and much deeper and broader interpretation of these facts. On the whole the same people should attempt both the fact collecting and the interpretation. The job of collecting data is rarely done well enough unless it is animated by the prospects of theoretical interpretation, while such interpretation is almost always likely to be best done by someone who knows the feel of a wire or a rope when a messenger is running down to trip a water bottle, who has experienced a north wind while he is collecting material through a hole in the ice, or who knows the glory of autumn foliage reflected in the still surface of a lake in October.

Before proceeding to particular aspects of limnology, we might mention one aspect of technique. Very few of us have actually seen what we study. The developments of the aqualung and particularly of underwater cameras and television apparatus, which can be small enough and sufficiently gently lowered not to create a disturbance, are beginning to provide more sensory reality to our science, as Ohle's (1959) fascinating pictures of lake bottoms clearly demonstrate.

The problems of physical limnology, at least in the strict sense of the study of standing bodies of water, mainly reduce to those involving the effect of wind stress on the surface of a body of water on a rotating planet and those involving the flux of solar energy across such a surface. The two problems overlap, and in any given case the non-overlapping areas give rise to interacting phenomena. It is a matter of some interest that these are theoretically the simplest kinds of limnological problems and the only ones that can at present be explored with the help of an extensive deductive mathematical apparatus. Yet here as elsewhere, the use of ordinary physical theory immediately involves either quite intractable mathematics or approximations and models that in some senses are quite unrealistic. The extreme difficulty of providing any satisfactory theory of the formation of one of the most familiar phenomena of limnology, namely thermal stratification and thermocline formation, may be mentioned as an example.

The purely physical problems of limnology obviously grade into those of oceanography. The main difference is that in limnology one can rarely neglect the boundaries of the water mass with which he is dealing. As a special case of this, the existence of oscillations of a kind that are stable in the sea only in narrow inlets, i.e., open-ended lakes filled with sea water, becomes important. No developments in recent limnology have had as far-reaching effects on the science as Mortimer's studies of internal seiches, but there are still a great many details of the water movements of stratified lakes that need elucidation.

A second very different aspect of the boundary effect arises in all problems concerning water balance, in which the relation of the drainage basin to the lake obviously acquires special local features that are not individually apparent in considering total drainage into the ocean. The nature of water movements and the problems of energy and water balance are likely to remain matters of importance, and it must not be forgotten that experimental manipulation of small bodies of water has been and will probably continue to be of importance in the study of the genesis of surface waves.

The analytical study of energy budgets, particularly of large lakes, initiated by Johnsson (1946), developed by Anderson and Pritchard (1951) and Neumann (1953), and extended by the various investigations on Lake Hefner and quite recently by the studies of Rodgers and Anderson (1961) on Lake Ontario, is likely to become important in relation to local meteorological studies, as well as in providing very beautiful analyses of the events within single lakes.

In all these aspects and several others, notably the optical properties of lakes, no real distinction can be made between oceanography and limnology, and both intergrading sciences have profited and will continue to profit by exchanges of points of view with meteorology. A good example of such an exchange is provided by Mortimer's (1959) use of Richardson's number in elucidating mixing in the metalimnion.

Chemical limnology differs profoundly from chemical oceanography, except perhaps in its most general biochemical problems. Too little attention has hitherto been paid to the purely inorganic aspects of lake water. There is, of course, much information on the inorganic composition of lake waters, which will at last be available in its full form in D. A. Livingstone's contribution to the new edition of *The Data of Geochemistry,* and Rodhe (1949) and Gorham (e.g., 1961) have made very interesting studies of its interpretation. One of the fundamental problems, however, has hardly been attacked, namely a detailed simultaneous study of the geochemistry of a limited drainage basin, the water of a lake within that basin, and the sediments laid down in that lake. This should be done in several areas of varying geology and climate. A large number of really detailed studies of this sort, in which at least twenty elements were determined, would be of great geochemical interest as well as highly significant to biogeochemical limnology.

The experience of various workers who have determined titration curves in connection with photosynthesis measurements suggests that more can be learned about the bicarbonate equilibrium in natural waters. The very extensive recent study of Garrells et al. (1961) makes a good foundation for this type of investigation. Other problems of the physical chemistry of iron, manganese, and the rarer trace elements dissolved or suspended in lake water involve biogeochemical cycles. Much work has been done on iron and some on copper and manganese, but the states of most of the minor elements are almost unelucidated. Almost any of them would provide exciting fields of study, for example, the biologically important trace elements boron, zinc, molybdenum, cobalt, and vanadium. Furthermore, the cycle of silver in the biosphere is almost unstudied, and there is some reason to suspect that an investigation of chromium would not be without interest.

Perhaps the most exciting immediate aspect of the inorganic chemistry of lakes, insofar as it is linked to biogeochemical processes, is that of the isotopic chemistry of water, solutes, organisms, and sediments. Many sporadic studies in relation to deuterium, O^{18}, C^{14} dating, and radioactive waste and fallout problems have, of course, been made, but there is clearly room for a great development of the subject along the lines of the recent but fundamental contribution of Oana and Deevey (1959). Extension of this work with addition of other elements such as sulfur, as is now being undertaken, should throw much light on the chemical kinetics of lakes.

The most popular biogeochemical problem, of course, concerns primary productivity, and here we are back in a region of limnology closely linked to oceanography. The initial problem relates to the fixation of carbon as carbon dioxide by photosynthesis. Light and chlorophyll are both clearly involved, and the plant physiologist has much to say about mechanisms and the probable course of the reaction in nature. Insofar as these mechanisms are relevant to the ecological aspects of photosynthesis in nature, no one has had so much to say nor said it so learnedly as Talling (1961) in a recent review.

Much of the ecological work has been methodological, a number of more or less imperfect methods, such as light- and dark-bottle oxygen determination, C^{14} fixation, pH changes caused by CO_2 uptake, and estimation from light and chlorophyll content, being the important ones. None gives quite unequivocal results, and a great deal of effort has been put into their improvement. As they are perfected, it will become worthwhile to try to disengage ourselves from preconceived ideas concerning what determines photosynthetic rate in nature. It should then be possible to enquire what variables in nature are actually involved in determining primary productivity. Vollenweider's (1960) comparative results using C^{14} and Wright's (1961) beautiful Canyon Ferry studies using light and dark bottles seem to indicate the right direction; however, it is quite likely that the general approach of studying pH changes *in situ* but at many depths (Verduin, 1956), perhaps with a more refined approach to the titration curve of the water (see also Beyers and Odum, 1959), may ultimately give results least distorted by disturbance of the ecosystem. A renewed study with such improved technique, somewhat along the lines of Riley's (1940) early study of Linsley Pond, in which a statistical analysis of the effects of many environmental variables on primary productivity was made, is clearly necessary.

It is quite certain that if the lake contained no primary producers, its primary production would be zero. It is easy to see that productivity must be some sort of function of standing crop at least when the latter is low; at high values of standing crop the concomitant decrease in transparency may obscure the relationship completely if the whole water column is considered. Although it is widely believed that the biomass of phytoplankton is likely to be determined by the concentrations of combined dissolved nitrogen and dissolved phosphate, the evidence that this is so is

confined largely to a few field experiments in lake fertilization and some enrichment experiments with lake water in bottles. Experimental studies on lakes (e.g., Stross and Hasler, 1960) seem to indicate that lime, presumably largely as a source of bicarbonate, may be a major limiting factor. Some stratigraphic confirmation of this has been obtained (Cowgill and Hutchinson, 1962). That surprises with regard to minor elements are possible is shown by Goldman's (1960) work with molybdenum deficiency.

The whole problem of organic matter in lake waters, first investigated in detail in Wisconsin, has again begun to yield significant results; analogy with the ocean, which is perhaps more dangerous in this problem than in most areas of limnology, suggests that in some cases a lack of chelators rather than of the substances chelated may impose a limit on the standing crop. If this is so, then the yellow humolimnic acids under study by Shapiro (1957, 1958) are likely to be of considerable significance. The remarkable results of Rodhe (1955) on heterotrophic nutrition, even in very cold, deep, unproductive lakes, indicate that in both limnology and oceanography heterotrophy must be taken very seriously. This is of particular interest in view of the discovery by Fogg and Nalewajko (1961) that glycolic acid is a very widespread external product of algal photosynthesis, which can be used by organisms even in very dilute solutions. The very great importance of vitamin B_{12} and thiamin in the nutrition of many algae may make these substances as important as any in determining algal populations. A far more detailed study of both these vitamins in lakes of various kinds is clearly now needed.

The existence of intense nitrogen fixation in the open waters of lakes containing blue-green algae is now well established (Dugdale *et al.*, 1959), and the further study of this phenomenon will obviously be of great interest.

The study of primary productivity naturally leads to an examination of the phytoplankton. Although there is now a fair body of data on the events leading to phytoplankton pulses, the results remain puzzling. By far the greatest puzzle is the extreme specific diversity exhibited by phytoplankton even within a quite small volume of water. A permanent non-equilibrium assemblage of population seems possible; van Walen (personal communication) has pointed out that this is no more unreasonable than cases of seasonal variation in gene frequency in a given population, a phenomenon well established in population genetics. It is, however, a matter of some urgency to investigate to what extent the phytoplankton of small lakes represents temporary opportunistic expansion of the populations of ordinarily benthic species, a view that has been held by various of the early workers and which is believed by Patrick (personal communication) to underlie part of the diversity of the diatom plankton.

The study of the productivity relationship of higher levels in the food web naturally becomes a limnological part of animal ecology. Lindeman's (1942) concepts of efficiency at different levels in a food web were developed largely on a limnological basis. Perhaps the most exciting developments directly derived from such concepts are the experimental studies by H. T. Odum (1962) which include various freshwater models. The original statement of the trophic dynamic point of view (Lindeman, 1942) and many subsequent studies have regarded the matter without much reference to the kinds of organisms involved in each level. At the time such an abstraction led to a great advance in understanding, but now we must attempt, as always, to re-introduce what was discarded in the earlier effort to get some quantitative elementary understanding of the process. Recent studies, notably by MacArthur (1955), Margalef (1961), and Patten (1961), using concepts derived from information theory, have shown how the idea of the stability as well as the hierarchy of efficiencies of a food web may be expressed. This stability is largely a function of the existence of alternate paths in a trophic system, as many ecologists have felt intuitively in the past. The full utilization of the rapidly developing body of theoretical knowledge in this field is likely to yield rich results to the limnologist whose appreciation of biological reality is sufficient and who is also nimble enough to handle the mathematics. Certain special situations ultimately dependent on the behavioral properties of prey and predator, relative to distribution at random or in a superdispersed manner of the former and the mode of search of the latter, have been formalized and studied with great success by Ivlev (1961) in fishes. The same kind of approach is likely to be very important in the study of feeding in other animals, aquatic or terrestrial.

Study of the zooplankton has now proceeded from the mere record of changing abundance to an attempt to analyze these changes in terms of population dynamics. Animals that carry their eggs are particularly suitable for this type of investigation as Elster (1954) and Eichhorn (1959) have shown in copepods and Edmondson (1960) with rotifers. The results of such studies often indicate how erroneous crude conclusions based on seasonal collections, considered independently of the physiological effect of temperature, may be. The cause of intense apparent reproductive activity in winter may be merely that the females carry the same slowly developing eggs over a protracted period. In contrast the young stages produced by the much less apparent but more intense reproduction in summer may suffer a great mortality, so that in some cases naive interpretation may lead to the right conclusions for the wrong reasons. This type of work is not only of great interest in itself and from the standpoint of the productivity of higher levels of the food chain, but also in the hands of Ravera (1954), Eichhorn (1959), Bossone and Tonolli (1954), and Davis (1961), it has demonstrated interesting temporal separation of equivalent stages of potentially competing organisms. This work, together with that of Carlin (1943) and of Pejler (1957a) on planktonic rotifers, suggests that the paradoxical situation observed in the phytoplankton with respect to specific diversity is probably not a striking feature of the zooplankton, in which every species may well be found to have a characteristic niche.

The phenomenon of cyclomorphosis in certain planktonic animals is practically confined to inland waters and provides a limnological problem of great interest to students of morphogenesis. Most attention has been given to the phenomenon as exhibited by species of *Daphnia* and *Bosmina,* and it is in the former genus that most advance has been made, although Lieder's studies of the extraordinary North German forms of *Bosmina* are noteworthy. In *Daphnia,* thanks to the work of Coker and Addlestone (1938), Brooks (1946, 1947), Hrbáček (1959), and Jacobs (1961), it is now reasonably clear that the efficient cause of the cycle as observed in nature is the seasonal variation in temperature, although other factors, notably turbulence and nutrition, can be shown to have an effect in the laboratory.

Jacobs has further made the remarkable discovery that when a *Daphnia* that initially developed at a low temperature is transferred to a high temperature, it exhibits more rapid relative head growth than one reared throughout life at the high temperature, thus adjusting its form towards that appropriate to the high temperature. The reciprocal effect also occurs. He has (in press) also demonstrated that the relative growth rate of the head is a function of absolute growth rate. The physiological details of the process remain to be elucidated, but Brooks' initial approach, developed by Jacobs, clearly has provided a satisfactory outline of what happens. What is not clear, from an adaptive point of view, is why the process occurs, and many workers seem to regard the high summer head in *Daphnia* as an inevitable epiphenomenon which, if adaptive, is related to physiological characters of a non-obvious kind. To the present writer the summer forms of *D. retrocurva or D. cucullata* seem so odd that unless they are positively adaptive, they would almost certainly be maladaptive. Meanwhile a large field of study has been opened, and since the prominent workers are all very active, most interesting results are likely to be achieved.

The problem of cyclomorphosis in rotifers has received little attention in comparison with the phenomenon in the Cladocera; almost no work of interest has been done recently in the New World. The main difficulty here is a fundamental taxonomic problem. At least in the genus *Keratella* there is presumptive evidence, from the work of Pejler (1957*b*), that a single lake may contain various more or less isolated and morphologically slightly different populations with maxima at different seasons. The replacement of one population by another may well give rise to the appearance of true cyclomorphosis. At least in some cases, the method of allometric plotting, used so successfully by Brooks for *Daphnia*, appears to permit the separation of such populations. Interesting work has been done in the Old World by Green (1960) and by Buchner and Mulzer (1961), but the most dramatic discovery is that of de Beauchamp (1952*a*, 1952*b*) that the lateral spines of *Brachionus calyciflorus* are evoked by a substance secreted by species of the predatory *Asplanchna*. A very wide field awaits anyone who seriously investigates these problems.

The vertical migratory behavior of the plankton, illuminated as it is by many excellent recent studies (e.g., Harris and Wolfe, 1955; Harris and Mason, 1956) which mainly involve optical stimuli, is almost certainly incompletely understood. This is indicated by the fact that in some Crustacea a sense organ exists which permits appreciation of falling through water (Grasser *et al.*, 1953; Hantschmann, 1961). Such a sense organ permits organisms possessing it to adjust the strength of the locomotory movements to compensate for falling speed. It is evident that the existence of such a process implies a re-interpretation of much earlier work on vertical migration.

Another link between limnology and ethology is provided by the recent and rapidly developing field of study on fish orientation in which Hasler and his co-workers (notably Hasler *et al.*, 1958) are achieving great success. There is probably also a very large number of behavioral problems connected with the movements and timing of emergence of the benthic larval insect fauna, the natural history of which is still not fully understood in spite of an enormous amount of excellent work. The whole relationship of active planktonic and resting benthic stages, studied in copepods so effectively by Elgmork (1959), will certainly be greatly extended, and we may hope soon to have a much greater understanding of the littoral biota, with its potentially enormous niche specificity.

While North America lacks ancient lakes in the evolutionary sense in which Baikal, Tanganyika, and Ohrid are ancient, the time has surely come for a truly evolutionary study of our great river system, the Mississippi, which provides in its fantastic molluscan fauna a fluviatile analogue of these ancient bodies of standing water. That the large Tertiary lakes of North America, so brilliantly discussed by Bradley in the present volume, seem, in spite of their long durations, not to have produced the astonishing diversity of some other existing ancient lakes is a problem that requires attention. The coregonids of the existing Great Lakes provide a respectable field for evolutionary study, and as Brooks has pointed out in another contribution to this volume, there are many interesting problems relating to landlocked fishes, notably *Salmo, Salvelinus,* and *Osmerus,* which have usually been considered either solely in terms of taxonomy or as matters strictly for the fishery biologist. Perhaps the most interesting evolutionary studies, however, are concerned with the micro-taxonomic approach, so far developed mainly in Italy. Price's (1958) demonstration that the cope-pod, ordinarily referred to *Cyclops vernalis* in North America, consists of half a dozen repro-ductively isolated but morphologically hardly separable species provides a challenge not yet taken up on a large scale. It is hard to avoid won-dering whether many other species of small fresh-water animals actually are composite entities, sep-arated beyond the dreams of the wildest schizo-taxonomist.

The paleolimnological approach to the study of recent lakes seems to some limnologists, in-cluding the present writer, one of the most interesting modern developments. The approach developed initially from various pollen analytical studies, from Lundquist's important work on the sediment succession in Swedish Lakes, and from various Russian studies (e.g., Messiatzev, 1924) on animal microfossils. The first attempt to use animal microfossils as typological indicators is Thienemann's note in Gams' (1927) study of the Lunzerseen. The first comprehensive reconstruc-tion aided by chemical data of both plant and animal succession was made by Deevey (1942) and by Patrick (1943) in their studies on Linsley Pond cores. Several other studies have now been made, the most extensive being those of Korde (1961) and her associates on Russian lakes, but in no case is the whole potential information available. The micropaleontological work of Frey (e.g., 1958) in this field is outstanding. Ideally a full study would involve C^{14} dates, pollen anal-yses, structural and microscopic analyses, chem-ical studies of all the inorganic and organic com-ponents that can be determined, studies of clay minerals by appropriate methods (X-ray diffrac-tion, differential thermal analysis, and exchange-able cation determinations), and determinations of all possible kinds of microfossils. At present no single lake has been subjected to all methods. Enough has been done in certain cases to suggest that with technical refinement the amount that can be learned about the history of a lake and its basin is enormous. Any picture that can be built up becomes available to further understand-ing of how all biological communities change over long periods of time. Lakes are ideal for this sort of study, and the development of community paleolimnology is likely to be one of the great contributions that limnology can make to science.

The problems already reviewed show the close connection of limnology not only with the sister science of oceanography but with geology, geo-chemistry, plant physiology, all aspects of ecology, developmental biology, ethology, and evolutionary studies. There is, however, another important aspect of limnology, namely its application to human welfare, and in many ways the wise de-velopment of applied limnology is vital to all the kinds of purely scientific studies already dis-cussed. Lakes are very beautiful and very useful parts of the landscape, but they are also naturally transitory and so peculiarly fragile.

Until recently most attention has been given to the problems involving increasing the produc-tivity of waters to yield more products, mainly fish, in the capture and consumption of which man is greatly interested. With the increase in urbanization, however, the main problem in many areas has become the prevention of excessive pro-ductivity of an undesirable kind.

Although large lakes are of great importance in transport and many natural and artificial lakes are essential sources of hydroelectric power and of water, all lakes can play an increasing role in providing an aesthetically satisfactory background to human life, and it is by no means unlikely that, great as the immediate practical value of an increasing number of lakes may be, the less obvious role may prove to be the more impor-tant. This aesthetic aspect of limnology may well prove to be inversely associated with the in-creasingly significant problems of mental health that develop in highly industrialized and urban societies. With proper planning, of course, the most utilitarian dam lake may give enormous recreational value in the deepest sense to many people not involved in hydroelectric power or navigation.

To a greater or lesser degree, all the human uses of lakes depend on some control of pollu-tion and the various consequences of excessive productivity, either heterotrophic or autotrophic. Fortunately, many of the more important pollu-tants are plant nutrients, and as really efficient ways of utilizing them before they reach the lake are developed, there is likely to be a decrease in what we politely call cultural eutrophy. In many cases this may come too late unless some public funds are used to subsidize the reclama-tion, for instance, of phosphate from sewage. In the long run and considering public welfare, any such expenditure, if devoted to technically sound procedures, is highly desirable. That applied limnology has significant affinities with many aspects of engineering and with nutritional science has long been obvious. In the future all the sciences of landscape, of which limnology is one, may appear to have great significance to psychiatry, which in its preventive aspects is in large measure concerned with what images the mind can take from the whole external world.

The aspects of limnology that have been discussed serve mainly as examples of the interrelation of the study of lakes to other sciences. As these advance, so will limnology. Other writers would have chosen other fields; many areas and many investigators are omitted, not because they lack merit but because the writer is less able to form judgments of the direction and the likely results in these areas. The whole subject of rivers, now ordinarily though not philologically subsumed in limnology, appears to him as a marvelous foreign territory explored by workers whose audacity is admirable in view of the difficulty of getting a theoretical grasp of the subject. Whatever the analytical interest of particular parts of limnology may be, one synthetic aspect will always be paramount as long as lakes exist and people study them. We have in lakes units that are satisfactorily unitary from many points of view. The lake as a microcosm was the first important theoretical construct to develop in American limnology. The idea has become a guiding principle of limnologists everywhere and will continue to give intellectual content to our science.

References

ANDERSON, E. R., AND D. W. PRITCHARD. 1951. Physical limnology of Lake Mead. U.S. Navy Electronics Lab., San Diego, California, Rept. 258, 152 p.

BEAUCHAMP, P. DE. 1952a. Un facteur de la variabilité chez les rotifères du genre *Brachionus*. Compt. Rend. Acad. Sci. Paris, **234**: 573–575.

——. 1952b. Variation chez les rotifères du genre *Brachionus*. Compt. Rend. Acad. Sci. Paris, **235**: 1355–1356.

BEYERS, R. J., AND H. T. ODUM. 1959. The use of carbon dioxide to construct pH curves for the measurement of productivity. Limnol. Oceanogr., **4**: 499–502.

BOSSONE, A., AND V. TONOLLI. 1954. Il problema della convivenza di *Arctodiaptomus bacillifer* (Koelb.), di *Acanthodiaptomus denticornis* (Wierz.) e di *Heterocope saliens* (Lill.). Mem. Ist. Ital. Idrobiol., **8**: 81–94.

BROOKS, J. L. 1946. Cyclomorphosis in *Daphnia*. I. An analysis of *D. retrocurva* and *D. galeata*. Ecol. Monogr., **16**: 409–447.

——. 1947. Turbulence as an environmental determinant of relative growth in *Daphnia*. Proc. Natl. Acad. Sci. Washington, **33**: 141–148.

BUCHNER, H., AND F. MULZER. 1961. Untersuchungen über die Variabilität der Rädertiere. II. Der Ablauf des Variation im Freien. Z. Morph. Ökol. Tiere, **50**: 330–374.

CARLIN, B. 1943. Die Planktonrotatorien des Motalaström. Medd. Lunds Univ. Limnol. Inst., No. 5, 256 p.

COKER, R. E., AND H. H. ADDLESTONE. 1938. Influence of temperature on cyclomorphosis in *Daphnia longispina*. J. Elisha Mitchell Sci. Soc., **54**: 45–75.

COWGILL, U. M., AND G. E. HUTCHINSON. 1962. Cultural eutrophication in Lago di Monterosi during Roman antiquity. Communicated to the XV Intern. Cong. Limnol., Madison, 1962.

DAVIS, C. C. 1961. Breeding of calanoid copepods in Lake Erie. Verh. intern. Ver. Limnol., **14**: 933–941.

DEEVEY, E. S. 1942. Studies on Connecticut lake sediments. III. The biostratonomy of Linsley Pond. Amer. J. Sci., **240**: 233–264, 313–338.

DUGDALE, R., V. DUGDALE, J. NEESS, AND J. GOERING. 1959. Nitrogen fixation in lakes. Science, **130**: 859–860.

EDMONDSON, W. T. 1960. Reproductive rates of rotifers in natural populations. Mem. Ist. Ital. Idrobiol., **12**: 21–77.

EICHHORN, R. 1959. Zur Populationsdynamik der calanoiden Copepoden in Titisee und Feldsee. Arch. Hydrobiol., suppl., **24**: 186–246.

ELGMORK, K. 1959. Seasonal occurrence of *Cyclops strenuus strenuus* in relation to environment in small water bodies in southern Norway. Folia Limnol. Scand., No. 11, 196 p.

ELSTER, H.-J. 1954. Über die Populationsdynamik von *Eudiaptomus gracilis* Sars und *Heterocope borealis* Fischer im Bodensee-Obersee. Arch. Hydrobiol., suppl., **20**: 546–614.

FOGG, G. E., AND C. NALEWAJKO. 1961. Extracellular products of phytoplankton. 1st Progr. Rept. to the Develop. Comm., 13 p.; 2nd Progr. Rept. to the Develop. Comm., 13 p. Also communicated to the XV Intern. Cong. Limnol., Madison, 1962.

FREY, D. G. 1958. The late-glacial cladoceran fauna of a small lake. Arch. Hydrobiol., **54**: 209–275.

GAMS, H. 1927. Die Geschichte der Lunzer Seen, Moore und Wälder. Intern. Rev. Hydrobiol. Hydrogr., **18**: 304–387.

GARRELLS, R. M., M. E. THOMPSON, AND R. SIEVER. 1961. Control of carbonate solubility by carbonate complexes. Amer. J. Sci., **259**: 24–45.

GOLDMAN, C. R. 1960. Molybdenum as a factor limiting primary productivity in Castle Lake, California. Science, **132**: 1016–1017.

GORHAM, E. 1961. Factors influencing supply of major ions to inland waters, with special reference to the atmosphere. Bull. Geol. Soc. Amer., **72**: 795–840.

GREEN, J. 1960. Zooplankton of the River Sokoto. The Rotifera. Proc. Zool. Soc., London, **135**: 491–523.

GROSSER, B. I., E. R. BAYLOR, AND F. E. SMITH. 1953. Analysis of geotactic responses in *Daphnia magna*. Ecology, **34**: 804–805.

HANTSCHMANN, S. C. 1961. Active compensation for the pull of gravity by a planktonic cladoceran *Daphnia schødleri* Sars. Ph.D. Thesis, Yale Univ.

HARRIS, J. E., AND P. MASON. 1956. Vertical migration in eyeless *Daphnia*. Proc. Roy. Soc. London, B, **145**: 280–290.

HARRIS, J. E., AND V. K. WOLFE. 1955. A laboratory study of vertical migration. Proc. Roy. Soc. London, B, **144**: 329–354.

HASLER, A. D., R. M. HORRALL, W. J. WISBY, AND W. BRAEMER. 1958. Sun-orienting and homing in fishes. Limnol. Oceanogr., **3**: 353–361.

HRBÁČEK, J. 1959. Circulation of water as a main factor influencing the development of helmets in *Daphnia cucullata* Sars. Hydrobiologia, **13**: 170–185.

IVLEV, V. S. 1961. Experimental ecology of the feeding of fishes (transl. of original Russian work of 1955). New Haven and London, Yale Univ. Press. 302 p.

JACOBS, J. 1961. Cyclomorphosis in *Daphnia galeata mendotae* Birge, a case of environmentally controlled allometry. Arch. Hydrobiol., **58**: 7–71.

JOHNSSON, H. 1946 Termisk-hydrologiska Studier i Sjön Klämmingen. Geograph. Ann. Stockholm, **28**: 1–154.

KORDE, N. W. 1961. Characteristische Merkmale der Stratifikation der Bodenablagerungen in Seen mit verschiedenartigem Zufluss. Verh. intern. Ver. Limnol., **14**: 524–531.

LIEDER, U. 1954. Der Stand der Zyklomorphoseforschung. Naturwissenschaften, **38**: 39–44.

LINDEMAN, R. L. 1942. The trophic dynamic aspect of ecology. Ecology, **23**: 399–418.

MacARTHUR, R. 1955. Fluctuations of animal populations and a measure of community stability. Ecology, **36**: 533–536.

MARGALEF, R. 1961. Communication of structure in planktonic populations. Limnol. Oceanogr., **6**: 124–128.

MESSIATZEV, I. I. 1924. Die fossile Fauna der Seen in Kossino. Arb. Biol. Sta. Kossino, **1**: 16–26, 35.

MORTIMER, C. H. 1959. Book review. Limnol. Oceanogr., **4**: 108–114.

NEUMANN, J. 1953. Energy balance and evaporation from sweetwater lakes of the Jordan Rift. Bull. Research Council Israel, **2**: 337–357.

OANA, S., AND E. S. DEEVEY. 1959. Carbon-13 in lake waters, and its possible bearing on paleo-

limnology. Amer. J. Sci. (Bradley Vol.), **258A**: 253–272.

ODUM, H. T. 1962. Discussion. 1st Conf. Marine Biol., Amer. Inst. Biol. Sci. (In press.)

OHLE, W. 1959. Blick in die Tiefe des Grossen Plöner Sees mit Fernseh- und Photo-Kameras. Natur u. Volk, **89**: 177–188.

PATRICK, R. 1943. The diatoms of Linsley Pond, Connecticut. Proc. Acad. Nat. Sci. Philadelphia, **95**: 53–110.

PATTEN, B. 1961. Negentropy flow in communities of plankton. Limnol. Oceanogr., **6**: 26–30.

PEJLER, B. 1957a. Taxonomical and ecological studies on planktonic Rotatoria from northern Swedish Lapland. Kgl. Svenska Vetenskapsakad. Handl., Ser. 4, **6**(5), 68 p.

———. 1957b. On variation and evolution in planktonic Rotatoria. Zool. Bidrag Uppsala, **32**: 1–66.

PRICE, J. L. 1958. Cryptic speciation in the vernalis group of Cyclopidae. Canadian J. Zool., **36**: 285–303.

RAVERA, O. 1954. La struttura demografica dei Copepodi del Lago Maggiore. Mem. Ist. Ital. Idrobiol., **8**: 109–150.

RILEY, G. A. 1940. Limnological studies in Connecticut. III. The plankton of Linsley Pond. Ecol. Monogr., **10**: 279–306.

RODGERS, G. K., AND D. V. ANDERSON. 1961. A preliminary study of the energy budget of Lake Ontario. J. Fish. Research Board Canada, **18**: 617–636.

RODHE, W. 1949. The ionic composition of lake waters. Verh. intern. Ver. Limnol., **10**: 377–386.

———. 1955. Can phytoplankton production proceed during winter darkness in subarctic lakes? Verh. intern. Ver. Limnol., **12**: 117–122.

SHAPIRO, J. 1957. Chemical and biological studies on the yellow organic acids of lake water. Limnol. Oceanogr., **2**: 161–179.

———. 1958. Yellow acid-cation complexes in lake waters. Science, **127**: 702–704.

STROSS, R. G., AND A. D. HASLER. 1960. Some lime induced changes in lake metabolism. Limnol. Oceanogr., **5**: 265–272.

TALLING, J. F. 1961. Photosynthesis under natural conditions. Ann. Rev. Plant Physiol., **12**: 133–154.

VERDUIN, J. 1956. Primary production in lakes. Limnol. Oceanogr., **1**: 85–91.

VOLLENWEIDER, R. A. 1960. Beiträge zur Kenntnis optischer Eigenschaften der Gewässer und Primärproduktion. Mem. Ist. Ital. Idrobiol., **12**: 201–244.

WRIGHT, J. C. 1961. The limnology of Canyon Ferry Reservoir. IV. The estimation of primary production from physical limnological data. Limnol. Oceanogr., **6**: 330–337.

Index

Ice-damned lakes: in British Columbia, 464, 466, 469; in northern North America, 561
Ictalurids: in Minnesota soft-water lakes, 306
Ictalurus furcatus, 603
Ictalurus melas, 74, 181
Ictalurus natalis, 181, 603
Ictalurus natalis prothistius, 224
Ictalurus nebulosus, 142, 612, 613
Ictalurus nebulosus marmoratus, 603
Ictalurus punctatus. See Channel catfish
Ictiobus. See Buffalo
Ictiobus bubalus, 603, 613
Ictiobus cyprinellus, 603, 613
Ide, F. P., 533, 678,
Identification Service: of LSA, 671
Ikrowik Lake (Alaska): influence of salt spray on, 562; ionic composition of, 563; growth and mortality of fishes in, 570; benthos and plankton in, 571
Illinois: physiography, 163; climate, 164; limnological resources of, 164–66; municipal water supplies of, 164–65; regional hardness of surface waters, 166; early ichthyologists in, 179; distribution of fishes in, 181–82; floristic and faunistic studies, 184; Sphagnum bogs dying out in, 184; recommendations for pond stocking, 604
Illinois Academy of Science, 169
Illinois Biological Station, 167–68
Illinois Department of Conservation, 169
Illinois-Mississippi Canal, 164
Illinois Natural History Survey, 168, 660
Illinois River: lakes in Havana region, 167; surveys of, 168, 660; plankton of, 169–71, 185, 655; origin of plankton in, 170; annual production of plankton, 170; benthos, 173–74, 185; alkalinity of, 177; species of fishes in, 182
Illinois State Geological Survey, 169
Illinois State Laboratory of Natural History, 166–67
Illinois State Sanitary Water Board, 169
Illumination: factor in geography of photosynthesis, 571
Ilopango Lake (El Salvador): location of, 399; high phosphorus, 415, 417; thermal structure, 416; mentioned, 400
Imerksungk Lake (Alaska), 571
Imikpuk Lake (Alaska): freezing out of solutes, 563, 564; seasonal water and sediment temperatures, 565–67; heat budget, 567; life histories of a copepod and *Daphnia,* 570, 572; phytoplankton, 571; primary productivity, 571
Impoundments. *See* Reservoirs; Farm ponds
Incodel: work on Delaware River, 219–20
Indiana: glacial lakes in, 253; sedimentation in lakes of, 253–56; cave plankton in, 262
Indiana University Biological Station: early history, 239; location of, 241; founded by Eigenmann, 263
Indicator organisms: of pollution, 283–84, 661–63; Crustacea, in alpine lakes, 354; algal, of lake types, 463; of fresh and saline stages in Lake Bonneville sediments, 647; typological, animal microfossils, 688. *See also* Lake types; Paleolimnology; Pollution
Indices: summed, for plankton, benthos, and fish, 477
Industrial pollution. *See* Pollution
Inert materials: type of pollutant, 660
Information theory: in limnology, 686
Inland Seas: research vessel on Great Lakes, photograph of, 552
Inman Lake (Kan.), 330

Insecticides: bioassay with *Daphnia,* 215; pollution by, 296. *See also* DDT; Pollution
Insects: ecological studies in Wisconsin, 42; biology of, in streams, 103; emergence related to larval populations, 257; at Highlands Biological Station, 271; in cenotes, 410; fossil, 641, 644; simultaneous emergence of, 687. *See also* Benthos
Institute for Fisheries Research (Mich.): lake-mapping program, 97; establishment and history, 102; activities of, 102–3; support of graduate students, 112
Institute of Fisheries (B.C.), 473
Institute of Radiation Ecology: in Georgia, 271
Instituto Mexicano de Recursos Naturales Renovables, 398
Instrumented buoys: for collecting basic data in Great Lakes, 554
Insular and Coast Mountains region (B.C.), 465, 467–68
Insular Lowland region (B.C.), 465, 468
Insulosity: of Gosiute Lake (Eocene), 636
Integral photosynthesis: in Great Lakes, 551
Interflow: defined and discussed, 585, 586; photography in model system, 585. *See also* Density currents; Reservoirs
Interior System (B.C.), 466–67
Intermittent streams: limnological studies of, 249–50, 321; metabolism of, 249–50; survival of biota in, 252, 321; spawning of fishes in, 321
Internal seiches. *See* Seiches
International Association of Limnology, 673, 674, 668
International Board of Inquiry for the Great Lakes, 546
Internationale Revue der gesamten Hydrobiologie und Hydrographie, 672, 673
International Pacific Salmon Fisheries Commission, 452, 473, 474
International Paper Company of Canada, 533
Interspecific competition: in stock tanks, 419
Invasion: of fresh waters by marine animals, 272, 509
Invertebrates: aquatic, dispersal in West via farm ponds, 363
Ionic composition: of New England waters, 132; of western meromictic lakes, 376; of lakes in Lower Grand Coulee (Wash.), 379; of Lakes Nicaragua and Managua, 402; of Salt River (Ariz.), 423; of waters in northern North America, 563. *See also* Chemistry, lake
Ion transport: induced by artificial circulation, 59
Iowa Cooperative Fisheries Research Unit, 318, 319, 334
Iowa Lakeside Laboratory, 318, 319, 334
Irénée-Marie, Brother, 508
Iron: in surface waters of Wisconsin lakes, 32; concentration changed by adding lime, 56; relation of midges to, 59; balance in Lake Mendota, 80; limiting productivity in marl lakes, 103; effect on trophic dynamics, 225
Iroquois River (Ill.), 164
Irrigation: plan diagram of system in Colorado, 357; canals, limnology of, 418–19; photograph of spillway, 579; mentioned, 356, 373
Irwin, W. H., 105–6, 318
Isaacs, J. D., 678
Isle Royal, 536
Isoetes: compositional index of, 64; in acid mine drainage, 262
Isopods: studies in Michigan, 103
Isotopes: tools in limnology and paleolimnology, 119,